Dietary Reference Intakes: RDA, AI*

	Vitamins													
Life-Stage Group	Vitamin A (μg/d)[a]	Vitamin D (μg/d)[b]	Vitamin E (mg/d)[c]	Vitamin K (μg/d)	Thiamin (mg/d)	Riboflavin (mg/d)	Niacin (mg/d)[d]	Pantothenic Acid (mg/d)	Biotin (μg/d)	Vitamin B6 (mg/d)	Folate (μg/d)[e]	Vitamin B12 (μg/d)	Vitamin C (mg/d)	Choline (mg/d)
Infants														
0–6 mo	400*	10	4*	2.0*	0.2*	0.3*	2*	1.7*	5*	0.1*	65*	0.4*	40*	125*
7–12 mo	500*	10	5*	2.5*	0.3*	0.4*	4*	1.8*	6*	0.3*	80*	0.5*	50*	150*
Children														
1–3 y	300	15	6	30*	0.5	0.5	6	2*	8*	0.5	150	0.9	15	200*
4–8 y	400	15	7	55*	0.6	0.6	8	3*	12*	0.6	200	1.2	25	250*
Males														
9–13 y	600	15	11	60*	0.9	0.9	12	4*	20*	1.0	300	1.8	45	375*
14–18 y	900	15	15	75*	1.2	1.3	16	5*	25*	1.3	400	2.4	75	550*
19–30 y	900	15	15	120*	1.2	1.3	16	5*	30*	1.3	400	2.4	90	550*
31–50 y	900	15	15	120*	1.2	1.3	16	5*	30*	1.3	400	2.4	90	550*
51–70 y	900	15	15	120*	1.2	1.3	16	5*	30*	1.7	400	2.4	90	550*
>70 y	900	20	15	120*	1.2	1.3	16	5*	30*	1.7	400	2.4	90	550*
Females														
9–13 y	600	15	11	60*	0.9	0.9	12	4*	20*	1.0	300	1.8	45	375*
14–18 y	700	15	15	75*	1.0	1.0	14	5*	25*	1.2	400	2.4	65	400*
19–30 y	700	15	15	90*	1.1	1.1	14	5*	30*	1.3	400	2.4	75	425*
31–50 y	700	15	15	90*	1.1	1.1	14	5*	30*	1.3	400	2.4	75	425*
51–70 y	700	15	15	90*	1.1	1.1	14	5*	30*	1.5	400	2.4	75	425*
>70 y	700	20	15	90*	1.1	1.1	14	5*	30*	1.5	400	2.4	75	425*
Pregnancy														
≤18 y	750	15	15	75*	1.4	1.4	18	6*	30*	1.9	600	2.6	80	450*
19–30 y	770	15	15	90*	1.4	1.4	18	6*	30*	1.9	600	2.6	85	450*
31–50 y	770	15	15	90*	1.4	1.4	18	6*	30*	1.9	600	2.6	85	450*
Lactation														
≤18 y	1200	15	19	75*	1.4	1.6	17	7*	35*	2.0	500	2.8	115	550*
19–30 y	1300	15	19	90*	1.4	1.6	17	7*	35*	2.0	500	2.8	120	550*
31–50 y	1300	15	19	90*	1.4	1.6	17	7*	35*	2.0	500	2.8	120	550*

Data from: Reprinted with permission from the Dietary Reference Intakes series, National Academies Press. Copyright 1997, 1998, 2000, 2001, 2011 by the National Academy of Sciences. These reports may be accessed via www.nap.edu. Courtesy of the National Academies Press, Washington, DC.

Note: This table is adapted from the DRI reports; see www.nap.edu. It lists Recommended Dietary Allowances (RDAs), with Adequate Intakes (AIs) indicated by an asterisk (*). RDAs and AIs may both be used as goals for individual intake. RDAs are set to meet the needs of almost all (97 percent to 98 percent) individuals in a group. For healthy breastfed infants, the AI is the mean intake. The AI for other life stage and gender groups is believed to cover the needs of all individuals in the group, but lack of data prevent being able to specify with confidence the percentage of individuals covered by this intake.

[a] Given as retinal activity equivalents (RAE).
[b] Also known as calciferol. The DRI values are based on the absence of adequate exposure to sunlight.
[c] Also known as α-tocopherol.
[d] Given as niacin equivalents (NE), except for infants 0–6 months, which are expressed as preformed niacin.
[e] Given as dietary folate equivalents (DFE).

Dietary Reference Intakes: RDA, AI*

Life-Stage Group	Elements												
	Calcium (mg/d)	Phosphorus (mg/d)	Magnesium (mg/d)	Iron (mg/d)	Zinc (mg/d)	Selenium (µg/d)	Iodine (µg/d)	Copper (µg/d)	Manganese (mg/d)	Fluoride (mg/d)	Chromium (µg/d)	Molybdenum (µg/d)
Infants												
0–6 mo	200	100*	30*	0.27*	2*	15*	110*	200*	0.003*	0.01*	0.2*	2*
7–12 mo	260	275*	75*	11	3	20*	130*	220*	0.6*	0.5*	5.5*	3*
Children												
1–3 y	700	460	80	7	3	20	90	340	1.2*	0.7*	11*	17
4–8 y	1000	500	130	10	5	30	90	440	1.5*	1*	15*	22
Males												
9–13 y	1300	1250	240	8	8	40	120	700	1.9*	2*	25*	34
14–18 y	1300	1250	410	11	11	55	150	890	2.2*	3*	35*	43
19–30 y	1000	700	400	8	11	55	150	900	2.3*	4*	35*	45
31–50 y	1000	700	420	8	11	55	150	900	2.3*	4*	35*	45
51–70 y	1000	700	420	8	11	55	150	900	2.3*	4*	30*	45
>70 y	1200	700	420	8	11	55	150	900	2.3*	4*	30*	45
Females												
9–13 y	1300	1250	240	8	8	40	120	700	1.6*	2*	21*	34
14–18 y	1300	1250	360	15	9	55	150	890	1.6*	3*	24*	43
19–30 y	1000	700	310	18	8	55	150	900	1.8*	3*	25*	45
31–50 y	1000	700	320	18	8	55	150	900	1.8*	3*	25*	45
51–70 y	1200	700	320	8	8	55	150	900	1.8*	3*	20*	45
>70 y	1200	700	320	8	8	55	150	900	1.8*	3*	20*	45
Pregnancy												
≤18 y	1300	1250	400	27	12	60	220	1000	2.0*	3*	29*	50
19–30 y	1000	700	350	27	11	60	220	1000	2.0*	3*	30*	50
31–50 y	1000	700	360	27	11	60	220	1000	2.0*	3*	30*	50
Lactation												
≤18 y	1300	1250	360	10	13	70	290	1300	2.6*	3*	44*	50
19–30 y	1000	700	310	9	12	70	290	1300	2.6*	3*	45*	50
31–50 y	1000	700	320	9	12	70	290	1300	2.6*	3*	45*	50

Data from: Reprinted with permission from the Dietary Reference Intakes series, National Academies Press. Copyright 1997, 1998, 2000, 2001, 2011 by the National Academy of Sciences. These reports may be accessed via www.nap.edu. Courtesy of the National Academies Press, Washington, DC.

Note: This table is adapted from the DRI reports; see www.nap.edu. It lists Recommended Dietary Allowances (RDAs), with Adequate Intakes (AIs) indicated by an asterisk (*). RDAs and AIs may both be used as goals for individual intake. RDAs are set to meet the needs of almost all (97 percent to 98 percent) individuals in a group. For healthy breastfed infants, the AI is the mean intake. The AI for other life stage and gender groups is believed to cover the needs of all individuals in the group, but lack of data prevent being able to specify with confidence the percentage of individuals covered by this intake.

the science of nutrition

Canadian Edition

Janice L. Thompson, Ph.D., FACSM
University of Bristol
University of New Mexico

Melinda M. Manore, Ph.D., RD, CSSD, FACSM
Oregon State University

Linda A. Vaughan, Ph.D., RD
Arizona State University

Kathy Gottschall-Pass, Ph.D., RD
University of Prince Edward Island

Debbie L. MacLellan, Ph.D., RD, FDC
University of Prince Edward Island

PEARSON

Toronto

Vice-President, Editorial Director: Gary Bennett
Editor-in-Chief: Nicole Lukach
Acquisitions Editor: Lisa Rahn
Vice President, Marketing: Marlene Olsavsky
Supervising Developmental Editor: Maurice Esses
Project Manager: Richard di Santo
Manufacturing Manager: Jane Schell
Production Editor: Niraj Bhatt, Aptara®, Inc.

Copy Editor: Cat Haggert
Proofreaders: Leanne Rancourt, Deborah Cooper-Bullock
Permissions Researcher: Debbie Henderson
Compositor: Aptara®, Inc.
Art Director: Julia Hall
Interior and Cover Designer: Anthony Leung
Cover Image: Iain Bagwell/Gettyimages

Credits and acknowledgments for materials borrowed from other sources and reproduced, with permission, in this textbook appear on the appropriate page within the text, and on page CR-1.

Original edition published by Pearson Education, Inc., Upper Saddle River, New Jersey, USA. Copyright © 2011 Pearson Education, Inc. This edition is authorized for sale only in Canada. If you purchased this book outside the United States or Canada, you should be aware that it has been imported without the approval of the publisher or the author.

10 9 8 7 6 5 4 3 2 1 CKV

Library and Archives Canada Cataloguing in Publication

The science of nutrition / Janice L. Thompson . . . [et al.].—Canadian ed.

Includes index.
ISBN 978-0-321-62473-4

1. Nutrition—Textbooks.   I. Thompson, Janice, 1962–

TX354.S35 2012   613.2   C2012-906496-3

ISBN 978-0-321-62473-4

Dedication

This book is dedicated to my amazing family, friends, and colleagues—you provide constant support, encouragement, and unconditional love. It is also dedicated to my students—you continue to inspire me, challenge me, and teach me. —JLT

This book is dedicated to my wonderful colleagues, friends, and family—your guidance, support, and understanding have allowed this book to happen. —MMM

This book is dedicated to my strong circle of family, friends, and colleagues. Year after year, your support and encouragement sustain me. —LAV

This book is dedicated to my family—it would never have been completed without your support and patience. —KGP

This book is dedicated to my family—your encouragement and support have motivated me to complete the project. —DM

About the Authors

Janice L. Thompson, Ph.D., FACSM

University of Bristol
University of New Mexico

Janice Thompson earned a doctorate in exercise physiology and nutrition at Arizona State University. She is currently Professor of Public Health Nutrition at the University of Bristol in the Department of Exercise and Health Sciences and is also an adjunct faculty member at the University of New Mexico Health Sciences Center. Her research focuses on designing and assessing the impact of nutrition and physical activity interventions to reduce the risks for obesity, cardiovascular disease, and type 2 diabetes in high-risk populations. She also teaches nutrition and research methods courses and mentors graduate research students.

Janice is a Fellow of the American College of Sports Medicine (ACSM) and a member of the American Society for Nutrition (ASN), the British Association of Sport and Exercise Science (BASES), and The Nutrition Society. Janice won an undergraduate teaching award while at the University of North Carolina, Charlotte. In addition to *The Science of Nutrition,* Janice coauthored the Benjamin Cummings textbooks *Nutrition: An Applied Approach* and *Nutrition for Life* with Melinda Manore.

Janice loves hiking, yoga, travelling, and cooking and eating delicious food. She likes almost every vegetable except fennel and believes chocolate should be listed as a food group.

Melinda M. Manore, Ph.D., RD, CSSD, FACSM

Oregon State University

Melinda Manore earned a doctorate in human nutrition with a minor in exercise physiology at Oregon State University (OSU). She is the past chair of the Department of Nutrition and Food Management at OSU and is currently a professor in the Department of Nutrition and Exercise Sciences. Prior to her tenure at OSU, she taught at Arizona State University for 17 years. Melinda's area of expertise is nutrition and exercise, especially the role of diet and exercise in health and prevention of chronic disease, exercise performance, weight control, and micronutrient needs. She has a special focus on the energy and nutritional needs of active women and girls across the life cycle.

Melinda is an active member of the Academy of Nutrition and Dietetics and the American College of Sports Medicine (ACSM). She is the past chair of the ADA Research Committee and the Research Dietetic Practice Group and served on the ADA Obesity Steering Committee. She is a Fellow and current Vice-President of the ACSM.

Melinda is also a member of the American Society of Nutrition (ASN) and The Obesity Society and serves as chair of the USDA Nutrition and Health Committee for Program Guidance and Planning. Melinda writes the nutrition column and is an associate editor for the ACSM's *Health and Fitness Journal,* serves on editorial boards of numerous research journals, and has won awards for excellence in research and teaching. She has also coauthored the Benjamin Cummings textbooks *Nutrition: An Applied Approach* and *Nutrition for Life* with Janice Thompson.

Melinda is an avid walker, hiker, and former runner who loves to garden, cook, and eat great food. She is also an amateur birder.

Linda A. Vaughan, Ph.D., RD
Arizona State University

Linda Vaughan is a professor and past chair of the Department of Nutrition at Arizona State University. Linda earned a doctorate in agricultural biochemistry and nutrition at the University of Arizona. She currently teaches, advises graduate students, and conducts research about independent-living older adults and the nutrient content of donated and distributed food from community food banks. Her area of specialization is older adults and life-cycle nutrition.

Linda is an active member of the Academy of Nutrition and Dietetics, the American Society of Nutrition (ASN), and the Arizona Dietetic Association. She has served as chair of the Research and Dietetic Educators of Practitioners practice groups of the American Dietetic Association. Linda has received numerous awards, including the Arizona Dietetic Association Outstanding Educator Award (1997) and the Arizona State University Supervisor of the Year award (2004).

Linda enjoys swimming, cycling, and baking bread in her free time.

Kathy Gottschall-Pass, Ph.D., RD
University of Prince Edward Island

Kathy Gottschall-Pass is a professor and chair of the Department of Applied Human Sciences at the University of Prince Edward Island (UPEI). She obtained her doctorate in Human Nutrition from the University of Saskatchewan. She is a registered Dietitian who previously worked in research and development for the food industry and taught at St. Francis Xavier University prior to her tenure at UPEI. She teaches in the areas of food science, introductory nutrition and human metabolism. Kathy's research interests focus on food components and nutritional factors involved in the prevention of chronic diseases and the mechanisms of their action. She is an active member of Dietitians of Canada (DC) and the Canadian Nutrition Society (CNS). She enjoys reading, cooking and learning about all things technological from her teenage children.

Debbie L. MacLellan, Ph.D., RD, FDC
University of Prince Edward Island

Debbie MacLellan earned a doctorate in nutrition at the University of Saskatchewan. She is currently a professor in the Department of Applied Human Sciences at the University of Prince Edward Island (UPEI) where she teaches in the areas of professional practice, research, food-service management, and introductory nutrition. She is also the Director of the Integrated Dietetic Internship program at UPEI. Debbie's research interests include school nutrition policy implementations, nutrition education and counselling, and the professional socialization of dietitians. Prior to her tenure at UPEI, Debbie worked as a registered dietitian in long term and acute care. She is an active member of Dietitians of Canada (DC) and is a past-Chair of the Board of Directors. Debbie has also served on the Professional Standards Advisory Committee for DC and is currently Chair of the Scientific Review Committee for the Canadian Foundation for Dietetic Research. She enjoys spending time with her family, especially her grandchildren, and reading mystery novels.

Preface

Nutrition is a dynamic, evolving, and exciting science. Learning about the scientific fundamentals of nutrition—the essential components of food and their functions in biological processes—can be challenging. Accordingly, we have designed this text's organization and pedagogy to make the material accessible, and to engage nutrition and other health science majors.

Maintaining health and preventing chronic disease is a main theme of this text. By organizing the text's contents around the functions of vitamins and minerals and their effects on the body we aim to help students appreciate that groups of micronutrients have crucial interconnected roles. In our teaching, we have found that this functional approach enhances understanding and discourages the simple rote memorization of lists of nutrients.

Students must be able to use scientific knowledge to assess diets, to evaluate research, and to appraise nutrition information. But to achieve these goals, they must learn about current scientific knowledge and how to evaluate future findings. Accordingly, the text emphasizes an evidence-informed approach to practice and promotes active learning through critical thinking. Each chapter incorporates Case Studies and Evidence-Informed Decision Making discussions to promote the development of these skills.

The Canadian Edition

Our primary goal in writing the Canadian edition of *The Science of Nutrition* was to create a reliable, accessible nutrition resource for Canadian students and instructors. Throughout the book you will find current Canadian material, including the following:

- Material from *Eating Well with Canada's Food Guide*
- Canadian food regulations
- Canadian research and innovations
- Nutrition issues unique to Canadian populations
- Canadian data
- Canadian references
- Links to Canadian websites

Organization

The book is divided into 19 chapters plus 7 appendices (4 of which are in the printed book and 3 of which are available online).

In Chapter 1 we provide an introductory overview of how nutrition contributes to good health. After briefly describing the essential nutrients, we discuss current nutrition recommendations and how they are used in dietary assessment. We conclude the chapter with an overview of the scientific method where students are challenged to think critically about the nutrition information and advice provided by the media and on the internet.

In Chapter 2 we outline the key components of a healthy diet and introduce students to *Eating Well with Canada's Food Guide* and to nutrition labelling rules and regulations.

In Chapter 3 we begin with a discussion about why we eat the foods that we do. Then we present an overview of the processes of digestion, absorption, and elimination of food and nutrients.

In Chapters 4, 5, and 6 we describe the macronutrients in detail. Each chapter includes a discussion of the important roles these nutrients play in the human body and a more detailed description of how they are digested, absorbed, and metabolized. Here we also discuss important food sources and the health-related disorders associated with particular nutrients.

In Chapter 7 we examine the metabolism of the macronutrients and their important role in energy production. We also include a discussion on the metabolic responses to feeding and fasting and the hormonal regulation of metabolism.

In Chapter 8 we present a brief introduction to the micronutrients, phytochemicals, and functional foods. This chapter sets the stage for a more detailed discussion of these nutrients in Chapters 9, 10, 11, 12, and 13. We have used a functional approach for the discussion of the essential micronutrients. In Chapter 9 we examine the nutrients involved in energy metabolism. In Chapter 10 we explore the various nutrients involved in fluid and electrolyte balance. Then, in Chapter 11, we move into a discussion of the nutrients involved in antioxidant function. Chapter 12 follows with a consideration of the nutrients involved in bone health. Chapter 13 closes this group of chapters with a discussion of the nutrients involved in blood health and immunity.

In Chapters 14 and 15 we explore the concepts of energy balance and weight control and the role of physical activity in achieving health. We discuss the various methods used to evaluate body weight and composition and the factors that contribute to excess body weight. We also consider strategies that can be used to achieve and maintain a healthy weight through diet and exercise.

In Chapters 16 through 18 we concentrate on nutrition issues through the lifecycle. We explore the role that food and nutrients play in the promotion of health from preconception to older adulthood, and we discuss nutrients and nutrition-related concerns in the various life stages.

In Chapter 19 we discuss the issues related to food security and insecurity in Canada and around the world. We look at the populations most affected by food insecurity and possible ways to address the problem.

Special Features of This Canadian Edition

Students learn effectively when they are interested, enthusiastic, and actively engaged. We have taken care to incorporate features that facilitate teaching and learning the science of nutrition.

- Each chapter opens with a brief quiz entitled **Test Yourself**. These true–false questions pique interest in the topics to be covered in the chapter by raising and dispelling some common misconceptions about nutrition. Answers to these questions are provided at the end of each chapter.

- **Chapter Objectives** follow the chapter-opening quiz and outline the knowledge and skills to be learned. By providing a roadmap at the beginning of each chapter, the Objectives will help students to read and understand the material more efficiently and more effectively.

- **Key Terms** are boldfaced in the body of the text where they are defined. They are also restated with their definitions in the margin. For convenience, they are also collected in a **Glossary** near the end of the book.

- **Did You Know?** boxes bring attention to important Canadian research and issues.

- **Highlight** boxes provide additional information about a particular topic.

- **Nutrition Label Activities** guide students in how to critically assess the information given in particular Canadian food labels.

- **Nutrition: Myth or Fact?** boxes dispel common misconceptions and encourage students to critically evaluate information from advertising, mass media, and their peers.

Test Yourself **True** or **False?**

1. A kilocalorie is a measure of the amount of fat in a food. (T) or (F)
2. Proteins are not a primary source of energy for our bodies. (T) or (F)

Chapter Objectives | *After reading this chapter, you will be able to:*

1. Define the term *nutrition, p. 4.*
2. Discuss why nutrition is important to health, *pp. 6–8.*
3. Identify the six classes of nutrients essential for health, *pp. 10–15.*

Did You Know?

Eating Well with Canada's Food Guide has been translated into ten different languages in addition to English and French. Translations include Arabic, Chinese, Farsi (Persian), Korean, Punjabi, Russian, Spanish, Tagalog, Tamil, and Urdu. You can download copies of these translations from www.hc-sc.gc.ca/fn-an/food-guide-aliment/order-commander/guide_trans-trad-eng.php.

NUTRITION LABEL ACTIVITY

Recognizing Carbohydrates on the Label

Figure 4.17 on page 142 shows labels for two breakfast cereals. The cereal on the left (a) is a whole-grain product with no added sugar, whereas the one on the right (b) is a processed and sweetened cereal. Consider the information shown and work through the questions below.

2. Examine the information listed as a subgroup on the label under *total carbohydrate.* How much sugar and how much fibre does each cereal contain?
3. What is the % Daily Value for carbohydrates for each cereal? What does this number mean?
4. For each cereal, calculate the number of calories and

NUTRITION MYTH OR FACT?

Do Athletes Need More Protein Than Inactive People?

Roula is a competitive figure skater who trains five days a week. She tries to eat a healthy diet but often finds it difficult because of her busy training schedule and the fact that she has recently adopted a vegetarian lifestyle. Roula has been told that she needs to eat more protein to build muscle and ensure optimal performance. She decides to add a 20 gram protein supplement to her fruit juice after each practice, which increases her usual protein intake to 90 grams per day. Roula's kcal intake is usually about 2400 kcal per day. She weighs 55 kg.

- **You Do the Math** boxes provide examples and opportunities to work out quantitative calculations.
- A **Case Study** (with a set of Critical Thinking Questions) in each chapter presents a scenario that encourages students to apply the material they have learned in the chapter. All the Case Studies in the book are listed immediately following the Table of Contents.
- A **See for Yourself** box immediately preceding the Chapter Review offers brief, targeted activities that encourage active learning. This self-assessment feature provides students with the opportunity to learn about their own nutrition and health habits.
- A **Chapter Review** appears at the end of each chapter, and consists of the following elements:
  - **Test Yourself Answers** consisting of answers to the chapter-opening quiz.
  - A **Summary** that briefly reviews the key concepts of the chapter.
  - **Review Questions** that consist of multiple-choice and short-essay questions. Answers to all the Review Questions may be found near the end of the book.
  - Annotated **Weblinks** that help students start to explore particular topics in more detail.
- A robust **Evidence-Informed Decision Making** feature at the end of each chapter focuses on an important current issue. Here students are encouraged to think critically about the issue and to answer the Using the Evidence questions. All the Evidence-Informed Decision Making sections are listed immediately following the Table of Contents.
- For convenience, various **Tables of Dietary Reference Intakes** are given on the inside of the front and back covers.

Instructor Supplements

Instructor's Resource CD-ROM

We have carefully prepared an *Instructor's Resource CD-ROM* (ISBN: 978-0321-83711-0) to aid in presenting engaging lectures, providing additional activities, assessing students' answers to all the questions in the book, and preparing tests and exams. It includes the following items:

- **Instructor's Manual** that includes additional activities as well as answers to all the questions in the book (except for the answers to the Review Questions, which are given in the book itself).
- A **Testbank** available either in Word (called a **Test Item File**) or in a computerized format (called **Pearson TestGen**). Pearson TestGen is a powerful program that enables instructors to view and edit existing questions, create new questions, and generate quizzes, tests, exams, or homework. With Pearson TestGen instructors can also administer tests on a local area network, have the tests graded electronically, and have the results prepared in electronic or printed reports.
- **PowerPoint Slides** that can be used to help create lectures.
- An **Image Library** consisting of electronic files of all the figures and tables in the textbook.

CourseSmart eTextbook

The **CourseSmart eTextbook** (978-0321-62474-1) version of this book represents a new way for instructors and students to access textbooks online, anytime, from anywhere. With thousands of titles across hundreds of courses, CourseSmart helps instructors choose the best textbook for their class and give their students a new option for buying the assigned textbook as an eTextbook at a lower cost. For more information, visit www.coursesmart.com.

Acknowledgements

We are very grateful to the following instructors who provided us with formal reviews of parts of the manuscript. Many of their suggestions have helped make the book stronger:

Nick Bellissimo (*Mount Saint Vincent University*)
Lindsay Benoit (*University of Northern British Columbia*)
Teresa Bosse (*Athabasca University*)
Tristaca Caldwell (*Acadia University)*
Alvin Chan (*University of Ottawa*)
Karen Davison (*Langara College*)
Mireille Dobost (*Université de Montréal*)
Matthew Durant (*Acadia University*)
Julia Ewaschuk (*University of Alberta*)
Rhona M. Hanning (*University of Waterloo*)
Gene Herzberg (*Memorial University*)
Christine Johnson (*St. Francis Xavier University*)
Shelley Lang (*Mohawk College*)
Donna Law (*Algonquin College*)
Paul J. LeBlanc (*Brock University*)
David W. L. Ma (*University of Guelph*)
Karen B. McLaren (*Canadore College*)
Brid NicNiocaill (*Dawson College*)
Jill Parnell (*Mount Royal University*)
Danny M. Pincivero (*Wilfrid Laurier University*)
Judy Sheeshka (*University of Guelph*)
Dave Steindl (*College of New Caledonia*)
Louise Thibault (*McGill University*)
Apollinaire Tsopmo (*Carleton University*)
Sabina Valentine (*University of Alberta*)
Christine Wellington (*University of Windsor*)

We would also like to extend an additional thanks to Jill Parnell (Mount Royal University) for technically checking pages during production.

When we decided to take on the task of writing the Canadian edition of this text, we really had no idea how much work this would entail. There are a myriad of little details that needed to be attended to in addition to the gathering of information related to Canadian nutrition research and practice. We would like to thank our student assistant, Sarah Nabuurs, for helping us check all of those details and for asking us questions from a student's point of view, which has made this book more student-centred. We would also like to thank the students in our introductory nutrition classes who have helped us test out some of our ideas and provided us with valuable feedback. We would like to thank all of the wonderful staff at Pearson for their dedication and commitment to this book. They are an incredibly professional group of individuals and we are extremely grateful to them for their patience and guidance. In particular, our developmental editor, Maurice Esses, provided us with invaluable support and encouragement throughout the writing process. His attention to detail and critical eye kept us on track and helped us to make improvements along the way. Finally, we would like to thank our colleagues, friends, and family members who have motivated us to keep going. This really has been a team effort.

Kathy Gottschall-Pass
Debbie L. MacLellan

MasteringNutrition®

MasteringNutrition (www.masteringnutrition.pearson.com) is a course management system that makes it easy to organize your class, personalize your students' educational experience, and push their learning to the next level.

Designed to help you maximize class time, MasteringNutrition offers customizable, easy-to-assign and automatically graded assessments and pedagogical tools that motivate students to learn outside of class, and arrive prepared for lecture.

Developed by science educators for science students and professors, the Mastering platform has over one million active users, and a proven history with over 9 years of student use in 30 countries.

Assignable Content

With MasteringNutrition, you can assign publisher-created pre-built assignments—pre-lecture tests, NutriCase Studies, and testbank questions—to get started quickly. You can import your own questions, and edit any of our questions or answers to match the precise language that you use.

The system automatically grades every assignment that features machine-graded questions (multiple choice and fill-in-the-blank), and students' results appear in the gradebook. Note that instructor-graded questions (short answer and essay questions) must be graded by the professor.

NutriTools

Students can experiment with 21 NutriTools—Build-a-Salad, Build-a-Pizza, Build-a-Meal, and more—to combine different food options, and thereby learn how to create healthier meals. NutriTools activities offer assignable questions.

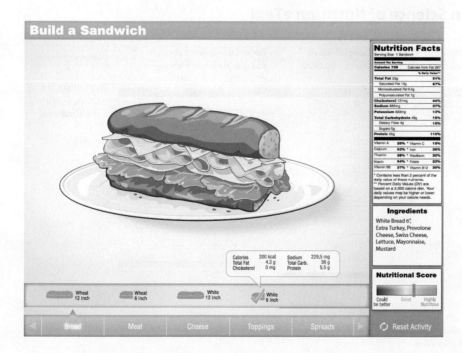

Animations

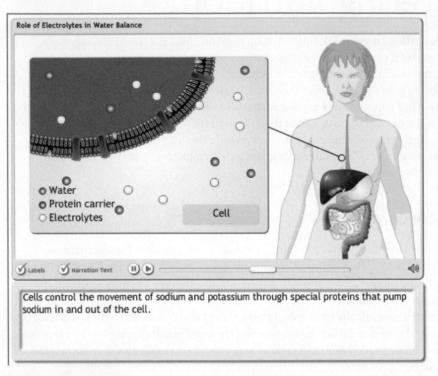

Pre-Lecture Quiz

Ensure that students come to lectures prepared by assigning a Pre-Lecture Quiz featuring multiple choice, fill-in-the-blank, and short answer questions based on chapter content.

Pearson Science of Nutrition eText

Highlight function allows students to highlight whatever they want to remember.

Google®-based search function.

Zoom lets students zoom in and out for better viewing.

Hyperlinks link to quizzes, activities, and animations.

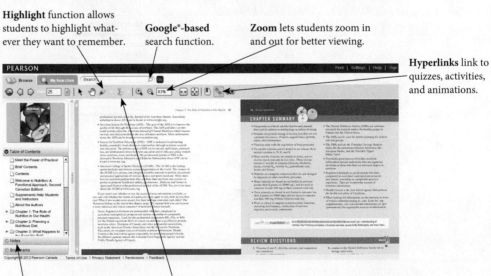

Notes give you, the educator, the opportunity to push out any content that you highlight and notes to your class.

Annotation function provides students with the opportunity to take notes.

NutriCase Studies

These audio case studies walk listeners through a real life nutrition challenge, and pose compelling questions that apply the chapter concepts to the case study. NutriCase Studies feature assignable multiple choice and true-false questions.

Study Area

The Study Area of MasteringNutrition offers a plethora of resources that allow students to assess their knowledge of the material, and their progress.

Prep Materials

Students have access to Get Ready for Nutrition, which features extra math and chemistry content related to nutrition.

Cumulative Exam

Students can assemble their own practice cumulative exam by selecting the chapters they want to test their knowledge, and the number of questions per chapter. The system then draws on a variety of questions. Note that these questions are different than the ones offered in the test bank to which you have access. MasteringNutrition automatically grades answers, so students can get feedback and check their understanding right away.

Gradebook

Get easy-to-interpret insights into students performance using the gradebook. MasteringNutrition automatically grades every assignment that features machine-grade questions. At a glance, you can see vulnerable students and challenging assignments.

The gradebook's diagnostics provide unique insight into the class, and student performance. Charts summarize the most difficult problems, students-at-risk, grade distribution, and score improvement over the duration of the course.

Instructor Resources

You can access all of the resources that accompany The Science of Nutrition, Canadian Edition—the Instructor's Guide, PowerPoint, Image Library, PRS Questions, Test Item File, and TestGen—from MasteringNutrition.

Study on the Go

Students will find a unique QR code featured at the end of each chapter that provides access to Study on the Go, an unprecedented mobile integration between text and online content. Students link to Pearson's unique Study on the Go content directly from their smartphones, allowing them to study whenever and wherever they wish! Go to one of the sites below to see how to download an app to your smartphone for free. Once the app is installed, the phone will scan the code and link to a website containing Pearson's Study on the Go content, including the popular study tools Glossary Flashcards, Animations, and Quizzes, which can be accessed anytime.

ScanLife
http://get.scanlife.com/
NeoReader
http://get.neoreader.com/
QuickMark
http://www.quickmark.com.tw/

MyDietAnalysis

Accessible via MasteringNutrition, MyDietAnalysis offers an accurate, reliable, easy-to-use program that helps students assess their lifestyles. Featuring a database of nearly 20 000 foods, the program assists in the tracking of diet and activity levels. Students can generate and submit reports electronically.

MyDiet Analysis

Logged in as   Logout

| Home | Profiles | Diet Tracker | Activity Tracker | Reports | My Class | Help |

Profile: Lisa

Diet Tracker - Day 1

| Day 1 | Day 2 | Day 3 | Day 4 | Day 5 | Day 6 | Day 7 |

Search: [   ] [Search] Search Tips   [Fast Entry] [Create a new food]

Name This Day: [Day 1]

Delete	Meal	Serving Size What's a serving size?		Food	Calories
☐	Breakfast ▼	1	each ▼	Cereal, hot, oatmeal, plain, inst, pkt (Quaker)	100
☐	Breakfast ▼	1	serving ▼	Blueberries	25
				Total Calories	125

[Save Changes]

MyDiet Analysis

Logged in as   Logout

| Home | Profiles | Diet Tracker | Activity Tracker | Reports | My Class | Help |

Profile: Lisa

Activity Tracker - Day 1

| Day 1 | Day 2 | Day 3 | Day 4 | Day 5 | Day 6 | Day 7 |

Search: [   ] [Search] Search Tips

Name This Day: [Day 1]

Delete	Duration		Activity	Calories
☐	55	minutes ▼	running, jogging, general	443
			Sedentary Activities of Daily Living *	1,863
			Total Calories	2,306

The current Activity list indicates an Activity Level of Low Active.   The Calorie Recommendation for this Profile is based on an Activity Level of Active.

Footnotes

* The sedentary activity level includes basic daily tasks such as brushing your teeth and bathing, housework, walking to work or class, and light yard work. These tasks are called Activities of Daily Living (ADL). If you engage in physical activity beyond the activities of daily living, you may increase your activity level. Strive for an active lifestyle for optimal health.

[Save Changes]

Brief Contents

Contents

1   The Role of Nutrition in Our Health 3

What Is the Science of Nutrition and How Did It Evolve? 4

HIGHLIGHT: Solving the Mystery of Pellagra 5

How Does Nutrition Contribute to Health? 6

Nutrition Is One of Several Factors Supporting Health 6

A Healthy Diet Can Prevent Some Diseases and Reduce Your Risk for Others 7

The Integrated Pan-Canadian Healthy Living Strategy 8

What Are Nutrients? 10

Carbohydrates, Lipids, and Proteins Provide Energy 11

HIGHLIGHT: What Is a Kilocalorie? 12

YOU DO THE MATH Calculating Energy Contribution of Carbohydrates, Lipids, and Proteins 13

Vitamins Assist in the Regulation of Physiologic Processes 14

Minerals Assist in the Regulation of Many Body Functions 15

Water Supports All Body Functions 15

What Are the Current Dietary Recommendations and How Are They Used? 15

DID YOU KNOW? 16

The Dietary Reference Intakes Identify a Healthy Person's Nutrient Needs 16

Diets Based on the DRIs Promote Health 19

How Do Nutrition Professionals Assess the Nutritional Status of Clients? 20

A Physical Examination Is Conducted by a Healthcare Provider 21

Questionnaires Elicit Self-Reported Information 21

Anthropometric and Biochemical Assessments Provide Objective Data 22

A Finding of Malnutrition Requires Further Classification 23

CASE STUDY Assessing Nutritional Status 24

Research Study Results: Who Can We Believe? 25

2 Designing a Healthy Diet 43

3 The Human Body: Are We Really What We Eat? 77

5 Lipids: Essential Energy-Supplying Nutrients 161

6 Proteins: Crucial Components of All Body Tissues 201

7 Metabolism: From Food to Life 237

8 Micronutrients, Phytochemicals, and Functional Foods 273

9 Nutrients Involved in Energy Metabolism 301

10 Nutrients Involved in Fluid and Electrolyte Balance 331

14 Achieving and Maintaining a Healthy Body Weight 485

15 Nutrition and Physical Activity: Keys to Good Health 535

16 Nutrition Through the Life Cycle: Pregnancy and the First Year of Life 579

17 Nutrition Through the Life Cycle: Childhood and Adolescence 627

18 Nutrition Through the Life Cycle: The Later Years 663

19 Malnutrition at Home and Around the World 693

Appendices

Case Studies

Evidence-Informed Decision Making

the science of nutrition

Canadian Edition

The Role of Nutrition in Our Health

Test Yourself   True *or* False?

1. A kilocalorie is a measure of the amount of fat in a food.   T *or* F

2. Proteins are not a primary source of energy for our bodies.   T *or* F

3. All vitamins must be consumed daily to support optimal health.   T *or* F

4. The Recommended Dietary Allowance is the maximum amount of a nutrient that people should consume to support normal body functions.   T *or* F

5. Government health agencies are typically poor sources of reliable nutrition information.   T *or* F

Test Yourself answers are located in the Chapter Review.

Chapter Objectives | *After reading this chapter, you will be able to:*

1. Define the term *nutrition, p. 4.*
2. Discuss why nutrition is important to health, *pp. 6–8.*
3. Identify the six classes of nutrients essential for health, *pp. 10–15.*
4. Identify the Dietary Reference Intakes for nutrients, *pp. 15–20.*
5. Describe the process for assessing an individual's nutritional status, *pp. 20–24.*
6. Discuss the four steps of the scientific method, *pp. 25–27.*
7. List at least four sources of reliable and accurate nutrition information, *pp. 27–33.*

Marilyn is 58 years old and works as a clerk at a small gift shop. During the last year, she has noticed that she is becoming increasingly tired at work and feels short of breath when performing tasks that she used to do easily, such as stocking shelves. This morning, she had her blood pressure checked for free at a local market and was told by the woman conducting the test that the reading was well above average. Assuming the woman's white lab coat meant that she was a healthcare professional, Marilyn asked her whether or not high blood pressure could explain her fatigue. The woman replied that fatigue was certainly a symptom and advised Marilyn to see her physician. When Marilyn explained that she had no family physician, the woman said, "Well, I'm not a physician, but I *am* a nutritionist, and I can certainly tell you that the best thing you can do to reduce your high blood pressure is to lose weight. We're running a special all month on our most popular weight-loss supplement. You take it 30 minutes before a meal and, since it's high in fibre, it makes you feel satisfied with less food. I can personally recommend it, because it helped me to lose 14 kilograms."

Marilyn wasn't convinced that she needed to lose weight. Sure, she was stocky, but she'd been that way all her life, and her fatigue had only started in the past year. But then she remembered that lately she'd been having trouble getting her rings on and off and that her shoes were feeling tight. So maybe the nutritionist was right. Noticing Marilyn wavering, the nutritionist added, "A few weeks after I started taking this product, my blood pressure went from sky-high to perfectly normal." She certainly looked slender and healthy, and her personal testimonial convinced Marilyn to spend $12 of her weekly grocery budget on the smallest-size bottle of the supplement.

What do you think of the advice Marilyn received? Was the nutritionist's assessment of her nutritional status adequate? Was the treatment plan sound? Just what is a "nutritionist" anyway? In this chapter, we'll begin to answer these questions as we explore the role of nutrition in human health, identify the six classes of nutrients, and describe what constitutes a professional assessment of a person's nutritional status. You'll also learn how to evaluate nutrition-related research studies, and how to distinguish science from scams. But first, let's take a quick look at the evolution of nutrition as a distinct scientific discipline.

The study of nutrition encompasses everything about food.

food The plants and animals we consume.

nutrition The scientific study of food and how it nourishes the body and influences health.

What Is the Science of Nutrition and How Did It Evolve?

Although many people think that *food* and *nutrition* mean the same thing, they don't. **Food** refers to the plants and animals we consume. These foods contain the energy and nutrients our bodies need to maintain life and support growth and health. **Nutrition**, in contrast, is a science. Specifically, it is the science that studies food and how food nourishes our bodies and influences our health. It identifies the processes by which we consume, digest, metabolize, and store the nutrients in foods, and how these nutrients affect our bodies. Nutrition also involves studying the factors that influence our eating patterns, making recommendations about the amount we should eat of each type of food, maintaining food safety, and addressing issues related to the global food supply.

When compared with other scientific disciplines such as chemistry, biology, and physics, nutrition is a relative newcomer. The cultivation, preservation, and preparation of food has played a critical role in the lives of humans for millennia, but in the West, the recognition of nutrition as an important contributor to health has developed slowly only during the past 400 years.

It started when researchers began to make the link between diet and illness. For instance, in the mid-1700s, long before vitamin C itself had been identified, researchers discovered that the vitamin C–deficiency disease *scurvy* could be prevented by consuming citrus fruits. By the mid-1800s, the three energy-providing nutrients—carbohydrates, lipids, and proteins—had been identified, as well as a number of essential minerals. Nutrition was coming into its own as a developing scientific discipline.

HIGHLIGHT

Solving the Mystery of Pellagra

In the first few years of the 20th century, Dr. Joseph Goldberger successfully controlled outbreaks of several fatal infectious diseases, from yellow fever in Louisiana to typhus in Mexico. So it wasn't surprising that, in 1914, the Surgeon General of the United States chose him to tackle another disease thought to be infectious that was raging throughout the South. Called *pellagra,* the disease was characterized by a skin rash, diarrhea, and mental impairment. At the time, it afflicted more than 50 000 people each year, and in about 10% of cases it resulted in death.

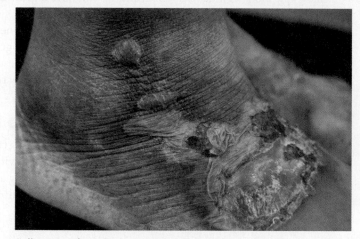

Pellagra is often characterized by a scaly skin rash.

Goldberger began studying the disease by carefully observing its occurrence in groups of people. He asked, if it is infectious, then why would it strike children in orphanages and prison inmates yet leave their nurses and guards unaffected? Why did it overwhelmingly affect impoverished mill workers and share croppers while leaving their affluent (and well-fed) neighbours healthy? Could a dietary deficiency cause pellagra? To confirm his hunch, he conducted a series of trials in which he fed afflicted orphans and prisoners, who had been consuming a limited, corn-based diet, a variety of nutrient-rich foods, including meats. They recovered. Moreover, orphans and inmates who did not have pellagra and ate the new diet did not develop the disease. Finally, Goldberger recruited eleven healthy prison inmates, who in return for a pardon of their sentence, agreed to consume a corn-based diet. After five months, six of the eleven developed pellagra.

Still, many skeptics were unable to give up the idea that pellagra was an infectious disease. So to prove that pellagra was not spread by germs, Goldberger and his colleagues deliberately injected and ingested patients' scabs, nasal secretions, and other bodily fluids. He and his team remained healthy.

Although Goldberger could not identify the precise component in the new diet that cured pellagra, he eventually found an inexpensive and widely available substance, brewer's yeast, that when added to the diet prevented or reversed the disease. Shortly after Goldberger's death in 1937, scientists identified the precise nutrient that was deficient in the diet of pellagra patients: niacin, one of the B-vitamins, which is plentiful in brewer's yeast.

Data from: Kraut, A. Dr. Joseph Goldberger and the war on pellagra. National Institutes of Health, Office of NIH History. Retrieved February 2009, from http://history.nih.gov/exhibits/goldberger; and H. Markel. 2003. The New Yorker who changed the diet of the South. *New York Times,* August 12, p. D5.

Still, vitamins were entirely unrecognized, and some fatal diseases that we now know to be due to vitamin deficiency were then thought to be due to infection. For instance, when Dutch scientist Christiaan Eijkman began studying the fatal nerve disease *beriberi* in the 1880s, he conducted experiments designed to ferret out the causative bacterium. Finally, Eijkman discovered that replacing the polished white rice in a patient's diet with whole-grain brown rice cured the disease. Still, he surmised that something in the brown rice conferred resistance to the beriberi "germ." It was not until the 20th century that the substance missing in polished rice—the B-vitamin *thiamin*—was identified and beriberi was definitively classified as a deficiency disease.[1] Another B-vitamin, niacin, was discovered through the work of Dr. Joseph Goldberger in the early 1900s. The accompanying Highlight box describes Dr. Goldberger's daring work.

Nutrition research continued to focus on identifying and preventing deficiency diseases through the first half of the 20th century. Then, as the higher standard of living after World War II led to an improvement in the North American diet, nutrition research began pursuing a new objective: supporting overall health and preventing and treating **chronic diseases**—that is, diseases that come on slowly and can persist for years, often despite treatment. Chronic diseases of particular interest to nutrition researchers include heart disease, obesity, type 2 diabetes, and various cancers. This new research has raised as many questions as it has answered, and we still have a great deal to learn about the relationship between nutrition and chronic disease.

In the closing decades of the 20th century, an exciting new area of nutrition research began to emerge. Reflecting our growing understanding of genetics, *nutrigenomics* seeks to uncover links between our genes, our environment, and our diet. The Evidence-informed Decision Making feature on pages 39–41 describes this new field of research.

How Does Nutrition Contribute to Health?

Proper nutrition can help us improve our health, prevent certain diseases, achieve and maintain a desirable weight, and maintain our energy and vitality. When you consider that most people eat on average three meals per day, during a 10-year period this results in almost 11 000 opportunities to affect our health through nutrition. The following section provides more detail on how nutrition supports health.

Nutrition Is One of Several Factors Supporting Health

Traditionally, **health** was defined simply as the absence of disease. However, as we have learned more about our health and what it means to live a healthy lifestyle, our definition has expanded. Health is now considered to be a multidimensional process, one that includes physical, emotional, and spiritual components (**Figure 1.1**).

In this book, we focus on two critical aspects of health: nutrition and physical activity. The two are so closely related that you can think of them as two sides of the same coin: our overall state of nutrition is influenced by how much energy we expend doing daily activities, and our level of physical activity has a major impact on how we use the nutrients in our food. We can perform more strenuous activities for longer periods of time when we eat a nutritious diet, whereas inadequate or excessive food intake can make us lethargic. A poor diet, inadequate physical activity, or a combination of these also can lead to serious health problems. Finally, several studies have suggested that adequate nutrition and regular physical activity can increase feelings of well-being and reduce feelings of anxiety and depression.[2,3] In other words, wholesome food and physical activity just plain feel good!

chronic disease A disease characterized by a gradual onset and long duration, with signs and symptoms that are difficult to interpret and which respond poorly to medical treatment.

health A multidimensional, lifelong process that includes physical, emotional, and spiritual components.

Physical health includes nutrition and physical activity

Occupational health meaningful work or vocation

Social health includes family, community, and social environment

Spiritual health spiritual values and beliefs

Emotional health includes positive feelings about oneself and life

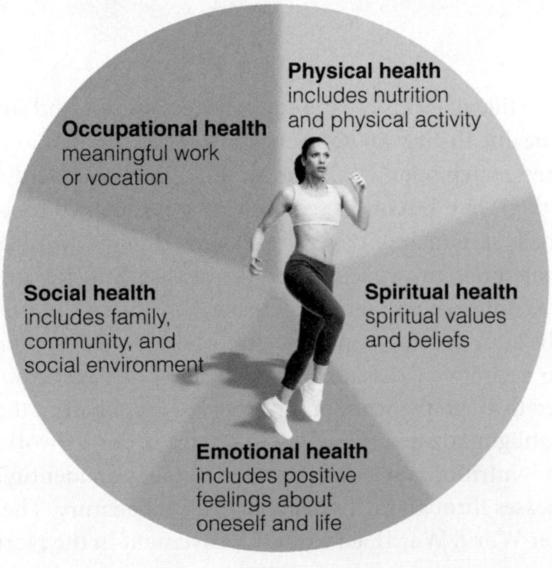

Figure 1.1 Many factors contribute to an individual's health. Primary among these are a nutritious diet and regular physical activity.

A Healthy Diet Can Prevent Some Diseases and Reduce Your Risk for Others

Nutrition appears to play a role—from a direct cause to a mild influence—in the development of many diseases (**Figure 1.2**). As we noted earlier, poor nutrition is a direct cause of deficiency diseases such as scurvy and pellagra. Thus, early nutrition research focused on identifying the causes of nutrient-deficiency diseases and the means to prevent them. These discoveries led nutrition experts to develop guidelines for nutrient intakes that are high enough to prevent deficiency diseases, and to lobby for **fortification** of foods with nutrients of concern. These measures, along with a more abundant and reliable food supply, have ensured that the majority of nutrient-deficiency diseases are no longer of concern in developed countries. However, they are still major problems in many developing nations (see Chapter 19, Malnutrition at Home and Around the World).

In addition to directly causing disease, poor nutrition can have a more subtle influence on our health. For instance, it can contribute to the development of brittle bones, a disease called *osteoporosis,* as well as to the progression of some forms of cancer. These associations are considered mild; however, poor nutrition is also strongly associated with three chronic diseases that are among the top ten causes of death in Canada (**Figure 1.3**). These are heart disease, stroke, and diabetes.

fortification The addition of nutrients to a food that were either not originally present in that food or were present in insignificant amounts.

Diseases in which nutrition plays some role
Osteoporosis
Osteoarthritis
Some forms of cancer

Diseases with a strong nutritional component
Type 2 diabetes
Heart disease
High blood pressure
Obesity

Diseases caused by nutritional deficiencies or toxicities
Pellagra
Rickets
Scurvy
Iron-deficiency anemia
Other vitamin and mineral deficiencies
Nutrient toxicities

Figure 1.2 The relationship between nutrition and human disease. Notice that whereas nutritional factors are only marginally implicated in the diseases of the top row, they are strongly linked to the development of the diseases in the middle row and truly causative of those in the bottom row.

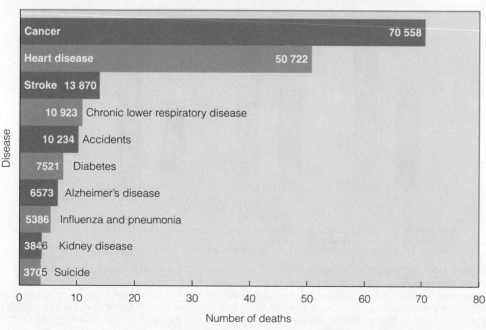

Cancer — 70 558
Heart disease — 50 722
Stroke — 13 870
10 923 — Chronic lower respiratory disease
10 234 — Accidents
7521 — Diabetes
6573 — Alzheimer's disease
5386 — Influenza and pneumonia
3846 — Kidney disease
3705 — Suicide

Disease

0   10   20   30   40   50   60   70   80
Number of deaths

Figure 1.3 Of the ten leading causes of death in Canada in 2008, three – heart disease, stroke and diabetes – are strongly associated with nutrition. In addition, nutrition plays a limited role in the development of some forms of cancer.
Data from: Statistics Canada. Ranking and Ten leading causes of death in Canada, 2008. Available online at http://www.statcan.gc.ca/daily-quotidien/111101/t111101b1-eng.htm (Accessed June 26, 2012). Reproduced and distributed on an "as is" basis with the permission of Statistics Canada.

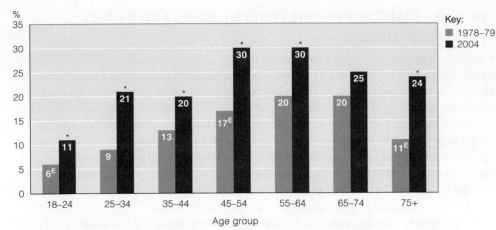

Figure 1.4 Obesity rates, by age group, household population aged 18 or older, Canada excluding territories, 1978–79 and 2004. (*Graph from* Nutrition: Findings from the Canadian Community Health Survey - Adult Obesity in Canada: Measured height and weight. Available at www.statcan.gc.ca/pub/82-620-m/2005001/article/adults-adultes/8060-eng.htm#2. Accessed September 11, 2010). Reproduced and distributed on an "as is" basis with the permission of Statistics Canada.

It probably won't surprise you to learn that the primary link between poor nutrition and mortality from these chronic diseases is obesity. That is, obesity is fundamentally a consequence of eating more energy than is expended. At the same time, obesity is a well-established risk factor for heart disease, stroke, type 2 diabetes, and some forms of cancer. Unfortunately, the prevalence of obesity has dramatically increased throughout Canada during the past 30 years (**Figures 1.4** and **1.5**). Throughout this text, we will discuss in detail how nutrition and physical activity affect the development of obesity and other chronic diseases.

The Integrated Pan-Canadian Healthy Living Strategy

In Canada, health is a provincial mandate. Each province is responsible for deciding how its healthcare budget will be spent and what its priorities are. However, every province and territory in Canada is dealing with the impact of the increasing prevalence of obesity and chronic diseases. The need for a pan-Canadian healthy living approach to address these issues in a collaborative and coordinated manner was first recognized in 2002 by the federal, provincial, and territorial ministers of health. An extensive consultation process was undertaken, including a two-day symposium that brought together almost 300 participants

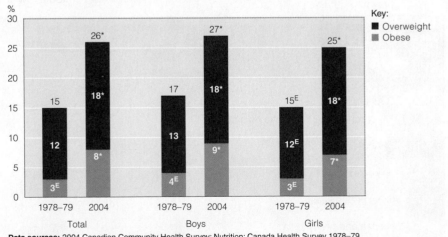

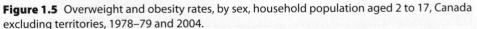

Figure 1.5 Overweight and obesity rates, by sex, household population aged 2 to 17, Canada excluding territories, 1978–79 and 2004. (*Graph from* Nutrition: Findings from the Canadian Community Health Survey - Overweight Canadian Children and Adolescents. Available at www.statcan.gc.ca/pub/82-620-m/2005001/article/child-enfant/8061-eng.htm#2. Accessed September 11, 2010). Reproduced and distributed on an "as is" basis with the permission of Statistics Canada.

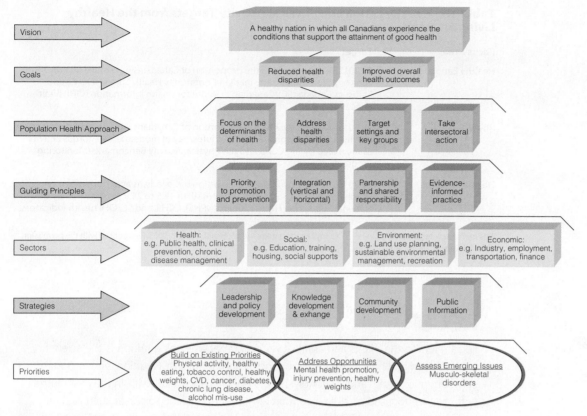

Figure 1.6 Strengthened Pan-Canadian Healthy Living Strategy Framework.
(*Source:* The Integrated Pan-Canadian Healthy Living Strategy – 2005. Health Canada, 2005. Reproduced with the permission of the Minister of Health, 2012.

from across the country to discuss a framework for healthy living. Consensus was achieved on objectives, overall priorities and directions, short-term actions, and partnerships. The result of these consultations was the Integrated Pan-Canadian Healthy Living Strategy. In 2010, this strategy was strengthened to make the need to take a population approach more explicit (**Figure 1.6**). A population health approach focuses on improving the health status of a population by addressing some of the root causes that lead to poor health outcomes. The overall vision of the Healthy Living Strategy is a healthy nation in which all Canadians have access to the conditions that support good health. The two main goals of the Strategy are to (1) improve overall health outcomes and (2) reduce health disparities. Health disparities refer to differences in health status due to factors associated with socio-economic status, geographic location, culture, disability, and Aboriginal identity. For example, the results of the Canadian Community Health Survey (CCHS cycle 3.1) indicated that the prevalence of type 2 diabetes in the lowest income group is 4.14 times higher than in the highest income group.[4] Infant mortality rates have been shown to be more than twice as high among First Nations as non-First Nations people.[5] Only by reducing these health disparities can we hope to improve overall health outcomes for Canadians.

The Strategy has four strategic directions: (1) leadership and policy development, (2) knowledge development and transfer, (3) community development and infrastructure, and (4) public information. An integrated research and surveillance agenda on healthy eating and physical activity is also a critical component of the Healthy Living Strategy.

Because of the importance of healthy eating and physical activity and their relationship to healthy weight and the health of all Canadians, it was agreed that these would be the first areas of emphasis. Table 1.1 identifies the specific targets related to nutrition and physical activity from the Healthy Living Strategy. The complete document is available on the Public Health Agency of Canada website at www.phac-aspc.gc.ca/hl-vs-strat/pdf/hls_e.pdf (accessed January 12, 2012).

Table 1.1 Healthy Eating and Physical Activity Targets from the Healthy Living Strategy

Focus Area	Target
Healthy Eating	By 2015, increase by 20% the proportion of Canadians who make healthy food choices according to the Canadian Community Health Survey (CCHS) and Statistics Canada (SC)/Canadian Institute for Health Information (CIHI) health indicators.
Physical Activity	By 2015, increase by 20% the proportion of Canadians who participate in regular physical activity based on 30 minutes/day of moderate to vigorous activity as measured by the CCHS and the Physical Activity Benchmarks/Monitoring Program.
Healthy Weights	By 2015, increase by 20% the proportion of Canadians at a "normal" body weight based on a Body Mass Index (BMI) of 18.5 to 24.9 as measured by the National Population Health Survey (NPHS), CCHS, and SC/CIHI health indicators.

Data from: The Integrated Pan-Canadian Healthy Living Strategy – 2005. Health Canada, 2005. Reproduced with the permission of the Minister of Health, 2012.

RECAP

Food refers to the plants and animals we consume, whereas nutrition is the scientific study of food and how food affects our bodies and our health. Nutrition is an important component of health and is strongly associated with physical activity. In the past, nutrition research focused on the prevention of nutrient-deficiency diseases such as scurvy and pellagra; currently, a great deal of nutrition research is dedicated to identifying dietary patterns that can lower the risk for chronic diseases such as type 2 diabetes and heart disease. The Integrated Pan-Canadian Healthy Living Strategy has set population health goals to promote optimal health for Canadians.

What Are Nutrients?

We enjoy eating food because of its taste, smell, and the pleasure and comfort it gives us. However, we rarely stop to think about what our food actually contains. Foods are composed of many chemical substances, some of which are not useful to the body, and others that are critical to human growth and function. These latter chemicals are referred to as **essential nutrients**. The six groups of essential nutrients found in foods are (**Figure 1.7**):

- carbohydrates
- lipids (including fats and oils)
- proteins
- vitamins
- minerals
- water

These latter chemicals are referred to as essential nutrients if they cannot be made by the human body in sufficient amounts; they must be supplied in the diet. As you may know, the term *organic* is commonly used to describe foods that are grown with little or no use of chemicals. But when scientists describe individual nutrients as **organic**, they mean that these nutrients contain an element called *carbon* that is an essential component of all living organisms. Carbohydrates, lipids, proteins, and vitamins are organic, because they contain carbon. Minerals and water are **inorganic** because they do not contain carbon. Both organic and inorganic nutrients are equally important for sustaining life but differ in their structures, functions, and basic chemistry. You will learn more about the details of these nutrients in subsequent chapters; a brief review is provided here.

essential nutrients Chemicals found in foods that are critical to human growth and function.

organic A substance or nutrient that contains the element carbon.

inorganic A substance or nutrient that does not contain carbon.

Carbohydrates, Lipids, and Proteins Provide Energy

Carbohydrates, lipids, and proteins are the only nutrients in foods that provide energy. By this we mean that these nutrients break down and reassemble into a fuel that the body uses to support physical activity and basic physiologic functioning. Although taking a multivitamin and a glass of water might be beneficial in some ways, it will not provide you with the energy you need to do your 20 minutes on the stair-climber! The energy nutrients are also referred to as **macronutrients**. *Macro* means "large," and thus macronutrients are those nutrients needed in relatively large amounts to support normal function and health.

Alcohol is found in certain beverages and foods, and it provides energy—but it is not considered a nutrient. This is because it does not support the regulation of body functions or the building or repairing of tissues. In fact, alcohol is considered to be both a drug and a toxin. Details about alcohol metabolism are provided in Chapter 7.

We express energy in units of *kilocalories* (kcal) or *kilojoules* (KJ). Refer to the Highlight box "What Is a Kilocalorie?" on page 12 for a definition of this term. Both carbohydrates and proteins provide 4 kcal per gram, alcohol provides 7 kcal per gram, and lipids provide 9 kcal per gram. Thus, for every gram of lipids we consume, we obtain more than twice the energy as compared with a gram of carbohydrate or protein. Refer to the You Do the Math box on page 13 to learn how to calculate the energy contribution of carbohydrates, lipids, and proteins in one day's diet.

Carbohydrates Are a Primary Fuel Source

Carbohydrates are the primary source of fuel for the human body, particularly for neurologic functioning and physical exercise (**Figure 1.8**). A close look at the word *carbohydrate* reveals the chemical structure of this nutrient. *Carbo-* refers to carbon, and *-hydrate* refers to water. You may remember that water is made up of hydrogen and oxygen. Thus, carbohydrates are composed of chains of carbon, hydrogen, and oxygen.

Carbohydrates are found in a wide variety of foods: rice, wheat, and other grains, as well as vegetables and fruits. Carbohydrates are also found in *legumes* (foods that include lentils, beans, and peas), seeds, nuts, and milk and other dairy products. Fibre is also classified as a type of carbohydrate. Carbohydrates and their role in health are the focus of Chapter 4.

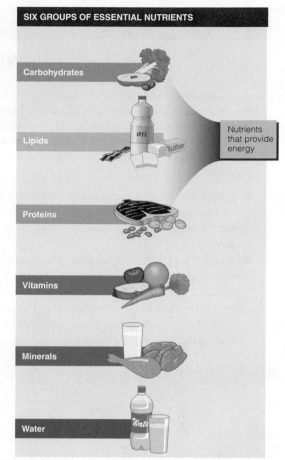

SIX GROUPS OF ESSENTIAL NUTRIENTS

Carbohydrates

Lipids

Nutrients that provide energy

Proteins

Vitamins

Minerals

Water

Figure 1.7 The six groups of nutrients found in the foods we consume.

Carbohydrates are the primary source of fuel for the body, particularly for the brain.

macronutrients Nutrients that the body requires in relatively large amounts to support normal function and health. Carbohydrates, lipids, and proteins are macronutrients.

carbohydrates The primary fuel source for the body, particularly for the brain and for physical exercise.

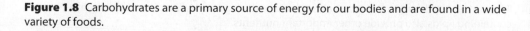

Carbohydrates

• Primary source of energy for the body
• Composed of carbon, hydrogen, and oxygen

Figure 1.8 Carbohydrates are a primary source of energy for our bodies and are found in a wide variety of foods.

HIGHLIGHT

What Is a Kilocalorie?

Have you ever wondered what the difference is between the terms *energy, kilocalories,* and *calories*? Should these terms be used interchangeably, and what do they really mean? The brief review provided in this Highlight should broaden your understanding. First, some precise definitions:

■ *Energy* is defined as the capacity to do work. We derive energy from the energy-containing nutrients in the foods we eat—namely, carbohydrates, lipids, and proteins.

■ A *kilocalorie (kcal)* is the amount of heat required to raise the temperature of 1 kilogram (kg) of water by 1 degree Celsius (°C). It is a unit of measurement that nutrition researchers use to quantify the amount of energy in food that can be supplied to the body. For instance, the energy found in 1 gram (g) of carbohydrate is equal to

4 kcal. In science, the term *Calorie (C)* is used to indicate a kilocalorie.

■ In the International System of Units (SI) used in Canada, the unit of energy is the *kilojoule (kJ)*. To convert kilocalories or dietary Calories to kilojoules, multiply by 4.182 (usually rounded off to 4.2). To convert kilojoules to kilocalories or dietary Calories, divide by 4.182.

It is most appropriate to use the term *energy* when you are referring to the general concept of energy intake or energy expenditure. If you are discussing the specific units related to energy you can use either *kcalories, Calories,* or *kilojoules.* The term *kcalories* is commonly used by nutrition professionals in Canada. The term *Calorie* is used on Canadian food labels. The use of *kilojoules* is optional on food labels. In this textbook we use the term *kilocalorie (or kcal)* as a unit of energy.

Lipids Provide Energy and Other Essential Nutrients

Lipids are an important energy source for our bodies at rest and can be broken down for energy during periods of fasting, for example, while we are asleep.

lipids A diverse group of organic substances that are insoluble in water; includes triglycerides, phospholipids, and sterols.

Lipids are another important source of energy for the body (**Figure 1.9**). Lipids are a diverse group of organic substances that are largely insoluble in water. Lipids include triglycerides, phospholipids, and sterols. Like carbohydrates, lipids are composed mainly of carbon, hydrogen, and oxygen (and in phospholipids, phosphorous and sometimes nitrogen); however, they contain proportionately much less oxygen and water than do carbohydrates. This quality partly explains why they yield more energy per gram than either carbohydrates or proteins.

Triglycerides (more commonly known as fats) are by far the most common lipid in foods. They are composed of an alcohol molecule called *glycerol* attached to three acid molecules called *fatty acids*. As we'll discuss throughout this book, triglycerides in foods

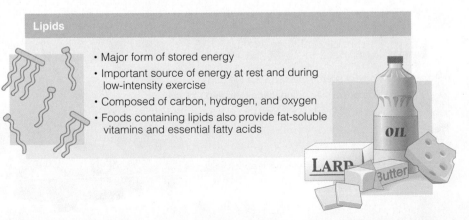

Lipids

- Major form of stored energy
- Important source of energy at rest and during low-intensity exercise
- Composed of carbon, hydrogen, and oxygen
- Foods containing lipids also provide fat-soluble vitamins and essential fatty acids

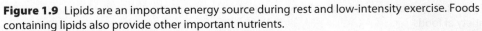

Figure 1.9 Lipids are an important energy source during rest and low-intensity exercise. Foods containing lipids also provide other important nutrients.

YOU DO THE MATH

Calculating Energy Contribution of Carbohydrates, Lipids, and Proteins

One of the most useful skills to learn as you study nutrition is how to determine the percentage of the total energy someone eats that comes from carbohydrates, lipids, or proteins. These data are an important first step in evaluating the quality of an individual's diet. Fortunately, a simple equation is available to help you calculate these values.

To begin, you need to know how much total energy someone consumes each day, as well as how many grams of carbohydrates, lipids, and proteins. You also need to know the kilocalorie (kcal) value of each of these nutrients. The energy value for carbohydrates and proteins is 4 kcal per gram, the energy value for alcohol is 7 kcal per gram, and the energy value for lipids is 9 kcal per gram. Working along with the following example will help you perform the calculations:

1. Let's say you have completed a personal diet analysis for your mother, and she consumes 2500 kcal per day. From your diet analysis you also find that she consumes 300 g of carbohydrates, 90 g of lipids, and 123 g of proteins.
2. To calculate her percentage of total energy that comes from carbohydrates, you must do two things:
   a. Take her total grams of carbohydrates and multiply by the energy value for carbohydrates to determine how many kilocalories of carbohydrates she has consumed.

   300 g of carbohydrates × 4 kcal/g = 1200 kcal of carbohydrates

   b. Take the kilocalories of carbohydrates she has consumed, divide this number by the total number of

kilocalories she has consumed, and multiply by 100. This will give you the percentage of total energy that comes from carbohydrates.

(1200 kcal/2500 kcal) × 100 = 48% of total energy from carbohydrates

3. To calculate her percentage of total energy that comes from lipids, you follow the same steps but incorporate the energy value for lipids:
   a. Take her total grams of lipids and multiply by the energy value for lipids to find the kilocalories of lipids consumed.

   90 g of fats × 9 kcal/g = 810 kcal of lipids

   b. Take the kilocalories of lipids she has consumed, divide this number by the total number of kilocalories she consumed, and multiply by 100 to get the percentage of total energy from lipids.

   (810 kcal/2500 kcal) × 100 = 32.4% of total energy from lipids

4. Now try these steps to calculate the percentage of the total energy she has consumed that comes from proteins. Make sure that the total equals 100%.

These calculations will be useful throughout this course as you learn more about how to design a healthy diet. Later in this book, you will learn how to estimate someone's energy needs and determine the appropriate amount of energy to consume from carbohydrates, fats, and proteins.

exert different health effects according to the type of fatty acids they contain. Some fatty acids are associated with an increased risk of chronic disease, whereas others—including essential fatty acids—are protective of our health. Triglycerides are an important energy source when we are at rest and during low- to moderate-intensity exercise. The human body is capable of storing large amounts of triglycerides as adipose tissue, or body fat. These fat stores can be broken down for energy during periods of fasting, such as while we are asleep. Foods that contain lipids are also important in providing fat-soluble vitamins.

Phospholipids are a type of lipid that contain phosphate. The body synthesizes phospholipids, and they are found in a few foods. Cholesterol is a form of lipid that is synthesized in the liver and other body tissues. It is also available in foods of animal origin such as meat and eggs. Chapter 5 provides a thorough review of lipids.

Proteins Support Tissue Growth, Repair, and Maintenance

Proteins also contain carbon, hydrogen, and oxygen, but they differ from carbohydrates and lipids in that they contain the element *nitrogen* (**Figure 1.10**). Within proteins, these four elements assemble into small building blocks known as *amino acids*. We break down

proteins Large, complex molecules made up of amino acids and found as essential components in all living cells.

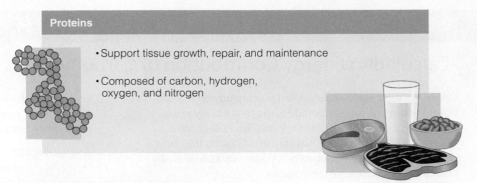

Proteins

• Support tissue growth, repair, and maintenance

• Composed of carbon, hydrogen, oxygen, and nitrogen

Figure 1.10 Proteins contain nitrogen in addition to carbon, hydrogen, and oxygen. Proteins support the growth, repair, and maintenance of body tissues.

dietary proteins into amino acids and reassemble them to build our own body proteins—for instance, the proteins in muscles and blood.

Although proteins can provide energy, they are not usually a primary energy source. Proteins play a major role in building new cells and tissues, maintaining the structure and strength of bone, repairing damaged structures, and assisting in regulating metabolism and fluid balance.

Proteins are found in many foods. Meats and dairy products are primary sources, as are seeds, nuts, and legumes. We also obtain small amounts of protein from vegetables and whole grains. Proteins are explored in detail in Chapter 6.

Vitamins Assist in the Regulation of Physiologic Processes

Vitamins are organic compounds that assist in the regulation of the body's physiologic processes. Contrary to popular belief, vitamins do not contain energy (or kilocalories); however, they do play an important role in the release and utilization of the energy found in carbohydrates, lipids, and proteins. They are also critical in building and maintaining healthy bone, blood, and muscle; supporting our immune system so we can fight illness and disease; and ensuring healthy vision. Because we need relatively small amounts of these nutrients to support normal health and body functions, the vitamins (in addition to minerals) are referred to as **micronutrients**. Some vitamins can be destroyed by heat, light, excessive cooking, exposure to air, and an alkaline (or basic) environment.

Vitamins are classified according to their solubility in water as either **fat-soluble** or **water-soluble** vitamins (Table 1.2). Their solubility in water affects how vitamins are absorbed, transported, and stored in body tissues. As our bodies cannot synthesize most vitamins, we must consume them in our diets. Both fat-soluble and water-soluble vitamins are essential for our health and are found in a variety of foods. Chapters 8 through 13 discuss individual vitamins in detail.

Fat-soluble vitamins are found in a variety of fat-containing foods, including dairy products.

vitamins Micronutrients that contain carbon and assist us in regulating our bodies' processes. They are classified as water-soluble or fat-soluble.

micronutrients Nutrients needed in relatively small amounts to support normal health and body functions. Vitamins and minerals are micronutrients.

fat-soluble vitamins Vitamins that are not soluble in water but soluble in fat. These include vitamins A, D, E, and K.

water-soluble vitamins Vitamins that are soluble in water. These include vitamin C and the B-vitamins.

Table 1.2 Overview of Vitamins

Type	Names	Distinguishing Features
Fat-soluble	A, D, E, and K	Soluble in fat Stored in the human body Toxicity can occur from consuming excess amounts, which accumulate in the body
Water-soluble	C, B-vitamins (thiamin, riboflavin, niacin, vitamin B_6, vitamin B_{12}, pantothenic acid, biotin, and folate)	Soluble in water Not stored to any extent in the human body Excess excreted in urine Toxicity generally only occurs as a result of vitamin supplementation

Table 1.3 Overview of Minerals

Type	Names	Distinguishing Features
Major minerals	Calcium, phosphorous, sodium, potassium, chloride, magnesium, sulphur	Needed in amounts greater than 100 mg/day in our diets Amount present in the human body is greater than 5 g (or 5000 mg)
Trace minerals	Iron, zinc, copper, manganese, fluoride, chromium, molybdenum, selenium, iodine	Needed in amounts less than 100 mg/day in our diets Amount present in the human body is less than 5 g (or 5000 mg)

Minerals Assist in the Regulation of Many Body Functions

Minerals are inorganic substances, meaning that they do not contain carbon. Some important dietary minerals include sodium, potassium, calcium, magnesium, zinc, and iron. Minerals differ from the macronutrients and vitamins in that they are not broken down during digestion or when the body uses them to promote normal function; and unlike certain vitamins, they are not destroyed by heat or light. Thus, all minerals maintain their structure no matter what environment they are in. This means that the calcium in our bones is the same as the calcium in the milk we drink, and the sodium in our cells is the same as the sodium in our table salt.

Minerals have many important physiologic functions. They assist in fluid regulation and energy production, are essential to the health of our bones and blood, and help rid the body of harmful by-products of metabolism. Minerals are classified according to the amounts we need in our diet and according to how much of the mineral is found in the body. The two categories of minerals in our diets and bodies are the **major minerals** and the **trace minerals** (Table 1.3). Chapters 9 through 13 discuss individual minerals in detail.

Peanuts are a good source of magnesium and phosphorous, which play an important role in the formation and maintenance of the skeleton.

Water Supports All Body Functions

Water is an inorganic nutrient that is vital for our survival. We consume water in its pure form, in juices, soups, and other liquids, and in solid foods such as fruits and vegetables. Adequate water intake ensures the proper balance of fluid both inside and outside of our cells and also assists in the regulation of nerve impulses and body temperature, muscle contractions, nutrient transport, and excretion of waste products. Because of the key role that water plays in our health, Chapter 10 focuses on water and its function in the body.

RECaP

The six essential nutrient groups found in foods are carbohydrates, lipids, proteins, vitamins, minerals, and water. Carbohydrates, lipids, and proteins are energy nutrients. Carbohydrates are the primary energy source; lipids provide fat-soluble vitamins and essential fatty acids and act as energy-storage molecules; and proteins support tissue growth, repair, and maintenance. Vitamins are organic compounds that assist with regulating a multitude of body processes. Minerals are inorganic elements that have critical roles in virtually all aspects of human health and function. Water is essential for survival and is important for regulating nerve impulses and body temperature, muscle contractions, nutrient transport, and excretion of waste products.

What Are the Current Dietary Recommendations and How Are They Used?

Now that you know what the six classes of nutrients are, you are probably wondering how much of each a person needs each day. But before you can learn more about specific nutrients and how to plan a healthy diet, you need to become familiar with current dietary standards and how these standards shape nutrition recommendations.

minerals Inorganic substances that are not broken down during digestion and absorption and are not destroyed by heat or light. Minerals assist in the regulation of many body processes and are classified as major minerals or trace minerals.

major minerals Minerals we need to consume in amounts of at least 100 mg per day and of which the total amount in our bodies is at least 5 g (or 5000 mg).

trace minerals Minerals we need to consume in amounts less than 100 mg per day and of which the total amount in our bodies is less than 5 g (or 5000 mg).

Did You Know?

The first dietary standards in Canada were issued by the Canadian Council on Nutrition (CCN) in 1939. The CCN was an organization that provided advice to the federal government on nutrition issues. In 1941, the first edition of the *Recommended Dietary Allowances* (RDAs), the dietary standards used in the United States, was published. These standards defined recommended intake values for various nutrients and were used to plan diets for both individuals and groups. The CCN adopted the RDAs for use in Canada for the sake of uniformity in 1942. However, because the RDAs were misused in evaluating group nutrient intakes, the CCN advised discontinuing their use in 1945 and a new Canadian standard was released. The 1983 version was the first to be called the *Recommended Nutrient Intakes* (RNIs). In 1995, Health Canada approached the Food and Nutrition Board (FNB) of the Institute of Medicine in the United States to collaborate on the development of harmonized nutrient-based recommendations. Thus, once again, Canada and the United States have the same dietary standards, now known as the *Dietary Reference Intakes* (DRIs).

The Dietary Reference Intakes Identify a Healthy Person's Nutrient Needs

In the past, as previously noted, dietary standards were set with the goal of preventing nutrient-deficiency diseases; however, in developed countries like Canada and the United States, these diseases are now extremely rare. The new **Dietary Reference Intakes (DRIs)** (**Figure 1.11**) are aimed at preventing and reducing the risk of chronic disease and promoting optimal health. These standards include and expand upon the former RDA and RNI values, and set new recommendation standards for nutrients that did not have RDA or RNI values.

The DRIs are dietary standards for healthy people only; they do not apply to people with diseases or those who are suffering from nutrient deficiencies. Like the RDAs and RNIs, they identify the amount of a nutrient needed to prevent deficiency diseases in healthy individuals, but they also consider how much of this nutrient may reduce the risk for chronic diseases in healthy people. The DRIs establish an upper level of safety for some nutrients and represent one set of values for both the United States and Canada.

Dietary Reference Intakes (DRIs) A set of nutritional reference values for the United States and Canada that applies to healthy people.

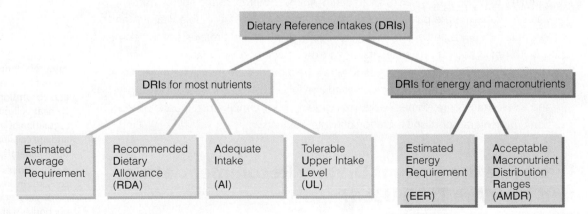
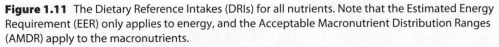

Figure 1.11 The Dietary Reference Intakes (DRIs) for all nutrients. Note that the Estimated Energy Requirement (EER) only applies to energy, and the Acceptable Macronutrient Distribution Ranges (AMDR) apply to the macronutrients.

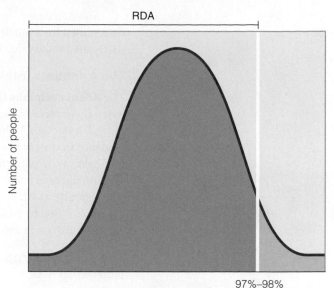

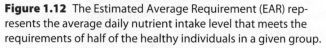

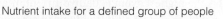

Figure 1.12 The Estimated Average Requirement (EAR) represents the average daily nutrient intake level that meets the requirements of half of the healthy individuals in a given group.

Figure 1.13 The Recommended Dietary Allowance (RDA) represents the average daily nutrient intake level that meets the requirements of almost all (97% to 98%) healthy individuals in a given life stage or gender group.

The DRIs for most nutrients consist of four values:

- Estimated Average Requirement (EAR)
- Recommended Dietary Allowance (RDA)
- Adequate Intake (AI)
- Tolerable Upper Intake Level (UL)

In the case of energy and the macronutrients, different standards are used. The standards for energy and the macronutrients include the Estimated Energy Requirement (EER) and the Acceptable Macronutrient Distribution Ranges (AMDR). The definitions for each of these DRI values are presented in the following section.

The Estimated Average Requirement Guides the Recommended Dietary Allowance

The first step in determining our nutrient requirements is to calculate the EAR. The **Estimated Average Requirement (EAR)** represents the average daily nutrient intake level estimated to meet the requirement of half of the healthy individuals in a particular life stage or gender group.[6] **Figure 1.12** provides a graph representing this value. As an example, the EAR for iron for women between the ages of 19 and 30 years represents the average daily intake of iron that meets the requirements of half of the women in this age group. The EAR is used by scientists to define the Recommended Dietary Allowance (RDA) for a given nutrient. Obviously, if the EAR meets the needs of only half the people in a group, then the recommended intake will be higher.

The Recommended Dietary Allowance Meets the Needs of Nearly All Healthy People

The **Recommended Dietary Allowance (RDA)** represents the average daily nutrient intake level that meets the nutrient requirements of 97% to 98% of healthy individuals in a particular life stage and gender group (**Figure 1.13**).[6] For example, the RDA for iron is 18 mg per day for women between the ages of 19 and 30 years. This amount of iron will meet the nutrient requirements of almost all women in this age category.

Estimated Average Requirement (EAR) The average daily nutrient intake level estimated to meet the requirements of half of the healthy individuals in a particular life stage or gender group.

Recommended Dietary Allowance (RDA) The average daily nutrient intake level that meets the nutrient requirements of 97% to 98% of healthy individuals in a particular life stage and gender group.

Again, scientists use the EAR to establish the RDA. In fact, if an EAR cannot be determined for a nutrient, then this nutrient cannot have an RDA. When this occurs, an Adequate Intake value is determined for a nutrient.

The Adequate Intake Is Based on Estimates of Nutrient Intakes

The **Adequate Intake (AI)** value is a recommended average daily nutrient intake level based on observed or experimentally determined estimates of nutrient intake by a group of healthy people.[6] These estimates are assumed to be adequate and are used when the evidence necessary to determine an RDA is not available. There are numerous nutrients that have an AI value, including vitamin K and fluoride. More research needs to be done on human requirements for the nutrients assigned an AI value so that an EAR, and subsequently an RDA, can be established.

In addition to establishing RDA and AI values for nutrients, an upper level of safety for nutrients, or Tolerable Upper Intake Level, has also been defined.

The Tolerable Upper Intake Level Is the Highest Level That Poses No Health Risk

The **Tolerable Upper Intake Level (UL)** is the highest average daily nutrient intake level likely to pose no risk of adverse health effects to almost all individuals in a particular life stage and gender group.[6] This does not mean that we should consume this intake level or that we will receive more benefits from a nutrient by meeting or exceeding the UL. In fact, as our intake of a nutrient increases in amounts above the UL, the potential for toxic effects and health risks increases. The UL value is a helpful guide to assist you in determining the highest average intake level that is deemed safe for a given nutrient. Note that there is not enough research to define the UL for all nutrients.

The Estimated Energy Requirement Is the Intake Predicted to Maintain a Healthy Weight

The **Estimated Energy Requirement (EER)** is defined as the average dietary energy intake that is predicted to maintain energy balance in a healthy adult. This dietary intake is defined by a person's age, gender, weight, height, and level of physical activity that is consistent with good health.[7] Thus, the EER for an active person is higher than the EER for an inactive person even if all other factors (age, gender, and so forth) are the same.

To calculate your EER you need to know your age (in years), weight (in kilograms), height (in metres), and physical activity (PA) value (see Table 1.4). The mathematical equations

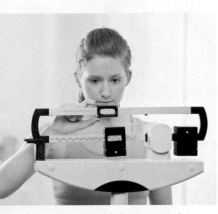

Knowing your daily Estimated Energy Requirement (EER) is a helpful step toward maintaining a healthy body weight. Your EER is defined by your age, gender, weight, height, and physical activity level.

Adequate Intake (AI) A recommended average daily nutrient intake level based on observed or experimentally determined estimates of nutrient intake by a group of healthy people.

Tolerable Upper Intake Level (UL) The highest average daily nutrient intake level likely to pose no risk of adverse health effects to almost all individuals in a particular life stage and gender group.

Estimated Energy Requirement (EER) The average dietary energy intake that is predicted to maintain energy balance in a healthy person.

Table 1.4 Physical Activity (PA) Categories and Values for Men and Women 19+ Years

Activity Level Category	Physical Activity Value		Description
	Men	**Women**	
Sedentary	1.00	1.00	Typical daily living activities (e.g., household tasks, walking to the bus)
Low active	1.11	1.12	Typical daily living activities plus 30 to 60 minutes daily of moderate activity (e.g., walking at 5 to 7 km/hr)
Active	1.25	1.27	Typical daily living activities plus at least 60 minutes daily of moderate activity
Very active	1.48	1.45	Typical daily living activities plus at least 60 minutes daily of moderate activity plus an additional 60 minutes of vigorous activity (e.g., jogging a 6 minute kilometre or skipping rope) or 120 minutes of moderate activity

Source: Dietary Reference Intakes Tables. Health Canada, 2010. Reproduced with the permission of the Minister of Health, 2012.

needed to determine the EER for children and adolescents and men and women of healthy weight (BMI = 18.5 − 24.9) are:

Children and Adolescents 3–18 years

Boys

3–8 yrs $EER = 88.5 - (61.9 \times age) + PA \times [(26.7 \times weight) + (903 \times height) + 20$

9–18 yrs $EER = 88.5 - (61.9 \times age) + PA \times [(26.7 \times weight) + (903 \times height) + 25$

Girls

3–8 yrs $EER = 135.3 - (30.8 \times age) + PA \times [(10.0 \times weight) + (934 \times height) + 20$

9–18 yrs $EER = 135.3 - (30.8 \times age) + PA \times [(10.0 \times weight) + (934 \times height) + 25$

Adults 19 years and older

Men $EER = 662 - [9.53 \times age] + PA \times [(15.91 \times weight) + (539.6 \times height)]$

Women $EER = 354 - [6.91 \times age] + PA \times [(9.36 \times weight) + (726 \times height)]$

Additional EER equations and the PA values can be found on the Health Canada website (www.hc-sc.gc.ca/fn-an/nutrition/reference/table/index-eng.php#eeer. Accessed January 12, 2012).

Source: Dietary Reference Intakes Tables. Health Canada, 2010. Reproduced with the permission of the Minister of Health, 2012.

The Acceptable Macronutrient Distribution Ranges Are Associated with Reduced Risk for Chronic Diseases

The **Acceptable Macronutrient Distribution Ranges (AMDR)** are ranges of intakes for a particular energy source that is associated with reduced risk of chronic disease while providing adequate intakes of essential nutrients.[7] The AMDR is expressed as a percentage of total energy or as a percentage of total kcal. The AMDR also has a lower and upper boundary; if we consume nutrients above or below this range, there is a potential for increasing our risk for poor health. The AMDRs for carbohydrate, fat, and protein are listed in Table 1.5.

Diets Based on the DRIs Promote Health

The primary goal of dietary planning is to develop an eating plan that is nutritionally adequate, meaning that the chances of consuming too little or too much of any nutrient are very low. To determine if your diet is adequate, you need to compare your nutrient intake with the DRI values. Since it is not possible to determine your individual nutrient requirements or your usual intake of nutrients with any degree of accuracy, experts have developed the following guidelines.[8]

Acceptable Macronutrient Distribution Ranges (AMDR) A range of intakes for a particular energy source that is associated with reduced risk of chronic disease while providing adequate intakes of essential nutrients.

a. If your usual intake is equal to or greater than the RDA, there is a low probability that your intake of that nutrient is inadequate, since intake at this level meets or exceeds the needs of almost all healthy individuals.

Table 1.5 Acceptable Macronutrient Distribution Ranges (AMDR) for Healthy Diets

Nutrient	AMDR*
Carbohydrate	45%–65%
Fat	20%–35%
Protein	10%–35%

*AMDR values expressed as percent of total energy or as percent of total calories.
Data from: Institute of Medicine, Food and Nutrition Board. 2005. *Dietary Reference Intakes for Energy, Carbohydrates, Fiber, Fat, Fatty Acids, Cholesterol, Protein, and Amino Acids (Macronutrients).* Washington, DC: National Academies Press. Reprinted by permission.

b. If your usual intake is between the RDA and the EAR, there is a 3% to 50% probability that your intake of that nutrient is inadequate.

c. If your usual intake is below the EAR, there is a high probability that your intake of that nutrient is inadequate.

d. For nutrients that have an AI instead of an EAR and RDA, if your usual intake exceeds the AI you are almost certainly achieving an adequate intake. However, if your nutrient intake is below the AI, it is impossible to say with any certainty whether or not your intake is adequate.

e. For nutrients that have a UL, if your usual intake is below the UL there is essentially no risk of adverse health effects. Be sure to check whether or not the UL refers to supplement intake only.

You should aim to achieve nutrient intakes that meet or exceed the RDA or AI and that remain below the UL. Your diet should also meet your needs for energy and your macronutrient distribution (% of energy from carbohydrate, protein, and fat) should fall within the AMDRs.

The DRI values are listed in a table on the inside cover of this book; they are also reviewed with each nutrient as it is introduced throughout this text. Find your own life-stage group and gender in the left-hand column, then simply look across to see each nutrient's value that applies. Using the DRI values in conjunction with diet planning tools such as *Eating Well with Canada's Food Guide* will ensure a healthy and adequate diet. Chapter 2 provides details on how you can use these tools to develop a healthy diet.

RECAP

The Dietary Reference Intakes (DRIs) are dietary standards for nutrients established for healthy people in a particular life stage or gender group. The Estimated Average Requirement (EAR) represents the nutrient intake level that meets the requirement of half of the healthy individuals in a group. The Recommended Dietary Allowance (RDA) represents the level that meets the requirements of 97% to 98% of healthy individuals in a group. The Adequate Intake (AI) is based on estimates of nutrient intake by a group of healthy people when there is not enough information to set an RDA. The Tolerable Upper Intake Level (UL) is the highest daily nutrient intake level that likely poses no health risk. The Estimated Energy Requirement (EER) is the average daily energy intake that is predicted to maintain energy balance in a healthy adult. The Acceptable Macronutrient Distribution Ranges (AMDR) are ranges of intakes associated with reduced risk of chronic disease and adequate intakes of essential nutrients.

How Do Nutrition Professionals Assess the Nutritional Status of Clients?

Before nutrition professionals can make valid recommendations about a client's diet, they need to have a thorough understanding of a client's current nutritional status, including weight, ratio of lean body tissue to body fat, and intake of energy and nutrients. The results of this assessment are extremely important, because they will become the foundation of any dietary or lifestyle changes that are recommended and will provide a baseline against which the success of any recommended changes are evaluated. For instance, if assessments reveal that an adolescent client is 10 kg underweight and consumes less than half the recommended amount of calcium each day, these baseline data are used to support a recommendation of increased energy and calcium intake and to evaluate the success of these recommendations in the future.

A client's nutritional status may fall anywhere along a continuum from healthy to imbalanced. Nutrition professionals use three terms to describe serious nutritional problems.

Malnutrition refers to a situation in which a person's nutritional status is out of balance; the individual is either getting too much or too little of a particular nutrient or energy over a significant period of time. **Undernutrition** refers to a situation in which someone consumes too little energy or too few nutrients over time, causing significant weight loss or a nutrient-deficiency disease. **Overnutrition** occurs when a person consumes too much energy or too much of a given nutrient over time, causing conditions such as obesity, heart disease, or nutrient toxicity.

Nutrition professionals use a number of tools to determine the nutritional status of a client. As you read about these in the following section, keep in mind that no one method is sufficient to indicate malnutrition. Instead, a combination of tools is used to confirm the presence or absence of nutrient imbalances.

A Physical Examination Is Conducted by a Healthcare Provider

Physical examinations should be conducted by a trained healthcare provider such as a physician, nurse, nurse practitioner, or physician assistant. The tests conducted during the examination depend on the client's medical history, disease symptoms, and risk factors. Typical tests may include vital signs (pulse, blood pressure, body temperature, and respiration rate) and auscultation of heart and lung sounds. Nutritional imbalances may be detected by examining the client's hair, skin, tongue, eyes, and fingernails.

A person's age and health status determine how often he or she needs a physical examination. It is typically recommended that a healthy person younger than 30 years of age have a thorough exam every 2 to 3 years. Adults aged 30 to 50 years should have an examination every 1 to 2 years, and individuals older than 50 years of age should have an exam on a yearly basis. However, individuals with established diseases or symptoms of malnutrition may require more frequent examinations.

Questionnaires Elicit Self-Reported Information

Health-history questionnaires are tools that assist in cataloguing a person's history of health, illness, drug use, exercise, and diet. These questionnaires are typically completed just prior to the physical examination by a nurse or other healthcare professional, or the patient may be asked to complete one independently. The questions included in health-history questionnaires usually relate to the following:

- Demographic information, including name, age, contact information, and self-reported height and body weight
- Current medication status, potential drug allergies, and history of drug use
- Family history of disease
- Personal history of illnesses, injuries, and surgeries
- History of menstrual function (for females)
- Exercise history
- Socio-economic factors such as education level, access to shopping and cooking facilities, marital status, and racial/ethnic background

In addition, specific questionnaires can be used to assess a person's nutrient and energy intakes. Examples include a diet history, 24-hour dietary recalls, food-frequency questionnaires, and diet records. As you read about each of these tools, bear in mind that they are all subjective; that is, they rely on a person's ability to self-report. The accuracy of the data cannot be empirically verified, as it can, for example, by repeating a measurement of a person's weight. Of these tools, the one or two selected by nutrition professionals will depend on what questions they wish to answer, the population they are working with, and the available resources. Following is a brief description of each.

Diet History

A diet history is typically conducted by a trained nutrition professional. Diet history information is gathered using either an interview process or a questionnaire. Information that is

malnutrition A nutritional status that is out of balance; an individual is either getting too much or not enough of a particular nutrient or energy over a significant period of time.
undernutrition A situation in which too little energy or too few nutrients are consumed over time, causing significant weight loss or a nutrient-deficiency disease.
overnutrition A situation in which too much energy or too much of a given nutrient is consumed over time, causing conditions such as obesity, heart disease, or nutrient toxicity.

generally included in the diet history includes current weight, usual weight, and body weight goals; factors affecting appetite and food intake; typical eating patterns (including time, place, dietary restrictions, frequency of eating out, and so forth); disordered eating behaviours (if any); economic status; educational level; living, cooking, and food-purchasing arrangements; medication and/or dietary supplement use; and physical activity patterns. A diet history can help identify any nutrition or eating problems and highlight a person's unique needs.

Twenty-Four-Hour Dietary Recalls

The 24-hour dietary recall is used to assess recent food intake. A trained nutrition professional interviews the person and records all of the person's responses. The person recalls all of the foods and beverages consumed in the previous 24-hour period. Information that the person needs to know to provide an accurate recall includes serving sizes, food-preparation methods, and brand names of convenience foods or fast foods that were eaten. The 24-hour recall has serious limitations, including the fact that it does not give an indication of a person's usual food intake; other limitations include reliance on a person's memory and his or her ability to estimate portion sizes.

Food-Frequency Questionnaires

Food-frequency questionnaires can assist in determining a person's usual dietary pattern over a predefined period of time, such as 1 month, 6 months, or 1 year. These questionnaires include lists of foods with questions regarding the number of times these foods are eaten during the specified time period. Some questionnaires only assess qualitative information, meaning they include only a list of typical foods that are eaten but do not include amounts of foods eaten. Semi-quantitative questionnaires are also available; these assess specific foods eaten and the quantity consumed.

Diet Records

A diet record is a list of all foods and beverages consumed over a specified time period, usually 3 to 7 days. The days selected for recording the person's diet should be representative of usual dietary and activity patterns.

The client is responsible for filling out the record accurately, and both training and take-home instructions are essential. The record is more accurate if all foods consumed are weighed or measured, labels of all convenience foods are saved, and labels of supplements are provided. Providing a food scale and measuring utensils can also assist people in improving the information obtained from diet records.

Although diet records can provide a reasonably good estimate of a person's energy and nutrient intakes, they are challenging to complete accurately and in sufficient detail. Because of this burden, people may change their intake to simplify completing the diet record. They may also change their intake simply because they know it will be analyzed; for example, a client who typically eats ice cream after dinner might forego this indulgence for the duration of the diet record. In addition, analyses are time-consuming and costly.

Diet records are forms that clients fill out to document all foods and beverages consumed over a specific time period.

Anthropometric and Biochemical Assessments Provide Objective Data

Anthropometric assessments are, quite simply, measurements of human beings (*anthropos* is a Greek word meaning "human"). The most common anthropometric measurements used include height and body weight. Other measurements that may be taken include head circumference in infants and waist circumference in adults. It is critical that the person taking anthropometric measurements is properly trained and uses the correct tools. Measurements are then compared with standards specific for a given age and gender. This allows health practitioners to determine if a person's body size or growth is normal for his or her age and gender. Repeated measurements can also be taken on the same person over time to assess trends in nutritional status and growth.

Although not technically considered an anthropometric assessment tool, body composition may also be measured. That is, the health practitioner will use one of several available methods to determine the ratio of fat tissue to non-fat tissue (or lean body mass) of which the client's body is composed. Specific details about body composition assessment are discussed in Chapter 14.

Biochemical assessments involve the laboratory analysis of a biological sample, usually blood or urine. For example, a person's iron status can be assessed by measuring the hemoglobin content of the blood. Biochemical assessments are more specific than anthropometric assessments in that they can help determine a specific nutrient deficiency or excess. However, laboratory values can be influenced by many factors and must always be interpreted in light of all other components of a complete nutritional assessment. For example, if an individual is dehydrated, their laboratory values will be artificially inflated and a true nutrient deficiency may be missed.

Think back to the advice that the nutritionist gave to Marilyn in our chapter-opening scenario. Now that you have learned about both subjective and objective methods for assessing a person's nutritional status, you probably recognize that the nutritionist failed to perform even a basic nutritional assessment; instead, she based her weight-loss recommendation solely on a measurement of Marilyn's blood pressure! Later in this chapter, we'll explore what the term *nutritionist* really means and discuss what it means to work within one's scope of practice. But for now, let's look at an example of how healthcare professionals use subjective and objective assessments to determine malnutrition.

Measuring height is a common anthropometric assessment, and when repeated over time can help determine a person's nutritional status.

A Finding of Malnutrition Requires Further Classification

If the results of nutrition assessment lead to a finding of malnutrition, the nutrition professional classifies the finding further as overnutrition or undernutrition (see page 21). Nutrient deficiencies are further classified as *primary* or *secondary*. **Primary deficiency** occurs when a person does not consume enough of a nutrient in the diet; thus, the deficiency occurs as a direct consequence of an inadequate intake. **Secondary deficiency** occurs when a person cannot absorb enough of a nutrient in his or her body, when too much of a nutrient is excreted from the body, or when a nutrient is not utilized efficiently by the body. Thus, a secondary deficiency is secondary to, or a consequence of, some other disorder.

Symptoms of a nutrient deficiency are not always obvious. A deficiency in its early stages, when few or no symptoms are observed, is referred to as a **subclinical deficiency**. The symptoms of a subclinical deficiency are typically **covert**, meaning they are hidden and require laboratory tests or other invasive procedures to detect. Once the symptoms of a nutrient deficiency become obvious, they are referred to as **overt**.

Figure 1.14 describes the stages in the development of a nutrient deficiency and shows which assessment methods can be used to determine whether an individual has a nutrient deficiency. Let's take vitamin C as an example.

The first stage of a deficiency develops as a result of an inadequate dietary intake of vitamin C (primary deficiency) or because an individual's body does not absorb enough, excretes too much, or is unable to use it (secondary deficiency). Conducting a diet history, food-frequency questionnaire, or 24-hour recall can provide clues to alert you to a primary deficiency. A more complete health history could identify any medical problems that might lead to a secondary deficiency.

Typically, the body will use its nutrient stores when insufficient amounts of a nutrient are being consumed. This leads to decreased nutrient stores, which can be detected by biochemical tests (subclinical deficiency). Vitamin C is a water-soluble nutrient so we have to consume it on a regular basis; any excess is excreted rather than stored. Thus, the next stage of the development of a vitamin C deficiency occurs when body functions are impaired (subclinical deficiency). At this stage, no outward signs or symptoms will be observed. However, measuring serum vitamin C levels can determine if vitamin C status is impaired.

Finally, after about one month, an individual will start to show physical signs and symptoms of a vitamin C deficiency (overt deficiency), such as bleeding gums, loose teeth, and hemorrhages around the hair follicles. A physical exam would identify these symptoms.

primary deficiency A deficiency that occurs when not enough of a nutrient is consumed in the diet.

secondary deficiency A deficiency that occurs when a person cannot absorb enough of a nutrient, excretes too much of a nutrient from the body, or cannot utilize a nutrient efficiently.

subclinical deficiency A deficiency in its early stages, when few or no symptoms are observed.

covert symptom A symptom that is hidden from a client and requires laboratory tests or other invasive procedures to detect.

overt symptom A symptom that is obvious to a client, such as pain, fatigue, or a bruise.

Stage		Assessment Method
Primary deficiency (caused by inadequate dietary intake)	→	Diet history, food-frequency questionnaire, 24-hour recall
or		
Secondary deficiency (secondary to another disorder)	→	Diet/health history
↓		
Decreased nutrient stores (subclinical deficiency)	→	Biochemical tests
↓		
Abnormal body functions (subclinical deficiency)	→	Biochemical tests
↓		
Physical signs and symptoms (overt deficiency)	→	Physical examination Anthropometric assessment

Figure 1.14 Stages in the development of a nutrient deficiency.

CASE STUDY ▶ Assessing Nutritional Status

Krista, a 15-year-old girl, has been referred by her doctor to the dietitian. Laboratory test results had indicated that Krista is suffering from a deficiency of iron. The dietitian conducts a complete nutritional assessment. The findings reveal that Krista follows a vegan diet, is physically active, and was in good health until the past six months. She is underweight and has pale skin. The dietitian asks Krista to complete three days of diet records and uses them to analyze her diet. She finds that, on average, Krista consumes 200 grams of carbohydrate, 40 grams of protein, and 90 grams of fat each day. Her average intake of iron is about 10 mg/day.

Thinking Critically

1. **Why did the dietitian ask Krista to complete a three-day food record rather than conduct a 24-hour recall?**
2. **How would you classify the type of deficiency that Krista has? Why?**
3. **What is Krista's average total daily kilocalorie intake?**
4. **What percentage of Krista's kilocalories come from fat? Carbohydrate? Protein?**
5. **How do these percentages compare with the appropriate AMDRs?**
6. **How does Krista's iron intake compare with the RDA for this nutrient?**

RECAP

Malnutrition refers to a person's nutritional status being out of balance; undernutrition is a situation in which someone consumes too little energy or too few nutrients over time, and overnutrition occurs when a person consumes too much energy or too much of a nutrient. Assessment tools that can be used to determine if malnutrition exists include a physical examination, a health-history questionnaire, a diet history, a 24-hour dietary recall, a food-frequency questionnaire, a diet record, and anthropometric and biochemical measures.

Research Study Results: Who Can We Believe?

"Eat more carbohydrates! Fats cause obesity!"

"Eat more protein and fat! Carbohydrates cause obesity!"

Do you ever feel overwhelmed by the abundant and often conflicting advice in media reports related to nutrition? If so, you are not alone. In addition to the "high-carb, low-carb" controversy, we've been told that calcium supplements are essential to prevent bone loss and that calcium supplements have no effect on bone loss; that high fluid intake prevents constipation and that high fluid intake has no effect on constipation; that coffee and tea could be bad for our health and that both can be beneficial! How can you navigate this sea of changing information? What constitutes valid, reliable evidence, and how can you determine whether or not research findings apply to you?

To become a more informed critic of product claims and nutrition news items, you need to understand the research process and how to interpret the results of different types of studies. Let's now learn more about research.

Research Involves Applying the Scientific Method

When confronted with a claim about any aspect of our world, from "The Earth is flat" to "Carbohydrates cause obesity," scientists, including nutritionists, must first consider whether or not the claim can be tested. In other words, can evidence be presented to substantiate the claim, and if so, what data would qualify as evidence? Scientists worldwide use a standardized method of looking at evidence called the *scientific method*. This method ensures that certain standards and processes are used in evaluating claims. The scientific method usually includes the following steps, which are described in more detail below and summarized in **Figure 1.15**:

- The researcher makes an *observation* and description of a phenomenon.
- The researcher proposes a *hypothesis* or educated guess to explain why the phenomenon occurs.
- The researcher develops an *experimental design* that will test the hypothesis.
- The researcher *collects and analyzes data* that will either support or reject the hypothesis.

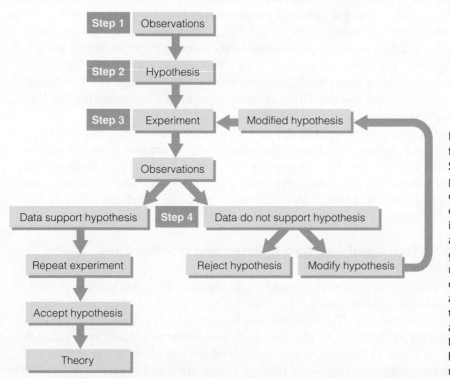

Figure 1.15 The scientific method, which forms the framework for scientific research. **Step 1:** Observations are made regarding some phenomenon, which lead researchers to ask a question. **Step 2:** A hypothesis is generated to explain the observations. **Step 3:** An experiment is conducted to test the hypothesis. Observations are made during the experiment, and data are generated and documented. **Step 4:** The data may either support or refute the hypothesis. If the data support the hypothesis, more experiments are conducted to test and confirm support for the hypothesis. A hypothesis that is supported after repeated testing may be called a theory. If the data do not support the hypothesis, the hypothesis is either rejected or modified and then retested.

- If the data do not support the original hypothesis, then an *alternative hypothesis* is proposed and tested.
- If the data support the original hypothesis, then a *conclusion* is drawn.
- The experiment must be *repeatable*, so other researchers can obtain similar results.
- Finally, a *theory* is proposed offering a conclusion drawn from repeated experiments that have supported the hypothesis time and time again.

Observation of a Phenomenon Initiates the Research Process

The first step in the scientific method is the observation and description of a phenomenon. As an example, let's say you are working in a healthcare office that caters to mostly older adult clients. You have observed that many of these clients have high blood pressure, but some have normal blood pressure. After talking with a large number of clients, you notice a pattern developing in that the clients who report being more physically active are also those having lower blood pressure readings. This observation leads you to question the relationship that might exist between physical activity and blood pressure. Your next step is to develop a *hypothesis*.

A Hypothesis Is a Possible Explanation for an Observation

A **hypothesis** is a possible explanation for your observation. In this example, your hypothesis might be, "Adults over age 65 with high blood pressure who begin and maintain a program of 45 minutes of aerobic exercise daily will experience a decrease in blood pressure." Your hypothesis must be written in such a way that it can be either supported or rejected. In other words, it must be testable.

An Experiment Is Designed to Test the Hypothesis

An *experiment* is a scientific study that is conducted to test a hypothesis. A well-designed experiment should include several key elements:

- The *sample size* or the number of people being studied should be adequate enough to ensure that the results obtained are not due to chance alone. For example, would you be more likely to believe a study that tested 5 people or 500?
- Having a *control group* is essential for comparison between treated and untreated individuals. A control group is a group of people who are as much like the treated group as possible except with respect to the *variable* being tested. For instance, in your study, 45 minutes of daily aerobic exercise would be the variable; the experimental group would consist of people over age 65 with high blood pressure who perform the exercise, and the control group would consist of people of the same age with high blood pressure who do not exercise. Using a control group helps a researcher to judge if a particular treatment has worked or not.
- A good experimental design also attempts to control for other variables that may coincidentally influence the results. For example, what if someone in your study was on a diet, smoked, or took blood-pressure-lowering medication? Because any of these factors could affect the results, researchers try to design experiments that have as many *constants* as possible. In doing so, they increase the chance that their results will be valid. To use an old saying, you can think of validity as "Comparing apples to apples."

Data Are Collected and Analyzed to Determine Whether They Support or Reject the Hypothesis

As part of the design of the experiment, the researcher must determine the type of data to collect and how it will be collected. For example, in your study the data being collected are blood pressure readings. These values could be collected by a person or a machine, but because the data will be closely scrutinized by other scientists, they should be as accurate as technology allows. In this case, an automatic blood pressure gauge would provide more reliable and consistent data than blood pressure measurements taken by research assistants.

hypothesis An educated guess as to why a phenomenon occurs.

Once the data have been collected, they must be interpreted or analyzed. Often, the data will begin to make sense only after being organized and put into different forms, such as tables or graphs, that reveal patterns that at first were not obvious. In your study, you can create a graph comparing blood pressure readings from both your experimental group and your control group to see if there is a significant difference between the blood pressure readings of those who exercised and those who did not.

Most Hypotheses Need to Be Refined

Remember that a hypothesis is basically a guess as to what causes a particular phenomenon. Rarely do scientists get it right the first time. The original hypothesis is often refined after the initial results are obtained, usually because the answer to the question is not clear and leads to more questions. When this happens, an alternative hypothesis is proposed, a new experiment is designed, and the new hypothesis is tested.

An Experiment Must Be Repeatable

One research study does not prove or disprove a hypothesis. Ideally, multiple experiments are conducted over many years to thoroughly test a hypothesis. Indeed, repeatability is a cornerstone of scientific investigation. Supporters and skeptics alike must be able to replicate an experiment and arrive at similar conclusions or the hypothesis becomes invalid. Have you ever wondered why the measurements used in scientific textbooks are always in the metric system? The answer is repeatability. Scientists use the metric system because it is a universal system and thus allows repeatability in any research facility worldwide.

Unfortunately, media reports on the findings of a research study that has just been published rarely include a thorough review of the other studies conducted on that topic. Thus, you should never accept one report in a newspaper or magazine as absolute fact on any topic.

A Theory May Be Developed Following Extensive Research

If the results of multiple experiments consistently support a hypothesis, then scientists may advance a **theory**. A theory represents a scientific consensus (agreement) as to why a particular phenomenon occurs. Although theories are based on data drawn from repeated experiments, they can still be challenged and changed as the knowledge within a scientific discipline evolves. For example, at the beginning of this chapter, we said that the prevailing theory held that beriberi was an infectious disease. Experiments were conducted over several decades before their consistent results finally confirmed that the disease was due to thiamin deficiency. We continue to apply the scientific method to test hypotheses and challenge theories today.

RECAP

The steps in the scientific method are (1) observing a phenomenon, (2) creating a hypothesis, (3) designing and conducting an experiment, and (4) collecting and analyzing data that support or refute the hypothesis. If the data are rejected, then an alternative hypothesis is proposed and tested. If the data support the original hypothesis, then a conclusion is drawn. A hypothesis that is supported after repeated experiments may be called a theory.

Different Types of Research Studies Tell Us Different Stories

Establishing nutrition guidelines and understanding the role of nutrition in health involve constant experimentation. Depending upon how the research study is designed, we can gather information that tells us different stories. Let's take a look at the different types of research.

theory A scientific consensus, based on data drawn from repeated experiments, as to why a phenomenon occurs.

Epidemiological studies indicate relationships between factors, such as between exercise and blood pressure in older adults, but cannot prove cause and effect.

Epidemiological Studies

Epidemiological studies are also referred to as observational studies. They involve assessing nutritional habits, disease trends, or other health phenomena of large populations and determining the factors that may influence these phenomena. However, these studies can only indicate relationships between factors, not specifically a cause-and-effect relationship. For example, let's say that an epidemiological study finds that the blood pressure values of physically active older adults are lower than those of inactive older adults. These results do not indicate that regular physical activity reduces blood pressure or that inactivity causes high blood pressure. All these results can tell us is that there is a relationship between higher physical activity and lower blood pressure in older adults.

Model Systems

Humans are not very good experimental models because it is difficult to control for all of the variables that affect their lives. Humans also have long lifespans, so it would take a long time to determine the effects of certain nutritional studies. For these reasons, laboratory studies generally involve experiments with animals. In many cases, animal studies provide preliminary information that can assist us in designing and implementing human studies. Animal studies also are used to conduct research that cannot be done with humans. For instance, it is possible to study nutritional deficiencies in animals by causing a deficiency and studying its adverse health effects over the lifespan of the animal; this type of experiment is not acceptable to perform with humans.

Animals with relatively short reproduction times can be studied when researchers need to look at the effects of specific drugs or treatments over many generations. Such animals can also be bred so they display specific traits such as certain diseases or metabolic conditions. One drawback of animal studies is that the results may not apply directly to humans. Another drawback is the ethical implications of studies involving animals, especially when the research reduces the animal's quality of life.

Human Studies

The two primary types of studies conducted with humans include case control studies and clinical trials. *Case control studies* are epidemiological studies done on a smaller scale. Case control studies involve comparing a group of individuals with a particular condition (for instance, older adults with high blood pressure) to a similar group without this condition (for instance, older adults with low blood pressure). This comparison allows the researcher to identify factors other than the defined condition that differ between the two groups. By identifying these factors, researchers can gain a better understanding of things that may cause and help prevent disease. In the case of your experiment, you may find that older adults with low blood pressure are not only more physically active, but also eat more fruits and vegetables and less sodium. These findings would indicate that other factors in addition to physical activity may play a role in affecting the blood pressure levels of older adults.

Clinical trials are tightly controlled experiments in which an intervention is given to determine its effect on a certain disease or health condition. Interventions may include medications, nutritional supplements, controlled diets, or exercise programs. Clinical trials include the experimental group, whose members are given the intervention, and the control group, whose members are not given the intervention. To minimize bias, individuals would be randomly assigned to these groups and unaware of which group they were in (blinded). The responses of the intervention group are compared to those of the control group. In the case of your experiment, you could assign one group of older adults with high blood pressure to an exercise program and assign a second group to a program in which no exercise is done. After the intervention phase was completed, you could compare the blood pressure of the people who exercised to those who did not. If the blood pressure of the intervention group decreased significantly and the blood pressure of the control group did not, then you could propose that the exercise program caused a decrease in blood pressure.

Among clinical trials, the type considered most likely to produce valid, reliable data is the *double-blind, placebo-controlled study*. In a double-blind study, neither researchers nor participants know which group is really getting the treatment. Blinding helps prevent the researchers from seeing only the results they want to see. A *placebo* is an imitation treatment that has no scientifically recognized therapeutic value, for instance, a sugar pill that looks, feels, smells, and tastes identical to the medication being tested. In a double-blind, placebo-controlled study, neither the researchers providing the treatment nor the study participants receiving it know whether the treatment being administered is the one being tested or a placebo.

Another important variable that cannot be overlooked in clinical trials is the effect of participation in the study on the subject's state of mind. This is known as the *psychosomatic effect* or *placebo effect*. Sometimes, just knowing they're in a study will cause individuals to experience physiological changes that they may interpret as therapeutic. For example, because the older adults in your study know they are part of a study concerning high blood pressure, they may subconsciously be more relaxed and content because they feel validated and important. They may therefore show a decrease in blood pressure. Similarly, people who take an "herbal supplement" believing that it will help relieve their insomnia may fall asleep more easily because of that belief, even if the pill that they swallow is actually a placebo.

Use Your Knowledge of Research to Help You Evaluate Media Reports

How can all of this research information assist you in becoming a better consumer and critic of media reports? By having a better understanding of the research process and types of research conducted, you are more capable of discerning the truth or fallacy within media reports. Keep the following points in mind when examining any media report:

- Who is reporting the information? If the report is made by a person or group who may financially benefit from you buying their products, you should be skeptical of the reported results. Also, many people who write for popular magazines and newspapers are not trained in science and are capable of misinterpreting research results.
- Who conducted the research, and who paid for it? Was the study funded by a company that stands to profit from certain results? Are the researchers receiving goods, personal travel funds, speaking fees, or other perks from the research sponsor, or do they have investments in companies or products related to their study? If the answer to

To become a more informed critic of nutrition reports in the media, and a smarter consumer, you need to understand the research process and how to interpret the results of different types of studies.

any of these questions is yes, there exists a conflict of interest between the researchers and the funding agency. If a conflict of interest does exist, it may seriously compromise the researchers' ability to conduct unbiased research and report the results in an accurate and responsible manner.

- Is the report based on reputable research studies? Did the research follow the scientific method, and were the results reported in a reputable scientific journal? Ideally, the journal is peer-reviewed; that is, the articles are critiqued by other specialists working in the same scientific field. A reputable report should include the reference, or source of the information, and should identify researchers by name. This allows the reader to investigate the original study and determine its merit. Some reputable nutrition journals are identified later in this chapter.

- Is the report based on testimonials about personal experiences? Are sweeping conclusions made from only one study? Be aware of personal testimonials, as they are fraught with bias. In addition, one study cannot answer all of our questions or prove any hypothesis, and the findings from individual studies should be placed in their proper perspective.

- Are the claims in the report too good to be true? Are claims made about curing disease or treating a multitude of conditions? If something sounds too good to be true, it probably is. Claims about curing diseases or treating many conditions with one product should be a signal to question the validity of the report.

As you may know, *quackery* is the misrepresentation of a product, program, or service for financial gain. Marilyn, the woman with high blood pressure from our opening story, was a victim of quackery. She probably would not have purchased that weight-loss supplement if she had understood that it was no more effective in promoting weight loss than a generic fibre supplement costing less than half the price. Throughout this text we provide you with information to assist you in becoming a more educated consumer regarding nutrition. You will learn about labelling guidelines, the proper use of supplements, and whether various nutrition topics are myths or facts. Armed with the information in this book, plus plenty of opportunities to test your knowledge, you will become more confident when trying to evaluate nutrition claims.

RECAP

Epidemiological studies involve large populations, model studies involve animals, and human studies include case control studies and clinical trials. Each type of study can be used to gather a different kind of data. When evaluating media reports, consider who is reporting the information, who conducted and paid for the research, whether or not the research was published in a reputable journal, and whether it involves testimonials or makes claims that sound too good to be true. Quackery is the misrepresentation of a product, program, or service for financial gain.

Nutrition Advice: Whom Can You Trust?

After reading this chapter, you can see that nutrition is a relatively new science that plays a critical role in preserving health and preventing and treating disease. As recognition of this vital role has increased over the past few decades, the public has become more and more interested in understanding how nutrition affects their health. One result of this booming interest has been the publication of an almost overwhelming quantity of nutritional information and claims on television infomercials; on websites; in newspapers, magazines, newsletters, and journals; on product packages; and via many other forums. Most individuals do not have the knowledge or training to interpret and evaluate the reliability of this information and thus are vulnerable to misinformation and potentially harmful quackery.

Evaluating Internet Information

The World Wide Web can provide you with a wealth of information but the quality of that information can vary widely, from very good to very bad. You need to be able to critically evaluate the information found on the internet to be able to decide if a particular website is credible and reliable. Consider the following criteria:

- Accuracy
  - Is the information fact or fiction? Is there a bibliography? If so, what is the quality of the sources being cited? Are there grammatical and spelling errors?
- Authority
  - Who is the author? What are his/her credentials? Is the sponsor, publisher, or website reputable?
- Purpose
  - Who is the information intended for and for what purpose? Is there any advertising on the page? If so, is it separate from the information provided?
- Currency
  - How old is the information? How often is it updated? How current are the links?
- Coverage
  - Is the information provided covered in sufficient depth? Does the information appear one-sided or biased?
- Site design
  - Is the website well organized? Easy to navigate?

For more information on evaluating sources on the internet, go to Evaluating Internet Research Sources (Robert Harris), www.virtualsalt.com/evalu8it.htm (accessed January 13, 2012).

Nutrition professionals are in a perfect position to work in a multitude of settings to counsel and educate their clients and the general public about sound nutrition practices. The following discussion identifies some key characteristics of reliable sources of nutrition information.

Trustworthy Experts Are Educated and Credentialed

It is not possible to list here all of the types of health professionals who provide reliable and accurate nutrition information. The following is a list of the most common groups:

- *Registered dietitian:* To become a **registered dietitian** in Canada requires a minimum of a bachelor's degree (specializing in foods and nutrition) from a Dietitians of Canada accredited university program, completion of a supervised internship program, a passing grade on a national examination, and registration with a provincial regulatory body. Dietitians who have met these criteria can use one of the following designations RD, RDN, PDt, or RDt (or the French equivalent Dt.P). Each province in Canada has its own laws regulating dietitians. Individuals who practise dietetics without the required registration can be prosecuted for breaking the law. You can contact Dietitians of Canada at www.dietitians.ca or the provincial regulatory body to obtain a list of dietitians in your area.[9]
- *Nutritionist:* The term *nutritionist* is not protected by law in all provinces, so people with different levels of training and knowledge can call themselves a nutritionist. There is no guarantee that a person calling himself or herself a nutritionist is necessarily educated, trained, and experienced in the field of nutrition. It is important to research the credentials and experience of anyone calling himself or herself a nutritionist. You should contact your provincial regulatory body to ensure that you are receiving services from a dietitian.
- *Professional with an advanced degree* (a master's degree [MA or MSc] or doctoral degree [PhD]) *in nutrition:* Many individuals hold an advanced degree in nutrition

registered dietitian (RD) A professional designation that requires a minimum of a bachelor's degree in nutrition, completion of a supervised internship experience, a passing grade on a national examination, and maintenance of registration with a provincial regulatory body. RDs are qualified to work in a variety of settings.

Medical doctors may have limited experience and training in the area of nutrition, but they can refer clients to a registered dietitian to assist them in meeting their dietary needs.

and have years of experience in a nutrition-related career. For instance, they may teach at community colleges or universities or work in fitness or healthcare settings. Unless these individuals are licensed or registered dietitians, they are not likely trained to provide clinical dietary counselling or treatment for individuals with disease. However, they are reliable sources of information about nutrition and health.

- *Physician:* The term *physician* encompasses a variety of healthcare professionals. A medical doctor (MD) is educated, trained, and licensed to practise medicine in Canada. However, MDs typically have very limited experience and training in the area of nutrition. Medical students in Canada are not required to take any nutrition courses throughout their academic training, although some may take courses out of personal interest. On the other hand, a number of individuals who started their careers in nutrition go on to become medical doctors and thus have a solid background in nutrition. Nevertheless, if you require a dietary plan to treat an illness or disease, most medical doctors will refer you to a dietitian. In contrast, an osteopathic physician, referred to as a doctor of osteopathy (DO), may have studied nutrition extensively, as may a naturopathic physician, a homeopathic physician, or a chiropractor. Thus, it is prudent to determine a physician's level of expertise rather than assuming that he or she has extensive knowledge of nutrition.

Government Sources of Information Are Usually Trustworthy

There are several government health agencies concerned with the nutritional health and well-being of Canadians. Three of the main ones are Health Canada, the Canadian Food Inspection Agency, and the Public Health Agency of Canada.

Health Canada is responsible for:[10]

- Establishing policies, setting standards, and providing advice and information on the safety and nutritional value of food.
- Promoting the nutritional health and well-being of Canadians by collaboratively defining, promoting, and implementing evidence-based nutrition policies and standards.
- Administering the provisions of the Food and Drugs Act that relate to public health, safety, and nutrition.
- Regulating the use of natural health products (NHPs) through the Natural Health Products regulations.

Health Canada Federal department responsible for helping Canadians maintain and improve their health.

Within Health Canada, the Office of Nutrition Policy and Promotion (ONPP) and Food Directorate are the main groups responsible for nutrition-related issues:

- The ONPP[11] is responsible for defining, promoting, and implementing evidence-based nutrition policies. It works collaboratively with its partners to develop nutrition policies and programs and to conduct nutrition research, monitor the nutritional health of Canadians, and evaluate policies and programs. Among its many activities, the ONPP supports the development and implementation of Canada's Food Guide and the Dietary Reference Intakes. It is also involved with food and nutrition surveillance and monitoring activities including the Canadian Community Health Survey (CCHS), and maintains the Canadian Nutrient File (CNF), the standard reference food composition database reporting the amount of nutrients in foods commonly consumed in Canada.
- The Food Directorate[12] is the federal health authority responsible for establishing policies, setting standards, and providing advice and information on the safety and nutritional value of food. Key activities of the Food Directorate include conducting scientific research and health risk/benefit assessments; developing policies, standards,

Lifestyle behaviours, such as eating an unhealthy diet, can increase your risk for chronic disease.

and guidelines; evaluating submissions from the food industry; and providing information to support Canadians in their decisions about food and diet.

The **Canadian Food Inspection Agency (CFIA)**[13] is responsible for the safety of our food supply. It develops and delivers programs designed to protect Canadians from food safety hazards, to ensure that food safety issues are handled in an efficient manner and that the Canadian public is aware of food safety issues including food allergens, food recalls, and causes of food-borne illness.

The **Public Health Agency of Canada's (PHAC)** main goal is to protect and improve the health of Canadians.[14] There are two main branches of the PHAC: Planning and Public Health Integration and Infectious Disease and Emergency Preparedness. The Centre for Health Promotion (CHP)[15] is situated within the Planning and Public Health Integration branch of the PHAC and is responsible for implementing policies and programs that enhance the health and wellness of Canadians. The Centre is composed of:

- Healthy Communities Division
- Division of Childhood and Adolescence
- Division of Aging and Seniors
- Health Surveillance and Epidemiology Division

The CHP is involved in many health promotion activities including the Pan-Canadian Healthy Living Strategy, the Canada Prenatal Nutrition Program (CPNP), Aboriginal Head Start (AHS), and the Community Action Program for Children.

To find out more about these agencies and their programs, see the Web Links at the end of this chapter.

Professional Organizations Provide Reliable Nutrition Information

There are several professional organizations and societies in Canada that represent nutrition professionals, scientists, and educators. These organizations publish nutrition research studies and provide educational information both for their members and the public. Some of these organizations include:

- *Dietitians of Canada (DC):* Dietitians of Canada is the national organization of food and nutrition professionals in Canada. The vision of this organization is to advance health through food and nutrition. The American equivalent is the Academy of Nutrition and Dietetics (AND). DC publishes a professional journal called the *Canadian Journal of Dietetic Practice and Research.*
- *Canadian Nutrition Society (CNS):* The CNS brings together various disciplines and professions interested in nutrition. Their mandate is to promote nutrition science and education and to advocate for the application of best practice and policies for the promotion of health and the prevention and treatment of disease. It was formed by a merger of the Canadian Society for Clinical Nutrition and the Canadian Society for Nutritional Sciences and became operational on January 1, 2010. The CNS supports the *Journal of Applied Physiology, Nutrition and Metabolism.*
- *The Canadian Public Health Association (CPHA):* The CPHA is a national association representing public health in Canada. Its mission is to advocate for the improvement and maintenance of personal and community health according to the public health principles of disease prevention, health promotion and protection, and healthy public policy. The CPHA publishes a peer-reviewed journal called the *Canadian Journal of Public Health.*

For more information on any of these organization, see the Web Links at the end of this chapter.

Canadian Food Inspection Agency (CFIA) A government agency that is responsible for the safety of the food supply, protecting the environment, and contributing to the health of Canadians.

Public Health Agency of Canada (PHAC) A government agency that is responsible for health promotion in Canada. Its mandate is to prevent and control chronic and infectious diseases and injuries and to prepare and respond to public health emergencies.

RECAP

Health Canada is the leading federal agency in Canada that protects human health and safety. Health Canada's Office of Nutrition Policy and Promotion and Food Directorate are the main groups responsible for nutrition-related issues. The Centre for Health Promotion is situated within the Public Health Agency of Canada and is responsible for policies and programs that enhance the health of Canadians. Dietitians of Canada, the Canadian Nutrition Society, and the Canadian Public Health Association are examples of professional organizations that provide reliable nutrition information.

SEE FOR YOURSELF

Take a piece of lined paper and divide it into four equal columns, labelled as follows:

■ Food Item
■ Serving Size
■ Time of Day
■ Location

The document you create will resemble a standard form used for a 24-hour dietary recall. Fill it out as carefully and thoroughly as you can, listing each food you ate yesterday, beginning and ending at midnight.

Now answer the following questions:

1. How confident are you that you documented every single item that you ate all day yesterday?
2. How confident are you that you recalled accurately the serving size of each food you ate?
3. Given your experience filling out a 24-hour dietary recall, what would you identify as the main limitations of this assessment tool?

Chapter Review

Test Yourself Answers

1. **F** A kilocalorie is a measure of the energy in a food. More precisely, a kilocalorie is the amount of heat required to raise the temperature of 1 kilogram of water by 1 degree Celsius.

2. **T** Carbohydrates and lipids are the primary energy sources for the body.

3. **F** Most water-soluble vitamins need to be consumed daily. However, we can consume foods that contain fat-soluble vitamins less frequently because our bodies can store these vitamins.

4. **F** The Recommended Dietary Allowance is the average daily nutrient intake level that meets the nutrient requirements of 97% to 98% of healthy individuals in a particular life stage and gender group.

5. **F** Other good sources are professional organizations in the field of nutrition research and education and individuals who are licensed or registered as nutrition professionals.

Summary

- Nutrition is the scientific study of food and how food nourishes the body and influences health.

- Early nutrition research focused on identifying, preventing, and treating nutrient-deficiency diseases. As the Western diet improved, obesity and its associated chronic diseases became an important subject for nutrition research. In the late 20th century, nutrigenomics emerged as a new field of nutrition research.

- Nutrition is an important component of health. Healthy nutrition plays a critical role in eliminating deficiency diseases and can help reduce our risks for various chronic diseases.

- The Pan-Canadian Healthy Living Strategy is a conceptual framework designed to promote optimal health using a population approach.

- Nutrients are chemicals found in food that are critical to human growth and function.

- The six essential nutrients found in the foods we eat are carbohydrates, lipids, and proteins, which provide energy and are known as the macronutrients; vitamins and minerals, which are micronutrients; and water.

- Carbohydrates are composed of carbon, hydrogen, and oxygen. Carbohydrates are the primary energy source for the human body, particularly for the brain.

- Lipids provide us with fat-soluble vitamins and essential fatty acids in addition to storing large quantities of energy.

- Proteins can provide energy if needed, but they are not a primary fuel source. Proteins support tissue growth, repair, and maintenance.

- Vitamins assist with the regulation of body processes.

- Minerals are inorganic substances that are not changed by digestion or other metabolic processes.

- Water is critical to support numerous body functions, including fluid balance, conduction of nervous impulses, and muscle contraction.

- The Dietary Reference Intakes (DRIs) are reference standards for nutrient intakes for healthy people in the United States and Canada.

- The DRIs include the Estimated Average Requirement, the Recommended Dietary Allowance, the Adequate Intake, the Tolerable Upper Intake Level, the Estimated Energy Requirement, and the Acceptable Macronutrient Distribution Range.

- Malnutrition occurs when a person's nutritional status is out of balance. Undernutrition occurs when someone consumes too little energy or nutrients, and overnutrition occurs when too much energy or too much of a given nutrient is consumed over time.

- Nutrition assessment methods include a physical examination, health-history questionnaire, dietary intake tools, and biochemical and anthropometric assessments. Specific dietary intake tools include a diet history, 24-hour recalls, food-frequency questionnaires, and diet records.

- A primary nutrient deficiency occurs when a person does not consume enough of a given nutrient in the diet. A secondary nutrient deficiency occurs when a person cannot absorb enough of a nutrient, when too much of a nutrient is excreted, or when a nutrient is not efficiently utilized.

- The steps in the scientific method are (1) observing a phenomenon, (2) creating a hypothesis, (3) designing and conducting an experiment, and (4) collecting and analyzing data that support or refute the hypothesis.

- A hypothesis that is supported after repeated experiments may be called a theory.

- Epidemiological studies involve large populations, model studies involve animals, and human studies include case control studies and clinical trials. A double-blind, placebo-controlled study is considered the most trustworthy form of clinical trial.

- When evaluating media reports, consider who is reporting the information, who conducted and paid for the research, whether or not the research was published in a reputable journal, and whether it involves testimonials or makes claims that sound too good to be true. Quackery is the misrepresentation of a product, program, or service for financial gain.

- Potentially good sources of reliable nutrition information include individuals who are registered dietitians, licensed nutritionists, or who hold an advanced degree in nutrition. Medical professionals such as physicians, osteopaths, and registered nurses have variable levels of training in nutrition.

- Health Canada is the leading federal agency that protects the health and safety of Canadians.

- The Office of Nutrition Policy and Promotion is responsible for defining, promoting, and implementing evidence-based nutrition policies and programs.

- The Food Directorate is the federal health authority responsible for establishing policies, setting standards, and providing advice and information on the safety and nutritional value of food.

- The Public Health Agency of Canada's goal is to protect and improve the health of Canadians.

Review Questions

1. Vitamins A and C, thiamin, calcium, and magnesium are considered
   a. water-soluble vitamins.
   b. fat-soluble vitamins.
   c. energy nutrients.
   d. micronutrients.

2. Malnutrition plays a role in which of the following?
   a. obesity
   b. iron-deficiency anemia
   c. scurvy
   d. all of the above

3. Ten grams of fat
   a. contain 40 kcal of energy.
   b. contain 90 kcal of energy.
   c. constitute the Dietary Reference Intake for an average adult male.
   d. constitute the Tolerable Upper Intake Level for an average adult male.

4. Which of the following assessment methods provides objective data?
   a. 24-hour dietary recall
   b. history of illnesses, injuries, and surgeries
   c. measurement of height
   d. diet record

5. Which of the following statements about hypotheses is true?
   a. Hypotheses can be proven by clinical trials.
   b. If the results of multiple experiments consistently support a hypothesis, it is confirmed as fact.
   c. "A high-protein diet increases the risk for porous bones" is an example of a valid hypothesis.
   d. "Many inactive people have high blood pressure" is an example of a valid hypothesis.

6. Explain the difference between organic and inorganic nutrients.

7. How do the new dietary standards (DRIs) differ from the old standards (RNIs)?

8. What is the difference between a primary nutrient deficiency and a secondary nutrient deficiency?

9. Explain the role of the control group in a clinical trial.

10. Compare the Estimated Average Requirement with the Recommended Dietary Allowance.

11. Imagine that you are in a gift shop and meet Marilyn, from the chapter-opening scenario. Learning that you are studying nutrition, she tells you of her experience and states that the supplements "didn't seem to do much of anything." She asks you, "How can I find reliable nutrition information?" How would you answer?

12. Your mother, who is a self-described "chocolate addict," phones you. She has read in the newspaper a summary of a research study suggesting that the consumption of a moderate amount of bittersweet chocolate reduces the risk of heart disease in older women. You ask her who funded the research. She says she doesn't know and asks you why it would matter. Explain why such information is important.

13. Intrigued by the idea of a research study on chocolate, you obtain a copy of the full report. In it, you learn that:
    - twelve women participated in the study;
    - the women's ages ranged from 65 to 78;
    - the women had all been diagnosed with high blood pressure;
    - they all described themselves as sedentary; and
    - six of the twelve smoked at least half a pack of cigarettes a day, but the others did not smoke.

Your mother is 51 years old, walks daily, and takes a weekly swim class. Her blood pressure is on the upper end of the normal range. She does not smoke. Identify at least three aspects of the study that would cause you to doubt its relevance to your mother.

Web Links

www.dietitians.ca
Dietitians of Canada
Obtain a list of registered dietitians in your community and information about careers in dietetics. Resources are also available for the public on planning a healthy diet.

www.eatracker.ca
eaTracker
Visit this website to evaluate the nutrient composition of your diet and to track your daily physical activity.

www.statcan.gc.ca
Statistics Canada
Get the latest information on prevalence of nutrition-related diseases and conditions, including trends in adult and childhood obesity in Canada.

www.hc-sc.gc.ca/fn-an/index-eng.php
Health Canada (Food and Nutrition)
Find out more about what Health Canada is doing to promote the nutritional health and well-being of Canadians.

www.hc-sc.gc.ca/dhp-mps/prodnatur/index-eng.php
Natural Health Products Directorate
Learn more about the regulations regarding the use of natural health products in Canada.

www.phac-aspc.gc.ca/index-eng.php
Public Health Agency of Canada
Look for additional information on policies and programs related to health promotion and illness prevention. The Integrated Pan-Canadian Healthy Living Strategy (2005) and Obesity in Canada: A Snapshot are just two of the many reports related to nutrition that can be found on this website.

www.inspection.gc.ca/english/fssa/fssae.shtml
Canadian Food Inspection Agency
Go to this site to find fact sheets on food recalls, food allergens, and causes of food-borne illness.

www.cns-scn.ca/HOME/default.asp
Canadian Nutrition Society
Go to this site for additional information on the CNS and its goals to promote nutrition science and education.

www.cpha.ca/en/default.aspx
Canadian Public Health Association
Obtain information on conferences, publications, and resources related to public health in Canada.

www.cancer.ca
Canadian Cancer Society
Provides up-to-date information on cancer incidence and mortality rates.

www.diabetes.ca
Canadian Diabetes Association
Obtain information on the prevalence and cost of diabetes in Canada.

www.heartandstroke.ca
Heart and Stroke Foundation of Canada
Access relevant and current statistics on heart disease and stroke as well as their related risk factors in Canada.

www.osteoporosis.ca
Osteoporosis Canada
Learn more about the status of osteoporosis care in Canada.

MasteringNutrition®

www.masteringnutrition.pearson.com

Assignments
Animation: Dietary Reference Intakes (DRI) Determination
Activities: NutriTools

Study Area
Practice Tests • Study Tools • Diet Analysis • eText

Study on the Go
At the end of every chapter, you will find a QR code like the one here that provides access to Study on the Go, linking you to extra resources including quizzes and glossary flashcards. You can link to Study on the Go content through your smartphone, allowing you to study whenever and wherever you wish.

References

1. Carpenter, K. J. 2000. *Beriberi, White Rice, and Vitamin B: A Disease, a Cause, and a Cure.* Berkeley, CA: University of California Press.

2. Jacka, F., J. A. Pasco, L. J. Williams, A. M. Hodge, S. L. O'Reilly, G. C. Nicholson, M. A. Kotowicz, and M. Berk. 2010. Association of western and traditional diets with depression and anxiety in women. *Am. J. Psychiatry* 167:305–311.

3. Fox, K. R. 1999. The influence of physical activity on mental well-being. *Public Health Nutrition* 2:411–418.

4. Dinca-Panaitescu, S., M. Dinca-Panaitescu, T. Bryant, I. Daiski, B. Pilkington, and D. Raphael. 2010. Diabetes prevalence and income: Results of the Canadian Community Health Survey. *J. Health Policy* (July 18), Epub Doi:10.1016/j.healthpol.2010.07.018.

5. Statistics Canada. 2004. Infant mortality among First Nations and non-First Nations people in British Columbia 1981 to 2000. Available at www.statcan.gc.ca/daily-quotidien/041109/dq041109c-eng.htm.

6. Institute of Medicine, Food and Nutrition Board. 2003. *Dietary Reference Intakes: Applications in Dietary Planning.* Washington, DC: National Academies Press.

7. Institute of Medicine, Food and Nutrition Board. 2005. *Dietary Reference Intakes for Energy, Carbohydrates, Fiber, Fat, Protein and Amino Acids (Macronutrients).* Washington, DC: National Academies Press.

8. Barr, S. I. 2006. Applications of dietary reference intakes in dietary assessment and planning. *Applied Physiology, Nutrition and Metabolism* 31:66–73.

9. Dietitians of Canada. 2010. What is the difference between a dietitian and a nutritionist? Available at www.dietitians.ca/public/content/career_in_nutrition/difference_dietitian_nutritionist.asp.

10. Health Canada. 2010. Food and Nutrition. Available at www.hc-sc.gc.ca/fn-an/index-eng.php.

11. Health Canada. 2005. Office of Nutrition Policy and Promotion. Available at www.hc-sc.gc.ca/ahc-asc/branch-dirgen/hpfb-dgpsa/onpp-bppn/index-eng.php.

12. Health Canada. 2005. Food Directorate. Available at www.hc-sc.gc.ca/ahc-asc/branch-dirgen/hpfb-dgpsa/fd-da/index-eng.php.

13. Canadian Food Inspection Agency. 2010. Available at www.inspection.gc.ca/english/agen/agene.shtml.

14. Public Health Agency of Canada. 2010. About the Agency. Available at www.phac-aspc.gc.ca/about_apropos/index-eng.php.

15. Public Health Agency of Canada. 2010. Centre for Health Promotion. Available at www.phac-aspc.gc.ca/chhd-sdsh/index-eng.php.

16. Watters, E. 2006. DNA is not destiny. *Discover* 27(11):32–75.

17. Johnson, N., and J. Kaput. 2003. Nutrigenomics: An emerging scientific discipline. *Food Technology* 57(4):60–67.

18. Grierson, B. 2003. What your genes want you to eat. *New York Times*, May 4.

19. Fontaine-Bisson, B., T. Wolever, P. Connelly, P. Corey, and A. Sohemy. 2009. NF-$_k$B-94Ins/Del ATTG polymorphism modifies the association between dietary polyunsaturated fatty acids and HDL-cholesterol in two distinct populations. *Atherosclerosis* 204:465–470.

20. Ozsunger, S., D. Brenner, and A. El-Sohemy. 2009. Fourteen well described caffeine withdrawal symptoms factor into three clusters. *Psychopharmacology* 201:541–548.

21. Eny, K., T. Wolever, B. Fontain-Bisson, and A. El-Sohemy. 2008. Genetic variant in the glucose transporter type 2 is associated with higher intakes of sugars in two distinct populations. *Physiological Genomics* 33:355–360.

22. Wallace, K. 2007. Diet, exercise may lower colon cancer risk [television broadcast]. CBS News, March 15.

23. Kaput, J., and R. Rodriguez. 2004. Nutritional genomics: The next frontier in the post-genomic era. *Physiological Genomics* 16:166–177.

24. Human Genome Project Information. 2008. How many genes are in the human genome? Retrieved February 2009 from www.ornl.gov/sci/techresources/Human_Genome/faq/genenumber.shtml.

25. Underwood, A., and J. Adler. 2005. Diet and genes. *Newsweek*, January 17, p. 40.

26. Sterling, R. 2008. The on-line promotion and sale of nutrigenomic services. *Genet Med.*, November, 10(11):784–796.

27. Ryan-Harshman, M., E. Vogel, H. Jones-Taggart, J. Green-Johnson, D. Castle, Z. Austin, and K. Anderson. 2008. Nutritional genomics and dietetic professional practice. *Can. J. Diet. Pract. Res.* 69:177–182.

28. Mathers, J. 2004. The biological revolution—towards a mechanistic understanding of the impact of diet on cancer risk. *Mutation Res.* 551:43–49.

29. Patterson, R., D. Eaton, and J. Potter. 1999. The genetic revolution: change and challenge for the dietetics profession. *J. Am. Diet. Assoc.* 99:1412–1420.

Nutrigenomics: Personalized Nutrition or Pie in the Sky?

Agouti mice are specifically bred for scientific studies. These mice are normally yellow in colour, obese, and prone to cancer and diabetes, and they typically have a short lifespan. When agouti mice breed, these traits are passed on to their offspring. Look at the picture of the agouti mice on this page; do you see a difference? The mouse on the right is obviously brown and of normal weight, but what you can't see is that it did not inherit its parents' susceptibility to disease and therefore will live a longer, healthier life. What caused this dramatic difference between parent and offspring? The answer is diet![16]

In 2000, researchers at Duke University found that when they changed the mother's diet just before conception, they could "turn off" the agouti gene, and any offspring born to that mother would appear normal.[16] As you might know, a *gene* is a segment of DNA, the substance responsible for inheritance, or the passing on of traits from parents to offspring, in both animals and humans. An organism's *genome* is its complete set of DNA, which is found packed into the nucleus of its body cells. Genes are precise regions of DNA that encode instructions for making specific proteins. In other words, genes are *expressed* in proteins; for instance, one way that the agouti gene is expressed is in the pigment proteins that produce yellow fur. We'll discuss genes and proteins in more detail in Chapter 6.

The Duke University researchers interfered with normal gene expression in their agouti mice by manipulating the mice's diet. Specifically, they fed the mother a diet that was high in methyl donors, compounds that can transfer a methyl group (CH_3) to another molecule. Methylation is thought to play a role in genetic expression. Sure enough, the methyl donors attached to the agouti gene and, in essence, turned it off. When the mother conceived, her offspring still carried the agouti gene on their DNA, but their cells no longer used the gene to make proteins. In short, the gene was no longer expressed; thus, the traits such as obesity that were linked to the agouti gene did not appear in the offspring.[16] These Duke University studies were some of the first to directly link a dietary intervention to a genetic modification and contributed significantly to the emerging science of *nutrigenomics* (or *nutritional genomics*).

Prompted only by a change in her diet before she conceived, an inbred agouti mouse (left) gave birth to a young mouse (right) that differed not only in appearance but also in its susceptibility to disease.

What Is Nutrigenomics?

Nutrigenomics is a scientific discipline studying the interactions between genes, the environment, and nutrition.[17] Scientists have known for some time that diet and environmental factors can contribute to disease, but what has not been understood before is *how*—namely, by altering how our genes are expressed. Until the late 20th century, scientists believed that the genes a person is born with determined his or her traits rigidly; in other words, that gene expression was not susceptible to outside influences. But the theory behind nutrigenomics is that genetic expression is indeed influenced—perhaps significantly—by foods we eat and substances in our environment to which our cells are exposed.

Nutrigenomics proposes that foods and environmental factors can act like a switch in body cells, turning on some genes while turning off others. When a gene is activated, it will instruct the cell to create a protein that will show up as a physical characteristic or functional ability, such as a protein that facilitates the storage of fat. When a gene is switched off, the cell will not create that protein, and the organism's form or function will differ. Some of the factors thought most likely to affect gene activation include tobacco, drugs, alcohol, environmental toxins, radiation, exercise, and the foods most common to an individual's diet.[17]

In addition, nutrigenomics scientists are discovering that what we expose our genes to—such as food and smoke—can affect gene expression not only in the exposed organism but in his or her offspring.[16] In the Duke University study, switching off the agouti gene caused beneficial changes in the offspring mice. But sometimes flipping the switch can be harmful, as when paternal exposure to radiation causes changes in sperm cells that increase the likelihood of birth defects in the offspring.

In short, nutrigenomics proposes that foods and environmental factors can influence the expression of our genes and possibly influence the traits of our children. It's an intriguing theory—but beyond the agouti study, what evidence supports it?

Evidence for Nutrigenomics

Several observations over many decades certainly suggest that the theory has merit. For example, nutrition researchers have long noted that some people will lose weight on a specific diet and exercise program, whereas others following the same diet and exercise program will experience no weight loss or will even gain weight.[17, 18] The varying results are now thought to depend to a certain extent upon how the foods in that diet affect the study participants' genes.

Evidence of nutrigenomics influencing future generations includes the breakthrough study of agouti mice, as well as recent historical data that suggest a link between the availability of food and type 2 diabetes. Researchers have found that when one generation experiences a food surplus during critical periods of reproductive development, their offspring are more likely to develop type 2 diabetes.[16]

Dr. El-Sohemy, a Canada Research Chair in Nutrigenomics at the University of Toronto, and colleagues have investigated how genetic influences modify the association between dietary polyunsaturated fatty acids and HDL-cholesterol and the subsequent development of coronary heart disease,[19] the genetics of our response to caffeine,[20] and genetic determinants of sugar consumption.[21] The overall goal of his research program is to identify biomarkers of dietary exposure and, ultimately, to develop an understanding of the basis for the variability in nutrient response and dietary preferences in humans.

Promises of Nutrigenomics

Currently, researchers involved in nutrigenomics are making predictions not unlike that of the famous inventor Thomas Edison: "The doctor of the future will give no medicine but will interest his patients in the care of the human frame, in diet, and in the cause and prevention of disease."

One promise of nutrigenomics is that it can assist people in optimizing their health by reducing their risk of developing diet-related diseases and possibly even by treating existing conditions through diet alone.[17] For example, some research is now studying how leafy green vegetables may "turn on" an important gene that suppresses cancerous tumours.[22]

Another promise of nutrigenomics is personalized nutrition. Today, dietary advice is based primarily on observations of large populations. Typically, these epidemiological studies do not consider variations within the group.[17] But advice that is generally appropriate for a population might not be appropriate for every individual

Nutrigenomics suggests that dietary and environmental factors can either activate or turn off some of the genes a person inherits from his or her parents.

within that population. For example, most Canadians are overweight or obese and need dietary advice that can help them lose weight. But some Canadians are chronically underweight and need advice for increasing their energy intake. Advances in nutrigenomics could eliminate this concern by making it possible to provide each individual with a personalized diet. In this future world, you would provide a tissue sample to a healthcare provider who would send it to a lab for genetic analysis. The results would guide the provider in creating a diet tailored to your specific genetic makeup. By identifying both foods to eat and foods to avoid, this personalized diet would help you to turn on beneficial genes and turn off genes that could be harmful.

Another promise of nutrigenomics is increased understanding of the role of physical activity in human health. Recent research shows that exercise can influence genes involved in certain diseases, such as colon cancer. Dr. Anne McTiernan of the Fred Hutchinson Cancer Research Center in Seattle has found that exercise can reduce the risk of colon cancer by 50%. McTiernan has observed that study participants who exercised at least four hours a week turned abnormal-looking cells that had the potential to develop into polyps and even colon cancer into normal-functioning cells.[22] Thus, nutrigenomics is finding that the conventional advice to "eat a balanced diet and exercise" holds true for the majority of people.

Challenges of Nutrigenomics

If the promises of nutrigenomics strike you as pie in the sky, you're not alone. Many researchers caution, for example, that dietary "prescriptions" to prevent or treat chronic diseases would be extremely challenging because multiple genes may be involved, and environmental, emotional, and even social factors may also play a role.[23] In addition, genetics researchers currently believe that there are about 20 000 to 25 000 genes in human DNA, representing only about 2% of the human genome.[24] The remaining regions of DNA are considered non-coding but are thought to have other functions, many of which may influence nutrition and health. Moreover, the pathways for genetic expression are extremely complex, and turning on a gene may have a beneficial effect on one body function but a harmful effect on another. To complicate the matter further, other factors such as age, gender, and lifestyle will also affect how different foods interact with these different genetic pathways. In short, the number of variables that must be considered in order to develop a "personalized diet" is staggering.

Even by themselves, food interactions are extremely complicated because when one eats a meal, hundreds of nutrient compounds are consumed at one time. Think about all the ingredients found in just one food item, such as pancakes. Each one of these ingredients may interact with a variety of genes directly or indirectly in an uncontrollable and inestimable number of ways.[23] As an example, scientists have determined that at least 150 different genes are linked to type 2 diabetes, and 300 or more have been linked to obesity. Which of the ingredients consumed affect what gene and how? It will be years before researchers are capable of mapping out these complex interactions.[25]

This daunting complexity has not stopped companies from offering naïve consumers nutrigenomics products and services ranging from at-home testing kits to "personalized" diets. One study of online sales of nutrigenomics services called such practices premature and concluded that organizations did not provide adequate information about their offerings.[26] Considering these challenges, regulation of the nutrigenomics industry is a growing concern. But what agency should be responsible? Currently Health Canada monitors and regulates food production and food safety, as well as the safety of medications and many medical devices. In the absence of such oversight, the safety of nutrigenomics services is likely to become a real concern as increasing numbers of consumers fall prey to fraudulent or even dangerous dietary advice.

Ethical Issues and Nutrigenomics

Major scientific advancements are often associated with ethical dilemmas.[27] There is still a great deal of uncertainty related to the potential impact of nutrigenomics on the public's health. On the one hand, having genetic information related to disease risk can empower individuals to take charge of their own health. However, being able to predict whether one is at risk of a particular disease does not necessarily mean that the disease can be prevented. There is the potential for this genetic information to result in a sense of fatalism that may lead to high-risk behaviours rather than encouraging individuals to change their behaviours to improve overall health.[28] Further, Patterson and colleagues raise a concern about the potential psychosocial effects of being labelled as "disease susceptible" or "disease resistant."[29] Ethical questions might also arise in relation to Canada's universal healthcare system. If population-based genotype screening can reduce healthcare costs, should all Canadians be required

to undergo genetic testing for the common good? Clearly, ethics is an important issue to consider in the debate about nutrigenomics.

When Will Nutrigenomics Become a Viable Healthcare Option?

Delivering on the promises of nutrigenomics will require a multidisciplinary approach involving researchers in genetics, nutrition, chemistry, molecular biology, physiology, pathology, sociology, ethics, and many more. The number and complexity of nutritional, environmental, and genetic interactions these scientists will have to contend with are so staggering that decades may pass before nutrigenomics is able to contribute significantly to human health.

Consumers will probably first encounter nutrigenomics in diagnostic testing. In this process, a blood or tissue sample of DNA will be genetically analyzed to determine how food and food supplements interact with that individual's genes and how a change in diet might affect those interactions. Genetic counselling will be required to help consumers understand the meaning and recommendations suggested by their genetic profile.[17]

Second, consumers will probably begin to see more specialized foods promoted for specific conditions. For example, consumers currently have an array of foods they can choose from if they want to lower their cholesterol or enhance their bone health. More such foods will likely be developed, and food packages of the future might even be coded for certain genetic profiles.

We may be decades away from a "personalized diet," but one thing is clear right now: nutrigenomics is showing us the importance of nutrition and environmental factors in preserving our health. In doing so, nutrigenomics is changing not only the way we look at food but the science of nutrition itself.

Using the Evidence

1. Are personalized diets and food packages coded for certain genetic profiles part of our future?

2. When you experience poor health, will you consult a nutrigenomics professional instead of a physician and get a prescription for foods instead of medicines?

3. Will nutrigenomics advance preventive medicine and reduce our rate of obesity and other chronic diseases?

4. If so, will it lower healthcare costs?

5. What might some of the challenges be to acting upon information provided by nutrigenomics?

2

Designing a Healthy Diet

Test Yourself | True *or* False?

1. A healthy diet is made up predominantly of fruits and vegetables. T *or* F

2. All foods sold in Canada must display a food label. T *or* F

3. *Eating Well with Canada's Food Guide* was developed by Health Canada as an education tool to promote healthy eating. T *or* F

4. *Eating Well with Canada's Food Guide* recommends that all Canadians should limit alcohol consumption. T *or* F

5. It is impossible to eat a healthy diet when eating out. T *or* F

Test Yourself answers are located in the Chapter Review.

Chapter Objectives | *After reading this chapter, you will be able to:*

1. Define the components of a healthy diet, *pp. 44–47.*

2. Read a food label and use the Nutrition Facts table to determine the nutritional adequacy of a given food, *pp. 47–50.*

3. Distinguish between label claims related to nutrient content or health, *pp. 49–50.*

4. Identify the food groups, number of servings, and serving sizes included in Canada's Food Guide, *pp. 52–61.*

5. Describe how Canada's Food Guide can be used to design a healthy diet, *pp. 62–65.*

6. List at least four ways to practise moderation and apply healthy dietary guidelines when eating out, *pp. 67–70.*

Each person needs to determine her or his own pattern of healthy eating.

S hivani and her parents moved to Canada from India when Shivani was 6 years old. Although delicate in comparison to her Canadian peers, Shivani was healthy and energetic, excelling in school and riding her new bike in her suburban neighbour-hood. By the time Shivani entered high school, her weight had caught up to that of her Canadian classmates. Now a first-year college student, she has joined the more than 26% of Canadian teens who are overweight.[1] Shivani explains, "In India, the diet is mostly rice, lentils, and vegetables. Many people are vegetarians, and many others eat meat only once or twice a week, and very small portions. Desserts are only for special occasions. When we moved to Canada, I wanted to eat like all the other kids: hamburgers, French fries, soft drinks, and sweets. I gained a lot of weight on that diet, and now my doctor says my cholesterol, my blood pressure, and my blood sugar levels are all too high. I wish I could start eating like my relatives back in India again, but they don't serve rice and lentils at the dorm cafeteria."

What influence does diet have on health? What exactly qualifies as a "poor diet," and what makes a diet healthy? Is it more important to watch how much we eat, or what kinds of foods we choose? Is low-carb better, or low-fat? What do the national dietary guidelines advise, and do they apply to "real people" like you?

Many factors contribute to the confusion surrounding healthy eating. First, nutrition is a relatively young science. In contrast with physics, chemistry, and astronomy, which have been studied for thousands of years, the science of nutrition emerged around the mid 1800s with the identification of the three energy nutrients and a number of essential minerals. The first vitamin was discovered in 1897. Canada's first food guide, the *Official Food Rules*, was introduced to the public in July 1942.[2] Although we have made substan-tial discoveries in the area of nutrition during the past century, nutritional research is still considered to be in its infancy. Thus, a growing number of new findings on the benefits of foods and nutrients are discovered almost daily. These new findings contribute to regular changes in how a healthy diet is defined. Second, as stated in Chapter 1, the popular media typically report the results of only selected studies, usually the most recent. This practice does not give a complete picture of all the research conducted in any given area. Indeed, the results of a single study are often misleading. Third, there is no one right way to eat that is healthy and acceptable for everyone. We are individuals with unique needs, food prefer-ences, and cultural influences. For example, a female athlete may need more iron than a sedentary male. One person might prefer to eat three cooked meals a day, whereas another might prefer to eat several smaller snacks, salads, and other quick foods. People following certain religious practices may limit or avoid foods like specific meats and dairy products. There are literally millions of different ways to design a healthy diet to fit individual needs.

Given all this potential confusion, it's a good thing there are tools to guide people in designing a healthy diet. In this chapter, we introduce these tools, including food labels, *Eating Well with Canada's Food Guide*, and others. Before exploring the question of how to design a healthy diet, however, it is important to understand what a healthy diet *is*.

What Is a Healthy Diet?

A **healthy diet** provides the proper combination of energy and nutrients. It has four char-acteristics: it is adequate, moderate, balanced, and varied. No matter if you are young or old, overweight or underweight, healthy or coping with illness, if you keep in mind these characteristics of a healthy diet, you will be able to consciously select foods that provide you with the appropriate combination of nutrients and energy each day.

A Healthy Diet Is Adequate

An **adequate diet** provides enough of the energy, nutrients, and fibre to maintain a person's health. A diet may be inadequate in only one area. For example, many people in Canada do not eat enough vegetables and therefore are not consuming enough of the fibre and micronutrients found in vegetables. However, their intake of protein, fat, and carbohydrate

healthy diet A diet that provides the proper combination of energy and nutrients and that is adequate, moderate, balanced, and varied.

adequate diet A diet that provides enough of the energy, nutrients, and fibre to maintain a person's health.

may be adequate. In fact, some people who eat too few vegetables are overweight or obese, which means that they are eating a diet that exceeds their energy needs.

On the other hand, a generalized state of undernutrition can occur if an individual's diet contains an inadequate level of several nutrients for a long period of time. To maintain a thin figure some individuals may skip one or more meals each day, avoid foods that contain any fat, and limit their meals to only a few foods such as a bagel, a banana, or a diet soft drink. This type of restrictive eating pattern practised over a prolonged period can cause low energy levels, loss of bone and hair, impaired memory and cognitive function, and menstrual dysfunction in women.

Consuming a variety of nutrient-dense foods and beverages while choosing foods that are limited in saturated and trans fats, cholesterol, added sugars, salt, and alcohol is an important consideration when planning an adequate diet. **Nutrient-dense foods** are foods that give the highest amount of nutrients for the least amount of energy (or kilocalories). **Figure 2.1** compares one day of meals that are high in nutrient density to meals that are low in nutrient density.

A Healthy Diet Is Moderate

Moderation is one of the keys to a healthy diet. **Moderation** refers to eating any foods in moderate amounts—not too much and not too little. If a person eats too much or too little of certain foods, health goals cannot be reached. For example, some people drink as much as 2 L of soft drinks on some days. Drinking this much contributes an extra 800 kcal of energy to a person's diet. To allow for these extra kilocalories and avoid weight gain, a person would need to reduce his or her food intake. This could lead to a person cutting healthy food choices from his or her diet. In contrast, people who drink mostly water or other beverages that contain little or no energy can consume more nourishing foods that will support their health.

A Healthy Diet Is Balanced

A **balanced diet** is one that contains combinations of foods that provide the proper proportions of nutrients. As you will learn in this text, the body needs many types of foods in varying amounts to maintain health. For example, fruits and vegetables are excellent sources of fibre, vitamin C, potassium, and magnesium. In contrast, meats are not good sources of fibre and these various nutrients. However, meats are excellent sources of protein, iron, zinc, and copper. By eating the proper balance of healthy foods, including fruits, vegetables, and meats or meat substitutes, we can be confident that we are consuming the balanced nutrition we need to maintain health.

A Healthy Diet Is Varied

Variety refers to eating many different foods from the different food groups on a regular basis. With literally thousands of healthy foods to choose from, trying new foods on a regular basis is a fun and easy way to vary your diet. Eat a new vegetable each week or substitute one food for another, such as raw spinach on your turkey sandwich in place of iceberg lettuce. Selecting a wide variety of foods increases the likelihood of consuming the multitude of nutrients the body needs. As an added benefit, eating a varied diet prevents boredom and avoids the potential of getting into a "food rut." Later in this chapter, we provide suggestions for eating a varied diet.

A Healthy Diet Considers Food Safety

In addition to the characteristics described above, a healthy diet is also one that is safe from food-borne illnesses like those caused by micro-organisms and their toxins. Important tips to remember include storing and cooking foods at the proper temperatures, avoiding unpasteurized juices and milk products and raw or undercooked meats and shellfish, and washing hands and cooking surfaces before cooking and after handling raw meats, shellfish, and eggs.

A diet that is adequate for one person may not be adequate for another. A woman who is lightly active will require fewer kilocalories of energy per day than a highly active male.

nutrient-dense foods Foods that give the highest amount of nutrients for the least amount of energy (or kilocalories).

moderation Eating the right amounts of foods to maintain a healthy weight and to optimize the body's metabolic processes.

balanced diet A diet that contains the combinations of foods that provide the proper proportions of nutrients.

variety Eating many different foods from the different food groups on a regular basis.

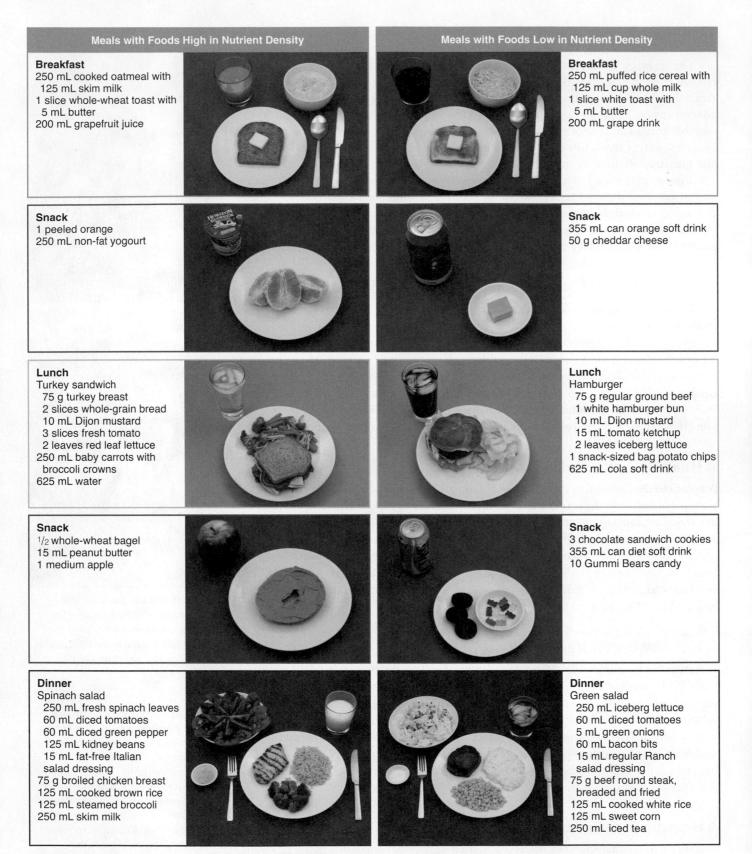

Figure 2.1 A comparison of one day's meals that contain foods high in nutrient density to meals that contain foods low in nutrient density.

Meals with Foods High in Nutrient Density

Breakfast
250 mL cooked oatmeal with
  125 mL skim milk
1 slice whole-wheat toast with
  5 mL butter
200 mL grapefruit juice

Snack
1 peeled orange
250 mL non-fat yogourt

Lunch
Turkey sandwich
  75 g turkey breast
  2 slices whole-grain bread
  10 mL Dijon mustard
  3 slices fresh tomato
  2 leaves red leaf lettuce
250 mL baby carrots with
  broccoli crowns
625 mL water

Snack
1/2 whole-wheat bagel
15 mL peanut butter
1 medium apple

Dinner
Spinach salad
  250 mL fresh spinach leaves
  60 mL diced tomatoes
  60 mL diced green pepper
  125 mL kidney beans
  15 mL fat-free Italian
  salad dressing
75 g broiled chicken breast
125 mL cooked brown rice
125 mL steamed broccoli
250 mL skim milk

Meals with Foods Low in Nutrient Density

Breakfast
250 mL puffed rice cereal with
  125 mL cup whole milk
1 slice white toast with
  5 mL butter
200 mL grape drink

Snack
355 mL can orange soft drink
50 g cheddar cheese

Lunch
Hamburger
  75 g regular ground beef
  1 white hamburger bun
  10 mL Dijon mustard
  15 mL tomato ketchup
  2 leaves iceberg lettuce
1 snack-sized bag potato chips
625 mL cola soft drink

Snack
3 chocolate sandwich cookies
355 mL can diet soft drink
10 Gummi Bears candy

Dinner
Green salad
  250 mL iceberg lettuce
  60 mL diced tomatoes
  5 mL green onions
  60 mL bacon bits
  15 mL regular Ranch
  salad dressing
75 g beef round steak,
  breaded and fried
125 mL cooked white rice
125 mL sweet corn
250 mL iced tea

What Tools Can Help Me Design a Healthy Diet?

Many people feel it is impossible to eat a healthy diet. They may mistakenly believe that the foods they would need to eat are too expensive or not available to them or they may feel too busy to do the necessary planning, shopping, and cooking. Some people rely on dietary supplements to get enough nutrients instead of focusing on eating a variety of foods. But is it really that difficult to eat a healthy diet?

Although designing and maintaining a healthy diet is not as simple as eating whatever you want, most of us can improve our diets with a little practice and a little help. Let's look now at some tools that can help us eat a healthy diet.

Reading Food Labels

To design and maintain a healthy diet, it's important to read and understand food labels. It may surprise you to learn that a few decades ago, there were no Canadian regulations dealing with the use of nutrition information on food labels! In December 2002, the Food and Drug Regulations were amended to make bilingual nutrition labelling mandatory on most food labels, update requirements for nutrient content claims, and permit the use of diet-related health claims on foods. As a result, nutrition labelling became mandatory for most prepackaged foods in December 2005, with smaller businesses having until December 2007 to comply with the new regulations.[3]

Eating a new vegetable each week is a fun way to vary your diet. Kale is a member of the cabbage family and is an excellent source of calcium.

Almost all prepackaged foods are required to have a Nutrition Facts table. Some exceptions are allowed for products that contain few nutrients or when it would be difficult to include a Nutrition Facts table. These exceptions are:

- fresh fruit and vegetables
- raw meat, poultry, fish, and seafood
- foods prepared or processed at the store such as bakery items, sausages, and salads
- foods that contain very few nutrients such as coffee beans, tea leaves, and spices
- alcoholic beverages
- foods sold at roadside stands, craft shows, flea markets, fairs, and farmers' markets
- individual servings of food intended for immediate consumption such as foods in canteens or vending machines.

Four Components Provide Nutrition-Related Information on Food Labels

Canadian regulations stipulate the requirements for four different types of nutrition-related information on food labels: ingredient lists, Nutrition Facts tables, nutrient content claims, and diet-related health claims (**Figure 2.2**).[4]

1. **Ingredient List:** The ingredients must be listed by their common names, in descending order by weight. This means that the first product listed in the ingredient list is the predominant ingredient in that food. This information can be useful in many situations, such as when you are looking for foods that are lower in fat or sugar, when you are attempting to identify foods that contain whole-grain flour

In this text you will learn how to read labels, a skill that can help you to meet your nutritional goals.

Figure 2.2 The four nutrition components that can be included on food labels. The ingredient list and Nutrition Facts table are mandatory. Nutrient content claims and health claims are optional but must meet specific composition criteria when used on food labels.

Nutrition Facts table The label on a food package that contains the nutrition information required by Health Canada.

The serving size on a nutrition label may not be the same as the amount you eat.

instead of white flour, or when you need to avoid certain ingredients because of an allergy. Ingredient lists are mandatory on all food labels.

2. **Nutrition Facts Table:** The **Nutrition Facts table** is a mandatory component on the label of most prepackaged foods. It has a consistent format and provides information on calories and a core list of 13 nutrients: fat, saturated fat, trans fat, cholesterol, sodium, carbohydrate, fibre, sugars, protein, vitamin A, vitamin C, calcium, and iron (**Figure 2.3**). Food manufacturers may include other nutrients in addition to this core list; however, they must fall within the expanded format template (**Figure 2.4**). You can use the information on the Nutrition Facts table to learn more about an individual food, and you can also use the panel to compare one food with another. Let's start at the top of the table and work our way down to better understand how to use the core information.

   a. **Serving Size:** describes the serving size in a common household measure (e.g., cup) and a metric unit (e.g., grams). Serving size is based on the amount of food a person typically eats at one sitting; these reference amounts have been set by Health Canada. However, keep in mind that the serving size listed on the package may not be the same as an *Eating Well with Canada's Food Guide* serving, or the amount you eat. You must factor in how much of the food you eat when determining the amount of nutrients that this food contributes to your actual food intake.

   b. **Calories per Serving:** describes the total number of kilocalories per serving of that food. By looking at this section of the table, you can determine the nutrient density of the food.

   c. **List of Nutrients:** describes various nutrients that are found in the food. Those nutrients listed near the top include fat, saturated fat and trans fat, cholesterol, and

Nutrition Facts
Per 125 mL (87 g)

Amount	% DV*
Calories 80	
Fat 0.5 g	1%
Saturated 0 g	0%
+ *Trans* 0 g	
Cholesterol 0 mg	
Sodium 0 mg	0%
Carbohydrate 18 g	6%
Fiber 2 g	8%
Sugars 2 g	
Protein 3 g	
Vitamin A	2%
Vitamin C	10%
Calcium	0%
Iron	2%

*DV = Daily Value

1. Serving size and servings per container
2. Calories and calories from fat per serving
3. List of nutrients and
4. % Daily Values

Figure 2.3 The Nutrition Facts table is a mandatory component on the label of most prepackaged foods. It has a consistent format and provides information on calories and 13 nutrients.
Data from: The Nutrition Facts Table. Health Canada, 2008. Reproduced with the permission of the Minister of Health, 2012.

Nutrition Facts
Serving Size 125 mL (35 g)
Servings Per Container 13

Amount Per Serving

Calories 90	Calories from fat 9
	Calories from Saturated + Trans 0

	% Daily Value*
Total Fat 1 g	**2** %
Saturated 0 g	**0** %
+ Trans 0 g	
Omega-6 Polyunsaturated 0.5 g	
Omega-3 Polyunsaturated 0 g	
Monounsaturated 0.2 g	
Cholesterol 0 mg	**0** %
Sodium 300 mg	**12** %
Potassium 410 mg	**12** %
Total Carbohydrate 27 g	**9** %
Dietary Fibre 12 g	**48** %
Soluble Fibre 0 g	
Insoluble Fibre 11 g	
Sugars 6 g	
Sugar Alcohols 0 g	
Starch 9 g	
Protein 4 g	

Vitamin A	0%	Vitamin C	0%
Calcium	2%	Iron	35%
Vitamin D	0%	Vitamin E	6%
Vitamin K	10%	Thiamin	55%
Riboflavin	4%	Niacin	25%
Vitamin B6	10%	Folate	10%
Vitamin B12	0%	Biotin	30%
Pantothenate	8%	Phosphorous	30%
Iodide	0%	Magnesium	50%
Zinc	25%	Selenium	6%
Copper	20%	Manganese	10%
Chromium	10%	Molybdenum	10%
Chloride	10%		

*Percent Daily Values are based on a 2000 Calorie diet. Your daily values may be higher or lower depending on your Calorie needs:

	Calories:	2000	2500
Total Fat	Less than	65 g	80 g
Saturated + Trans	Less than	20 g	25 g
Cholesterol	Less than	300 mg	300 mg
Sodium	Less than	2400 mg	2400 mg
Potassium		3500 mg	3500 mg
Total Carbohydrate		300 g	375 g
Dietary Fibre		25 g	30 g

Calories per gram:
Fat 9   Carbohydrate 4   Protein 4

Figure 2.4 Food manufacturers may include other nutrients in addition to the core list; however, they must fall within the expanded format template shown here.
Data from: The Nutrition Facts Table. Health Canada, 2008. Reproduced with the permission of the Minister of Health, 2012.

sodium. These are generally nutrients we strive to limit in a healthy diet. Some of the nutrients listed toward the bottom are those we try to consume more of, including fibre, vitamins A and C, calcium, and iron.

   d. Percent Daily Value (%DV): you can use the **percent daily values (%DVs)** to make informed food choices. Because we are all individuals with unique nutrient needs, it is impractical to include nutrition information that applies to each person consuming a food. That would require thousands of different labels! Instead, the %DV is a benchmark to evaluate the nutrient content of food and is based on a set of standards compiled by Health Canada for a 2000-kcal healthy diet. For example, if you want to increase the amount of a nutrient in your diet such as calcium, iron, or fibre you would look for foods with ≥ 15% of the DV. If you are interested in decreasing a specific nutrient such as fat or sodium, you would look for foods that contain ≤ 5% DV. By comparing the %DV between foods for any nutrient, you can quickly tell which food is higher or lower in that nutrient without having to know anything about how much of that nutrient you need (see **Figure 2.5** on page 50).

3. **Nutrient Content Claims:** Nutrient content claims are statements based on current science that can be made when a food meets a certain set of criteria. Nutrient content claims provide information about the amount of one specific nutrient in a food, such as fibre or fat. The statement "source of omega-3 polyunsaturates" on a cracker package or "25% less sodium" on a soup label are examples of nutrient content claims. While nutrient content claims are optional, they must meet government regulations before appearing on a package (Table 2.1).

4. **Diet-Related Health Claims:** Health Canada defines health claims as statements that link a food or a food component to a reduced risk of a disease or to a condition. Currently, there is scientific agreement for claims related to foods suitable for diets that reduce risk of high blood pressure, heart disease, some types of cancer, and osteoporosis (Table 2.2). To use a specific health claim, the food must meet specific content criteria. For example, to say that a food may lower the risk of hypertension, it must be low in sodium and contain at least 350 mg of potassium.

percent daily values (%DVs)
Information on a Nutrition Facts table that is a benchmark to evaluate the nutrient content of a food, and is based on a set of standards for a 2000–kcal healthy diet.

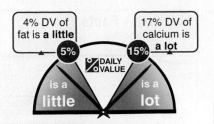

Figure 2.5
Data from: % Daily Value. Health Canada, 2010. Reproduced with the permission of the Minister of Health, 2012.

Note: When a nutrient content claim or diet-related health claim is made about a nutrient that is not one of the 13 core nutrients, that nutrient must be included in the Nutrition Facts table. This is also true for foods fortified with nutrients that are core nutrients, for example, vitamin D added to milk.

Table 2.1 Examples of Common Nutrient Content Claims on Labels

Source of fibre	"Source of fibre" means the food contains 2 grams of fibre or more per reference amount and serving of stated size.
Low fat	"Low fat" means that the food contains no more than 3 grams of fat per reference amount and serving of stated size and, if the reference amount is 30 g or 30 mL, or less, per 50 g; or 3 g or less of fat per 100 g with 30% or less of the energy from fat, if the food is a prepackaged meal.
Cholesterol-free	"Cholesterol-free" means that the product has less than 2 mg of cholesterol per reference amount and serving of stated size, or per serving of stated size, if the food is a prepackaged meal and also meets the conditions for "low in saturated fatty acids".
Low in saturated fatty acids	"Low in saturated fatty acids" means that the food contains 2 g or less of saturated fatty acids and *trans* fatty acids combined per reference amount and serving stated size or per 100 g if the food is a prepackaged meal. The food must provide 15% or less energy from the sum of saturated fatty acids and *trans* fatty acids.
No sodium	"No sodium" means that the food contains less than 5 mg of sodium per reference amount and serving of stated size; or less than 5 mg of sodium per serving of stated size, if the food is a prepackaged meal.
Reduced in Calories	"Reduced in Calories" means that the food has been modified so that it provides at least 25% less energy per reference amount of the food, than the reference amount of the similar reference food or per 100 g, than 100 g of the similar reference food if the food is a prepackaged meal.

Data from: The Department of Justice. Food and Drug Regulations, http://laws-lois.justice.gc.ca/eng/regulations/C.R.C.%2C_c._870/ (accessed June 20, 2012)

RECAP

The ability to read and interpret nutrition labels is important for planning and maintaining a healthy diet. Nutrition labels must list the ingredients in the food and provide a Nutrition Facts table containing a core list of 13 nutrients. Nutrition labels may also have nutrient content claims and health claims, provided that the food meets the specified compositional criteria outlined in the labelling regulations.

Table 2.2 Examples of Approved Health Claims on Labels

Disease risk reduction claims with respect to sodium and potassium	"A healthy diet containing foods high in potassium and low in sodium may reduce the risk of high blood pressure, a risk factor for stroke and heart disease. (Naming the food) is sodium-free."
Disease risk claims with respect to calcium and vitamin D	"A healthy diet with adequate calcium and vitamin D, and regular physical activity, help to achieve strong bones and may reduce the risk of osteoporosis. (Naming the food) is a good source of calcium."
Disease risk reduction claims with respect to saturated and trans fat	"A healthy diet low in saturated and trans fat may reduce the risk of heart disease. (Naming the food) is free of saturated and trans fats."
Disease risk reduction claims with respect to cancer risk reduction	"A healthy diet rich in a variety of vegetables and fruit may help reduce the risk of some types of cancer"
Disease risk reduction claims with respect to dental caries	"Does not promote tooth decay."

Data from: Guide to Food Labelling and Advertising - www.inspection.gc.ca/english/fssa/labeti/guide/toce.shtml, Canadian Food Inspection Agency, September 21, 2011. Reproduced with the permission of the Minister of Public Works and Government Services Canada, 2012.

YOU DO THE MATH

What Is % Daily Value, and How Is It Calculated?

The % Daily Value is a simple benchmark for evaluating the nutrient content of foods quickly and easily. The % Daily Value can be used to determine whether there is a lot or a little of a nutrient in a serving of the food.

The % Daily Values are based on reference standards for a 2000-calorie diet. We use these reference standards to determine the relative contribution of a food to a specific nutrient.

Nutrient	Amount
Total Fat	< 65 g
Saturated + Trans	< 20 g
Cholesterol	< 300 mg
Sodium	< 2400 mg
Potassium	3500 mg
Total Carbohydrate	300 g
Dietary Fibre	25 g

Example 1: A Nutrition Facts table lists the fat content of a food as 18 g. We know that the reference standard for fat is 65 g. What is the %DV for total fat?

$$(18 \text{ g} \div 65 \text{ g}) \times 100 = ?$$

A product with 18 g of fat would have a % Daily Value of 28%.

Example 2: The combined saturated and trans fat on a food label is 7.5 g. We know that the reference standard for combined saturated and trans fat is 20 g.

$$(7.5 \text{ g} \div 20 \text{ g}) \times 100 = ?$$

A product with 7.5 g of saturated and trans fats would have a % Daily Value of 38%.

Recommended Daily Intakes have been set for each vitamin and mineral that may appear in a Nutrition Facts table (Table 2.3). We can use the Recommended Daily Intakes to calculate the amount of any vitamin or mineral listed on the table.

Example 3: A 250 mL glass of skim milk has a %DV for calcium of 30%. We know that the Recommended Daily Intake for calcium is 1100 mg.

$$(? \text{ Mg} \div 1100 \text{ mg}) \times 100 = 30\%$$

The 250 mL glass of skim milk has 330 mg of calcium.

Table 2.3 Recommended Daily Intakes Used to Calculate the %DV for Vitamins and Minerals

Vitamin or Mineral	Units	Persons 2 years of age or older
Vitamin A	RE[a]	1000
Vitamin D	µg[b]	5
Vitamin E	mg[c]	10
Vitamin C	mg	60
Thiamin, Thiamine, or Vitamin B$_1$	mg	1.3
Riboflavin or Vitamin B$_2$	mg	1.6
Niacin	NE[d]	23
Vitamin B$_6$	mg	1.8
Folacin or Folate	µg	220
Vitamin B$_{12}$	µg	2
Pantothenic Acid or Pantothenate	mg	7
Vitamin K	µg	80
Biotin	µg	30
Calcium	mg	1100
Phosphorous	mg	1100
Magnesium	mg	250
Iron	mg	14
Zinc	mg	9
Iodide	µg	160
Selenium	µg	50
Copper	mg	2
Manganese	mg	2
Chromium	µg	120
Molybdenum	µg	75
Chloride	mg	3400

[a] RE = retinol equivalents
[b] µg = micrograms
[c] mg = milligrams
[d] NE = niacin equivalents
Data from: % Daily Value. Health Canada, 2010. Reproduced with the permission of the Minister of Health, 2012.

When grocery shopping, try to select foods that are moderate in total fat, sugar, and salt.

Eating Well with Canada's Food Guide

Canada's first food guide, the *Official Food Rules*, was introduced to the public in July 1942. Its purpose was to prevent nutritional deficiencies and improve the health of Canadians during wartime food rationing. Since that time, the food guide has been transformed many times. In 1961, it was renamed **Canada's Food Guide** and revised to include more diverse food choices such as citrus fruits and meat alternatives. The inclusion of colourful graphics and reduction to four food groups by combining vegetables and fruit occurred in 1977. The 1982 revision was the first to consider the role of diet in reducing chronic illnesses and to include the concept of energy balance. This approach was expanded in 1992 with the inclusion of the total diet approach to eating (**Figure 2.6**).[2]

Eating Well with Canada's Food Guide was released in 2007 after an extensive consultative process. The resulting guide is a practical pattern of food choices that incorporates variety and flexibility, and is based on the current science of nutrient requirements.[5] *Eating Well with Canada's Food Guide* is an evolving document and will continue to change as we learn more about the roles of specific nutrients and foods in promoting health and preventing certain diseases.

Eating Well with Canada's Food Guide is intended to help Canadians:

- Meet their needs for vitamins, minerals, and other nutrients.
- Reduce their risk of obesity, type 2 diabetes, heart disease, certain types of cancer, and osteoporosis.
- Contribute to their overall health and vitality.

Did You Know?

Eating Well with Canada's Food Guide has been translated into ten different languages in addition to English and French! Translations include Arabic, Chinese, Farsi (Persian), Korean, Punjabi, Russian, Spanish, Tagalog, Tamil, and Urdu. You can download copies of these translations from www.hc-sc.gc.ca/fn-an/food-guide-aliment/order-commander/guide_trans-trad-eng.php.

Eating Well with Canada's Food Guide Is Represented by a Rainbow Design

A rainbow design was chosen to represent the recommendations outlined in *Eating Well with Canada's Food Guide* (see **Figure 2.7** on page 54). The varying sizes of the arcs in the rainbow represent the proportional contribution of each of the four food groups to healthy eating. The four food groups are vegetables and fruit, grain products, milk and alternatives, and meat and alternatives. The pictures representing each food group were selected to reflect the multicultural diversity of popular food choices in Canada.

Let's take a look at each food group.

Canada's Food Guide A practical pattern of food choices that incorporates variety and flexibility, and is based on current science for nutrient recommendations.

Vegetables and Fruit   The vegetables and fruit arc of *Eating Well with Canada's Food Guide* is the largest, indicating that foods from this group should be consumed the most and emphasizing the importance of this group in preventing chronic disease. The foods in this group are clustered together because they provide carbohydrate, fibre, vitamins A, C, B_6, and folate, potassium, and magnesium (Table 2.4).

CANADA'S OFFICIAL FOOD RULES

These are the Health-Protective Foods
Be sure you eat them every day in at least these amounts.
(Use more if you can)

MILK—Adults—1/2 pint. Children—more than 1 pint. And some CHEESE, as available.

FRUITS—One serving of tomatoes daily, or of a citrus fruit, or of tomato or citrus fruit juices, and one serving of other fruits, fresh, canned or dried.

VEGETABLES (In addition to potatoes of which you need one serving daily)— Two servings daily of vegetables, preferably leafy green, or yellow, and frequently raw.

CEREALS AND BREAD—One serving of a whole-grain cereal and 4 to 6 slices of Canada Approved Bread, brown or white.

MEAT, FISH, etc.—One serving a day of meat, fish, or meat substitutes. Liver, heart, or kidney once a week.

EGGS—At least 3 or 4 eggs weekly.

Eat these foods first, then add these and other foods you wish.

Some source of Vitamin D such as fish liver oils, is essential for children, and may be advisable for adults.

(a)

Figure 2.6 Evolution of Canada's Food Guide. (a) *Canada's Food Rules* (1942); (b) *Canada's Food Guide* (1961); (c) *Canada's Food Guide* (1982); (d) *Canada's Food Guide to Healthy Eating* (1992).
Data from: Canada's Food Guide: 1942 to 1992. Health Canada, 2007. Reproduced with the permission of the Minister of Health, 2012.

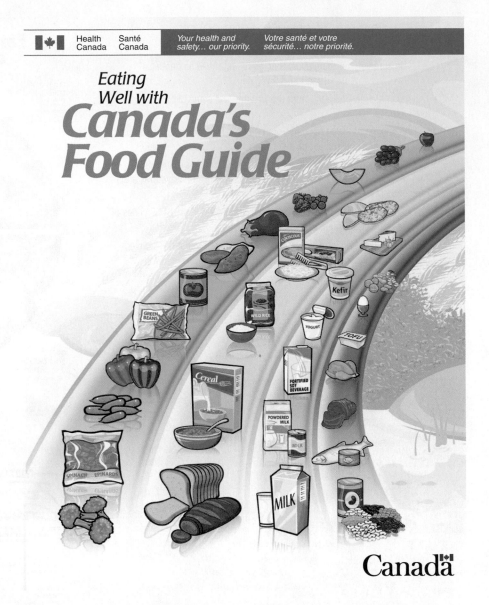

Figure 2.7 *Eating Well with Canada's Food Guide* was introduced in 2007.
Data from: Canada's Food Guide. Health Canada, 2011. Reproduced with the permission of the Minister of Health, 2012.

Some of your daily fruit servings can come from canned fruits.

phytochemicals Chemicals found in plants (*phyto-* is from the Greek word for plant), such as pigments and other substances, that may reduce our risk for diseases such as cancer and heart disease.

The guide recommends that Canadians eat at least one dark green and one orange vegetable each day to ensure an adequate intake of folate and vitamin A. Dark green vegetables (e.g., asparagus, broccoli, and romaine lettuce) are important sources of folate. Orange vegetables (e.g., carrots, pumpkin, and sweet potato) are rich in carotenoids such as beta-carotene. Some orange-coloured fruit, such as apricots, cantaloupe, and mango, are also high in vitamin A and can replace an orange vegetable. Canadians are also encouraged to choose vegetables and fruit prepared with little or no added fat, sugar, or salt. Most vegetables and fruit are naturally low in fat and kilocalories, but become high sources of fat when they are breaded, fried, or served with sauces, butter, or cream. Canadians should steam, bake, or stir-fry instead of deep-frying. Finally, choosing vegetables and fruit more often than juice will ensure a higher intake of fibre.

Vegetables and fruit also contain differing amounts and types of **phytochemicals**, which are naturally occurring plant chemicals (such as pigments) that enhance health. These substances appear to work together in whole foods in a unique way to provide health

Table 2.4 Each of the Four Food Groups Contributes a Certain Combination of Nutrients to the Healthy Eating Pattern

Key Nutrient	Some Important Nutrients in the Food Groups			
	Vegetables and Fruit	Grain Products	Milk and Alternatives	Meat and Alternatives
Protein			✓	✓
Fat			✓	✓
Carbohydrate	✓	✓	✓	
Fibre	✓	✓		
Thiamin		✓		✓
Riboflavin		✓	✓	✓
Niacin		✓		✓
Folate	✓	✓		
Vitamin B_6	✓			✓
Vitamin B_{12}			✓	✓
Vitamin C	✓			
Vitamin A	✓		✓	
Vitamin D			✓	
Calcium			✓	
Iron		✓		✓
Zinc		✓	✓	✓
Magnesium	✓	✓	✓	✓
Potassium	✓	✓	✓	✓

Data from: Health Canada. 2007. Eating Well with Canada's Food Guide: A Resource for Educators and Communicators. Available online at www.hc-sc.gc.ca/fn-an/alt_formats/hpfb-dgpsa/pdf/pubs/res-educat-eng.pdf. © Her Majesty the Queen in Right of Canada, represented by the Minister of Health Canada, 2011.

benefits. Taking vitamin and mineral supplements does not provide the same benefits as eating whole foods, as supplements may not contain phytochemicals or contain them in the right combinations to optimize their effect. Other plant products such as soy, garlic, and onions contain phytochemicals, as do green and black tea and even coffee and chocolate. The scientific study of phytochemicals is in its infancy, but there is growing evidence that these substances may reduce the risk for chronic diseases such as cancer and cardiovascular disease.[6] A detailed explanation of phytochemicals and their impact on health is presented in Chapter 8.

Grain Products The grain products arc of *Eating Well with Canada's Food Guide* is the second largest, indicating that foods from this group should be consumed in the second highest proportion. The foods in this group are clustered together because they provide fibre-rich carbohydrates and are good sources of the nutrients riboflavin, thiamin, niacin, iron, folate, zinc, potassium, and magnesium (Table 2.4).

The guide recommends that Canadians should make at least half of their grain products whole grain each day to ensure an adequate intake of fibre and magnesium. A diet rich in whole grains (e.g., barley, oats, brown rice, or wild rice) may help reduce the risk of cardiovascular disease.[7]

Canadians are also encouraged to choose grain products that are lower in fat, sugar, or salt. Most grain products are naturally low in fat, but the way you eat them can add extra kilocalories and increase the total fat consumed. For example, if you add spreads or sauces to your pasta or bread, use small amounts. Make sandwiches on whole-grain bagels,

Eating a diet rich in whole-grain foods, such as whole-wheat bread and brown rice, can enhance your overall health.

baguettes, bread, buns, and tortillas instead of croissants. Trade your morning cinnamon bun for an English muffin spread with nut butter. Buy lower-fat and lower-salt (sodium) versions of crackers.

Milk and Alternatives   The milk and alternatives arc of *Eating Well with Canada's Food Guide* is the third largest, indicating that foods from this group should be consumed in the third highest proportion. The foods in this group are clustered together because they are good sources of protein, fat, and carbohydrate; contain vitamins A, D, B$_{12}$, and riboflavin; and the minerals calcium, zinc, magnesium, and potassium (Table 2.4).

Canadians are encouraged to drink at least 500 mL of skim, 1%, or 2% milk daily to encourage an adequate intake of vitamin D. Fortified soy beverages can be used as an alternative to milk; however, they should contain added vitamins and minerals to make them a nutritionally adequate alternative to milk. Look for the word *fortified* on the package. Canadians should select lower-fat milk alternatives. Milk products with high milk fat (MF) content such as cheese and some yogourt contain high amounts of fat, saturated fat, and kilocalories. Look for lower-fat yogourt (2% MF or less), and lower-fat cheese (15% to 20% MF or less), and replace half the cheese in a recipe with a variety of cheese that is lower in fat. Serve lower-fat vanilla or fruit-flavoured yogourt as a dip for fruit.

Meat and Alternatives   The meat and alternatives arc of *Eating Well with Canada's Food Guide* is the smallest, indicating that foods from this group should be consumed in the lowest proportion. The foods in this group are clustered together because they are good sources of protein and fat; contain vitamins B$_6$, B$_{12}$, thiamin, riboflavin, and niacin; and the minerals iron, zinc, magnesium, and potassium (Table 2.4).

When it comes to meat consumption, times have changed. Today, a balanced meal includes meat alternatives or smaller amounts of meat. Canadians are encouraged to have meat alternatives such as beans, lentils, and tofu more often to lower their saturated fat and increase their fibre intake. Regular consumption of fish helps reduce the risk of heart disease; therefore, it is suggested that two servings of fish be consumed each week. All fish contains at least some omega-3 fats, which are important for health. Good choices include Arctic char, herring, mackerel, rainbow trout, salmon, and sardines because these have very high amounts of omega-3 fats.

Canadians are also encouraged to select lean meat and alternatives prepared with little or no added fat or salt to help reduce the amount of saturated fat consumed. *Eating Well with Canada's Food Guide* further emphasizes choosing lean cuts of meat and skinless poultry; baking, broiling, poaching, or roasting instead of frying or deep-frying meats; and letting the fat drip off cooked meats. Luncheon meats, processed meats, and sausages add extra fat and sodium and should be chosen less often, or lower-fat and lower-salt varieties should be chosen.

Seafood, meat, poultry, dry beans, eggs, and nuts are examples of foods that are high in protein.

Number of Recommended Servings per Day

Eating Well with Canada's Food Guide also helps Canadians decide the amount of food they should eat. The recommended number of food guide servings chart (**Figure 2.8**) shows how much food is needed from each of the four food groups every day. The recommendations are based on age and gender. A range of recommended servings is suggested for some food groups and some age categories. For example, it is recommended that men aged 19–50 years consume 8–10 vegetables and fruit servings daily. Less active men can choose the lower recommendation; men who are more active can choose the higher recommendation.

Serving Sizes in Canada's Food Guide   What is considered a serving size for the foods recommended in *Eating Well with Canada's Food Guide*? **Figure 2.9** shows examples

Recommended Number of *Food Guide Servings* per Day

	Children			Teens		Adults			
Age in Years	2-3	4-8	9-13	14-18		19-50		51+	
Sex	Girls and Boys			Females	Males	Females	Males	Females	Males
Vegetables and Fruit	4	5	6	7	8	7-8	8-10	7	7
Grain Products	3	4	6	6	7	6-7	8	6	7
Milk and Alternatives	2	2	3-4	3-4	3-4	2	2	3	3
Meat and Alternatives	1	1	1-2	2	3	2	3	2	3

The chart above shows how many Food Guide Servings you need from each of the four food groups every day.

Having the amount and type of food recommended and following the tips in *Canada's Food Guide* will help:

- Meet your needs for vitamins, minerals and other nutrients.
- Reduce your risk of obesity, type 2 diabetes, heart disease, certain types of cancer and osteoporosis.
- Contribute to your overall health and vitality.

Figure 2.8 The recommended number of food guide servings per day is based on age and gender.
Data from: Canada's Food Guide. Health Canada, 2011. Reproduced with the permission of the Minister of Health, 2012.

What is One Food Guide Serving?
Look at the examples below.

Figure 2.9 *Eating Well with Canada's Food Guide* suggested serving sizes for each food group. Some household items can help you estimate serving size. For example, use four stacked dice to estimate 50 g of cheese; ½ a tennis ball for roughly 125 mL of grapes; a portion the size of a deck of playing cards is approximately 75 g of meat, fish, or poultry; and a hockey puck has a similar diameter and thickness as a whole bagel (2 servings of grain products).
Data from: Canada's Food Guide. Health Canada, 2011. Reproduced with the permission of the Minister of Health, 2012.

How do I count Food Guide Servings in a meal?

Here is an example:

Vegetable and beef stir-fry with rice, a glass of milk and an apple for dessert		
250 mL (1 cup) mixed broccoli, carrot and sweet red pepper	=	2 **Vegetables and Fruit** Food Guide Servings
75 g (2 ½ oz.) lean beef	=	1 **Meat and Alternatives** Food Guide Serving
250 mL (1 cup) brown rice	=	2 **Grain Products** Food Guide Servings
5 mL (1 tsp) canola oil	=	part of your **Oils and Fats** intake for the day
250 mL (1 cup) 1% milk	=	1 **Milk and Alternatives** Food Guide Serving
1 apple	=	1 **Vegetables and Fruit** Food Guide Serving

Figure 2.10 Example of how to classify foods and count servings according to *Eating Well with Canada's Food Guide*.
Data from: Canada's Food Guide. Health Canada, 2011. Reproduced with the permission of the Minister of Health, 2012.

of serving sizes for each of the four food groups. For example, the serving size for fresh, frozen, or canned vegetables is 125 mL and for bread, 1 slice or 35 g. *Eating Well with Canada's Food Guide* uses food images with specific amounts indicated (in metric and imperial measures) and the illustration of a measuring cup, where appropriate, to help demonstrate the amount of one food guide serving.

It is important to understand that no national standardized definition for a serving size for any food exists. A food guide serving is simply a reference amount. It is a consistent measure to compare how much you eat to what is recommended in *Eating Well with Canada's Food Guide* and is meant to help you understand how much food is recommended from each of the four food groups (**Figure 2.10**). In some cases, a food guide serving may be close to what you typically eat in one sitting, such as an apple. In other cases, such as rice or pasta, you may serve yourself more than a food guide serving. Food guide servings are also not necessarily the same as serving sizes identified on a food label. Try the Nutrition Label Activity to determine whether the serving sizes listed on assorted food labels match the serving sizes that you normally consume.

NUTRITION LABEL ACTIVITY

How Realistic Are the Serving Sizes Listed on Food Labels?

Many people read food labels to determine the energy (i.e., caloric) value of foods, but it is less common to pay close attention to the actual serving size that corresponds to the listed caloric value. To test how closely your "naturally selected" serving size meets the actual serving size of certain foods, try these label activities:

■ Choose a breakfast cereal that you commonly eat. Pour the amount of cereal that you would normally eat into a bowl. Before adding milk to your cereal, use a measuring cup to measure the amount of cereal you poured. Now read the label of the cereal to determine the serving size (e.g., 125 mL or 250 mL) and the caloric value listed on the label. How do your "naturally selected" serving size and the label-defined serving size compare?

■ At your local grocery store, locate various boxes of snack crackers. Look at the number of crackers and total

calories per serving listed on the labels of crackers such as regular Triscuits, reduced-fat Triscuits, Vegetable Thins, and Ritz crackers. How do the number of crackers and total calories per serving differ for the serving size listed on each box? How do the serving sizes listed in the Nutrition Facts table compare to how many crackers you would usually eat?

These activities are just two examples of ways to understand how nutrition labels can assist the consumer with making balanced and healthy food choices. As many people do not know what constitutes a serving size, they are inclined to consume too much of some foods (such as snack foods and meat) and too little of other foods (such as fruits and vegetables).

Serving sizes in restaurants, cafes, and movie theatres have grown substantially over the past 30 years.[8] This "supersizing" phenomenon, now seen even at home, indicates a major shift in accessibility to foods and in accepted eating behaviours, and emphasizes the importance of becoming educated about portion size control. In addition to being a potentially important contributor to the rise in obesity rates around the world, this increase in serving size leads to confusion among consumers. Refer to the You Do the Math activity on pages 60–61 to estimate how much physical activity you would need to do to expend the excess energy you consume because of increasing food portion sizes.

YOU DO THE MATH

How Much Exercise Is Needed to Combat Increasing Food Portion Sizes?

Although the causes of obesity are complex and multifactorial, it is speculated that one reason obesity rates are rising around the world is a combination of increased energy intake due to expanding food portion sizes and a reduction in overall daily physical activity. This activity should help you to better understand how portion sizes have increased over the past 20 years and how much physical activity you would need to do to expend the excess energy resulting from these larger portion sizes.

The photos in **Figure 2.11** give examples of foods whose portion sizes have increased substantially. A bagel 20 years ago had a diameter of approximately 7½ cm and contained 140 kcal. A bagel in today's society is about 15 cm in diameter and contains 350 kcal. Similarly, a cup of coffee 20 years ago was 250 mL and was typically served with a small amount of whole milk and sugar. It contained about 45 kcal. A standard coffee mocha commonly consumed today is 500 mL and contains 350 kcal; this excess energy comes from the addition of sugar, milk, and flavoured syrup.

On her morning break at work, Asha routinely consumes a bagel and a coffee drink like the ones described here. Asha has type 2 diabetes, and her doctor has advised her to lose weight. How much physical activity would Asha need to do to "burn" this excess energy? Let's do some simple math to answer this question.

1. Calculate the excess energy Asha consumes from both of these foods:
   a. Bagel: 350 kcal in larger bagel − 140 kcal in smaller bagel = 210 kcal extra
   b. Coffee: 350 kcal in large coffee mocha − 45 kcal in small regular coffee = 305 kcal extra
      total excess energy for these two larger portions = 515 kcal
2. Asha has started walking each day in an effort to lose weight. Asha currently weighs 90 kg. Based on her relatively low fitness level, Asha walks at a slow pace (approximately 3 km per hour); it is estimated that walking at this pace expends 2.6 kcal per kg of body weight per hour. How long does Asha need to walk each day to expend 515 kcal?

20 years ago   **Today**

7½ cm diameter, 140 kilocalories   15 cm diameter, 350 kilocalories

(a) Bagel

250 mL, 45 kilocalories   500 mL, 350 kilocalories

(b) Coffee

Figure 2.11 Examples of increases in food portion sizes over the past 20 years. (a) A bagel has increased in diameter from 7½ cm to 15 cm; (b) a cup of coffee has increased from 250 mL to 500 mL, and now commonly contains calorie-dense flavoured syrup as well as steamed whole milk.

   a. First, calculate how much energy Asha expends if she walks for a full hour by multiplying her body weight by the energy cost of walking per hour = 2.6 kcal/kg body weight × 90 kg = 234 kcal.

b. Next, you need to calculate how much energy she expends each minute she walks by dividing the energy cost of walking per hour by 60 minutes = 234 kcal/hour ÷ 60 minutes/hour = 3.9 kcal/minute

c. To determine how many minutes she would need to walk to expend 515 kcal, divide the total amount of energy she needs to expend by the energy cost of walking per minute = 515 kcal ÷ 3.9 kcal/minute = 132 minutes

Thus, Asha would need to walk for approximately 132 minutes, or about 2 hours and 15 minutes, to expend the excess energy she consumes by eating the larger bagel and coffee. If she wanted to burn off all of the energy in her morning snack, she would have to walk even longer, especially if she enjoyed her bagel with cream cheese!

Now use your own weight in these calculations to determine how much walking you would have to do if you consumed these same foods:

a. 2.6 kcal/kg × (your weight in kgs) = _____ kcal/hour

(If you walk at a brisk pace, use 5.2 kcal/kg)

b. _____ kcal/hour ÷ 60 minutes/hour = _____ kcal/minute

c. 515 extra kcal in bagel and coffee ÷ _____ kcal/minute = _____ minutes

For more information about large portion sizes and the physical activities one needs to do to avoid weight gain, take the National Heart, Lung, and Blood Institute's Portion Distortion Quiz at http://hp2010.nhlbihin.net/portion/index.htm.

Fats and Oils *Eating Well with Canada's Food Guide* also recommends that Canadians include a small amount (30 to 45 mL) of unsaturated fat as part of the healthy eating pattern that includes mostly lower-fat foods (**Figure 2.12**). This will ensure people have enough essential fat. Oils and fats that are mostly unsaturated include vegetable oils such as canola, olive, and soybean, and soft margarines. Canadians are also encouraged to limit the amount of saturated and trans fats from foods such as butter, hard margarine, lard, and shortening.

Water *Eating Well with Canada's Food Guide* also recommends that Canadians drink water regularly (**Figure 2.13**). It can satisfy thirst and provide hydration without adding kilocalories. Further, they should drink more water in hot weather or when they are very active.

Oils and Fats
- Include a small amount – 30 to 45 mL (2 to 3 Tbsp) – of unsaturated fat each day. This includes oil used for cooking, salad dressings, margarine and mayonnaise.
- Use vegetable oils such as canola, olive and soybean.
- Choose soft margarines that are low in saturated and trans fats.
- Limit butter, hard margarine, lard and shortening.

Figure 2.12 *Eating Well with Canada's Food Guide* recommends 30 to 45 mL of unsaturated fat each day.
Data from: Canada's Food Guide. Health Canada, 2011. Reproduced with the permission of the Minister of Health, 2012.

Satisfy your thirst with water!

Drink water regularly. It's a calorie-free way to quench your thirst. Drink more water in hot weather or when you are very active.

Figure 2.13 *Eating Well with Canada's Food Guide* encourages Canadians to satisfy their thirst with water.
Data from: Canada's Food Guide. Health Canada, 2011. Reproduced with the permission of the Minister of Health, 2012.

Advice for different ages and stages...

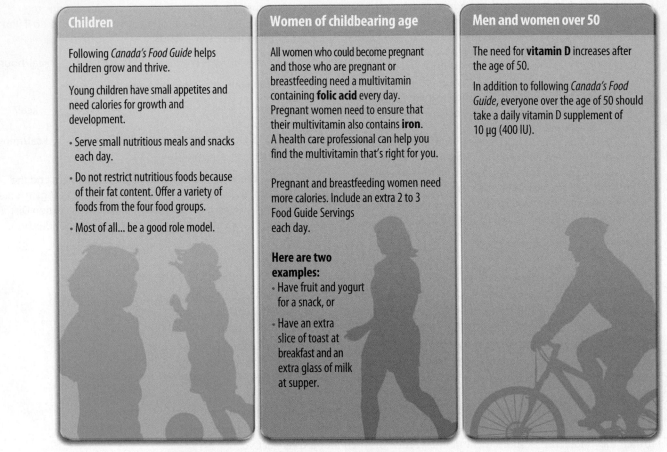

Children

Following *Canada's Food Guide* helps children grow and thrive.

Young children have small appetites and need calories for growth and development.

- Serve small nutritious meals and snacks each day.
- Do not restrict nutritious foods because of their fat content. Offer a variety of foods from the four food groups.
- Most of all... be a good role model.

Women of childbearing age

All women who could become pregnant and those who are pregnant or breastfeeding need a multivitamin containing **folic acid** every day. Pregnant women need to ensure that their multivitamin also contains **iron**. A health care professional can help you find the multivitamin that's right for you.

Pregnant and breastfeeding women need more calories. Include an extra 2 to 3 Food Guide Servings each day.

Here are two examples:
- Have fruit and yogurt for a snack, or
- Have an extra slice of toast at breakfast and an extra glass of milk at supper.

Men and women over 50

The need for **vitamin D** increases after the age of 50.

In addition to following *Canada's Food Guide*, everyone over the age of 50 should take a daily vitamin D supplement of 10 µg (400 IU).

Figure 2.14 *Eating Well with Canada's Food Guide* provides specific advice for different age groups. *Data from:* Canada's Food Guide. Health Canada, 2011. Reproduced with the permission of the Minister of Health, 2012.

Advice for Different Ages and Stages

Eating Well with Canada's Food Guide provides additional guidance for children, women of childbearing age, and adults over 50 (**Figure 2.14**).

Children   Young children need to eat small amounts of food throughout the day because they have small stomachs that tend to fill up quickly. One food guide serving from a food group can be divided up into smaller amounts and served throughout the day. For example, a food guide serving of meat and alternatives can be split and served at two different meals; one egg can be served at lunch and about 30 g of chicken for dinner. Nutritious food should not be restricted because of its fat content since children need kilocalories for development and growth. In addition, children look to role models such as parents and caregivers to learn eating behaviours and develop a taste for healthy food.

Women of Childbearing Age   Although folic acid is found in some foods, such as dark green vegetables, beans, lentils, orange juice, and some grain products, all women who could become pregnant and those who are pregnant or breastfeeding need a daily multivitamin containing 400 micrograms (0.4 mg) of folic acid. This supplement, together with the amount of folic acid obtained by following *Eating Well with Canada's Food Guide*, will help decrease the risk of neural tube defects and meet the extra folic acid needs for those pregnant and breastfeeding. In addition, pregnant women need to ensure that their multivitamin also contains enough iron. A healthcare provider can help them find the right multivitamin. The food guide recommends that pregnant and breastfeeding women add an extra 2 or 3 servings daily from any of the food groups. For example, one piece of fruit and 175 g of yogourt.

Adults Over 50 Vitamin D needs increase after the age of 50 and are higher than can be obtained by following the food guide. In older adults, vitamin D intake is associated with highest bone mineral density, improved muscle strength, reduced fracture rates, reduced rates of falling, and improved mobility. Therefore, all adults over 50 should take a supplement containing 400 IU of vitamin D in addition to following *Eating Well with Canada's Food Guide* recommendations to meet their vitamin D needs.

Physical Activity

Along with eating well, being active is also an important part of being healthy. There are many reasons for eating well and being active regularly. These include better overall health, lower risk of disease, a healthy body weight, feeling and looking better, more energy, and stronger muscles and bones. The Canadian Physical Activity Guidelines recommend that adults aged 18–64 accumulate 150 minutes of moderate- to vigorous-intensity aerobic physical activity per week in periods of at least 10 minutes at a time. Children and youth should aim for 60 minutes of moderate- to vigorous-intensity physical activity daily. Note the difference in this recommendation compared to that in *Eating Well with Canada's Food Guide* (**Figure 2.15**). This will be discussed in more detail in Chapter 14.

Eating Well with Canada's Food Guide—First Nations, Inuit, and Métis

Health Canada has published a version of the food guide tailored to reflect the values, traditions, and food choices of First Nations, Inuit, and Métis (see **Figure 2.16** on page 64).[9] This version contains unique images and content developed for Aboriginal populations.

Being physically active for at least 30 minutes each day can reduce your risk for chronic diseases.

Eat well and be active today and every day!

The benefits of eating well and being active include:

- Better overall health.
- Lower risk of disease.
- A healthy body weight.
- Feeling and looking better.
- More energy.
- Stronger muscles and bones.

Be active

To be active every day is a step towards better health and a healthy body weight.

It is recommended that adults accumulate at least 2 ½ hours of moderate to vigorous physical activity each week and that children and youth accumulate at least 60 minutes per day. You don't have to do it all at once. Choose a variety of activities spread throughout the week.

Start slowly and build up.

Eat well

Another important step towards better health and a healthy body weight is to follow *Canada's Food Guide* by:

- Eating the recommended amount and type of food each day.
- Limiting foods and beverages high in calories, fat, sugar or salt (sodium) such as cakes and pastries, chocolate and candies, cookies and granola bars, doughnuts and muffins, ice cream and frozen desserts, french fries, potato chips, nachos and other salty snacks, alcohol, fruit flavoured drinks, soft drinks, sports and energy drinks, and sweetened hot or cold drinks.

Figure 2.15 *Eating Well with Canada's Food Guide* advises Canadians to engage in daily physical activity. *Data from:* Canada's Food Guide. Health Canada, 2011. Reproduced with the permission of the Minister of Health, 2012.

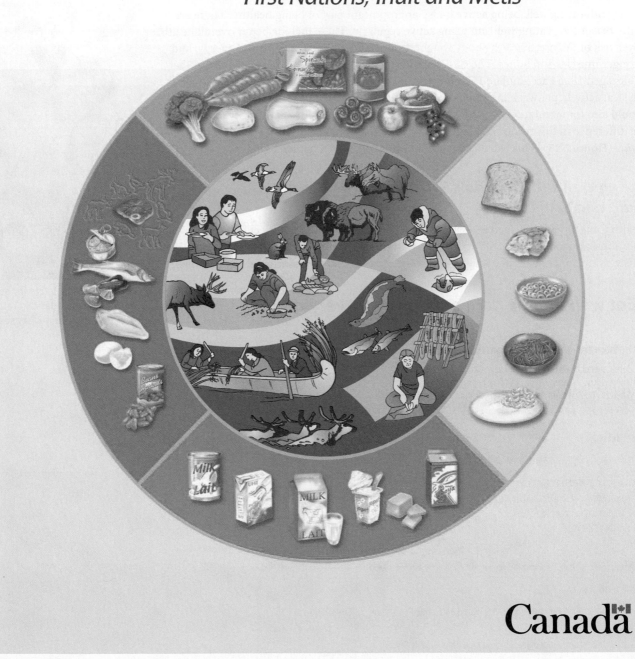

Figure 2.16 *Eating Well with Canada's Food Guide—First Nations, Inuit, Métis*
Data from: Eating Well with Canada's Food Guide for First Nations, Inuit and Metis. Health Canada, 2007. Reproduced with the permission of the Minister of Health, 2012.

For example, it uses a circle rather than a rainbow format. The centre of the circle presents ways Aboriginal peoples are physically active. The perimeter contains both traditional foods such as moose, char, and bannock, and shows pictures of store-bought foods that are generally available in rural and remote locations. *Eating Well with Canada's Food Guide— First Nations, Inuit, and Métis* is available in Cree, Ojibwe, and Inuktitut languages.

RECaP

Eating Well with Canada's Food Guide can be used to plan a healthy, balanced diet that includes foods from the vegetables and fruit, grain products, milk and alternatives, and meat and alternatives groups. Each food group is structured around provision of key nutrients to a healthy diet. The serving sizes defined by *Eating Well with Canada's Food Guide* are typically smaller than the amounts we normally eat or are served. Health Canada has published a version of the food guide tailored to reflect the values, traditions, and food choices of Aboriginal Canadians.

HIGHLIGHT

The Mediterranean Diet

Mediterranean diets have been associated with increased life expectancy and a reduction in chronic disease.[10] It has been suggested that following the Mediterranean diet, together with regular physical activity and not smoking, could prevent over 80% of coronary heart disease, 70% of stroke, and 90% of type 2 diabetes.[11] These are the same chronic diseases that are prevalent in the Canadian population. Therefore, a comparison of the current recommendations outlined in *Eating Well with Canada's Food Guide* with the Mediterranean dietary pattern may be warranted. There is actually not a single Mediterranean diet, as this region of the world includes Portugal, Spain, Italy, France, Greece, Turkey, and Israel. Each of these countries has different dietary patterns; however, there are similarities that have led to speculation that this type of diet is more healthy than the typical Canadian diet:

■ Meat is eaten monthly, and eggs, poultry, fish, and sweets are eaten weekly, making the diet low in saturated fats and refined sugars.

■ The predominant fat used for cooking and flavour is olive oil, making the diet high in monounsaturated fats.

■ Foods eaten daily include grains such as bread, pasta, couscous, and bulgur; fruits; beans and other legumes; nuts; vegetables; and cheese and yogurt. These choices make this diet high in fibre and rich in vitamins and minerals.

As you can see in **Figure 2.17** on page 66, the base of the Mediterranean Pyramid includes breads, cereals, and other grains, foods also emphasized in *Eating Well with Canada's Food Guide*. Another similarity is the daily intake of fruits and vegetables. Finally, both food guides highlight daily physical activity.

The two guides differ in several important aspects. The Mediterranean Pyramid recommends beans, other legumes, and nuts as daily sources of protein; fish, poultry, and eggs are eaten weekly; and red meat is eaten only about once each month. The Mediterranean Pyramid highlights cheese and yogourt as the primary dairy sources and recommends daily consumption of olive oil. Another feature of the Mediterranean diet is the inclusion of wine.

Interestingly, the Mediterranean diet is not lower in fat; in fact, about 40% of the total energy in this diet is derived from fat, which is much higher than the dietary fat recommendations made in Canada. This fact has led some nutritionists to criticize the Mediterranean diet; however, supporters point out that the majority of fats in the Mediterranean diet are plant oils, which are more healthy than the animal fats found in the Canadian diet, and make the Mediterranean diet more protective against cardiovascular disease. The potential benefits of plant oils in reducing our cholesterol levels and our risk for heart disease are discussed in Chapter 5.

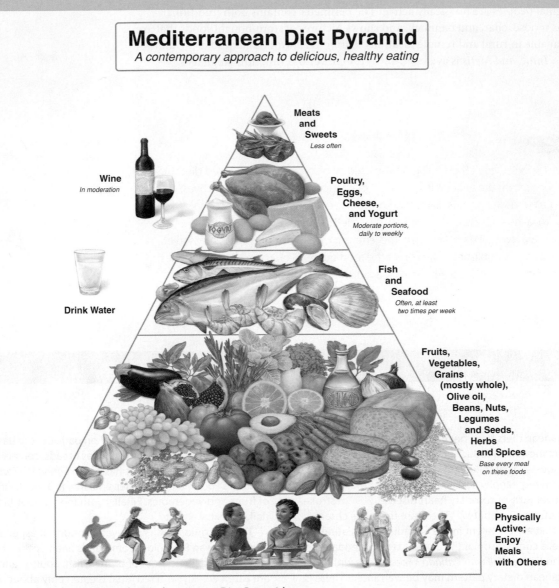

Figure 2.17 The Mediterranean Diet Pyramid.
(© 2009 Oldways Preservation and Exchange Trust. The Food Issues Think Tank. Healthy Eating Pyramids & Other Tools. www.oldwayspt.org.)

Encouraging Healthy Eating

Maribeth works part-time at the campus library. When her boss, a 42-year-old librarian, finds out that Maribeth is majoring in nutrition, she asks her to evaluate her diet. Maribeth asks the librarian to record her intake for two days, a weekend and weekday, and then reviews her dietary choices.

Food Records:

Sunday	**Monday**
Brunch:	**Breakfast:**

Sunday

Brunch:
Pancakes, 3–8 cm diameter
  with syrup, 45 mL
Bacon, 3 strips
Coffee, 250 mL
  with 10% cream, 15 mL

Snack:
Potato chips, 50 g
Diet Cola, 355 mL

Dinner:
Roast beef, 75 g
Mashed potatoes, 125 mL
Peas, 125 mL
Tea, 25 mL
  with sugar, 5 mL

Snack:
Chocolate cake, 75 g
Vanilla ice cream, 125 mL

Monday

Breakfast:
White bread toast, 2 slices
  with margarine, 10 mL
Banana, 1 medium
Coffee, 250 mL
  with 10% cream, 15 mL

Lunch:
Sandwich on white bread, 2 slices
  Processed ham, 50 g
  Processed cheese, 25 g
  Lettuce, 1 leaf
Chocolate chip cookies, 2
Diet Cola, 355 mL

Snack:
Chocolate bar, 45 g

Dinner:
Fish sticks, 5 each
French fries, 40 pieces
Carrots, 125 mL
Tea, 25 mL
  with sugar, 5 mL

Snack:
Potato chips, 50 g

Thinking Critically

1. Using *Eating Well with Canada's Food Guide*, compare the librarian's diet to the recommended number of servings for each food group for her age and gender.
2. Assess the choice of food in each food group. How does the librarian's diet compare?
3. Evaluate your groupings. Which food groups are over- or underrepresented?
4. Predict which nutrients the librarian might be at risk of consuming in inadequate amounts.
5. Suggest some specific changes that would improve the librarian's diet.

Can Eating Out Be Part of a Healthy Diet?

How many times each week do you eat out? A recent report from the Nielson Company states that about one-third of Canadians eat out once per week, while another 35% eats out two or more times per week.[12] When Canadians eat out, what sort of restaurants do they frequent? Statistics Canada found that 25% of Canadians report consuming something that had been prepared in a fast-food outlet in the previous 24-hour period.[13] Over the past 20 years, there has been a phenomenal growth in the restaurant industry, particularly in the fast-food market. During this same time period, rates of obesity have increased. Almost 23% of the total adult population are considered obese and another 36% overweight.[14]

Table 2.5 Nutritional Value of Selected Fast Foods

Menu Item	Kcal	Fat (g)	Fat (% kcal)	Sodium (mg)
Burger King				
Hamburger	260	11	38.1	500
Cheeseburger	300	14	42.0	710
Whopper	670	40	53.7	910
Whopper with cheese	760	47	55.7	1320
Double Whopper	910	58	57.4	980
Bacon Double Cheeseburger	510	30	52.9	1140
French fries, small	240	10	37.5	330
French fries, medium	340	15	39.7	490
French fries, large	410	18	39.5	570

Foods served at fast-food chains are often high in kilocalories, total fat, and sodium.

The Hidden Costs of Eating Out

Table 2.5 shows an example of foods served at Burger King restaurants. As you can see, a regular Burger King hamburger has only 260 kcal, whereas the Whopper has 670 kcal. A meal of the Double Whopper and a Large French provides 1320 kcal. This meal has almost enough energy to support an entire day's needs for a small, lightly active woman! Similar meals at other fast-food chains are also very high in kilocalories, not to mention total fat and sodium.

Fast-food restaurants are not alone in serving large portions. Most sit-down restaurants also serve large meals that may include bread with butter, a salad with dressing, sides of vegetables and potatoes, and free refills of sugar-filled drinks. Combined with a high-fat appetizer like potato skins, fried onions, fried mozzarella sticks, or buffalo wings, it is easy to eat more than 2000 kcal at one meal!

Does this mean that eating out cannot be a part of a healthy diet? Not necessarily. By becoming an educated consumer and making wise meal choices while dining out, you can enjoy both a healthy diet and the social benefits of eating out.

The Healthy Way to Eat Out

Most restaurants, even fast-food restaurants, offer lower-fat menu items that you can choose. For instance, eating a regular Burger King hamburger, a small order of French fries, and a diet beverage or water provides 500 kcal and 21 g of fat (or 38% of kcal from fat). To provide some vegetables for the day, you could add a side salad with low-fat or non-fat salad dressing. Other fast-food restaurants also offer smaller portions, sandwiches made with whole-grain bread, grilled chicken or other lean meats, and side salads. Many sit-down restaurants offer "lite" menu items such as grilled chicken and a variety of vegetables, which are usually a much better choice than eating from the regular menu.

Here are some other suggestions on how to eat out in moderation. Practise some of these suggestions every time you eat out:

When ordering your favourite coffee drink, avoid those made with flavoured syrups, cream, or whipping cream, and request reduced-fat or skim milk instead.

- Avoid coffee drinks made with syrups, as well as those made with cream, whipping cream, or whole milk; select reduced-fat or skim milk in your favourite coffee drink.

- Avoid eating appetizers that are breaded, fried, or filled with cheese or meat; you may want to skip the appetizer completely. Alternatively, you may want to order a healthy appetizer as an entrée instead of a larger meal.
- Share an entrée with a friend! Many restaurants serve entrées large enough for two people.
- Order broth-based soups instead of cream-based soups.
- Order any meat dish grilled or broiled, and avoid fried or breaded meat dishes.
- If you order a meat dish, select lean cuts of meat, such as chicken or turkey breast, extra-lean ground beef, pork loin chop, or filet mignon.
- Order a meatless dish filled with vegetables and whole grains. Avoid dishes with cream sauces and a lot of cheese.
- Order a salad with low-fat or non-fat dressing served on the side. Many restaurants smother their salads in dressing, and you will eat less by controlling how much you put on the salad.
- Order steamed vegetables on the side instead of potatoes or rice. If you order potatoes, make sure you get a baked potato (with very little butter or sour cream on the side).
- Order beverages with few or no kilocalories, such as water, tea, or diet drinks.
- Eat no more than half of what you are served, and take the rest home for another meal.
- Skip dessert or share one dessert with a lot of friends! Another healthy alternative is to order fresh fruit for dessert.

Eating out can be part of a healthy diet, if you are careful to choose wisely.

Table 2.6 lists examples of low-fat foods you can choose when you eat out.[15] Although provided as examples for people with diabetes, they are useful for anyone who is interested in making healthier food choices while eating out. By choosing healthy foods and appropriate portion sizes, you can eat out regularly and still maintain a healthy body weight.

RECaP

Healthy ways to eat out include choosing menu items that are smaller in size, ordering meats that are grilled or broiled, avoiding fried foods, choosing items with steamed vegetables, avoiding energy-rich appetizers and desserts, and eating less than half of the food you are served.

SEE FOR YOURSELF

Go to your local grocery store and compile a list of ten examples of nutrient content or health claims made on the labels of various foods. Record the name of the food, the actual claim, and any information related to supporting the claim given on the packaging. For each item, note whether or not you found the claim convincing enough to persuade you that the item would be part of a healthy diet.

Table 2.6 Tips for Making Healthy Food Choices Wherever You Eat

	Choose <u>more</u> often	Choose <u>less</u> often
Cooking methods	• Baked, steamed, poached, grilled, roasted or stir-fried • Tomato-based sauce, sauces on the side	• Fried, breaded, battered • Au gratin (with cheese), sweet or creamy sauces • Dishes with soy sauce or MSG
Snacks on-the-go	• Vegetables, fruit, low-fat cheeses or yogourt, boiled eggs • Whole-grain crackers with peanut butter • Unsalted nuts or seeds	• Cheese puffs, chips, cookies, donuts, buttered/salted popcorn, chocolate bars, candy
Beverages	• Water, milk (skim, 1%, or 2%) • Sugar-free/diet drinks • Clear tea, herbal tea, black coffee	• Milkshakes, fruit drinks, regular pop • Alcohol, specialty drinks (e.g., iced cappuccino)
Fast food	• Garden salad • Mini subs, pita sandwiches, plain burgers/wraps/sandwiches (ask for extra vegetables) • Vegetarian or cheese pizza with whole-grain crust	• Burgers/sandwiches with bacon, cheese, and high-fat sauces • French fries, fried chicken, fried fish, poutine, hash browns • Pizza with pepperoni, sausage, bacon, or extra cheese
Starters	• Raw vegetables, salads (garden, spinach, fruit) • Vegetable juice, clear or vegetable soups • Seafood cocktail, sushi • Whole-grain breads and rolls	• Salads with high-fat dressings or toppings • Cream soups • Wings, egg rolls, onion rings, nachos • White or garlic bread
Main courses	**Grains & Starches** (amount equal to ¼ of your plate) • Oatmeal, high-fibre/lower-sugar cereals • Whole-grain breads, rice, pasta, barley, couscous • Plain or sweet potatoes	• Sugary, low-fibre cereals • Large bagels, muffins, croissants, white bread • French fries, hash browns, fried rice
	Meat & Alternatives (amount equal to ¼ of your plate) • Lean meats, poultry, fish, eggs, low-fat cheese • Tofu, soy products, vegetable protein • Legumes (e.g., lentils, chickpeas, beans)	• High-salt and/or high-fat meats (e.g., ribs, wings, sausages, wieners, poultry with skin on, processed luncheon meats)
	Vegetables (amount equal to ½ of your plate) • Salads (Greek, garden, spinach), plain vegetables • Vegetables on sandwiches, wraps, pizza	• Salads with creamy, high-fat dressings and toppings like bacon bits, croutons, cheese
Desserts	• Fresh fruit, frozen yogourt, skim milk latte	• Cakes, pies, pastries, ice cream, cheesecake

PLATE METHOD

Vegetables

Grains & Starches   Meat & Alternatives

Data from: Reprinted with permission from the Canadian Diabetes Association (diabetes.ca).

Chapter Review

2

1. (F) A healthy diet can come in many forms, and particular attention must be paid to adequacy, variety, moderation, and balance. While consuming at least seven servings of fruits and vegetables each day is important to maintain optimal health, a healthy diet should also include whole grains and cereals, meat or meat alternatives, milk products, and small amounts of healthy fats.

2. (F) Detailed food labels are not required for meat or poultry. Coffee and most spices are not required to have food labels, as they contain insignificant amounts of all the nutrients that must be listed on food labels.

3. (T) *Eating Well with Canada's Food Guide* can be used by most Canadians to design a healthy diet. This tool is flexible and allows for modifications as needed; there are also many ethnic variations available.

4. (T) *Eating Well with Canada's Food Guide* recommends that Canadians limit alcohol consumption in addition to sugar, fat, and salt consumption.

5. (F) Eating out poses many challenges to healthy eating, but it is possible to eat a healthy diet when dining out. Ordering and/or consuming smaller portion sizes, selecting foods that are lower in fat and added sugars, and selecting eating establishments that serve more healthy foods can assist you in eating healthily while dining out.

Summary

- A healthy diet is adequate, moderate, balanced, varied, and considers food safety.

- Health Canada regulates the content of food labels; food labels must contain an ingredient list and Nutrition Facts table.

- The Nutrition Facts table on a food label contains core nutrition information about serving size; total calories; a list of various macronutrients, vitamins, and minerals; and the % Daily Values for the nutrients on the panel.

- Health Canada regulates nutrient and health claims found on food labels.

- *Eating Well with Canada's Food Guide* was created in 2007 to provide a conceptual framework for the types and amounts of foods that make up a healthy diet. The groups in *Eating Well with Canada's Food Guide* include vegetable and fruit, grain products, milk and alternatives, and meat and alternatives.

- Specific serving sizes are defined for foods in each group of the food guide and are generally smaller than those listed on food labels or the servings generally sold to consumers.

- There are many ethnic and cultural variations of *Eating Well with Canada's Food Guide* for example, Chinese, Punjabi, and Inuktitut.

- Eating out is challenging because of the high fat content and large serving sizes of many fast-food and sit-down restaurant menu items.

- Behaviours that can improve the quality of your diet when eating out include choosing lower-fat meats that are grilled or broiled, eating vegetables and salads as side or main dishes, asking for low-fat salad dressing on the side, skipping high-fat desserts and appetizers, and drinking low-calorie or non-caloric beverages.

Review Questions

1. The Nutrition Facts table identifies which of the following?
   a. all of the nutrients and calories in the package of food
   b. the Recommended Dietary Allowance for each nutrient found in the package of food
   c. a footnote identifying the Tolerable Upper Intake Level for each nutrient found in the package of food
   d. the % Daily Values of selected nutrients in a serving of the packaged food

2. An adequate diet is defined as a diet that
   a. provides enough energy to meet minimum daily requirements.
   b. provides enough of the energy, nutrients, and fibre to maintain a person's health.
   c. provides a sufficient variety of nutrients to maintain a healthy weight and to optimize the body's metabolic processes.
   d. contains combinations of foods that provide healthy proportions of nutrients.

3. *Eating Well with Canada's Food Guide* recommends eating
   a. at least half your grains as whole grains each day.
   b. 6 to 11 servings of milk, cheese, and yogourt each day.
   c. 200 kcal to 500 kcal of discretionary kilocalories each day.
   d. 2 to 3 servings of fruit juice each day.

4. What does it mean to choose foods for their nutrient density?
   a. Dense foods such as peanut butter or chicken are more nutritious choices than transparent foods such as mineral water or gelatin.
   b. Foods with a lot of nutrients per kilocalorie such as fish are more nutritious choices than foods with fewer nutrients per kilocalorie such as candy.
   c. Calorie-dense foods such as cheesecake should be avoided.
   d. Fat makes foods dense, and thus foods high in fat should be avoided.

5. Which of the following is an alternative choice for meats in *Eating Well with Canada's Food Guide*?
   a. nuts
   b. bacon
   c. lard
   d. peas

6. John is a 21-year-old university student. His girlfriend wants him to start eating more fruit and vegetables; John thinks he is doing fine. On a typical day he eats a banana or orange for breakfast, ½ cup of applesauce and 1 cup of orange juice for lunch, and an apple or ½ cup of grapes for dessert with his supper. Throughout the day he snacks on drink boxes that contain 25% real juice and occasionally will have a fruit roll-up.

   Compare John's fruit and vegetable intake with the recommended number of food guide servings. Should John listen to his girlfriend?

7. The Nutrition Facts table on Quaker Apples and Cinnamon Oatmeal states that one packet contains 35% DV of iron. Explain how Marianne can use this information to plan her diet.

8. Defend the statement that no single diet can be appropriate for every human being.

9. You work for a food company that is introducing a new variety of soup. Design a label for this new soup, including all four nutrition-related label components allowed by Health Canada.

10. Explain why *Eating Well with Canada's Food Guide* identifies a range in the number of suggested daily servings of each food group instead of telling us exactly how many servings of each food to eat each day.

11. If the label on a box of cereal claims that the cereal is "High in fibre," at least how much fibre does it provide per serving?

12. You are chatting with your nutrition classmate, Sylvia, about her attempts to lose weight. "I tried one of those low-carb diets," Sylvia confesses, "but I couldn't stick with it because bread and pasta are my favourite foods! Now I'm on the Mediterranean diet. I like it because it's a low-fat diet, so I'm sure to lose weight, plus I can eat all the bread and pasta that I want!" Do you think Sylvia's assessment of the Mediterranean diet is accurate? Why or why not?

Web Links

www.inspection.gc.ca/english/fssa/labeti/guide/toce.shtml
Canadian Food Inspection Agency
Access the Guide to Food Labelling and Advertising.

www.hc-sc.gc.ca/fn-an/surveill/atlas/index-eng.php
Canada's Nutrition and Health Atlas
Here you'll find maps and tables that make it easy to access information about the health and nutrition of Canadians.

www.dietitians.ca
Dietitians of Canada
Visit this site to find nutrition labelling and healthy eating resources.

www.eatracker.ca
eaTracker
Track your daily food and activity choices and compare them to Health Canada guidelines.

www.hc-sc.gc.ca/fn-an/food-guide-aliment/index-eng. php
Health Canada
Here you can create a personalized version of Canada's Food Guide, track your servings from each food group, and access resources on nutrition labelling.

www.eatwise.ca
Eat Wise
Check out this site to look up common Canadian foods and view their nutrient content.

MasteringNutrition®

www.masteringnutrition.pearson.com

Assignments
Animation: Reading Labels
Activities: NutriTools

Study Area
Practice Tests • Diet Analysis • eText

References

1. Statistics Canada. 2005. *Nutrition: Findings from the Canadian Community Health Survey: Measured obesity.* Ottawa: Statistics Canada Cat. No. 82-620-MWE.

2. Health Canada. 2010. *Background on the food guide.* Available at www.hc-sc.gc.ca/fn-an/food-guide-aliment/context/hist-eng.php (accessed June 2, 2010).

3. Canadian Food Inspection Agency. 2007. *Guide to Food Labelling and Advertising.* Available at www.inspection.gc.ca/english/fssa/labeti/guide/toce.shtml (accessed June 15, 2010).

4. Health Canada. 2010. *Nutrition Labelling.* Available at www.hc-sc.gc.ca/fn-an/label-etiquet/nutrition/educat/te_quest-eng.php#a13 (accessed June 20, 2010).

5. Health Canada. 2007. *Eating Well with Canada's Food Guide.* Available at www.hc-sc.gc.ca/fn-an/alt_formats/hpfb-dgpsa/pdf/food-guide-aliment/print_eatwell_bienmang-eng.pdf (accessed June 7, 2010).

6. Lui, R. H. 2003. Health benefits of fruit and vegetables are from additive and synergistic combinations of phytochemicals. *Am. J. Clin. Nutr.* 78 (suppl): 517S–520S.

7. Jacobs, D. R., and D. D. Gallaher. 2004. Whole grain intake and cardiovascular disease: A review. *Curr. Atheroscler. Rep.* 5:415–423.

8. Nielsen, S. J., and B. M. Popkin. 2003. Patterns and trends in food portion sizes, 1977–1998. *JAMA* 289(4):450–453.

9. Health Canada. 2010. *Eating Well with Canada's Food Guide—First Nations, Inuit, Métis.* Available online at www.hc-sc.gc.ca/fn-an/alt_formats/fnihb-dgspni/pdf/pubs/fnim-pnim/2007_fnim-pnim_food-guide-aliment-eng.pdf (accessed June 20, 2010).

10. Downs, S. M., and N. D. Willows. 2008. Should Canadians eat according to the traditional Mediterranean diet pyramid or Canada's Food Guide? *Appl. Physiol. Nutr. Metabol.* 33:527–535.

11. Willet, W. C., and R. L, Leibel. 2006. The Mediterranean diet: Science and practice. *Public Health Nutr.* 9:106–110.

12. Neilson Company. 2009. *Food for thought: Out of home dining.* Available at http://blog.nielsen.com/nielsenwire/wp-content/uploads/2009/06/canada-out-of-home-dining_may-2009.pdf (accessed June 25, 2010).

13. Statistics Canada. 2004. *Findings from the Canadian Community Health Survey: Overview of Canadians Eating Habits.* Ottawa: Statistics Canada Cat. No. 82-620-MIE.

14. Tjepkema, M. 2005. *Adult obesity in Canada: Measured height and weight.* Available at: http://www.statcan.gc.ca/pub/82-003-x/2005003/article/9276-eng.pdf

15. Canadian Diabetes Association. 2008. *Eating away from home.* Available at www.diabetes.ca/files/EatingEnglish.pdf (accessed June 26, 2010).

16. Katamay, S. W., K. A. Esslinger, M. Vigneault, J. L. Johnston, B. A. Junkins, L. G. Robbins, I. V. Sirois, E. M. Jones-McLean, A. F. Kennedy, M. A. A. Bush, D. Brulé, and C. Marineau. 2007. Eating Well with Canada's Food Guide (2007): Development of the food intake pattern. *Nutr. Rev.* 65:155–166.

17. Andresen, M. 2007. Mixed reviews for Canada's new food guide. *CMAJ* 176:752–753.

18. Corby, L. 2007. Eating Well. *CMAJ* 177:176.

19. Health Canada. 2007. *My Food Guide.* Available at www.hc-sc.gc.ca/fn-an/food-guide-aliment/myguide-monguide/index-eng.php (accessed October 12, 2010).

Will *Eating Well with Canada's Food Guide* Help You Find the Perfect Diet?

As you learned in this chapter, the previous Canada's Food Guide was revised in 1992. A lot has changed in the past two decades. Canadians have more food choices than ever before; bok choy, couscous, and naan are as likely to be eaten as apples, eggs, and pasta. And, Canadians are not the same people they were in 1992. Today, they rely heavily on the internet for information about diet and lifestyle, a medium that was in its infancy in the early 1990s.

Eating Well with Canada's Food Guide[5] was released in 2007 after a multi-year process that incorporated the advice of a scientific advisory committee and input through public and professional consultations. The eating pattern recommended in the guide was developed using a modelling process to ensure that it met nutrient standards and energy recommendations and was consistent with evidence linking food with the risk of developing certain chronic diseases.[16]

A two-step process was used to develop the recommended pattern. First, food composites were created for 16 age and gender groups. These food composites were then used to create 500 simulated diets for each age and gender group. The nutrient distributions from these simulated diets were assessed relative to the Dietary Reference Intakes. Any simulated diets that didn't meet the DRIs were revised to produce a better pattern and the process was repeated. The final patterns were reviewed to ensure associations between foods and the risk of chronic disease were considered.[16] However, even after this extensive development process, when it was released, the food guide received mixed reviews.

One major criticism reported extensively in the media concerned the composition of the advisory committee that was set up to oversee the revision. The 12 members included dietitians and scientists. However, it also included representatives from the food and grocery industries.

Eating Well with Canada's Food Guide includes more culturally specific foods that reflect diversity of the Canadian diet.

Critics argued that food manufacturers had too much of a voice. Health Canada defended the role of the food industry on the advisory committee saying that to understand the issues, all stakeholders needed to be at the table.

A second criticism levelled at the food guide was that it did nothing to halt the current obesity epidemic. In fact, some critics suggested that following *Eating Well with Canada's Food Guide* would promote weight gain.[17] They pointed to the number of servings recommended from each food group and the fact that the food guide does not provide recommended daily caloric intakes. However, proponents argue that it is important for everyone to balance healthy eating and daily physical exercise, as recommended by the food guide. They also pointed out that the number of kilocalories any one person needs can only be calculated after careful consideration, in consultation with a registered dietitian. Focusing on calorie counting alone can result in very unhealthy dietary practices.[18]

A third criticism of *Eating Well with Canada's Food Guide* is that the serving sizes suggested are unrealistic or do not coincide with typical serving sizes of food listed on food labels. For instance, the new guide considers half of a whole-grain muffin to be a single serving; who eats half a muffin? And, while it may be easy to picture 125 mL of cereal or 30 mL of peanut butter, it is more of a challenge to envision 125 mL of chicken when it is on the bone or to dish out 75 grams of beef without weighing individual portions. Dietitians agree that the food guide is not perfect, but they concede that it is more personal, more adaptable, and more reflective of the Canadian demographic than its predecessor.

The food guide contains information that is more targeted to specific groups—children, teens, women, men, and older adults.[5] Scientific advances that have occurred since 1992 are also incorporated into the guide. For instance, there is a recommendation that people over

50 take daily supplements of vitamin D to prevent osteoporosis, and a recommendation to include two fish servings each week to lower their risk of cardiovascular disease.

Further recommendations encourage Canadians to eat foods with little or no added salt and strive to get their vegetables and fruit servings from fresh vegetables and fruit instead of juice. It also recommends that Canadians include some fats and oils in their diet, with the focus on unsaturated fats such as olive and canola oils. The guide recommends that people limit as much as possible their consumption of trans fats.[5]

The revised food guide includes far more culturally specific foods.[5] For example, if you're having a stir-fry for dinner, 250 mL of mixed broccoli, carrot, and sweet red pepper would give you two vegetables and fruit servings, and 75 grams of chicken would constitute a meat and alternatives serving. However, if you don't eat meat you could substitute 175 mL of lentils or 150 grams of tofu. Or, you could include cheese, kefir, or paneer in your diet instead of 250 mL of milk.

Finally, the food guide has adopted an online interactive element called My Food Guide, which can be found at www.hc-sc.gc.ca/fn-an/food-guide-aliment/myguide-monguide/index-eng.php. Canadians can provide their age, gender, and physical activity levels to My Food Guide. The website then takes the information and creates a personal food guide.[19] It also includes a list of sample servings based on individual preferences for foods in each of the food groups.

Eating Well with Canada's Food Guide is a fundamental tool for healthy eating, but it cannot be expected to meet every need. It is designed to promote a pattern of healthy eating and daily physical activity over a lifetime.

What has changed?

- Recommendations are tailored by age and gender.
- More prominence is given to vegetables and fruit.
- Ethnic food selections are included.
- The food guide suggests that at least half of the grain products consumed daily should be whole grains.
- Limiting salt consumption is recommended.
- Recommendations include consuming 30–45 mL of unsaturated fats each day.
- Canadians over the age of 50 are encouraged to take a vitamin D supplement to help prevent osteoporosis.
- Specific advice is provided to include physical activity in daily activities.
- An interactive component called My Food Guide is available that allows users to personalize nutrition information.
- There exist versions for First Nations, Inuit, and Métis peoples.

Using the Evidence

1. How confident are you in using *Eating Well with Canada's Food Guide* to plan a healthy diet?

2. Are the criticisms directed at *Eating Well with Canada's Food Guide* valid?

3. Will following the guidelines described in *Eating Well with Canada's Food Guide* minimize our risk of chronic disease?

The Human Body: Are We Really What We Eat?

Test Yourself | **True** *or* **False?**

1. Sometimes you may have an appetite even though you are not hungry. T *or* F

2. Your stomach is the primary organ responsible for telling you when you are hungry. T *or* F

3. If you eat only small amounts of food, over time, your stomach will permanently shrink. T *or* F

4. The entire process of digestion and absorption of one meal takes about 24 hours. T *or* F

5. Most ulcers result from a type of infection. T *or* F

Test Yourself answers are located in the Chapter Review.

Chapter Objectives | *After reading this chapter, you will be able to:*

1. Distinguish between appetite and hunger, describing the mechanisms that stimulate each, *pp. 78–82.*
2. Draw a picture of the gastrointestinal tract, including all major and accessory organs, *p. 83.*
3. Describe the contribution of each organ of the gastrointestinal tract to the digestion, absorption, and elimination of food, *pp. 84–91.*
4. Identify the source and function of the key enzymes involved in digesting foods, *pp. 91–92.*
5. Identify the four major hormones involved in the regulation of the gastrointestinal tract and describe their primary action, *pp. 92–93.*
6. Discuss the roles of the gallbladder, pancreas, and liver in digestion, absorption, and processing of nutrients, *pp. 93–94.*
7. List and describe the four types of absorption that occur in the small intestine, *pp. 94–96.*
8. Describe the causes, symptoms, and treatments of gastroesophageal reflux disease, ulcers, food allergies, celiac disease, diarrhea, constipation, and irritable bowel syndrome, *pp. 99–108.*

Two months ago, Padma's lifelong dream of becoming a lawyer came one step closer to reality; she moved out of her parents' home in Regina to attend law school in Toronto. Unfortunately, the adjustments to a new city, new friends, and her intensive course load were more stressful than she'd imagined, and Padma has been experiencing insomnia and exhaustion. What's more, her always "sensitive stomach" has been getting worse. After every meal she gets cramps so bad that she can't stand up, and twice she has missed classes because of sudden attacks of pain and diarrhea. She suspects that the problem is related to stress and wonders if she is going to experience it throughout her life. She is even thinking of dropping out of school if that would make her feel well again.

Almost everyone experiences brief episodes of abdominal pain, diarrhea, or other symptoms from time to time. Such episodes are usually caused by food poisoning or an infection such as influenza. But do you know anyone who experiences these symptoms periodically for days, weeks, or even years? If so, has it made you wonder why? What are the steps in normal digestion and absorption of food, and at what points can the process break down?

We begin this chapter with a look at some of the factors that make us feel as if we want to eat. We then discuss the physiologic processes by which the body digests and absorbs food and eliminates waste products. Finally, we look at some disorders that affect these processes.

Foods that are artfully prepared, arranged, or ornamented, like the cakes and pies in this bakery display case, appeal to our sense of sight.

Why Do We Want to Eat What We Want to Eat?

You've just finished eating at your favourite Thai restaurant. As you walk back to the block where you parked your car, you pass a bakery window displaying several cakes and pies, each of which looks more enticing than the last, and through the door wafts a complex aroma of coffee, cinnamon, and chocolate. You stop. You know you're not hungry . . . but you go inside and buy a slice of chocolate torte and an espresso anyway. Later that night, when the caffeine from the chocolate and espresso keep you awake, you wonder why you succumbed.

Two mechanisms prompt us to seek food. **Hunger** is a physiologic drive for food that occurs when the body senses that we need to eat. The drive is *non-specific*; when you're hungry, a variety of different foods could satisfy you. If you've recently finished a nourishing meal, then hunger probably won't compel you toward a slice of chocolate torte. Instead, the pull is likely to be **appetite**, a psychological desire to consume *specific* foods. It is aroused when environmental cues—such as the sight of chocolate cake or the smell of coffee—stimulate our senses, prompting pleasant emotions and often memories.

People commonly experience appetite in the absence of hunger. That's why you can crave cake and coffee even after eating a full meal. On the other hand, it is possible to have a physiologic need for food yet have no appetite. This state, called **anorexia**, can accompany a variety of illnesses from infectious diseases to mood disorders. It can also occur as a side effect of certain medications, such as the chemotherapy used in treating cancer patients. Although in the following sections we describe hunger and appetite as separate entities, ideally the two states coexist: we seek specific, appealing foods to satisfy a physiologic need for nutrients.

Hunger is a physiologic stimulus that prompts us to find food and eat.

hunger A physiologic drive to eat. Chronic hunger results in physical discomfort, weakness, or pain.

appetite A psychological desire to consume specific foods.

anorexia An absence of appetite.

The Hypothalamus Prompts Hunger in Response to Various Signals

Because hunger is a physiologic stimulus that drives us to find food and eat, it is often felt as a negative or unpleasant sensation. The primary organ producing that sensation is the

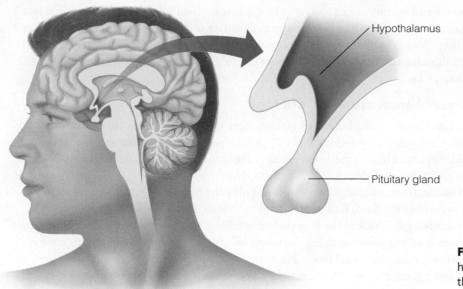

Hypothalamus

Pituitary gland

Figure 3.1 The hypothalamus triggers hunger by integrating signals from nerve cells throughout the body, as well as from messages carried by hormones.

brain. That's right—it's not our stomachs, but our brains that tell us when we're hungry. The region of brain tissue that is responsible for prompting us to seek food is called the **hypothalamus** (**Figure 3.1**). It's located just above the pituitary gland and brain stem in a region of the brain responsible for regulating many types of involuntary activity. The hypothalamus triggers feelings of hunger or satiation (fullness) by integrating signals from nerve cells in other body regions and from chemical messengers called hormones. Even the amount and type of food we eat influence the hypothalamus to cause us to feel hungry or full. Let's now review these three types of signals generated from nerve cells, hormones, and the food we eat.

The Role of Nerve Cells

One hunger-regulating signal comes from special cells lining the stomach and small intestine that detect changes in pressure according to whether the organ is empty or distended with food. The cells relay these data to the hypothalamus. For instance, if you have not eaten for many hours and your stomach and small intestine do not contain food, these data are sent to the hypothalamus, which in turn prompts you to experience the sensation of hunger.

The Role of Hormones

Hormones are chemical messengers that are secreted into the bloodstream by one of the many *endocrine glands* of the body. Their presence in the blood helps regulate one or more body functions. Insulin and glucagon are two hormones produced in the pancreas. They are responsible for maintaining blood glucose levels. Glucose is our bodies' most readily available fuel supply. It's not surprising, then, that its level in our blood is an important signal regulating hunger. When we have not eaten for a while, our blood glucose levels fall, prompting a change in the level of insulin and glucagon. This chemical message is relayed to the hypothalamus, which then prompts us to eat to supply our bodies with more glucose.

After we eat, the hypothalamus picks up the sensation of a distended stomach, other signals from the gut, and a rise in blood glucose levels. When it integrates these signals, you have the experience of feeling full, or *satiated*. However, as we have noted, even though the brain sends us clear signals about hunger, most of us become adept at ignoring them . . . and eat when we are not truly hungry.

In addition to insulin and glucagon, a variety of other hormones and hormonelike substances signal the hypothalamus to cause us to feel hungry or satiated. Examples of

hypothalamus A region of the brain below (*hypo-*) the thalamus and cerebral hemispheres and above the pituitary gland and brain stem where visceral sensations such as hunger and thirst are regulated.

hormone A chemical messenger that is secreted into the bloodstream by one of the many endocrine glands of the body. Hormones act as a regulator of physiologic processes at a site remote from the gland that secreted them.

hormones and hormonelike substances that stimulate food intake include neuropeptide Y and galanin, while those that create feelings of satiety include leptin, cholecystokinin, and serotonin.[1] More details about the various hormones involved in digestion are provided later in this chapter. For information about the role of hormones in weight management, see Chapter 14.

The Role of Amount and Type of Food

Foods containing protein have the highest satiety value.[1] This means that a ham-and-egg breakfast will cause us to feel satiated for a longer period of time than will pancakes with maple syrup, even if both meals have exactly the same number of calories. High-fat diets have a higher satiety value than high-carbohydrate diets.

Another factor affecting hunger is how bulky the meal is—that is, how much fibre and water are within the food. Bulky meals tend to stretch the stomach and small intestine, which sends signals back to the hypothalamus telling us that we are full, so we stop eating. Beverages tend to be less satisfying than semi-solid foods, and semi-solid foods have a lower satiety value than solid foods. For example, if you were to eat a bunch of grapes, you would feel a greater sense of fullness than if you drank a glass of grape juice.

RECAP

In contrast to appetite, hunger is a physiologic sensation triggered by the hypothalamus in response to cues about stomach and intestinal distention and the levels of certain hormones and hormonelike substances. Foods containing protein have the highest satiety value, and bulky meals fill us up quickly, causing the distention that signals us to stop eating.

Environmental Cues Trigger Appetite

Whereas hunger is prompted by internal signals, appetite is triggered by aspects of our environment. The most significant factors influencing our appetite are sensory data, social and cultural cues, and learning (**Figure 3.2**).

Figure 3.2 Appetite is a drive to consume specific foods, such as popcorn at the movies. It is aroused by social and cultural cues and sensory data, and influenced by learning.

The Role of Sensory Data

Foods stimulate our five senses. Foods that are artfully prepared, arranged, or ornamented, with several different shapes and colours, appeal to our sense of sight. Food producers know this and spend millions of dollars annually in Canada to promote and package their products in an appealing way.

The aromas of foods, such as freshly brewed coffee and baked goods, can also be powerful stimulants. Interestingly, the sense of smell is so acute that newborn babies can distinguish the scent of their own mother's breast milk from that of other mothers.[2] Much of our ability to taste foods actually comes from our sense of smell. This is why foods are not as appealing when we have a stuffy nose due to a cold. Certain tastes, such as sweetness, are almost universally appealing, whereas others, such as the astringent taste of foods like spinach and kale, are quite individual. Because many natural poisons and spoiled foods are bitter, our distaste for bitterness is thought to be protective.[3]

Texture, or "mouth feel," is also important in food choices, as it stimulates nerve endings sensitive to touch in our mouths and on our tongues. Do you prefer mashed potatoes, thick French fries, or rippled potato chips? Even your sense of hearing can be stimulated by foods, from the fizz of cola to the crunch of peanuts to the "snap, crackle, and pop" of Rice Krispies® cereal.

The Role of Social and Cultural Cues

In addition to sensory cues, the brain's association with certain social events, such as birthday parties or holiday gatherings, can stimulate our appetite. At these times, our culture gives us permission to eat more than usual or to eat "forbidden" foods. Even when we feel full, these cues can motivate us to accept a second helping.

For some people, being in a certain location, such as at a hockey game or a movie theatre, can trigger appetite. Others may be triggered by certain activities such as watching television or studying, or at certain times of day associated with mealtimes. Many people feel an increase or decrease in appetite according to whom they are with; for example, they may eat more when at home with family members and less when out on a date. Even visual cues and sounds in the environment can trigger appetite. Do you start thinking about food every time you pass your refrigerator? At the end of a class period, how many of your classmates head for the vending machines?

In some cases, appetite masks an emotional response to an external event. For example, after receiving a failing grade or arguing with a close friend, a person might experience a desire for food rather than a desire for emotional comfort. Many people crave food when they're frustrated, worried, or bored, or when they are at a party or other gathering where they feel anxious or awkward. Others subconsciously seek food as a "reward." For example, have you ever found yourself heading out for a burger and fries after handing in a term paper?

The Role of Learning

Pigs' feet, anyone? What about blood sausage, stewed octopus, or tripe? These are delicacies in various European cultures. Would you eat grasshoppers? If you'd grown up in certain parts of Africa or Central America you probably would. That's because your preference for particular foods is largely a learned response. The family, community, religion, and/or culture in which you are raised teach you what plant and animal products are appropriate to eat. If your parents fed you cubes of plain tofu throughout your toddlerhood, then you are probably still eating tofu now.

That said, early introduction to foods is not essential; we can learn to enjoy new foods at any point in our lives. Immigrants from developing nations settling in Canada often adopt a typical Western diet, especially when their traditional foods are not readily available. This happens temporarily when we travel; the last time you were away from home, you probably enjoyed sampling a variety of dishes that are not normally part of your diet.

Food preferences are influenced by the family and culture in which you are raised.

Food preferences also change when people learn what foods are healthiest in terms of nutrient density and prevention of chronic diseases. Since reading Chapters 1 and 2, has your diet changed at all? Chances are, as you learn more about the health benefits of specific types of carbohydrates, fats, and proteins, you'll quite naturally start incorporating more of these foods in your diet.

We can also "learn" to dislike foods we once enjoyed. For example, if we experience an episode of food poisoning after eating undercooked scrambled eggs, we might develop a strong distaste for all types of cooked eggs. Many adults who become vegetarians do so after learning about the treatment of animals in slaughterhouses; they might have eaten meat daily when young but no longer have any appetite for it.

RECAP

In contrast to hunger, appetite is a psychological desire to consume specific foods. It is triggered when external stimuli arouse our senses, and often occurs in combination with social and cultural cues. Our preference for certain foods is largely learned from the culture in which we were raised, but our food choices can change with exposure to new foods or with new learning experiences.

SEE FOR YOURSELF

Do You Eat in Response to External or Internal Cues?

So far in this chapter you have learned the differences between appetite and hunger, as well as the influence of learning on food choices. So now you might be curious to investigate your own reasons for eating what and when you do. Whether you're trying to lose weight, gain weight, or maintain your current healthy weight, you'll probably find it intriguing to keep a log of the reasons behind your decisions about what, when, where, and why you eat. Are you eating in response to internal sensations telling you that your body *needs* food, or in response to your emotions, situation, or a prescribed diet? Keeping a "cues" log for one full week would give you the most accurate picture of your eating habits, but even logging two days of meals and snacks should increase your cue awareness.

Each day, every time you eat a meal, snack, or beverage other than water, make a quick note of:

- **When you eat.** Many people eat at certain times (for example, 6 p.m.) whether they are hungry or not.
- **What you eat, and how much.** A cup of yogourt and a handful of nuts? An apple? A 355 mL cola?
- **Where you eat.** At home at the dining room table, watching television, driving in the car, and so on.
- **With whom you eat.** Are you alone or with others? If with others, are they eating as well? Have they offered you food?
- **Your emotions.** Many people overeat when they are happy, especially when celebrating with others. Some

people eat excessively when they are anxious, depressed, bored, or frustrated. Still others eat as a way of denying feelings because they don't want to identify and deal with them. For some, food becomes a substitute for emotional fulfillment.

- **Your sensations: what you see, hear, or smell.** Are you eating because you walked past the kitchen and spied that batch of homemade cookies, or smelled coffee roasting?
- **Any diet restrictions.** Are you choosing a particular food because it is allowed on your current diet plan? Or are you hungry, but drinking a diet soft drink to stay within a certain allowance of kilocalories? Are you restricting yourself because you feel guilty about having eaten too much at another time?
- **Your physiologic hunger.** Rate your hunger on a scale from 1 to 5 as follows:
  1 = you feel full or even stuffed
  2 = you feel satisfied but not uncomfortably full
  3 = neutral; you feel no discernible satiation nor hunger
  4 = you feel hungry and want to eat
  5 = you feel strong physiologic sensations of hunger and need to eat

After keeping a log for two or more days, you might become aware of patterns you'd like to change. For example, maybe you notice that you often eat when you are not actually hungry but are worried about homework or personal relationships. Or maybe you notice that you can't walk past the snack bar without going in. This self-awareness may prompt you to take positive steps to change those patterns. For instance, instead of stifling your worries with food, sit down with a pen and paper and write down exactly what you are worried about, including steps you can take to address your concerns. And the next time you approach the snack bar, before going in, check with your gut: are you truly hungry? If so, then purchase a healthy snack, maybe a yogourt, a piece of fruit, or a bag of peanuts. If you're not really hungry, then take a moment to acknowledge the strength of this visual cue—and then walk on by.

What Happens to the Food We Eat?

When we eat, the food we consume is digested, then the useful nutrients are absorbed, and, finally, the waste products are eliminated. But what does each of these processes really entail? In the simplest terms, **digestion** is the process by which foods are broken down into their component molecules, either mechanically or chemically. **Absorption** is the process of taking these products of digestion through the wall of the intestine. **Elimination** is the process by which the undigested portions of food and waste products are removed from the body.

The processes of digestion, absorption, and elimination occur in the **gastrointestinal (GI) tract**, the organs of which work together to process foods. The GI tract is a long tube: if held out straight, an adult GI tract would be close to 9 m in length. Food within this tube is digested; in other words, food is broken down into molecules small enough to be absorbed by the cells lining the GI tract and thereby passed into the body.

The GI tract begins at the mouth and ends at the anus (**Figure 3.3**). It is composed of several distinct organs, including the mouth, esophagus, stomach, small intestine, and

digestion The process by which foods are broken down into their component molecules, either mechanically or chemically.

absorption The physiologic process by which molecules of food are taken from the gastrointestinal tract into the circulation.

elimination The process by which the undigested portions of food and waste products are removed from the body.

gastrointestinal (GI) tract A long, muscular tube consisting of several organs: the mouth, esophagus, stomach, small intestine, and large intestine.

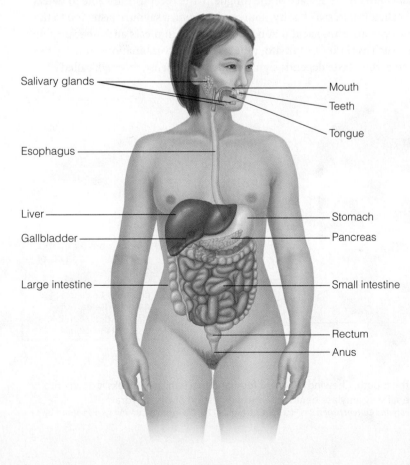

Salivary glands
Mouth
Teeth
Tongue
Esophagus
Liver
Stomach
Gallbladder
Pancreas
Large intestine
Small intestine
Rectum
Anus

Figure 3.3 An overview of the gastrointestinal (GI) tract. The GI tract begins at the mouth and ends at the anus and is composed of numerous organs.
Data from: Johnson, M., *Human Biology: Concepts and Current Issues,* *5/e,* Fig. 14.1, Copyright © 2010 Benjamin Cummings. Reprinted by permission of Pearson Education, Inc.

Digestion of a sandwich starts before you even take a bite.

large intestine. The flow of food between these organs is controlled by muscular **sphincters**, which are tight rings of muscle that open when a nerve signal indicates that food is ready to pass into the next section. Surrounding the GI tract are several accessory organs, including the salivary glands, liver, pancreas, and gallbladder, each of which has a specific role in digestion and absorption of nutrients.

Now let's take a look at the role of each of these organs in processing the food we eat. Imagine that you ate a turkey sandwich for lunch today. It contained two slices of bread spread with mayonnaise, some turkey, two lettuce leaves, and a slice of tomato. Let's travel along with the sandwich and see what happens as it enters your GI tract and is digested and absorbed into your body.

Digestion Begins in the Mouth

Believe it or not, the first step in the digestive process is not your first bite of that sandwich. It is your first thought about what you wanted for lunch and your first whiff of turkey and freshly baked bread as you stood in line at the deli. In this **cephalic phase** of digestion, hunger and appetite work together to prepare the GI tract to digest food. The nervous system stimulates the release of digestive juices in preparation for food entering the GI tract, and sometimes we experience some involuntary movement commonly called "hunger pangs."

Now, let's stop smelling that sandwich and take a bite and chew! Chewing moistens the food and mechanically breaks it down into pieces small enough to swallow (**Figure 3.4**). The presence of food not only initiates mechanical digestion via chewing but also initiates chemical digestion through the secretion of hormones and other substances throughout the gastrointestinal tract. As the teeth cut and grind the different foods in the sandwich, more surface area of the foods is exposed to the digestive juices in the mouth. Foremost among these is **saliva**, which is secreted from the **salivary glands**.

Without saliva, we could not taste the foods we eat. That's because taste occurs when chemicals dissolved in saliva bind to chemoreceptors called *taste receptors* located in structures called *taste buds* on the surface of the tongue. Taste receptors are able to detect at least five distinct tastes: bitter, sweet, salty, sour, and *umami*, a savoury taste due to the presence of glutamic acid, an amino acid that occurs naturally in meats and other protein-rich foods. Flavours, such as turkey or tomato, reflect complex combinations of these five basic tastes. As noted earlier, taste depends significantly on the sense of smell, called

sphincter A tight ring of muscle separating some of the organs of the GI tract and opening in response to nerve signals indicating that food is ready to pass into the next section.

cephalic phase The earliest phase of digestion in which the brain thinks about and prepares the digestive organs for the consumption of food.

saliva A mixture of water, mucus, enzymes, and other chemicals that moistens the mouth and food, binds food particles together, and begins the digestion of carbohydrates.

salivary glands A group of glands found under and behind the tongue and beneath the jaw that releases saliva continually as well as in response to the thought, sight, smell, or presence of food.

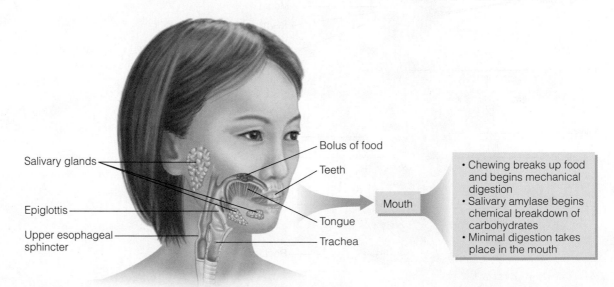

Salivary glands

Epiglottis

Upper esophageal sphincter

Bolus of food

Teeth

Tongue

Trachea

Mouth

- Chewing breaks up food and begins mechanical digestion
- Salivary amylase begins chemical breakdown of carbohydrates
- Minimal digestion takes place in the mouth

Figure 3.4 Where your food is now: the mouth. Chewing moistens food and mechanically breaks it down into pieces small enough to swallow, while salivary amylase begins chemical digestion of carbohydrates.
Data from: Johnson, M., *Human Biology: Concepts and Current Issues, 5/e*, Fig. 3.3, Copyright © 2010 Benjamin Cummings. Reprinted by permission of Pearson Education, Inc.

olfaction. To achieve olfaction, odourants dissolved in mucus bind to chemoreceptors in the nasal cavity called *olfactory receptor cells.* These cells then transmit their data to the olfactory bulb of the brain.

Saliva also initiates the chemical digestion of carbohydrates. It accomplishes this through the actions of salivary amylase, a digestive enzyme. **Enzymes** are complex chemicals, usually proteins, that induce chemical changes in other substances to speed up bodily processes. They can be reused because they essentially are unchanged by the chemical reactions they catalyze. Salivary amylase is only one of many enzymes that assist the body in digesting foods. We make hundreds of enzymes in our bodies, and not only digestion but many other biochemical processes could not happen without them. By the way, enzyme names usually end in *-ase,* so they are easy to recognize as we go through the digestive process. Various amylases assist in the digestion of carbohydrates, lipases are involved with lipid digestion, and proteases help digest proteins.

Saliva contains many other components, including:

- bicarbonate, which helps neutralize acids
- mucus, which moistens the food and the oral cavity, ensuring that food travels easily down the esophagus
- antibodies, proteins that defend against bacteria entering the mouth
- lysozyme, an enzyme that inhibits bacterial growth in the mouth and may assist in preventing tooth decay

In reality, very little digestion occurs in the mouth. This is because we do not hold food in our mouths for very long and because all of the enzymes needed to break down foods are not present in saliva. Salivary amylase starts the digestion of carbohydrates in the mouth, and this digestion continues until food reaches the stomach. Once in the stomach, salivary amylase is no longer active because it is destroyed by the acidic environment of the stomach.

RECaP

The cephalic phase of digestion begins before you take your first bite of food and involves hunger and appetite working together to prepare the GI tract for digestion and absorption. Chewing initiates mechanical digestion of food by breaking it into smaller components and mixing all nutrients together. Chewing also stimulates chemical digestion through the secretion of digestive juices such as saliva. Saliva allows for the sensation of taste, moistens food, and starts the process of carbohydrate digestion through the action of the enzyme salivary amylase. This action continues during the transport of food through the esophagus and stops when food reaches the acidic environment of the stomach.

The Esophagus Propels Food into the Stomach

The mass of food that has been chewed and moistened in the mouth is referred to as a **bolus**. This bolus is swallowed (**Figure 3.5**) and propelled to the stomach through the esophagus. Most of us take swallowing for granted. However, it is a very complex process involving voluntary and involuntary motion. A tiny flap of tissue called the *epiglottis* acts like a trapdoor covering the entrance to the trachea (or windpipe). The epiglottis is normally open, allowing us to breathe freely even while chewing (Figure 3.5a). As our bite of sandwich moves to the very back of the mouth, the brain is sent a signal to temporarily raise the soft palate and close the openings to the nasal passages, preventing aspiration of food or liquid into the sinuses (Figure 3.5b). The brain also signals the epiglottis to close during swallowing so food and liquid cannot enter the trachea. Sometimes this protective mechanism goes awry; for instance, when we try to eat and talk at the same time. When

enzymes Small chemicals, usually proteins, that act on other chemicals to speed up bodily processes but are not changed during those processes.

bolus A mass of food that has been chewed and moistened in the mouth.

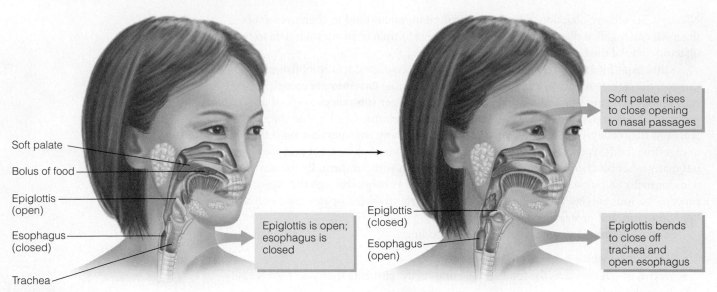

Soft palate

Bolus of food

Epiglottis
(open)

Esophagus
(closed)

Trachea

(a) Chewing

Epiglottis is open;
esophagus is
closed

Soft palate rises
to close opening
to nasal passages

Epiglottis
(closed)

Esophagus
(open)

Epiglottis bends
to close off
trachea and
open esophagus

(b) Swallowing

Figure 3.5 Chewing and swallowing are complex processes. (a) During the process of chewing, the epiglottis is open and the esophagus is closed so that we can continue to breathe as we chew. (b) During swallowing, the epiglottis closes so that food does not enter the trachea and obstruct our breathing. The soft palate also rises to seal off the nasal passages to prevent aspiration of food or liquid into the sinuses.
Data from: Johnson, M., *Human Biology: Concepts and Current Issues, 5/e,* Fig. 3.3, Copyright © 2010 Benjamin Cummings. Reprinted by permission of Pearson Education, Inc.

this happens, we experience the sensation of choking and typically cough involuntarily and repeatedly until the offending food or liquid is expelled from the trachea.

As the trachea closes, the sphincter muscle at the top of the esophagus, called the *upper esophageal sphincter*, opens to allow the passage of food. The **esophagus** then transports the food to the stomach (**Figure 3.6**). A muscular tube, the esophagus propels food along its length by contracting two sets of muscles: inner sheets of circular muscle squeeze the food, while outer sheets of longitudinal muscle push food along the length of the tube. Together, these rhythmic waves of squeezing and pushing are called **peristalsis**. We will see later in this chapter that peristalsis occurs throughout the GI tract.

Gravity also helps transport food down the esophagus, which is one reason why it is wise to sit or stand upright while eating. Together, peristalsis and gravity can transport a bite of food from the mouth to the opening of the stomach in 5 to 8 seconds. At the end of the esophagus is another sphincter muscle, the *gastroesophageal sphincter* (*gastro-* indicates

esophagus A muscular tube of the GI tract connecting the back of the mouth to the stomach.

peristalsis Waves of squeezing and pushing contractions that move food, chyme, and feces in one direction through the length of the GI tract.

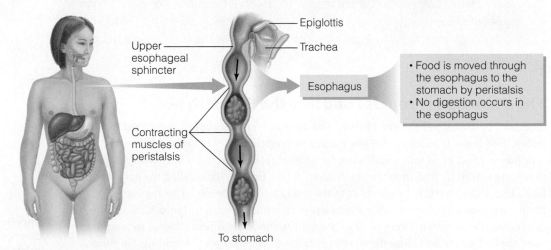

Upper esophageal sphincter

Epiglottis

Trachea

Esophagus

Contracting muscles of peristalsis

• Food is moved through the esophagus to the stomach by peristalsis
• No digestion occurs in the esophagus

To stomach

Figure 3.6 Where your food is now: the esophagus. Peristalsis, the rhythmic contraction and relaxation of both circular and longitudinal muscles in the esophagus, propels food toward the stomach. Peristalsis occurs throughout the GI tract.
Data from: Johnson, M., *Human Biology: Concepts and Current Issues, 5/e,* Fig. 3.3, Copyright © 2010 Benjamin Cummings. Reprinted by permission of Pearson Education, Inc.

the stomach), also referred to as the *lower esophageal sphincter,* which is normally tightly closed. When food reaches the end of the esophagus, this sphincter relaxes to allow the passage of food into the stomach. In some people, this sphincter is continually somewhat relaxed. Later in the chapter, we'll discuss this disorder and the unpleasant symptoms experienced when this sphincter does not function properly.

Recap

Swallowing causes the nasal passages to close and the epiglottis to cover the trachea to prevent food from entering the sinuses and lungs. The upper esophageal sphincter opens as the trachea closes. The esophagus is a muscular tube that transports food from the mouth to the stomach via peristalsis. Gravity also helps move food toward the stomach. Once food reaches the stomach, the gastroesophageal sphincter opens to allow food into the stomach.

The Stomach Mixes, Digests, and Stores Food

The **stomach** is a J-shaped organ. Its size varies with different individuals; in general, its volume is about 185 mL when it is empty. The stomach wall contains four layers, the innermost of which is crinkled into large folds called *rugae* that flatten progressively to accommodate food. This allows the stomach to expand to hold about 1 L of food and liquid.[4] As food is released into the small intestine, the rugae reform, and the stomach gradually returns to its baseline size.

Before any food reaches the stomach, the brain sends signals to the stomach to stimulate and prepare it to receive food. For example, the hormone *gastrin,* secreted by stomach-lining cells called *G cells,* stimulates gastric glands to secrete a digestive fluid referred to as **gastric juice**. Gastric glands are lined with two important types of cells—**parietal cells** and **chief cells**—that secrete the various components of gastric juice, as follows:

- *Hydrochloric acid (HCl),* which is secreted by parietal cells, keeps the stomach interior very acidic—more so than citrus juices (**Figure 3.7**). This acidic environment kills any bacteria and/or germs that may have entered the body with the sandwich. HCl is also

stomach A J-shaped organ where food is partially digested, churned, and stored until released into the small intestine.

gastric juice Acidic liquid secreted within the stomach; it contains hydrochloric acid, pepsin, and other compounds.

parietal cells Cells lining the gastric glands that secrete hydrochloric acid and intrinsic factor.

chief cells Cells lining the gastric glands that secrete pepsinogen and gastric lipase.

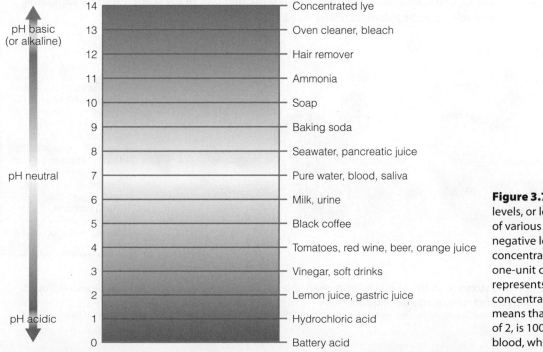

pH basic (or alkaline)	14	Concentrated lye
	13	Oven cleaner, bleach
	12	Hair remover
	11	Ammonia
	10	Soap
	9	Baking soda
	8	Seawater, pancreatic juice
pH neutral	7	Pure water, blood, saliva
	6	Milk, urine
	5	Black coffee
	4	Tomatoes, red wine, beer, orange juice
	3	Vinegar, soft drinks
	2	Lemon juice, gastric juice
pH acidic	1	Hydrochloric acid
	0	Battery acid

Figure 3.7 This chart illustrates the pH levels, or levels of acidity or alkalinity, of various substances. The pH is the negative logarithm of the hydrogen–ion concentration of any substance. Each one-unit change in pH from high to low represents a tenfold increase in the concentration of hydrogen ions. This means that gastric juice, which has a pH of 2, is 100 000 times more acidic than blood, which has a pH of 7.

extremely important for digestion because it starts to denature proteins, which means it uncoils the bonds that maintain their structure. This is an essential preliminary step in breaking down the proteins in the turkey and bread.

- HCl also converts *pepsinogen,* an inactive enzyme secreted by chief cells, into the active enzyme *pepsin,* which begins to digest the denatured proteins into smaller components. Recall that salivary amylase begins to digest carbohydrates in the mouth. In contrast, proteins and lipids enter the stomach largely unchanged. Pepsin begins the digestion of protein and activates many other GI enzymes needed to digest your sandwich.
- *Gastric lipase,* secreted by the chief cells, is an enzyme responsible for lipid digestion. Thus, it begins to break apart the lipids in the turkey and mayonnaise in your sandwich. However, only minimal digestion of lipids occurs in the stomach.
- *Intrinsic factor,* secreted by parietal cells, is a protein critical to the absorption of vitamin B_{12} (discussed in more detail in Chapter 13), which is present in the turkey.

Because gastric juice is already present in the stomach, chemical digestion of proteins and lipids begins as soon as food enters (**Figure 3.8**). The stomach also plays a role in mechanical digestion by mixing and churning the food with the gastric juice until it becomes a liquid called **chyme**. This mechanical digestion facilitates chemical digestion, because enzymes can access the liquid chyme more easily than solid forms of food.

Despite the acidity of gastric juice, the stomach itself is not eroded because *mucous neck cells* in gastric glands and *mucous surface cells* in the stomach lining secrete a protective layer of mucus (**Figure 3.9**). Any disruption of this mucous barrier can cause gastritis (inflammation of the stomach lining) or an ulcer (a condition that is discussed later in this chapter). Other lining cells secrete bicarbonate, which neutralizes acid near the surface of the stomach's lining and also assists in protecting this lining.[5]

Although most absorption occurs in the small intestine, some substances are absorbed through the stomach lining and into the blood. These include water, fluoride, some medium-chain fatty acids, and some drugs, including aspirin, caffeine and alcohol.[6]

Another of the stomach's jobs is to store chyme while the next part of the digestive tract, the small intestine, gets ready for the food. Remember that the stomach can hold about 1 L of food. If this amount were to move into the small intestine all at once, it would overwhelm it. Chyme stays in the stomach for about 2 hours before it is released periodically in spurts into the duodenum, which is the first part of the small intestine. Regulating this release is the *pyloric sphincter* (see Figure 3.8).

chyme A semi-fluid mass consisting of partially digested food, water, and gastric juices.

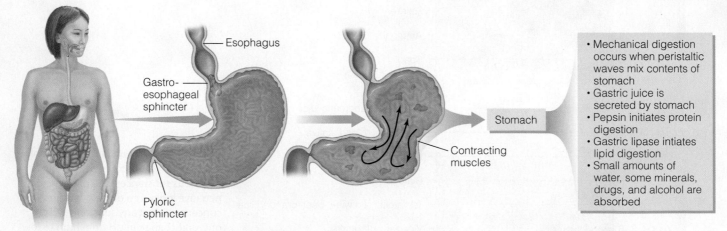

Figure 3.8 Where your food is now: the stomach. In the stomach, the protein and lipids in your sandwich begin to be digested. Your meal is churned into chyme and stored until release into the small intestine.
Data from: Johnson, M., *Human Biology: Concepts and Current Issues, 5/e,* Fig. 3.3, Copyright © 2010 Benjamin Cummings. Reprinted by permission of Pearson Education, Inc.

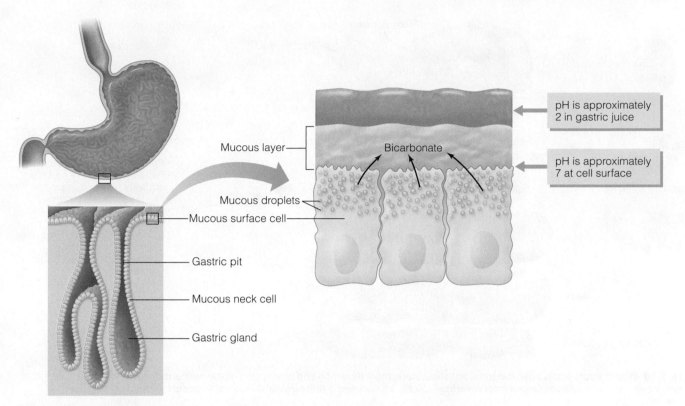

Mucous layer

Bicarbonate

pH is approximately 2 in gastric juice

pH is approximately 7 at cell surface

Mucous droplets

Mucous surface cell

Gastric pit

Mucous neck cell

Gastric gland

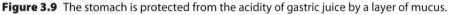

Figure 3.9 The stomach is protected from the acidity of gastric juice by a layer of mucus.

RECAP

Gastric glands in the stomach secrete gastric juice, which contains hydrochloric acid, the enzymes pepsin and gastric lipase, and intrinsic factor. Mucous neck cells and surface cells secrete mucus to protect the stomach lining from erosion. Digestion of proteins and lipids begins in the stomach. The stomach mixes food into a substance called chyme, which is released periodically into the small intestine through the pyloric sphincter.

Most Digestion and Absorption Occurs in the Small Intestine

The **small intestine** is the longest portion of the GI tract, accounting for about two-thirds of its length. However, at only 2.5 cm in diameter, it is comparatively narrow.

The small intestine is composed of three sections (**Figure 3.10**). The *duodenum* is the section of the small intestine that is connected via the pyloric sphincter to the stomach. The *jejunum* is the middle portion, and the last portion is the *ileum*. It connects to the large intestine at another sphincter, called the *ileocecal valve*.

Most digestion and absorption take place in the small intestine. Here, the carbohydrates, lipids, and proteins in your turkey sandwich are broken down into their smallest components, molecules that the body can then absorb into the circulation. Digestion and absorption are achieved in the small intestine through the actions of enzymes, accessory organs (the pancreas, gallbladder, and liver), and some unique anatomical features. The details of how these enzymes, organs, and features do their job are described later in this chapter. Once digestion and absorption are completed in the small intestine, the residue is passed into the large intestine.

small intestine The longest portion of the GI tract where most digestion and absorption take place.

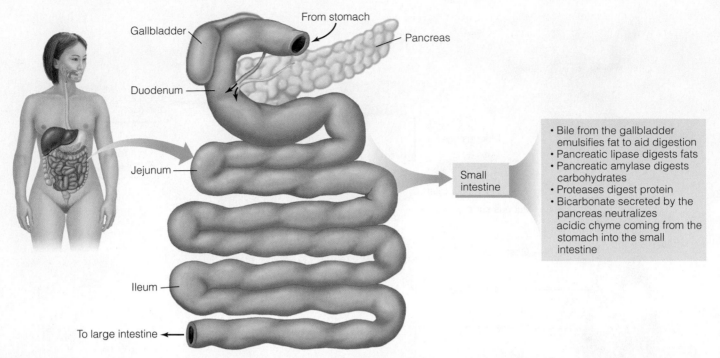

Figure 3.10 Where your food is now: the small intestine. Here, most digestion and absorption of the nutrients in your sandwich take place.
Data from: Johnson, M., *Human Biology: Concepts and Current Issues, 5/e,* Fig. 3.3, Copyright © 2010 Benjamin Cummings. Reprinted by permission of Pearson Education, Inc.

Recap

Most digestion and absorption occurs in the small intestine. Its three sections include the duodenum, the jejunum, and the ileum. Digestion and absorption are achieved through the actions of enzymes, accessory organs, and unique anatomical features.

The Large Intestine Stores Food Waste Until It Is Excreted

large intestine The final organ of the GI tract consisting of the cecum, colon, rectum, and anal canal and in which most water is absorbed and feces are formed.

The **large intestine** is a thick tubelike structure that frames the small intestine on three-and-one-half sides (**Figure 3.11**). It is also referred to as the *colon.* It begins with a tissue sac called the *cecum,* which explains the name of the sphincter—the *ileocecal valve*—that connects it to the ileum of the small intestine. From the cecum, the large intestine continues

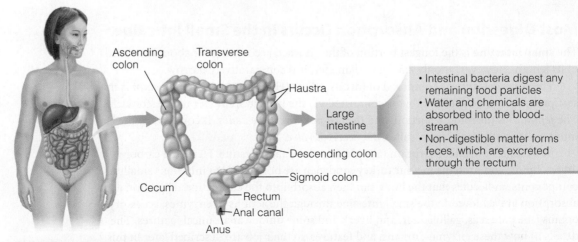

Figure 3.11 Where your food is now: the large intestine. Most water absorption occurs here, as does the formation of food wastes into semi-solid feces.
Data from: Johnson, M., *Human Biology: Concepts and Current Issues, 5/e,* Fig. 3.3, Copyright © 2010 Benjamin Cummings. Reprinted by permission of Pearson Education, Inc.

up along the right side of the small intestine as the *ascending colon*. The *transverse colon* runs across the top of the small intestine, and then the *descending colon* comes down on the left. These regions of the colon are characterized by *haustra*, regular, saclike segmentations that contract to move food toward the *sigmoid colon*, which extends from the bottom left corner to the *rectum*. The last segment of the large intestine is the *anal canal*, which is about 3.8 cm long.

What has happened to our turkey sandwich? The residue that finally reaches the large intestine bears little resemblance to the chyme that left the stomach several hours before. This is because a majority of the nutrients have been absorbed, leaving mostly water, bacteria, and non-digestible food material such as the outer husks of the tomato seeds and the fibres in the lettuce. The bacteria present are normal and helpful residents of your large intestine, because they finish digesting some of the nutrients remaining from your sandwich. In fact, these bacteria are so helpful that many people consume them deliberately! The by-products of this bacterial digestion, such as short-chain fatty acids, are reabsorbed into the body, where they return to the liver and are either stored or used as needed.

No other digestion occurs in the large intestine. Instead, while it stores the digestive mass for 12 to 24 hours, it absorbs water, short-chain fatty acids, and electrolytes from it, leaving a semi-solid mass called *feces*. Peristalsis occurs weakly to move the feces through the colon, except for one or more stronger waves of peristalsis each day that force the feces more powerfully toward the rectum for elimination.

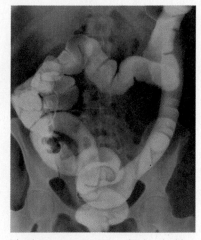

The large intestine is a thick tubelike structure that stores the undigested mass leaving the small intestine and absorbs any remaining nutrients and water.

ReCap

The large intestine is composed of seven sections: the cecum, ascending colon, transverse colon, descending colon, sigmoid colon, rectum, and anal canal. Small amounts of undigested food, undigestible food material, bacteria, and water enter the large intestine from the small intestine. The bacteria assist with final digestion of any remaining food particles. No other digestion occurs in the large intestine. The main functions of the large intestine are to store the digestive mass and absorb water, short-chain fatty acids, and electrolytes over a 12- to 24-hour period. The remaining semi-solid mass, called feces, is then eliminated from the body.

How Does the Body Accomplish Chemical Digestion?

Now that you have learned about the structure and functions of the GI tract, you are ready to delve more deeply into the specific activities of the various enzymes, hormones, and accessory organs involved in digestion.

Enzymes Speed Up Digestion via Hydrolysis

Enzymes are released into the gastrointestinal tract as needed, in a process controlled by the nervous system and various hormones. Upon release, they guide the digestion of foods through the process of **hydrolysis**, which is a chemical reaction that breaks down substances by the addition of water. In this process, which is described in detail in Chapter 7, a reactant such as a portion of a protein is broken down into two products.

Although a few digestive enzymes are produced in the mouth and stomach, most are synthesized by the pancreas and small intestine. Table 3.1 lists many of the enzymes that play a critical role in digestion and specifies where they are produced and their primary actions. Enzymes are usually specific to the substance they act upon, and this is true for the digestive enzymes. As you can see in this table, there are enzymes specific to the digestion of carbohydrates, lipids, and proteins, all of which are too large to be directly absorbed from the gastrointestinal tract. However, water, single-sugar units called monosaccharides,

hydrolysis A catabolic process by which a large, chemically complex compound is broken apart with the addition of water.

Table 3.1 Digestive Enzymes Produced in the Gastrointestinal Tract and Their Actions

Organ Where Produced	Enzyme	Site of Action	Primary Action
Mouth	Salivary amylase	Mouth	Digests carbohydrates
Stomach	Salivary lipase Pepsin Gastric lipase	Stomach	Digests fats Digests proteins Digests lipids
Pancreas	Proteases (trypsin, chymotrypsin, carboxypolypeptidase) Elastase Pancreatic lipase Cholesterol esterase Pancreatic amylase (amylase)	Small intestine	Digest proteins Digests fibrous proteins Digests lipids Digests cholesterol Digests carbohydrates
Small intestine	Carboxypeptidase, aminopeptidase, dipeptidase Lipase Sucrase Maltase Lactase	Small intestine	Digest proteins Digests lipids Digests sucrose Digests maltose Digests lactose

amino acids, fatty acids, vitamins, minerals, and alcohol do not require enzymatic digestion because they are much smaller molecules and therefore can be absorbed in their original form.

Hormones Assist in Regulating Digestion

As introduced earlier in this chapter, hormones are regulatory chemicals produced by endocrine glands. Hormones are released into the bloodstream and travel to target cells that contain the receptor protein specific to that given hormone. Generally, the receptor proteins for hormones are located on the cell membrane. When the hormone arrives at the target cell, it binds to the receptor protein and activates what is referred to as a *second messenger system* within the cell (**Figure 3.12**). This second messenger system achieves the targeted response, such as release of a particular digestive enzyme.

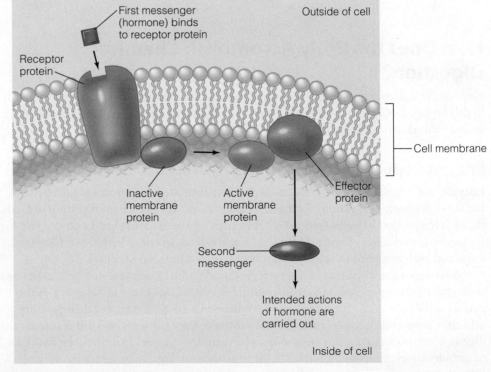

Figure 3.12 Hormones travel to target cells to initiate specific actions. When a hormone arrives at its target cell, it binds to the receptor protein on the cell membrane. This binding activates a protein on the interior cell membrane that initiates a second messenger system within the cell. The second messenger system then carries out the action directed by the hormone's "message."

Table 3.2 Hormones Involved in the Regulation of Digestion

Hormone	Production Site	Target Organ	Actions
Gastrin	Stomach	Stomach	Stimulates secretion of HCl and pepsinogen (inactive form of pepsin) Stimulates gastric motility Promotes proliferation of gastric mucosal cells
Secretin	Small intestine (duodenum)	Pancreas	Stimulates secretion of pancreatic bicarbonate (which neutralizes acidic chyme)
		Stomach	Decreases gastric motility
Cholecystokinin (CCK)	Small intestine (duodenum and jejunum)	Pancreas	Stimulates secretion of pancreatic digestive enzymes
		Gallbladder	Stimulates gallbladder contraction
		Stomach	Slows gastric emptying
Gastric inhibitory peptide (GIP)	Small intestine	Stomach	Inhibits gastric acid secretion
			Slows gastric emptying
		Pancreas	Stimulates insulin release

Regulation of the gastrointestinal tract involves the action of more than 80 hormones and hormonelike substances. Table 3.2 identifies four of the most important of these hormones and the actions they initiate. These are gastrin, secretin, cholecystokinin (CCK), and gastric inhibitory peptide (GIP).[7] Other hormones have recently received attention for their potential roles in digestion. Somatostatin acts to inhibit the release of various hormones and enzymes involved in digestion, and it is being used to treat pancreatic cancer and disorders of the gastrointestinal tract such as diarrhea.[8] Ghrelin is a hormone secreted by cells in the gastrointestinal tract, and it has been identified as playing a role in eating behaviour and weight regulation.[9] It may also have a beneficial effect on the cardiovascular system by improving blood flow and decreasing blood pressure. As the research studying the impact of ghrelin on obesity and cardiovascular health is in its infancy, there is still much to learn about this hormone.

Accessory Organs Produce, Store, and Secrete Chemicals That Aid in Digestion

The gallbladder, pancreas, and liver are considered accessory organs to the gastrointestinal tract. As you will learn in the following sections, these organs are critical to the production, storage, and secretion of enzymes and other substances that are involved in digestion.

The Gallbladder Stores Bile

As noted in Table 3.2, cholecystokinin (CCK) is released in the small intestine in response to the presence of proteins and lipids. This hormone signals the **gallbladder** to contract. The gallbladder is located beneath the liver (see Figure 3.3) and stores a greenish fluid, **bile**, produced by the liver. Contraction of the gallbladder sends bile through the *common bile duct* into the duodenum. Bile then *emulsifies* the lipids; that is, it reduces the lipids into smaller globules and disperses them so they are more accessible to digestive enzymes.

The Pancreas Produces Digestive Enzymes and Bicarbonate

The **pancreas** manufactures, holds, and secretes digestive enzymes. It is located behind the stomach (see Figure 3.3). The pancreas stores these enzymes in their inactive forms, and they are activated in the small intestine; this is important because if the enzymes were active in the pancreas, they would digest the pancreas. Enzymes secreted by the pancreas include *pancreatic amylase,* which continues the digestion of carbohydrates, and *pancreatic lipase,* which continues the digestion of lipids. *Proteases* secreted in pancreatic juice digest

gallbladder A pear-shaped organ beneath the liver that stores bile and secretes it into the small intestine.

bile Fluid produced by the liver and stored in the gallbladder; it emulsifies lipids in the small intestine.

pancreas A gland located behind the stomach that secretes digestive enzymes.

proteins. The pancreas is also responsible for manufacturing hormones that are important in metabolism. Insulin and glucagon, two hormones necessary to regulate the amount of glucose in the blood, are produced by the pancreas.

Another essential role of the pancreas is to secrete bicarbonate into the duodenum. Bicarbonate is a base and, like all bases, is capable of neutralizing acids. Recall that chyme leaving the stomach is very acidic. The pancreatic bicarbonate neutralizes this acidic chyme. This allows the pancreatic enzymes to work effectively and ensures that the lining of the duodenum is not eroded. When the acidic chyme first enters the duodenum, this portion of the small intestine is protected by mucus produced by special glands until the bicarbonate is released and has neutralized the chyme.

The Liver Produces Bile and Regulates Blood Nutrients

The **liver** is a triangular, wedge-shaped organ of about 1.4 kg of tissue that rests almost entirely within the protection of the rib cage on the right side of the body (see Figure 3.3). It is the largest digestive organ; it is also one of the most important organs in the body, performing more than 500 discrete functions. One important job of the liver is to synthesize many of the chemicals used by the body in carrying out metabolic processes. For example, the liver synthesizes bile, which, as we just discussed, is then stored in the gallbladder until needed for the emulsification of lipids.

Another important function of the liver is to receive the products of digestion via the **portal vein**, remove them from the bloodstream and process them for storage, and then release back into the bloodstream those nutrients needed throughout the body. For instance, after we eat a meal, the liver picks up excess glucose from the blood and stores it as glycogen, releasing it into the bloodstream when we need energy later in the day. It also stores certain vitamins and manufactures blood proteins. The liver can even make glucose when necessary to ensure that our blood levels stay constant. Thus, the liver plays a major role in regulating the level and type of fuel circulating in our blood.

Have you ever wondered why people who abuse alcohol are at risk for damaging the liver? That's because another of its functions is to filter the blood, removing wastes and toxins such as alcohol, medications, and other drugs. When you drink, your liver works hard to replace the cells poisoned with alcohol, but, over time, scar tissue forms. The scar tissue blocks the free flow of blood through the liver, so that any further toxins accumulate in the blood, causing confusion, coma, and, ultimately, death. Alcohol is discussed in Chapter 7.

ReCap

Enzymes speed up the digestion of food through hydrolysis. Hormones act as chemical messengers to regulate digestion. The key hormones involved in digestion include gastrin, secretin, cholecystokinin, and gastric inhibitory peptide. The digestive accessory organs include the gallbladder, pancreas, and liver. The gallbladder stores bile, which is produced by the liver. Bile emulsifies lipids into pieces that are more easily digested. The pancreas synthesizes and secretes digestive enzymes that break down carbohydrates, lipids, and proteins. The liver processes all nutrients absorbed from the small intestine, regulates blood glucose levels, and stores glucose as glycogen.

liver The largest auxiliary organ of the GI tract and one of the most important organs of the body. Its functions include production of bile and processing of nutrient-rich blood from the small intestine.

portal vein A vessel that carries blood and various products of digestion from the digestive organs and spleen to the liver.

How Does the Body Absorb and Transport Digested Nutrients?

Although some nutrient absorption occurs in the stomach and large intestine, the majority occurs in the small intestine. The small intestine is ideally equipped to handle this responsibility because of its extensive surface area and specialized absorptive cells. Let's now learn more about how we absorb the nutrients from our food.

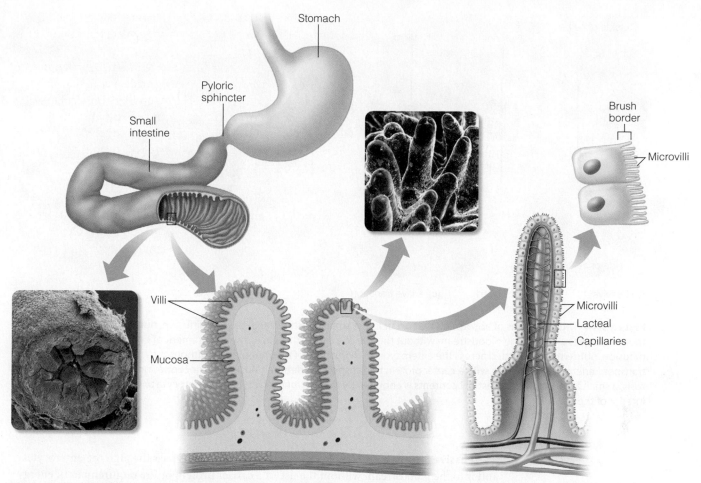

Figure 3.13 Absorption of nutrients occurs via the specialized lining of the small intestine. The lining of the small intestine is heavily folded and has thousands of fingerlike projections called *villi*. The cells covering the villi end in hairlike projections called *microvilli* that together form the brush border. These features significantly increase the absorptive capacity of the small intestine.

A Specialized Lining Enables the Small Intestine to Absorb Food

The lining of the small intestine is especially well suited for absorption. If you looked at the inside of the lining, which is also referred to as the *mucosal membrane,* you would notice that it is heavily folded (**Figure 3.13**). This feature increases the surface area of the small intestine and allows it to absorb more nutrients than if it were smooth. Within these larger folds, you would notice even smaller fingerlike projections called *villi,* whose constant movement helps them to encounter and trap nutrient molecules. The villi are composed of numerous specialized absorptive cells called **enterocytes**. Inside each villus are capillaries and a **lacteal**, which is a small lymph vessel. (The role of the lymphatic system is discussed shortly.) The capillaries and lacteals absorb some of the end products of digestion. Water-soluble nutrients are absorbed directly into the bloodstream, whereas fat-soluble nutrients are absorbed into lymph. Each enterocyte of each villus has hairlike projections called *microvilli*. The microvilli look like tiny brushes and are sometimes collectively referred to as the **brush border**. These intricate folds increase the surface area of the small intestine by more than 500 times, tremendously increasing its absorptive capacity as well.

Four Types of Absorption Occur in the Small Intestine

Nutrients are absorbed across the mucosal membrane and into the bloodstream or lymph via four mechanisms: passive diffusion, facilitated diffusion, active transport, and endocytosis. These are illustrated in **Figure 3.14**.

enterocytes Specialized absorptive cells in the villi of the small intestine.

lacteal A small lymph vessel located inside the villi of the small intestine.

brush border A term that describes the microvilli of the small intestine's lining. These microvilli tremendously increase the small intestine's absorptive capacity.

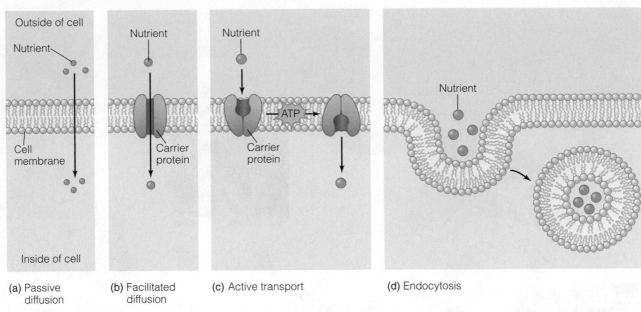

Figure 3.14 The four types of absorption that occur in the small intestine. (a) In passive diffusion, nutrients pass through the enterocytes and into the bloodstream without the use of a carrier protein or the requirement of energy. (b) In facilitated diffusion, nutrients are shuttled across the enterocytes with the help of a carrier protein without the use of energy. (c) In active transport, energy is used along with a carrier protein to transport nutrients against their concentration gradient. (d) In endocytosis, a small amount of the intestinal contents is engulfed by the cell membrane of the enterocyte and released into the interior of the cell.

passive diffusion The simple absorptive process in which nutrients pass through the enterocytes and into the bloodstream without the use of a carrier protein or the requirement of energy.

facilitated diffusion The absorptive process that occurs when nutrients are shuttled across the enterocytes with the help of a carrier protein.

active transport An absorptive process that requires the use of energy to transport nutrients and other substances in combination with a carrier protein.

endocytosis An absorptive process by which a small amount of the intestinal contents is engulfed by the cell membrane (also called pinocytosis).

Passive diffusion is a simple process in which nutrients pass through the enterocytes and into the bloodstream without the use of a carrier protein or the requirement of energy (Figure 3.14a). Passive diffusion can occur when the wall of the intestine is permeable to the nutrient and the concentration of the nutrient in the GI tract is higher than its concentration in the enterocytes. Thus, the nutrient is moving from an area of higher concentration to an area of lower concentration. Lipids, water, vitamin C, and some minerals are absorbed via passive diffusion.

Facilitated diffusion occurs when nutrients are shuttled across the enterocytes with the help of a carrier protein (Figure 3.14b). This process is similar to passive diffusion in that it does not require energy and is driven by a concentration gradient. The monosaccharide fructose is transported via facilitated diffusion.

Active transport requires the use of energy to transport nutrients in combination with a carrier protein (Figure 3.14c). The energy derived from ATP and the assistance of the carrier protein allow for absorption of nutrients against their concentration gradient, meaning the nutrients can move from areas of low to high concentration. Glucose, galactose, sodium, potassium, magnesium, calcium, iron, and amino acids are some of the nutrients absorbed via active transport. In addition to being absorbed via passive diffusion, vitamin C can also be absorbed via active transport.

Endocytosis (also called pinocytosis) is a form of active transport by which a small amount of the intestinal contents is engulfed by the enterocyte's cell membrane and incorporated into the cell (Figure 3.14d). Some proteins and other large particles are absorbed in this way, as are the antibodies contained in breast milk.

Blood and Lymph Transport Nutrients and Wastes

Two circulating fluids transport nutrients and waste products throughout the body: blood travels through the cardiovascular system, and lymph travels through the lymphatic system (**Figure 3.15**). The oxygen we inhale into our lungs is carried by our red blood cells. This oxygen-rich blood then travels to the heart, where it is pumped out to the body. Blood travels to all of our tissues to deliver nutrients and other materials and to pick up waste products. In the GI tract, blood in the capillaries picks up most nutrients, including water, that have been absorbed through the mucosal membrane of the small intestine. The lacteals pick up most lipids and fat-soluble vitamins, as well as any fluids that have escaped from the capillaries, and these are now transported in the lymph. Lymph nodes are clusters of immune cells that filter microbes and other harmful agents from the lymph fluid (see Figure 3.15). The lymph eventually returns to the bloodstream in an area near the heart where the lymphatic and blood vessels join together.

As the blood leaves the GI system, it is transported to the liver, whose role in digestion was described earlier. The waste products picked up by the blood as it circulates around the body are filtered and excreted by the kidneys. In addition, much of the carbon dioxide remaining in the blood once it reaches the lungs is exhaled into the outside air, making room for oxygen to attach to the red blood cells and repeat this cycle of circulation again.

RᴇᴄaP

The mucosal membrane of the small intestine contains multiple villi and microvilli that significantly increase absorptive capacity. Nutrients are absorbed through one of four mechanisms: passive diffusion, facilitated diffusion, active transport, and endocytosis. Most nutrients and waste products are transported throughout the body via the blood, whereas lipids and fat-soluble vitamins are transported through lymph.

How Does the Body Coordinate and Regulate Digestion?

Now that you can identify the organs involved in digestion and absorption and the complex tasks they each perform, you might be wondering— who's the boss? In other words, what organ or system controls all of these interrelated processes? The answer is the neuromuscular system. Its two components, nerves and muscles, partner to coordinate and regulate the digestion and absorption of food and the elimination of waste.

The Muscles of the Gastrointestinal Tract Mix and Move Food

The purposes of the muscles of the GI tract are to mix food, ensure efficient digestion and optimal absorption of nutrients, and move the intestinal contents from the mouth toward the anus. Once we swallow a bolus of food, peristalsis begins in the esophagus and continues throughout the remainder of the gastrointestinal tract. Peristalsis is accomplished through the actions of circular muscles and longitudinal muscles that run along the entire GI tract (**Figure 3.16a**). The circular and longitudinal muscles continuously contract and relax, causing subsequent constriction and bulging of the tract. This action pushes the contents from one area to the next.

The stomach is surrounded by its own set of longitudinal, circular, and diagonal muscles that assist in digestion (see **Figure 3.17**). These muscles alternately contract and relax, churning the stomach contents and moving them toward the pyloric sphincter.

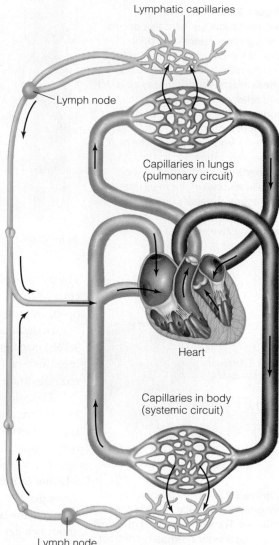

Figure 3.15 Blood travels through the cardiovascular system to transport nutrients and fluids and to pick up waste products. Lymph travels through the lymphatic system and transports most lipids and fat-soluble vitamins.

Water is readily absorbed along the entire length of the GI tract.

Figure 3.16 Peristalsis and segmentation. (a) Peristalsis occurs through the actions of circular muscles and longitudinal muscles that run along the entire GI tract. These muscles continuously contract and relax, causing subsequent constriction and bulging of the tract. This action pushes the intestinal contents from one area to the next. (b) Segmentation occurs through the rhythmic contraction of the circular muscles of the small intestine. This action squeezes the chyme, mixes it, and enhances its contact with digestive enzymes and enterocytes.

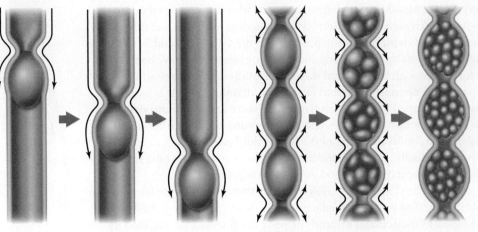

(a) Peristalsis   (b) Segmentation

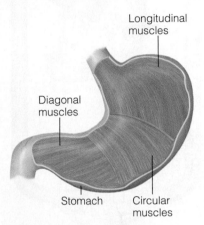

Figure 3.17 The stomach has longitudinal, circular, and diagonal muscles. These three sets of muscles aid digestion by alternately contracting and relaxing; these actions churn the stomach contents and move them toward the pyloric sphincter. *Data from:* Bauman, R. *Microbiology,* Fig. 2.14, © 2003 Benjamin Cummings; and Moyes, C. and Shutle, PL. *Principles of Animal Physiology,* Fig. 2.15, © 2006 Benjamin Cummings. Used by permission of Pearson Education.

segmentation Rhythmic contraction of the circular muscles of the intestines that squeezes chyme, mixes it, and enhances digestion and absorption of nutrients from the chyme.

haustration Involuntary, sluggish contraction of the haustra of the proximal colon that moves wastes toward the sigmoid colon.

mass movement Involuntary, sustained, forceful contraction of the colon that occurs two or more times a day to push wastes toward the rectum.

enteric nervous system (ENS) The nerves of the GI tract.

The pyloric sphincter stays closed while gastric juices are secreted and the chyme is completely liquefied. Once the chyme is liquefied, the pyloric sphincter is stimulated to open, and small amounts of chyme are regularly pushed into the small intestine.

In the small intestine, a unique pattern of motility called **segmentation** occurs (**Figure 3.16b**). Segmentation, accomplished by the rhythmic contraction of circular muscles in the intestinal wall, squeezes the chyme, mixes it, and enhances its contact with digestive enzymes and enterocytes.

The colon also exhibits a unique pattern of motility, called **haustration**, in which the haustra contract sluggishly to move wastes toward the sigmoid colon. However, two or more times each day, a much stronger and more sustained **mass movement** of the colon occurs, pushing wastes forcibly toward the rectum.

The muscles of the GI tract contract at varying rates depending on their location and whether or not food is present. The stomach tends to contract more slowly, about three times per minute, whereas the small intestine may contract up to ten times per minute when chyme is present. The contractions of haustra are very slow, occurring at a rate of about two per hour. As with an assembly line, the entire GI tract functions together so that materials are moved in one direction, absorption of nutrients is maximized, and wastes are removed as needed.

To process the large amount of food we consume daily, we use both voluntary and involuntary muscles. Muscles in the mouth are primarily voluntary; that is, they are under our conscious control. Once we swallow, the involuntary muscles just described largely take over to propel food through the rest of the GI tract. This enables us to continue digesting and absorbing food while we're working, exercising, and even sleeping. Let's now identify the master controller behind these involuntary muscular actions.

Nerves Control the Contractions and Secretions of the Gastrointestinal Tract

The contractions and secretions of the gastrointestinal tract are controlled by nerves from three divisions of the nervous system:

- a specialized division localized in the wall of the gastrointestinal tract, called the **enteric nervous system (ENS)**
- the parasympathetic and sympathetic branches of the autonomic nervous system, which is part of the peripheral nervous system (PNS)
- the central nervous system (CNS), which includes the brain and spinal cord

Some digestive functions are carried out entirely within the ENS. For instance, control of peristalsis and segmentation is enteric, occurring without PNS or CNS involvement. In addition, enteric nerves regulate the secretions of the various digestive glands whose roles we have discussed in this chapter.

Enteric nerves also work in collaboration with the PNS and CNS. For example, we noted earlier in this chapter that in response to fasting, receptors in the stomach and intestinal walls (ENS receptors) stimulate peripheral nerves to signal the hypothalamus, part of the CNS. We then experience the sensation of hunger.

Finally, some functions, such as secretion of saliva, are achieved without enteric involvement. A variety of stimuli from the smell, sight, taste, and tactile sensations from food trigger special salivary cells in the CNS; these cells then increase PNS activity to the salivary glands. Activation of the salivary glands through this mechanism causes an increase of salivary secretions.

RECAP

The coordination and regulation of digestion are directed by the neuromuscular system. Voluntary muscles assist us with chewing and swallowing. Once food is swallowed, involuntary muscles of the GI tract function together so that materials are processed in a coordinated manner. Involuntary movements include the mixing and churning of chyme by muscles in the stomach wall, as well as peristalsis, segmentation, haustration, and mass movement. The enteric nerves of the GI tract work with the peripheral and central nervous systems to achieve digestion, absorption, and elimination of food.

What Disorders Are Related to Digestion, Absorption, and Elimination?

Considering the complexity of digestion, absorption, and elimination, it's no wonder that sometimes things go wrong. Disorders of the neuromuscular system, hormonal imbalances, infections, allergies, and a host of other disorders can disturb gastrointestinal functioning, as can merely consuming the wrong types or amounts of food for our unique needs. Whenever there is a problem with the GI tract, absorption of nutrients can be affected. If absorption of a nutrient is less than optimal for a long period of time, malnutrition can result. Let's look more closely at some GI tract disorders and what you might be able to do if they affect you.

Belching and Flatulence Are Common

Many people complain of problems with belching (or eructation) and/or flatulence (passage of intestinal gas). The primary cause of belching is swallowed air. Eating too fast, wearing improperly fitting dentures, chewing gum, sucking on hard candies or a drinking straw, and gulping food or fluid can increase the risk of swallowing air. To prevent or reduce belching, avoid these behaviours.

Although many people find *flatus* (intestinal gas) uncomfortable and embarrassing, its presence in the GI tract is completely normal, as is its expulsion. Flatus is a mixture of many gases, including nitrogen, hydrogen, oxygen, methane, and carbon dioxide. Interestingly, all of these are odourless. It is only when flatus contains sulphur that it causes the embarrassing odour associated with flatulence.

Foods most commonly reported to cause flatus include those rich in fibres, starches, and sugars, such as beans, dairy products, and some vegetables. The partially digested carbohydrates from these foods pass into the large intestine, where they are acted upon by bacteria, producing gas. Other food products that may cause flatus, intestinal cramps, and diarrhea include products made with the fat substitute olestra and sugar alcohols.

Because many of the foods that can cause flatus are healthy, it is important not to avoid them. Eating smaller portions can help reduce the amount of flatus produced and passed. In addition, products such as Beano® can offer some relief. Beano® is an over-the-counter supplement that contains alpha-galactosidase, an enzyme that digests the complex sugars in gas-producing foods. Although flatus is generally normal, some people have malabsorption diseases that cause painful bloating and require medical treatment. Some of these disorders are described later in this section.

Heartburn and Gastroesophageal Reflux Disease (GERD) Are Caused by Reflux of Stomach Acid

When you eat food, your stomach secretes hydrochloric acid (HCl) to start the digestive process. In many people, the amount of HCl secreted is occasionally excessive or the gastroesophageal sphincter opens too soon. In either case, the result is that HCl seeps back up into the esophagus (**Figure 3.18**). Although the stomach lining is protected from HCl by a thick coat of mucus, the esophagus does not have this mucous coating. Thus, the HCl burns it. When this happens, a person experiences a painful sensation in the region of his or her chest above the sternum (breastbone). This condition is commonly called **heartburn**. People often take over-the-counter antacids to neutralize the HCl, thereby relieving the heartburn. A non-drug approach is to repeatedly swallow: This action causes any acid within the esophagus to be swept down into the stomach, eventually relieving the symptoms.

Gastroesophageal reflux disease (GERD) is a more painful type of heartburn that occurs more than twice per week. On average, 5 million Canadians experience heartburn and/or acid regurgitation at least once each week.[10] Although people who experience occasional heartburn usually have no structural abnormalities, many people with GERD have an overly relaxed or damaged esophageal sphincter or damage to the esophagus itself. Symptoms of GERD include persistent heartburn and acid regurgitation. Some people have GERD without heartburn and instead experience chest pain, trouble swallowing, burning in the mouth, the feeling that food is stuck in the throat, or hoarseness in the morning.[11]

heartburn The painful sensation that occurs over the sternum when hydrochloric acid backs up into the lower esophagus.

gastroesophageal reflux disease (GERD) A painful type of heartburn that occurs more than twice per week.

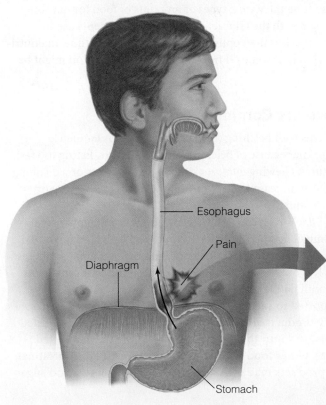

Figure 3.18 The mechanism of heartburn and gastroesophageal reflux disease is the same: acidic gastric juices seep backward through an open or relaxed sphincter into the lower portion of the esophagus, burning its lining. The pain is felt above the sternum, over the heart.
Data from: Johnson, M., *Human Biology: Concepts and Current Issues, 5/e,* Fig. 10.13, Copyright © 2010 Benjamin Cummings. Reprinted by permission of Pearson Education, Inc.

Esophagus

Pain

Diaphragm

Gastroesophageal sphincter remains partially opened, allowing gastric juice to seep backward and burn the esophageal lining

Stomach

The exact causes of GERD are unknown. However, a number of factors may contribute, including the following:[11]

- A *hiatal hernia,* which occurs when the upper part of the stomach lies above the diaphragm muscle. Normally, the diaphragm muscle separates the stomach from the chest and helps keep acid from coming into the esophagus. Stomach acid can more easily enter the esophagus in people with a hiatal hernia.
- Cigarette smoking.
- Alcohol use.
- Overweight.
- Pregnancy.
- Foods such as citrus fruits, chocolate, caffeinated drinks, fried foods, garlic and onions, spicy foods, and tomato-based foods such as chili, pizza, and spaghetti sauce.
- Large, high-fat meals. These meals stay in the stomach longer and increase stomach pressure, making it more likely that acid will be pushed up into the esophagus.
- Lying down within 1 to 2 hours after a meal. This is almost certain to bring on symptoms, because it positions the body so that it is easier for the stomach acid to back up into the esophagus.

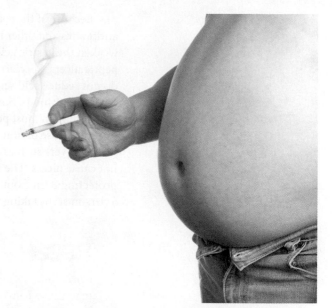

Although the exact causes of gastroesophageal reflux disease (GERD) are unknown, smoking and being overweight may be contributing factors.

There are ways to reduce the symptoms of GERD. One way is to identify the types of foods or situations that trigger episodes and then avoid them. Eating smaller meals also helps. After a meal, waiting at least 3 hours before lying down is recommended. Some people relieve their nighttime symptoms by elevating the head of the bed 10 to 15 cm, for instance by placing a wedge between the mattress and the box spring. This keeps the chest area elevated and minimizes the amount of acid that can back up into the esophagus. It is also suggested that if people smoke, they should stop, and if they are overweight, they should lose weight. Taking an antacid before a meal can help, and many prescription medications are available to treat GERD. The most effective medications currently available are called *proton pump inhibitors*; these drugs reduce the secretion of HCl from the stomach's parietal cells.

Left untreated, GERD can cause serious health problems, including bleeding and ulceration of the esophagus. Scar tissue can develop in the esophagus, making swallowing very difficult. Some people can also develop a condition called Barrett esophagus, which can lead to cancer. Asthma can also be aggravated or even caused by GERD.[11]

An Ulcer Is an Area of Erosion in the GI Tract

A **peptic ulcer** is an area of the GI tract that has been eroded away by a combination of hydrochloric acid and the enzyme pepsin (**Figure 3.19**). In almost all cases, it is located in the stomach area (*gastric ulcer*) or the part of the duodenum closest to the stomach (*duodenal ulcer*). It causes a burning pain in the abdominal area, typically 1 to 3 hours after eating a meal. In serious cases, eroded blood vessels bleed into the GI tract, causing vomiting of blood and/or blood in the stools, as well as anemia. If the ulcer entirely perforates the tract wall, stomach contents can leak into the abdominal cavity, causing a life-threatening infection.

The bacterium *Helicobacter pylori* (*H. pylori*) plays a key role in development of most peptic ulcers, which include both gastric and duodenal ulcers.[12] It is thought that *H. pylori* burrow through the thick mucous layer of the stomach exposing the sensitive layers of tissue to acidic gastric juice. *H. pylori* infects about 20% of people younger than 40 years of age and about 50% of people older than 60 years of age; however, most people with *H. pylori* infection do not develop ulcers, and the reason for this is not known.[13]

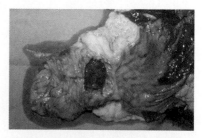

Figure 3.19 A peptic ulcer.

peptic ulcer An area of the GI tract that has been eroded away by the acidic gastric juice of the stomach. The two main causes of peptic ulcers are *Helicobacter pylori* infection or use of non-steroidal anti-inflammatory drugs.

Because of the role of *H. pylori* in ulcer development, treatment usually involves antibiotics and other types of medications to reduce gastric secretions. Antacids are used to weaken the gastric acid, and the same medications used to treat GERD can be used to treat peptic ulcers. Special diets are not recommended as often as they once were because they do not reduce acid secretion. In fact, we now know that ulcers are not caused by stress or eating spicy foods, however, stress and spicy foods will worsen the symptoms.

Although most peptic ulcers are caused by *H. pylori* infection, some are caused by prolonged use of non-steroidal anti-inflammatory drugs (NSAIDs); these drugs include pain relievers such as aspirin, ibuprofen, and naproxen sodium. Acetaminophen use does not cause ulcers. The NSAIDs appear to cause ulcers by preventing the stomach from protecting itself from acidic gastric juices. Ulcers caused by NSAID use generally heal once a person stops taking the medication.[14]

RECaP

Belching is commonly caused by behaviours that cause us to swallow air. Foods that may cause flatulence include those rich in fibres, starches, and sugars. Heartburn is caused by the seepage of gastric juices into the esophagus. Gastroesophageal reflux disease (GERD) is a painful type of heartburn that occurs more than twice per week. GERD can cause serious health consequences such as esophageal bleeding, ulcers, and cancer. Peptic ulcers are caused by erosion of the GI tract by hydrochloric acid and pepsin. The two major causes of peptic ulcers are *Helicobacter pylori* infection and the use of non-steroidal anti-inflammatory drugs. Peptic ulcers are typically treated with antibiotics and other medications.

Did You Know?

Northern Canadian Aboriginal people are among the ethnic groups most at risk of *H. pylori* infection and its consequences, such as gastric cancer. Some reports show prevalence rates double that of non-Aboriginal groups. It has been suggested that *H. pylori* infection may contribute to the widespread anemia reported in indigenous populations, despite their abundant intake of heme iron. It is possible that *H. pylori* reduces gastric acid secretion and consequently impacts iron absorption.[15]

Some People Experience Disorders Related to Specific Foods

You check out the ingredients list on your energy bar, and you notice that it says, "Produced in a facility that processes peanuts." The carton of soy milk you're drinking from proclaims: "Gluten free!" What's all the fuss about? To some people, consuming certain food ingredients can be dangerous, even life-threatening. That is why Health Canada's food allergen labelling guidelines were implemented in 2012 to identify those ingredients most frequently associated with food allergies. These are currently defined as peanuts, tree nuts, sesame seeds, milk, eggs, fish, crustaceans, shellfish, soy, and wheat. Sulphites are considered a food additive, but are treated with the same degree of concern as food allergens since they can also cause anaphylaxis-type reactions in sensitive individuals.[16]

Disorders related to specific foods can be clustered into three main groupings: food intolerances, food allergies, and genetic disorders such as celiac disease. We discuss these separately.

Food Intolerance

A **food intolerance** is a cluster of GI symptoms (often gas, pain, and diarrhea) that occur following consumption of a particular food. The immune system plays no role in intolerance, and although episodes are unpleasant, they are usually transient, resolving after the offending food has been eliminated from the body. An example is lactose intolerance. It occurs in people whose bodies do not produce sufficient quantities of the enzyme lactase, which is needed for the breakdown of the milk sugar lactose. (Lactose intolerance is discussed in more detail in Chapter 4.) People can also have an intolerance to wheat, soy, and other foods, but as with lactose intolerance, the symptoms pass once the offending food is out of the person's system.

Food Allergy

A **food allergy** is a hypersensitivity reaction of the immune system to a particular component (usually a protein) in a food. This reaction causes the immune cells to release chemicals that cause either limited or systemic (whole-body) inflammation. About 6%–8% of infants and young children and 2.5% of adults experience food allergies.[17] Although this makes them much less common than food intolerances, food allergies can be far more serious. Reports suggest that hospitalizations due to food-induced anaphylaxis have increased by 350% over the past decade.[17]

For some people, eating a meal of grilled shrimp with peanut sauce would cause a severe allergic reaction.

You may have heard stories of people being allergic to foods as common as peanuts. This is the case for Liz. She was out to dinner with her parents, celebrating her birthday, when the dessert cart came around. The caramel custard looked heavenly and was probably a safe choice, but she asked the waiter just to be sure that it contained no peanuts. He checked with the chef, then returned and assured her that, no, the custard was peanut-free—but within minutes of consuming it, Liz's skin became flushed, and she struggled to breathe. As her parents were dialing 911, she lost consciousness. Fortunately, the paramedics arrived within minutes and were able to resuscitate her. It was subsequently determined that, unknown to the chef, the spoon that his prep cook had used to scoop the baked custard into serving bowls had been resting on a cutting board where he had chopped peanuts for a different dessert. Just this small exposure to peanuts was enough to cause a severe allergic reaction in Liz.

How can a food that most people consume regularly, such as peanuts, shellfish, eggs, or milk, cause another person's immune system to react so violently? In Liz's case, a trace amount of peanut stimulated immune cells throughout her body to release their inflammatory chemicals. In many people, the inflammation is localized, so the damage is limited; for instance, a person's mouth and throat might itch whenever they eat cantaloupe. What made Liz's experience so terrifyingly different was that the inflammation was widespread. Thus, her airways became constricted and clogged with mucus, leading to respiratory collapse. At the same time, her blood vessels dilated and became so permeable that her blood pressure plummeted, leading to circulatory collapse. This state, called *anaphylactic shock*, is nearly always fatal if not treated immediately. For this reason, many people with known food allergies carry with them a kit containing an injection of a powerful stimulant called epinephrine (epi pen). This drug can reduce symptoms long enough to buy the victim time to get emergency medical care.

Celiac Disease

Celiac disease, also known as *celiac sprue*, is a digestive disease that severely damages the lining of the small intestine and interferes with absorption of nutrients.[18] As in food allergy, the body's immune system causes the disorder. However, there is a strong genetic predisposition to celiac disease, with the risk now linked to specific gene markers.

In celiac disease, the offending food component is *gliadin*, a fraction of a protein called *gluten* that is found in wheat, rye, and barley. When people with celiac disease eat one of these grains, their immune system triggers an inflammatory response that erodes the villi

food intolerance Gastrointestinal discomfort caused by certain foods that is not a result of an immune system reaction.

food allergy An allergic reaction to food caused by a reaction of the immune system.

celiac disease A disorder characterized by an immune reaction that damages the lining of the small intestine when the individual is exposed to a component of a protein called gluten.

For people with celiac disease, corn is a gluten-free source of carbohydrates.

of the small intestine. If the person is unaware of the disorder and continues to eat gluten, repeated immune reactions cause the villi to become greatly decreased so that there is less absorptive surface area. In addition, the enzymes located at the brush border of the small intestine become reduced. As a result, the person becomes unable to absorb certain nutrients properly—a condition known as *malabsorption*. Over time, malabsorption can lead to malnutrition (poor nutrient status). Deficiencies of fat-soluble vitamins A, D, E, and K, as well as iron, folic acid, and calcium, are common in those suffering from celiac disease, as are inadequate intakes of protein and total energy.[19]

Symptoms of celiac disease often mimic those of other intestinal disturbances such as irritable bowel syndrome (discussed shortly), and so the condition is often misdiagnosed. Some of the symptoms of celiac disease include fatty stools (due to poor fat absorption); frequent stools, either watery or hard, with an odd odour; cramping; anemia; pallor; weight loss; fatigue; and irritability. However, other puzzling symptoms do not appear to involve the GI tract. These include an intensely itchy rash called *dermatitis herpetiformis*, osteoporosis (poor bone density), infertility, epilepsy, anxiety, irritability, depression, and migraine headaches, among others.[19]

Diagnostic tests for celiac disease include a variety of blood tests that screen for the presence of immune proteins called antibodies, or for the genetic markers of the disease. However, the "gold standard" for diagnosis is a biopsy of the small intestine showing atrophy of the intestinal villi. Because long-term complications of undiagnosed celiac disease include an increased risk for intestinal cancer, early diagnosis can be life-saving. Unfortunately, celiac disease is currently thought to be widely underdiagnosed in Canada.[20] We'll explore some reasons for this in the Evidence-informed Decision Making section on pages 114–115.

Currently there is no cure for celiac disease. Treatment is with a special diet that excludes all forms of wheat, rye, and barley. Oats are allowed, but they are often contaminated with wheat flour from processing, and even a microscopic amount of wheat can cause an immune response. The diet is especially challenging because many binding agents and other unfamiliar ingredients in processed foods are derived from gluten. Thus, nutritional counselling is essential. Fortunately, many gluten-free foods are now available.

Crohn's Disease and Ulcerative Colitis Are Inflammatory Disorders

Two inflammatory bowel diseases are Crohn's disease and ulcerative colitis. The precise causes of these disorders are unknown, but both have been linked to an immune response to a virus or bacterium. Both also are associated with similar symptoms.

Crohn's Disease

Crohn's disease can cause inflammation anywhere along the gastrointestinal tract, and usually affects the entire thickness of the wall. About 50% of cases involve both the ileum and the colon; an additional 25% involve only the small or large intestine. Some experts speculate that the inflammation is related to the reaction of the immune system to a virus or bacterium.[21] It has been suggested that Canada has the highest incidence of Crohn's disease reported worldwide.[21]

The symptoms of Crohn's disease include diarrhea, abdominal pain, rectal bleeding, weight loss, and fever. People with this disease may also suffer from anemia due to the persistent bleeding that occurs, and children with Crohn's disease can experience delayed physical and mental development. If allowed to progress, Crohn's disease can cause blockage of the intestine and the development of ulcers that tunnel through the areas surrounding the inflammation, such as the bladder, vagina, skin, anus, or rectum. These tunnels are referred to as *fistulas,* and they become infected and commonly require surgical treatment. Crohn's disease also results in deficiencies in protein, energy, and vitamins and is associated with arthritis, kidney stones, gallstones, and diseases of the liver.

Crohn's disease A bowel disease that causes inflammation in the small intestine leading to diarrhea, abdominal pain, rectal bleeding, weight loss, and fever.

Because it shares many of the same symptoms as other intestinal disorders, Crohn's disease can be difficult to diagnose. Treatment may involve a combination of prescription drugs and nutritional supplements, as well as surgery to control inflammation, correct nutritional deficiencies, and relieve pain, diarrhea, and bleeding.[21]

Ulcerative Colitis

Ulcerative colitis is a chronic disease characterized by inflammation and ulceration of the mucosa, or innermost lining, of the colon. Ulcers form on the surface of the mucosa, where they bleed and produce pus and mucus. The causes of ulcerative colitis are unknown. Many of the scientists who study this disease believe it results from an interaction between an outside virus or bacterium and the immune system. This interaction might either trigger the disease or directly cause the damage to the intestinal wall.

The resulting symptoms are similar to Crohn's disease and include diarrhea (which may be bloody), abdominal pain, weight loss, anemia, nausea, fever, and severe urgency to have a bowel movement. Complications of ulcerative colitis include profuse bleeding, rupture of the bowel, severe abdominal distention, dehydration, and nutritional deficiencies.

Treatment usually involves taking anti-inflammatory medications. Surgery may be needed for those people who do not successfully respond to pharmacologic treatment.[22] No particular foods cause ulcerative colitis, but it may be necessary for people with this disease to avoid foods that cause intestinal discomfort.

RECaP

Food intolerances are digestive problems caused by consumption of certain foods, but not due to an immune reaction. Food allergies are hypersensitivities to food ingredients caused by an immune reaction. Food allergies can cause mild symptoms, such as hives and swelling, or life-threatening inflammation and anaphylactic shock. People with celiac disease cannot eat gluten, a protein found in wheat, rye, and barley, as it causes an immune reaction that damages the lining of the small intestine and leads to malabsorption of nutrients and malnutrition. Crohn's disease and ulcerative colitis are inflammatory bowel diseases. Crohn's disease usually affects the entire thickness of the ileum of the small intestine, whereas colitis is an inflammation and ulceration of the innermost lining of the colon. The causes of Crohn's disease and ulcerative colitis are unknown.

Diarrhea, Constipation, and Irritable Bowel Syndrome Are Functional Disorders

As their name implies, functional disorders affect the regular function of the gastrointestinal tract. Food may move through the small or large intestine too quickly or too slowly, prompting discomfort, bloating, or other symptoms.

Diarrhea

Diarrhea is the frequent (more than three times in one day) passage of loose, watery stools. Other symptoms may include cramping, abdominal pain, bloating, nausea, fever, and blood in the stools. Diarrhea is usually caused by an infection of the gastrointestinal tract, stress, food intolerances, reactions to medications, or an underlying bowel disorder or other chronic disease.[23]

Acute diarrhea lasts less than three weeks and is usually caused by an infection from bacteria, a virus, or a parasite. Chronic diarrhea, which lasts more than three weeks, affects about 3% to 5% of the Canadian population and is usually caused by allergies to cow's milk,

ulcerative colitis A chronic disease of the large intestine, or colon, indicated by inflammation and ulceration of the mucosa, or innermost lining of the colon.

diarrhea A condition characterized by the frequent passage of loose, watery stools.

Table 3.3 Signs and Symptoms of Dehydration in Adults and Children

Signs and Symptoms in Adults	Signs and Symptoms in Children
Thirst	Dry mouth and tongue
Light-headedness	No tears when crying
Less frequent urination	No wet diapers for 3 hours or more
Dark-coloured urine	High fever
Fatigue	Sunken abdomen, eyes, or cheeks
Dry skin	Irritability or listlessness
	Skin that does not flatten when pinched and released

Data from: National Digestive Diseases Information Clearinghouse (NDDIC). 2001. Diarrhea. NIH publication no. 01–2749. Available online at http://digestive.niddk.nih.gov/ddiseases/pubs/diarrhea/index.htm.

irritable bowel syndrome (discussed shortly), lactose intolerance, celiac disease, or conditions such as Crohn's disease or ulcerative colitis.

Whatever the cause, diarrhea can be harmful if it persists for a long period of time because the person can lose large quantities of water and electrolytes and become severely dehydrated. Table 3.3 reviews the signs and symptoms of dehydration, which is particularly dangerous in infants and young children. In fact, a child can die from dehydration in just a few days. Adults, particularly older adults, can also become dangerously ill if severely dehydrated.

A condition referred to as *traveller's diarrhea* has become a common health concern because of the expansion in global travel.[24] Traveller's diarrhea is discussed in the Highlight box on the next page.

Constipation

constipation A condition characterized by the absence of bowel movements for a period of time that is significantly longer than normal for the individual. When a bowel movement does occur, stools are usually small, hard, and difficult to pass.

irritable bowel syndrome (IBS) A bowel disorder that interferes with normal functions of the colon. Symptoms are abdominal cramps, bloating, and constipation or diarrhea.

At the opposite end of the spectrum is **constipation**, which is typically defined as a condition in which no stools are passed for two or more days; however, it is important to recognize that some people normally experience bowel movements only every second or third day. Thus, the definition of constipation varies from one person to another. In addition to being infrequent, the stools are usually hard, small, and difficult to pass.

Constipation is frequent in people who have disorders affecting the nervous system, which in turn affect the muscles of the large bowel, as they do not receive the appropriate neurologic signals needed for involuntary muscle movement to occur. For these individuals, drug therapy is often needed to keep the large bowel functioning.

Many people experience temporary constipation at some point in their lives in response to a variety of factors. Often people have trouble with it when they travel, when their schedule is disrupted, if they change their diet, or if they are on certain medications. Increasing fibre and fluid in the diet is one of the mainstays of preventing constipation. Seven or more servings of fruits and vegetables each day and six or more servings of whole grains is helpful to most people. If you eat breakfast cereal, make sure you buy a cereal containing at least 2 to 3 g of fibre per serving. The dietary recommendation for fibre and the role it plays in maintaining healthy elimination is discussed in detail in Chapter 4. Staying well-hydrated by drinking lots of water is especially important when increasing fibre intake. Exercising also helps reduce the risk of constipation.

Irritable Bowel Syndrome

Irritable bowel syndrome (IBS) is a disorder that interferes with normal functions of the colon. Symptoms include abdominal cramps, bloating, and either constipation or diarrhea. It is one of the most common medical diagnoses.[24] Five million Canadians suffer from IBS, with 120 000 Canadians developing IBS each year.[25] Three times more women than men are diagnosed with IBS, which typically first appears in early adulthood.[26]

Consuming caffeinated drinks is one of several factors that have been linked with irritable bowel syndrome (IBS), a disorder that interferes with normal functions of the colon.

IBS shows no sign of disease that can be observed or measured.[26] However, it appears that the colon is more sensitive to physiologic or emotional stress in people with IBS than in healthy people. Some researchers believe that the problem stems from conflicting messages between the central nervous system and the enteric nervous system. The immune system may also trigger symptoms of IBS. Whatever the cause, the normal movement of the colon appears to be disrupted. In some people with IBS, food moves too quickly through the colon and fluid cannot be absorbed fast enough, which causes diarrhea. In others, the movement of the colon is too slow and too much fluid is absorbed, leading to constipation. Some of the foods thought to cause physiologic stress linked to IBS include:

- caffeinated drinks, such as tea, coffee, and colas;
- foods such as chocolate, alcohol, dairy products, and wheat; and
- large meals.

Some women with IBS find that their symptoms worsen during their menstrual period, indicating a possible link between reproductive hormones and IBS. Certain medications may also increase the risk.

The high prevalence of the diagnosis in Canada, along with the lack of any sign of physical disease, has led to charges that IBS is overdiagnosed or misdiagnosed. Some physicians do not even agree that IBS qualifies as a disease, pointing out that the stresses of everyday life have always led to digestive problems, and probably always will.[26] Other researchers argue that physicians too often apply the diagnosis of IBS before screening for more serious disorders. In more than one study, a significant percentage of patients who had been diagnosed with IBS were determined upon screening to have celiac disease; thus, some researchers are arguing that all diarrhea-predominant IBS patients should be screened for celiac disease.[27]

HIGHLIGHT

Traveller's Diarrhea—What Is It and How Can I Prevent It?

Diarrhea is the rapid movement of fecal matter through the large intestine, often accompanied by large volumes of water. *Traveller's diarrhea* (also called *dysentery*) is experienced by people travelling to countries outside of their own and is usually caused by viral or bacterial infection. Diarrhea represents the body's way of ridding itself of the invasive agent. The large intestine and even some of the small intestine become irritated by the microbes and the resulting immune response. This irritation leads to increased secretion of fluid and increased peristalsis of the large intestine, causing watery stools and a higher-than-normal frequency of bowel movements.

People generally get traveller's diarrhea from consuming water or food that is contaminated with fecal matter. High-risk destinations include developing countries in Africa, Asia, Latin America, and the Middle East. However, hikers and others travelling in any remote region are at increased risk if they drink untreated water from lakes, rivers, and streams.

Traveller's diarrhea usually starts about 5 to 15 days after you arrive at your destination. Symptoms include fatigue, lack of appetite, abdominal cramps, and watery diarrhea. In some cases, you may also experience nausea, vomiting, and low-grade fever. Usually, this diarrhea passes within

When travelling in developing countries, it is wise to avoid food from street vendors.

four to six days, and people recover completely. However, infants and toddlers, older people, and people with compromised immunity are at greater risk for serious illness resulting from traveller's diarrhea. This is also true for people with digestive disorders such as celiac disease and ulcers.[23]

What can you do to prevent traveller's diarrhea? Table 3.4 lists foods and beverages to avoid and those that are considered relatively safe when travelling. In general, it is smart to assume that all local water is contaminated, including ice, so you should wipe all chilled bottles clean before drinking bottled beverages. Beverages made with boiling water are typically safe. Chemicals such as chorine bleach and iodine can be used to sterilize drinking water, but boiling is more effective.

If you do suffer from traveller's diarrhea, it is important to replace the fluid and nutrients lost as a result of the illness. Specially formulated oral rehydration solutions are usually available in most countries at local pharmacies or stores. Antibiotics may also be prescribed to kill the bacteria. Once treatment is initiated, the diarrhea should cease within two to three days. If the diarrhea persists for more than 10 days after the initiation of treatment, or if there is blood in your stools, you should return to a physician immediately to avoid serious medical consequences.

Table 3.4 Foods and Beverages Linked with Traveller's Diarrhea

Foods/Beverages That Can Cause Traveller's Diarrhea	Foods/Beverages Considered Safe to Consume
Tap water	Boiled tap water
Local bottled water	Brand-name bottled water
Iced tea	Hot coffee and hot tea
Unpasteurized dairy products or juices	Wine and beer
Ice (in alcoholic or non-alcoholic beverages)	Well-cooked foods
Undercooked or raw foods (includes meats, vegetables, and most fruits)	Fruit that can be peeled (for example, bananas and oranges)
Cooked foods that are no longer hot in temperature	
Shellfish	
Food from street vendors	

Data from: Public Health Agency of Canada. *Traveller's Diarrhea.* Available at www.phac-aspc.gc.ca/tmp-pmv/info/diarrhea-eng.php.

If you think you have IBS, it is important to have a complete physical examination to rule out any other health problems, including celiac disease. Treatment options include certain medications to treat diarrhea or constipation, stress management, regular physical activity, eating smaller meals, avoiding foods that exacerbate symptoms, eating a higher-fibre diet, and drinking at least six to eight glasses of water each day.[28] Although IBS is uncomfortable, it does not appear to endanger long-term health. However, severe IBS can be disabling and prevent people from leading normal lives; thus, accurate diagnosis and effective treatment are critical.

RECAP

Diarrhea is the frequent passage of loose or watery stools, whereas constipation is failure to have a bowel movement for two or more days or within a time period that is normal for the individual. Diarrhea should be treated quickly to avoid dehydration. Constipation often can be corrected by increasing your intake of fibre and water. Irritable bowel syndrome (IBS) causes abdominal cramps, pain, bloating, and constipation or diarrhea. Factors linked by some studies to exacerbation of IBS include stress, consumption of certain foods and fluids, large meals, and certain medications. IBS can be treated with medications and dietary and lifestyle changes.

CASE STUDY ▸ Preventing Gastrointestinal Upset

This is Sam's first year at university; he is earning good grades and working hard at his part-time job. However, Sam's eating habits are poor and he has gained about 5 kg. Sam has a busy schedule so he typically grabs food between classes and after he finishes work in the evening. Lately, he finds it difficult to fall asleep and has been experiencing heartburn at night. Sam has tried taking antacids, but they don't seem to help for long. Recently, a friend suggested Sam's problems were likely due to his diet. At first he ignored the advice, but now his heartburn is getting so bad he is willing to try anything so he decides to increase his fibre intake by eating high-fibre cereal bars for breakfast.

Sam's typical diet includes:

9:00	Large blueberry muffin
	250 mL coffee with sugar and cream
12:30	Cheeseburger with ketchup, mustard, and pickles
	Medium fries with gravy
	355 mL cola
4:00	Spicy chicken wings or nachos and cheese
	1 apple or 125 mL of grapes
11:30	30 cm pepperoni pizza
	250 mL Caesar salad
	355 mL cola
12:00	Chocolate chip cookies or potato chips
	500 mL apple or orange juice

Thinking Critically

1. **What is the probable cause of the symptoms Sam is experiencing?**
2. **Sam tries taking antacids. Is this a good idea? Why or why not?**
3. **Will including high-fibre cereal bars help improve Sam's indigestion? Why or why not?**
4. **What advice would you give Sam about his lifestyle and eating habits?**
5. **What are the long-term consequences if Sam continues to eat this way?**

Chapter Review

3

Test Yourself | Answers

1. **T** Sometimes you may have an appetite even though you are not hungry. These feelings are referred to as "cravings" and are associated with physical or emotional cues.

2. **F** Your brain, not your stomach, is the primary organ responsible for telling you when you are hungry.

3. **F** Even extreme food restriction, such as near-starvation, does not cause the stomach to permanently shrink. Likewise, the stomach doesn't permanently stretch. The folds in the wall of the stomach flatten as it expands to accommodate a large meal, but they reform over the next few hours as the food empties into the small intestine. Only after gastric surgery, when a very small stomach "pouch" remains, can stomach tissue stretch permanently.

4. **T** Although there are individual variations in how we respond to food, the entire process of digestion and absorption of one meal usually takes about 24 hours.

5. **T** Most ulcers result from an infection by the bacterium *Helicobacter pylori* (*H. pylori*). Contrary to popular belief, ulcers are not caused by stress or spicy food.

Summary

- Hunger is a physiologic drive that prompts us to eat.

- Appetite is a psychological desire to consume specific foods; this desire is influenced by sensory data, social and cultural cues, and learning.

- In response to signals from the gastrointestinal tract and from hormones, the hypothalamus causes us to feel hungry or satiated.

- Foods that contain fibre, water, and large amounts of protein have the highest satiety value.

- Digestion is the process of breaking down foods into molecules small enough to be transported into enterocytes, absorption is the process of taking molecules of food out of the gastrointestinal tract and into the circulation, and elimination is the process of removing undigested food and waste products from the body.

- In the mouth, chewing starts mechanical digestion of food. Saliva contains salivary amylase, an enzyme that initiates the chemical digestion of carbohydrates.

- Food moves down to the stomach through the esophagus via a process called peristalsis. Peristalsis involves rhythmic waves of squeezing and pushing food through the gastrointestinal tract.

- The stomach mixes and churns food together with gastric juices. Hydrochloric acid and the enzyme pepsin initiate protein digestion, and a minimal amount of fat digestion begins through the action of gastric lipase.

- The stomach periodically releases the partially digested food, referred to as chyme, into the small intestine.

- Most digestion and absorption of nutrients occur in the small intestine.

- The large intestine digests any remaining food particles, absorbs water and chemicals, and moves feces to the rectum for elimination.

- Enzymes guide the digestion of food via the process of hydrolysis. Most digestive enzymes are synthesized by the pancreas and small intestine.

- The four primary hormones that regulate digestion are gastrin, secretin, cholecystokinin, and gastric inhibitory peptide.

- The gallbladder stores bile and secretes it into the small intestine to assist with the digestion of lipids.

- The pancreas manufactures and secretes digestive enzymes into the small intestine. Pancreatic amylase digests carbohydrates, pancreatic lipase digests lipids, and proteases digest proteins. The pancreas also synthesizes two hormones that play a critical role in carbohydrate metabolism, insulin and glucagon.

- The liver processes all absorbed nutrients, alcohol, and drugs, and it stores various nutrients. The liver also synthesizes bile and regulates metabolism of monosaccharides, fatty acids, and amino acids.

- The lining of the small intestine has folds, villi, and microvilli that increase its surface area and absorptive capacity.

- The four types of absorption that occur in the small intestine are passive diffusion, facilitated diffusion, active transport, and endocytosis.

- The neuromuscular system involves coordination of the muscles as well as the enteric, peripheral, and central nervous systems to move food along the gastrointestinal tract and to control all aspects of digestion, absorption, and elimination.

- Belching results from swallowed air, and flatulence can be caused by consumption of foods rich in fibres, starches, and sugars, such as beans, dairy products, and some vegetables.

- Heartburn occurs when hydrochloric acid seeps into the esophagus and burns its lining. Gastroesophageal reflux disease (GERD) is a more painful type of heartburn that occurs more than twice per week.

- A peptic ulcer is an area in the stomach or duodenum that has been eroded away by hydrochloric acid and pepsin.

- Food allergies can cause either localized reactions such as minor skin rashes or systemic inflammation resulting in respiratory and circulatory collapse.

- People with celiac disease cannot eat gluten, a protein found in wheat, rye, and barley, as it causes an immune reaction that damages the lining of the small intestine and leads to malabsorption of nutrients and malnutrition.

- Crohn's disease is an inflammatory bowel disease that usually affects the small intestine, whereas ulcerative colitis damages the mucosal lining of the colon. The causes of these diseases are unknown.

- Diarrhea is the frequent (more than three times per day) elimination of loose, watery stools. Constipation is a condition in which no stools are passed for two or more days or for a length of time considered abnormally long for the individual. Irritable bowel syndrome is a bowel disorder that interferes with normal functions of the colon, causing pain and diarrhea or constipation.

Review Questions

1. Which of the following processes moves food along the entire GI tract?
   a. mass movement
   b. peristalsis
   c. haustration
   d. segmentation

2. Bile is a greenish fluid that
   a. is produced by the gallbladder.
   b. is stored by the pancreas.
   c. denatures proteins.
   d. emulsifies lipids.

3. The region of brain tissue that is responsible for prompting us to seek food is the
   a. pituitary gland.
   b. enteric nervous system.
   c. hypothalamus.
   d. thalamus.

4. Heartburn is caused by seepage of
   a. gastric acid into the esophagus.
   b. gastric acid into the cardiac muscle.
   c. bile into the stomach.
   d. salivary amylase into the stomach.

5. Which of the following foods is likely to keep a person satiated for the longest period of time?
   a. a bean and cheese burrito
   b. a serving of full-fat ice cream
   c. a bowl of rice cereal in whole milk
   d. a tossed salad with oil and vinegar dressing

6. Pierre considers breakfast to be the most important meal of the day. Each morning he makes sure that he has at least one food from at least three of the four food groups. For example, he might eat whole wheat toast with peanut butter and a piece of fresh fruit. Katia, on the other hand, usually grabs some coffee and a donut on her way to class. Who will feel full longer?

7. Gastric bypass surgery is becoming a common treatment for obesity. This surgery reduces the size of the stomach and shortens the length of the intestine. What implications would this surgery have for normal digestion?

8. Explain why it can be said that you are what you eat.

9. Imagine that the lining of your small intestine were smooth, like the inside of a rubber tube. Would this design be efficient in performing the main function of this organ? Why or why not?

10. Why doesn't the acidic environment of the stomach cause it to digest itself?

11. Create a table comparing the area of inflammation, symptoms, and treatment options for celiac disease, Crohn's disease, and ulcerative colitis.

12. After dinner, your roommate lies down to rest for a few minutes before studying. When he gets up, he complains of a sharp, burning pain in his chest. Offer a possible explanation for his pain.

Web Links

www.aaia.ca/en/index.htm
Allergy/Asthma Information Association
Discover educational information for treating and preventing allergies and asthma.

www.anaphylaxis.ca
Anaphylaxis Canada
Visit this site to learn more about common food allergies.

www.cag-acg.org
Canadian Association of Gastroenterology
Explore this site for the latest research, education, and patient care information on digestive tract health and disease.

www.celiac.ca
Canadian Celiac Association
Get information on celiac disease, treatment options, educational resources, and lists of gluten-free products.

www.cdhf.ca
Canadian Digestive Health Foundation
Search this site for resources, news, and research on digestive disorders.

www.liver.ca
Canadian Liver Foundation
Explore this site for the latest research, education, and patient care information on liver disorders.

www.ccfc.ca
Crohn's and Colitis Foundation of Canada
Search this site to learn more about recent research, news, and educational information for people with ulcerative colitis and Crohn's disease.

www.hc-sc.gc.ca/fn-an/securit/allerg/index-eng.php
Health Canada
Find information on food allergen labelling and allergy alerts.

MasteringNutrition®

www.masteringnutrition.pearson.com

Assignments
Animations: Basic Absorption Mechanisms • Overview of Digestion & Absorption • Role of Enzymes • Control of Appetite: Hunger & Satiety
Activities: NutriTools

Study Area
eText • Video: Understanding Digestion & Absorption • Practice Tests • Diet Analysis • eText

References

1. Orr, J., and B. Davy. 2005. Dietary influences on peripheral hormones regulating energy intake: potential applications for weight management. *J. Am. Diet. Assoc.* 105:1115–1124.
2. Gardner, S. L., and E. Goldson. 2002. The neonate and the environment: impact on development. In: Merenstein, G. G., and S. L. Gardner, eds. *Handbook of Neonatal Intensive Care*, 5th ed., pp. 219–282. St. Louis: Mosby.
3. Marieb, E., and K. Hoehn. 2007. *Human Anatomy and Physiology*, 7th ed. San Francisco: Benjamin Cummings, p. 582.
4. Kim, D.-Y., M. Camilleri, J. A. Murray, D. A. Stephens, J. A. Levine, and D. D. Burton. 2001. Is there a role for gastric accommodation and satiety in asymptomatic obese people? *Obesity Res.* 9:655–661.
5. Germann, W. J., and C. L. Stanfield. 2005. *Principles of Human Physiology*, 2nd ed. San Francisco: Benjamin Cummings, p. 653.
6. Davidson, N. O. 2003. Intestinal lipid absorption. In: Yamada, T., D. H. Alpers, N. Kaplowitz, L. Laine, C. Owyang, and D. W. Powell, eds. *Textbook of Gastroenterology*, vol. 1. 4th ed. Philadelphia: Lippincott Williams & Wilkins.
7. Moran, T. H. 2009. Gut peptides in the control of food intake. *Int. J. Obes.* 33(Suppl 1):S7–10.
8. Gurusamy, K. S., R. Koti, G. Fusai, and B. R. Davidson. 2010. Somatostatin analogues for pancreatic surgery. *Cochrane Database Syst Rev.* Feb 17(2):CD008370.
9. Eisenstein, J., and A. Greenberg. 2003. Ghrelin: Update 2003. *Nutr.Rev.* 61(3):101–104.
10. Canadian Digestive Health Foundation. GERD. www.cdhf.ca (accessed April 25, 2010).
11. National Digestive Diseases Information Clearinghouse (NDDIC). 2003. Heartburn, hiatal hernia, and gastroesophageal reflux disease (GERD). NIH Publication No. 03–0882. Available online at http://digestive.niddk.nih.gov/ddiseases/pubs/gerd/index.htm.

12. Chan, F. K. L., and W. K. Leung. 2002. Peptic-ulcer disease. *Lancet* 360:933–941.

13. Goodman, K. J., K. Jacobson, and S. Veldhuyzen van Zanten. 2007. *Helicobacter pylori* infection in Canadian and related arctic aboriginal populations. *Can. J. Gastroenterol.* 22:289–295.

14. National Digestive Diseases Information Clearinghouse (NDDIC). 2002. NSAIDs and peptic ulcers. NIH Publication No. 02–4644. Available online at http://digestive.niddk.nih.gov/ddiseases/pubs/nsaids/index.htm.

15. Jamieson, J. A. and H. V. Kuhnlein. 2008. The paradox of anemia with high meat intake: a review of the multifactorial etiology of anemia in the Inuit of North America. *Nutr. Rev.* 66:256–271.

16. Health Canada. Food Allergen Labelling. www.hc-sc.gc.ca/fn-an/label-etiquet/allergen/index-eng.php (accessed June 30, 2012).

17. Ben-Shoshan, M., D. W. Harrington, L. Soller, J. Fragapane, L. Joseph, Y. St Pierre, S. B. Godefroy, S. J. Elliot, and A. E. Clarke. 2010. A population-based study on peanut, tree nut, fish, shellfish, and sesame allergy prevalence in Canada. *J. Allergy Clin. Immunol.* 125:1327–1335.

18. National Institutes of Health (NIH). June 26, 2008. Celiac disease awareness campaign. Available online at http://celiac.nih.gov/default.aspx.

19. National Institutes of Health (NIH). June 2004. *NIH consensus development conference on celiac disease.* Available online at http://consensus.nih.gov/2004/2004CeliacDisease118html.htm.

20. Bernstein, C. N., A. Wajda, L. W. Svenson, A. MacKenzie, M. Koehoorn, M. Jackson, R. Fedorak, D. Isreal, and J. F. Blanchard. 2006. The epidemiology of inflammatory bowel disease in Canada: a population-based study. *Am. J. Gasteroenterol.* 101:1559–1568.

21. National Digestive Diseases Information Clearinghouse (NDDIC). 2003. Crohn's disease. NIH Publication No. 03–3410. Available online at http://digestive.niddk.nih.gov/ddiseases/pubs/crohns/index.htm.

22. Crohn's & Colitis Foundation of America (CCFA). 2005. Introduction to ulcerative colitis. Available online at www.ccfa.org/research/info/aboutuc.

23. National Digestive Diseases Information Clearinghouse (NDDIC). 2001. Diarrhea. NIH Publication No. 01–2749. Available online at http://digestive.niddk.nih.gov/ddiseases/pubs/diarrhea/index.htm.

24. DuPont, H. L. 2006. New insights and directions in traveler's diarrhea. *Gastroenterol. Clin. N. Am.* 35(2):337–353, viii–ix.

25. Canadian Digestive Health Foundation. Understanding irritable bowel syndrome IIBS). www.cdhf.ca (accessed May 24, 2012).

26. Lewis, C. July–August 2001. Irritable bowel syndrome: a poorly understood disorder. *FDA Consumer Magazine.* Available online at www.fda.gov/fdac/features/2001/401_ibs.html.

27. Mein, S. M., and U. Ladabaum. Serological testing for coeliac disease in patients with symptoms of irritable bowel syndrome: a cost-effective analysis. *Aliment Phamacol Ther* April 29, 2004 19(11):1199–1210; National Institutes of Health. March 12, 2002. Celiac disease meeting summary. DDICC meeting minutes. Available online at http://digestive.niddk.nih.gov/federal/ddicc/minutes_3-12-02.pdf.

28. National Digestive Diseases Information Clearinghouse (NDDIC). 2003. Irritable bowel syndrome. NIH Publication No. 03–693. Available online at http://digestive.niddk.nih.gov/ddiseases/pubs/ibs/index.htm.

29. Early, E. 2003. Celiac disease more prevalent in diabetic children. Medical College of Wisconsin. Available online at http://healthlink.mcw.edu/article/1009402816.html.

30. North American Society for Pediatric Gastroenterology, Hepatology, and Nutrition. 2005. Diagnosis and treatment of celiac disease in children: Clinical practice guideline summary. *Journal of Pediatric Gastroenterology and Nutrition* 40(1):1–19. Available online at www.naspghan.org.

31. National Digestive Diseases Information Clearinghouse (NDDIC). October 2005. Celiac disease. NIH Publication No. 06-4269. Available online at http://digestive.niddk.nih.gov.

Should School-Aged Children Be Screened for Celiac Disease?

A *screening test* is a diagnostic procedure that elicits data about the presence or absence of characteristic signs of a disorder. Every baby born in a Canadian hospital undergoes at least two screening tests within the first 48 hours of life. These are for the metabolic disorder phenylketonuria, discussed in Chapter 6, and congenital hypothyroidism, a disorder affecting the thyroid gland. Most school-aged children in Canada are also screened for vision and hearing deficits, learning disorders, head lice, and other problems. With all this screening going on, should school-aged children also be screened for celiac disease?

Researchers and healthcare professionals in favour of screening children for celiac disease point to several factors in support of their position. First, the prevalence in Canada is high enough to be of general concern: about 1 in every 133 Canadians are believed to have celiac disease.[20] This is even higher than the 1:300 prevalence rates in the United States and Europe, where celiac disease is the most common genetic disease.

In addition, celiac disease is thought to be greatly underdiagnosed. There are three reasons for this: many doctors and healthcare providers in Canada are not knowledgeable about celiac disease; only a small number of Canadian laboratories are experienced and skilled in testing for celiac disease; and celiac symptoms can be attributed to other problems. Although in many people celiac disease presents as a "classic" syndrome of diarrhea, weight loss, abdominal bloating, and excessive intestinal gas, the symptoms are in reality highly variable, with some patients experiencing constipation, vomiting, or abdominal pain. In people with neurologic and other non-digestive symptoms, celiac disease may never even be considered without routine, population-wide screening.

Moreover, general screening both in Europe and in limited studies in the United States reveals a significant prevalence of "silent celiac disease"; that is, the individual is not aware of having symptoms, but has a positive antibody test and upon biopsy is shown to have atrophy of the intestinal villi. Although asymptomatic, the intestinal damage in these people puts them at risk for all of the complications of untreated celiac disease. In Italy, where the prevalence of celiac disease is about 1 in 250 people, all children are screened by age 6 so that even asymptomatic disease is caught early.[29] Guidelines for pediatricians from the North

American Society for Pediatric Gastroenterology, Hepatology, and Nutrition (NASPGHAN) recommend that all children with type 1 diabetes be screened for celiac disease, as an association between the two diseases has been recognized for some time.[30] A recent U.S. study showed that at least 4.6% of children with type 1 diabetes also have celiac disease.[29] NASPGHAN also recommends that children with Down syndrome be screened.[30] In these children the prevalence is 5% to 12%.[18] In addition, NASPGHAN recommends testing for children with unexplained short stature, delayed puberty, and poor bone density.[30]

Further considerations in favour of routine screening are the potentially serious consequences of a missed diagnosis. In children, short stature results when childhood celiac disease prevents nutrient absorption during the years when nutrition is critical to a child's normal growth and development.[31] Children who are diagnosed and treated before their growth period ends may be able to catch up to the growth of their peers, but after that time, the short stature is irreversible. Other possible consequences of a missed diagnosis include an increased risk of depression, anxiety, learning disorders, epilepsy, autoimmune disorders, type 1 diabetes, thyroid disease, liver disease, poor bone density, and GI cancers.[31]

Finally, a simple blood test that is highly sensitive and specific to antibodies produced in celiac disease is available. Routine screening would provide a financial incentive for laboratories to make the antibody test more widely available, benefiting all Canadians.

School-aged children may have celiac disease and not know it. Undiagnosed celiac disease can lead to a variety of serious health problems as children grow.

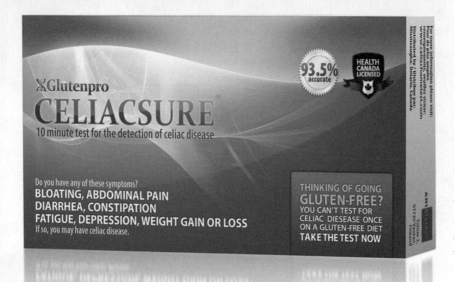

A simple blood test can identify celiac disease.

Arguments against routine testing centre on invasiveness and questions of reliability of the available tests. Unlike the screening tests for vision, hearing, or head lice, the antibody test for celiac disease is invasive, requiring that the healthcare provider draw a small amount of blood. Some families object to invasive medical tests for religious or other reasons. Second, although the antibody test is considered generally reliable for diagnosing celiac disease, false negatives are not uncommon. Indeed, the reliability of the test for children younger than 5 is controversial.[31] The only definitive proof of celiac disease is via a biopsy of the small intestine that shows atrophy of the villi. Because few people would argue that all children should undergo a biopsy, should routine screening wait until a reliable but non-invasive test is developed?

Another area of controversy exists over the benefit of identifying people with "latent celiac disease," that is, people who test positive with the antibody screen but do not currently have symptoms or any damage to the intestinal villi. Do these people need to go on the highly restrictive gluten-free diet? Because current data do not indicate a clear benefit of a gluten-free diet in people with latent disease, this question is the subject of debate.[19]

Finally, the concept of routine screening itself is a matter of some controversy. While few would argue against simple, low-cost screening tests such as those for vision or hearing problems, some people hesitate when tests become more costly. Canada does not currently require screening of all children for type 1 or type 2 diabetes, obesity, or many other serious health problems, so why should the public be burdened with screening for celiac disease?

In 2004, the National Institutes of Health Consensus Development Conference on Celiac Disease concluded that, at this time, there are insufficient data to recommend routine screening for celiac disease. Instead, the Conference recommended further research into the benefits and cost-effectiveness of screening in the general population. Ongoing with this research, the Conference recommends heightened awareness of the disease; education of physicians, registered dietitians, and other healthcare providers is imperative.[19]

Using the Evidence

1. Now that you've read the arguments for and against routine screening of Canadian children for celiac disease, do you think that all children should have the test? Why or why not?

2. If you said yes, who should pay for it? Parents? School districts? The public health department?

3. Given the number of children who are home-schooled or in private schools, how could we ensure that all families were offered screening?

4. Would you be in favour of routine screening of children for type 2 diabetes, hypertension, obesity, and other disorders?

5. What factors seem most important to consider when deciding which diseases we screen for in Canadian children?

4

Carbohydrates: Plant-Derived Energy Nutrients

Test Yourself | True *or* False?

1. Carbohydrates are the primary fuel source for the brain and body tissues.
   T *or* F

2. Carbohydrates are fattening. T *or* F

3. Type 2 diabetes is seen only in adults. T *or* F

4. Diets high in sugar cause hyperactivity in children. T *or* F

5. Alternative sweeteners, such as aspartame, are safe for us to consume.
   T *or* F

Test Yourself answers are located in the Chapter Review.

Chapter Objectives | *After reading this chapter, you will be able to:*

1. Describe the difference between simple and complex carbohydrates, *pp. 119–122.*
2. Describe the difference between alpha and beta bonds, and discuss how these bonds are related to the digestion of fibre and lactose intolerance, *pp. 121–122.*
3. Compare and contrast soluble and insoluble fibres, *pp. 123–124.*
4. Discuss how carbohydrates are digested and absorbed by the body, *pp. 124–127.*
5. List four functions of carbohydrates in the body, *pp. 130–132.*
6. Define the Acceptable Macronutrient Distribution Range for carbohydrates, the Adequate Intake for fibre, and the recommended intake of added sugars, *pp. 134–139.*
7. Identify the potential health risks associated with diets high in simple sugars, *pp. 135–137.*
8. List five foods that are good sources of carbohydrates, *pp. 139–140.*
9. Identify at least three alternative sweeteners, *pp. 142–145.*
10. Describe type 1 and type 2 diabetes, and discuss how diabetes differs from hypoglycemia, *pp. 145–150.*

It was a typical day at a large medical centre in downtown Toronto: two patients were having toes amputated, another had nerve damage, one was being treated for kidney failure, another for infection, and another was blind. Despite their variety, these problems were due to just one disease: diabetes. In 2000, it was estimated that total healthcare costs related to diabetes in Canada were $4.66 billion.[1] That figure is expected to increase to $8.14 billion by the year 2016. Older Canadians, those experiencing household food insufficiency, and Aboriginal people have a significantly higher risk of developing diabetes; however, more and more children are being diagnosed with the disease.[2,3] It is expected that the incidence of type 2 diabetes in children in Canada will increase by up to 50% by the year 2025.[4]

What is diabetes, and why are we discussing it in a chapter on carbohydrates? Does the consumption of carbohydrates somehow lead to diabetes—or, for that matter, to obesity or any other disorder? Several popular diets—including the Zone Diet,[5] Sugar Busters,[6] and Dr. Atkins' New Diet Revolution[7]—claim that carbohydrates are bad for your health and advocate reducing **carbohydrate** consumption and increasing protein and fat intake. Are carbohydrates a health menace, and should we reduce our intake? If you noticed that a friend regularly consumed four or five soft drinks a day, plus chips, cookies, candy, and other high-carbohydrate snacks, would you say anything?

In this chapter, we explore the differences between simple and complex carbohydrates and learn why some carbohydrates are better than others. We also learn how our bodies break down carbohydrates and use them to maintain our health and to fuel our activity and exercise. Because carbohydrate metabolism sometimes does go wrong, we'll also discuss its relationship to some common health disorders.

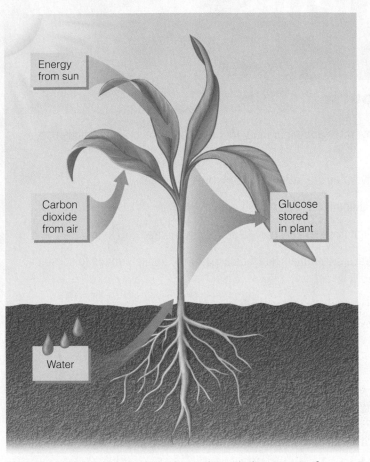

Figure 4.1 Plants make carbohydrates through the process of photosynthesis. Water, carbon dioxide, and energy from the sun are combined to produce glucose.

carbohydrate One of the three macronutrients, a compound made up of carbon, hydrogen, and oxygen that is derived from plants and provides energy.

glucose The most abundant sugar molecule, a monosaccharide generally found in combination with other sugars; the preferred source of energy for the brain and an important source of energy for all cells.

photosynthesis A process by which plants use sunlight to fuel a chemical reaction that combines carbon and water into glucose, which is then stored in their cells.

What Are Carbohydrates?

As we mentioned in Chapter 1, carbohydrates are one of the three macronutrients. As such, they are an important energy source for the entire body and are the preferred energy source for nerve cells, including those of the brain. We will say more about their functions later in this chapter.

The term *carbohydrate* literally means "hydrated carbon." Water (H_2O) is made of hydrogen and oxygen, and when something is said to be *hydrated*, it contains water. Thus, the chemical abbreviation for carbohydrate (CHO) indicates the atoms it contains: carbon, hydrogen, and oxygen.

We obtain carbohydrates predominantly from plant foods such as fruits, vegetables, and grains. Plants make the most abundant form of carbohydrate, called **glucose**, through a process called **photosynthesis**. During photosynthesis, the green pigment of plants, called *chlorophyll,* absorbs sunlight, which provides the energy needed to fuel the manufacture of glucose. As shown in **Figure 4.1**, water absorbed from the earth by the roots of plants combines with carbon dioxide present in the leaves to produce the carbohydrate glucose. Plants continually store glucose and use it to support their own growth. Then, when we eat plant foods, our bodies digest, absorb, and use the stored glucose.

What's the Difference Between Simple and Complex Carbohydrates?

Carbohydrates can be classified as *simple* or *complex*. Simple carbohydrates contain either one or two molecules, whereas complex carbohydrates contain hundreds to thousands of molecules.

Simple Carbohydrates Include Monosaccharides and Disaccharides

Simple carbohydrates are commonly referred to as *sugars*. Four of these sugars are called **monosaccharides** because they consist of a single sugar molecule (*mono*, meaning "one," and *saccharide*, meaning "sugar"). The other three sugars are **disaccharides**, which consist of two molecules of sugar joined together (*di*, meaning "two").

Glucose, Fructose, Galactose, and Ribose Are Monosaccharides

Glucose, fructose, and *galactose* are the three most common monosaccharides in our diet. Each of these monosaccharides contains 6 carbon atoms, 12 hydrogen atoms, and 6 oxygen atoms (**Figure 4.2**). Very slight differences in the structure of these three monosaccharides cause major differences in their level of sweetness.

Given what you've just learned about how plants manufacture glucose, it probably won't surprise you to discover that glucose is the most abundant monosaccharide found in our diets and in our bodies. Glucose does not generally occur by itself in foods but attaches to other sugars to form disaccharides and complex carbohydrates. In our bodies, glucose is the preferred source of energy for the brain, and it is a very important source of energy for all cells.

Fructose, the sweetest natural sugar, occurs naturally in fruits and vegetables. Fructose is also called *levulose*, or *fruit sugar*. In many processed foods, it is a component of *high-fructose corn syrup*. This syrup is made from corn and is used to sweeten soft drinks, desserts, candies, and jellies.

Galactose does not occur alone in foods. It joins with glucose to create lactose, one of the three most common disaccharides.

Ribose is a five-carbon monosaccharide. Very little ribose is found in our diets; our bodies produce ribose from the foods we eat, and ribose is contained in the genetic material of our cells: deoxyribonucleic acid (DNA) and ribonucleic acid (RNA).

In our bodies, glucose is the preferred source of energy for the brain.

simple carbohydrate Commonly called *sugar;* a monosaccharide or disaccharide such as glucose.

monosaccharide The simplest of carbohydrates. Consists of one sugar molecule, the most common form of which is glucose.

disaccharide A carbohydrate compound consisting of two monosaccharide molecules joined together.

fructose The sweetest natural sugar; a monosaccharide that occurs in fruits and vegetables; also called *levulose*, or *fruit sugar*.

galactose A monosaccharide that joins with glucose to create lactose, one of the three most common disaccharides.

ribose A five-carbon monosaccharide that is located in the genetic material of cells.

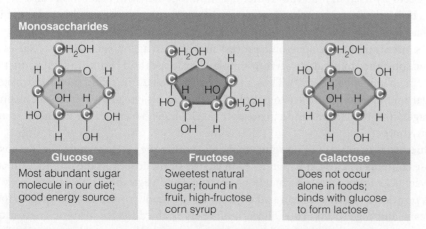

Monosaccharides

Glucose	Fructose	Galactose
Most abundant sugar molecule in our diet; good energy source	Sweetest natural sugar; found in fruit, high-fructose corn syrup	Does not occur alone in foods; binds with glucose to form lactose

Figure 4.2 The three most common monosaccharides. Notice that all three monosaccharides contain identical atoms: 6 carbon, 12 hydrogen, and 6 oxygen. It is only the arrangement of these atoms that differs.

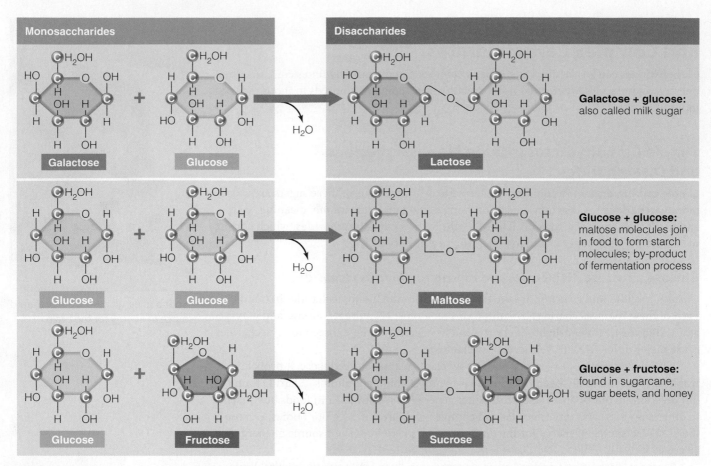

Figure 4.3 Galactose, glucose, and fructose join together in different combinations to make the disaccharides lactose, maltose, and sucrose.

Lactose, Maltose, and Sucrose Are Disaccharides

The three most common disaccharides found in foods are *lactose, maltose,* and *sucrose* (**Figure 4.3**). **Lactose** (also called *milk sugar*) consists of one glucose molecule and one galactose molecule. Interestingly, human breast milk has a higher amount of lactose than cow's milk, which makes human breast milk taste sweeter.

Maltose (also called *malt sugar*) consists of two molecules of glucose. It does not generally occur by itself in foods but rather is bound together with other molecules. As our bodies break these larger molecules down, maltose results as a by-product. Maltose is also the sugar that results from *fermentation* during the production of beer and liquor products. **Fermentation** is the anaerobic process in which an agent, such as yeast, causes an organic substance to break down into simpler substances and results in the production of adenosine triphosphate (ATP). Thus, maltose is formed during the anaerobic breakdown of sugar into alcohol. Contrary to popular belief, very little maltose remains in alcoholic beverages after the fermentation process; thus, alcoholic beverages are not good sources of carbohydrate.

Sucrose is composed of one glucose molecule and one fructose molecule. Because sucrose contains fructose, it is sweeter than lactose or maltose. Sucrose provides much of the sweet taste found in honey, maple syrup, fruits, and vegetables. Table sugar, brown sugar, powdered sugar, and many other products are made by refining the sucrose found in sugarcane and sugar beets. You will learn more about the different forms of sucrose commonly used in foods later in this chapter. Are honey and other naturally occurring forms of sucrose healthier than manufactured forms? The Nutrition Myth or Fact? box investigates this question.

lactose Also called *milk sugar*, a disaccharide consisting of one glucose molecule and one galactose molecule; found in milk, including human breast milk.

maltose A disaccharide consisting of two molecules of glucose; does not generally occur independently in foods but results as a by-product of digestion; also called *malt sugar*.

fermentation The anaerobic process in which an agent causes an organic substance to break down into simpler substances and results in the production of ATP.

sucrose A disaccharide composed of one glucose molecule and one fructose molecule; sweeter than lactose or maltose.

NUTRITION MYTH OR FACT?

Is Honey More Nutritious Than Table Sugar?

Ming is dedicated to eating nutritious foods. She works hard to avoid white sugar and to eat foods that contain honey, molasses, or raw sugar. Ming believes that these sweeteners are more natural and nutritious than refined white sugar. To critically assess her belief, consider Table 4.1 and work through the questions below.

Thinking Critically

1. **How does the carbohydrate composition of white sugar compare with that of honey?**
2. **How does the nutrient composition of white sugar compare with that of honey?**
3. **How do the micronutrients in honey compare to the recommended dietary reference intakes (DRI) for a 22-year-old female?**
4. **Is raw sugar more nutritious than table sugar?**

5. **Blackstrap molasses is the syrup that remains when sucrose is made from sugarcane. Is blackstrap molasses a more nutritious choice than white sugar?**
6. **What advice would you give to Ming about sweeteners?**

Table 4.1 Nutrient Comparison of 15 mL of Four Different Sweeteners

	White Sugar	Honey	Blackstrap Molasses	"Raw" Sugar
Energy (kcal)	49.0	65.0	49.0	49.0
Carbohydrate (g)	12.7	17.7	12.6	12.7
Sugars, total (g)	12.7	17.6	8.9	12.7
Fat (g)	0	0	0	0
Protein (g)	0	0.06	0	0
Fibre (g)	0	0	0	0
Vitamin C (mg)	0	0.1	0	0
Vitamin A (IU)	0	0	0	0
Thiamine (mg)	0	0	0.007	0.001
Riboflavin (mg)	0.002	0.008	0.01	0.001
Folate (µg)	0	0	0	0
Calcium (mg)	0	1.0	179.0	11.0
Iron (mg)	0	0.09	3.6	0.24
Sodium (mg)	0	1.0	11.0	5.0
Potassium (mg)	0	11.0	518.0	45.0

Data from: The Canadian Nutrient File. Health Canada, 2012. Reproduced with the permission of the Minister of Health, 2012.

The two monosaccharides that compose a disaccharide are attached by a bond between an oxygen atom and one carbon atom on each of the monosaccharides (**Figure 4.4**). Two forms of this bond occur in nature: an **alpha bond** and a **beta bond**. As you can see in Figure 4.4a, sucrose is produced by an alpha bond joining a glucose molecule and a fructose molecule. The disaccharide maltose is also produced by an alpha bond. In contrast, lactose is produced by

alpha bond A type of chemical bond that can be digested by enzymes found in the human intestine.

beta bond A type of chemical bond that cannot be easily digested by enzymes found in the human intestine.

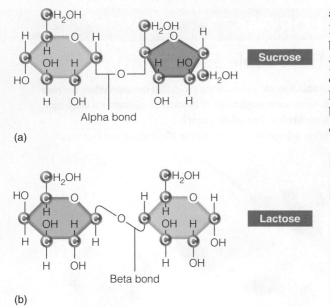

(a)

(b)

Figure 4.4 The two monosaccharides that compose a disaccharide are attached by either an (a) alpha bond or (b) beta bond between an oxygen atom and one carbon atom of each monosaccharide.

a beta bond joining a glucose molecule and a galactose molecule (see Figure 4.4b). Alpha bonds are easily digestible by humans, whereas beta bonds are very difficult to digest and may even be non-digestible. As you will learn later in this chapter, some people do not possess enough of the enzyme lactase that is needed to break the beta bond present in lactose. This causes the condition referred to as *lactose intolerance*. Beta bonds are also present in high-fibre foods, leading to our inability to digest most forms of fibre.

RECaP

Carbohydrates contain carbon, hydrogen, and oxygen. Simple carbohydrates include monosaccharides and disaccharides. Glucose, fructose, galactose, and ribose are monosaccharides; lactose, maltose, and sucrose are disaccharides. In disaccharides, two monosaccharides are linked together with either an alpha bond or a beta bond. Alpha bonds are easily digestible by humans, whereas beta bonds are not easily digestible.

Complex Carbohydrates Include Oligosaccharides and Polysaccharides

Complex carbohydrates, the second major classification of carbohydrate, generally consist of long chains of glucose molecules. Technically, any carbohydrate with three or more monosaccharides is considered to be a complex carbohydrate.

Oligosaccharides are carbohydrates that contain 3 to 10 monosaccharides (*oligo,* meaning "few"). Two of the most common oligosaccharides found in our diets are **raffinose** and **stachyose**. Raffinose is composed of galactose, glucose, and fructose. It is commonly found in beans, cabbage, Brussels sprouts, broccoli, and whole grains. Stachyose is composed of two galactose molecules, a glucose molecule, and a fructose molecule. It is found in many beans and legumes.

Raffinose and stachyose are part of the raffinose family of oligosaccharides (RFOs).[8] Because humans do not possess the enzyme needed to break down these RFOs, they pass into the large intestine undigested. Once they reach the large intestine, they are fermented by bacteria that produce gases such as carbon dioxide, methane, and hydrogen. The product Beano® contains the enzyme alpha-galactosidase; this is the enzyme needed to break down the RFOs in the intestinal tract. Thus, this product can help to reduce the intestinal gas caused by eating beans and various vegetables.

Most **polysaccharides** consist of hundreds to thousands of glucose molecules (*poly,* meaning "many").[8] The polysaccharides include starch, glycogen, and most fibres (**Figure 4.5**).

Starch Is a Polysaccharide Stored in Plants

Plants store glucose not as single molecules but as polysaccharides in the form of **starch**. The two forms of starch are amylose and amylopectin (see Figure 4.5). Amylose is a straight chain of glucose molecules, whereas amylopectin is highly branched. Both forms of starch are found in starch-containing foods. The more open-branched structure of amylopectin increases its surface area and thus its exposure to digestive enzymes. Consequently, amylopectin is more rapidly digested than amylose, and thus it raises blood glucose more quickly than amylose.

Excellent food sources of starch include grains (wheat, rice, corn, oats, and barley), legumes (peas, beans, and lentils), and tubers (potatoes and sweet potatoes). Our cells cannot use the complex starch molecules exactly as they occur in plants. Instead, the body

complex carbohydrate A nutrient compound consisting of long chains of glucose molecules, such as starch, glycogen, and fibre.

oligosaccharides Complex carbohydrates that contain 3 to 10 monosaccharides.

raffinose An oligosaccharide composed of galactose, glucose, and fructose. Also called melitose, it is found in beans, cabbage, broccoli, and other vegetables.

stachyose An oligosaccharide composed of two galactose molecules, a glucose molecule, and a fructose molecule. Found in the Chinese artichoke and various beans and legumes.

polysaccharide A complex carbohydrate consisting of long chains of glucose.

starch A polysaccharide stored in plants; the storage form of glucose in plants.

must break them down into the monosaccharide glucose, from which we can then fuel our energy needs.

Our bodies easily digest most starches, in which alpha bonds link the numerous glucose units; however, starches linked by beta bonds are largely indigestible and are called *resistant*. Technically, resistant starch is classified as a type of fibre. When our intestinal bacteria ferment resistant starch, a short-chain fatty acid called *butyrate* is produced. Consuming resistant starch may be beneficial: some research suggests that butyrate reduces the risk of cancer.[9] Legumes contain more resistant starch than do grains, fruits, or vegetables. This quality, plus their high protein and fibre content, makes legumes a healthy food.

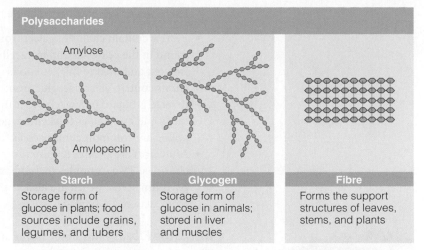

Polysaccharides		
Amylose / Amylopectin		
Starch	**Glycogen**	**Fibre**
Storage form of glucose in plants; food sources include grains, legumes, and tubers	Storage form of glucose in animals; stored in liver and muscles	Forms the support structures of leaves, stems, and plants

Figure 4.5 Polysaccharides, also referred to as complex carbohydrates, include starch, glycogen, and fibre.

Glycogen Is a Polysaccharide Stored by Animals

Glycogen is the storage form of glucose for animals, including humans. After an animal is slaughtered, most of the glycogen is broken down by enzymes found in animal tissues. Thus, very little glycogen exists in meat. Glycogen does not exist at all in plants either. Therefore, glycogen is not a dietary source of carbohydrate. We can very quickly break down the glycogen stored in the body into glucose when we need it for energy. We store glycogen in our muscles and liver; the storage and use of glycogen are discussed in more detail on pages 126–127.

Fibre Is a Polysaccharide That Gives Plants Their Structure

Like starch, fibre is composed of long polysaccharide chains; however, the body does not easily break down the bonds that connect fibre molecules. This means that most fibres pass through the digestive system without being digested and absorbed, so they contribute no energy to our diet. However, fibre offers many other health benefits (see page 132).

There are currently a number of definitions of fibre. Recently, the Food and Nutrition Board of the Institute of Medicine proposed three distinctions: *dietary fibre, functional fibre,* and *total fibre*:[8]

Tubers, such as these sweet potatoes, are excellent food sources of starch.

- **Dietary fibre** (also referred to as resistant starch) is the non-digestible part of plants that form the support structures of leaves, stems, and seeds (see Figure 4.5). In a sense, you can think of dietary fibre as the plant's "skeleton."
- **Functional fibre** consists of non-digestible forms of carbohydrates that are extracted from plants or manufactured in a laboratory and have known health benefits. Functional fibre is added to foods and is the form found in fibre supplements. Examples of functional fibre sources you might see on nutrition labels include cellulose, guar gum, pectin, and psyllium.
- **Total fibre** is the sum of dietary fibre and functional fibre.

Fibre can also be classified according to its chemical and physical properties as soluble or insoluble.

Soluble Fibres **Soluble fibres** dissolve in water. They are also **viscous**, forming a gel when wet, and they are fermentable; that is, they are easily digested by bacteria in the colon. Soluble fibres are typically found in citrus fruits, berries, oat products, and beans.

Research suggests that regular consumption of soluble fibres reduces the risks for cardiovascular disease and type 2 diabetes by lowering blood cholesterol and blood glucose levels. The possible mechanisms by which fibre reduces the risk for various diseases are discussed in more detail on pages 132–134.

glycogen A polysaccharide stored in animals; the storage form of glucose in animals.

dietary fibre The non-digestible carbohydrate parts of plants that form the support structures of leaves, stems, and seeds.

functional fibre The non-digestible forms of carbohydrate that are extracted from plants or manufactured in the laboratory and have known health benefits.

total fibre The sum of dietary fibre and functional fibre.

soluble fibres Fibres that dissolve in water.

viscous A term referring to a gel-like consistency; viscous fibres form a gel when dissolved in water.

Examples of soluble fibres include the following:

- *Pectins* contain chains of galacturonic acid and other monosaccharides. Pectins are found in the cell walls and intracellular tissues of many fruits and berries. They can be isolated and used to thicken foods such as jams and yogourts.
- *Gums* contain galactose, glucuronic acid, and other monosaccharides. Gums are a diverse group of polysaccharides that are viscous. They are typically isolated from seeds and are used as thickening, gelling, and stabilizing agents. Guar gum and gum arabic are common gums used as food additives.
- *Mucilages* are similar to gums and contain galactose, mannose, and other monosaccharides. Two examples include psyllium and carrageenan. Psyllium is the husk of psyllium seeds, which are also known as plantago or flea seeds. Carrageenan comes from seaweed. Mucilages are used as food stabilizers.

Insoluble Fibres   **Insoluble fibres** are those that do not typically dissolve in water. These fibres are usually non-viscous and cannot be fermented by bacteria in the colon. They are generally found in whole grains such as wheat, rye, and brown rice and are also found in many vegetables. These fibres are not associated with reducing cholesterol levels but are known for promoting regular bowel movements, alleviating constipation, and reducing the risk for a bowel disorder called diverticulosis (discussed later in this chapter). Examples of insoluble fibres include the following:

- *Lignins* are non-carbohydrate forms of fibre. Lignins are found in the woody parts of plant cell walls and are found in carrots and in the seeds of fruits and berries. Lignins are also found in brans (or the outer husk of grains such as wheat, oats, and rye) and other whole grains.
- *Cellulose* is the main structural component of plant cell walls. Cellulose is a chain of glucose units similar to amylose, but unlike amylose, cellulose contains beta bonds that are non-digestible by humans. Cellulose is found in whole grains, fruits, vegetables, and legumes. It can also be extracted from wood pulp or cotton, and it is added to foods as an agent for anti-caking, thickening, and texturizing of foods.
- *Hemicelluloses* contain glucose, mannose, galacturonic acid, and other monosaccharides. Hemicelluloses are found in plant cell walls and they surround cellulose. They are the primary component of cereal fibres and are found in whole grains and vegetables. Although many hemicelluloses are insoluble, some are also classified as soluble.

Wheat bran is a source of insoluble fibre.

Recap

Complex carbohydrates include oligosaccharides and polysaccharides. Raffinose and stachyose are two of the most common oligosaccharides found in our diet. The three types of polysaccharides are starch, glycogen, and fibre. Starch is the storage form of glucose in plants, while glycogen is the storage form of glucose in animals. Fibre forms the support structures of plants. Soluble fibres dissolve in water, are viscous, and can be digested by bacteria in the colon, whereas insoluble fibres do not dissolve in water, are not viscous, and cannot be digested.

How Do Our Bodies Break Down Carbohydrates?

Glucose is the form of sugar that our bodies use for energy, and the primary goal of carbohydrate digestion is to break down polysaccharides and disaccharides into monosaccharides that can then be converted to glucose. Chapter 3 provided an overview of digestion of the three types of macronutrients, as well as vitamins and minerals. Here, we focus specifically and in more detail on the digestion and absorption of carbohydrates. **Figure 4.6** provides a visual tour of carbohydrate digestion.

insoluble fibres Fibres that do not dissolve in water.

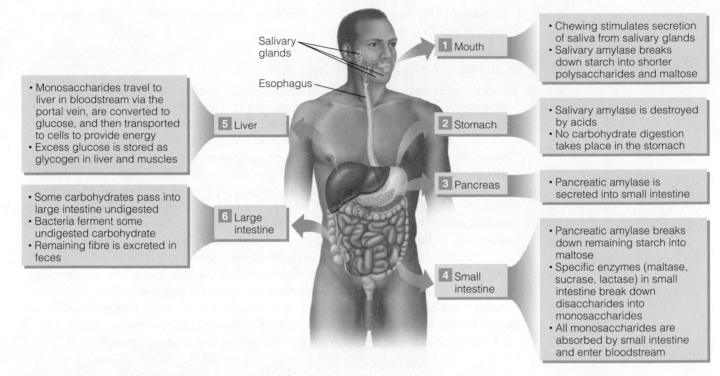

Figure 4.6 A review of carbohydrate digestion and absorption.
Data from: Johnson, M., *Human Biology: Concepts and Current Issues, 5/e*, page 89, Copyright © 2010 Benjamin Cummings. Reprinted by permission of Pearson Education, Inc.

Carbohydrate Digestion

Carbohydrate digestion begins in the mouth (Figure 4.6, step 1). As you saw in Chapter 3, the starch in the foods you eat mixes with your saliva during chewing. Saliva contains an enzyme called **salivary amylase**, which breaks down starch into smaller particles and eventually into the disaccharide maltose. The next time you eat a piece of bread, notice that you can actually taste it becoming sweeter; this indicates the breakdown of starch into maltose. Disaccharides are not digested in the mouth.

As the bolus of food leaves the mouth and enters the stomach, all digestion of carbohydrates ceases. This is because the acid in the stomach inactivates the salivary amylase enzyme (Figure 4.6, step 2).

The majority of carbohydrate digestion occurs in the small intestine. As the contents of the stomach enter the small intestine, an enzyme called *pancreatic amylase* is secreted by the pancreas into the small intestine (Figure 4.6, step 3). **Pancreatic amylase** continues to digest any remaining starch into maltose. Additional enzymes found in the microvilli of the mucosal cells that line the intestinal tract work to break down disaccharides into monosaccharides. Maltose is broken down into glucose by the enzyme **maltase**. Sucrose is broken down into glucose and fructose by the enzyme **sucrase**. The enzyme **lactase** breaks down lactose into glucose and galactose (Figure 4.6, step 4). Enzyme names are identifiable by the suffix *-ase*.

Carbohydrate Absorption

Once digestion of carbohydrates is complete, all monosaccharides are then absorbed into the mucosal cells lining the small intestine, where they pass through and enter into the bloodstream. Glucose and galactose are absorbed across the enterocytes via active transport using a carrier protein saturated with sodium. This process requires energy from the breakdown of ATP. Fructose is absorbed via facilitated diffusion and therefore requires no energy. (Refer back to Chapter 3 for a description of these transport processes.) The absorption of fructose takes longer than that of glucose or galactose. This slower absorption rate means that fructose stays in the small intestine longer and draws water into the intestines

salivary amylase An enzyme in saliva that breaks starch into smaller particles and eventually into the disaccharide maltose.

pancreatic amylase An enzyme secreted by the pancreas into the small intestine that digests any remaining starch into maltose.

maltase A digestive enzyme that breaks maltose into glucose.

sucrase A digestive enzyme that breaks sucrose into glucose and fructose.

lactase A digestive enzyme that breaks lactose into glucose and galactose.

via osmosis. This not only results in a smaller rise in blood glucose when consuming fructose, but it can also lead to diarrhea.

Carbohydrate Metabolism

Once the monosaccharides enter the bloodstream, they travel to the liver, where fructose and galactose are converted to glucose (Figure 4.6, step 5). If needed immediately for energy, the glucose is released into the bloodstream, where it can travel to the cells to provide energy. If glucose is not immediately needed by the body for energy, it is stored as glycogen in the liver and muscles. Enzymes in liver and muscle cells combine glucose molecules to form glycogen (an anabolic, or building, process) and break glycogen into glucose (a catabolic, or destructive, process), depending on the body's energy needs. On average, the liver can store 70 g (or 280 kcal) and the muscles can store about 120 g (or 480 kcal) of glycogen. Between meals, our bodies draw on liver glycogen reserves to maintain blood glucose levels and support the needs of our cells, including those of our brain, spinal cord, and red blood cells (**Figure 4.7**).

The glycogen stored in our muscles continually provides energy to the muscles, particularly during intense exercise. Endurance athletes can increase their storage of muscle glycogen from two to four times the normal amount through a process called *glycogen,* or *carbohydrate, loading* (see Chapter 15). Any excess glucose is stored as glycogen in the liver and muscles and saved for such future energy needs as exercise. Once the carbohydrate storage capacity of the liver and muscles is reached, any excess glucose can be stored as fat in adipose tissue.

Carbohydrate Excretion

As previously mentioned, humans do not possess enzymes in the small intestine that can break down fibre. Thus, fibre passes through the small intestine undigested and enters the large intestine, or colon. There, bacteria ferment some previously undigested carbohydrates, causing the production of gases such as hydrogen, methane, and sulphur and a few short-chain fatty acids such as acetic acid, butyric acid, and propionic acid. The cells of the large intestine use these short-chain fatty acids for energy. It is estimated that fermented fibres yield about 1.5 to 2.5 kcal/g.[8,9] This is less than the 4 kcal/g provided by carbohydrates that are digested and absorbed in the small intestine; the discrepancy is due to the fact that fermentation of the

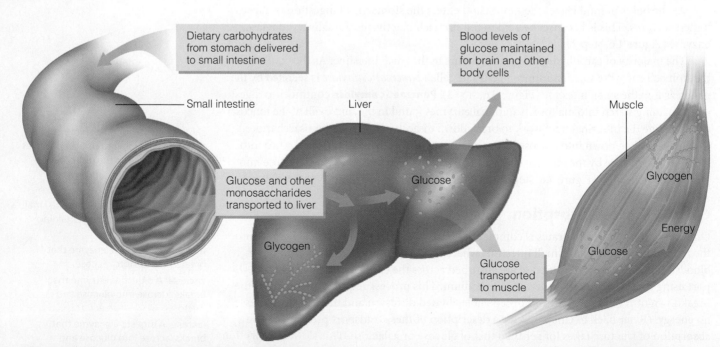

Figure 4.7 Glucose is stored as glycogen in both the liver and muscle. The glycogen stored in the liver maintains blood glucose between meals; muscle glycogen provides immediate energy to the muscle during exercise and cannot be released back into the blood.

fibres in the colon is an anaerobic process, which yields less energy than the aerobic digestive process of other carbohydrates. Obviously, the fibres that remain totally undigested contribute no energy to our bodies. Fibre remaining in the colon adds bulk to our stools and is excreted in feces (Figure 4.6, step 6). In this way, fibre assists in maintaining bowel regularity. The health benefits of fibre are discussed later in this chapter (pages 132–134).

Regulation of Blood Glucose Levels

Our bodies regulate blood glucose levels within a fairly narrow range to provide adequate glucose to the brain and other cells. A number of hormones, including insulin, glucagon, epinephrine, norepinephrine, cortisol, and growth hormone, assist the body with maintaining blood glucose.

When we eat a meal, our blood glucose level rises. But glucose in our blood cannot help the nerves, muscles, and other tissues to function unless it can cross into their cells. Glucose molecules are too large to cross the cell membranes of our tissues independently. To get in, glucose needs assistance from the hormone **insulin**, which is secreted by the beta cells of the pancreas (**Figure 4.8a**). Insulin is transported in the blood to the cells of tissues throughout the body, where it stimulates special carrier proteins, called *glucose transporters,* located in cells. The arrival of insulin at the cell membrane stimulates glucose transporters to travel to the surface of the cell, where they assist in transporting glucose across the cell membrane and into the cell. Insulin can thus be thought of as a key that opens the gates of the cell membrane, enabling the transport of glucose into the cell interior, where it can be used for energy. Insulin also stimulates the liver and muscles to take up glucose and store it as glycogen.

When you have not eaten for some period of time, your blood glucose level declines. This decrease in blood glucose stimulates the alpha cells of the pancreas to secrete another hormone, **glucagon** (**Figure 4.8b**). Glucagon acts in an opposite way to insulin: it causes the liver to convert its stored glycogen into glucose, which is then secreted into the bloodstream and transported to the cells for energy. Glucagon also assists in the breakdown of body proteins to amino acids so the liver can stimulate **gluconeogenesis** (or "generating new glucose"), the production of glucose from amino acids.

Epinephrine, norepinephrine, cortisol, and growth hormone are additional hormones that work to increase blood glucose. Epinephrine and norepinephrine are secreted by the adrenal glands and nerve endings when blood glucose levels are low. They act to increase glycogen breakdown in the liver, resulting in a subsequent increase in the release of glucose into the bloodstream. They also increase gluconeogenesis. These two hormones are also responsible for our "fight or flight" reaction to danger; they are released when we need a burst of energy to respond quickly. Cortisol and growth hormone are secreted by the adrenal glands to act upon liver, muscle, and adipose tissue. Cortisol increases gluconeogenesis and decreases the use of glucose by muscles and other body organs. Growth hormone decreases glucose uptake by the muscles, increases our mobilization and use of fatty acids stored in our adipose tissue, and also increases the liver's output of glucose.

Normally, the effects of these hormones balance each other to maintain blood glucose within a healthy range. If this balance is altered, it can lead to health conditions such as diabetes (pages 145–148) or hypoglycemia (pages 149–150).

RECAP

Carbohydrate digestion starts in the mouth and continues in the small intestine. Glucose and other monosaccharides are absorbed into the bloodstream and travel to the liver, where non-glucose monosaccharides are converted to glucose. Glucose is either used by the cells for energy, converted to glycogen and stored in the liver and muscles for later use, or converted to fat and stored in adipose tissue. Various hormones are involved in regulating blood glucose. Insulin lowers blood glucose levels by facilitating the entry of glucose into cells. Glucagon, epinephrine, norepinephrine, cortisol, and growth hormone raise blood glucose levels by a variety of mechanisms.

insulin A hormone secreted by the beta cells of the pancreas in response to increased blood levels of glucose; facilitates uptake of glucose by body cells.

glucagon A hormone secreted by the alpha cells of the pancreas in response to decreased blood levels of glucose; causes breakdown of liver stores of glycogen into glucose.

gluconeogenesis The generation of glucose from the breakdown of proteins into amino acids.

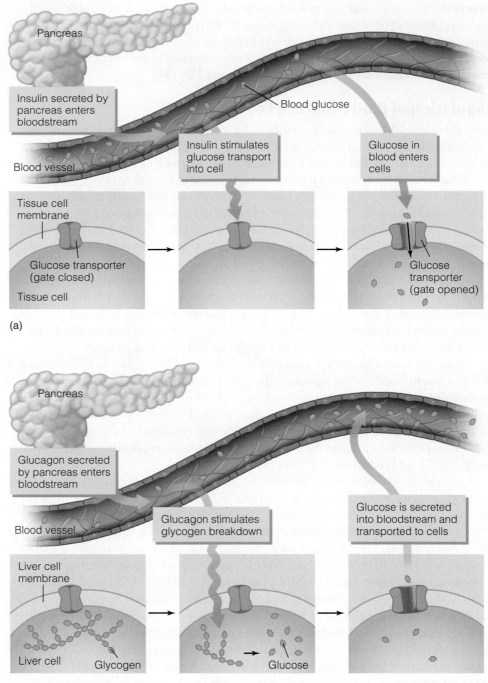

Figure 4.8 Regulation of blood glucose by the hormones insulin and glucagon. (a) When blood glucose levels increase after a meal, the pancreas secretes insulin. Insulin opens gates in the cell membranes of body tissues to allow the passage of glucose into the cell. (b) When blood glucose levels are low, the pancreas secretes glucagon. Glucagon enters the cell, where it stimulates the breakdown of stored glycogen into glucose. This glucose is then released into the bloodstream.

The Glycemic Index Shows How Foods Affect Our Blood Glucose Levels

glycemic index Rating of the potential of foods to raise blood glucose and insulin levels.

The **glycemic index** refers to the potential of foods to raise blood glucose levels. Foods with a high glycemic index cause a sudden surge in blood glucose. This in turn triggers a large increase in insulin, which may be followed by a dramatic drop in blood glucose. Foods with a low glycemic index cause low to moderate fluctuations in blood glucose. When foods are assigned a glycemic index value, they are often compared with the glycemic effect of pure glucose or white bread.

The glycemic index of a food is not always easy to predict. **Figure 4.9** ranks certain foods according to their glycemic index. Do any of these rankings surprise you? Most people assume that foods containing simple sugars have a higher glycemic index than starches, but this is not always the case. For instance, compare the glycemic index for apples and instant potatoes. Although instant potatoes are a starchy food, they have a glycemic index value of 83, while the value for an apple is only 36!

An apple has a much lower glycemic index (36) than a serving of white rice (56).

The type of carbohydrate, the way the food is prepared, and its fat and fibre content can all affect how quickly the body absorbs it. It is important to note that we eat most of our foods combined into a meal. In this case, the glycemic index of the total meal becomes more important than the ranking of each food.

For determining the effect of a food on a person's glucose response, some nutrition experts believe the **glycemic load** is more useful than the glycemic index. The glycemic load of a food is the total grams of carbohydrate it contains multiplied by the glycemic index of that particular carbohydrate. For instance, carrots are recognized as a vegetable having a relatively high glycemic index of about 68; however, the glycemic load of carrots is only 3.[10] This is because there is very little total carbohydrate in a serving of carrots. The low glycemic load of carrots means that carrot consumption is unlikely to cause a significant rise in glucose and insulin.

Why do we care about the glycemic index and glycemic load? Foods or meals with a lower glycemic load are a better choice for someone with diabetes because they will not

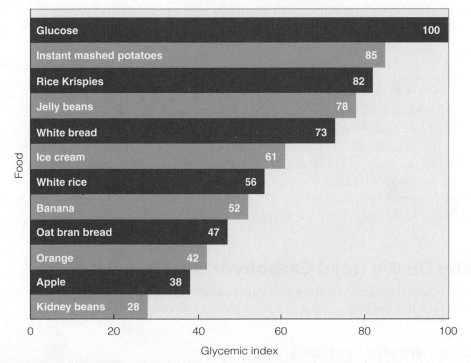

Food

Glucose	100
Instant mashed potatoes	85
Rice Krispies	82
Jelly beans	78
White bread	73
Ice cream	61
White rice	56
Banana	52
Oat bran bread	47
Orange	42
Apple	38
Kidney beans	28

Glycemic index (0, 20, 40, 60, 80, 100)

Figure 4.9 Glycemic index values for various foods as compared to pure glucose.
(*Data adapted from:* Foster-Powell, K., S. H. A. Holt, and J. C. Brand-Miller. 2002. International table of glycemic index and glycemic load values. *Am. J. Clin. Nutr.* 76:5–56.)

glycemic load The amount of carbohydrate in a food multiplied by the glycemic index of the carbohydrate.

trigger dramatic fluctuations in blood glucose. They may also reduce the risk of heart disease and colon cancer because they generally contain more fibre, and it is known that fibre helps decrease fat levels in the blood. Recent studies have shown that people who eat lower-glycemic-index diets have higher levels of high-density lipoprotein, or HDL (a healthy blood lipid), and lower levels of low-density lipoprotein, or LDL (a blood lipid associated with increased risk for heart disease), and their blood glucose values are more likely to be normal.[11-13] Diets with a low glycemic index and load are also associated with a reduced risk for prostate cancer.[14] Despite some encouraging research findings, the glycemic index and glycemic load remain controversial. Many nutrition researchers feel that the evidence supporting their health benefits is weak. In addition, many believe the concepts of the glycemic index/load are too complex for people to apply to their daily lives. Other researchers insist that helping people to choose foods with a lower glycemic index/load is critical to the prevention and treatment of many chronic diseases. Until this controversy is resolved, people are encouraged to eat a variety of fibre-rich and less-processed carbohydrates such as beans and lentils, fresh vegetables, and whole-wheat bread, because we know these forms of carbohydrates are lower in glycemic load and they also contain a multitude of important nutrients.

Did You Know?

The glycemic index (GI) was developed in the early 1980s by a team of researchers at the University of Toronto, led by Dr. David Jenkins. They challenged the notion that all simple carbohydrates cause a rapid rise in blood glucose levels and, conversely, that eating complex carbohydrates results in a slow release of glucose into the bloodstream. They found that carbohydrates in white bread caused subjects' blood glucose to rise higher than those in ice cream and coined the term "glycemic index" to describe the effect of foods on blood glucose levels in the body.[15] Ongoing research by this team has assessed the relevance of using the GI in planning diets and its effects on type 2 diabetes.

Recap

The glycemic index is a value that indicates the potential of foods to raise blood glucose and insulin levels. The glycemic load is the amount of carbohydrate in a food multiplied by the glycemic index of the carbohydrate in that food. Foods with a high glycemic index/load cause sudden surges in blood glucose and insulin, whereas foods with a low glycemic index/load cause low to moderate fluctuations in blood glucose. Diets with a low glycemic index/load are associated with a reduced risk for chronic diseases such as cardiovascular disease, type 2 diabetes, and prostate cancer.

Why Do We Need Carbohydrates?

We have seen that carbohydrates are an important energy source for our bodies. Let's learn more about this and discuss other functions of carbohydrates.

Carbohydrates Provide Energy

Carbohydrates, an excellent source of energy for all of our cells, provide 4 kcal of energy per gram. Some of our cells can also use lipids and even protein for energy if necessary.

Our red blood cells can use only glucose and other monosaccharides, and the brain and other nervous tissues primarily rely on glucose. This is why you get tired, irritable, and shaky when you have not eaten for a prolonged period of time.

However, our red blood cells can use only glucose, and the brain and other nervous tissues rely primarily on glucose. This is why you get tired, irritable, and shaky when you have not eaten carbohydrates for a prolonged period of time.

Carbohydrates Fuel Daily Activity

Many popular diets—such as Dr. Atkins' New Diet Revolution and the Sugar Busters plan—are based on the idea that our bodies actually "prefer" to use dietary fats and/or protein for energy. They claim that current carbohydrate recommendations are much higher than we really need.

In reality, the body relies mostly on both carbohydrates and fats for energy. In fact, as shown in **Figure 4.10**, our bodies always use some combination of carbohydrates and fats to fuel daily activities.

Fats are the predominant energy source used by our bodies at rest and during low-intensity activities such as sitting, standing, and walking. Even during rest, however, our brain cells and red blood cells still rely on glucose.

Carbohydrates Fuel Exercise

When we exercise, whether running, briskly walking, bicycling, or performing any other activity that causes us to breathe harder and sweat, we begin to use more glucose than lipids. Whereas lipid breakdown is a slow process and requires oxygen, we can break down glucose very quickly either with or without oxygen. Even during very intense exercise, when less oxygen is available, we can still break down glucose very quickly for energy. That's why when you are exercising at maximal effort, carbohydrates are providing the majority of the energy your body requires.

If you are physically active, it is important to eat enough carbohydrates to provide energy for your brain, red blood cells, and muscles. In Chapter 15, we discuss in more detail the carbohydrate recommendations for active people. In general, if you do not eat enough carbohydrate to support regular exercise, your body will have to rely on fat and protein as alternative energy sources (the consequences of which are discussed shortly). If you or someone you know is trying to lose weight, you may be wondering whether exercising at a lower intensity will result in more stored fat being burned for energy. This is a question that researchers are still trying to answer. Weight-loss studies show that, to lose weight and keep it off, it is important to exercise daily. A low-intensity activity such as walking is generally recommended because it is easy to do and can be done for longer periods of time than high-intensity exercise; thus, it can result in the expenditure of more energy. Also, we know that fat stores provide much of the energy we need for walking. However, a study of highly trained athletes found that they actually lost more body fat when they performed very-high-intensity exercise![16] Although the exact mechanism for this fat loss is unknown, the researchers speculated that very-high-intensity exercise activated enzymes that increased the metabolism of fat, leading to a reduction in body fat. Based on the evidence currently available, the recommended activities for weight loss combine aerobic-type exercises, such as walking, jogging, or bicycling, with strength-building exercises. (For more information on weight loss, see Chapter 14.)

Low Carbohydrate Intake Can Lead to Ketoacidosis

When we do not eat enough carbohydrates, the body seeks an alternative source of fuel for the brain and begins to break down stored fat. This process, called **ketosis**, produces an

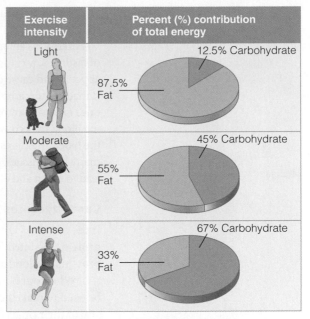

Exercise intensity	Percent (%) contribution of total energy
Light	12.5% Carbohydrate / 87.5% Fat
Moderate	45% Carbohydrate / 55% Fat
Intense	67% Carbohydrate / 33% Fat

Figure 4.10 Amounts of carbohydrate and fat used during light, moderate, and intense exercise.
(*Data adapted from:* Romijn, J. A., E. F. Coyle, L. S. Sidossis, A. Gastaldelli, J. F. Horowitz, E. Endert, and R. R. Wolfe. 1993. Regulation of endogenous fat and carbohydrate metabolism in relation to exercise intensity and duration. *Am. J. Physiol.* 265 [Endocrinol. Metab. 28]:E380–E391.)

When we exercise at relatively high intensities, or perform any other activity that causes us to breathe harder and sweat, we begin to use more glucose than fat.

ketosis The process by which the breakdown of fat during fasting results in the production of ketones.

alternative fuel called **ketones**. The metabolic process of ketosis is discussed in more detail in Chapter 7.

Ketosis is an important mechanism for providing energy to the brain during situations of fasting, low carbohydrate intake, or vigorous exercise.[17] However, ketones also suppress appetite and cause dehydration and acetone breath (the breath smells like nail polish remover). If inadequate carbohydrate intake continues for an extended period of time, the body will produce excessive amounts of ketones. Because many ketones are acids, high ketone levels cause the blood to become very acidic, leading to a condition called **ketoacidosis**. The high acidity of the blood interferes with basic body functions, causes the loss of lean body mass, and damages many body tissues. People with untreated diabetes are at high risk for ketoacidosis, which can lead to coma and even death. (See pages 145–149 for further details about diabetes.)

Carbohydrates Spare Protein

If the diet does not provide enough carbohydrate, the body will make its own glucose from protein. As noted earlier, this process, called gluconeogenesis, involves breaking down the proteins in blood and tissues into amino acids, then converting them to glucose.

When our bodies use proteins for energy, the amino acids from these proteins cannot be used to make new cells, repair tissue damage, support the immune system, or perform any of their other functions. During periods of starvation or when eating a diet that is very low in carbohydrate, our body will take amino acids from the blood first, and then from other tissues such as muscles and the heart, liver, and kidneys. Using amino acids in this manner over a prolonged period of time can cause serious, possibly irreversible, damage to these organs. (See Chapter 6 for more details on using protein for energy.)

Complex Carbohydrates Have Health Benefits

Complex carbohydrates contain fibre and other nutrients that can reduce the risk for obesity, heart disease, and type 2 diabetes. The relationship between carbohydrates and these chronic diseases is the subject of considerable controversy. On the one hand, proponents of low-carbohydrate diets claim that eating carbohydrates makes you overweight and promotes changes in blood lipids and insulin that contribute to heart disease and type 2 diabetes. However, fat is more than twice as energy-dense as carbohydrate, and anyone who consumes extra kilocalories, whether in the form of sugar, starch, protein, or fat, may eventually become obese. As we'll discuss later in this chapter, studies indicate that people who are obese have a significantly increased risk of both heart disease and type 2 diabetes. On the other hand, eating carbohydrates that are high in fibre and other nutrients has been shown to reduce the risk for obesity, heart disease, and type 2 diabetes. Thus, all carbohydrates are not bad, and complex carbohydrates are significantly beneficial. Even small amounts of simple carbohydrates can be included in a healthy diet. People who are very active and need more calories can eat more simple carbohydrates, whereas those who are older, less active, or overweight should limit their consumption of simple carbohydrates and focus on complex carbohydrates.

Fibre Helps Us Stay Healthy

Although we cannot digest fibre, it is still an important substance in our diet. Research indicates that it helps us stay healthy and may play a role in preventing many digestive and chronic diseases. The potential benefits of fibre consumption include the following:

- May reduce the risk of colon cancer. While there is still some controversy surrounding this issue, many researchers believe that fibre binds cancer-causing substances and speeds their elimination from the colon.
- Helps prevent hemorrhoids, constipation, and other intestinal problems by keeping our stools moist and soft. Fibre gives gut muscles "something to push on" and makes it easier to eliminate stools.

ketones Substances produced during the breakdown of fat when carbohydrate intake is insufficient to meet energy needs. Provide an alternative energy source for the brain when glucose levels are low.

ketoacidosis A condition in which excessive ketones are present in the blood, causing the blood to become very acidic, which alters basic body functions and damages tissues. Untreated ketoacidosis can be fatal. This condition is found in individuals with untreated diabetes mellitus.

Brown rice is a good source of dietary fibre.

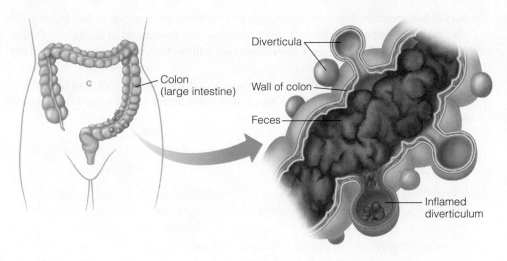

Figure 4.11 Diverticulosis occurs when bulging pockets form in the wall of the colon. These pockets become infected and inflamed, demanding proper treatment. *Data from: Johnson, M., Human Biology: Concepts and Current Issues, 5/e,* Fig. 3.3, Fig. 13.5, and page 88, Copyright © 2010 Benjamin Cummings. Reprinted by permission of Pearson Education, Inc.

- Reduces the risk of *diverticulosis,* a condition that is caused in part by trying to eliminate small, hard stools. A great deal of pressure must be generated in the large intestine to pass hard stools. This increased pressure weakens intestinal walls, causing them to bulge outward and form pockets (**Figure 4.11**). Feces and fibrous materials can get trapped in these pockets, which become infected and inflamed. This painful condition is typically treated with antibiotics or surgery.
- May reduce the risk of heart disease by delaying or blocking the absorption of dietary cholesterol into the bloodstream (**Figure 4.12**).

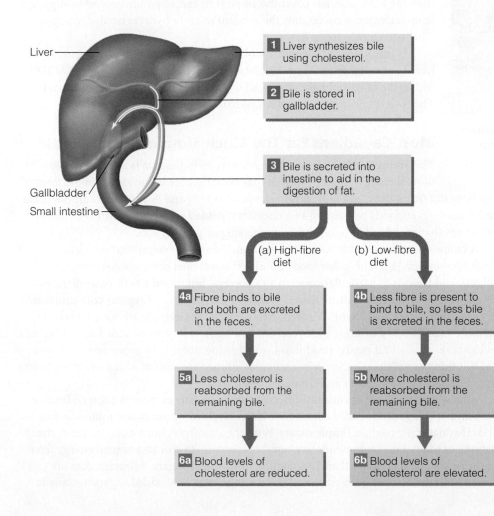

Figure 4.12 How fibre might help decrease blood cholesterol levels. (a) When eating a high-fibre diet, fibre binds to the bile that is produced from cholesterol, resulting in relatively more cholesterol being excreted in the feces. (b) When a lower-fibre diet is consumed, less fibre (and thus cholesterol) is bound to bile and excreted in the feces.

- May enhance weight loss, as eating a high-fibre diet causes a person to feel fuller. Fibre absorbs water, expands in our intestine, and slows the movement of food through the upper part of the digestive tract. People who eat a fibre-rich diet tend to eat fewer fatty and sugary foods.
- May lower the risk of type 2 diabetes. In slowing digestion and absorption, fibre also slows the release of glucose into the blood. It thereby improves the body's regulation of insulin production and blood glucose levels.

RecaP

Carbohydrates are an important energy source at rest and during exercise and provide 4 kcal of energy per gram. Carbohydrates are necessary in the diet to spare body protein and prevent ketosis. Complex carbohydrates contain fibre and other nutrients that can reduce the risk for obesity, heart disease, and type 2 diabetes. Fibre helps prevent hemorrhoids, constipation, and diverticulosis, may reduce risk of colon cancer, and may assist with weight loss.

Many popular diets claim that current carbohydrate recommendations are much higher than we really need.

added sugars Sugars and syrups that are added to food during processing or preparation.

Foods with added sugars, such as candy, have lower levels of vitamins, minerals, and fibre than foods that naturally contain simple sugars.

How Much Carbohydrate Should We Eat?

Carbohydrates are an important part of a balanced, healthy diet. The Recommended Dietary Allowance (RDA) for carbohydrate is based on the amount of glucose the brain uses.[8] The current RDA for carbohydrate for adults 19 years of age and older is 130 g of carbohydrate per day. It is important to emphasize that this RDA does not cover the amount of carbohydrate needed to support daily activities; it covers only the amount of carbohydrate needed to supply adequate glucose to the brain.

As introduced in Chapter 1, carbohydrates and the other macronutrients have been assigned an Acceptable Macronutrient Distribution Range (AMDR). This is the range of intake associated with a decreased risk of chronic diseases. The AMDR for carbohydrates is 45% to 65% of total energy intake.

Most Canadians Eat Too Much Simple Carbohydrate

The average carbohydrate intake per person in Canada is approximately 50% of total energy intake.[18] Most of that carbohydrate is consumed in the form of breads, pasta, rice, grains, and milk; however, between 16% and 20% of total carbohydrate intake comes from foods containing added sugars.[19] **Added sugars** are defined as sugars and syrups that are added to foods during processing or preparation.

A common source of added sugars in the Canadian diet is sweetened soft drinks, which account for 11.3% of "other food" calories.[18] Sweetened beverage consumption by children and teens is of particular concern. On average, boys aged 14–18 years drink one 355 mL can of a regular soft drink daily.[20] Consider that one can of regular cola contains 33.4 g of sugar, or almost 35 mL. If a teenage boy drinks the average amount, he is consuming more than 11 750 g of sugar each year! Other common sources of added sugars include cookies, cakes, pies, and candy. In addition, a surprising number of processed foods you may not think of as "sweet" actually contain a significant amount of added sugar, including many brands of peanut butter and flavoured rice mixes.

Added sugars are not chemically different from naturally occurring sugars. However, foods and beverages with added sugars have lower levels of vitamins and minerals than foods that naturally contain simple sugars. With these nutrient limitations in mind, the Institute of Medicine recommends that our diets contain 25% or less of total energy from simple sugars, with no more than 10% coming from added sugars. Although data are limited in Canada, it has been estimated that average intakes of added sugars in Canada are approximately 13% of total energy intake.[21] People who are very physically active have a higher daily energy expenditure and therefore are able to consume relatively more added sugars, whereas smaller or less active people should consume relatively less. The Nutrition Facts table found on products includes a listing of total sugars, but does not distinguish between added and naturally occurring sugars. Thus, you should check the ingredient list. (See Highlight: Forms of Sugars Commonly Used in Foods for a list of terms indicating added sugars.) To eat a diet low in added sugars, limit foods in which a form of added sugar is listed as one of the first few ingredients on the label.

Simple Carbohydrates Are Blamed for Many Health Problems

Why do simple carbohydrates have such a bad reputation? First, they are known to contribute to tooth decay. Second, they have been criticized as a possible cause of hyperactivity in children. Third, many researchers believe that eating a lot of simple carbohydrates increases the levels of unhealthy lipids in our blood, increasing our risk for heart disease. High intakes of simple carbohydrates have also been blamed for causing diabetes and obesity. Let's now learn the truth about these accusations related to simple carbohydrates.

HIGHLIGHT

Forms of Sugars Commonly Used in Foods

Brown sugar   A highly refined sweetener made up of approximately 99% sucrose and produced by adding either molasses or burnt table sugar to white table sugar for colouring and flavour.

Concentrated fruit juice sweetener   A form of sweetener made with concentrated fruit juice, commonly pear juice.

Confectioner's sugar   A highly refined, finely ground white sugar; also referred to as powdered sugar.

Corn sweeteners   A general term for any sweetener made with corn starch.

Corn syrup   A syrup produced by the partial hydrolysis of corn starch.

Dextrose   An alternative term for glucose.

Fructose   A monosaccharide that occurs in fruits and vegetables. Also called levulose, or fruit sugar.

Galactose   A monosaccharide that joins with glucose to create lactose.

Glucose   The most abundant monosaccharide; it is the preferred source of energy for the brain and an important source of energy for all cells.

Granulated sugar   Another term for white sugar or table sugar.

High-fructose corn syrup   A type of corn syrup in which part of the sucrose is converted to fructose, making it sweeter than sucrose or regular corn syrup; most high-fructose corn syrup contains 42% to 55% fructose.

Honey   A sweet, sticky liquid sweetener made by bees from the nectar of flowers; contains glucose and fructose.

Invert sugar   A sugar created by heating a sucrose syrup with a small amount of acid. Inverting sucrose results in its breakdown into glucose and fructose, which reduces the size of the sugar crystals. Because of its smooth texture, it is used in making candies such as fondant and some syrups.

Lactose   A disaccharide formed by one molecule of glucose and one molecule of galactose. Occurs naturally in milk and other dairy products.

Levulose   Another term for fructose, or fruit sugar.

Maltose   A disaccharide consisting of two molecules of glucose. Does not generally occur independently in foods but results as a by-product of digestion. Also called malt sugar.

Mannitol   A type of sugar alcohol.

Maple sugar   A sugar made by boiling maple syrup.

Molasses   A thick brown syrup that is separated from raw sugar during manufacturing. It is considered the least refined form of sucrose.

Natural sweeteners   A general term used for any naturally occurring sweeteners, such as sucrose, honey, and raw sugar.

Raw sugar   The sugar that results from the processing of sugar beets or sugarcane. It is approximately 96% to 98% sucrose. True raw sugar contains impurities and is not stable in storage; the raw sugar available to consumers has been purified to yield an edible sugar.

Sorbitol   A type of sugar alcohol.

Turbinado sugar   The form of raw sugar that is purified and safe for human consumption. Sold as "Sugar in the Raw" in Canada.

White sugar   Another name for sucrose, or table sugar.

Xylitol   A type of sugar alcohol.

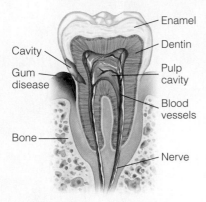

Figure 4.13 Eating simple carbohydrates can cause an increase in cavities and gum disease. This is because bacteria in the mouth consume simple carbohydrates present on the teeth and gums and produce acids, which eat away at these tissues.

Simple Carbohydrates Cause Tooth Decay

Simple carbohydrates do play a role in dental problems because the bacteria that cause tooth decay thrive on them. These bacteria produce acids that eat away at tooth enamel and can eventually cause cavities and gum disease (**Figure 4.13**). Eating sticky foods that adhere to teeth—such as caramels, crackers, sugary cereals, and licorice—and sipping sweetened beverages over a period of time increase the risk of tooth decay. This means that people shouldn't slowly sip soda or juice and that babies should not be put to sleep with a bottle unless it contains water. As we have seen, even breast milk contains sugar, which can slowly drip onto the baby's gums. As a result, infants should not routinely be allowed to fall asleep at the breast.

To reduce your risk for tooth decay, brush your teeth after each meal and especially after drinking sugary drinks and eating candy. Drinking fluoridated water and using a fluoride toothpaste also will help protect your teeth.

There Is No Link Between Simple Carbohydrates and Hyperactivity in Children

Although many people believe that eating simple carbohydrates, particularly sugar, causes hyperactivity and other behavioural problems in children, there is little scientific evidence to support this claim. However, it is important to emphasize that most studies of sugar and children's behaviour have only looked at the effects of sugar a few hours after ingestion. We know very little about the long-term effects of sugar intake on the behaviour of children. Behavioural and learning problems are complex issues, most likely caused by a multitude of factors. Because of this complexity, the Institute of Medicine has stated that, overall, there currently does not appear to be enough evidence that eating too much sugar causes hyperactivity or other behavioural problems in children.[8] Thus, a Tolerable Upper Intake Level has not been set for sugar.

High Simple Carbohydrates Intake Can Lead to Unhealthy Levels of Blood Lipids

Research evidence suggests that consuming a diet high in simple carbohydrates, particularly fructose, can lead to unhealthy changes in blood lipids. You will learn more about blood lipids (including cholesterol and lipoproteins) in Chapter 5. Briefly, higher intakes of simple carbohydrates are associated with increases in our blood of both triglycerides and LDLs; LDL is commonly referred to as "bad cholesterol." At the same time, high simple carbohydrate intake appears to *decrease* our HDLs, which are protective and are often referred to as "good cholesterol."[8,22] These changes are of concern, as increased levels of triglycerides and LDLs and decreased levels of HDLs are known risk factors for heart disease. However, there is not enough scientific evidence at the present time to state with confidence that eating a diet high in simple carbohydrates causes heart disease. Based on our current knowledge, it is prudent for a person at risk for heart disease to eat a diet low in simple carbohydrates. Because high-fructose corn syrup is a component of many processed foods, careful label reading is advised.

High Simple Carbohydrate Intake Does Not Cause Diabetes but May Contribute to Obesity

There is no scientific evidence that eating a diet high in simple carbohydrates causes diabetes. In fact, studies examining the relationship between simple carbohydrate intake and type 2 diabetes are equivocal, reporting either no association between simple carbohydrate intake and diabetes, an increased risk of diabetes associated with increased simple carbohydrate intake and weight gain, or a decreased risk of diabetes with increased simple carbohydrate intake.[23-25] However, people who have diabetes need to moderate their intake of simple carbohydrates and closely monitor their blood glucose levels.

We have somewhat more evidence linking simple carbohydrate intake with obesity. For example, a recent study found that overweight children consumed more sugared soft drinks than did children of normal weight.[26] Another study found that for every extra sugared soft drink consumed by a child per day, the risk of obesity increases by 60%.[27] We also know that if you consume more energy than you expend, you will gain weight. It makes intuitive sense that people who consume extra energy from high-sugar foods are at risk for obesity, just as people who consume extra energy from fat or protein gain weight. In addition to the increased potential for obesity, another major concern about high-sugar diets is that they tend to be low in nutrient density because the intake of high-sugar foods tends to replace that of more nutritious foods. The relationship between sugared soft drinks and obesity is highly controversial and discussed in more detail in the Evidence-informed Decision Making section on pages 157–159.

Recap

The RDA for carbohydrate is 130 g per day; this amount is sufficient only to supply adequate glucose to the brain. The AMDR for carbohydrate is 45% to 65% of total energy intake. Added sugars are sugars and syrups added to foods during processing or preparation. Our intake of simple carbohydrates should be 25% or less of our total energy intake each day, with no more than 10% coming from added sugars. Simple carbohydrates contribute to tooth decay but do not appear to cause hyperactivity in children. Higher intakes of simple carbohydrates are associated with increases in triglycerides and low-density lipoproteins. Diets high in simple carbohydrates are not confirmed to cause diabetes but may contribute to obesity.

Most Canadians Eat Too Little Complex Carbohydrate

Do you eat enough complex carbohydrate each day? If you are like most people in Canada, you eat fewer than five servings of fruits or vegetables (including legumes) each day; this is far below the recommended amount.

Breads and cereals are another potential source of complex carbohydrates, and they're part of most Canadians' diets. But are the breads and cereals you eat made with whole grains? If you're not sure, check out the ingredients lists on the labels of your favourite breads and breakfast cereals. Do they list *whole-wheat flour* or just *wheat flour*? And what's the difference? To help you answer this question, we've defined some terms in Table 4.2 commonly used on labels for breads and cereals. As you can see, whole-wheat flour is made from whole grains: only the germ and some of the bran have been removed. In contrast, the term *wheat flour* can be used to signify a flour that has been highly refined, with the bran and other fibre-rich portions removed.

Whole-grain foods provide more nutrients and fibre than foods made with enriched flour.

Table 4.2 Terms Used to Describe Grains and Cereals on Nutrition Labels

Flour, white flour, enriched flour or enriched white flour[1]	Refined flour made from wheat that has been fortified with added thiamine, riboflavin, niacin, folic acid, and iron and may be bleached
Whole wheat flour or entire wheat flour[1]	Flour made from wheat from which a part of the outer bran may have been separated; must contain not less than 95% of the total weight of the wheat from which it was milled
Whole grain[2]	Contain all parts of the grain (bran, germ, and endosperm) in the same relative proportions found in the original grain
Refined grains[2]	Whole grains that have had the germ and the bran removed
Enriched white bread[1]	Bread made from enriched flour and fortified with skim milk solids, whey powder or proteins from pea or soy
Whole-grain bread[2]	Bread made from whole-grain flour
Whole-wheat bread[1]	Bread which is made from not less than 60% whole wheat flour

[1]*Data adapted from:* Guide to Food Labelling and Advertising - www.inspection.gc.ca/english/fssa/labeti/guide/toce.shtml, Canadian Food Inspection Agency, September 21, 2011. Reproduced with the permission of the Minister of Public Works and Government Services Canada, 2012.
[2]Health Canada. Whole Grains–Get the Facts. Health Canada, 2012. Reproduced with the permission of the Minister of Health, 2012.

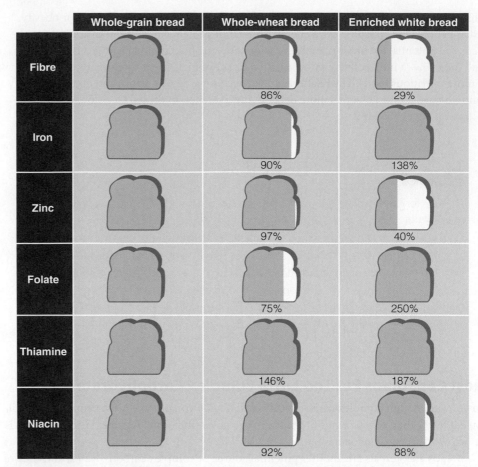

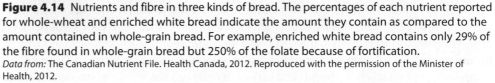

Figure 4.14 Nutrients and fibre in three kinds of bread. The percentages of each nutrient reported for whole-wheat and enriched white bread indicate the amount they contain as compared to the amount contained in whole-grain bread. For example, enriched white bread contains only 29% of the fibre found in whole-grain bread but 250% of the folate because of fortification.
Data from: The Canadian Nutrient File. Health Canada, 2012. Reproduced with the permission of the Minister of Health, 2012.

In addition to stripping a grain of its fibre, the refining process reduces many of the grain's original nutrients. To make up for some of the lost nutrients, manufacturers sometimes enrich the product. **Enriched foods** are foods in which nutrients that were lost during processing have been added back so the food meets a specified standard. Notice that the terms *enriched* and *fortified* are not synonymous: **fortified foods** have nutrients added that did not originally exist in the food (or existed in insignificant amounts). For example, some breakfast cereals have been fortified with iron, a mineral that is not present in cereals naturally. **Figure 4.14** compares the nutrients and fibre in whole-grain bread versus whole-wheat and enriched white breads.

We Need at Least 25 Grams of Fibre Daily

How much fibre do we need? The Adequate Intake for fibre is 25 g per day for women and 38 g per day for men, or 14 g of fibre for every 1000 kcal per day that a person eats. Most people in Canada eat between 13 to 22 g of fibre each day. Although fibre supplements are available, it is best to get fibre from food because foods contain additional nutrients such as vitamins and minerals.

As recommended in *Eating Well with Canada's Food Guide*, eating at least half of your grain products as whole grains and eating the suggested number of vegetables and fruit each day will ensure that you get enough fibre-rich carbohydrate foods in your diet. **Figure 4.15** lists some common foods and their fibre content. You can use this information to design a diet that includes adequate fibre.

enriched foods Foods in which nutrients that were lost during processing have been added back so the food meets a specified standard.

fortified foods Foods in which nutrients are added that did not originally exist in the food or existed in insignificant amounts.

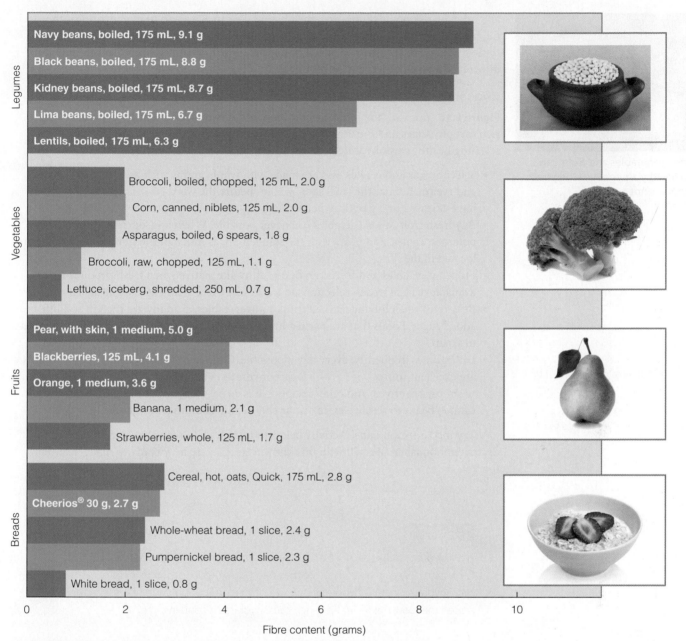

Figure 4.15 Fibre content of common foods. *Notes:* The Adequate Intake for fibre is 25 g per day for women and 38 g per day for men. The serving sizes shown are those recommended by *Eating Well with Canada's Food Guide.*
Data from: The Canadian Nutrient File. Health Canada, 2012. Reproduced with the permission of the Minister of Health, 2012.

It is important to drink plenty of fluid as you increase your fibre intake, as fibre binds with water to soften stools. Inadequate fluid intake with a high-fibre diet can actually result in hard, dry stools that are difficult to pass through the colon. At least 3L of fluid each day are commonly recommended.

Can you eat too much fibre? Excessive fibre consumption can lead to problems such as intestinal gas, bloating, and constipation. Because fibre binds with water, it causes the body to eliminate more water in the feces, so a very-high-fibre diet could result in dehydration. Fibre also binds with minerals, so a high-fibre diet can reduce our absorption of important nutrients such as iron, zinc, and calcium. However, mineral binding does not seem to be a problem when mineral intake is adequate. In children, some older adults, the chronically ill,

Frozen vegetables and fruits can be a healthy alternative when fresh produce is not available.

and other at-risk populations, extreme fibre intake can even lead to malnutrition—they feel full before they have eaten enough to provide adequate energy and nutrients. So whereas some societies are accustomed to a very-high-fibre diet, most people in Canada find it difficult to tolerate more than 50 g of fibre per day.

Choosing Complex Carbohydrates

Figure 4.16 compares the food and fibre content of two diets, one high in complex, fibre-rich carbohydrates and the other high in simple carbohydrates. Here are some hints for selecting healthy carbohydrate sources:

- Select breads and cereals that are made with whole grains such as wheat, oats, barley, and rye (make sure the label says "whole" before the word *grain*). Choose foods that have at least 2 or 3 g of fibre per serving.
- Buy fresh fruits and vegetables whenever possible. When appropriate, eat foods such as potatoes, apples, and pears with the skin left on, as much of the fibre and nutrients are located in the skin.
- Frozen vegetables and fruits can be a healthy alternative when fresh produce is not available. Check frozen selections to make sure there is no extra sugar or salt added.
- Be careful when buying canned fruits and vegetables, as many are high in sodium and added sugar. Foods that are packed in their own juice are healthier than those packed in syrup.
- Eat legumes frequently, every day if possible. Canned or fresh beans, peas, and lentils are excellent sources of fibre-rich carbohydrates, vitamins, and minerals. Add them to soups, casseroles, and other recipes—it is an easy way to eat more of them. Rinse canned beans to remove extra salt or choose low-sodium alternatives.

Try the Nutrition Label Activity below to learn how to recognize various carbohydrates on food labels. Armed with this knowledge, you are now ready to make healthier food choices.

RECAP

The Adequate Intake for fibre is 25 g per day for women and 38 g per day for men. Most Canadians only eat half of the fibre they need each day. Foods high in fibre and complex carbohydrates include whole grains and cereals, fruits, and vegetables. The more processed the food, the fewer fibre-rich carbohydrates it contains.

NUTRITION LABEL ACTIVITY

Recognizing Carbohydrates on the Label

Figure 4.17 on page 142 shows labels for two breakfast cereals. The cereal on the left (a) is a whole-grain product with no added sugar, whereas the one on the right (b) is a processed and sweetened cereal. Consider the information shown and work through the questions below.

Thinking Critically

1. Compare the total carbohydrate composition between the two products.

2. Examine the information listed as a subgroup on the label under total carbohydrate. How much sugar and how much fibre does each cereal contain?

3. What is the % Daily Value for carbohydrates for each cereal? What does this number mean?

4. For each cereal, calculate the number of calories and percentage of total calories per serving that come from carbohydrates.

5. Which cereal would you recommend?

High Complex Carbohydrate Diet	High Simple Carbohydrate Diet

Breakfast:
40 g Cheerios
250 mL skim milk
2 slices whole-wheat toast
with 15 mL light margarine
1 medium banana
250 mL fresh orange juice

Breakfast:
40 g Fruit Loops cereal
250 mL skim milk
2 slices white bread toasted,
with 15 mL light margarine
250 mL fresh orange juice

Lunch:
250 mL low-fat blueberry
yogourt
Tuna sandwich (2 slices
whole-wheat bread; 63 mL
tuna packed in water,
drained; 5 mL Dijon mustard;
10 mL low-calorie
mayonnaise)
2 carrots, raw, with peel
250 mL raw cauliflower
15 mL peppercorn ranch
salad dressing
(for dipping vegetables)

Lunch:
McDonald's Quarter Pounder—
1 sandwich
1 large order French fries
500 mL cola beverage
30 jelly beans

Snack:
750 mL cups non-fat popcorn

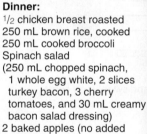

Snack:
1 cinnamon raisin bagel (9 cm
diameter)
30 mL cream cheese
250 mL low-fat strawberry
yogourt

Dinner:
1/2 chicken breast roasted
250 mL brown rice, cooked
250 mL cooked broccoli
Spinach salad
(250 mL chopped spinach,
1 whole egg white, 2 slices
turkey bacon, 3 cherry
tomatoes, and 30 mL creamy
bacon salad dressing)
2 baked apples (no added
sugar)

Dinner:
1 whole chicken breast,
roasted
500 mL mixed green salad
30 mL ranch salad dressing
1 serving macaroni and
cheese
375 mL cola beverage
Cheesecake (1/9 of cake)

(No Snack)

Late Night Snack:
500 mL gelatin dessert
(cherry flavoured)
3 raspberry oatmeal no-fat
cookies

Nutrient Analysis:
2034 kcal
54% of energy from carbohydrates
27% of energy from fat
19% of energy from protein
32.6 grams of dietary fibre

Nutrient Analysis:
3956 kcal
62% of energy from carbohydrates
24% of energy from fat
14% of energy from protein
11.2 grams of dietary fibre

Figure 4.16 Comparison of two high-carbohydrate diets. (*Note*: Diets were analyzed using eaTracker (Dieticians of Canada).)

Nutrition Facts
Valeur Nutritive

Serving Size: 1/3 cup (40 g) / portion
1/3 tasse (40 g)

Amount	% Daily Value
Teneur	% Valeur Quotidienne
Calories / Calories 150	
Fat / Lipides 2.5 g	4%
Saturated / Saturés 0.5 g	
+ Trans / Trans 0 g	3%
Cholesterol / Cholestérol 0 mg	0%
Sodium / Sodium 4 mg	0%
Carbohydrates / Glucides 27 g	9%
Fibre / Fibres 4 g	16%
Sugars / Sucres 1 g	
Protein / Protéines 6 g	
Vitamin A / Vitamin A	0%
Vitamin C / Vitamin C	0%
Calcium / Calcium	2%
Iron / Fer	15%

(a)

Nutrition Facts
Valeur Nutritive

Serving Size: 3/4 cup (30 g) / portion 3/4 tasse (30 g)

Amount		% Daily Value
Teneur		% Valeur Quotidienne
	Cereal Only	With 1/2 Cup Skim Milk
Calories / Calories	120	160
Fat / Lipides 2.5 g*	2%	2%
Saturated / Saturés 0 g		
+ Trans / Trans 0 g	0%	0%
Cholesterol / Cholestérol 0 mg	0%	1%
Sodium / Sodium 220 mg	9%	12%
Carbohydrates / Glucides 26 g	9%	11%
Fibre / Fibres 1 g	3%	3%
Sugars / Sucres 13 g		
Protein / Protéines 1 g		
Vitamin A / Vitamin A	0%	4%
Vitamin C / Vitamin C	0%	2%
Calcium / Calcium	0%	15%
Iron / Fer	25%	25%
Vitamin D	0%	25%
Thiamine	25%	25%
Riboflavin	25%	35%
Niacin	25%	25%
Vitamin B$_6$	25%	25%
Folate	25%	25%
Zinc	25%	25%
*Amount in cereal		

(b)

Figure 4.17 Labels for two breakfast cereals: (a) whole-grain cereal with no sugar added; (b) processed and sweetened cereal.

What's the Story on Alternative Sweeteners?

Most of us love sweets but want to avoid the extra kilocalories and tooth decay that go along with eating simple sugars. Remember that all carbohydrates, whether simple or complex, contain 4 kcal of energy per gram. Because sweeteners such as sucrose, fructose, honey, and brown sugar contribute energy, they are called **nutritive sweeteners**.

Other nutritive sweeteners include the *sugar alcohols* such as mannitol, sorbitol, isomalt, and xylitol. Popular in sugar-free gums, mints, and diabetic candies, sugar alcohols are less sweet than sucrose (**Figure 4.18**). Foods with sugar alcohols have health benefits that foods made with sugars do not have, such as a reduced glycemic response and decreased risk of dental caries. Also, because sugar alcohols are absorbed slowly and incompletely from the intestine, they provide less energy than sugar, usually only 2 to 3 kcal of energy per gram. However, because they are not completely absorbed from the intestine, they can attract water into the large intestine and cause diarrhea.

nutritive sweeteners Sweeteners such as sucrose, fructose, honey, and brown sugar that contribute calories (or energy).

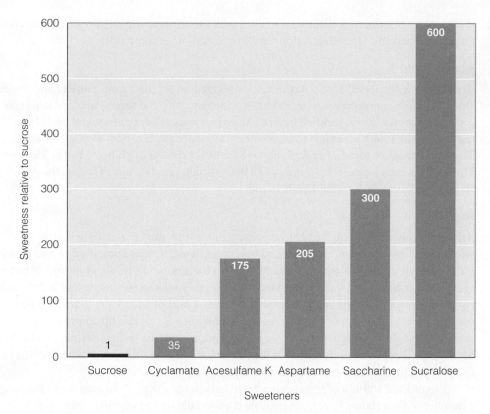

Figure 4.18 Relative sweetness of alternative sweeteners as compared to sucrose.
(*Data adapted from:* Food Safety Network. 2012. *Sweeteners.* Available at www.uoguelph.ca/foodsafetynetwork/sweeteners (accessed March 6, 2012).

Alternative Sweeteners Are Non-Nutritive

A number of other products have been developed to sweeten foods without promoting tooth decay and weight gain. As these products provide little or no energy, they are called **non-nutritive**, or **alternative sweeteners**.

Limited Use of Alternative Sweeteners Is Not Harmful

Contrary to popular belief, alternative sweeteners have been determined as safe for adults, children, and individuals with diabetes. Women who are pregnant should discuss the use of alternative sweeteners with their healthcare provider. In general, it appears safe for most pregnant women to consume alternative sweeteners in amounts within Health Canada guidelines. The **Acceptable Daily Intake (ADI)** is an estimate made by Health Canada of the amount of a sweetener that someone can consume each day over a lifetime without adverse effects. The estimates are based on studies conducted on laboratory animals, and they include a 100-fold safety factor. It is important to emphasize that actual intake by humans is typically well below the ADI.

In recent years, concerns have been raised about the increased ingestion of artificial sweeteners and their effects on appetite and food intake.[28] The number of food products containing non-caloric artificial sweeteners has risen dramatically over the past decade and there is increasing evidence that this might be a contributing factor in the epidemic of obesity in North America.[29] However, additional research is needed to determine the mechanisms by which this might occur. In the meantime, it is wise to limit your intake of foods containing artificial sweeteners to ensure that more nutrient-dense foods are not excluded from your diet.

Saccharin

Discovered in the late 1800s, *saccharin* is about 300 times sweeter than sucrose (see Figure 4.18). Evidence to suggest that saccharin may cause bladder tumours in rats surfaced in the 1970s; however, more than 20 years of scientific research has shown that saccharin is not related to bladder cancer in humans. Health Canada's scientists have thoroughly reviewed

Contrary to recent media reports claiming severe health consequences related to consumption of alternative sweeteners, major health agencies have determined that these products are safe for us to consume.

non-nutritive sweeteners Also called *alternative sweeteners;* manufactured sweeteners that provide little or no energy.

Acceptable Daily Intake (ADI) An estimate made by Health Canada of the amount of a non-nutritive sweetener that someone can consume each day over a lifetime without adverse effects.

the scientific information available and as a result are considering relisting saccharin in the Canadian Food and Drug Regulations to allow its use in certain foods.

Acesulfame-K

Acesulfame-K (or acesulfame potassium) is marketed under the names Sunette and Sweet One. It is a kilocalorie-free sweetener that is approximately 200 times sweeter than sugar. It is used to sweeten gums, candies, beverages, instant tea, coffee, gelatins, and puddings. The taste of acesulfame-K does not change when it is heated, so it can be used in cooking. The body does not metabolize acesulfame-K, so it is excreted unchanged by the kidneys. The ADI for acesulfame-K is 15 mg per kg body weight per day. For example, the ADI for an adult weighing 68 kg would be 1020 mg.

Aspartame

Aspartame, also called Equal or NutraSweet, is one of the most popular alternative sweeteners currently found in foods and beverages. Aspartame is composed of two amino acids: phenylalanine and aspartic acid. When these amino acids are separate, one is bitter and the other has no flavour—but joined together, they make a substance that is 200 times sweeter than sucrose. Although aspartame contains 4 kcal of energy per gram, it is so sweet that only small amounts are necessary. Consequently, it ends up contributing little or no energy. Because aspartame is made from amino acids, its taste is destroyed with heat because the dipeptide bonds that bind the two amino acids are destroyed when heated (see Chapter 6); thus, it cannot be used in cooking.

A significant amount of research has been done to test the safety of aspartame. Although a number of false claims have been published, especially on the internet, there is no scientific evidence to support the claim that aspartame causes brain tumours, Alzheimer's disease, or nerve disorders.

The ADI for aspartame is 40 mg per kg body weight per day. For example, the ADI for an adult weighing 68 kg would be 2720 mg. Table 4.3 shows how many servings of aspartame-sweetened foods would have to be consumed to exceed the ADI. Although eating less than the ADI is considered safe, note that children who consume many powdered drinks, diet sodas, and other aspartame-flavoured products could potentially exceed this amount. Drinks sweetened with aspartame are extremely popular among children and teenagers, but they are very low in nutritional value and should not replace healthier beverages such as milk, water, and 100% fruit juice.

There are some people who should not consume aspartame at all: those with the disease *phenylketonuria (PKU).* This is a genetic disorder that prevents the breakdown of the amino acid phenylalanine. Because the person with PKU cannot metabolize phenylalanine, it builds up to toxic levels in the tissues of the body and causes irreversible brain damage. In Canada, all newborn babies are tested for PKU; those who have it are placed on a phenylalanine-limited diet. Some foods that are common sources of protein and other nutrients for many growing children, such as meats and milk, contain phenylalanine. Thus, it is critical that children with PKU not waste what little phenylalanine they can consume on nutrient-poor products sweetened with aspartame.

Table 4.3 The Amount of Food That a 22.7 kg Child and a 68 kg Adult Would Have to Consume Daily to Exceed the ADI for Aspartame

Food	22.7 kg Child	68 kg Adult
375 mL carbonated soft drink	7	20
125 mL gelatin dessert	14	42
Packets of tabletop sweetener	32	97

Data from: International Food Information Council Foundation. 2009. Lowdown on Low-Calorie Sweeteners. Available at http://www.foodinsight.org/Content/3848/LCS%20CPE%20Module_Updated%20w-2010%20DGA%205.pdf (accessed March 19, 2012).

Sucralose

Sucralose is a high-intensity sweetener marketed under the name Splenda. It is made from sucrose, but chlorine atoms are substituted for the hydrogen and oxygen normally found in sucrose, and it passes through the digestive tract unchanged, without contributing any energy. It is 600 times sweeter than sucrose and is stable when heated, so it can be used in cooking. It has been approved for use in many foods, including chewing gum, salad dressings, beverages, gelatin and pudding products, canned fruits, frozen dairy desserts, and baked goods. Safety studies have not shown sucralose to cause cancer or to have other adverse health effects. The ADI for sucralose is 9 mg per kg body weight per day. For example, the ADI of sucralose for an adult weighing 68 kg would be 612 mg.

Stevia

The stevia plant is native to South and Central America and sweeteners derived from this plant are up to 300 times sweeter than sucrose. Health Canada has not approved the use of stevia or its extracts for use as an additive in food because of insufficient evidence regarding its safety. However, it does allow for the use of these sweeteners as non-medicinal ingredients in natural health products.

> ## RecaP
>
> Alternative sweeteners can be used in place of sugar to sweeten foods. Most of these products do not promote tooth decay and contribute little or no energy. The alternative sweeteners approved for use in Canada are considered safe when eaten in amounts less than the acceptable daily intake.

What Disorders Are Related to Carbohydrate Metabolism?

Health conditions that affect the body's ability to absorb and/or use carbohydrates include diabetes, hypoglycemia, and lactose intolerance.

Diabetes: Impaired Regulation of Glucose

Hyperglycemia is the term referring to higher-than-normal levels of blood glucose. **Diabetes** is a chronic disease in which the body can no longer regulate blood glucose within normal limits, and consequently blood glucose levels become dangerously high. It is imperative to detect and treat the disease as soon as possible because excessive fluctuations in glucose injure tissues throughout the body. As we noted at the beginning of this chapter, if not controlled, diabetes can lead to blindness, seizures, kidney failure, nerve disease, amputations, stroke, and heart disease. Uncontrolled diabetes can also lead to ketoacidosis, which may result in coma and death. Diabetes is the sixth leading cause of death in Canada.[30]

Approximately 6% of Canadians aged 12 years or older have diabetes.[31] It is speculated that many more people have diabetes but do not know it. Diabetes is of particular concern for Canada's Aboriginal population. Aboriginal people are three to five times more likely to have type 2 diabetes than non-Aboriginal Canadians.[32]

The two main forms of diabetes are type 1 and type 2. Some women develop a third form, *gestational diabetes,* during pregnancy; we will discuss this in more detail in Chapter 16.

In Type 1 Diabetes, the Body Does Not Produce Enough Insulin

Approximately 10% of people with diabetes have **type 1 diabetes**, in which the beta cells of the pancreas are not able to produce insulin. When people with type 1 diabetes eat a meal and their blood glucose rises, the pancreas is unable to secrete insulin in response.

hyperglycemia A condition in which blood glucose levels are higher than normal.

diabetes A chronic disease in which the body can no longer regulate glucose.

type 1 diabetes A disorder in which the body cannot produce enough insulin.

Table 4.4 Signs and Symptoms of Diabetes

Unusual thirst
Frequent urination
Weight change (gain or loss)
Extreme fatigue or lack of energy
Blurred vision
Frequent or recurring infections
Cuts and bruises that are slow to heal
Tingling or numbness in the hands and feet
Trouble getting or maintaining an erection

Note: The Canadian Diabetes Association does not separate the signs and symptoms of type 1 and type 2 diabetes. Many people who have type 2 diabetes may display no symptoms.
Data from: Reprinted with permission from the Canadian Diabetes Association (diabetes.ca).

Figure 4.19 Monitoring blood glucose requires pricking the fingers several times each day and measuring the blood glucose level using a glucometer.

As a result, blood glucose levels soar, and the body tries to expel the excess glucose by excreting it in the urine. In fact, the medical term for the disease is *diabetes mellitus* (from the Greek *diabainein,* "to pass through," and Latin *mellitus,* "sweetened with honey"), and frequent urination is one of its warning signs (see Table 4.4 for other symptoms). If blood glucose levels are not controlled, a person with type 1 diabetes will become confused and lethargic and have trouble breathing. This is because the brain is not getting enough glucose to properly function. As discussed earlier, uncontrolled diabetes can lead to ketoacidosis; left untreated, the ultimate result is coma and death.

The cause of type 1 diabetes is unknown, but it may be an *autoimmune disease.* This means that the body's immune system attacks and destroys its own tissues, in this case the beta cells of the pancreas.

Most cases of type 1 diabetes are diagnosed in adolescents around 10 to 14 years of age, although the disease can appear in infants, young children, and adults. Because it has a genetic link, siblings and children of those with type 1 diabetes are at greater risk than the general population.[33]

The only treatment for type 1 diabetes is administration of insulin by injection or pump several times daily. Insulin is a hormone composed of protein, so it would be digested in the intestine if taken as a pill. Individuals with type 1 diabetes must also monitor their blood glucose levels closely to ensure that they remain within a healthy range (**Figure 4.19**). The Highlight box below describes how one young man with type 1 diabetes stays healthy.

HIGHLIGHT

Living with Diabetes

Vincent is a young man who was diagnosed with type 1 diabetes when he was 10 years old. At first, Vincent and his family were frightened by the disease and found it difficult to adapt their lifestyles to provide a safe and health-promoting environment for Vincent. For example, Vincent's mother felt frustrated because her son could no longer eat the cakes, pies, and other sweets she had always enjoyed baking for her family, and his sister found herself watching over her brother's meals and snacks, running to her parents whenever she feared that he was about to eat something that would harm him. Within a few months, though, Vincent's mother learned to adapt her recipes and cooking techniques to produce a variety of foods that Vincent could enjoy, and the entire family learned to allow Vincent the responsibility for his food choices and his health.

Vincent is now a college student and has been living with diabetes for nine years, but what he still hates most about the disease is that food is always a major issue. Vincent is smart and a good student, but if his blood glucose declines, he has trouble concentrating. He has to eat three nutritious meals a day on a regular schedule and needs to limit his snacks unless his blood sugar is low. When his friends eat candy, chips, or other snacks, he can't join them. In general, he knows these dietary changes are very healthy, but sometimes he wishes he could eat like all of his friends. On the other hand, he cannot skip a meal, even if he isn't hungry. It is also important for Vincent to stay on a regular schedule for exercise and sleep.

Vincent must test his blood sugar many times each day. He has to prick his fingers to do this, and they get tender and develop calluses. During his first few years with diabetes, he had to give himself two to four shots of insulin each day. He learned to measure the insulin into a syringe, and he had to monitor where the shots were injected because each insulin shot should be given in a different place on his body to avoid damaging the skin and underlying tissue. Technological advances now offer easier alternatives than a needle and syringe. Vincent uses an insulin infusion pump, which looks like a small pager and delivers insulin into the body through a long, thin tube in very small amounts throughout

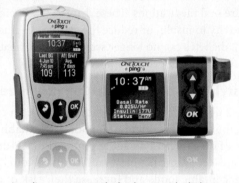

Insulin pumps can help those with diabetes eat a wider range of foods.

the day. One of Vincent's friends also has diabetes but can't use a pump; instead, he uses an insulin pen, which includes a needle and a cartridge of insulin. Now that Vincent uses the insulin pump, he can choose to eat more of the foods he loves and deliver his insulin accordingly.

Although diabetes is challenging, it does not prevent Vincent from playing soccer and basketball almost every day. In fact, he knows that people with diabetes should be active. As long as he takes his insulin regularly, keeps an eye on his blood sugar, drinks plenty of water, and eats when he should, he knows that he can play sports and do most of the things he wants to do. There are numerous professional and Olympic athletes and other famous people who have diabetes, showing that this disease should not prevent Vincent from leading a healthy life and realizing his dreams.

Currently, there is no cure for type 1 diabetes. However, there are many new treatments and potential cures being researched, such as devices that measure blood glucose without pricking the finger. Some of them can read glucose levels through the skin, and others insert a small needle into the body to monitor glucose continually. Tests are also being conducted on insulin nasal sprays and inhalers. Advances in genetic engineering may soon make it possible to transplant healthy beta cells into the pancreas of virtually anyone with type 1 diabetes, so that the normal cells will secrete insulin. Vincent looks forward to seeing major changes in the treatment of diabetes in the next few years.

In Type 2 Diabetes, Cells Become Less Responsive to Insulin

In **type 2 diabetes**, body cells become resistant (less responsive) to insulin. This type of diabetes develops progressively, meaning that the biological changes resulting in the disease occur over a long period of time.

Obesity is the most common trigger for a cascade of changes that eventually results in the disorder. Specifically, the cells of many obese people are less responsive to insulin, exhibiting a condition called *insulin insensitivity* (or insulin resistance). The pancreas attempts to compensate for this insensitivity by secreting more insulin. At first, the increased secretion of insulin is sufficient to maintain normal blood glucose levels. However, over time, a person who is insulin insensitive will have to circulate very high levels of insulin to use glucose for energy. The cycle continues and eventually even the excessive insulin production becomes insufficient for preventing the rise in blood glucose. The resulting condition is referred to as **impaired glucose tolerance**, meaning glucose levels are higher than normal but not high enough to lead to a diagnosis of type 2 diabetes. Some health

type 2 diabetes A progressive disorder in which body cells become less responsive to insulin.

impaired glucose tolerance Fasting blood glucose levels that are higher than normal but not high enough to lead to a diagnosis of type 2 diabetes.

Jerry Garcia, a member of the band The Grateful Dead, had type 2 diabetes.

professionals refer to this condition as *pre-diabetes*, as people with impaired glucose tolerance are more likely to get type 2 diabetes than people with normal fasting glucose levels. Eventually the pancreas becomes incapable of secreting these excessive amounts of insulin, and the beta cells stop producing the hormone altogether. Thus, blood glucose levels may be elevated in a person with type 2 diabetes (1) because of insulin insensitivity, (2) because the pancreas can no longer secrete enough insulin, or (3) because the pancreas has entirely stopped insulin production.

Many factors can cause type 2 diabetes. Genetics plays a role, so relatives of people with type 2 diabetes are at increased risk. Obesity and physical inactivity also increase the risk. A cluster of risk factors referred to as the *metabolic syndrome* is also known to increase the risk for type 2 diabetes. The criteria for metabolic syndrome include having a waist circumference ≥88 cm (or 35 in.) for women and ≥102 cm (or 40 in.) for men, elevated blood pressure, and unhealthy levels of certain blood lipids and blood glucose.[34] Increased age is another risk factor: Most cases of type 2 diabetes develop after age 45.

Once commonly known as *adult-onset diabetes,* type 2 diabetes in children was virtually unheard of until recently. Unfortunately, the disease is increasing dramatically among children and adolescents, posing serious health consequences for them and their future children.[35]

Type 2 diabetes can be treated in a variety of ways. Weight loss, healthy eating patterns, and regular exercise can control symptoms in some people. More severe cases may require oral medications. These drugs work in either of two ways: they improve body cells' sensitivity to insulin or reduce the amount of glucose the liver produces. If a person with type 2 diabetes can no longer secrete enough insulin, the patient must take daily injections of insulin just like people with type 1 diabetes.

Lifestyle Choices Can Help Control or Prevent Diabetes

Type 2 diabetes is thought to have become an epidemic in Canada.[31] Many factors have contributed to this, including poor eating habits, sedentary lifestyles, increased prevalence of obesity, and an aging population. Underlying these risk factors are a multitude of socio-economic factors that limit individuals' access to safe, nutritious, and culturally acceptable foods and increase their risk of developing type 2 diabetes.[3] Addressing these root causes of poor health through a population health approach is the major goal of the Integrated Pan-Canadian Healthy Living Strategy discussed in Chapter 1. But what can individuals do to control or prevent diabetes? We can't control our age, but we can adopt a healthy diet, increase our physical activity, and maintain a healthy body weight.

In general, people with diabetes should follow many of the same dietary guidelines recommended for those without diabetes. One difference is that people with diabetes may need to eat less carbohydrate and slightly more fat or protein to help regulate their blood glucose levels. Carbohydrates are still an important part of the diet, but their intake may need to be reduced. Precise nutritional recommendations vary according to each individual's responses to foods. In addition, people with diabetes should avoid alcoholic beverages, which can cause hypoglycemia. The symptoms of alcohol intoxication and hypoglycemia are very similar. The person with diabetes and his or her companions may confuse these conditions; this can result in a potentially life-threatening situation.

Moderate daily exercise may prevent the onset of type 2 diabetes more effectively than dietary changes alone.[36] See Chapter 15 for examples of moderate exercise programs. Exercise will also assist in weight loss, and studies show that losing only 5% to 10% of body weight can reduce or eliminate the symptoms of type 2 diabetes.[37]

In summary, by eating a healthy diet, staying active, and maintaining a healthy body weight, you should be able to keep your risk for diabetes low.

RecaP

Diabetes is a disease that results in dangerously high levels of blood glucose. Type 1 diabetes typically appears at a young age; the pancreas cannot secrete sufficient insulin, so insulin injections are required. Type 2 diabetes develops over time and may be triggered by obesity. In type 2 diabetes body cells are no longer sensitive to the effects of insulin or the pancreas no longer secretes sufficient insulin for bodily needs. Supplemental insulin may or may not be needed to treat type 2 diabetes. Diabetes increases the risk of dangerous complications such as heart disease, blindness, kidney disease, and amputations. Many cases of type 2 diabetes could be prevented or delayed with a balanced diet, regular exercise, and achieving and/or maintaining a healthy body weight.

CASE STUDY — Dietary Fibre and Type 2 Diabetes

Bruno, a 60-year-old accountant, has been diagnosed with type 2 diabetes. He had been suffering from blurred vision, constant fatigue, and increased urination. His doctor has referred him to a dietitian and Bruno arrives at the dietitian's office fearing the worst. He knows that he has put on too much weight over the last few years and that his father died at age 68 from complications related to diabetes, but Bruno thinks that he is too old to change his habits now. The dietitian asks Bruno what he eats in a typical day and finds out the following information:

Breakfast:
- 500 mL cornflakes
- 175 mL whole milk
- 15 mL sugar
- 500 mL coffee with cream and sugar

Lunch:
- 2 roast beef sandwiches on white bread with mayonnaise and mustard
- 250 mL coffee with cream and sugar

Dinner:
- 200 g roast chicken
- 250 mL mashed potatoes with gravy
- 125 mL boiled carrots
- 2 slices white bread with margarine
- 250 mL coffee with cream and sugar

Snack:
- 4 slices cheddar cheese
- 10 soda crackers

Thinking Critically

1. What risk factors for type 2 diabetes does Bruno have?
2. Explain why Bruno was experiencing blurred vision, constant fatigue, and increased urination.
3. What are the sources of soluble fibre in Bruno's diet? Insoluble fibre?
4. How does the consumption of dietary fibre affect the risk for type 2 diabetes?
5. What dietary recommendations would you make to Bruno?

Hypoglycemia: Low Blood Glucose

In **hypoglycemia**, fasting blood sugar falls to lower-than-normal levels (**Figure 4.20**). One cause of hypoglycemia is excessive production of insulin, which lowers blood glucose too far. People with diabetes can develop hypoglycemia if they inject too much insulin or if

hypoglycemia A condition marked by blood glucose levels that are below normal fasting levels.

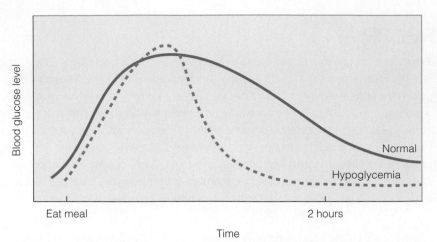

Figure 4.20 Changes in blood glucose after a meal for people with hypoglycemia (lower than normal) and without hypoglycemia (normal).

they exercise and fail to eat enough carbohydrates. Two types of hypoglycemia can develop in people who do not have diabetes: reactive and fasting.

Reactive hypoglycemia occurs when the pancreas secretes too much insulin after a high-carbohydrate meal. The symptoms of reactive hypoglycemia usually appear about 1 to 4 hours after the meal and include nervousness, shakiness, anxiety, sweating, irritability, headache, weakness, and rapid or irregular heartbeat. Although many people experience these symptoms from time to time, they are rarely caused by true hypoglycemia. A person diagnosed with reactive hypoglycemia must eat smaller meals more frequently to level out blood insulin and glucose levels.

Fasting hypoglycemia occurs when the body continues to produce too much insulin, even when someone has not eaten. This condition is usually secondary to another disorder such as cancer, liver infection, alcohol-induced liver disease, or a tumour in the pancreas. Its symptoms are similar to those of reactive hypoglycemia but occur more than four hours after a meal.

RecaP

Hypoglycemia refers to lower-than-normal blood glucose levels. Reactive hypoglycemia occurs when the pancreas secretes too much insulin after a high-carbohydrate meal. Fasting hypoglycemia occurs when the body continues to produce too much insulin even when someone has not eaten.

Lactose Intolerance: Inability to Digest Lactose

Sometimes our bodies do not produce enough of the enzymes necessary to break down certain carbohydrates before they reach the colon. A common example is **lactose intolerance**, in which the body does not produce sufficient amounts of the enzyme lactase in the small intestine and therefore cannot digest foods containing lactose.

Lactose intolerance should not be confused with a milk allergy. People who are allergic to milk experience an immune reaction to the proteins found in cow's milk. Symptoms of milk allergy include skin reactions such as hives and rashes; intestinal distress such as nausea, vomiting, cramping, and diarrhea; and respiratory symptoms such as wheezing, runny nose, and itchy and watery eyes. In severe cases, anaphylactic shock can occur. In contrast, symptoms of lactose intolerance are limited to the GI tract and include intestinal gas, bloating, cramping, nausea, diarrhea, and discomfort. These symptoms resolve spontaneously within a few hours.

Milk products, such as ice cream, are hard to digest for people who are lactose intolerant.

lactose intolerance A disorder in which the body does not produce sufficient lactase enzyme and therefore cannot digest foods that contain lactose, such as cow's milk.

Although some infants are born with lactose intolerance, it is more common to see lactase enzyme activity decrease after two years of age. In fact, it is estimated that up to 70% of the world's adult population will lose some ability to digest lactose as they age.

Not everyone experiences lactose intolerance to the same extent. Some people can digest small amounts of dairy products, whereas others cannot tolerate any. Suarez and colleagues found that many people who reported being lactose intolerant were able to consume multiple small servings of dairy products without symptoms, which enabled them to meet their calcium requirements.[38] Thus, it is not necessary for everyone with lactose intolerance to avoid all dairy products; they may simply need to eat smaller amounts and experiment to find foods that do not cause intestinal distress.

People with lactose intolerance need to find foods that can supply enough calcium for normal growth, development, and maintenance of bones. Many can tolerate specially formulated milk products that are low in lactose, whereas others take pills or use drops that contain the lactase enzyme when they eat dairy products. Calcium-fortified soy milk and orange juice are excellent substitutes for cow's milk. Many lactose-intolerant people can also digest yogourt and aged cheese, as the bacteria or moulds used to ferment these products break down the lactose during processing.

How can you tell if you are lactose intolerant? Many people discover that they have problems digesting dairy products by trial and error. But because intestinal gas, bloating, and diarrhea may indicate other health problems, you should consult a physician to determine the cause.

Tests for lactose intolerance include drinking a lactose-rich liquid and testing blood glucose levels over a 2-hour period. If you do not produce the normal amount of glucose, you will be unable to digest the lactose present. Another test involves measuring hydrogen levels in the breath, as lactose-intolerant people breathe out more hydrogen when they drink a beverage that contains lactose.

Lactose intolerance results from the inability to digest lactose due to insufficient amounts of the enzyme lactase. Symptoms include intestinal gas, bloating, cramping, diarrhea, and nausea. The extent of lactose intolerance varies from mild to severe.

SEE FOR YOURSELF

Are You at Risk?

You could be one of many Canadians who have type 2 diabetes and don't know it. If you are age 40 or over, you are at risk for type 2 diabetes and should be tested at least every three years. If you check any of the boxes below, you should be tested for diabetes earlier or more often.

☐ I have a parent, brother, or sister with diabetes.

☐ I am a member of a high-risk group (Aboriginal, Hispanic, South Asian, Asian, or African descent).

☐ I have health complications that are associated with diabetes.

☐ I gave birth to a baby that weighed over 4 kg (9 lb) at birth.

☐ I had gestational diabetes.

☐ I have been told I have impaired glucose tolerance or impaired fasting glucose.

☐ I have high blood pressure.

☐ I have high cholesterol or other fats in my blood.

☐ I am overweight (especially if I carry most of my weight around my middle).

☐ I have been diagnosed with polycystic ovary syndrome, acanthosis nigricans, or schizophrenia.

Data from: Reprinted with permission from the Canadian Diabetes Association (diabetes.ca).

Chapter Review

Test Yourself | Answers

1. **T** Our brains rely almost exclusively on glucose for energy, and our body tissues utilize glucose for energy both at rest and during exercise.

2. **F** At 4 kcal/g, carbohydrates have less than half the energy of a gram of fat. Eating a high-carbohydrate diet will not cause people to gain body fat unless their total diet contains more energy (or kcal) than they expend. In fact, eating a diet high in complex, fibre-rich carbohydrates is associated with a lower risk for obesity.

3. **F** Although specific estimates are not yet available, significantly higher rates of type 2 diabetes are now being reported in children and adolescents; these higher rates are attributed to increasing obesity rates in young people.

4. **F** There is no evidence that diets high in sugar cause hyperactivity in children.

5. **T** Contrary to recent reports claiming harmful consequences related to consumption of alternative sweeteners, major health agencies have determined that these products are safe for most of us to consume in limited quantities.

Summary

- Carbohydrates contain carbon, hydrogen, and oxygen. Plants make the carbohydrate glucose during photosynthesis.

- Simple sugars include monosaccharides and disaccharides. The three primary monosaccharides are glucose, fructose, and galactose.

- Two monosaccharides joined together are called disaccharides. Glucose and fructose join to make sucrose; glucose and glucose join to make maltose; and glucose and galactose join to make lactose.

- The two monosaccharides that compose a disaccharide are attached by a bond between an oxygen atom and one carbon atom on each of the monosaccharides. There are two forms of this bond: alpha bonds are easily digestible by humans, whereas beta bonds are very difficult to digest.

- Oligosaccharides are complex carbohydrates that contain 3 to 10 monosaccharides.

- Polysaccharides are complex carbohydrates that typically contain hundreds to thousands of monosaccharides. The three types of polysaccharides are starches, glycogen, and fibre.

- Starches are the storage form of glucose in plants.

- Glycogen is the storage form of glucose in humans. Glycogen is stored in the liver and in muscles.

- Dietary fibre is the non-digestible parts of plants, whereas functional fibre is a non-digestible form of carbohydrate extracted from plants or manufactured in the laboratory. Fibre may reduce the risk of many diseases and digestive illnesses.

- Carbohydrate digestion starts in the mouth, where chewing and an enzyme called salivary amylase start breaking down the carbohydrates in food.

- Digestion continues in the small intestine. Specific enzymes are secreted to break starches into smaller mono- and disaccharides. As disaccharides pass through the intestinal cells, they are digested into monosaccharides.

- Glucose and other monosaccharides are absorbed into the bloodstream and travel to the liver, where all non-glucose molecules are converted to glucose.

- Glucose is transported in the bloodstream to the cells, where it is either used for energy, stored in the liver or muscle as glycogen, or converted to fat and stored in adipose tissue.

- Insulin is secreted when blood glucose increases sufficiently, and it assists with the transport of glucose into cells thereby lowering blood glucose levels.

- Glucagon, epinephrine, norepinephrine, cortisol, and growth hormone are secreted when blood glucose levels are low, and they assist with the conversion of glycogen to glucose, with gluconeogenesis, and with reducing the use of glucose by muscles and other organs therefore increasing blood glucose levels.

- The glycemic index and the glycemic load are values that indicate how much a food increases glucose levels. High-glycemic foods can trigger detrimental increases in blood glucose for people with diabetes.

- All cells can use glucose for energy. The red blood cells, brain, and central nervous system prefer to use glucose exclusively.

- Using glucose for energy helps spare body proteins, and glucose is an important fuel for the body during exercise.

- Fibre helps us maintain the healthy elimination of waste products. Eating adequate fibre may reduce the risk of colon cancer, type 2 diabetes, obesity, heart disease, hemorrhoids, and diverticulosis.

- The Acceptable Macronutrient Distribution Range for carbohydrate is 45% to 65% of total energy intake. Our diets should contain less than 25% of total energy from simple sugars.

- High added-sugar intake can cause tooth decay, elevate triglyceride and low-density lipoprotein levels in the blood, and contribute to obesity. It does not appear to cause hyperactivity in children.

- The Adequate Intake for fibre is 25 g per day for women and 38 g per day for men, or 14 g of fibre for every 1000 kcal of energy consumed.

- Foods high in fibre-rich carbohydrates include whole grains and cereals, fruits, and vegetables. Eating 6 to 8 servings of grains products (at least half of which are whole grains) and 7 to 10 servings of fruits and vegetables helps ensure that you meet your fibre-rich carbohydrate goals.

- Alternative sweeteners are added to some foods because they sweeten foods without promoting tooth decay and add little or no calories to foods.

- All alternative sweeteners approved for use in Canada are believed to be safe when eaten at levels at or below the Acceptable Daily Intake levels defined by Health Canada.

- Diabetes is caused by insufficient insulin or by the cells becoming resistant or insensitive to insulin. It causes dangerously high blood glucose levels. The two primary types of diabetes are type 1 and type 2.

- A lower-than-normal blood glucose level is defined as hypoglycemia. There are two types: reactive and fasting. Reactive hypoglycemia occurs when too much insulin is secreted after a high-carbohydrate meal; fasting hypoglycemia occurs when blood glucose drops even though no food has been eaten.

- Lactose intolerance results from an insufficient amount of the lactase enzyme. Symptoms include intestinal gas, bloating, cramping, diarrhea, and discomfort.

Review Questions

1. The glycemic index rates
   a. the acceptable amount of alternative sweeteners to consume in one day.
   b. the potential of foods to raise blood glucose and insulin levels.
   c. the risk of a given food for causing diabetes.
   d. the ratio of soluble to insoluble fibre in a complex carbohydrate.

2. Carbohydrates contain
   a. carbon, nitrogen, and water.
   b. carbonic acid and a sugar alcohol.
   c. hydrated sugar.
   d. carbon, hydrogen, and oxygen.

3. The most common source of added sugar in the Canadian diet is
   a. table sugar.
   b. white flour.
   c. alcohol.
   d. sweetened soft drinks.

4. Glucose, fructose, and galactose are
   a. monosaccharides.
   b. disaccharides.
   c. polysaccharides.
   d. complex carbohydrates.

5. Aspartame should not be consumed by people who have
   a. phenylketonuria.
   b. type 1 diabetes.
   c. lactose intolerance.
   d. diverticulosis.

6. Compare and contrast soluble fibres with insoluble fibres.

7. What is the difference between the glycemic index and the glycemic load?

8. Describe the role of insulin in regulating blood glucose levels.

9. Identify at least four ways in which fibre helps us maintain a healthy digestive system.

10. Your niece, Lilly, is 6 years old and is learning about *Eating Well with Canada's Food Guide* in her Grade 1 class. She

points out the grain products group and proudly lists her favourite food choices from this group: "saltine crackers, pancakes, cinnamon toast, and spaghetti." Explain to Lilly, in words she can understand, the difference between fibre-rich carbohydrates and highly processed carbohydrates and why fibre-rich carbohydrates are healthier food choices.

11. When Kenton returns from his doctor's appointment with the news that he has been diagnosed with type 2 diabetes and must lose weight, his wife looks skeptical. "I thought that diabetes runs in families," she says. "No one in your family has diabetes, and your whole family is overweight! So how come your doctor thinks losing weight will solve your problems?" Defend the statement that obesity can trigger type 2 diabetes.

12. Create a table listing the molecular composition and food sources of each of the following carbohydrates: glucose, fructose, lactose, and sucrose.

Web Links

www.dietitians.ca
Dietitians of Canada
Visit this site to learn more about high- and low-carbohydrate diets, and discover resources for general healthy eating.

www.diabetes.ca
Canadian Diabetes Association
Find out more about risk factors for developing diabetes and the nutritional needs of people living with diabetes.

www.cda-adc.ca
Canadian Dental Association
Go to this site to learn more about dental caries and oral health.

www.hc-sc.gc.ca/fniah-spnia/pubs/index-eng.php
Canadian Health Program for First Nations, Inuit and Aboriginal Health

Learn more about the incidence of diabetes in Aboriginal populations and about culturally appropriate prevention and health promotion initiatives.

http://hc-sc.gc.ca/fn-an/index-eng.php
Health Canada
Here you can find a summary of dietary recommendations for the Canadian public, which includes recommendations for carbohydrate intake.

www.heartandstroke.com
Heart and Stroke Foundation
Read the position statement of the Heart and Stroke Foundation on low-carbohydrate diets and heart disease and stroke.

MasteringNutrition®

www.masteringnutrition.pearson.com

Assignments
Animations: Carbohydrate Absorption • Carbohydrate Digestion • Diverticulosis & Fibre • Hormonal Control of Blood Glucose • Alcohol Absorption

Study Area
Video: Understanding Carbohydrates • Practice Tests • Diet Analysis • eText

References

1. Ohinmaa, A., P. Jacobs, S. Simpson, and J. Johnson. 2004. The projection of prevalence and cost of diabetes in Canada: 2000 to 2016. *Can. J. Diabetes.* 28:1–8. Available at www.diabetes.ca/files/CostofDiabetesJohnsonJun04.pdf (accessed March 18, 2010).

2. Public Health Agency of Canada. 2008. *The Face of Diabetes in Canada.* Available at www.phac-aspc.gc.ca/cd-mc/diabetes-diabete/face-eng.php?opt (accessed January 31, 2010).

3. Vozoris, N. T., and V. S. Tarasuck. 2003. Household food insufficiency is associated with poorer health. *J. Nutr.* 133:120–126.

4. Canadian Diabetes Association. 2010. *Children and type 2 diabetes.* Available at www.diabetes.ca/about-diabetes/youth/type2/ (accessed February 7, 2010).

5. Sears, B. 1995. *The Zone. A Dietary Road Map.* New York: Harper Collins Publishers.

6. Steward, H. L., M. C. Bethea, S. S. Andrews, and L. A. Balart. 1995. *Sugar Busters! Cut Sugar to Trim Fat.* New York: Ballantine Books.

7. Atkins, R. C. 1992. *Dr. Atkins' New Diet Revolution.* New York: M. Evans & Company, Inc.

8. Institute of Medicine, Food and Nutrition Board. 2002. *Dietary Reference Intakes for Energy, Carbohydrates, Fiber, Fat, Protein and Amino Acids (Macronutrients).* Washington, DC: The National Academy of Sciences.

9. Topping, D. L., and P. M. Clifton. 2001. Short-chain fatty acids and human colonic function: roles of resistant starch and non-starch polysaccharides. *Physiol. Rev.* 81:1031–1064.

10. Foster-Powell K., S. H. A. Holt, and J. C. Brand-Miller. 2002. International table of glycemic index and glycemic load values: 2002. *Am. J. Clin. Nutr.* 76:5–56.

11. Liu, S., J. E. Manson, M. J. Stampfer, M. D. Holmes, F. B. Hu, S. E. Hankinson, and W. C. Willett. 2001. Dietary glycemic load assessed by food-frequency questionnaire in relation to plasma high-density-lipoprotein cholesterol and fasting plasma triacylglycerols in postmenopausal women. *Am. J. Clin. Nutr.* 73:560–566.

12. Sloth B., I. Krog-Mikkelsen, A. Flint, I. Tetens, I. Björck, S. Vinoy, H. Elmståhl, A. Astrup, V. Lang, and A. Raben. 2004. No difference in body weight decrease between a low-glycemic-index and a high-glycemic-index diet but reduced LDL cholesterol after 10-wk ad libitum intake of the low-glycemic-index diet. *Am. J. Clin. Nutr.* 80:337–347.

13. Buyken, A. E., M. Toeller, G. Heitkamp, G. Karamanos, B. Rottiers, R. Muggeo, and M. Fuller. 2001. Glycemic index in the diet of European outpatients with type 1 diabetes: relations to glycated hemoglobin and serum lipids. *Am. J. Clin. Nutr.* 73:574–581.

14. Augustin L. S. A., C. Galeone, L. Dal Maso, C. Pelucchi, V. Ramazzotti, D. J. A. Jenkins, M. Montella, R. Talamini, E. Negri, S. Franceschi, and C. La Vecchia. 2004. Glycemic index, glycemic load and risk of prostate cancer. *Int. J. Cancer* 112: 446–450.

15. Jenkins, D. J., T. M. Wolever, R. H. Taylor, H. Barker, H. Fielden, J. M. Baldwin, A. C. Bowling, H. C. Newman, A. L. Jenkins, and D. V. Goff. 1981. Glycemic index of foods: a physiological basis for carbohydrate exchange. *Am. J. Clin. Nutr.* 34:362–366.

16. Tremblay, A., J. A. Simoneau, and C. Bouchard. 1994. Impact of exercise intensity on body fatness and skeletal muscle metabolism. *Metabolism* 43:814–818.

17. Pan, J. W., D. L. Rothman, K. L. Behar, D. T. Stein, and H. P. Hetherington. 2000. Human brain ß-hydroxybutyrate and lactate increase in fasting-induced ketosis. *J. Cereb. Blood Flow Metab.* 20:1502–1507.

18. Garriguet, D. 2007. Overview of Canadians' Eating Habits. *Health Rep.* 18(2):17–32.

19. Johnson-Down, L., H. Ritter, L. Jacobs Starkey, and K. Gray-Donald. 2006. Primary food sources of nutrients in the diet of Canadian adults. *Can. J. Diet. Prac. Res.* 67:7–13.

20. Garriguet D. 2008. Beverage consumption of children and teens. *Health Rep.* 19(4): 1–6.

21. Langlois, K. and Didier Garriguet. 2011. Sugar consumption among Canadians of all ages. *Health Rep.* 22(3):1–5.

22. Howard, B. V., and J. Wylie-Rosett. 2002. Sugar and cardiovascular disease. A statement for healthcare professionals from the Committee on Nutrition of the Council on Nutrition, Physical Activity, and Metabolism of the American Heart Association. *Circulation* 106:523–527.

23. Meyer, K. A., L. H. Kushi, D. R. Jacobs, J. Slavin, T. A. Sellers, and A. R. Folsom. 2000. Carbohydrates, dietary fiber, and incidence of type 2 diabetes in older women. *Am. J. Clin. Nutr.* 71:921–930.

24. Colditz, G. A., J. E. Manson, M. J. Stampfer, B. Rosner, W. C. Willett, and F. E. Speizer. 1992. Diet and risk of clinical diabetes in women. *Am. J. Clin. Nutr.* 55:1018–1023.

25. Schultz, M. B., J. E. Manson, D. S. Ludwig, G. A. Colditz, M. J. Stampfer, W. C. Willett, and F. B. Hu. 2004. Sugar-sweetened beverages, weight gain, and incidence of type 2 diabetes in young and middle-aged women. *JAMA.* 292:927–934.

26. Troiano, R. P., R. R. Briefel, M. D. Carroll, and K. Bialostosky. 2000. Energy and fat intakes of children and adolescents in the United States: Data from the National Health and Nutrition Examination Surveys. *Am. J. Clin. Nutr.* 72:1343S–1353S.

27. Ludwig, D. S., K. E. Peterson, and S. L. Gortmaker. 2001. Relation between consumption of sugar-sweetened drinks and childhood obesity: a prospective, observational analysis. *Lancet* 357:505–508.

28. Mattesk, R. D., and B. M. Popkin. 2009. Nonnutritive sweetener consumption in humans: effects on appetite and food intake and their putative mechanisms. *Am. J. Clin. Nutr.* 89:1–14.

29. Yang Q. 2010. Gain weight by "going diet?" Artificial sweeteners and the neurobiology of sugar cravings. *Yale Journal of Biology and Medicine* 83:101–108.

30. Statistics Canada. *Selected leading causes of death in Canada, by sex.* www.40.statcan.gc.ca/l01/cst01/hlth36a-eng.htm (accessed February 10, 2010).

31. Sanmartin, C., and J. Gilmore. 2008. *Diabetes: Prevalence and care practices.* Ottawa, ON: Statistics Canada.

32. Health Canada. 2010. *First Nations, Inuit and Aboriginal Health.* Available at www.hc-sc.gc.ca/fniah-spnia/diseases-maladies/diabete/index-eng.php (accessed February 7, 2010).

33. American Diabetes Association. 2005. *The genetics of diabetes.* Available online at www.diabetes.org/genetics.jsp.

34. Grundy, S. M., J. I. Cleeman, S. R. Daniels, K. A. Donato, R. H. Eckel, B. A. Franklin, D. J. Gordon, R. M. Krauss, P. J. Savage, S. C. Smith, J. A. Spertus, and F. Costa. 2005. Diagnosis and management of the metabolic syndrome: an American Heart Association/National Heart, Lung, and Blood Institute scientific statement. *Circulation* 112(17):2735–2752.

35. Centers for Disease Control and Prevention (CDC). 2007. National diabetes fact sheet: 2007. Available online at www.cdc.gov/diabetes/pubs/pdf/ndfs_2007.pdf.

36. Pan, X.-P., G.-W. Li, Y.-H. Hu, J. X. Wang, W. Y. Yang, Z. X. An, Z. X. Hu, J. Lin, J. Z. Xiao, H. B. Cao, P. A. Liu, X. G. Jiang, Y. Y. Jiang, J. P Wang, H. Zheng, H. Zhang, P. H. Bennett, and B. V. Howard. 1997. Effects of diet and exercise in preventing NIDDM in people with impaired glucose tolerance. *Diabetes Care* 20:537–544.

37. Canadian Diabetes Association Clinical Practice Guidelines Expert Committee. 2008. Canadian Diabetes Association 2008 clinical practice guidelines for the prevention and management of diabetes in Canada. *Can J Diabetes* 32(Suppl 1):S1-S201.

38. Suarez, F. L., J. Adshead, J. K. Furne, and M. D. Levitt. 1998. Lactose maldigestion is not an impediment to the intake of 1500 mg calcium daily as dairy products. *Am. J. Clin. Nutr.* 68:1118–1122.

39. Public Health Agency of Canada. 2009. *Obesity in Canada: A Snapshot.* Available at www.phac-aspc.gc.ca (accessed October 3, 2010).

40. Shields, M. 2005. *Measured obesity. Overweight children and adolescents.* Ottawa: Statistics Canada Cat.

41. Obesity Canada Clinical Practice Guidelines Expert Panel. 2007. 2006 Canadian clinical practice guidelines on the management

and prevention of obesity in adults and children. *Can. Med. Assoc. J.* (April 10). Epub DOI:10.1503/cmaj.061409.

42. Bray G. A., S. J. Nielsen, and B. M. Popkin. 2004. Consumption of high-fructose corn syrup in beverages may play a role in the epidemic of obesity. *Am. J. Clin. Nutr.* 79:537–543.

43. Ebbeling, C. B., D. B. Pawlak, and D. S. Ludwig. 2002. Childhood obesity: public-health crisis, common sense cure. *Lancet.* 360:473–482.

44. Wilkinson Enns, C., S. J. Mickle, and J. D. Goldman. 2002. Trends in food and nutrient intakes by children in the United States. *Family Econ. Nutr. Rev.* 14:56–68.

45. Harnack, L., J. Stang, and M. Story. 1999. Soft drink consumption among U.S. children and adolescents: nutritional consequences. *J. Am. Diet. Assoc.* 99:436–441.

46. Ebbeling, C. B., H. A. Feldman, S. K. Osganian, V. R. Chomitz, S. H. Ellenbogen, and D. S. Ludwig. 2006. Effects of decreasing sugar-sweetened beverage consumption on body weight in adolescents: a randomized, controlled pilot study. *Pediatrics* 117:673–680.

47. Ontario Ministry of Education. 2010. *Nutrition Standards for Ontario Schools. Policy/Program Memorandum No. 150, School Food and Beverage Policy.* Available at www.edu.gov.on.ca/extra/eng/ppm/150.html (accessed January 15, 2010).

48. British Columbia Ministries of Health and Education. 2007. *Guidelines for Food and Beverage Sales in BC Schools.* Available at www.bced.gov.bc.ca/health/guidelines_sales07.pdf (accessed March 30, 2010).

49. New Brunswick Department of Education. 2008. Policy 711, *Healthier Foods and Nutrition in Public Schools.* Available at www.gnb.ca/0000/pol/e/711A.pdf (accessed March 30, 2010).

50. White, J. 2009. Misconceptions about high-fructose corn syrup. *J. Nutr.* 139:1219s–1227s.

51. Jones. J. J. 2009. Dietary sweeteners containing fructose: overview of a workshop on the state of the science. *J. Nutr.* 139:1210S–1213S.

52. Monsivais, P., M. M. Perrigue, and A. Drewnowski. 2007. Sugars and satiety: does the type of sweetener make a difference? *Am. J. Clin. Nutr.* 86: 116–123.

53. Murphy, S. P. 2009. The state of science on dietary sweeteners containing sucrose: summary and issues to be resolved. *J. Nutr.* 139: 1269s–1270s.

54. Moran, T. H. 2009. Fructose and satiety. *J. Nutr.* 139:1253s–1256s.

55. Elliott S. S., N. L. Keim, J. S. Stern, K. Teff, and P. J. Havel. 2002. Fructose, weight gain, and the insulin resistance syndrome. *Am. J. Clin. Nutr.* 76:911–922.

56. White, J. S. (2009). Misconceptions about high-fructose corn syrup: is it uniquely responsible for obesity, reactive dicarbonyl compounds, and advanced glycation endpoints? *J. Nutr.* 139:1219S–1227S.

57. Bell, E. A, L. S. Roe, and B. J. Rolls. 2003. Sensory-specific satiety is affected more by volume than by energy content of a liquid food. *Physiol. Behav.* 78:593–600.

58. Rolls, B. J., I. C. Fedoroff, J. F. Guthrie, and L. J. Laster. 1990. Foods with different satiating effects in humans. *Appetite.* 15:115–126.

59. DiMegliio, D. P., and R. D. Mattes. 2000. Liquid versus solid carbohydrate: effects on food intake and body weight. *Int. J. Obes.* 24:794–800.

60. Jacobson, M. F. 2004. Letter to the editor. High-fructose corn syrup and the obesity epidemic. *Am. J. Clin. Nutr.* 80:1081–1090.

61. Forshee, R.A., A.D.B. Storey, D.B. Allison, W.H. Glinsmann, G.L. Hein, D.R. Lineback, S.A. Miller, T.A. Nicklas, G.A. Weaver, and J.S. White. 2007. A critical examination of the evidence relating high fructose corn syrup and weight gain. *Crit. Rev. Food Sci Nutr.* 47:561–582.

62. Lê K.-A., D. Faeh, R. Stettler, M. Ith, R. Kreis, P. Vermathen, C. Boesch, E. Ravussin, and L. Tappy. 2006. A 4-wk high-fructose diet alters lipid metabolism without affecting insulin sensitivity or ectopic lipids in healthy humans. *Am. J. Clin. Nutr.* 84: 1374–1379.

63. Public Health Agency of Canada. 2008. *Reducing the risk of diabetes.* Available at www.phac-aspc.gc.ca/cd-mc/diabetes-diabete/risk-risques-eng.php (accessed October 3, 2010).

64. Murphy, S. P. 2009. The state of the science on dietary sweeteners containing fructose: summary and issues to be resolved. *J. Nutr.* 139:1269S–1270S.

Does High-Fructose Corn Syrup Play a Role in Childhood Obesity?

Almost every day in the news we see headlines about obesity: "More Canadians Overweight!" "The Fattening of North America," "Obesity is a National Epidemic!" Over the past 25 years, obesity rates have increased dramatically in Canada.[39] It has become public health enemy number one, as many chronic diseases such as type 2 diabetes, heart disease, high blood pressure, and arthritis go hand in hand with obesity.

Of particular concern are the rising obesity rates in children. The results of the 2004 Canadian Community Health Survey (CCHS) indicate that the prevalence of obesity is 6.3% in young children aged 2 to 5 years, 8.0% in children aged 6 to 11 years, and 9.4% in adolescents aged 12 to 17 years.[40] This is a 250% increase in obesity rates since the late 1970s and translates into about half a million children and youth.

Why should we concern ourselves with fighting obesity in children? First, it is well established that the treatment of existing obesity is extremely challenging, and our greatest hope of combating this disease is through prevention. Most agree that prevention should start with children at a very early age. Second, there is a tendency for obese children to remain obese as adults, suffering all of the health problems that accompany this disease.[41] Young children are now experiencing type 2 diabetes, high blood pressure, and high cholesterol at increasingly younger ages, only compounding the devastating effects of these illnesses as they get older. We have reached the point at which serious action must be taken immediately to curb this growing crisis.

How can we prevent obesity? This is a difficult question to answer. One way is to better understand the factors that contribute to obesity, and then take actions to alter these factors. We know of many factors that contribute to

overweight and obesity. These include genetic influences, lack of adequate physical activity, and eating foods that are high in fat, added sugar, and energy. While it is easy to blame our genetics, they cannot be held entirely responsible for the rapid rise in obesity that has occurred over the past 25 years. Our genetic makeup takes thousands of years to change; thus, humans who lived 50 or 100 years ago have essentially the same genetic makeup as humans who live now. The fact that obesity rates have risen so dramatically in recent years indicates that we need to look more closely at how changes in our lifestyle and environment over this same period have contributed to obesity.

One factor that has been the topic of much discussion and debate in recent years is the contribution of added sugars, particularly in the form of *high-fructose corn syrup (HFCS)* to overweight and obesity. Researchers in the United States have linked the increased use and consumption of HFCS in beverages and foods with the rising rates of obesity since the 1970s, when HFCS was first developed and marketed (see Figure 4a).[42, 43] HFCS use in Canada is not tracked separately from total sweeteners and appears on food labels as the generic term "glucose/fructose." Consequently, similar correlations can't be examined. However, it is known that HFCS provides about 95% of the caloric sweeteners used by the Canadian soft drink industry,[29] which is on par with the 100% usage in the United States.

How significant a problem is soft drink consumption in children? Studies from the United States show that girls and boys ages 6 to 11 years drank about twice as many soft drinks in 1998 as compared to 1977, and consumption of milk over this same time period dropped by about 30%.[44] Equally alarming is the finding that one-fourth of a group of adolescents studied were heavy consumers of sugared soft drinks, drinking at least 770 mL of soft drinks each day.[45] In Canada, boys aged 14–18 years consume on average 359 mL of sweetened soft drinks daily, roughly equivalent to one 355 mL can.[28] This intake is equivalent to almost 150 extra calories! So, it's not surprising that researchers have shown that for each extra sugared soft drink that children consume each day, the risk of obesity increases by 60%.[27] A recent pilot intervention study found that replacing sweetened soft drinks with non-caloric beverages in the diets of 13- to 18-year-old adolescents resulted in a significant decrease in body mass index in the adolescents who were the most overweight when starting the study.[46]

All of this alarming information has led to dramatic changes in the availability of soft drinks in schools and at school-sponsored events. Most provinces in Canada have school food and nutrition policies that limit the sale of

It is estimated that the rate of overweight in children in Canada has almost tripled since 1981.

sweetened drinks including fruit drinks, energy drinks, and soft drinks on school grounds.[47–50] Despite these positive changes in the school environment, foods and beverages containing HFCS are still widely available in the marketplace.

What is HFCS? It is a mixture of two monosaccharides, fructose and glucose; it is made by first converting the starch in corn to glucose, and then converting some of the glucose to fructose through a process referred to as *enzymatic isomerization*. The result is an inexpensive, corn-based syrup that has replaced sucrose and other simple carbohydrates as a sweetener in foods and beverages. It is referred to as high-fructose corn syrup not because it is all fructose or even very high in fructose, but because the corn syrup from which it is derived is virtually fructose-free.[51] The most commonly used forms of HFCS contain 55% (HFCS 55) or 42% (HFCS 42) free fructose; what remains is free glucose.[52] Thus it is similar in composition to the disaccharide sucrose (50% glucose, 50% fructose).[53]

How might the consumption of HFCS contribute to obesity? Early studies on the metabolic effects of HFCS focused on the differences between glucose and fructose metabolism. Fructose is absorbed further down in the small intestine and, unlike glucose, does not stimulate insulin release from the pancreas; it also enters the cell by a transport protein that does not require the presence of insulin. Insulin increases the release of leptin and both of these hormones inhibit food intake in humans.[54] Bray

et al. speculated that HFCS could lead to lower circulating levels of both insulin and leptin, resulting in an increase in appetite and food intake, excessive energy intake, and thus increased obesity.[42] At the same time, HFCS could contribute to obesity because people consume significant amounts of excess energy in the form of HFCS-sweetened soft drinks and foods. Consumption of fructose has also been reported to increase the production of triglycerides in the blood significantly more than glucose and, in animals, can lead to insulin resistance and impaired glucose regulation—factors that can lead to weight gain and type 2 diabetes.[55] However, these studies have been criticized for using pure fructose and pure glucose at much higher concentrations than would be found in the American diet,[56] and equating the metabolism of fructose with HFCS.[51] Further, many of these early studies were in vitro (in test tubes) or laboratory feeding studies.

More specifically, it has been suggested that the consumption of sweetened soft drinks is more likely to cause weight gain than consumption of sugary foods. Some researchers believe that liquid calories are less satiating than calories from solid foods, possibly because of the higher water content.[57, 58] However, other researchers have shown that solid foods are more satiating.[59]

Although the evidence pinpointing HFCS as a major contributor to the obesity epidemic originally appeared strong, a growing number of researchers disagree with these speculations about HFCS.[56] It has been proposed

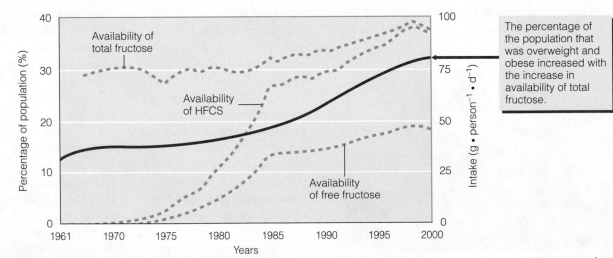

The percentage of the population that was overweight and obese increased with the increase in availability of total fructose.

Figure 4a Availability of total fructose, high-fructose corn syrup (HFCS), and free fructose in relation to obesity prevalence in the United States. (*Data adapted from:* Bray, G. A., S. J. Nielsen, and B. M. Popkin. 2004. Consumption of high fructose corn syrup in beverages may play a role in the epidemic of obesity. *Am. J. Clin. Nutr.* 79:537–543. Used with permission.)

that soft drinks would have contributed to the obesity epidemic no matter whether the sweetener was sucrose or fructose, and that their contribution to obesity arises from the increased consumption resulting from massive increases in advertising, substantial increases in serving sizes of soft drinks, and virtually unlimited access to soft drinks throughout our everyday lives.[60]

Forshee and colleagues conducted a search of the literature related to HFCS and weight gain and found that few studies directly explored the relationship between HFCS, body weight, and BMI.[61] The only evidence linking HFCS consumption and rising BMI rates was ecological data. A recent study has also indicated that though four weeks of increased fructose consumption in humans does cause an increased production of triglycerides as previously stated, it does not cause weight gain or increased resistance to insulin.[61] Thus, it may be that animals respond differently than humans to diets high in fructose. Other researchers argue that the timing of sugar administration influences satiety, not the chemical structure.[63] Therefore, it is entirely possible that the obesity epidemic has resulted from increased consumption of energy (predominantly in the form of sweetened soft drinks and other high-energy foods) and a reduction in physical activity levels, and HFCS has nothing to do with this epidemic. Evidence to support this supposition stems from the fact that obesity rates are rising around the world, and many of the countries experiencing this epidemic do not use HFCS as a sweetener.

There is also little evidence that HFCS is less satiating than other dietary sweeteners.[64] Monsivais and colleagues gave commercially available cola beverages, sweetened with sucrose, HFCS 42, or HFCS 55 to 37 volunteers to determine the relative effects on hunger, satiety, and energy intakes at the next meal.[52] They found no significant differences between the sucrose and HFCS-sweetened beverages.

Clearly, this issue is extremely complex. It has been suggested that more research needs to be done in humans before we can fully understand how HFCS contributes to our diet, and whether its consumption adversely affects our health.[39,55]

Aggressive marketing and easy availability of soft drinks make them a tempting choice for children and adults, adding HFCS and calories to their diets.

Using the Evidence

1. After reading this, do you think HFCS is a major contributor to the obesity epidemic?

2. Should HFCS be banned from our food supply? Please justify.

3. Should soft drink companies be encouraged to replace HFCS with sucrose or some other form of caloric sweetener?

4. Should reducing soft drink consumption be up to individuals, or should it be mandatory for those at high risk for obesity?

5. Should families, schools, and our government play a central role in controlling the types of foods and beverages offered to young people throughout their day?

Lipids: Essential Energy-Supplying Nutrients

Test Yourself True *or* False?

1. Fat is unhealthy, and we should consume as little as possible.
   T *or* **F**

2. Fat is an important fuel source during rest and exercise. **T** *or* **F**

3. Fried foods are relatively nutritious as long as vegetable shortening is used to fry the foods. **T** *or* **F**

4. Certain fats protect against heart disease. **T** *or* **F**

5. High-fat diets cause cancer. **T** *or* **F**

Test Yourself answers are located in the Chapter Review.

Chapter Objectives | *After reading this chapter, you will be able to:*

1. List and describe the three types of lipids found in foods, *pp. 162–170.*
2. Discuss how the level of saturation of a fatty acid affects its shape and the form it takes, *pp. 164–165.*
3. Identify the primary difference between a *cis* fatty acid and a *trans* fatty acid, *pp. 165–166.*
4. Compare and contrast the two essential fatty acids, *pp. 166–168.*
5. Describe the steps involved in fat digestion, absorption, and transport, *pp. 170–174.*
6. List at least three functions of fat in the body, *pp. 175–178.*
7. Define the recommended dietary intakes for total fat, saturated fat, and the two essential fatty acids, *pp. 178–180.*
8. Identify at least three food sources of omega-3 fatty acids, *pp. 180–182.*
9. Describe the role of dietary fat in the development of cardiovascular disease, *pp. 184–190.*
10. Identify lifestyle recommendations for the prevention or treatment of cardiovascular disease, *pp. 190–191.*

Many places around the world are considering charging a 'fat tax' to curb rising rates of obesity.

How would you feel if you purchased a bag of potato chips and were charged an extra 5% "fat tax"? What if you ordered fish and chips in your favourite restaurant only to be told that, in an effort to avoid lawsuits, fried foods were no longer being served? Sound surreal? Believe it or not, these and dozens of similar scenarios are being proposed, threatened, and defended in the current "obesity wars" raging around the globe. From Prince Edward Island to British Columbia, from Iceland to New Zealand, local and national governments and healthcare policy advisors are scrambling to find effective methods for combating their rising rates of obesity. For reasons we explore in this chapter, many of their proposals focus on limiting consumption of foods high in saturated and *trans* fats—for instance, requiring food vendors and manufacturers to reduce the portion size of high-fat foods; taxing or increasing the purchase price of these foods; levying fines on manufacturers who produce them; removing these foods from vending machines; banning advertisements of these foods to children; and using food labels and public service announcements to warn consumers away from these foods.

Are saturated and *trans* fats really such a menace? Does a diet high in saturated and *trans* fats cause obesity, heart disease, or diabetes? What exactly are saturated and *trans* fats anyway?

Although some people think that all dietary fat should be avoided, a certain amount of fat is absolutely essential for life and health. In this chapter, we'll discuss the function of fat in the human body, explain how dietary fat is digested, absorbed, transported, and stored, and help you distinguish between beneficial and harmful types of dietary fat. You'll also assess how much fat you need in your diet and learn about the role of dietary fat in the development of heart disease and other disorders.

What Are Lipids?

Lipids are a large and diverse group of substances that are distinguished by the fact that they are insoluble in water. Think of a salad dressing made with vinegar (which is mostly water) and olive oil—a lipid. Shaking the bottle *disperses* the oil but doesn't *dissolve* it; that's why it separates back out again so quickly. Lipids are found in all sorts of living things, from bacteria to plants to human beings. In fact, their presence on your skin explains why you can't clean your face with water alone—you need some type of soap to break down the insoluble lipids before you can wash them away. In this chapter, we focus on lipids that are found in foods and some of the lipids synthesized within the body.

Some lipids, such as olive oil, are liquid at room temperature.

Many different forms of lipids occur in the body and in foods. In the body, lipids are stored in adipose tissues that protect and insulate organs, are combined with phosphorous in cell membranes, and occur as steroids in bile salts, sex hormones, and other substances.[1] In foods, lipids occur as both fats and oils. These two forms are distinguished by the fact that fats, such as butter and lard, are solid at room temperature, whereas oils such as olive oil are liquid at room temperature. Dietary guidelines, food labels, and other nutrition information intended for the general public use the term *fats* when referring to the lipid content of diets and foods. We adopt this practice throughout this textbook, reserving the term *lipids* for discussions of chemistry and metabolism.

Three types of lipids are commonly found in foods and in the cells and tissues of the human body. These are triglycerides, phospholipids, and sterols. Let's take a look at each.

Triglycerides Are the Most Common Food-Based Lipid

Most of the fat we eat (95%) is in the form of triglycerides (also called triacylglycerols), which is the same form in which most body fat is stored. As reflected in the prefix *tri,* a **triglyceride** is a molecule consisting of *three* fatty acids attached to a *three*-carbon glycerol backbone (**Figure 5.1a**). **Fatty acids** are long chains of carbon atoms bound to each other as well as to hydrogen atoms. They are acids because they contain an acid group (carboxyl group) at one end of their chain. **Glycerol**, the backbone of a triglyceride molecule, is an

triglyceride A molecule consisting of three fatty acids attached to a three-carbon glycerol backbone.

fatty acids Long chains of carbon atoms bound to each other as well as to hydrogen atoms.

glycerol An alcohol composed of three carbon atoms; it is the backbone of a triglyceride molecule.

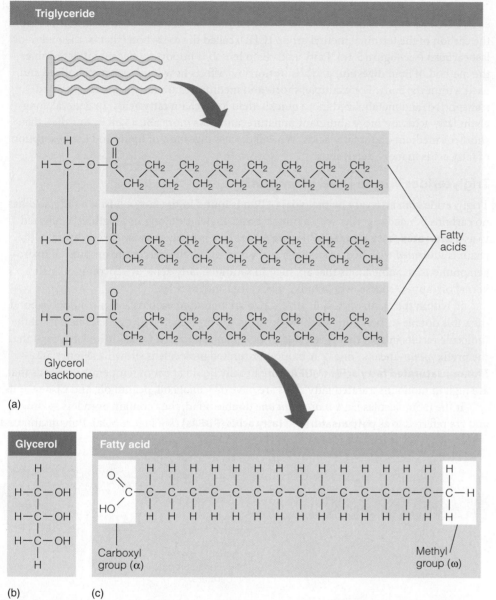

Figure 5.1 (a) A triglyceride consists of three fatty acids attached to a three-carbon glycerol backbone. (b) Structure of glycerol. (c) Structure of a fatty acid showing the carboxyl carbon (α) and the methyl carbon (ω) ends.

alcohol composed of three carbon atoms (Figure 5.1b). One fatty acid attaches to each of these three carbons to make the triglyceride.

Triglycerides can be classified by their chain length (number of carbons in each fatty acid), by their level of saturation (how much hydrogen is attached to each carbon atom in the fatty acid chain), and by their shape, which is determined in some cases by how they are commercially processed. All of these factors influence how the triglyceride is used within the body and how it affects our health.

Triglycerides Vary in Chain Length

The fatty acids attached to the glycerol backbone can vary in the number of carbons they contain, a quality referred to as their *chain length*.

- **Short-chain fatty acids** are usually fewer than six carbon atoms in length.
- **Medium-chain fatty acids** are six to twelve carbons in length.
- **Long-chain fatty acids** are 14 or more carbons in length.

short-chain fatty acids Fatty acids fewer than six carbon atoms in length.

medium-chain fatty acids Fatty acids that are six to twelve carbon atoms in length.

long-chain fatty acids Fatty acids that are 14 or more carbon atoms in length.

The carbons of a fatty acid can be numbered beginning with the carbon of the carboxyl end (COOH), which is designated the α-carbon (that is, the *alpha* or first carbon), or from the carbon of the terminal methyl group (CH$_3$), called the ω-carbon (that is, the *omega* or last carbon) (see Figure 5.1c). Fatty acid chain length is important because it determines the method of lipid digestion and absorption and affects how lipids are metabolized and used within the body. For example, short- and medium-chain fatty acids are digested, transported, and metabolized more quickly than long-chain fatty acids. In general, long-chain fatty acids are more abundant in nature, and thus more abundant in our diet, than short- or medium-chain fatty acids. We will discuss digestion of lipids and the absorption of fatty acids in more detail shortly.

Triglycerides Vary in Level of Saturation

Triglycerides can also vary by the types of bonds found in the fatty acids. If a fatty acid has no carbons bonded together with a double bond anywhere along its length, it is referred to as a **saturated fatty acid (SFA)** (**Figure 5.2a**). This is because every carbon atom in the chain is *saturated* with hydrogen. Each carbon atom has the maximum amount of hydrogen bound to it. Some foods that are high in saturated fatty acids are coconut oil, palm kernel oil, butter, cheese, whole milk, cream, lard, and beef fat.

If, within the chain of carbon atoms, two are bound to each other with a double bond, then this double carbon bond excludes hydrogen. This lack of hydrogen at *one* part of the molecule results in a fat that is referred to as *monounsaturated* (recall from Chapter 4 that the prefix *mono-* means "one"). A monounsaturated molecule is shown in Figure 5.2a. **Monounsaturated fatty acids (MUFAs)** are usually liquid at room temperature. Foods that are high in monounsaturated fatty acids are olive oil, canola oil, peanut oil, and cashew nuts.

If the fat molecules have *more than one* double bond, they contain even less hydrogen and are referred to as **polyunsaturated fatty acids (PUFAs)** (see Figure 5.2a). Polyunsaturated

saturated fatty acids (SFAs) Fatty acids that have no carbons joined together with a double bond; these types of fatty acids are generally solid at room temperature.

monounsaturated fatty acids (MUFAs) Fatty acids that have two carbons in the chain bound to each other with one double bond; these types of fatty acids are generally liquid at room temperature.

polyunsaturated fatty acids (PUFAs) Fatty acids that have more than one double bond in the chain; these types of fatty acids are generally liquid at room temperature.

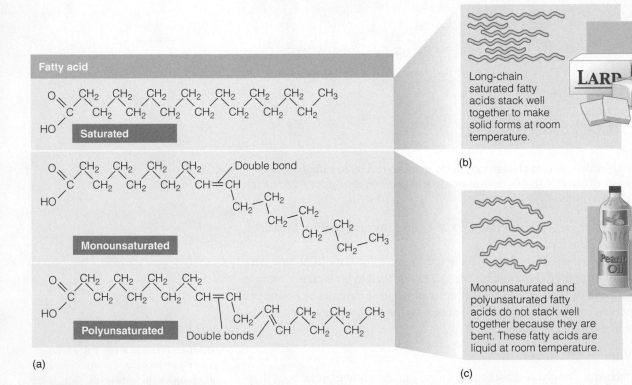

Figure 5.2 Examples of levels of saturation among fatty acids and how these levels of saturation affect the shape of fatty acids. (a) Saturated fatty acids are saturated with hydrogen, meaning they have no carbons bonded together with a double bond. Monounsaturated fatty acids contain two carbons bound by one double bond. Polyunsaturated fatty acids have more than one double bond linking carbon atoms. (b) Saturated fats have straight fatty acids packed tightly together and are solid at room temperature. (c) Unsaturated fats have "kinked" fatty acids at the area of the double bond, preventing them from packing tightly together; they are liquid at room temperature.

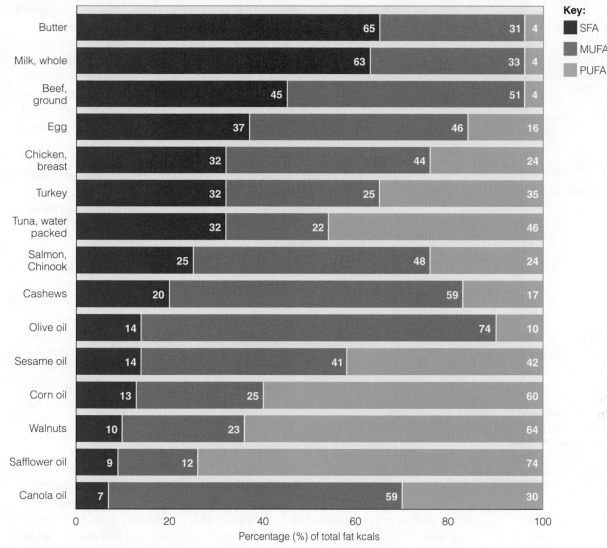

	SFA	MUFA	PUFA
Butter	65	31	4
Milk, whole	63	33	4
Beef, ground	45	51	4
Egg	37	46	16
Chicken, breast	32	44	24
Turkey	32	25	35
Tuna, water packed	32	22	46
Salmon, Chinook	25	48	24
Cashews	20	59	17
Olive oil	14	74	10
Sesame oil	14	41	42
Corn oil	13	25	60
Walnuts	10	23	64
Safflower oil	9	12	74
Canola oil	7	59	30

Percentage (%) of total fat kcals

Key:
SFA
MUFA
PUFA

Figure 5.3 Major sources of dietary fat.

fatty acids are also liquid at room temperature and include cottonseed, canola, corn, and safflower oils.

Foods vary in the types of fatty acids they contain. For example, animal fats provide approximately 40% to 60% of their energy from saturated fats, whereas plant fats provide 80% to 90% of their energy from monounsaturated and polyunsaturated fats (**Figure 5.3**). Notice that most oils are a good source of both MUFAs and PUFAs. Diets higher in plant foods will usually be lower in saturated fats than diets high in animal products. The impact that various types of fatty acids have on health will be discussed later in this chapter (beginning on page 184).

Carbon Bonding Affects Shape

Have you ever noticed how many toothpicks are packed into a small box? Two hundred or more! But if you were to break a bunch of toothpicks into V shapes anywhere along their length, how many could you then fit into the same box? It would be very few because the bent toothpicks would jumble together, taking up much more space. Molecules of saturated fat are like straight toothpicks: they have no double carbon bonds and always form straight, rigid chains. As they have no kinks, these chains can pack together tightly (Figure 5.2b). That is why saturated fats, such as the fat in meats, are solid at room temperature.

Walnuts and cashews are high in unsaturated fatty acids.

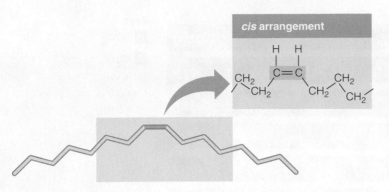

(a) *cis* polyunsaturated fatty acid

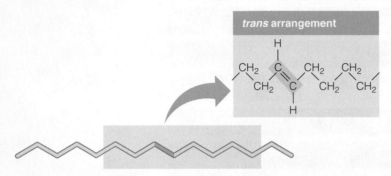

(b) *trans* polyunsaturated fatty acid

Figure 5.4 Structure of (a) a *cis* and (b) a *trans* polyunsaturated fatty acid. Notice that *cis* fatty acids have both hydrogen atoms located on the same side of the double bond. This positioning makes the molecule kinked. In *trans* fatty acids, the hydrogen atoms are attached on diagonally opposite sides of the double carbon bond. This positioning makes them straighter and more rigid.

Health Canada requires that both saturated and *trans* fats be listed as separate line items on Nutrition Facts tables for conventional foods and some dietary supplements. Research studies show that diets high in these fatty acids can increase the risk of cardiovascular disease.

hydrogenation The process of adding hydrogen to unsaturated fatty acids, making them more saturated and thereby more solid at room temperature.

In contrast, each double carbon bond of unsaturated fats gives them a kink along their length (Figure 5.2c). This means that they are unable to pack together tightly—for example, to form a stick of butter—and instead are liquid at room temperature. Monounsaturated and polyunsaturated fatty acids are fluid and flexible, qualities that are important in fatty acids that become part of cell membranes, as well as in those that transport substances in the bloodstream.

Unsaturated fatty acids can occur in either a *cis* or a *trans* shape. The prefix *cis* indicates a location on the same side, whereas *trans* is a prefix that denotes across or opposite. In lipid chemistry, these terms describe the positioning of the hydrogen atoms around the double carbon bond, as follows:

- A *cis fatty acid* has both hydrogen atoms located on the same side of the double bond (**Figure 5.4a**). This positioning gives the *cis* molecule a pronounced kink at the double carbon bond. We typically find the *cis* fatty acids in nature and thus in foods like olive oil.
- In contrast, in a *trans fatty acid,* the hydrogen atoms are attached on diagonally opposite sides of the double carbon bond (Figure 5.4b). This positioning makes *trans* fatty acid fats straighter and more rigid, just like saturated fats. Although a limited amount of *trans* fatty acids is found in such foods as dairy products, beef, and lamb (2% to 6% of the fat), the majority of *trans* fatty acids are commercially produced by manipulating the fatty acid during food processing. For example, in the **hydrogenation** of oils, such as corn or safflower oil, hydrogen are added to the fatty acids. In this process, some of the double bonds found in the monounsaturated and polyunsaturated fatty acids in the oil are broken, and additional hydrogen is inserted at diagonally opposite sides of the double bonds. This process straightens out the molecules, making the oil more solid at room temperature—and also more saturated. Thus, corn oil margarine is a partially hydrogenated fat made from corn oil. Margarines that are hydrogenated have more *trans* fatty acids than butter. The hydrogenation of fats helps foods containing these fats, such as cakes, cookies, and crackers, to resist rancidity, because the additional hydrogen reduces the tendency of the carbon atoms in the fatty acid chains to undergo oxidation.

Does the straight, rigid shape of the saturated and *trans* fats we eat have any effect on our health? Absolutely! Research during the past two decades has shown that both saturated and *trans* fatty acids raise blood cholesterol levels and appear to change cell membrane function and the way cholesterol is removed from the blood. For these reasons, diets high in saturated or *trans* fatty acids are associated with an increased risk of cardiovascular disease. Because of the concerns related to these fatty acids, food manufacturers are required to list the amount of saturated and *trans* fatty acids per serving on the Nutrition Facts table of food labels.

Some Triglycerides Contain Essential Fatty Acids

The length of the fatty acid chain (number of carbons) and the placement of the double bonds will determine the function of the fatty acid within the body. As noted earlier, the carbons of a fatty acid can be numbered beginning with the carbon of the terminal methyl group, called the ω-carbon (ω [omega] is the last letter in the Greek alphabet), or from the

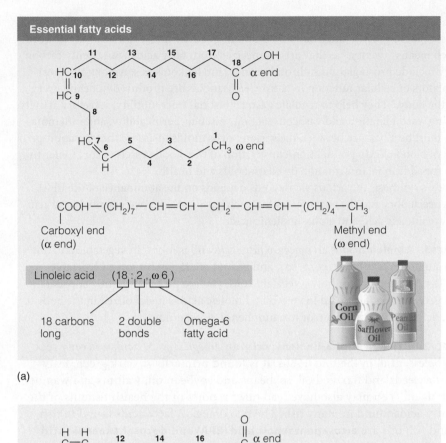

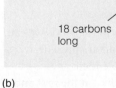

(a)

(b)

Figure 5.5 The two essential fatty acids. (a) In linoleic acid (omega-6 fatty acid), counting from the terminal methyl group (the ω-carbon), the first double bond occurs at the sixth carbon. (b) In alpha-linolenic acid (omega-3 fatty acid), counting from the terminal methyl group (the ω-carbon), the first double bond occurs at the third carbon.

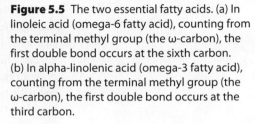

α-carbon of the beginning carboxyl group (α [alpha] is the first letter in the Greek alphabet). In **Figure 5.5**, we have illustrated this numbering system and have numbered the carbons from the ω-carbon. When synthesizing fatty acids, the body cannot insert double bonds before the ninth carbon from the ω-carbon.[2] For this reason, fatty acids with double bonds closer to the methyl end (at ω-3 and at ω-6) are considered **essential fatty acids (EFAs)**—because the body cannot synthesize them, they must be obtained from food.

essential fatty acids (EFAs) Fatty acids that must be consumed in the diet because they cannot be made by the body. The two essential fatty acids are linoleic acid and alpha-linolenic acid.

EFAs are precursors to important biological compounds called *eicosanoids* and are therefore essential to growth and health. Eicosanoids get their name from the Greek word *eicosa,* which means "twenty," as they are synthesized from fatty acids with twenty carbon atoms. They include prostaglandins, thromboxanes, and leukotrienes. Among the most potent regulators of cellular function in nature, eicosanoids are produced in nearly every cell within the body.[3] They help to regulate gastrointestinal tract motility, secretory activity, blood clotting, vasodilatation and vasoconstriction, vascular permeability, and inflammation. There must be a balance between the various eicosanoids to assure that the appropriate amount of blood clotting or dilation/constriction of the blood vessels occurs. Refer to Chapter 13 for additional information on eicosanoids and health.

The body's synthesis of various eicosanoids depends on the abundance of the EFAs available as precursors and the enzymes within each pathway. The two essential fatty acids in our diet are linoleic acid and alpha-linolenic acid.

Linoleic Acid   **Linoleic acid** is an *omega-6 fatty acid* and is found in vegetable and nut oils such as sunflower, safflower, corn, soy, and peanut oil. If you eat lots of vegetables or use vegetable-oil-based margarines or vegetable oils, you are probably getting adequate amounts of this essential fatty acid in your diet. Linoleic acid is metabolized in the body to arachidonic acid, which is a precursor to a number of eicosanoids.

Alpha-Linolenic Acid   **Alpha-linolenic acid**, an *omega-3 fatty acid,* was only recognized to be essential in the mid-1980s. It is found primarily in dark green, leafy vegetables, flaxseeds and flaxseed oil, soybeans and soybean oil, walnuts and walnut oil, and canola oil. You may also have read news reports of the health benefits of the omega-3 fatty acids found in many fish. The two omega-3 fatty acids found in fish, shellfish, and fish oils are **eicosapentaenoic acid (EPA)** and **docosahexaenoic acid (DHA)**. Fish that naturally contain more oil, such as salmon and tuna, are higher in EPA and DHA than lean fish such as cod or flounder. Research indicates that diets high in EPA and DHA stimulate the production of prostaglandins and thromboxanes that reduce inflammatory responses in the body, reduce blood clotting and plasma triglycerides, and thereby reduce an individual's risk of heart disease.

Shrimp are high in omega-3 fatty acid content.

linoleic acid An essential fatty acid found in vegetable and nut oils; also known as omega-6 fatty acid.

alpha-linolenic acid An essential fatty acid found in leafy green vegetables, flaxseed oil, soy oil, fish oil, and fish products; an omega-3 fatty acid.

eicosapentaenoic acid (EPA) A metabolic derivative of alpha-linolenic acid.

docosahexaenoic acid (DHA) A metabolic derivative of alpha-linolenic acid; together with EPA, it appears to reduce the risk of heart disease.

phospholipids A type of lipid in which a fatty acid is combined with another compound that contains phosphate; unlike other lipids, phospholipids are soluble in water.

RECaP

Fat is essential for health. Triglycerides are the most common fat found in food. A triglyceride is made up of glycerol and three fatty acids. These fatty acids can be classified based on chain length, level of saturation, and shape. The essential fatty acids, linoleic acid and alpha-linolenic acid, cannot be synthesized by the body and must be consumed in the diet.

Phospholipids Combine Lipids with Phosphate

Along with the triglycerides just discussed, we also find **phospholipids** in the foods we eat. They are abundant, for example, in egg yolks, peanuts, and soybeans and are present in processed foods containing emulsifiers, additives that help foods stay blended.

Phospholipids consist of a glycerol backbone with fatty acids attached at the first and second carbons and another compound that contains phosphate attached at the third carbon (**Figure 5.6a**). Because phosphates are soluble in water, phospholipids are soluble in water, a property that enables them to assist in transporting fats in the bloodstream. We discuss this concept in more detail later in this chapter (page 172).

The phospholipids are unique in that they have a hydrophobic (water-avoiding) end, which is their lipid "tail," and a hydrophilic (water-attracting) end, which is their phosphate "head." In the cell membrane, this quality helps them to regulate the transport of substances into and out of the cell (see Figure 5.6b). Phospholipids also help with digestion of

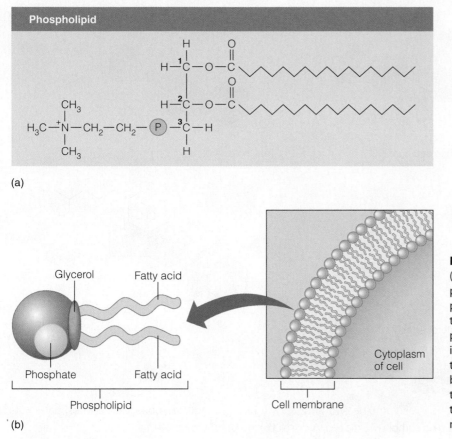

(a)

(b)

Figure 5.6 The structure of a phospholipid. (a) Detailed biochemical drawing of the phospholipid phosphatidylcholine, in which the phosphate is bound to choline and attached to the glycerol backbone at the third carbon. This phospholipid is commonly called lecithin and is found in foods such as egg yolks as well as in the body. (b) Phospholipids consist of a glycerol backbone with two fatty acids and a compound that contains phosphate. This diagram illustrates the placement of the phospholipids in the cell membrane structure.

dietary fats. In the liver, phospholipids called *lecithins* combine with bile salts and electrolytes to make bile. As you recall from Chapter 3, bile emulsifies lipids. Note that the body manufactures phospholipids, so they are not essential to include in the diet.

Sterols Have a Ring Structure

Sterols are a type of lipid found in both plant and animal foods and produced in the body, but their multiple-ring structure is quite different from that of triglycerides or phospholipids (**Figure 5.7a**). Plants contain some sterols, but they are not very well absorbed. Plant sterols appear to block the absorption of dietary cholesterol, the most commonly occurring sterol in the diet (Figure 5.7b). In food, cholesterol is found primarily as cholesterol esters, in which a fatty acid is attached to the cholesterol ring structure (Figure 5.7c). Endogenous (dietary) cholesterol is found in the fatty part of animal products such as butter, egg yolks, whole milk, meats, and poultry. Lean meats and low- or reduced-fat milk, yogourt, and cheeses have little cholesterol. Plant products do not naturally contain any cholesterol.

It is not necessary to consume cholesterol because the body continually synthesizes it, mostly in the liver, adrenal cortex, reproductive tissues, and intestines. This continuous production is vital because cholesterol is part of every cell membrane, where it works in conjunction with fatty acids and phospholipids to help maintain cell membrane integrity and modulate fluidity. It is particularly plentiful in the neural cells that make up the brain, spinal cord, and nerves.

The body uses cholesterol, whether exogenous or endogenous, to make several important sterol compounds, including sex hormones (estrogen, androgens such as testosterone, and progesterone), adrenal hormones, and vitamin D. In addition, cholesterol is the precursor for the bile salts that are a primary component of bile, which helps emulsify the lipids in the gut prior to digestion. Thus, despite cholesterol's bad reputation, it is absolutely essential to human health.

sterols A type of lipid found in foods and the body that has a ring structure; cholesterol is the most common sterol that occurs in our diets.

Figure 5.7 Sterol structure. (a) Sterols are lipids that contain multiple ring structures. (b) Cholesterol is the most commonly occurring sterol in the diet. (c) When a fatty acid is attached to the cholesterol molecule, it is called a cholesterol ester. Cholesterol esters are a common form of cholesterol in our diets.

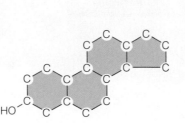

(a) Sterol ring structure

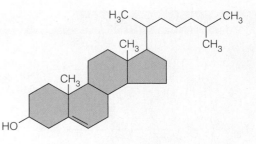

(b) Cholesterol

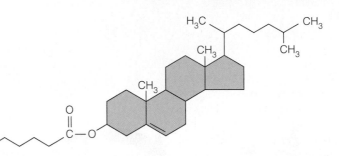

(c) Cholesterol ester

Recap

Phospholipids combine two fatty acids and a glycerol backbone with a phosphate-containing compound, making them soluble in water. Sterols have a multiple-ring structure; cholesterol is the most commonly occurring sterol in our diets.

How Does the Body Break Down Lipids?

Because lipids are not soluble in water, they cannot enter the bloodstream easily from the digestive tract. Thus, their digestion, absorption, and transport within the body differ from those of carbohydrates and proteins, which are water-soluble substances.

The digestion and absorption of lipids were discussed in detail in Chapter 3, but we briefly review the process here (**Figure 5.8**). Dietary fats are usually mixed with other foods. Lingual lipase, a salivary enzyme released during chewing, plays a minor role in the breakdown of lipids in food, so most lipids reach the stomach intact (see Figure 5.8, step 1). The primary role of the stomach in lipid digestion is to mix and break up the lipid into smaller droplets. Because lipids are not soluble in water, these droplets typically float on top of the watery digestive juices in the stomach until they are passed into the small intestine (see Figure 5.8, step 2).

The Gallbladder, Liver, and Pancreas Assist in Fat Digestion

Because lipids are not soluble in water, their digestion requires the help of bile from the gallbladder and digestive enzymes from the pancreas. Recall from Chapter 3 that the gallbladder is a sac attached to the underside of the liver and the pancreas is an oblong-shaped organ sitting below the stomach. Both have a duct connecting them to the small intestine. As lipids enter the small intestine from the stomach, the gallbladder contracts and releases bile (see Figure 5.8, step 3). The contraction of the gallbladder is primarily caused by the release of cholecystokinin (CCK) (also called pancreozymin) from the duodenal mucosal cells into the circulation. Secretin, another hormone released from the duodenal mucosa, also plays a role in gallbladder contraction. These same gut hormones also cause the release of the pancreatic aqueous phase (bicarbonate and water) and the pancreatic digestive enzymes into the gut.

Although bile is stored in the gallbladder, it is actually produced in the liver. It is composed primarily of bile salts made from cholesterol, lecithins and other phospholipids, and

Fats and oils do not dissolve readily in water.

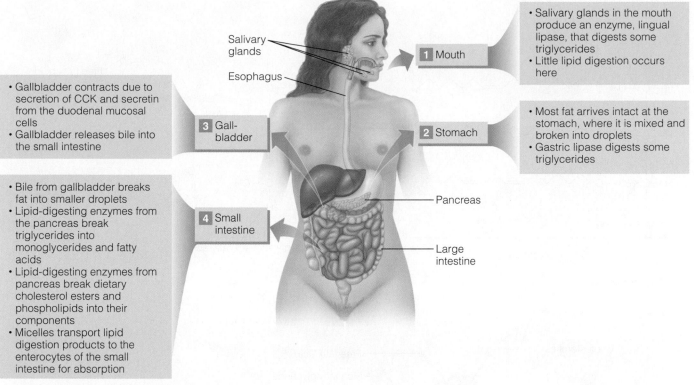

Salivary glands

Esophagus

1 Mouth
- Salivary glands in the mouth produce an enzyme, lingual lipase, that digests some triglycerides
- Little lipid digestion occurs here

- Gallbladder contracts due to secretion of CCK and secretin from the duodenal mucosal cells
- Gallbladder releases bile into the small intestine

3 Gall-bladder

2 Stomach
- Most fat arrives intact at the stomach, where it is mixed and broken into droplets
- Gastric lipase digests some triglycerides

- Bile from gallbladder breaks fat into smaller droplets
- Lipid-digesting enzymes from the pancreas break triglycerides into monoglycerides and fatty acids
- Lipid-digesting enzymes from pancreas break dietary cholesterol esters and phospholipids into their components
- Micelles transport lipid digestion products to the enterocytes of the small intestine for absorption

4 Small intestine

Pancreas

Large intestine

Figure 5.8 The process of lipid digestion.
Data from: Johnson, M., *Human Biology: Concepts and Current Issues, 5/e,* Fig. 3.3, Copyright © 2010 Benjamin Cummings. Reprinted by permission of Pearson Education, Inc.

electrolytes (for example, sodium, potassium, chloride, and calcium). *Lecithins* (also called phosphatidylcholine; see Figure 5.6a) are phospholipids in which a phosphate-containing compound and choline are combined and attached at the third carbon on the glycerol backbone. They are the primary emulsifiers in bile. The hydrophobic tails of lecithin molecules attract lipid droplets, clustering them together in tiny spheres, while the hydrophilic heads form a water-attracting shell. Lecithins enable bile to act much like soap, breaking up lipids into smaller and smaller droplets with a greater surface area. The more droplets there are, the greater the chance that digestive enzymes will be able to reach their target. Interestingly, lecithins are abundant in egg yolk, which is frequently used as an emulsifier in cooking—for instance, when oil and vinegar are combined to make mayonnaise.

At the same time the bile is mixing with the lipids to emulsify them, lipid-digesting enzymes produced in the pancreas travel through the pancreatic duct into the small intestine. Each lipid product requires a specific digestive enzyme or enzymes. For example, triglycerides require both pancreatic lipase and co-lipase for digestion. The co-lipase anchors the pancreatic lipase to the lipid droplet so that it can break the fatty acids away from their glycerol backbones. Each triglyceride molecule is broken down into two free fatty acids, which are removed from the first and third carbons on the glycerol backbone, and one *monoacylglyceride,* a glycerol molecule with one fatty acid still attached at the second carbon on the glycerol backbone (**Figure 5.9a**).

Specific enzymes also assist the digestion of cholesterol esters and phospholipids. As noted in Figure 5.7c, when a fatty acid is attached to cholesterol it is called a cholesterol ester. Some of the cholesterol in our diet is in this form; thus, we need cholesterol esterase, an enzyme released from the pancreas, to break the ester bond between cholesterol and its attached fatty acid and release a free cholesterol molecule and a free fatty acid. Phospholipase enzymes are responsible for breaking phospholipids into smaller parts. Thus, the end products of digestion are much smaller molecules that can be more easily captured and transported to the enterocytes for absorption.

Lecithins are abundant in egg yolk, which is used as an emulsifier in products such as mayonnaise.

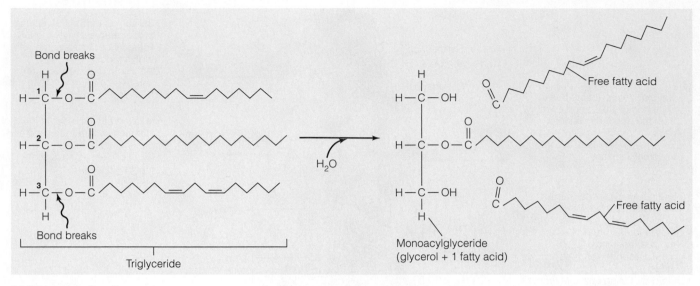

(a) Triglyceride digestion

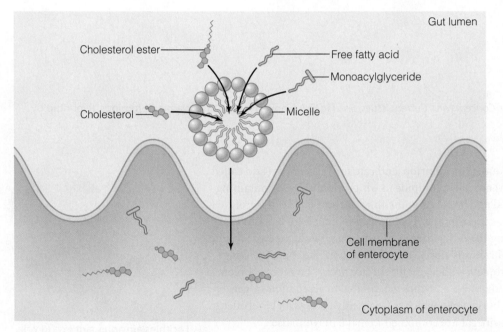

(b) Micelle transport into enterocyte

Figure 5.9 Lipid digestion and absorption. **(a)** In the presence of enzymes, triglycerides are broken down into fatty acids and monoacyl-glycerides. **(b)** These products, along with cholesterol and cholesterol esters, are trapped in the micelle, a spherical compound made up of bile salts and biliary phospholipids. The micelle then transports these lipid digestion products to the intestinal mucosal cell, and these products are then absorbed into the cell.

Absorption of Lipids Occurs Primarily in the Small Intestine

The majority of lipid absorption occurs in the mucosal lining of the small intestine with the help of micelles (see Figure 5.8, step 4). A **micelle** is a spherical compound made up of bile salts and biliary phospholipids that can capture the lipid digestion products, such as free fatty acids, free cholesterol, and the monoglycerides, and transport them to the enterocytes for absorption (Figure 5.9b). The micelle has a hydrophobic core and a hydrophilic surface, which is excellent for transporting lipids in the watery environment of the gut.

How do the absorbed lipids—which do not mix with water—get into the bloodstream? Within the enterocytes, the fatty acids and monoglycerides are reformulated back into

micelle A spherical compound made up of bile salts and biliary phospho-lipids that transports lipid digestion products to the intestinal mucosal cell.

triglycerides and then packaged into lipoproteins before they're released into the bloodstream. A **lipoprotein** is a spherical compound with triglycerides clustered in the centre along with cholesterol esters, free cholesterol, and other hydrophobic lipids, and phospholipids and proteins forming the outside of the sphere (**Figure 5.10**). The specific lipoprotein produced in the enterocytes to transport lipids from a meal is called a **chylomicron**.

The process of forming a chylomicron begins with the re-creation of the triglycerides and the cholesterol esters in the enterocytes (**Figure 5.11**). These products are then loosely enclosed within an outer shell made of phospholipids and proteins. The chylomicron is now soluble in water because phospholipids and proteins are water soluble. Once chylomicrons are formed, they are transported out of the enterocytes to the lymphatic system, which empties into the bloodstream through the thoracic duct at the left subclavian vein in the neck. In this way, the dietary fat consumed in a meal is transported into the blood. Soon after a meal containing fat, there is an increase of chylomicrons in the blood as the fat is transported into the body. For most individuals, chylomicrons are cleared rapidly from the blood, usually within 6 to 8 hours after a moderate-fat meal, which is why patients are instructed to fast overnight before having blood drawn for a laboratory analysis of blood lipid levels.

As mentioned earlier, short- and medium-chain fatty acids (those less than 14 carbons in length) can be transported in the body more readily than long-chain fatty acids. This is because short- and medium-chain fatty acids transported to the muscosal cells do not have to be re-formed into triglycerides and incorporated into chylomicrons (see Figure 5.11). Instead, they can travel in the portal bloodstream bound to either the transport protein albumin or a phospholipid. In general, our diets are low in short- and medium-chain fatty acids; however, they can be extracted from certain oils for clinical use in feeding patients who cannot digest long-chain fatty acids.

Fat Is Stored in Adipose Tissues for Later Use

After a meal, the chylomicrons, which are filled with dietary triglycerides, begin to circulate through the blood, looking for a place to deliver their load. There are three primary fates of these dietary triglycerides:

1. They can immediately be taken up and used as a source of energy for the cells, especially by the muscle cells.
2. They can be used to make lipid-containing compounds in the body.
3. They can be stored in the muscle or adipose tissue for later use. (See **Figure 5.12** for an illustration of an adipose cell.)

How do the triglycerides get out of the chylomicrons and into the cells of the body, such as the adipose or muscle cells? This process occurs with the help of an enzyme called **lipoprotein lipase**, or LPL, which is found on the outside of our cells. For example, when chylomicrons touch the surface of an adipose cell, they come into contact with LPL. As a result of this contact, LPL breaks apart the triglycerides in the core of the chylomicrons. This process frees individual fatty acids to move into the adipose cell. If the adipose cell needs the fat for energy, these fatty acids will be quickly used as fuel. If the cell doesn't need the fatty acids for immediate energy, they will have to be stored. However, cells cannot store individual fatty acids; instead, cells convert these fatty acids back into a triglyceride for storage. Because adipose cells are the only

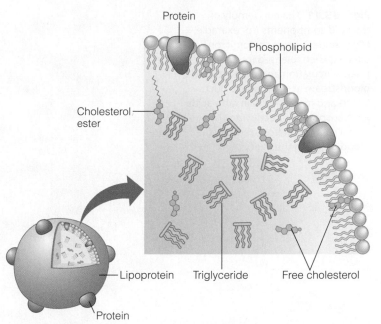
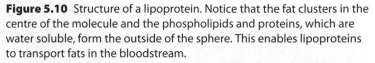

Figure 5.10 Structure of a lipoprotein. Notice that the fat clusters in the centre of the molecule and the phospholipids and proteins, which are water soluble, form the outside of the sphere. This enables lipoproteins to transport fats in the bloodstream.

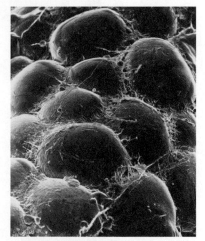

Adipose tissue. During times of weight gain, excess fat consumed in the diet is stored in the adipose tissue.

lipoprotein A spherical compound in which fat clusters in the centre and phospholipids and proteins form the outside of the sphere.

chylomicron A lipoprotein produced in the mucosal cell of the intestine; transports dietary fat out of the intestinal tract.

lipoprotein lipase An enzyme that sits on the outside of cells and breaks apart triglycerides so that their fatty acids can be removed and taken up by the cell.

Figure 5.11 The reassembly of the lipid components (for example, triglycerides) into a chylomicron, which is then released into the lymphatic circulation and then into the bloodstream at the thoracic duct. Short- and medium-chain fatty acids are transported directly into the portal circulation (for example, the blood going to the liver).

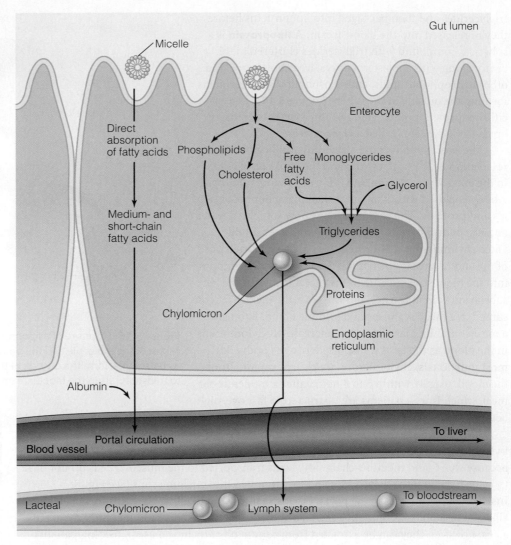

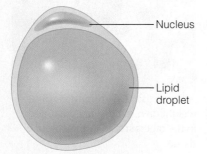

Figure 5.12 Diagram of an adipose cell.

body cells that have significant storage capacity for triglycerides, most fat not needed for energy is stored in adipose tissues for later use.

Although the primary storage site for triglycerides is the body's adipose tissues, if you are physically active, your body will preferentially store this extra fat in your muscle tissues. This ensures that, the next time you go out for a run, the fat will be readily available for energy. Thus, people who engage in physical activity are more likely to have extra triglyceride stored in the muscle tissue and to have less body fat—something many of us would prefer. Of course, fat stored in your adipose tissues can also be used for energy during exercise, but it must be broken down first and then transported to your muscle cells.

RECAP

Fat digestion begins when fats are emulsified by bile. Lipid-digesting enzymes from the pancreas subsequently digest the triglycerides into two free fatty acids and one monoglyceride. These are transported into the intestinal mucosal cells with the help of micelles. Once inside the mucosal cells, triglycerides are re-formed and packaged into lipoproteins called chylomicrons. Dietary fat, in the form of triglycerides, is transported by the chylomicrons to cells within the body that need energy. Triglycerides stored in the muscle tissue are used as a source of energy during physical activity. Excess triglycerides are stored in the adipose tissue and can be used whenever the body needs energy.

Why Do We Need Lipids?

Lipids, in the form of dietary fat, provide energy and help our bodies perform essential physiologic functions.

Dietary fat provides energy.

Lipids Provide Energy

Dietary fat is a primary source of energy because fat has more than twice the energy per gram as carbohydrate or protein. Fat provides 9 kilocalories (kcals) per gram, whereas carbohydrate and protein provide only 4 kcals per gram. This means that fat is much more energy dense. For example, 15 mL of butter or oil contains approximately 100 kcals, whereas it takes 625 mL of steamed broccoli or 1 slice of whole-wheat bread to provide 100 kcals.

Lipids Are a Major Fuel Source When We Are at Rest

At rest, we are able to deliver plenty of oxygen to our cells so that metabolic functions can occur. Just as a candle needs oxygen for the flame to continue burning, our cells need oxygen to use fat for energy. Thus, approximately 30% to 70% of the energy used at rest by the muscles and organs comes from lipids.[4] The exact amount of energy coming from lipids at rest will depend on how much fat you are eating in your diet, how physically active you are, and whether you are gaining or losing weight. If you are dieting, more lipid will be used for energy than if you are gaining weight. During times of weight gain, more of the fat consumed in the diet is stored in the adipose tissue, and the body uses more dietary protein and carbohydrate as fuel sources at rest.

Lipids Fuel Physical Activity

Lipids are the major energy source during physical activity, and one of the best ways to lose body fat is to exercise and reduce energy intake. During aerobic exercise, such as running or cycling, lipids can be mobilized from any of the following sources of body fat: muscle tissue, adipose tissue, and blood lipoproteins. A number of hormonal changes signal the body to break down stored energy to fuel the working muscles. The hormonal responses, and the amount and source of the lipids used, depend on your level of fitness; the type, intensity, and duration of the exercise; and how well fed you are before you exercise.

For example, adrenaline (that is, epinephrine) strongly stimulates the breakdown of stored fat. Within minutes of beginning exercise, blood levels of epinephrine rise dramatically. Through a cascade of events, this surge of epinephrine activates an enzyme within adipose cells called *hormone-sensitive lipase*. This enzyme works to remove single fatty acids from the stored triglycerides. When all three free fatty acids on the glycerol backbone have been removed, the free fatty acids and the glycerol are released into the blood.

Epinephrine also signals the pancreas to *decrease* insulin production. This is important, because insulin inhibits fat breakdown. Thus, when the need for fat as an energy source is high, blood insulin levels are typically low. As you might guess, blood insulin levels are high when we are eating, because during this time our need for energy from stored fat is low and the need for fat storage is high.

Once fatty acids are released from the adipose cells, they travel in the blood attached to the transport protein albumin, to the muscle cells. There, they enter the mitochondria, the cell's energy-generating structures, and use oxygen to produce ATP, which is the cell's energy source. Becoming more physically fit means you can deliver more oxygen to the muscle cells to use the fatty acids delivered there. In addition, you can exercise longer when you are fit. Because the body has only a limited supply of stored carbohydrate as glycogen in muscle tissue, the longer you exercise, the more fatty acids you use

The longer you exercise, the more fat you use for energy. Cyclists in a long-distance race make greater use of fat stores as the race progresses.

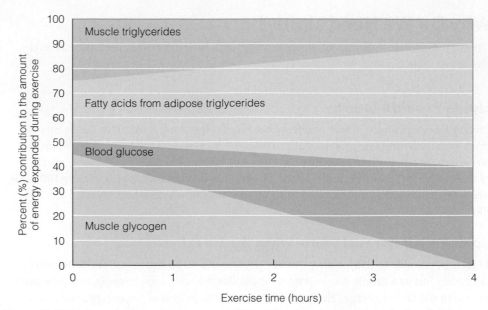

Figure 5.13 Various sources of energy used during exercise. As a person exercises for a prolonged period of time, fatty acids from adipose cells contribute relatively more energy than do carbohydrates stored in the muscle or circulating in the blood. (*Data from:* Coyle, E. F. 1995. Substrate utilization during exercise in active people. *Am. J. Clin. Nutr.* 61[Suppl.]:968S–979S. Used with permission.)

for energy. This point is illustrated in **Figure 5.13**. In this example, an individual is running for four hours at a moderate intensity. As the muscle glycogen levels become depleted, the body relies on fatty acids from the adipose tissue as a fuel source.

Fatty acids cannot be used to produce glucose; however, recall that the breakdown of triglycerides also frees molecules of glycerol into the bloodstream. Some of this free glycerol travels to the liver, where it can be used for the production of modest amounts of glucose (in the process of gluconeogenesis).

Body Fat Stores Energy for Later Use

The body stores extra energy in the form of body fat, which then can be used for energy at rest, during exercise, or during periods of low energy intake. Having a readily available energy source in the form of fat allows the body to always have access to energy even when we choose not to eat (or are unable to eat), when we are exercising, and while we are sleeping. The body has small amounts of stored carbohydrate in the form of glycogen—only enough to last about one to two days—and there is no place that the body can store extra protein. We cannot consider our muscles and organs as a place where "extra" protein is stored! For these reasons, the fat stored in adipose and muscle tissues is necessary to fuel the body between meals. Although too much stored adipose tissue can harm our health, some fat storage is essential to protect our health.

Essential Fatty Acids Are Components of Important Biological Compounds

As discussed earlier, EFAs are needed to make a number of important biological compounds. They also are important constituents of cell membranes, help prevent DNA damage, help fight infection, and are essential for fetal growth and development. In the growing fetus, EFAs are necessary for normal growth, especially for the development of the brain and visual centres.

Dietary Fat Enables the Transport of Fat-Soluble Vitamins

Dietary fat enables the absorption and transport of the fat-soluble vitamins (A, D, E, and K) needed by the body for many essential metabolic functions. The fat-soluble vitamins are transported in the gut to the intestinal cells for absorption as part of micelles, and they are transported in the blood to the body cells as part of chylomicrons.[5] The fat-soluble vitamins include vitamin A, which is important for normal vision and night vision. Vitamin D helps regulate blood calcium and phosphorous concentrations within normal ranges, which indirectly helps maintain bone health. Vitamin E keeps cell membranes healthy throughout the body, and vitamin K is important for proteins involved in blood clotting and bone health. We discuss these vitamins in detail in later chapters.

Lipids Help Maintain Cell Function and Provide Protection to the Body

Lipids, especially PUFAs and phospholipids, are a critical part of every cell membrane, where they help to maintain membrane integrity, determine what substances are transported in and out of the cell, and regulate what substances can bind to the cell. Thus, lipids strongly influence the function of cells.

In addition, lipids help maintain cell fluidity. For example, wild salmon live in very cold water and have high levels of omega-3 fatty acids in their cell membranes. These fatty acids stay fluid and flexible even at very low temperatures, thereby enabling the fish to swim in extremely cold water. In the same way, lipids help our membranes stay fluid and flexible. For example, red blood cells require flexibility to bend and move through the smallest capillaries in the body, delivering oxygen to all body cells.

PUFAs are also primary components of the tissues of the brain and spinal cord, where they facilitate the transmission of information from one cell to another. The body also uses lipids for the development, growth, and maintenance of these tissues.

Stored body fat also plays an important role in the body. Besides being the primary site of stored energy, adipose tissue pads the body and protects the organs, such as the kidneys and liver, when we fall or are bruised. Fat under the skin also acts as insulation to help retain body heat. Although we often think of body fat as "bad," it plays an important role in keeping the body healthy and functioning properly.

Adipose tissue pads the body and protects the organs when we fall or are bruised.

Fats Contribute to the Flavour and Texture of Foods

Dietary fat adds texture and flavour to foods. Fat makes salad dressings smooth and ice cream "creamy," and it gives cakes and cookies their moist, tender texture. Frying foods in melted fat or oil, as with donuts or French fries, gives them a crisp, flavourful coating; however, eating such foods regularly can be unhealthy because they are high in saturated and/or *trans* fatty acids.

Fats Help Us Feel Satiated Because They Are Energy Dense

We often hear that fats contribute to satiation and satiety. First, what does this mean? A food or nutrient is said to contribute to *satiation* if that food makes you feel full and causes you to stop eating. A food or nutrient is said to contribute to *satiety* if it contributes to a feeling of fullness that subsequently reduces the amount of food you eat at the next meal or lengthens the time between meals.

Fat adds texture and flavour to foods.

A number of research studies have compared the effects of fat and carbohydrate on both satiation and satiety. In general, this research has found little difference between these two macronutrients when palatability (taste) and energy density have been controlled.[6, 7] However, high-fat foods are often very palatable, so it is easy to overeat them. In addition, fats are more energy dense than carbohydrates and protein. For example, 250 mL of whole milk provides 8.4 g of fat and 157 kcal, whereas 250 mL of low-fat milk (1% fat) provides 2.5 g of fat and 108 kcal. For every gram of fat you consume, you get 2.25 times the amount of energy that you get with a gram of protein or carbohydrate. The energy density of a food affects the level of gastric distention produced by the food consumed and by how quickly food empties from the stomach. The rate at which foods reach the satiety receptors in the gut and release satiety hormones can also be influenced by the energy density of food.[6] Therefore, eating a high-fat meal tends to have a greater satiety value than a high-carbohydrate meal.

RECAP

Dietary fats play a number of important roles within the body. (1) Dietary fats provide the majority of energy required at rest and are a major fuel source during exercise, especially endurance exercise. (2) Dietary fats provide essential fatty acids (linoleic and alpha-linolenic acid). (3) Dietary fats help transport the fat-soluble vitamins into the body. (4) Dietary fats help regulate cell function and maintain membrane integrity. (5) Stored body fat in the adipose tissue helps protect vital organs and pads the body. (6) Fats contribute to the flavour and texture of foods, and because fats are energy dense, they are one factor that contributes to the satiety we feel after a meal.

How Much Dietary Fat Should We Eat?

The latest research comparing low-carbohydrate to low-fat diets has made Canadians wonder what, exactly, is a healthy level of dietary fat and what foods contain the most beneficial fats. We'll explore these issues here.

Dietary Reference Intake for Total Fat

The Acceptable Macronutrient Distribution Range (AMDR) for fat is 20% to 35% of total energy.[8] This recommendation is based on evidence indicating that higher intakes of fat increase the risk of obesity and its complications, especially heart disease and diabetes, but that diets too low in fat and too high in carbohydrate can also increase the risk of heart disease if they cause blood triglycerides to increase and high-density lipoprotein cholesterol to decrease.[8] Within this range of fat intake, it is also recommended that we minimize our intake of saturated and *trans* fatty acids; these changes will lower our risk of heart disease.

Because carbohydrate is essential in replenishing glycogen, athletes and other physically active people are advised to consume less fat and more carbohydrate than sedentary people.[9]

Although many people trying to lose weight consume less than 20% of their energy from fat, this practice may do more harm than good, especially if they are also limiting energy intake (eating fewer than 1500 kcals per day). Research suggests that very-low-fat diets, or those with less than 15% of energy from fat, do not provide additional health or performance benefits over moderate-fat diets and are usually very difficult to follow.[10] In fact, most people find they feel better, are more successful in weight maintenance, and are less preoccupied with food if they keep their fat intakes at 20% to 25% of energy intake. Additionally, people attempting to reduce their dietary fat frequently eliminate protein-rich foods, such as meat, dairy, eggs, and nuts. These foods are also potential sources of many essential vitamins and minerals important for good health and for maintaining an active lifestyle. Diets extremely low in fat may also be deficient in essential fatty acids.

Did You Know?

Canadian scientists first raised concerns about the harmful effects of *trans* fat and the rising levels in the Canadian diet in the early 1990s. At that time, it was estimated that Canadians had one of the highest intakes of *trans* fats in the world.[11] It wasn't until 2005, however, that the Government of Canada formed the Trans Fat Task Force to develop recommendations and strategies to reduce *trans* fat in Canadian foods.[12] The task force commissioned a literature review and consulted with scientific experts, industry representatives, and the public. They published their report in 2006,[11] which recommended limiting the *trans* fat content of vegetable oils and soft, spreadable margarines to 2% of the total fat content and for all other foods to 5% of the total fat content, including ingredients sold to restaurants.[12] These recommendations were adopted by Health Canada in 2007. In addition, Health Canada implemented a two-year Trans Fat Monitoring Program to ensure that the target levels were met. Foods that are significant sources of *trans* fat are analyzed and the results of these analyses are posted on the Health Canada website every six months. Canada is the first country in the world to publish this type of data.[12]

Dietary Reference Intakes for Essential Fatty Acids

Dietary Reference Intakes (DRIs) for the two essential fatty acids were set in 2002:[8]

- *Linoleic acid.* The Adequate Intake (AI) for linoleic acid is 14 to 17 g per day for men and 11 to 12 g per day for women 19 years and older. Using the typical energy intakes for adult men and women, this translates into an AMDR of 5% to 10% of energy.
- *Alpha-linolenic acid.* The AI for alpha-linolenic acid is 1.6 g per day for adult men and 1.1 g per day for adult women. This translates into an AMDR of 0.6% to 1.2% of energy.

For example, an individual consuming 2000 kcal per day should consume about 11 to 22 g per day of linoleic acid and about 1.3 to 2.6 g per day of alpha-linolenic acid. This level of intake would keep one within the 5:1 to 10:1 ratio of linoleic:alpha-linolenic acid recommended by the World Health Organization and supported by the Institute of Medicine.[8] Because these fatty acids compete for the same enzymes to produce various eicosanoids that regulate body functions, this ratio helps keep the eicosanoids produced in balance; that is, one isn't overproduced at the expense of another.

Most Canadians Eat Within the Recommended Percentage of Fat but Eat the Wrong Types

Many nutrition experts have been recommending the reduction of dietary fat for more than 20 years. Data have shown that total and saturated fat intake has declined in Canada since the 1970s.[13] According to the most recent Canadian Community Health Survey (CCHS 2.2), most Canadian adults (19 years of age and older) have total fat intakes within the AMDR (20%–35% of total kcal). However, 25% of males and 23% of females have fat intakes above the AMDR, and all Canadian adults have median intakes of linoleic acid less than the AI.[14]

Of the dietary fat we eat, saturated and *trans* fats are most highly correlated with an increased risk of heart disease because they increase blood cholesterol levels by altering the way cholesterol is removed from the blood. Thus, the recommended intake of saturated fat is less than 10% of our total energy; unfortunately, our average intake of saturated fats is approximately 10% of energy.[13] The Institute of Medicine also recommends that we keep our intake of *trans* fatty acids to an absolute minimum.[8] Determining the actual amount of *trans* fatty acids consumed in Canada has been hindered by the lack of an accurate and comprehensive database of foods containing *trans* fatty acids. It is estimated that Canadian's consumption of *trans* fat has declined by 40% over the past 10 years (from 8.3 g per day to 4.9 gram per day).[15]

Don't Let the Fats Fool You

The last time you picked up a frozen dinner in the grocery store, did you stop and read the Nutrition Facts table on the box? If you had, you might have been shocked to learn how much saturated fat was in the meal. As we discuss here, many processed foods are hidden sources of fat, especially saturated and *trans* fats. In contrast, many whole foods, such as oils and nuts, are rich sources of the healthy fats our bodies need.

Watch Out for Invisible Fats

Canadians not only eat lots of high-fat foods but also commonly add fat to foods to improve their taste. Added fats, such as oils, butter, cream, shortening, margarine, mayonnaise, and salad dressings are called **visible fats** because we can easily see that we are adding them to our food.

When we add cream to coffee or butter to pancakes, we know how much fat we are adding and what kind. In contrast, when fat is added in the preparation of a frozen entrée or a fast food burger and fries, we are less aware of how much or what type of fat is actually there. In fact, we might not be aware that a food contains any fat at all. We call fats in prepared and processed foods **invisible fats** because they are hidden within the food. In fact, their invisibility often tricks us into choosing them over healthier foods. For example, a slice of yellow cake is much higher in fat (40% of total energy) than a slice of angel food cake (1% of total energy). Yet many consumers assume that the fat content of these foods is the same, because they are both cake.

The majority of the fat in the average Canadian diet is invisible. Foods that can be high in invisible fats are baked goods, regular-fat dairy products, processed meats or meats that are highly marbled or not trimmed, and most convenience and fast foods, such as hamburgers, hot dogs, chips, ice cream, French fries, and other fried foods.

Because high-fat diets have been associated with obesity, many Canadians have tried to reduce their total fat intake. Food manufacturers have been more than happy to provide consumers with low-fat alternatives to their favourite foods. However, these lower-fat foods may not always have fewer calories. See the upcoming Highlight box "Low-Fat, Reduced-Fat, Non-Fat . . . What's the Difference?" and Table 5.1.

Select Beneficial Fats

In general, it is prudent to switch to healthier sources of fats without increasing your total fat intake. For example, use olive oil and canola oil in place of butter and margarine, and select fish more frequently instead of high-fat meat sources (hot dogs, hamburgers, sausage). Dairy products, including cheeses, can be high in saturated fats, so select low- and reduced-fat versions when possible. Read the Nutrition Label Activity, page 185, "How Much Fat Is in This Food?" to learn how to calculate the kilocalories from fat in the foods you buy.

As previously mentioned, recent data suggest that all Canadian adults have median intakes of linoleic acid (omega-6) lower than the AI.[14] This finding was surprising to many

Baked goods are often high in invisible fats.

visible fats   Fat we can see in our foods or see added to foods, such as butter, margarine, cream, shortening, salad dressings, chicken skin, and untrimmed fat on meat.

invisible fats   Fats that are hidden in foods, such as the fats found in baked goods, regular-fat dairy products, marbling in meat, and fried foods.

Table 5.1 Comparison of Full-Fat, Reduced-Fat, and Low-Fat Foods

Product	Serving Size	Energy (kcal)	Protein (g)	Carbohydrate (g)	Fat (g)
Milk, whole, 3.3% MF	250 mL	157	8.1	12.4	8.4
Milk, 2% MF	250 mL	129	8.5	12.4	5.1
Milk, 1% MF	250 mL	108	8.7	12.9	2.5
Milk, skim (non-fat)	250 mL	88	8.7	12.9	0.2
Cheese, cheddar, regular	50 g	202	12.5	0.6	16.6
Cheese, cheddar, reduced-fat	50 g	141	13.6	1.0	9.2
Cheese, cheddar, low-fat	50 g	86	12.2	1.0	3.5
Mayonnaise, regular	15 mL	101	0.1	0.4	11.1
Mayonnaise, reduced-fat	15 mL	39	0.1	3.5	2.8
Mayonnaise, fat-free	15 mL	14	0.03	2.5	0.4
Margarine, regular, tub	15 mL	103	0.03	0.1	11.5
Margarine, reduced-fat	15 mL	50	0.1	0.1	5.6
Peanut butter, regular	30 mL	191	8.1	6.4	16.3
Peanut butter, reduced-fat	30 mL	190	9.5	13.0	12.4
Cream cheese, soft regular	15 mL	50	0.9	0.6	5.0
Cream cheese, soft light	15 mL	31	1.2	1.2	2.3
Cream cheese, soft fat-free	15 mL	17	2.5	1.2	0.2
Crackers, wheat	4 (20g)	91	1.8	13.5	3.5
Crackers, wheat, reduced-fat	4 (18g)	74	1.8	11.6	2.2
Cookies, chocolate chip, regular (18%–28% fat)	1	47	0.5	6.4	2.3
Cookies, chocolate chip, reduced-fat (12%–17%)	1	45	0.6	7.3	1.5
Granola bar, chewy fruit and/or nut	1	142	2.8	24.5	4.1
Granola bar, chewy, low-fat	1	111	1.9	22.4	2.6

The Food and Drugs Act specifies allowable product descriptions for reduced-fat products. The following claims are defined for one serving:
Fat-free: less than 0.5 g of fat
Low-fat: 3 g or less of fat
Reduced-fat or lower-fat: at least 25% less fat as compared to a similar reference food
Light: food is reduced in fat
Data from: The Canadian Nutrient File. Health Canada, 2012. Reproduced with the permission of the Minister of Health, 2012.

experts given that linoleic acid deficiency is thought to be non-existent in Canada. This has led to speculation that the way the AI was set might be misleading. The AI was based on observed intakes from the United States, where the predominant oil is soybean oil. In Canada we eat primarily canola oil, which contains less linoleic acid.[14] If the AI values had been set based on observed intakes among Canadians, they may have been lower than the current DRI values.

It is assumed that there is a low prevalence of inadequate intakes of linolenic acid (omega-3) among adult Canadians since most have intakes above the AI.[14] However, people who do not eat dark green, leafy vegetables; fish or walnuts; soy products; canola oil; or flaxseeds or their oil may have low intakes of omega-3 fatty acids. Table 5.2 on page 182 identifies the omega-3 fatty acid content of various foods.

Table 5.2 Omega-3 Fatty Acid Content of Selected Foods

Food Item	Omega-3 Fatty Acid (grams per serving)
Salmon oil (fish oil) (15 mL)	4.87
Herring, Atlantic, broiled (75 g)	1.65
Herring oil (15 mL)	1.63
Canola oil (15 mL)	1.30
Trout, rainbow (farmed), baked (75 g)	0.92
Walnuts (15 mL)	0.69
Halibut, fillet, baked (75 g)	0.50
Salmon, Chinook, smoked (75 g)	0.38
Crab, Dungeness, steamed (75 g)	0.31
Shrimp, boiled (75 g)	0.26
Tuna, light in water (75 g)	0.20

Data from: The Canadian Nutrient File. Health Canada, 2012. Reproduced with the permission of the Minister of Health, 2012.

It is important to recognize that there can be some risk associated with eating large amounts of fish on a regular basis. Depending on the species of fish and the level of pollution in the water in which it is caught, the fish may contain high levels of poisons such as mercury, polychlorinated biphenyls (PCBs), and other environmental contaminants. Types of fish that are currently considered safe to consume include salmon (except from the Great Lakes region), farmed trout, flounder, sole, mahi mahi, and cooked shellfish. Fish more likely to be contaminated are shark, swordfish, golden bass, golden snapper, marlin, bluefish, and largemouth and smallmouth bass. Canned albacore tuna (also known as white tuna) should be limited in the diets of pregnant women and children (up to age 11) due to its higher mercury content. This advice does not apply to canned light tuna, because it contains other tuna species that are relatively low in mercury.

HIGHLIGHT

Low-Fat, Reduced-Fat, Non-Fat . . . What's the Difference?

Although most people love the taste of high-fat foods, most Canadians also know that eating too much fat isn't good for their health.[16] Food manufacturers have responded to this concern by producing a host of modified-fat foods—so you can have your cake and eat it too. Or can you? In Table 5.1 we list a number of full-fat foods with their lower-fat alternatives. These products, if incorporated in the diet on a regular basis, can significantly reduce the amount of fat consumed, but may or may not reduce the amount of energy consumed. For example, drinking non-fat (or skim) milk (88 kilocalories and 0.2 g of fat per serving) instead of whole milk (157 kilocalories and 8.4 g of fat per serving) will dramatically reduce both fat and energy intake. However, eating reduced-fat peanut butter (190 kilocalories and 12.4 g of fat per 30 mL) does not significantly reduce energy intake, even though it reduces fat intake by about 4 g per serving.

Thus, those who think that they can eat all the low-fat foods they want without gaining weight are mistaken. The reduced fat is often replaced with added carbohydrate, resulting in a sweeter taste and very similar total energy intake. If you want to reduce the amount of fat and the number of kilocalories you consume, you must read the labels of modified-fat foods carefully before you buy.

Be Aware of Fat Replacers

The rising rates of obesity and its associated health concerns have increased the demand for low-fat versions of our favourite foods, which in turn has created a booming industry for *fat replacers,* substances that mimic the palate-pleasing and flavour-enhancing properties of fats with fewer kilocalories. Snack foods and desserts have been the primary target for fat replacers because it is difficult to simply eliminate all or most of the fat in these products without dramatically changing their taste. In the mid-1990s, both food industry executives and nutritionists thought that fat replacers would be the answer to our growing obesity problem. They reasoned that if we could replace some of the fats in snack and fast foods with these products, we might be able to reduce both energy and fat intake and help Canadians manage their weight better.

Olestra (marketed as Olean), a fat replacer developed by Proctor & Gamble, hit U.S. grocery shelves in 1996. Olestra is a non-absorbable, non-caloric fat substitute that has properties that are similar to fat and is stable at temperatures used for baking and frying, making it an attractive choice for reducing the fat content of many types of foods.[17] It is not hydrolyzed by digestive enzymes and is too large to be absorbed; it therefore passes through the human digestive tract and is excreted. However, the consumption of olestra does reduce the absorption of carotenoids and fat-soluble vitamins and was initially thought to have gastrointestinal side effects, primarily causing loose stools and diarrhea. This caused the U.S. Food and Drug Administration (FDA) to require all olestra-containing food products to be fortified with fat-soluble vitamins and to include a label warning about the potential side effects. In 2003, the FDA announced that this warning was no longer necessary as research had shown that olestra caused only mild, infrequent discomfort.[18] Although there is some research that has shown that the substitution of olestra in a reduced-fat diet results in sustained weight loss[19, 20] and is more effective than a low-fat diet alone, only limited foods in the marketplace in the United States contain olestra and it is not allowed to be used in Canada. Health Canada commissioned a review of the scientific evidence related to olestra and in 2000 decided not to recommend olestra as a food additive.

Recently, a new group of fat replacers has been developed using proteins, such as the whey protein found in milk. Like their predecessors, these new fat replacers lower the fat content of food, but in addition, they improve the food's total nutrient profile and decrease its kilocalorie content. This means we can have a low-fat ice cream with the mouthfeel, finish, and texture of a full-fat ice cream that is also higher in protein and lower in kilocalories than traditional ice cream. So don't be surprised if you see more products containing protein-based fat replacers, such as Simplesse, on your supermarket shelves in the next few years.

RECAP

The AMDR for total fat is 20% to 35% of total energy. The AI for linoleic acid is 14 to 17 g per day for adult men and 11 to 12 g per day for adult women. The AI for alpha-linolenic acid is 1.6 g per day for adult men and 1.1 g per day for adult women. Because saturated and *trans* fatty acids can increase the risk of heart disease, health professionals recommend that we reduce our intake of saturated fat to less than 10% of our total energy intake and reduce our intake of *trans* fatty acids to the absolute minimum. Visible fats can be easily recognized, but invisible fats are added to our food during manufacturing or cooking, so we are not aware of how much we are consuming. A healthy dietary strategy is to switch from saturated and *trans* fats to MUFAs, PUFAs, and EFAs. Fat replacers are used to reduce the fat content of processed foods and, in some cases, improve the nutrient profile while reducing the number of calories.

What Role Do Lipids Play in Cardiovascular Disease and Cancer?

There appears to be a generally held assumption that if you eat fat-free or low-fat foods, you will lose weight and prevent chronic diseases. Certainly, we know that high-fat diets, especially those high in saturated and *trans* fatty acids, can contribute to chronic diseases, including heart disease and cancer; however, as we have explored in this chapter, unsaturated fatty acids do not have this negative effect and are essential to good health. Thus, a sensible health goal would be to eat the appropriate amounts and types of fat.

Fats Can Protect Against or Promote Cardiovascular Disease

Cardiovascular disease is a general term used to refer to any abnormal condition involving dysfunction of the heart or the body's blood vessels. A common form of this disease is *coronary artery disease* (CAD), which occurs when blood vessels supplying the heart (the coronary arteries) become blocked or constricted; such blockage reduces blood flow to the heart and so can result in a heart attack. Similar blockage can occur in the cerebral arteries and impair blood flow to the brain, a condition commonly called a *stroke*. According to Statistics Canada, diseases of the heart are the second leading cause of death in Canada, and stroke is the third leading cause of death. (See Figure 1.3 in Chapter 1.) Combined, these two disease categories account for about 30% of all deaths annually.[21] In 2007, 1.3 million Canadians reported having cardiovascular disease[21] and it is estimated that it costs the Canadian economy more than $22.2 billion every year in associated healthcare costs, lost wages, and reduced productivity.[22]

Risk Factors for Cardiovascular Disease

During the past two decades, researchers have identified a number of factors that contribute to an increased risk for cardiovascular disease. Following is a brief description of each of these major risk factors, many of which have a dietary component.[22]

Being overweight is associated with higher rates of death from cardiovascular disease.

cardiovascular disease A general term that refers to abnormal conditions involving dysfunction of the heart and blood vessels; cardiovascular disease can result in heart attack or stroke.

- *Overweight:* Being overweight is associated with higher rates of death from cardiovascular disease. The risk is due primarily to a greater occurrence of high blood pressure, abnormal blood lipids (discussed in more detail shortly), and higher rates of diabetes in overweight individuals. In general, an overweight condition develops from an energy imbalance from eating too much and exercising too little (see Chapter 14).
- *Physical inactivity:* Numerous research studies have shown that physical activity can reduce your risk of cardiovascular disease by improving blood lipid levels, lowering resting blood pressure, reducing body fat and weight, and improving blood glucose levels both at rest and after eating.
- *Smoking:* There is strong evidence that smoking increases your risk for cardiovascular disease. Research indicates that smokers have a 70% greater chance of developing cardiovascular disease than non-smokers. Without question, smoking cessation or never starting initially is one of the best ways to reduce your risk of cardiovascular disease. People who stop smoking live longer than those who continue to smoke, and a 15-year cessation period will reduce your risk factors for cardiovascular disease to those of a non-smoker.
- *High blood pressure:* High blood pressure stresses the heart and increases the chance that blockage or rupture of a blood vessel will occur. Elevated blood pressure is associated with a number of factors, including dietary factors (for example, high sodium intakes, low calcium and/or potassium intakes), elevated blood lipid levels, obesity, smoking, diabetes, and physical inactivity.

NUTRITION LABEL ACTIVITY

How Much Fat Is in This Food?

How do you know how much fat is in a food you buy? One simple way to determine the amount of fat in the food you eat is to read the Nutrition Facts label. By becoming a better label reader you can make healthier food choices.

The Nutrition Facts labels from two different types of crackers are shown in **Figure 5.14**; one cracker is a regular snack cracker and the other is marketed as a baked snack cracker. Consider the information shown on these labels and work through the following questions.

Thinking Critically

1. **Compare the fat content in each of these crackers. (Be sure to include in your answer a comparison of the different types of fat.)**
2. **How many kilocalories are coming from fat in each of these crackers?**
3. **What percentage of total kilocalories is coming from fat in each of these crackers?**
4. **Which cracker would you choose? Why?**

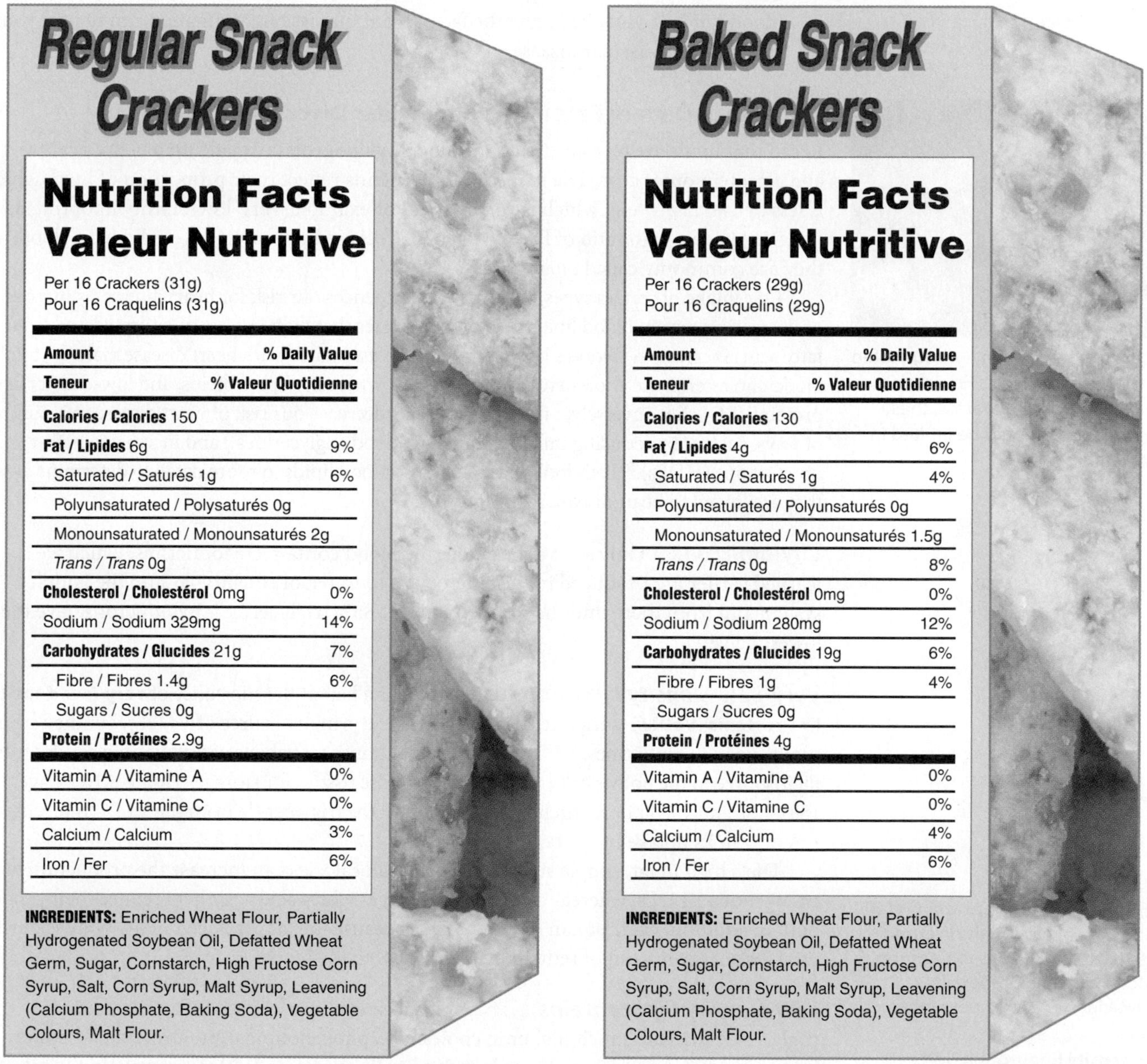

Regular Snack Crackers

Nutrition Facts
Valeur Nutritive

Per 16 Crackers (31g)
Pour 16 Craquelins (31g)

Amount	% Daily Value
Teneur	**% Valeur Quotidienne**
Calories / Calories 150	
Fat / Lipides 6g	9%
Saturated / Saturés 1g	6%
Polyunsaturated / Polysaturés 0g	
Monounsaturated / Monounsaturés 2g	
Trans / Trans 0g	
Cholesterol / Cholestérol 0mg	0%
Sodium / Sodium 329mg	14%
Carbohydrates / Glucides 21g	7%
Fibre / Fibres 1.4g	6%
Sugars / Sucres 0g	
Protein / Protéines 2.9g	
Vitamin A / Vitamine A	0%
Vitamin C / Vitamine C	0%
Calcium / Calcium	3%
Iron / Fer	6%

INGREDIENTS: Enriched Wheat Flour, Partially Hydrogenated Soybean Oil, Defatted Wheat Germ, Sugar, Cornstarch, High Fructose Corn Syrup, Salt, Corn Syrup, Malt Syrup, Leavening (Calcium Phosphate, Baking Soda), Vegetable Colours, Malt Flour.

(a)

Baked Snack Crackers

Nutrition Facts
Valeur Nutritive

Per 16 Crackers (29g)
Pour 16 Craquelins (29g)

Amount	% Daily Value
Teneur	**% Valeur Quotidienne**
Calories / Calories 130	
Fat / Lipides 4g	6%
Saturated / Saturés 1g	4%
Polyunsaturated / Polyunsaturés 0g	
Monounsaturated / Monounsaturés 1.5g	
Trans / Trans 0g	8%
Cholesterol / Cholestérol 0mg	0%
Sodium / Sodium 280mg	12%
Carbohydrates / Glucides 19g	6%
Fibre / Fibres 1g	4%
Sugars / Sucres 0g	
Protein / Protéines 4g	
Vitamin A / Vitamine A	0%
Vitamin C / Vitamine C	0%
Calcium / Calcium	4%
Iron / Fer	6%

INGREDIENTS: Enriched Wheat Flour, Partially Hydrogenated Soybean Oil, Defatted Wheat Germ, Sugar, Cornstarch, High Fructose Corn Syrup, Salt, Corn Syrup, Malt Syrup, Leavening (Calcium Phosphate, Baking Soda), Vegetable Colours, Malt Flour.

(b)

Figure 5.14 Labels for two types of crackers: (a) Regular snack crackers. (b) Baked snack crackers.

- *Diabetes mellitus:* As discussed in Chapter 4, in many individuals with diabetes the condition is directly related to being overweight or obese, which is also associated with abnormal blood lipids and high blood pressure. The risk for cardiovascular disease is three times higher in women with diabetes and two times higher in men with diabetes compared with individuals without diabetes.

- *Inflammation:* Inflammation is now considered a major initiator of cardiovascular disease.[23] As you may know, inflammation occurs as a response to tissue injury. In arterial walls, this injury may be due to any number of physiologic stresses, such as high blood pressure, smoking, high blood lipids, or poor glucose control. When injury occurs to the arteries, the resulting inflammatory response eventually leads to the deposition of plaque in the arterial walls. Plaque buildup increases the risk of a heart attack or stroke. C-reactive protein (CRP) is a non-specific marker of inflammation that is associated with cardiovascular disease. Risk of cardiovascular disease appears to be higher in individuals who have high CRP levels in addition to other risk factors such as high blood lipids.[24] Thus, reducing the factors that increase inflammation can reduce your risk of cardiovascular disease.

The Role of Dietary Fats in Cardiovascular Disease

Recall that lipids are transported in the blood by lipoproteins made up of a lipid centre and a protein outer coat. The names of lipoproteins reflect their proportion of lipid, which is less dense, to protein, which is very dense. For example, very-low-density lipoproteins (VLDLs) have a high ratio of lipid to protein. Because lipoproteins are soluble in blood, they are commonly called *blood lipids.*

Our intake of certain types of dietary fats influences our risk for heart disease by increasing or decreasing certain blood lipids. Research indicates that high intakes of saturated and *trans* fatty acids increase the blood's level of those lipids associated with heart disease, namely, total blood cholesterol, the cholesterol found in very-low-density lipoproteins, and low-density lipoproteins (LDLs). Conversely, omega-3 fatty acids decrease our risk of heart disease in a number of ways, such as by reducing inflammation and blood triglycerides[25] and increasing high-density lipoproteins (HDLs).[26] Let's look at each of these blood lipids in more detail to determine how they are linked to heart disease risk (**Figure 5.15**).

Chylomicrons   Only after a meal does the blood contain chylomicrons, which we learned earlier are produced in the enterocytes to transport dietary fat into the lymph system and from there into the bloodstream. At 85% triglyceride, chylomicrons have the lowest density.

Very-Low-Density Lipoproteins   More than half of the substance of **very-low-density lipoproteins (VLDLs)** is triglyceride. The liver is the primary source of VLDLs, but they are also produced in the intestines. VLDLs are primarily transport vehicles ferrying triglycerides from their source to the body's cells, including to adipose tissues for storage (**Figure 5.16a**, page 188). The enzyme lipoprotein lipase frees most of the triglyceride from the VLDL molecules, resulting in its uptake by the body's cells.

Diets high in fat, simple sugars, and extra kilocalories can increase the production of endogenous VLDLs, whereas diets high in omega-3 fatty acids can help reduce their production. In addition, exercise can reduce VLDLs because the fat produced in the body is quickly used for energy instead of remaining to circulate in the blood.

Low-Density Lipoproteins   The molecules resulting when VLDLs release their triglyceride load are much higher in cholesterol, phospholipids, and protein and therefore somewhat more dense. These **low-density lipoproteins (LDLs)** circulate in the blood, delivering their cholesterol to cells with specialized LDL receptors (see Figure 5.16b). Diets high in saturated fat *decrease* the removal of LDLs by body cells, apparently by blocking these receptor sites.

Because foods fried in hydrogenated vegetable oils, such as French fries, are high in *trans* fatty acids, these types of foods should be limited in our diet.

very-low-density lipoprotein (VLDL) A lipoprotein made in the liver and intestine that functions to transport endogenous lipids, especially triglycerides, to the tissues of the body.

low-density lipoprotein (LDL) A lipoprotein formed in the blood from VLDLs that transports cholesterol to the cells of the body. Often called the "bad cholesterol."

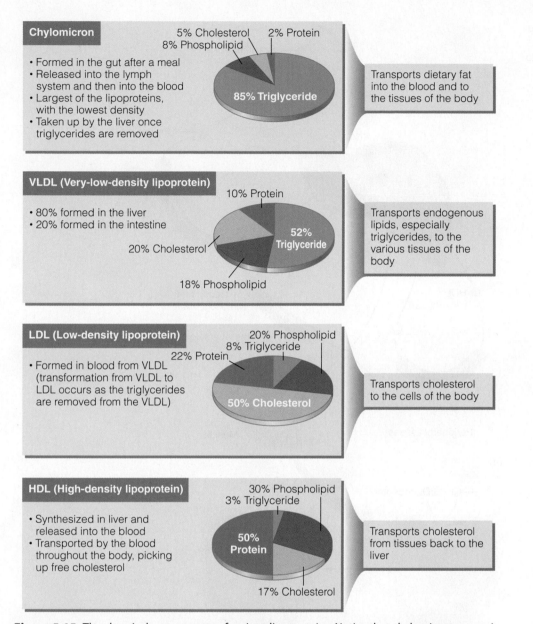

Chylomicron
5% Cholesterol
8% Phospholipid
2% Protein

- Formed in the gut after a meal
- Released into the lymph system and then into the blood
- Largest of the lipoproteins, with the lowest density
- Taken up by the liver once triglycerides are removed

85% Triglyceride

Transports dietary fat into the blood and to the tissues of the body

VLDL (Very-low-density lipoprotein)
10% Protein

- 80% formed in the liver
- 20% formed in the intestine

20% Cholesterol

52% Triglyceride

18% Phospholipid

Transports endogenous lipids, especially triglycerides, to the various tissues of the body

LDL (Low-density lipoprotein)
20% Phospholipid
8% Triglyceride
22% Protein

- Formed in blood from VLDL (transformation from VLDL to LDL occurs as the triglycerides are removed from the VLDL)

50% Cholesterol

Transports cholesterol to the cells of the body

HDL (High-density lipoprotein)
30% Phospholipid
3% Triglyceride

- Synthesized in liver and released into the blood
- Transported by the blood throughout the body, picking up free cholesterol

50% Protein

Transports cholesterol from tissues back to the liver

17% Cholesterol

Figure 5.15 The chemical components of various lipoproteins. Notice that chylomicrons contain the highest proportion of triglycerides, making them the least dense, and high-density lipoproteins (HDLs) have the highest proportion of protein, making them the most dense.

What happens to LDLs not taken up by body cells? As LDLs degrade over time, they release their cholesterol; thus, failure to remove LDLs from the bloodstream results in an increased load of cholesterol in the blood. The more cholesterol circulating in the blood, the greater the risk that some of it will adhere to the walls of the blood vessels. This adhesion causes "scavenger" white blood cells to rush to the site and bind cholesterol to their receptors. As more and more cholesterol binds to these cells, they burst to form a fatty patch, or *plaque,* that eventually becomes fibrous and calcified, blocking the artery (**Figure 5.17**). Because high blood levels of LDL-cholesterol increase the risk of heart disease, it is often labelled the "bad cholesterol." Studies have shown that losing weight helps to lower LDL-cholesterol levels in the blood. Foods that are low in saturated fat and high in soluble fibre have also been found to be helpful in lowering LDL.

High-Density Lipoproteins

As their name indicates, **high-density lipoproteins (HDLs)** are small, dense lipoproteins with a very low cholesterol content and a high protein

high-density lipoprotein (HDL) A lipoprotein made in the liver and released into the blood. HDLs function to transport cholesterol from the tissues back to the liver. Often called the "good cholesterol."

Figure 5.16 (a) Transport of blood lipoproteins throughout the body. (b) Illustration of the LDL binding to the LDL receptor and being internalized into the cell.

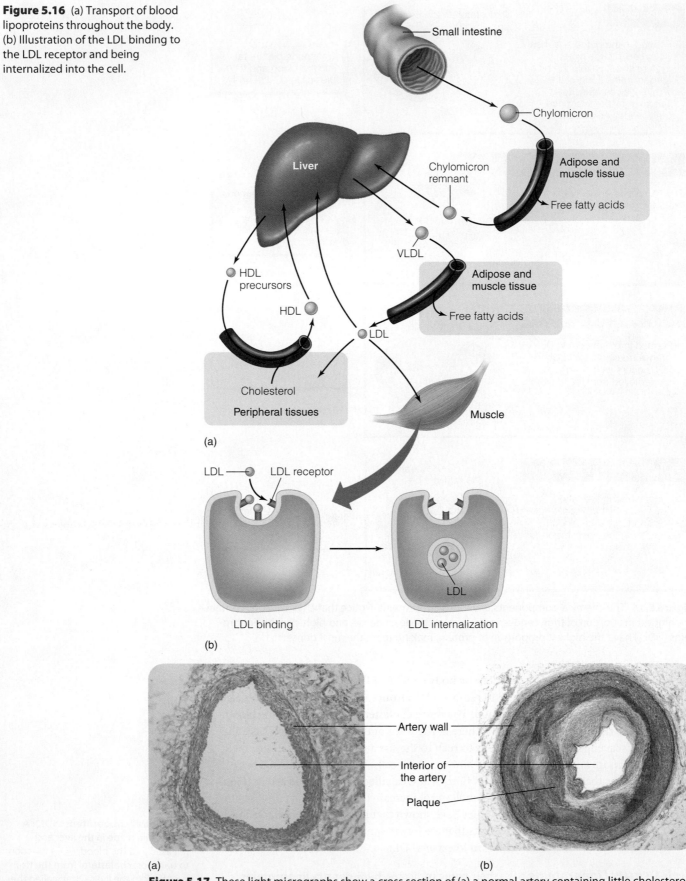

Small intestine

Chylomicron

Liver

Chylomicron remnant

Adipose and muscle tissue

Free fatty acids

VLDL

Adipose and muscle tissue

Free fatty acids

HDL precursors

HDL

LDL

Cholesterol

Peripheral tissues

Muscle

(a)

LDL — LDL receptor

LDL

LDL binding   LDL internalization

(b)

Artery wall

Interior of the artery

Plaque

(a)   (b)

Figure 5.17 These light micrographs show a cross section of (a) a normal artery containing little cholesterol-rich plaque and allowing adequate blood flow through the heart, and (b) an artery that is partially blocked with cholesterol-rich plaque, which can lead to a heart attack.

content. They are released from the liver and intestines to circulate in the blood, picking up cholesterol from dying cells and arterial plaques and transferring it to other lipoproteins, which return it to the liver (see Figure 5.16a). The liver takes up the cholesterol and uses it to synthesize bile, thereby removing it from the circulatory system. High blood levels of HDL-cholesterol are therefore associated with a low risk of coronary artery disease. That's why HDL-cholesterol is often referred to as the "good cholesterol." There is some evidence that diets high in omega-3 fatty acids and participation in regular physical exercise can modestly increase HDL-cholesterol levels.

Refer to the Highlight box "Blood Lipid Levels: Know Your Numbers!" below to gain more insight into your own blood lipid levels.

Total Serum Cholesterol Normally, as the dietary level of cholesterol increases, the body decreases the amount of cholesterol it makes, which keeps the body's level of cholesterol constant. Unfortunately, this feedback mechanism does not work well in everyone. For some individuals, eating dietary cholesterol doesn't decrease the amount of cholesterol produced in the body, and their total body cholesterol level rises. This also increases the level of cholesterol in the blood. These individuals benefit from reducing their intake of dietary cholesterol. Although this appears somewhat complicated, both dietary cholesterol and saturated fats are found in animal foods; thus, by limiting intake of animal products or selecting low-fat animal products, people reduce their intake of both saturated fat and cholesterol. Selecting low-fat meat, poultry, and dairy products and consuming egg whites without yolks can dramatically reduce the amount of cholesterol in the diet.

The Role of Trans Fatty Acids We have known for a long time that saturated fats increase blood levels of total cholesterol and LDL-cholesterol and increase the risk of heart disease. Because saturated fat is found primarily in the fats of animal products, many people believe that eating low-fat dairy and meat products eliminates this risk. But in vegetable

HIGHLIGHT

Blood Lipid Levels: Know Your Numbers!

One of the most important steps you can take to reduce your risk of heart disease is to know your "numbers"—that is, your blood lipid values. In addition, if you are considering a career in nutrition or healthcare, you'll need to be able to work with your clients to track their blood lipid levels as they change their diet and lifestyle to decrease their risk of heart disease. The current Canadian guidelines for the diagnosis of dyslipidemia (abnormal levels of lipids in the blood) recommend that men over the age of 40 and women over the age of 50 should have their blood lipids checked annually.[27] For children, the guidelines recommend screening if there is a family history of hypercholesterolemia or chylomicronemia, genetic conditions where there is a high level of cholesterol or chylomicrons in the blood.

How are blood lipids such as LDL-cholesterol or HDL-cholesterol actually measured? First, a fasting blood sample is taken (no eating or drinking for 12 hours prior to the test), and the lipoproteins in the blood are extracted. Total cholesterol is determined by breaking apart all the lipoproteins and measuring their combined cholesterol content. You can see

from Figure 5.15 that each of the lipoproteins contains some cholesterol and some triglycerides. This same process is used to determine total blood triglyceride level. The next step is to measure the amount of cholesterol in the LDLs and HDLs, because these two lipoproteins can either raise or lower an individual's risk of heart disease. These lipoproteins are separated and the amount of cholesterol in each one is determined to give an LDL-cholesterol value and an HDL-cholesterol value. Once these values are determined, you can compare them to the "target" levels, which identify healthy ranges for blood lipids, and see how you measure up. The target lipid values are as follows:[28]

Total Cholesterol:	< 5.2 mmol/L
LDL-Cholesterol:	< 3.5 mmol/L
HDL-Cholesterol	> 1.0 mmol/L for men and 1.3 mmol/L for women
Total Cholesterol/ HDL-Cholesterol Ratio:	< 5.0 mmol/L
Triglycerides:	< 1.7 mmol/L

Invisible and *trans* fats are hidden in processed and prepared foods, such as pies. Without a label, it is impossible to know the amount of fat in each serving of these types of foods, and so their intake should be limited.

oils converted to solids (for example, corn oil to corn-oil margarine), the level of saturated fat dramatically increases, as does the level of *trans* fatty acids. Research has shown that *trans* fatty acids can raise blood LDL-cholesterol levels as much as saturated fat.[29] *Trans* fats also lower blood levels of the healthy HDL-cholesterol. Thus, to reduce the risk of heart disease, we must reduce our intake of both high-fat animal products and hydrogenated vegetable products. Because many commercially prepared baked goods, as well as foods fried in hydrogenated vegetable oils, such as French fries, are also high in *trans* fatty acids, these types of foods should also be limited in our diet.

Health Canada requires that *trans* fatty acid content be listed on labels for conventional foods and some dietary supplements. Unfortunately, no federal regulations require restaurants to provide nutrition facts for any of their foods at the present time. Until all restaurants are required to identify the *trans* fatty acid content of their foods, avoid ordering fried foods and baked goods such as cakes, cookies, and pies to limit your intake of *trans* fatty acids.

Lifestyle Changes Can Prevent or Reduce Cardiovascular Disease

Diet and exercise interventions aimed at reducing the risk of cardiovascular disease centre on reducing high levels of triglycerides and LDL-cholesterol while raising HDL-cholesterol. The Centers for Disease Control and Prevention (CDC); the Expert Panel on Detection, Evaluation, and Treatment of High Blood Cholesterol in Adults (ATP III) the Heart and Stroke Foundation of Canada,[28] and the American Heart Association have made the following dietary and lifestyle recommendations to improve blood lipid levels and reduce the risk of cardiovascular disease:[23, 25, 30, 31]

Consuming whole fruits and vegetables can reduce your risk for cardiovascular disease.

- Maintain total fat intake to within 20% to 35% of energy.[8] Polyunsaturated fats (for example, soy and canola oil) can provide up to 10% of total energy intake, and monounsaturated fats (for example, olive oil) can provide up to 20% of total energy intake. For some people, a lower fat intake may help to maintain a healthy body weight.
- Decrease dietary saturated fat to less than 7% of total energy intake. Decrease cholesterol intake to less than 300 mg per day, and keep *trans* fatty acid intake to an absolute minimum (<1% of energy). Lowering the intakes of these fats will lower your LDL-cholesterol level. Replace saturated and *trans* fats (for example, butter, margarine, vegetable shortening, or lard) with healthier fats such as olive oil or canola oil. Select lean meats and vegetable alternatives and use fat-free (skim), 1%-fat, or low-fat dairy products.
- Increase intake of dietary omega-3 fatty acids from dark green, leafy vegetables; fatty fish; soybeans or soybean oil; walnuts or walnut oil; flaxseed meal or oil; or canola oil. Consuming fish, especially oily fish, at least twice a week will increase omega-3 fatty acid intake.
- Increase dietary intakes of whole grains, fruits, and vegetables so that total dietary fibre is 20 to 30 g per day, with 10 to 25 g per day coming from fibre sources such as oat bran, beans, and fruits. Foods high in fibre decrease blood LDL-cholesterol levels.
- Maintain blood glucose and insulin concentrations within normal ranges. High blood glucose levels are associated with high blood triglycerides. Consume whole foods (such as whole-wheat breads and cereals, whole fruits and vegetables, and beans and legumes), and select low-saturated-fat meats and dairy products, while limiting your intake of foods high in refined carbohydrates and saturated and *trans* fats (for example, cookies, high-sugar drinks and snacks, candy, fried foods, and convenience and fast foods).
- Eat throughout the day (for example, smaller meals and snacks) instead of eating most of your calories in the evening before bed.
- Consume no more than two alcoholic drinks per day for men and one drink per day for women.
- Maintain an active lifestyle. Exercise most days of the week for 30 to 60 minutes if possible. Exercise will increase HDL-cholesterol while lowering blood triglyceride levels.

Exercise also helps maintain a healthy body weight and a lower blood pressure and reduces your risk for diabetes.

- Balance kilocalorie intake and physical activity to achieve or maintain a healthy body weight. Blood lipids and glucose levels typically improve when obese individuals lose weight and engage in regular physical activity. Obesity promotes inflammation; thus, keeping body weight within a healthy range helps keep inflammation low.[24]

- Decrease salt intake by selecting and preparing foods with little or no salt to help keep blood pressure normal (<120/80 mm Hg). High blood pressure is an independent risk factor for cardiovascular disease.

The impact of diet on reducing the risk of cardiovascular disease was clearly demonstrated in the Dietary Approaches to Stop Hypertension (DASH) study, which is discussed in detail in Chapter 10. Although this study focused on dietary interventions to reduce hypertension (high blood pressure), the results of the study showed that eating the DASH way could also dramatically improve blood lipids. The DASH diet includes high intakes of fruits, vegetables, whole grains, low-fat dairy products, poultry, fish, and nuts and low intakes of fats, red meat, sweets, and sugar-containing beverages. Combining the DASH dietary approach with an active lifestyle significantly reduces the risk of cardiovascular disease.

Prescription Medications Can Reduce Cardiovascular Disease Risk

Sometimes medications are needed in addition to lifestyle changes to reduce cardiovascular risk. A number of medications on the market help lower LDL-cholesterol. The following are some of the most common:

- Endogenous cholesterol synthesis inhibitors: These types of drugs, typically called *statins,* block an enzyme in the cholesterol synthesis pathway. Thus, these drugs lower blood levels of LDL-cholesterol and VLDL-cholesterol. Statins also have an important anti-inflammatory effect that contributes to the reduction in cardiovascular disease risk independent of their effect on blood lipids.[32]

- Bile acid sequestrants: These types of drugs bind the bile acids, preventing them from being reabsorbed by the intestinal tract. Because bile acids are made from cholesterol, blocking their reabsorption means the liver must use cholesterol already in the body to make new bile acids. Continually eliminating bile acids from the body reduces the total cholesterol pool.

- Nicotinic acid: Therapeutic doses of nicotinic acid, a form of niacin, favourably affect all blood lipids when given pharmacologically. (The form of niacin found in multivitamin supplements does not affect lipids.) Unfortunately, this drug has a number of side effects, such as flushing of the skin, gastrointestinal distress, and liver problems.[33] Because of this, it is used less frequently than the other two drugs just discussed.

CASE STUDY ▶ **Reducing the Risk for Cardiovascular Disease**

Alaina is a 45-year-old Caucasian woman. She has just been to see her physician to get the results of her annual physical exam. Alaina's physician is concerned about her blood cholesterol levels. Her total cholesterol was 6.4 mmol/L, her LDL-cholesterol was 4.6 mmol/L, and her HDL-cholesterol was 0.8 mmol/L. Alaina has a family history of heart disease (her father had a stroke at age 50), is a smoker, and is overweight (1.6 m tall and 68 kg). Her waist circumference is 90 cm. Her physician recommends that she see a dietitian about a diet plan to help reduce her risk for heart disease.

The dietitian assesses Alaina's diet and finds that she does not eat the recommended number of servings of vegetables and fruit and she eats at least one serving of a high-fat food daily. She dislikes fish, her fibre intake is below the AI, and her sodium intake exceeds the AI. She typically eats 2500 kcal/day (38% of total kcal from fat, 42% from carbohydrates, and 20% from protein). Alaina has a very stressful job and she often has one or two glasses of red wine at night to calm her nerves. She does go for walks with her family on Sundays but other than that she gets very little exercise.

Thinking Critically

1. **Why was Alaina's physician concerned about her blood cholesterol levels?**
2. **Which aspects of Alaina's diet may affect her heart disease risk? Why?**
3. **Which aspects of Alaina's lifestyle may affect her heart disease risk? Why?**
4. **What suggestions could you make to Alaina to reduce her risk for heart disease?**

Does a High-Fat Diet Cause Cancer?

Cancer develops as a result of a poorly understood interaction between the environment and genetic factors. In addition, most cancers take years to develop, so examining the impact of diet on cancer development can be a long and difficult process. Diet and lifestyle are two of the most important environmental factors that have been identified in the development of cancer.[34, 35] Of the dietary factors, fat intake has been extensively researched. The relationship between type and amount of fat consumed and increased risk for breast cancer is controversial.[36, 37] Early research showed an association between animal fat intake and increased risk for colon cancer, whereas more recent research indicates that the association is between factors other than fat that are found in red meat. Because we now know that physical activity can reduce the risk of colon cancer, earlier diet and colon cancer studies that did not control for this factor are now being questioned. The strongest association between dietary fat intake and cancer is for prostate cancer. Research shows that there is a consistent link between prostate cancer risk and consumption of animal fats but not other types of fats. The exact mechanism by which animal fats may contribute to prostate cancer has not yet been identified. High fat diets may also contribute indirectly to cancer risk as they increase the risk for obesity, a risk factor for cancer.

RecaP

The types of fats we eat can significantly influence our health and risk of disease. Saturated and *trans* fatty acids increase our risk of heart disease, whereas omega-3 fatty acids can reduce our risk. Other risk factors for heart disease include being overweight, being physically inactive, smoking, having high blood pressure, and having diabetes. You can calculate your 10-year risk of heart disease by knowing a few facts about yourself: your blood cholesterol and HDL-cholesterol levels, blood pressure, age, and smoking status. High levels of LDL-cholesterol and low levels of HDL-cholesterol increase your risk of heart disease. Selecting appropriate types of fat in the diet may also reduce your risk of some cancers, especially prostate cancer.

SEE FOR YOURSELF

Tips for Heart-Healthy Eating

When preparing meals at home, as well as when dining out, try these simple strategies and see for yourself how easy it can be to tip the balance of your diet toward heart-healthy fats.

At Home

☐ Boost the omega-3 profile of your favourite breakfast cereal by adding 1 tablespoon of ground flaxseed meal.

☐ Select whole-grain breads, and try peanut, almond, or walnut butter as a spread for your toast.

☐ If you normally eat two eggs for breakfast, discard the yolk from one egg for half the cholesterol. Do the same in recipes calling for two eggs.

☐ Select low-fat or non-fat milk, coffee creamers, yogourt, cream cheese, cottage cheese, sour cream, mayonnaise, and salad dressings.

☐ Substitute lower-fat cheeses such as parmesan for higher-fat cheeses such as cheddar.

☐ If you use margarine, select one that is made from an oil high in omega-3, such as canola oil, and is *trans*-fat free.

☐ Start meals with a salad dressed with olive oil and vinegar or a fat-free soup.

☐ Select lean cuts of meat. Load your plate with vegetables, and make meat a "condiment."

☐ Instead of frying meats, fish, and vegetables, bake or broil them.

☐ Trim all visible fat from meats and poultry before cooking. Eat poultry without the skin.

☐ Instead of buttering your bread, dip it in a mixture of olive oil and a dribble of balsamic vinegar.

☐ Make sure that any crackers or cookies you buy are low in saturated fats and free of *trans* fatty acids.

☐ Choose ice milk, sorbet, or low-fat or non-fat yogourt and fruit for dessert instead of high-fat ice cream.

☐ For snacks, substitute raw vegetables, whole and dried fruits, pretzels, or air-popped popcorn for potato chips or sweets.

☐ Choose water, skim milk, soy milk, or unsweetened beverages over sugar-sweetened beverages.

☐ Read food labels. Select high-fat foods less often or use them in moderation.

☐ Control your portion size, especially when consuming high-fat foods.

Eating Out

☐ When dining out, select a fish high in omega-3 fatty acid, such as salmon, or try a vegetarian entrée made with tofu or tempeh. If you do choose meat, ask that it be trimmed of fat and baked rather than fried.

☐ Consider splitting an entrée with your dinner companion and complement it with a side salad.

☐ On your salad, choose olive oil and vinegar instead of a high-fat dressing. Also, use olive oil instead of butter for your bread.

☐ Order a baked potato or rice instead of French fries or potatoes au gratin.

☐ Share or skip dessert or choose a fat-free sorbet.

☐ The next time you order a fast food meal, either skip the French fries or order the kid's meal for portion control.

☐ Order pizza with vegetable toppings instead of pepperoni or sausage.

☐ Order coffee drinks with skim milk instead of cream or whole milk, and accompany them with a biscotti instead of a brownie.

Chapter Review

Test Yourself | Answers

1. **F** Eating too much fat, or too much of unhealthy fats such as saturated and *trans* fatty acids, can increase our risk for diseases such as cardiovascular disease and obesity. However, fat is an important part of a nutritious diet, and we need to consume a certain minimum amount to provide adequate levels of essential fatty acids and fat-soluble vitamins.

2. **T** Fat is our primary source of energy, both at rest and during low-intensity exercise. Fat is also an important fuel source during prolonged exercise.

3. **F** Even foods fried in vegetable shortening can be unhealthy because they are higher in *trans* fatty acids. In addition, fried foods are high in total fat and energy and can contribute to overweight and obesity.

4. **T** Certain essential fatty acids, including EPA and DHA, reduce inflammation, blood clotting, and plasma triglycerides and thereby reduce an individual's risk of heart disease.

5. **F** Cancer develops as a result of a poorly understood interaction between environmental and genetic factors. Some research indicates an association between high dietary fat consumption and certain cancers, but this research is inconclusive.

Summary

- Fats and oils are forms of a larger and more diverse group of substances called lipids; most lipids are insoluble in water.

- The three types of lipids commonly found in foods are triglycerides, phospholipids, and sterols.

- Most of the fat we eat is in the form of triglycerides; a triglyceride is a molecule that contains three fatty acids attached to a glycerol backbone.

- Short-chain fatty acids are usually less than six carbon atoms in length; medium-chain fatty acids are six to twelve carbons in length, and long-chain fatty acids are fourteen or more carbons in length.

- Saturated fatty acids have no carbons attached together with a double bond, which means that every carbon atom in the fatty acid chain is saturated with hydrogen. They are straight in shape and solid at room temperature.

- Monounsaturated fatty acids contain one double bond between two carbon atoms. Polyunsaturated fatty acids contain more than one double bond between carbon atoms. Unsaturated fatty acids are usually liquid at room temperature.

- A *cis* fatty acid has hydrogen atoms located on the same side of the double bond in an unsaturated fatty acid. This *cis* positioning produces a kink in the unsaturated fatty acid and is the shape found in naturally occurring fatty acids.

- A *trans* fatty acid has hydrogen atoms located on opposite sides of the double carbon bond. This positioning causes *trans* fatty acids to be straighter and more rigid, like saturated fats. This *trans* positioning results when oils are hydrogenated during food processing.

- The essential fatty acids (linoleic acid and alpha-linolenic acid) must be obtained from food. These fatty acids are precursors to important biological compounds called eicosanoids, which are essential for growth and health.

- Linoleic acid is found primarily in vegetable and nut oils, whereas alpha-linolenic acid is found in dark green, leafy vegetables; flaxseeds and oil; walnuts and walnut oil; soybean oil and soy foods; canola oil; and fish products and fish oil.

- Phospholipids consist of a glycerol backbone and two fatty acids with a phosphate group; phospholipids are soluble in water and assist with transporting fats in the bloodstream.

- Sterols have a ring structure; cholesterol is the most common sterol in our diets.

- The majority of fat digestion and absorption occurs in the small intestine. Fat is broken into smaller components by bile, which is produced by the liver and stored in the gallbladder.

- Lipid digestion products are transported to enterocytes by micelles.

- Because fats are not soluble in water, triglycerides are packaged into lipoproteins before being released into the bloodstream for transport to the cells.

- Dietary fat is primarily used either as an energy source for the cells or to make lipid-containing compounds in the body, or it is stored in the muscle and adipose tissue as triglyceride for later use.

- Fats are a primary energy source during rest and exercise, are our major source of stored energy, provide essential fatty acids, enable the transport of fat-soluble vitamins, help maintain cell function, provide protection for body organs, contribute to the texture and flavour of foods, and help us feel satiated after a meal.

- The AMDR for fat is 20% to 35% of total energy intake. Our intake of saturated fats and *trans* fatty acids should be kept to a minimum. Individuals who limit fat intake to less than 15% of energy intake need to make sure that essential fatty acid needs are met, as well as protein and energy needs.

- For the essential fatty acids, 5% to 10% of energy intake should be in the form of linoleic acid and 0.6% to 1.2% as alpha-linolenic acid.

- Watch for invisible fats found in cakes, cookies, marbling in meat, regular-fat dairy products, and fried foods.

- Diets high in saturated fat and *trans* fatty acids can increase our risk for cardiovascular disease. Other risk factors for cardiovascular disease are obesity, physical inactivity, smoking, high blood pressure, and diabetes.

- High levels of circulating low-density lipoproteins, or LDLs, increase total blood cholesterol concentrations and the formation of plaque on arterial walls, leading to an increased risk for cardiovascular disease. This is why LDL-cholesterol is sometimes called the "bad cholesterol."

- High levels of circulating high-density lipoproteins, or HDLs, reduce our blood cholesterol levels and our risk for cardiovascular disease. This is why HDL-cholesterol is sometimes called the "good cholesterol."

- Some studies suggest that diets high in fat may increase our risk for prostate cancer, while the role of dietary fat in breast and colon cancer is still controversial.

Review Questions

1. Omega-3 fatty acids are
   a. a form of *trans* fatty acid.
   b. metabolized in the body to arachidonic acid.
   c. synthesized in the liver and small intestine.
   d. found in flaxseeds, walnuts, and fish.

2. One of the most sensible ways to reduce body fat is to
   a. limit intake of dietary fat to less than 15% of total energy consumed.
   b. exercise regularly.
   c. avoid all consumption of *trans* fatty acids.
   d. restrict total energy to 1200 kcals per day.

3. Lipids in chylomicrons are taken up by cells with the help of
   a. lipoprotein lipase.
   b. micelles.
   c. sterols.
   d. pancreatic enzymes.

4. The risk of heart disease is reduced in people who have high blood levels of
   a. triglycerides.
   b. very-low-density lipoproteins.
   c. low-density lipoproteins.
   d. high-density lipoproteins.

5. Fatty acids with a double bond at one part of the molecule are referred to as
   a. monounsaturated.
   b. hydrogenated.
   c. saturated.
   d. essential.

6. Explain why fatty acid chain length is important.

7. What is the role of the gallbladder, liver, and pancreas in fat digestion?

8. Explain how the straight, rigid shape of the saturated and *trans* fatty acids we eat affects our health.

9. Explain the contribution of dietary fat to bone health.

10. You have volunteered to participate in a 32 km walk-a-thon to raise money for a local charity. You have been training for several weeks, and the event is now two days away. An athlete friend of yours advises you to "load up on carbohydrates" today and tomorrow and says you should avoid eating any foods that contain fat during the day of the walk-a-thon. Do you take this advice? Why or why not?

11. Caleb's father returns from an appointment with his doctor feeling down. He tells Caleb that his "blood test didn't turn out so good." He then adds, "My doctor told me I can't eat any of my favourite foods anymore. He says red meat and butter have too much fat. I guess I'll have to switch to cottage cheese and margarine!" What type of blood test do you think Caleb's father had? How should Caleb respond to his father's intention to switch to cottage cheese and margarine? Finally, suggest a non-dietary lifestyle choice that might improve his health.

12. Your friend Maria has determined that she needs to consume about 2000 kcals per day to maintain her healthy weight. Create a chart for Maria showing the recommended maximum number of calories she should consume in each of the following forms: unsaturated fat, saturated fat, linoleic acid, alpha-linolenic acid, and *trans* fatty acids.

Web Links

www.heartandstroke.ca
Heart and Stroke Foundation of Canada
Learn the best way to help lower your blood cholesterol level.
Check out the tips for choosing heart-healthy foods and cooking
methods.

www.dhaomega3.org
DHA.EPA Omega-3 Institute
Provides the latest evidence on omega-3 fatty acids and health.
All of the information on this site is written by Dr. Bruce Holub,
Professor Emeritus of Nutritional Sciences at the University of
Guelph.

www.phac-aspc.gc.ca
Public Health Agency of Canada
Learn more about the risk factors for cardiovascular disease and
initiatives and programs designed to reduce the prevalence of
heart disease in Canada.

www.obesitynetwork.ca
Canadian Obesity Network
Go to this site to use the Framingham Risk Score to estimate
your risk of cardiovascular diseases.

www.nlm.nih.gov/medlineplus
MedlinePlus Health Information
Search for "fats" or "lipids" to obtain additional resources and
the latest news on dietary lipids, heart disease, and cholesterol.

www.hsph.harvard.edu/nutritionsource
The Nutrition Source: Knowledge for Healthy Eating
Harvard University's Department of Nutrition
Go to this site and click on "What Should I Eat? Fats and Choles-
terol" to find out how selective fat intake can be part of a healthy diet.

http://ific.org
International Food Information Council Foundation
Access this site to find out more about fats and dietary fat replacers.

MasteringNutrition®

www.masteringnutrition.pearson.com

Assignments
Animations: Fat Digestion • Fats in Food • Lipid Absorption
• Lipoproteins: VLDL, LDL, and HDL
Study Area
Video: Understanding Lipids • Practice Tests • Diet Analysis • eText

References

1. Marieb, E. 2007. *Human Anatomy and Physiology.* 7th ed. San Francisco: Benjamin Cummings, p. 48.
2. Champe, P. C., R. A. Harvey, and D. R. Ferrier. 2008. *Lippincott's Illustrated Reviews: Biochemistry.* 4th ed. Philadelphia: Lippincott Williams & Wilkins.
3. Smith, C., A. D. Marks, and M. Lieberman. 2005. *Mark's Basic Medical Biochemistry: A Clinical Approach.* 2nd ed. Philadelphia: Lippincott Williams & Wilkins.
4. Jebb, S. A., A. M. Prentice, G. R. Goldberg, P. R. Murgatroyd, A. E. Black, and W. A. Coward. 1996. Changes in macronutrient balance during over- and underfeeding assessed by 12-d continuous whole-body calorimetry. *Am. J. Clin. Nutr.* 64:259–266.
5. Institute of Medicine (IOM), Food and Nutrition Board. 2000. *Dietary Reference Intakes for Vitamin C, Vitamin E, Selenium and Carotenoids.* Washington, DC: National Academies Press.
6. Rolls, B. J. 2000. The role of energy density in the overconsumption of fat. *J. Nutr.* 130:268S–271S.
7. Gerstein, D. E., G. Woodward-Lopez, A. E. Evans, K. Kelsey, and A. Drewnowski. 2004. Clarifying concepts about macronutrients' effects on satiation and satiety. *J. Am. Diet. Assoc.* 104:1151–1153.
8. Institute of Medicine (IOM), Food and Nutrition Board. 2002. *Dietary Reference Intakes for Energy, Carbohydrate, Fiber, Fat, Fatty Acids, Cholesterol, Protein, and Amino Acids (Macronutrients).* Washington, DC: National Academies Press.
9. Rodriguez, N. R., N. M. DiMarco, and S. Langley. 2009. Position of the Academy of Nutrition and Dietetics, Dietitians of Canada, and the American College of Sports Medicine: nutrition and athletic performance. *J. Am. Diet. Assoc.* 109:509–527.
10. Lichtenstein, A. H., and L. Van Horn. 1998. Very low fat diets. *Circulation* 98:935–939.
11. Trans Fat Task Force. TRANSforming the Food Supply: Report of the Trans Fat Task Force. Available at www.healthcanada.ca/transfat (accessed October 16, 2010).
12. Health Canada. 2006. Task Force on Trans Fat. Available at www.hc-sc.gc.ca/fn-an/nutrition/gras-trans-fats/tf-ge/index-eng.php (accessed October 16, 2010).
13. Gray-Donald, K., L. Jacobs-Starkey, and L. Johnson-Down. 2000. Food habits of Canadians: reduction in fat intake over a generation. *Can. J. Pub. Health* 91:381–385.
14. Health Canada. 2009. Do Canadian Adults Meet Their Nutrient Intakes Through Food Alone? Available at www.hc-sc.gc.ca/fn-an/alt_formats/pdf/surveill/nutrition/commun/art-nutr-adult-eng.pdf.
15. Health Canada. 2009. General Questions on Trans Fat. Available at www.hc-sc.gc.ca/fn-an/nutrition/gras-trans-fats/tfa-age_question-eng.php (accessed October 16, 2010).
16. Canadian Council of Food and Nutrition. 2008. Tracking Nutrition Trends VII. Available at www.ccfn.ca/membership/membersonly/content/Tracking%20Nutrition%20Trends/TNT_VII_FINAL_REPORT_full_report_Sept.pdf (accessed October 17, 2010).
17. Neuhouser, M. L., C. Rock, A. R. Kristal, R. E. Patterson, D. Neumark-Sztainer, L. J. Cheskin, and M. D. Thornquist. 2006. Olestra is associated with slight reductions in serum carotenoids

but does not markedly influence serum fat-soluble vitamin concentrations. *Am. J. Clin. Nutr.* 83:624–631.

18. Sandler, R. S., N. L. Zorich, T. G. Filloon, H. B. Wiseman, D. J. Lietz, M. H. Brock, M. G. Royer, and R. K. Miday. 1999. Gastrointestinal symptoms in 3181 volunteers ingesting snack foods containing olestra or triglycerides. A 6-week randomized, placebo-controlled trial. *Ann. Inter. Med.* 130:253–261.

19. Bray, G. A., J. C. Lovejoy, J. C., M. Most-Windhauser, S. R. Smith, J. Volaufova, Y. Denkins, L, deJonge, J. Rood, M. Lefevre, A. L. Eldridge, and J. C. Peters. 2002. A 9-mo randomized clinical trial comparing fat-substituted and fat-reduced diets in healthy obese men: Ole Study. *Am. J. Clin. Nutr.* 76:1242–1249.

20. Roy, J. H., M. M. Most, A. Sparti, J. C. Lovejoy, J. Volaufova, J. C. Peters, and G. A. Bray. 2002. Effect on body weight of replacing dietary fat with olestra for two or ten weeks in healthy men and women. *J. Am. Coll. Nutr.* 21:259–267.

21. Statistics Canada, May 4, 2010. CANSIM Table 102-0529: Deaths, by cause, Chapter IX: Diseases of the circulatory system (I00 to I99), age group and sex, Canada, annual (number), 2000 to 2006. Available at www.statcan.gc.ca/daily-quotidien/101130/dq101130b-eng.htm.

22. Heart and Stroke Foundation of Canada. Statistics. 2010. Available at www.heartandstroke.com/site/c.ikIQLcMWJtE/b.3483991/k.34A8/Statistics.htm#heartdisease (accessed October 16, 2010).

23. Wilson, P. W. F. 2004. CDC/AHA workshop on markers of inflammation and cardiovascular disease. Application to clinical and public health practice. Ability of inflammatory markers to predict disease in asymptomatic patients. A background paper. *Circulation* 110:e568–e571.

24. Libby, P., P. M. Ridker, and A. Maseri. 2002. Inflammation and atherosclerosis. *Circulation* 105:1135–1143.

25. Kris-Etherton, P. M., W. S. Harris, L. J. Appel, and the Nutrition Committee of the American Heart Association. 2002. Fish consumption, fish oil, omega-3 fatty acids and cardiovascular disease. *Circulation* 106:2747–2757.

26. Harris, W. S. 1997. n-3 fatty acids and serum lipoproteins: human studies. *Am. J. Clin. Nutr.* 65(Suppl.):1645S–1654S.

27. Genest, J., R. McPherson, J. Frohlich, T. Anderson, N. Campbell, A. Carpentier, P. Couture, R. Dufour, G. Fodor, G. A. Francis, S. Grover, M. Gupta, R. A. Hegele, D. C. Lau, L. Leiter, G. F. Lewis, E. Lonn, G. B. J. Mancini, D. Ng, G. G. Pearson, A. Sniderman, J. A. Stone, and E. Ur. 2009. Canadian Cardiovascular Society/Canadian guidelines for the diagnosis and treatment of dyslipidemia and prevention of cardiovascular disease in the adult—2009 recommendations. *Can. J. Cardiol.* 25(10):567–579.

28. Heart & Stroke Foundation of Canada. 2010. Living with Cholesterol: Cholesterol and Healthy Living. Available at www.heartandstroke.com/atf/cf/%7B99452D8B-E7F1-4BD6-A57D-B136CE6C95BF%7D/Living-with-cholesterol-en.pdf (accessed November 10, 2010).

29. Oomen, C. M., M. C. Ocké, E. J. Feskens, M. A. van Erp-Baart, F. J. Kok, and D. Kromhout. 2001. Association between *trans* fatty acid intake and 10-year risk of coronary heart disease in the Zutphen Elderly Study: a prospective population-based study. *Lancet* 357(9258):746–751.

30. National Center for Chronic Disease Prevention and Health Promotion (NCCDPHP). 2008. Division for Heart Disease and Stroke Prevention addressing the nation's leading killers. At a glance 2008. Available online at http://www.cdc.gov/nccdphp/publications/AAG/dhdsp.htm.

31. Lichtenstein A. H., L. J. Appel, M. Brands, M. Carnethon, S. Daniels, H. A. Franch, B. Franklin, P. Kris-Ethergon, W. S. Harris, B. Howard, N. Karanja, M. Lefevre, L. Rudel, F. Sancks, L. Van Horn, M. Winston, and J. Wylie-Rosett. 2006. Diet and lifestyle recommendations revision 2006: a scientific statement from the American Heart Association Nutrition Committee. *Circulation* 114:82–96.

32. Libby, P., Ridker, P. M., Maseri, A. 2002. Inflammation and atherosclerosis. *Circulation* 105:1135–1143.

33. National Institutes of Health (NIH). 2001. *Third report of the National Cholesterol Education Program: Detection, evaluation and treatment of high blood cholesterol in adults (ATP III)*. National Cholesterol Education Program, National Heart, Lung, and Blood Institute, NIH. Available online at www.nhlbi.nih.gov/guidelines/cholesterol/atp3xsum.pdf.

34. Kim, Y. I. 2001. Nutrition and cancer. In: Bowman, B. A., and R. M. Russell, eds. *Present Knowledge in Nutrition*. 8th ed. Washington, DC: International Life Sciences Institute Press, pp. 573–589.

35. Kris-Etherton, P. M., and S. Innis. 2007. Position of the Academy of Nutrition and Dietetics and Dietitians of Canada: Dietary fatty acid. *J. Am. Diet. Assoc.* 107:1599–1611.

36. Willett, W. C. 1999. Diet, nutrition and the prevention of cancer. In: Shils, M. E., J. A. Olsen, M. Shike, and A. C. Ross, eds. *Modern Nutrition in Health and Disease*. 9th ed. Baltimore: Williams & Wilkins.

37. Prentice, R. L., C. Bette, R. Chlebowski, et al. 2006. Low-fat dietary patterns and risk of invasive breast cancer. The Women's Health Initiative Randomized Controlled Dietary Modification Trial. *JAMA* 295:629–642.

38. Variyam, J. N. 2004. The price is right. Economics and the rise of obesity. *Amber Waves*. USDA Economic Research Service 3(1):20–27.

39. Glanz, K., M. Basil, E. Maibach, J. Goldberg, and D. Snyder. 1998. Why Americans eat what they do: taste, nutrition, cost, convenience, and weight control concerns as influences on food consumption. *J. Am. Diet. Assoc.* 98:1118–1126.

40. Brownell, K. D., and T. R. Frieden. 2009. Ounces of prevention—the public policy case for taxes on sugared beverages. *N. Engl. J. Med.* 360:1805–1808.

41. Guthrie, H. A.1986. There's no such thing as "junk food," but there are junk diets. *Healthline* 5:11–12.

42. Kant, A. K.1996. Indexes of overall diet quality: A review. *J. Am. Diet. Assoc.* 96:785–791.

43. Drewnowski, A. and V. Fulgoni III. 2008. Nutrient profiling of foods: creating a nutrient-rich food index. *Nutr. Rev.* 66:23–39.

44. Drewnowski, A. 2010. The Nutrient Rich Foods Index helps to identify healthy, affordable foods. *Am. J. Clin. Nutr.* 91(suppl):1095S–1101S.

45. Lackey, C. J., and K. M. Kolasa. 2004. Healthy eating: defining the nutrient quality of foods. *Nutr. Today* 39:26–29.

46. Drewnowski, A. 2005. Concept of a nutritious food: toward a nutrient density score. *Am J Clin Nutr.* 82:721–732.

47. Frieden, T. R., W. Dietz, and J. Collins. 2010. Reducing childhood obesity through policy change: acting now to prevent obesity. *Health Affairs* 29:357–362.

48. Jha, P., F. J. Chaloupka, J. Moore, V. Gajalakshmi, P. C. Gupta, R. Peck et al. Tobacco addiction: In Jamison, D. T., J. G. Breman, A. R. Measham, G. Alleyne, M. Claeson, D. B. Evans, P. Jha, A. Mills, and P. Musgrove. Eds. *Disease control priorities in developing countries*. 2nd ed. [internet]. pp. 869–885. New York: Oxford University Press; 2006. Available from http://files.dep2.org/pdf/DCP/DCP46.pdf.

49. Powell, L. M., J. Chriqui, and F. J. Chaloupka. 2009. Associations between state-level soda taxes and adolescent body mass index. *J. Adolescent Health* 45:S57–S63.

50. Mytton, O., A. Gray, M. Rayner, and H. Rutter. 2007. Could targeted food taxes improve health? *J. Epidemiol. Comm. Health* 61:689–694.

51. Epstein, L. H., K. K. Dearin, L. G. Roba, and E. Finkelstein. 2010. The influence of taxes and subsidies on energy purchased in an experimental purchasing study. *Psych. Sci.* 21:406–414.

52. Dellava, J. E., C. M. Bulik, and B. M. Popkin. 2010. Price changes alone are not adequate to produce long-term dietary change. *J. Nutr.* 140:1887–1891.

53. Powell, L. M., and F. J. Chaloupka. 2009. Food prices and obesity: evidence and policy implications for taxes and subsidies. *The Milbank Quarterly* 87:229–257.

54. Paquette, M-C. 2005. Perceptions of healthy eating: state of knowledge and research gaps. *Can. J. Pub. Health* 96 (suppl):S15–S19.

Should We Tax "Unhealthy" Foods?

Look around you. How many fast food restaurants are within walking distance of your home, place of work, or campus? These restaurants are generally well known for the high-fat, high-kilocalorie foods they serve. So why do consumers choose them? Fast food has three major advantages over traditional restaurant meals and home-cooked meals: it is quick to obtain, tastes good to a majority of consumers, and is relatively cheap for the number of kilocalories it provides.[38] Many Canadians view the large portions served in fast food restaurants as evidence that they are getting good "value" for their money, and consumer research has shown that food cost is the single most important factor influencing purchasing decisions.[39] Healthier food has become relatively more expensive than so-called "bad" or "unhealthy" food.[40] So what can be done to encourage Canadians to eat healthy foods and limit their intake of unhealthy foods?

One of the first challenges in answering this question is defining an "unhealthy" food. For many years, nutrition professionals told their clients that "all foods can fit" and that there are no junk foods, just junk diets.[41] The concept of "nutrient density" (see page 45) was developed in an attempt to help consumers make wise dietary choices and was initially applied only to overall dietary intake.[42] More recently, researchers have become interested in nutrient profiling of foods and a number of indices have been developed to rank foods on the basis of their nutrient density. Drewnowski and Fulgoni III created the Nutrient Rich Foods (NRF) index,[43] which has been shown to be useful in identifying healthy and affordable foods.[44] Despite this work, there is still no universal agreement on what constitutes a "healthy" food,[45] but it is generally recognized that foods high in total, saturated, and *trans* fats, sodium, and simple sugars are less nutrient dense than foods such as milk, vegetables, fruit, lean meats, and grains.[46]

Many experts are now recommending that governments implement tax policies to raise the price of foods higher in fat, sodium, and sugar and decrease costs of healthier foods, especially vegetables and fruit, as a way of improving overall diet quality and halting the epidemic of obesity.[47] They cite the beneficial effect of increasing the price of tobacco through higher taxes,[48] but would taxing unhealthy food have the same effect?

Powell and colleagues conducted a study to determine whether or not taxing soft drinks had an effect on weight among U.S. adolescents. They found no significant associations between state-level taxes on soft drinks and BMI in adolescents and concluded that taxes would have to be raised substantially to have a significant effect on weight.[49] In the United Kingdom, Mytton and colleagues used empirical economic data to predict the effect of tax increases on consumption of a wide variety of foods and found that raising taxes on foods high in saturated fat resulted in an increased consumption of salty foods. Further, reducing the intake of saturated fat also reduced the intake of mono- and polyunsaturated fats.[50] Conversely, Epstein and colleagues conducted a similar modelling exercise to examine the effects of increasing the price of energy-dense/nutrient-poor foods or reducing the price of low-energy/nutrient-dense foods on mothers' food purchases. They found that taxing the less healthy foods reduced kilocalorie and fat intake while subsidizing the healthy foods increased energy intake without changing the macronutrient profile of the diet.[51] Dellava and colleagues undertook a study to determine the short- and long-term effects of price changes on diet using data from the Russian Longitudinal Monitoring Survey and economic data collected in each community at the time of the survey each year.[52] During the 1990s, there was major economic upheaval in the former Soviet Union, which

resulted in major increases in the price of high-fat meat and dairy products. These researchers found that increased prices did not result in long-term dietary change. Fat consumption did decrease when prices were high but quickly went back to the original levels when prices fell. Finally, in a recent review of the literature, Powell and Chaloupka found that small taxes or subsidies were unlikely to have a significant effect on the prevalence of obesity in the United States and concluded that the price changes would have to be large to have a measurable effect on BMI.[53]

Paquette has suggested that we need to better understand the factors that influence eating behaviour to help Canadians eat a healthier diet.[54] Do we know enough about the role of the cost of food to recommend taxes and subsidies to encourage healthy eating?

Should we tax unhealthy foods to discourage people from eating them?

Using the Evidence

1. What is your perception of an "unhealthy" food? What is that perception based on?

2. Now that you know more about nutrition, do you agree that all foods can fit into a healthy diet, or do you think that some foods should be avoided completely?

3. Do you think that taxing foods high in fat, sugar, and salt would help to reduce the prevalence of obesity in Canada?

4. What else do we need to know about the factors that influence eating behaviour to help Canadians make positive dietary changes?

Proteins: Crucial Components of All Body Tissues

Test Yourself True *or* False?

1. Protein is a primary source of energy for our bodies. T *or* F

2. We must consume amino acid supplements in order to build muscle tissue. T *or* F

3. Any protein eaten in excess is excreted in your urine. T *or* F

4. Vegetarian diets are inadequate in protein. T *or* F

5. Most people in Canada consume more protein than they need. T *or* F

Test Yourself answers are located in the Chapter Review.

Chapter Objectives | *After reading this chapter, you will be able to:*

1. Describe how proteins differ from carbohydrates and lipids, *p. 202*.
2. Sketch an amino acid molecule and include its five essential components, *p. 203*.
3. Differentiate between essential amino acids, non-essential amino acids, and conditionally essential amino acids, *pp. 203–205*.
4. Explain the relationship between protein shape and function, *pp. 207–208*.
5. Discuss how proteins are digested, absorbed, and synthesized by the body, *pp. 210–212*.
6. Describe at least four functions of proteins in the body, *pp. 212–216*.
7. Calculate your recommended dietary allowance for protein, *pp. 218–219*.
8. Identify the potential health risks associated with high-protein diets, *pp. 219–220*.
9. List six foods that are good sources of protein, including at least three non-meat sources, *pp. 221–222*.
10. Describe two disorders related to inadequate protein intake or genetic abnormalities, *pp. 227–229*.

Proteins are an integral part of our body tissues, including our muscle tissue.

W hat do Canadian Olympic figure skater Charlene Wong, Ultimate Fighting Champion Mac Danzig, and hundreds of other athletes have in common? They are all vegetarians! Although few well-controlled long-term studies have been conducted to determine the effects of a vegetarian diet on physical performance, Barr and Rideout concluded that as long as protein intakes are adequate to meet the needs of an athlete, it doesn't really matter if the protein is from an animal or a plant source.[1]

What is a protein, and what makes it so different from carbohydrates and fats? How much protein do people really need, and do most people get enough in their daily diets? What exactly is a vegetarian, anyway? Do you qualify? If so, how do you plan your diet to include sufficient protein, especially if you play competitive sports?

It seems as if everybody has an opinion about protein, both how much you should consume and from what sources. In this chapter, we address these and other questions to clarify the importance of protein in the diet and dispel common myths about this crucial nutrient.

What Are Proteins?

Proteins are large, complex molecules found in the cells of all living things. Although proteins are best known as a part of our muscle mass, they are in fact critical components of all tissues of the human body, including bones, blood, and hormones. Proteins function in metabolism, immunity, fluid balance, and nutrient transport, and they can provide energy in certain circumstances. The functions of proteins will be discussed in detail later in this chapter.

How Do Proteins Differ from Carbohydrates and Lipids?

As we saw in Chapter 1, proteins are one of the three macronutrients. Like carbohydrates and lipids, proteins are found in a wide variety of foods, plus the human body is able to synthesize them. But unlike carbohydrates and lipids, proteins are made according to instructions provided by our genetic material, or DNA. See Appendix B for more information on how DNA dictates the structure of proteins.

Another key difference between proteins and the other macronutrients lies in their chemical makeup. In addition to the carbon, hydrogen, and oxygen also found in carbohydrates and lipids, proteins contain a special form of nitrogen that the body can readily use; 16% of protein is composed of nitrogen (1 g N/6.25 g protein). Our bodies are able to break down the proteins in foods and utilize the nitrogen for many important body processes. Carbohydrates and lipids do not provide nitrogen. In addition, two amino acids, cysteine and methionine, also contain sulphur; neither carbohydrates nor lipids contain sulphur.

The Building Blocks of Proteins Are Amino Acids

The proteins in our bodies are made from a combination of building blocks called **amino acids**, molecules composed of a central carbon atom connected to four other groups: an amine group, an acid group, a hydrogen atom, and a side chain (**Figure 6.1a**). The word *amine* means *nitrogen-containing*, and nitrogen is indeed the essential component of the amine portion of the molecule.

As shown in Figure 6.1b, the portion of the amino acid that makes each unique is its side chain. This side chain is referred to as the R group. The amine group, acid group, and carbon and hydrogen atoms do not vary. Variations in the structure of the R group give each amino acid its distinct properties.

The singular term *protein* is misleading, as there are potentially an infinite number of unique types of proteins in living organisms. Most of the body's proteins are made from

amino acids Nitrogen-containing molecules that combine to form proteins.

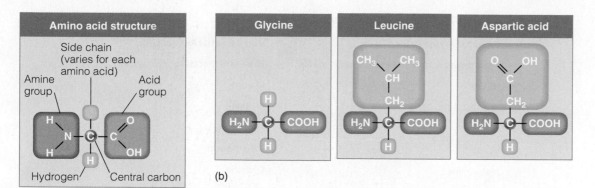

(a)

(b)

Figure 6.1 Structure of an amino acid. (a) All amino acids contain five parts: a central carbon atom, an amine group around the atom that contains nitrogen, an acid group, a hydrogen atom, and a side chain called the R group. (b) Only the side chain differs for each of the 20 amino acids, giving each its unique properties.

combinations of just 20 amino acids, identified in Table 6.1. By combining a few dozen to more than 300 of these 20 amino acids in various sequences, the body synthesizes an estimated 10 000 to 50 000 unique proteins. **Figure 6.2** illustrates how the components of a protein differ from that of a carbohydrate such as starch. As you can see, starch is composed of a chain of glucose molecules. In contrast, the protein insulin is composed of 51 amino acids connected in a specific order, or sequence.

Did You Know?

Insulin was discovered by a team of Canadian researchers at the University of Toronto in 1922. Drs. Frederick Banting and Charles Best along with Professor J. J. R. Macleod and biochemist J. B. Collip, following a series of experiments with dogs, were able to synthesize a purified "antidiabetic" extract from the pancreas. They injected this extract into a 14-year-old diabetic boy and within days his blood sugar returned to normal and his symptoms began to disappear. This extract was called insulin. In 1923, Banting and Macleod were awarded a Nobel prize for their discovery. Without a doubt this was one of the most important medical discoveries in the 20th century.[2]

We Must Obtain Essential Amino Acids from Food

Of the 20 amino acids in the body, nine are classified as essential. This does not mean that they are more important than the others. Instead, an **essential amino acid** is one that the body cannot produce at all or cannot produce in sufficient quantities to meet physiologic needs. Thus, essential amino acids must be obtained from food. Without the proper amount of essential amino acids in our bodies, we lose our ability to make the proteins and other nitrogen-containing compounds we need.

The Body Can Make Non-essential Amino Acids

Non-essential amino acids are just as important to the body as essential amino acids, but the body can synthesize them in sufficient quantities, so we do not need to consume them

essential amino acids Amino acids not produced by the body or not produced in sufficient amounts so that they must be obtained from food.

non-essential amino acids Amino acids that can be manufactured by the body in sufficient quantities and therefore do not need to be consumed regularly in our diet.

Table 6.1 Amino Acids of the Human Body

Essential Amino Acids	Non-essential Amino Acids
These amino acids must be consumed in the diet.	*These amino acids can be manufactured by the body.*
Histidine	Alanine
Isoleucine	Arginine
Leucine	Asparagine
Lysine	Aspartic acid
Methionine	Cysteine
Phenylalanine	Glutamic acid
Threonine	Glutamine
Tryptophan	Glycine
Valine	Proline
	Serine
	Tyrosine

transamination The process of transferring the amine group from one amino acid to another to manufacture a new amino acid.

in our diet. We make non-essential amino acids by transferring the amine group from an essential amino acid to a different acid group and R group. This process of transferring is called **transamination** and is shown in **Figure 6.3**. The acid groups and R groups can be donated by amino acids, or they can be made from the breakdown products of carbohydrates and fats. Thus, by combining parts of different amino acids, the necessary non-essential amino acid can be made.

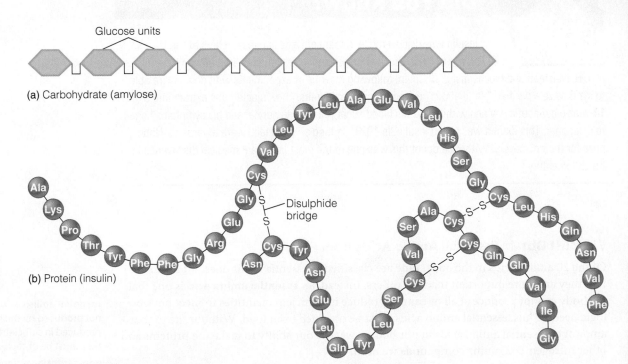

Figure 6.2 How proteins differ from starch. (a) Starch is composed of a chain of glucose molecules, whereas proteins are composed of multiple amino acids connected together. (b) Insulin is a protein that contains 51 amino acids in two chains that are connected by three disulphide bridges—two that connect the two amino acid chains and a third that connects a section of the shortest amino acid chain.

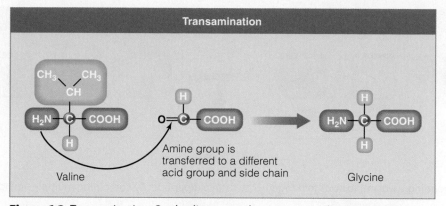

Figure 6.3 Transamination. Our bodies can make non-essential amino acids by transferring the amine group from an essential amino acid to a different acid group and side chain.

Under some conditions, a non-essential amino acid can become an essential amino acid. In this case, the amino acid is called a **conditionally essential amino acid**. Consider what occurs in the disease known as phenylketonuria (PKU). As discussed in Chapter 4, someone with PKU cannot metabolize phenylalanine (an essential amino acid). Normally, the body uses phenylalanine to produce the non-essential amino acid tyrosine, so the inability to metabolize phenylalanine results in failure to make tyrosine. If PKU is not diagnosed immediately after birth, it results in irreversible brain damage. In this situation, tyrosine becomes a conditionally essential amino acid that must be provided by the diet. Other conditionally essential amino acids include arginine, cysteine, and glutamine.

RecaP

Proteins are critical components of all tissues of the human body. Like carbohydrates and lipids, they contain carbon, hydrogen, and oxygen. Unlike the other macronutrients, they also contain nitrogen and some contain sulphur, and their structure is dictated by DNA. The building blocks of proteins are amino acids. The amine group of the amino acid contains nitrogen. The portion of the amino acid that changes, giving each amino acid its distinct identity, is the side chain (or R group). The body cannot make essential amino acids, so we must obtain them from our diet. The body can make non-essential amino acids from parts of other amino acids, carbohydrates, and fats.

How Are Proteins Made?

The body can synthesize proteins by selecting the needed amino acids from the "pool" of all amino acids available in the bloodstream at any given time. Let's look more closely at how this occurs.

Amino Acids Bond to Form a Variety of Peptides

Figure 6.4 shows that when two amino acids join together, the amine group of one binds to the acid group of another in a unique type of chemical bond called a **peptide bond**. In the process, a molecule of water is released as a by-product.

conditionally essential amino acids Amino acids that are normally considered non-essential but become essential under certain circumstances when the body's need for them exceeds the ability to produce them.

peptide bonds Unique types of chemical bonds in which the amine group of one amino acid binds to the acid group of another to manufacture dipeptides and all larger peptide molecules.

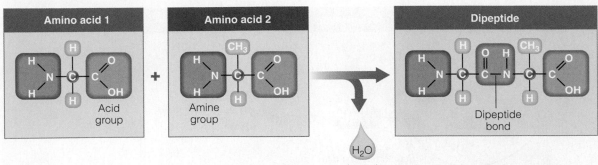

Figure 6.4 Amino acid bonding. Two amino acids join together to form a dipeptide. By combining multiple amino acids, proteins are made.

Two amino acids joined together form a *dipeptide,* and three amino acids joined together are called a *tripeptide.* The term *oligopeptide* is used to identify a string of four to nine amino acids, and a *polypeptide* is ten or more amino acids bonded together. As a polypeptide chain grows longer, it begins to fold into any of a variety of complex shapes that give proteins their sophisticated structure.

Genes Regulate Amino Acid Binding

Each of us is unique because we inherited a specific set of genes from our parents. Our genes encode a specific sequence of the amino acids for each individual protein molecule in our bodies. Minute differences in amino acid sequences can lead to significant differences in the proteins synthesized. These differences in proteins result in the unique physical and physiologic characteristics each one of us possesses. **Gene expression** is the process by which cells use genes to make proteins.

Protein Turnover Involves Synthesis and Degradation

Our bodies constantly require new proteins to function properly. *Protein turnover* involves both the synthesis of new proteins and the degradation of existing proteins to provide the building blocks for those new proteins (**Figure 6.5**). This process allows the cells to respond to the constantly changing demands of physiologic functions. For instance, skin cells live only for about 30 days and must continually be replaced. The amino acids needed

gene expression The process of using a gene to make a protein.

Figure 6.5 Protein turnover involves the synthesis of new proteins and breakdown of existing proteins to provide building blocks for new proteins. Amino acids are drawn from the body's amino acid pool and can be used to build proteins, fat, glucose, and non-protein nitrogen-containing compounds. Urea is produced as a waste product from any excess nitrogen, which is then excreted by the kidneys.

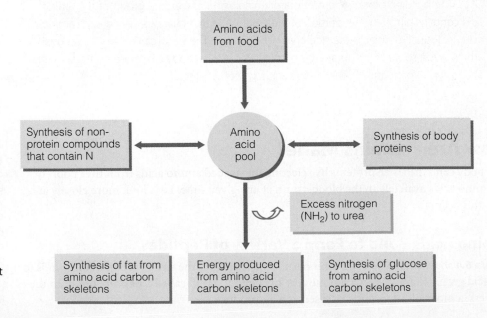

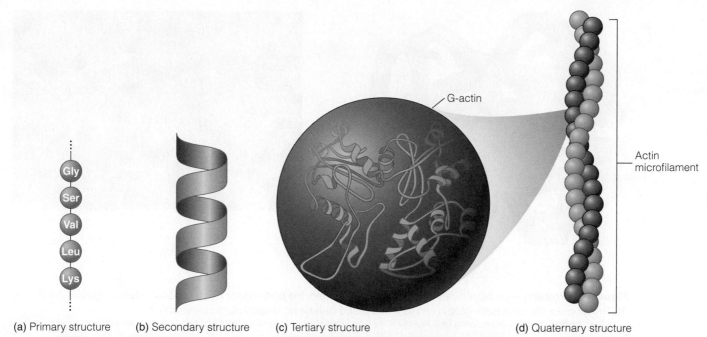

(a) Primary structure   (b) Secondary structure   (c) Tertiary structure   (d) Quaternary structure

Figure 6.6 Levels of protein structure. (a) The primary structure of a protein is the sequential order of amino acids. (b) The secondary structure of a protein is the folding of the amino acid chain. (c) The tertiary structure is a further folding that results in the three-dimensional shape of the protein. (d) The quaternary structure of a protein refers to the situation in which two or more polypeptides interact, join together, and form a larger protein such as the actin molecule illustrated here. In this figure, strands of actin molecules intertwine to form contractile elements involved in generating muscle contractions.

Fig. 6.6a: Adapted from Johnson, M., *Human Biology: Concepts and Current Issues, 5/e*, page 88, Copyright © 2010 Benjamin Cummings. Reprinted by permission of Pearson Education, Inc. Fig. 6.6b: From Germann, W. and Stanfield, C. *Principles of Human Physiology*, Fig. 2.9, Copyright © 2004 Benjamin Cummings. Fig. 6.6c: Copyright 2002 from Molecular Biology of the Cell by Alberts et al. Reproduced by permission of Garland Science/Taylor & Francis LLC.

to produce these new skin cells can be obtained from the body's *amino acid pool,* which includes those amino acids we consume in our diets as well as those that are released from the breakdown of other cells in our bodies. The body's pool of amino acids is used to produce not only new amino acids but also other products including glucose, fat, and urea.

Protein Organization Determines Function

Four levels of protein structure have been identified (**Figure 6.6**). The sequential order of the amino acids in a protein is called the *primary structure* of the protein. The different amino acids in a polypeptide chain possess unique chemical attributes that cause the chain to twist and turn into a characteristic spiral shape, also referred to as the protein's *secondary structure.* The stability of the secondary structure is achieved through the bonding of hydrogen atoms (referred to as hydrogen bonds) or sulphur atoms (referred to as a *disulphide bridge*); these bonds create a bridge between two protein strands or two parts of the same strand of protein (see Figure 6.2). The spiral of the secondary structure further folds into a unique three-dimensional shape referred to as the protein's *tertiary structure;* this structure is critically important because it determines that protein's function in the body. Often, two or more separate polypeptides bond to form a larger protein with a *quaternary structure* that may be *globular* or *fibrous.*

The importance of the shape of a protein to its function cannot be overemphasized. For example, the protein strands in muscle fibres are much longer than they are wide (see Figure 6.6d). This structure plays an essential role in enabling muscle contraction and relaxation. In contrast, the proteins that form red blood cells are globular in shape (see **Figure 6.7**), and they result in the red blood cells being shaped like flattened discs with depressed centres, similar to a miniature donut. This structure and the flexibility of the proteins in the red blood cells permit them to change shape and flow freely through even the tiniest capillaries to deliver oxygen and still return to their original shape.

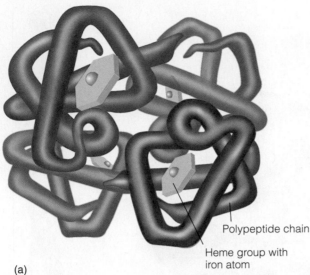

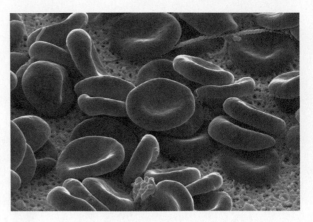

(b)

Polypeptide chain

Heme group with
iron atom

(a)

Figure 6.7 Protein shape determines function. (a) Hemoglobin, the protein that forms red blood cells, is globular in shape. (b) The globular shape of hemoglobin results in red blood cells being shaped like flattened discs.
Data from: Hemoglobin illustration, Irving Geis. Rights owned by Howard Hughes Medical Institute. Not to be reproduced without permission.

Stiffening egg whites denatures some of the proteins within them.

denaturation The process by which proteins uncoil and lose their shape and function when they are exposed to heat, acids, bases, heavy metals, alcohol, and other damaging substances.

limiting amino acid The essential amino acid that is missing or in the smallest supply in the amino acid pool and is thus responsible for slowing or halting protein synthesis.

incomplete proteins Foods that do not contain all of the essential amino acids in sufficient amounts to support growth and health.

Protein Denaturation Affects Shape and Function

Proteins can uncoil and lose their shape when they are exposed to heat, acids, bases, heavy metals, alcohol, and other damaging substances. The term used to describe this change in the shape of proteins is **denaturation**. Everyday examples of protein denaturation that we can see are stiffening of egg whites when they are whipped, the curdling of milk when lemon juice or another acid is added, and the solidifying of eggs as they cook.

Denaturation does not affect the primary structure of proteins, however, it does affect the secondary structure. When a protein is denatured, its function is also lost. For instance, denaturation of a critical enzyme due to exposure to heat or acidity is harmful, because it prevents the enzyme from doing its job. This type of denaturation can occur during times of high fever or when blood pH is out of the normal range. In some cases, denaturation is helpful. For instance, denaturation of proteins during the digestive process allows for their breakdown into amino acids and absorption of these amino acids from the digestive tract into the bloodstream.

Protein Synthesis Can Be Limited by Missing Amino Acids

For protein synthesis to occur, all essential amino acids must be available to the cell. If this is not the case, the amino acid that is missing or in the smallest supply is called the **limiting amino acid**. Without the proper combination and quantity of essential amino acids, synthesis of a particular protein slows and can even halt entirely. For instance, the protein hemoglobin contains the essential amino acid histidine. If we do not consume enough histidine, it becomes the limiting amino acid in hemoglobin production. As no other amino acid can be substituted, the body becomes unable to produce adequate hemoglobin and loses the ability to transport oxygen to cells.

Inadequate energy consumption also limits protein synthesis. If there is not enough energy available from the diet, the body will use any accessible amino acids for energy, thus preventing them from being used to build new proteins.

Protein Quality Can Be Assessed by Several Methods

The nutritional quality of dietary proteins is related to their content of essential amino acids. A protein that does not contain all of the essential amino acids in sufficient quantities to support growth and health is called an **incomplete** (or low-quality) **protein**. Proteins that have all nine of the essential amino acids in sufficient quantities are considered **complete** (or high-quality) **proteins**. The most complete protein sources are foods derived from animals and include egg whites, meat, poultry, fish, and milk. Soybeans and quinoa are the most complete sources of plant protein.

Protein quality was originally determined by long-term balance studies in animals and humans who were given various amounts of dietary protein. However, this method was time consuming and costly and was not ethically sound. Several alternate methods have been developed including biological value (BV), protein efficiency ratio (PER), amino acid or chemical score, the **protein digestibility corrected amino acid score (PDCAAS)**, and the indicator amino acid oxidation technique (IAAO).

The biological value of a protein refers to the proportion of absorbed protein from foods that is incorporated into body proteins. Egg protein has a BV of 100, which indicates that 100% of the nitrogen absorbed is retained and used by the body.

The protein efficiency ratio measures the amount of weight gained by a growing animal and compares it to that animal's protein intake. It is expressed as:

$$PER = weight\ gain\ (g)/protein\ intake\ (g)$$

The amino acid or chemical score is a comparison of the amount of the limiting amino acid in a food with the amount of that same amino acid in a reference food (usually egg protein). The amino acid that is found to have the lowest proportion in the test food as compared with the reference food is defined as the limiting amino acid. Thus, the amino acid or chemical score of a protein gives an indication of the lowest amino acid ratio calculated for any amino acid in a particular food.

The PDCAAS is the most preferred method and has been adopted by the WHO and the FDA to determine protein quality. This technique measures the quality of a protein based on the amino acid requirements (adjusted for digestibility) of a 2- to 5-year-old child (considered the most nutritionally demanding age group). More recently, Canadian researchers adapted the indicator amino acid oxidation technique to determine the metabolic activity of individual amino acids in order to assess the nutritional quality of dietary proteins.[3] For more information on this technique, read the Did You Know? box below.

Meats are highly digestible sources of dietary protein.

Did You Know?

Pioneering work in the area of amino acid requirements has been conducted by several Canadian scientists over the past three decades.[4] In the early 1980s, Kim and colleagues[5] at the University of Guelph developed a new method for the determination of amino acid requirements in young pigs, which they called the indicator amino acid oxidation (IAAO) technique. This technique is based on the concept that when one essential amino acid is deficient for protein synthesis (the limiting amino acid), then all other essential amino acids will be oxidized (that is, broken down into energy). As intakes of the limiting amino acid are increased, amino acid oxidation will decrease, reflecting protein synthesis. When the requirement for the limiting amino acid is met, there is no further change in the indicator oxidation.[6] This method was first applied to adult humans by Zello, Pencharz, and Ball in 1993.[7] Since then, studies have been conducted to determine amino acid requirements in children[8] and in disease.[9] The technique has also been used to determine the nutritional value of proteins.[10] In 2010, Elango and colleagues[11] determined that protein requirements using the IAAO technique were 50% higher than the current DRIs and suggested that there is an urgent need to reassess these recommendations.

complete proteins Foods that contain all nine essential amino acids.

protein digestibility corrected amino acid score (PDCAAS) A measurement of protein quality that considers the balance of amino acids as well as the digestibility of the protein in the food.

Protein Synthesis Can Be Enhanced by Mutual Supplementation

Many people believe that we must consume meat or dairy products to obtain complete proteins. Not true! Consider a meal of beans and rice. Beans are low in the amino acids methionine and cysteine but have adequate amounts of isoleucine and lysine. Rice is low in isoleucine and lysine but contains sufficient methionine and cysteine. By combining beans and rice, a complete protein source is created.

Mutual supplementation is the process of combining two or more incomplete protein sources to make a complete protein, and the two foods involved are called complementary foods; these foods provide **complementary proteins** (**Figure 6.8**) that, when combined, provide all nine essential amino acids. It is not necessary to eat these foods at the same meal. As previously mentioned, the body maintains a free pool of amino acids in the blood; these amino acids come from food and sloughed-off cells. When we eat one potentially complementary protein, its amino acids join those in the amino acid pool. These free amino acids can then combine to synthesize complete proteins. However, it is wise to eat complementary-protein foods during the same day, as partially completed proteins cannot be stored and saved for a later time. Mutual supplementation is important for people eating a vegetarian diet, particularly if they consume no animal products whatsoever.

Recap

Amino acids bind together to form proteins. Genes regulate the amino acid sequence, and thus the structure, of all proteins. Protein turnover involves the synthesis and degradation of proteins so that the body can constantly adapt to a changing environment. The shape of a protein determines its function. When a protein is denatured by heat or damaging substances such as acids, it loses its shape and its function. When a particular amino acid is limiting, protein synthesis will also be limited. A complete protein provides all nine essential amino acids. Methods used to determine protein quality include determination of biological value, protein efficiency ratio, chemical score, the protein digestibility corrected amino acid score, and the indicator amino acid oxidation technique. Mutual supplementation combines two or more complementary-protein sources to make a complete protein.

How Does the Body Break Down Proteins?

The body does not directly use proteins from the diet to make the proteins it needs. Dietary proteins are first digested and broken into amino acids so that they can be absorbed and transported to the cells. In this section, we will review how proteins are digested and absorbed. As you read about each step in this process, refer to **Figure 6.9** for a visual tour through the digestive system.

Stomach Acids and Enzymes Break Proteins into Short Polypeptides

Virtually no enzymatic digestion of proteins occurs in the mouth. As shown in step 1 in Figure 6.9, proteins in food are chewed, crushed, and moistened with saliva to ease swallowing and to increase the surface area of the protein for more efficient digestion. There is no further digestive action on proteins in the mouth.

When proteins reach the stomach, hydrochloric acid denatures the protein strands (Figure 6.9, step 2). It also converts the inactive enzyme, *pepsinogen*, into its active form, **pepsin**, which is a protein-digesting enzyme. Although pepsin is itself a protein, it is not

mutual supplementation The process of combining two or more incomplete protein sources to make a complete protein.

complementary proteins Proteins contained in two or more foods that together contain all nine essential amino acids necessary for a complete protein. It is not necessary to eat complementary proteins at the same meal.

pepsin An enzyme in the stomach that begins the breakdown of proteins into shorter polypeptide chains and single amino acids.

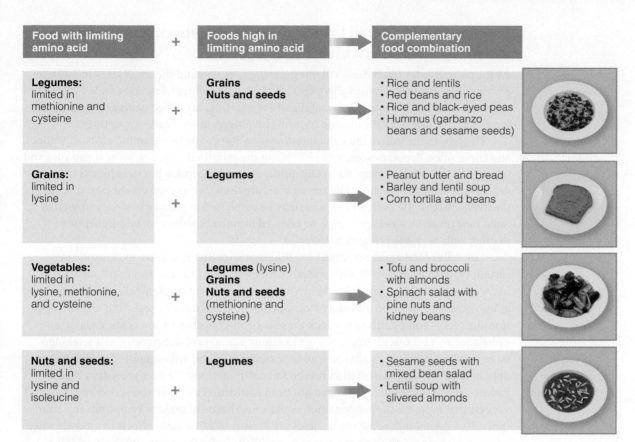

Food with limiting amino acid	+	Foods high in limiting amino acid	→	Complementary food combination	
Legumes: limited in methionine and cysteine	+	**Grains** **Nuts and seeds**	→	• Rice and lentils • Red beans and rice • Rice and black-eyed peas • Hummus (garbanzo beans and sesame seeds)	
Grains: limited in lysine	+	**Legumes**	→	• Peanut butter and bread • Barley and lentil soup • Corn tortilla and beans	
Vegetables: limited in lysine, methionine, and cysteine	+	**Legumes** (lysine) **Grains** **Nuts and seeds** (methionine and cysteine)	→	• Tofu and broccoli with almonds • Spinach salad with pine nuts and kidney beans	
Nuts and seeds: limited in lysine and isoleucine	+	**Legumes**	→	• Sesame seeds with mixed bean salad • Lentil soup with slivered almonds	

Figure 6.8 Complementary food combinations.

denatured by the acid in the stomach because it has evolved to work optimally in an acidic environment. The hormone *gastrin* controls both the production of hydrochloric acid and the release of pepsin; thinking about food or actually chewing food stimulates the gastrin-producing cells located in the stomach. Pepsin begins breaking proteins into single amino acids and shorter polypeptides via hydrolysis; these amino acids and polypeptides then travel to the small intestine for further digestion and absorption.

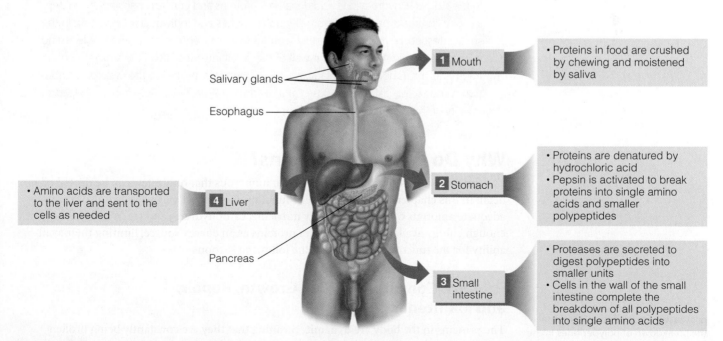

Salivary glands

Esophagus

1 Mouth
• Proteins in food are crushed by chewing and moistened by saliva

2 Stomach
• Proteins are denatured by hydrochloric acid
• Pepsin is activated to break proteins into single amino acids and smaller polypeptides

4 Liver
• Amino acids are transported to the liver and sent to the cells as needed

Pancreas

3 Small intestine
• Proteases are secreted to digest polypeptides into smaller units
• Cells in the wall of the small intestine complete the breakdown of all polypeptides into single amino acids

Figure 6.9 The process of protein digestion.

Enzymes in the Small Intestine Break Polypeptides into Single Amino Acids

As the polypeptides reach the small intestine, the pancreas and the small intestine secrete enzymes that digest them into oligopeptides, tripeptides, dipeptides, and single amino acids (Figure 6.9, step 3). The enzymes that digest polypeptides are called **proteases**; proteases found in the small intestine include trypsin, chymotrypsin, and carboxypeptidase.

The cells in the wall of the small intestine then absorb the single amino acids, dipeptides, and tripeptides. Peptidases, enzymes located in the intestinal cells, break the dipeptides and tripeptides into single amino acids. Dipeptidases break dipeptide bonds, whereas tripeptidases break tripeptide bonds. The amino acids are then transported via the portal vein to the liver. Once in the liver, amino acids may be converted to glucose or fat, combined to build new proteins, used for energy, or released into the bloodstream and transported to other cells as needed (Figure 6.9, step 4).

The cells of the small intestine have different sites that specialize in transporting certain types of amino acids, dipeptides, and tripeptides. This fact has implications for users of amino acid supplements. When very large doses of supplements containing single amino acids are taken on an empty stomach, they typically compete for the same absorption sites. This competition can block the absorption of other amino acids, causing an imbalance of amino acids and leading to various amino acid deficiencies. Also, taking large amounts of amino acids can lead to toxicity. Park and colleagues found that three days of arginine supplementation resulted in a stimulation of cancer growth in breast cancer patients.[12] These results have not been confirmed by other researchers but do suggest that arginine supplementation could cause harmful toxicity symptoms in certain individuals. Although some amino acids are known to cause toxic effects in animals when taken in high doses, the data necessary to establish a tolerable upper intake level (UL) for individual amino acids in humans are considered insufficient at this time.[13] For more information on the use of amino acid supplements to enhance exercise performance, refer to Chapter 15.

RECAP

In the stomach, hydrochloric acid denatures proteins and converts pepsinogen to pepsin; pepsin breaks proteins into smaller polypeptides and individual amino acids. In the small intestine, proteases break polypeptides into smaller fragments and single amino acids. Enzymes in the cells in the wall of the small intestine break the smaller peptide fragments into single amino acids, which are then transported to the liver for distribution to our cells. Taking high doses of individual amino acid supplements can lead to toxicity of those amino acids and deficiencies of others.

Why Do We Need Proteins?

The functions of proteins in the body are so numerous that only a few can be described in detail in this chapter. Note that proteins function most effectively when we also consume adequate amounts of the other energy nutrients, carbohydrates and fat. When there is not enough energy available, the body uses proteins as an energy source, limiting their availability for the functions described in the following sections.

Proteins Contribute to Cell Growth, Repair, and Maintenance

The proteins in the body are dynamic, meaning that they are constantly being broken down, repaired, and replaced. When proteins are broken down, many amino acids are

proteases Enzymes that continue the breakdown of polypeptides in the small intestine.

recycled into new proteins. Think about all of the new proteins that are needed to allow an embryo to develop and grow. In this case, an entirely new human body is being made! In fact, a newborn baby has more than 10 trillion body cells.

Even in the mature adult, all cells are constantly turning over, meaning old cells are broken down and parts are used to create new cells. In addition, the cellular damage that occurs on a regular basis must be repaired to maintain health. Red blood cells live for only three to four months and then are replaced by new cells that are produced in bone marrow. The cells lining the intestinal tract are replaced every three to six days. The "old" intestinal cells are treated just like the proteins in food; they are digested and the amino acids absorbed back into the body. The constant turnover of proteins from our diet is essential for such cell growth, repair, and maintenance.

Proteins Act as Enzymes and Hormones

Recall that enzymes are small chemicals, usually proteins, that speed up chemical reactions, without being changed by the chemical reaction themselves. Enzymes can act to bind substances together or break them apart and can transform one substance into another. **Figure 6.10** shows how an enzyme can bind two substances together.

Each cell contains thousands of enzymes that facilitate specific cellular reactions. For example, the enzyme phosphofructokinase (PFK) is critical to driving the rate at which we break down glucose and use it for energy during exercise. Without PFK, we would be unable to generate energy at a fast enough rate to allow us to be physically active.

Hormones are substances that act as chemical messengers in the body. Some hormones are made from amino acids, whereas others are made from lipids (refer to Chapter 5). Hormones are stored in various glands in the body, which release them in response to changes in the body's environment. They then act on the body's organs and tissues to restore the body to normal conditions. For example, recall that insulin, a hormone made from amino acids, acts on cell membranes to facilitate the transport of glucose into cells. Other examples of amino-acid-containing hormones are glucagon, which responds to conditions of low blood glucose, and thyroid hormone, which helps control our resting metabolic rate.

Proteins Help Maintain Fluid and Electrolyte Balance

Electrolytes are electrically charged particles that assist in maintaining fluid balance. For our bodies to function properly, fluids and electrolytes must be maintained at healthy levels

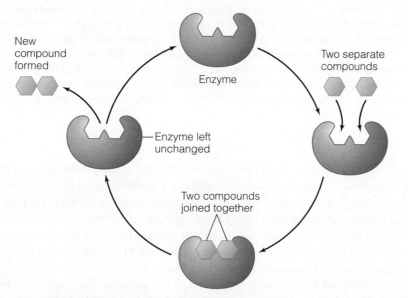

Figure 6.10 Proteins act as enzymes. Enzymes facilitate chemical reactions such as joining two compounds together.

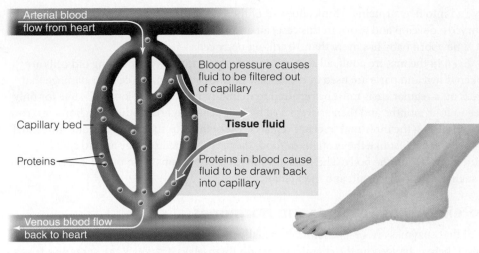

(a) Normal fluid balance

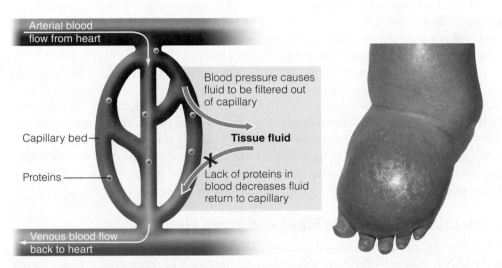

(b) Edema caused by insufficient protein in bloodstream

Figure 6.11 The role of proteins in maintaining fluid balance. The heartbeat exerts pressure that continually pushes fluids in the bloodstream through the arterial walls and out into the tissue spaces. By the time blood reaches the veins, the pressure of the heartbeat has greatly decreased. In this environment, proteins in the blood are able to draw fluids out of the tissues and back into the bloodstream. (a) This healthy (non-swollen) tissue suggests that body fluids in the bloodstream and in the tissue spaces are in balance. (b) When the level of proteins in the blood is insufficient to draw fluids out of the tissues, edema can result. This foot with edema is swollen due to fluid imbalance.

inside and outside cells and within blood vessels. Proteins attract fluids, and the proteins that are in the bloodstream, in the cells, and in the spaces surrounding the cells work together to keep fluids moving across these spaces in the proper quantities to maintain fluid balance and blood pressure. When protein intake is deficient, the concentration of proteins in the bloodstream is insufficient to draw fluid from the tissues and across the blood vessel walls; fluid then collects in the tissues, causing **edema** (**Figure 6.11**). In addition to being uncomfortable, edema can lead to serious medical problems.

Sodium (Na^+) and potassium (K^+) are examples of common electrolytes. Under normal conditions, Na^+ is more concentrated outside the cell, and K^+ is more concentrated inside the cell. This proper balance of Na^+ and K^+ is accomplished by the action of

edema A disorder in which fluids build up in the tissue spaces of the body, causing fluid imbalances and a swollen appearance.

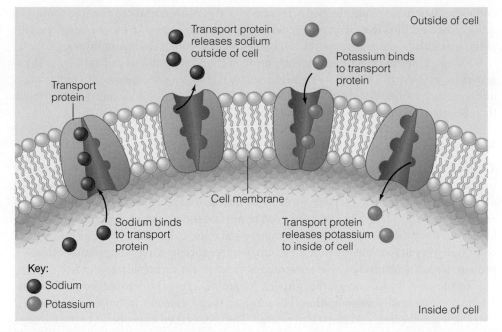

Figure 6.12 Transport proteins help maintain electrolyte balance. Transport proteins in the cell membrane pick up potassium and sodium and transport them across the cell membrane.

transport proteins located within the cell membrane. **Figure 6.12** shows how these transport proteins work to pump Na$^+$ outside and K$^+$ inside of the cell. Conduction of nerve signals and contraction of muscles depend on a proper balance of electrolytes. If protein intake is deficient, we lose our ability to maintain these functions, resulting in potentially fatal changes in the rhythm of the heart. Other consequences of chronically low protein intakes include muscle weakness and spasms, kidney failure, and, if conditions are severe enough, death.

Proteins Help Maintain Acid–Base Balance

The body's cellular processes result in the constant production of acids and bases. These substances are transported in the blood to be excreted through the kidneys and the lungs. The human body maintains very tight control over the **pH**, or the acid–base balance of the blood. The body goes into a state called **acidosis** when the blood becomes too acidic. **Alkalosis** results if the blood becomes too basic. Both acidosis and alkalosis can be caused by respiratory or metabolic problems. Acidosis and alkalosis can cause coma and death by denaturing body proteins.

Proteins are excellent **buffers**, meaning they help maintain proper acid–base balance. Acids contain hydrogen ions, which are positively charged. The side chains of proteins have negative charges that attract the hydrogen ions and neutralize their detrimental effects on the body. Proteins can release the hydrogen ions when the blood becomes too basic. By buffering acids and bases, proteins maintain acid–base balance and blood pH.

Proteins Help Maintain a Strong Immune System

Antibodies are special proteins that are critical components of the immune system. When a foreign substance attacks the body, the immune system produces antibodies to defend against it. Bacteria, viruses, toxins, and allergens (substances that cause allergic reactions) are examples of antigens that can trigger antibody production. (An *antigen* is any substance—but typically a protein—that our bodies recognize as foreign and that triggers an immune response.)

Each antibody is designed to destroy one specific invader. When that substance invades the body, antibodies are produced to attack and destroy the specific antigen. Once

transport proteins Protein molecules that help to transport substances throughout the body and across cell membranes.

pH Stands for percentage of hydrogen. It is a measure of the acidity—or level of hydrogen—of any solution, including human blood.

acidosis A disorder in which the blood becomes acidic; that is, the level of hydrogen in the blood is excessive. It can be caused by respiratory or metabolic problems.

alkalosis A disorder in which the blood becomes basic; that is, the level of hydrogen in the blood is deficient. It can be caused by respiratory or metabolic problems.

buffers Proteins that help maintain proper acid–base balance by attaching to, or releasing, hydrogen ions as conditions change in the body.

antibodies Defensive proteins of the immune system. Their production is prompted by the presence of bacteria, viruses, toxins, and allergens.

antibodies have been made, the body "remembers" this process and can respond more quickly the next time that particular invader appears. *Immunity* refers to the development of the molecular memory to produce antibodies quickly upon subsequent invasions.

Adequate protein is necessary to support the increased production of antibodies that occurs in response to a cold, flu, or allergic reaction. If we do not consume enough protein, our resistance to illnesses and disease is weakened. On the other hand, eating more protein than we need does not improve immune function.

Proteins Serve as an Energy Source

The body's primary energy sources are carbohydrate and fat. Remember that both carbohydrate and fat have specialized storage forms that can be used for energy—carbohydrate as glycogen and fat as triglycerides. Proteins do not have a specialized storage form for energy. This means that when proteins need to be used for energy, they are taken from the blood and body tissues such as the liver and skeletal muscle. In healthy people, proteins contribute very little to energy needs. Because we are efficient at recycling amino acids, protein needs are relatively low as compared with needs for carbohydrate and fat.

To use proteins for energy, the nitrogen (or amine) group is removed from the amino acid in a process called **deamination**. The nitrogen is converted to ammonia, which is transported to the liver and converted to *urea*. The urea is then transported to the kidneys, where it is excreted in the urine. The remaining fragments of the amino acid contain carbon, hydrogen, and oxygen. The body can directly metabolize these fragments for energy or use them to build carbohydrate. Certain amino acids can be converted into glucose via gluconeogenesis. This is a critical process during times of low carbohydrate intake or starvation. Fat cannot be converted into glucose, but body proteins can be broken down and converted into glucose to provide needed energy to the brain.

To protect the proteins in our body tissues, it is important that we regularly eat an adequate amount of carbohydrate and fat to provide energy. We also need to consume enough dietary protein to perform the required work without using up the proteins that already are playing an active role in our bodies. Unfortunately, the body cannot store excess dietary protein. As a consequence, eating too much protein results in the removal and excretion of the nitrogen in the urine and the use of the remaining components for energy.

Proteins Assist in the Transport and Storage of Nutrients

Proteins act as carriers for many important nutrients in the body. As discussed in Chapter 5, lipoproteins contain lipids bound to proteins, which allows the transport of hydrophobic lipids through the watery medium of blood. Another example of a transport protein is transferrin, which carries iron in the blood. Ferritin, in contrast, is an example of a storage protein: it is the compound in which iron is stored in the liver.

As discussed on page 215, transport proteins are located in cell membranes and allow for the proper transport of many nutrients across the cell membrane. These transport proteins also help in the maintenance of fluid and electrolyte balance and conduction of nerve impulses.

deamination The process by which an amine group is removed from an amino acid. The nitrogen is then transported to the kidneys for excretion in the urine, and the carbon and other components are metabolized for energy or used to make other compounds.

RECaP

Proteins serve many important functions, including (1) enabling growth, repair, and maintenance of body tissues; (2) acting as enzymes and hormones; (3) maintaining fluid and electrolyte balance; (4) maintaining acid–base balance; (5) making antibodies, which strengthen the immune system; (6) providing energy when carbohydrate and fat intake are inadequate; and (7) transporting and storing nutrients. Proteins function best when adequate amounts of carbohydrate and fat are consumed.

How Much Protein Should We Eat?

Consuming adequate protein is a major concern of many people. In fact, one of the most common concerns among active people and athletes is that their diets are deficient in protein (see the Nutrition Myth or Fact? box on page 227 for a discussion of this topic). This concern about dietary protein is generally unnecessary, as we can easily consume the protein our bodies need by eating an adequate and varied diet.

Nitrogen Balance Is a Method Used to Determine Protein Needs

A highly specialized procedure referred to as *nitrogen balance* is used to determine a person's protein needs. Nitrogen is excreted through the body's processes of recycling or using proteins; thus, the balance can be used to estimate if protein intake is adequate to meet protein needs.

Typically performed only in experimental laboratories, the nitrogen-balance procedure involves measuring both nitrogen intake and nitrogen excretion over a two-week period. A standardized diet, the nitrogen content of which has been measured and recorded, is fed to the study participant. The person is required to consume all of the foods provided. Because the majority of nitrogen is excreted in the urine and feces, laboratory technicians directly measure the nitrogen content of the subject's urine and fecal samples. Small amounts of nitrogen are excreted in the skin, hair, and body fluids such as mucus and semen, but because of the complexity of collecting nitrogen excreted via these routes, the measurements are estimated. Then, technicians add the estimated nitrogen losses to the nitrogen measured in the subject's urine and feces. Nitrogen balance is then calculated as the difference between nitrogen intake and nitrogen excretion.

People who consume more nitrogen than is excreted are considered to be in positive nitrogen balance (**Figure 6.13**). This state indicates that the body is retaining or adding protein, and it occurs during periods of growth, pregnancy, or recovery from illness or a protein deficiency. People who excrete more nitrogen than is consumed are in negative nitrogen balance. This situation indicates that the body is losing protein, and it occurs during starvation or when people are consuming very-low-energy diets. This is because when energy intake is too low to meet energy demands over a prolonged period of time, the body metabolizes body proteins for energy. The nitrogen from these proteins is excreted in the urine and feces. Negative nitrogen balance also occurs during severe illness, infections, high fever, serious burns, or injuries that cause significant blood loss. People in these situations require increased dietary protein. A person is in nitrogen balance when nitrogen intake equals nitrogen excretion. This indicates that protein intake is sufficient to cover protein needs. Healthy adults who are not pregnant are in nitrogen balance.

Recommended Dietary Allowance for Protein

How much protein should we eat? The RDA for protein is 0.8 g per kilogram of body weight per day. The recommended percentage of energy that should come from protein is 10% to 35% of total energy intake. Protein needs are higher for children, adolescents, and pregnant/lactating women because more protein is needed during times of growth and development (refer to Chapters 16 and 17 for details on protein needs during these phases of the life cycle). Protein needs can also be higher for active people (refer to Chapter 15 for more details) and for vegetarians.

Table 6.2 lists the daily recommendations for protein for a variety of lifestyles. How can we convert this recommendation into total grams of protein for the day? Using the You Do the Math box on the page 219, let's calculate your protein requirements.

Is it possible for you to eat this much protein each day? It may surprise you to discover that most Canadians eat 1.5 to 2 times the RDA for protein without any effort!

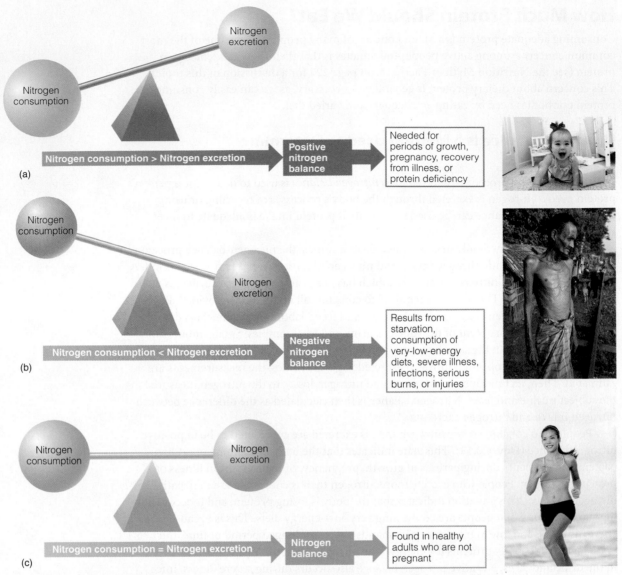

Figure 6.13 Nitrogen balance describes the relationship between how much nitrogen (or protein) we consume and excrete each day. (a) Positive nitrogen balance occurs when nitrogen consumption is greater than excretion. (b) Negative nitrogen balance occurs when nitrogen consumption is less than excretion. (c) Nitrogen balance is maintained when nitrogen consumption equals excretion.

Table 6.2 Recommended Protein Intakes

Group	Protein Intake (grams per kilogram body weight)
Most adults [1]	0.8
Non-vegetarian endurance athletes [2]	1.2 to 1.4
Non-vegetarian strength athletes [2]	1.2 to 1.7
Vegetarian endurance athletes [3]	1.3 to 1.5
Vegetarian strength athletes [3]	1.7 to 1.8

Data from: [1]Food and Nutrition Board, Institute of Medicine. 2002. *Dietary Reference Intakes for Energy, Carbohydrate, Fiber, Fat, Fatty Acids, Cholesterol, Protein, and Amino Acids (Macronutrients)*. Washington, DC: National Academies Press, pp. 465–608.
[2]Academy of Nutrition and Dietetics, Dietitians of Canada, and the American College of Sports Medicine. 2009. Position of the Academy of Nutrition and Dietetics, Dietitians of Canada, and the American College of Sports Medicine: Nutrition and Athletic Performance. *J. Am. Diet Assoc.* 109:509–527.
[3]American College of Sports Medicine, Academy of Nutrition and Dietetics, and Dietitians of Canada. 2001. Joint position statement. Nutrition and athletic performance. *Med. Sci. Sports Exerc.* 32:2130–2145.

YOU DO THE MATH

Calculating Your Protein Needs

How many grams of protein do you need to eat each day? For most healthy adults, this depends primarily on how much you weigh and whether or not you are a strength or endurance athlete. To calculate the total number of grams of protein that you should eat each day:

1. Determine your body weight in kilograms. If you know your weight in pounds, you can convert this measurement to kilograms by dividing by 2.2. For example, an individual who weighs 200 lbs would be 91 kg (200 lb/2.2 lb per kg).
2. Using the values in Table 6.2, multiply your weight in kilograms by your requirement for protein. For example,

if you are a non-vegetarian strength athlete who weighs 91 kg:

$$91 \text{ kg} \times 1.2 \text{ g/kg} = 109.2 \text{ g of protein per day}$$

$$91 \text{ kg} \times 1.7 \text{ g/kg} = 154.7 \text{ g of protein per day}$$

Your protein requirement ranges from approximately 109 g to 155 g daily.

Now calculate your recommended protein intake based on your weight and activity level.

Most Canadians Meet the AMDRs for Protein

Most Canadians eat an amount of protein that falls within the Adequate Macronutrient Distribution Range of 10% to 35% of total energy intake daily; the average protein intake among adults is 16.8%.[14] Between 18% and 24% of protein intake in the Canadian diet is from red meats, 10% to 13% from poultry, and 3% to 6% from fish and seafood. Milk products account for 15% of protein intake, while legumes, nuts, seeds, and eggs provide only 2%.[15] This data suggest that most Canadians appear to have no problems meeting their protein needs each day.

What are the typical protein intakes of active people? Research indicates that the self-reported protein intake of athletes participating in a variety of sports can well exceed current recommendations.[16] For instance, the protein intake for some female distance runners is 1.2 g per kilogram body weight per day, accounting for 15% of their total daily energy intake. In addition, some male bodybuilders consume 3 g per kilogram body weight per day, accounting for almost 38% of their total daily energy intake! However, there are certain groups of athletes who are at risk for low protein intakes. Athletes who consume inadequate energy and limit food choices, such as some distance runners, figure skaters, female gymnasts, and wrestlers who are dieting, are all at risk for low protein intakes. Unlike people who consume adequate energy, individuals who are restricting their total energy intake (kilocalories) need to pay close attention to their protein intake.

Too Much Dietary Protein Can Be Harmful

High protein intake may increase the risk of health problems. Three health conditions that have received particular attention include heart disease, bone loss, and kidney disease.

High Protein Intake Is Associated with High Cholesterol

High-protein diets composed of predominantly animal sources are associated with higher blood cholesterol levels. This is probably due to the saturated fat in animal products, which is known to increase blood cholesterol levels and the risk of heart disease.

One study showed that people with heart disease improved their health when they ate a diet that was high in whole grains, fruits, and vegetables and met the RDA for protein.[17] However, some of the people in this study chose to eat a high-protein diet, and their risk factors worsened. In addition, vegetarians have been shown to have a greatly reduced risk of heart disease.[18, 19]

High Protein Intake May Contribute to Bone Loss

How might a high-protein diet lead to bone loss? Until recently, nutritionists have been concerned about high-protein diets because they increase calcium excretion. This may be because animal products contain more of the sulphur amino acids (methionine and cysteine). Metabolizing these amino acids makes the blood more acidic, and calcium is pulled from the bone to buffer these acids. Although eating more protein can cause an increased excretion of calcium, it is very controversial whether high protein intakes actually cause bone loss. We do know that eating too little protein causes bone loss, which increases the risk of fractures and osteoporosis. Higher intakes of animal and soy protein have been shown to protect bone in middle-aged and older women.[20, 21] There does not appear to be enough direct evidence at this time to show that higher protein intakes cause bone loss in healthy people.

High Protein Intake Can Increase the Risk for Kidney Disease

A third risk associated with high protein intakes is kidney disease. People with kidney problems are advised to eat a low-protein diet because a high-protein diet can increase the risk of acquiring kidney disease in people who are susceptible. People with diabetes have higher rates of kidney disease and may benefit from a lower-protein diet.[22] The Canadian Diabetes Association in its *2008 Clinical Practice Guidelines*[23] recommends a protein intake of 15% to 20% of total energy for people with diabetes. This level of protein is deemed safe for diabetics who have normal renal function. However, there is no evidence that eating more protein causes kidney disease in healthy people who are not susceptible to this condition. In fact, one study found that athletes consuming up to 2.8 g of protein per kilogram body weight per day experienced no unhealthy changes in kidney function.[24] Experts agree that eating no more than 2 g of protein per kilogram body weight each day is safe for healthy people.

It is important for people who consume a lot of protein to drink more water. This is because eating more protein increases protein metabolism and urea production. As mentioned earlier, urea is a waste product that forms when nitrogen is removed during amino acid metabolism. Adequate fluid is needed to flush excess urea from the kidneys. This is particularly important for athletes, who need more fluid because of higher sweat losses.

CASE STUDY ▶ Nitrogen Balance

Colin is a seven-year-old boy who has been described by his mother as a "picky eater." He doesn't like meat and will only eat a few milk products. On a typical day, Colin has a bowl of cereal and milk for breakfast, a honey sandwich for lunch, and one or two chicken fingers and mashed potatoes for supper. Throughout the day he drinks a lot of apple juice and he enjoys salty snacks. An assessment of his diet reveals that he consumes an average of 1800 kcal and 21 g of protein daily. Biochemical analysis shows that Bobby's total daily nitrogen losses are 6 g. His energy requirement is determined to be 1750 kilocalories per day.

Thinking Critically

1. **What are the sources of protein in Colin's diet?**
2. **How would you describe Colin's present nitrogen balance?**
3. **How much protein does Colin have to eat to be in zero nitrogen balance?**
4. **What should Colin's nitrogen balance be? Why?**
5. **What suggestions would you have for Colin's mother to improve his diet?**

Good Food Sources of Protein

Table 6.3 compares the protein content of a variety of foods. In general, good sources of protein include meats (beef, pork, poultry, seafood), dairy products (milk-based products and eggs), soy products, legumes, whole grains, and nuts.

Although most people are aware that meats are an excellent source of protein, many people are surprised to learn that the quality of the protein in some legumes is almost equal to that of meat. Legumes include foods such as kidney beans, pinto beans, black beans,

Table 6.3 Protein Content of Commonly Consumed Foods

Food	Serving Size	Protein (g)	Food	Serving Size	Protein (g)
Beef:			Tempeh, cooked	100 g	18.2
Ground, lean, baked (well done)	75 g	22.7	Soy milk beverage	250 mL	11.6
Rib roast, roasted, (3 mm fat)	75 g	21.2	**Beans:**		
Top sirloin, broiled (3 mm fat)	75 g	21.1	Refried	125 mL	7.3
Poultry:			Kidney, red	125 mL	7.1
Chicken breast, broiled with skin	75 g	19.4	Black	125 mL	8.1
Chicken thigh, bone and skin removed	75 g	18.7	**Nuts:**		
Turkey breast, meat and skin, roasted	75 g	21.8	Peanuts, dry roasted	37 g	8.8
Seafood:			Peanut butter, smooth	30 mL	8.1
Cod, Atlantic, baked	75 g	17.1	Almonds, blanched	29.5 g	5.6
Salmon, Atlantic, wild, baked	75 g	19.1	**Cereals, Grains, Breads:**		
Shrimp, steamed	75 g	15.7	Oatmeal, instant, cooked	250 mL	5.4
Tuna, in water, drained	75 g	17.7	Cheerios	250 mL	2.8
Pork:			Grape Nuts	250 mL	12.4
Loin, rib chop, broiled	75 g	21.6	Raisin Bran	250 mL	5.1
Ham, boneless, regular, roasted	75 g	17	Brown rice, cooked	250 mL	4.8
Dairy:			Whole wheat bread	1 slice	3.4
Whole milk (3.3% fat)	250 mL	8.3	Oatbran bagel	1/2 bagel (44.5 g)	3.3
1% milk	250 mL	8.7	**Vegetables:**		
Skim milk	250 mL	8.7	Carrots, raw (14 cm long)	1	0.5
Yogourt, plain, <1% MF	175 g	8.8	Broccoli, raw, chopped	250 mL	2.6
Processed cheddar cheese	50 g	11.1	Spinach, raw	250 mL	0.9
Cottage cheese, 2% MF	125 mL	16.4	Peas, frozen, cooked	125 mL	4.4
Soy Products:					
Tofu	150 g	21.2			

Data from: The Canadian Nutrient File. Health Canada, 2012. Reproduced with the permission of the Minister of Health, 2012.

The quality of the protein in some legumes, such as these black-eyed peas, lentils, and garbanzo beans, is almost equal to that of meat.

soybeans, garbanzo beans (or chickpeas), lentils, green peas, black-eyed peas, and lima beans. Interestingly, the quality of soybean protein is almost identical to that of meat, and the protein quality of other legumes is relatively high. In addition to being excellent sources of protein, legumes are also high in fibre, iron, calcium, and many of the B-vitamins. They are also low in saturated fat and cholesterol. Legumes are not nutritionally complete, however, as they do not contain vitamins B_{12}, C, or A and are deficient in methionine, an essential amino acid. Eating legumes regularly and including foods made from soybeans (such as soy milk, tofu, textured soy protein, and tempeh) may help reduce the risk of heart disease by lowering blood cholesterol levels. Diets high in legumes and soy products are also associated with lower rates of some cancers.

Nuts are a healthy high-protein food. In the past, the high fat and energy content of nuts was assumed to be harmful, and people were advised to eat nuts only occasionally and in very small amounts. The results from clinical trials indicate that eating about 1.5 to 3.5 servings (50 to 100 grams) of nuts five or more times a week as part of a diet containing 35% energy as fat decreases total and LDL cholesterol levels, suggesting that nut consumption may reduce people's cardiovascular disease risk.[25, 26] Although the exact mechanism for the reduction in cardiovascular disease risk with increased nut intake is not known, nuts contain many nutrients and other substances that are associated with health benefits, including fibre, unsaturated fats, potassium, folate, and plant sterols that inhibit cholesterol absorption.

Fruits and many vegetables are not particularly high in protein; however, these foods provide fibre and many vitamins and minerals and are excellent sources of carbohydrates. Thus, eating these foods can help provide the carbohydrates and energy that our bodies need so that we can spare protein for use in building and maintaining our bodies rather than using it for energy. Try the Nutrition Label Activity on page 223 to determine how much protein you typically eat.

RECAP

The RDA for protein for most non-pregnant, non-lactating, non-vegetarian adults is 0.8 g per kg body weight. Children, pregnant women, nursing mothers, vegetarians, and active people need slightly more. Most people who eat enough kilocalories and carbohydrates have no problem meeting their RDA for protein. Eating too much protein, particularily from animal sources, may increase a person's risk for heart disease and kidney disease if he or she is already at risk for these diseases. Good sources of protein include meats, eggs, dairy products, soy products, legumes, whole grains, and nuts.

vegetarian A person who does not eat meat, poultry, or fish or products containing these foods.

Can a Vegetarian Diet Provide Adequate Protein?

A **vegetarian** is a person who does not eat meat, poultry, or fish or products containing these foods.[27] It is currently estimated that almost 1 million adults in Canada are vegetarians. Many vegetarians are university and college students; moving away from home and taking responsibility for one's eating habits appears to influence some young adults to try vegetarianism as a lifestyle choice.

Types of Vegetarian Diets

There are almost as many types of vegetarian diets as there are vegetarians. Some people who consider themselves vegetarians regularly eat poultry and fish. Others avoid the flesh of animals, but consume eggs, milk, and cheese liberally. Still others strictly avoid all products of animal origin, including milk and eggs, and even by-products such as candies and puddings made with gelatin. A type of "vegetarian" diet receiving significant media attention recently is the *flexitarian* diet:

Soy products are also a good source of dietary protein.

NUTRITION LABEL ACTIVITY

Calculating Protein Intake

Theo wants to know if his diet contains enough protein. To calculate his protein intake, he records all foods that he eats for three days in a food diary. The foods Theo consumed for one of his three days are listed below on the left, and the protein content of those foods is listed on the right. Theo recorded the protein content listed on the Nutrition Facts table for those foods with labels. For products without labels, he used the Health Canada website that lists the energy and nutrient content of thousands of foods (go to www.hc-sc. gc.ca/fn-an/nutrition/fiche-nutri-data/index-eng.php).

Foods Consumed	Protein Content (g)
BREAKFAST:	
Brewed coffee (500 mL) with 60 mL cream (18% MF)	1.7
1 large oatbran bagel (89 g)	9.5
Low-fat cream cheese (30 mL)	2.4
MID-MORNING SNACK:	
Cola beverage (1000 mL)	0
Low-fat strawberry yogourt (250 mL)	10
Snackwells Apple Cinnamon Bars®	2
(37 g each bar; 2 bars eaten)	
LUNCH:	
Ham and cheese sandwich:	
Whole-wheat bread (2 slices)	9
Mayonnaise (30 mL)	0.25
Lean ham (113.5 g)	21.4
Swiss cheese (50 g)	12.4
Iceberg lettuce (2 leaves)	0.5
Slice tomato (3 slices)	0.5
Banana (1 large)	1

Foods Consumed	Protein Content (g)
Triscuit® crackers (20 each)	7
Bottled water (625 mL)	0
DINNER:	
Cheeseburger:	
Broiled ground beef (227 g)	58
Processed cheese (31 g)	6.9
Seeded bun (1 large)	6
Ketchup (30 mL)	0.5
Mustard (15 mL)	0.7
Shredded lettuce (125 mL)	0.5
Sliced tomato (3 slices)	0.5
French fries (100 g; 20 strips)	4
Baked beans (500 mL)	25.5
2% milk (500 mL)	17
EVENING SNACK:	
Chocolate chip cookies (4 each of 7.6 cm diameter cookie)	3
2% milk (250 mL)	8.5
Total Protein Intake for the Day:	**208.8 g**

Thinking Critically

1. **Theo presently weighs 100 kg. He is active but does not qualify as an endurance or strength athlete. Calculate Theo's protein RDA.**
2. **Compare Theo's protein RDA with his protein intake.**
3. **Is Theo obtaining more protein from animal or non-animal sources?**
4. **Theo asks you if he should be taking an amino acid or protein supplement. What would you recommend?**

Flexitarians are considered semi-vegetarians who eat mostly plant foods, eggs, and dairy but occasionally eat red meat, poultry, and/or fish.

Table 6.4 identifies the various types of vegetarian diets, ranging from the most inclusive to the most restrictive. Notice that the more restrictive the diet, the more challenging it becomes to achieve an adequate protein intake.

Why Do People Become Vegetarians?

When discussing vegetarianism, one of the most often-asked questions is why people would make this food choice. The most common responses are included here.

Religious, Ethical, and Food-Safety Reasons

Some make the choice for religious or spiritual reasons. Several religions prohibit or restrict the consumption of animal flesh; however, generalizations can be misleading. For

Table 6.4 Terms and Definitions of a Vegetarian Diet

Type of Diet	Foods Consumed	Comments
Semi-vegetarian (also called partial vegetarian or flexitarian)	Vegetables, grains, nuts, fruits, legumes; sometimes seafood, poultry, eggs, and dairy products	Typically exclude or limit red meat; may also avoid other meats
Pescovegetarian	Similar to a semi-vegetarian but excludes poultry	*Pesco* means fish, the only animal source of protein in this diet
Lacto-ovo-vegetarian	Vegetables, grains, nuts, fruits, legumes, dairy products (*lacto*) and eggs (*ovo*)	Excludes animal flesh and seafood
Lactovegetarian	Similar to a lacto-ovo-vegetarian but excludes eggs	Relies on milk and cheese for animal sources of protein
Ovovegetarian	Vegetables, grains, nuts, fruits, legumes, and eggs	Excludes dairy, flesh, and seafood products
Vegan (also called strict vegetarian)	Only plant-based foods (vegetables, grains, nuts, seeds, fruits, legumes)	May not provide adequate vitamin B_{12}, zinc, iron, or calcium
Macrobiotic diet	Vegan type of diet; becomes progressively more strict until almost all foods are eliminated. At the extreme, only brown rice and small amounts of water or herbal tea are consumed.	Taken to the extreme, can cause malnutrition and death
Fruitarian	Only raw or dried fruit, seeds, nuts, honey, and vegetable oil	Very restrictive diet; deficient in protein, calcium, zinc, iron, vitamin B_{12}, riboflavin, and other nutrients

People who follow certain sects of Hinduism refrain from eating meat.

example, whereas certain sects within Hinduism forbid the consumption of meat, perusing the menu at any Indian restaurant will reveal that many other Hindus regularly consume small quantities of meat, poultry, and fish. Many Buddhists are vegetarians, as are some Christians, including Seventh Day Adventists.

Many vegetarians are guided by their personal philosophy to choose vegetarianism. These people feel that it is morally and ethically wrong to consume animals and any products from animals (such as dairy or egg products) because they view the practices in the modern animal industries as inhumane. They may consume milk and eggs but choose to purchase them only from family farms where they feel animals are treated humanely.

There is also a great deal of concern about meat-handling practices, because contaminated meat has occasionally made its way into our food supply. For example, in 2008 there was an outbreak of listeriosis in Canada that killed 23 people. This was eventually linked to the consumption of deli meats that were contaminated during packaging.

Ecological Benefits

Many people choose vegetarianism because of their concerns about the effect of meat industries on the global environment. Because of the high demand for meat in developed nations, meat production has evolved from small family farming operations into the larger system of agribusiness. Critics point to the environmental costs of agribusiness, including massive uses of water and grain to feed animals, methane gases and other wastes produced by animals themselves, and increased land use to support livestock. For an in-depth discussion of this complex and emotionally charged topic, refer to the Evidence-informed Decision Making feature at the end of this chapter.

Health Benefits

Still others practise vegetarianism because of its health benefits. Research over several years has consistently shown that a varied and balanced vegetarian diet can reduce the risk of many chronic diseases. Health benefits include:[28]

- Reduced intake of fat and total energy, which reduces the risk for obesity. This may in turn lower a person's risk for type 2 diabetes.

- Lower blood pressure, which may be due to a higher intake of fruits and vegetables. People who eat vegetarian diets tend to be non-smokers, drink little or no alcohol, and exercise more regularly, which are also factors known to reduce blood pressure and help maintain a healthy body weight.
- Reduced risk of heart disease, which may be due to lower saturated fat intake and a higher consumption of *antioxidants* that are found in plant-based foods. Anti-oxidants, discussed in detail in Chapter 11, are substances that can protect our cells from damage. They are abundant in fruits and vegetables.
- Fewer digestive problems such as constipation and diverticular disease, perhaps due to the higher fibre content of vegetarian diets. Diverticular disease, discussed in Chapter 4, occurs when the wall of the bowel (large intestine) pouches and becomes inflamed.
- Reduced risk of some cancers. Research shows that vegetarians may have lower rates of cancer, particularly colon cancer.[27] Many components of a vegetarian diet could contribute to reducing cancer risks, including higher fibre and antioxidant intakes, lower dietary fat intake, lower consumption of **carcinogens** (cancer-causing agents) that are formed when cooking meat, and higher consumption of soy protein, which may have anticancer properties.[29]
- Reduced risk of kidney disease, kidney stones, and gallstones. The lower protein contents of vegetarian diets, plus the higher intake of legumes and vegetable proteins such as soy, may be protective against these conditions.

What Are the Challenges of a Vegetarian Diet?

Although a vegetarian diet can be healthy, it also presents many challenges. Limiting consumption of flesh and dairy products introduces the potential for inadequate intakes of certain nutrients, especially for people consuming a vegan, macrobiotic, or fruitarian diet. Table 6.5 lists the nutrients that can be deficient in a vegan-type of diet plan and describes good non-animal sources that can provide these nutrients. Vegetarians who consume dairy and/or egg products obtain these nutrients more easily.

Research indicates that a sign of disordered eating in some female athletes is the switch to a vegetarian diet.[30] Instead of eating a healthy variety of non-animal foods, people with disordered eating problems may use vegetarianism as an excuse to restrict many foods from their diets.

Can a vegetarian diet provide enough protein? Because non-meat high-quality protein sources are quite easy to obtain in developed countries, a well-balanced vegetarian diet can

A well-balanced vegetarian diet can provide adequate protein.

Table 6.5 Nutrients of Concern in a Vegan Diet

Nutrient	Functions	Non-meat/Non-dairy Food Sources
Vitamin B$_{12}$	Assists with DNA synthesis; protection and growth of nerve fibres	Vitamin B$_{12}$ fortified cereals, yeast, soy products, and other meat analogs; vitamin B$_{12}$ supplements
Vitamin D	Promotes bone growth	Vitamin D fortified cereals, margarines, and soy products; adequate exposure to sunlight; supplementation may be necessary for those who do not get adequate exposure to sunlight
Riboflavin (vitamin B$_2$)	Promotes release of energy; supports normal vision and skin health	Whole and enriched grains, green leafy vegetables, mushrooms, beans, nuts, and seeds
Iron	Assists with oxygen transport; involved in making amino acids and hormones	Whole-grain products, prune juice, dried fruits, beans, nuts, seeds, leafy vegetables such as spinach
Calcium	Maintains bone health; assists with muscle contraction, blood pressure, and nerve transmission	Fortified soy milk and tofu, almonds, dry beans, leafy vegetables, calcium-fortified juices, fortified breakfast cereals
Zinc	Assists with DNA and RNA synthesis, immune function, and growth	Whole-grain products, wheat germ, beans, nuts, and seeds
Omega-3 fatty acids	Reduce inflammatory responses; reduces blood clotting and triglyceride levels	Canola, flax and soybean oils; ground flax seed, soybeans, tofu, hemp hearts, and walnuts

carcinogens Any substance or agent capable of causing the cellular mutations that lead to cancer, such as certain pesticides, industrial chemicals, and pollutants.

Vegetarians should eat two to three servings of beans, nuts, seeds, eggs, or meat substitutes, such as tofu, daily.

provide adequate protein. In fact, the Academy of Nutrition and Dietetics and the Dietitians of Canada endorse an appropriately planned vegetarian diet as healthy, nutritionally adequate, and providing many benefits in reducing and preventing various diseases.[27] As you can see, the emphasis is on a *balanced* and *adequate* vegetarian diet; thus, it is important for vegetarians to consume soy products, eat complementary proteins, and obtain enough energy from other macronutrients to spare protein from being used as an energy source. Although the digestibility of a vegetarian diet is potentially lower than that of an animal-based diet, there is no separate protein recommendation for vegetarians who consume complementary plant proteins.[5]

Using the Vegetarian Food Guide to Design a Healthy Diet

An example of a Vegetarian Food Guide based on *Eating Well with Canada's Food Guide* is illustrated in **Figure 6.14**. This guide can be used by vegetarians to design a healthy diet that contains all of the necessary nutrients.

For example, to meet their needs for protein and calcium, lactovegetarians can consume low-fat or non-fat dairy products. Vegans and ovovegetarians can consume calcium-fortified soy milk or one of the many protein bars now fortified with calcium.

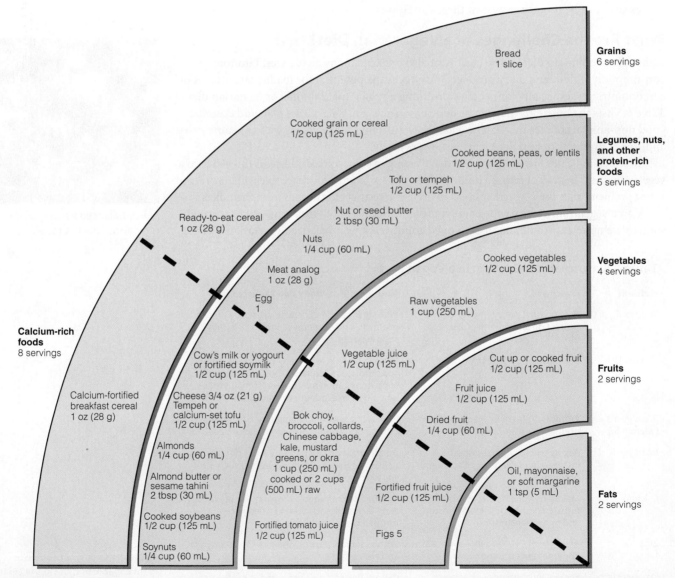

Figure 6.14 The North American Vegetarian Food Guide. This guides general food choices for vegetarians on a daily basis.
Data from: Reprinted from Journal of the American Dietetic Association, Vol 103/6, V. Messina, V. Melina, A. R. Mangels, A new food guide for North American vegetarians/ Pg. 774, Copyright 2003, with permission from Elsevier.

NUTRITION MYTH OR FACT?

Do Athletes Need More Protein Than Inactive People?

Roula is a competitive figure skater who trains five days a week. She tries to eat a healthy diet but often finds it difficult because of her busy training schedule and the fact that she has recently adopted a vegetarian lifestyle. Roula has been told that she needs to eat more protein to build muscle and ensure optimal performance. She decides to add a 20 gram protein supplement to her juice after each practice, which increases her usual protein intake to 90 grams per day. Roula's kcal intake is usually about 2400 kcal per day. She weighs 55 kg.

Thinking Critically

1. **Why do athletes need more protein?**
2. **How much protein does Roula need?**
3. **Does Roula need to take a protein supplement?**
4. **What advice would you give Roula about her protein intake?**

Some athletes who persistently diet are at risk for low protein intake.

In addition to protein and calcium, vegans need to pay special attention to consuming foods high in vitamins D, B_{12}, and riboflavin (B_2) and the minerals zinc and iron. Supplementation of these micronutrients may be necessary for certain individuals if they cannot consume adequate amounts in their diet.

ReCaP

A balanced vegetarian diet may reduce the risk of obesity, type 2 diabetes, heart disease, digestive problems, some cancers, kidney disease, kidney stones, and gallstones. Whereas varied vegetarian diets can provide enough protein, vegetarians who consume no animal products need to make sure they consume adequate plant sources of protein and supplement their diet with good sources of vitamin B_{12}, vitamin D, riboflavin, iron, calcium, and zinc.

What Disorders Are Related to Protein Intake or Metabolism?

As we have seen, consuming inadequate protein can result in severe illness and death. Typically, this occurs when people do not consume enough total energy, but a diet deficient specifically in protein can have similar effects.

Protein-Energy Malnutrition Can Lead to Debility and Death

When a person consumes too little protein and energy, the result is **protein-energy malnutrition** (also called *protein-calorie malnutrition*). Two diseases that can follow are marasmus and kwashiorkor (**Figure 6.15**).

Marasmus Results from Grossly Inadequate Energy Intake

Marasmus is a disease that results from grossly inadequate intakes of protein, energy, and other nutrients. Essentially, people with marasmus slowly starve to death. It is most common

protein-energy malnutrition A disorder caused by inadequate consumption of protein. It is characterized by severe wasting.

marasmus A form of protein-energy malnutrition that results from grossly inadequate intakes of protein, energy, and other nutrients.

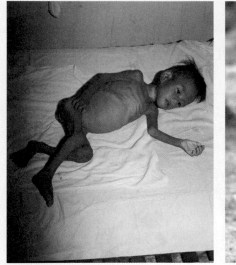

(a)   (b)

Figure 6.15 Two forms of protein-energy malnutrition are (a) marasmus and (b) kwashiorkor.

in young children (6 to 18 months of age) who are living in impoverished conditions. These children are fed diluted cereal drinks that are inadequate in energy, protein, and most nutrients. People suffering from marasmus have the look of "skin and bones," as their body fat and tissues are wasting. Consequences of marasmus include:

- Wasting and weakening of muscles, including the heart muscle
- Stunted brain development and learning impairment
- Depressed metabolism and little insulation from body fat, causing a dangerously low body temperature
- Stunted physical growth and development
- Deterioration of the intestinal lining, which further inhibits absorption of nutrients
- *Anemia* (abnormally low levels of hemoglobin in the blood)
- Severely weakened immune system
- Fluid and electrolyte imbalances

If marasmus is left untreated, death from dehydration, heart failure, or infection will result. Treating marasmus involves carefully correcting fluid and electrolyte imbalances. Protein and carbohydrates are provided once the body's condition has stabilized. Fat is introduced much later, as the protein levels in the blood must improve to the point at which the body can use them to carry fat (in the form of lipoproteins) so it can be safely metabolized by the body.

Kwashiorkor Results from a Low-Protein Diet

Kwashiorkor often occurs in developing countries when infants are weaned of breast milk early due to the arrival of a subsequent baby. This deficiency disease is typically seen in young children (one to three years of age) who no longer drink breast milk. Instead, they often are fed a low-protein, starchy cereal. Unlike marasmus, kwashiorkor often develops quickly and causes the person to look swollen, particularly in the belly. This is because the low protein content of the blood is inadequate to keep fluids from seeping into the tissue spaces. Other symptoms of kwashiorkor include:

- Some weight loss and muscle wasting, with some retention of body fat
- Retarded growth and development; less severe than that seen with marasmus
- Edema, which results in extreme distension of the belly and is caused by fluid and electrolyte imbalances
- Fatty degeneration of the liver
- Loss of appetite, sadness, irritability, apathy
- Development of sores and other skin problems; skin pigmentation changes
- Dry, brittle hair that loses its pigment, straightens, and falls out easily

Kwashiorkor can be reversed if adequate protein and energy are given in time. Because of their severely weakened immune systems, many individuals with kwashiorkor die from diseases they contract in their weakened state. Of those who are treated, many return home to the same impoverished conditions, only to develop this deficiency once again.

Many people think that only children in developing countries suffer from these diseases. However, protein-energy malnutrition occurs in all countries and affects both children and adults. In Canada, poor people living in inner cities and isolated rural areas are affected. Others at risk include older adults, the homeless, people with eating disorders, those addicted to alcohol and drugs, and individuals with wasting diseases such as AIDS and cancer. Despite the fact that Canada produces more than enough food, Canadians do experience malnutrition and hunger. Chapter 19 provides a detailed review of malnutrition in Canada and worldwide.

kwashiorkor A form of protein-energy malnutrition that is typically seen in developing countries in infants and toddlers who are weaned early because of the birth of a subsequent child. Denied breast milk, they are fed a cereal diet that provides adequate energy but inadequate protein.

Disorders Related to Genetic Abnormalities

Numerous disorders are caused by defective DNA. These genetic disorders include phenyl-ketonuria (or PKU), sickle cell anemia, and cystic fibrosis.

As discussed in Chapter 4, *phenylketonuria* is an inherited disease in which a person does not have the ability to break down the amino acid phenylalanine. As a result, phenyl-alanine and its metabolic by-products build up in tissues and can cause brain damage. Individuals with PKU must eat a diet that is severely limited in phenylalanine.

Sickle cell anemia is an inherited disorder of the red blood cells in which a single amino acid present in hemoglobin is changed. As shown in Figure 6.7, normal hemoglobin is globular, giving red blood cells a round, donutlike shape. The genetic alteration that occurs with sickle cell anemia causes the red blood cells to be shaped like a sickle or a crescent (**Figure 6.16**). Because sickled red blood cells are hard and sticky, they cannot flow smoothly through the smallest blood vessels. Instead, they block the vessels, depriving nearby tissues of their oxygen supply and eventually damaging vulnerable organs, particularly the spleen. Sickled cells also have a lifespan of only about 10 to 20 days, as opposed to the 120-day average for globular red blood cells. The body's greatly increased demand for new red blood cells leads to severe anemia. Other signs and symptoms of sickle cell anemia include impaired vision, headaches, convulsions, bone degeneration, and decreased function of various organs. This disease occurs in any person who inherits the sickle cell gene from both parents.

Cystic fibrosis is an inherited disease that primarily affects the respiratory system and digestive tract. It is caused by a defective gene that causes cells to build and then reject an abnormal version of a protein that normally allows passage of chloride into and out of certain cells. This alteration in chloride transport causes cells to secrete thick, sticky mucous. The linings of the lungs and pancreas are particularly affected, causing breathing difficulties, lung infections, and digestion problems that lead to nutrient deficiencies. Symptoms include wheezing, coughing, and stunted growth. The severity of this disease varies greatly; some individuals with cystic fibrosis live relatively normal lives, whereas others are seriously debilitated and die in childhood.

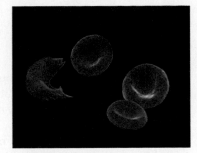

Figure 6.16 A sickled red blood cell.

RECAP

Protein-energy malnutrition can lead to marasmus and kwashiorkor. These diseases primarily affect impoverished children in developing nations. However, residents of developed countries are also at risk, especially older adults, the homeless, people who abuse alcohol or other drugs, and people with AIDS, cancer, and other wasting diseases. Genetic disorders involving abnormal proteins include phenylketonuria, sickle cell anemia, and cystic fibrosis.

sickle cell anemia A genetic disorder that causes red blood cells to be shaped like a sickle or crescent. These cells cannot travel smoothly through blood vessels, causing cell breakage and anemia.

cystic fibrosis A genetic disorder that causes an alteration in chloride transport, leading to the production of thick, sticky mucus that causes life-threatening respiratory and digestive problems.

SEE FOR YOURSELF

Tips for Adding Legumes to Your Daily Diet

They're high in protein and fibre, low in fat, and fill you up with fewer calories than meat sources of protein. What's more, they taste good! Maybe that's why nutrition experts consider legumes an almost perfect food. From main dishes to snacks, here are some simple ways to add legumes to your daily diet. By the way, some people experience uncomfortable intestinal gas after eating legumes. This is pro-duced when bacteria in the colon break down the starches. If you're one of those people, make sure you soak legumes thoroughly, changing the water once or twice, before cooking. You can also try using Beano®, an enzyme supplement available in most grocery stores. Taken before meals, it reduces intestinal gas.

Breakfast

- Instead of cereal, eggs, or a muffin, microwave a frozen bean burrito for a quick, portable breakfast.
- Make your pancakes with soy milk or pour soy milk on your cereal.
- If you normally have a side of bacon, ham, or sausage with your eggs, have a side of black beans.

Lunch and Dinner

- Try a sandwich made with hummus (a garbanzo bean spread), cucumbers, tomato, avocado, and/or lettuce in a whole-wheat pocket.
- Add garbanzo beans, kidney beans, or fresh peas to tossed salads or make a three-bean salad with kidney beans, green beans, and garbanzo beans.
- Make a side dish using legumes, such as peas with pearl onions or succotash (lima beans, corn, and tomatoes).

- Make black-bean soup, lentil soup, pea soup, minestrone soup, or a batch of dal (a type of yellow lentil used in Indian cuisine) and serve over brown rice. Top with plain yogourt, a traditional accompaniment in many Asian cuisines.
- Make burritos with black or pinto beans instead of shredded meat.
- Make a "meatloaf" using cooked, mashed lentils instead of ground beef.
- For fast food at home, keep canned beans on hand. Serve over rice with a salad for a complete and hearty meal.

Snacks

- Instead of potato chips or pretzels, try one of the new bean chips.
- Dip fresh vegetables in bean dip or hummus.
- Add roasted soy "nuts" to your trail mix.
- Keep frozen tofu desserts such as tofu ice cream in your freezer.

Chapter Review

6

Test Yourself | Answers

1. **F** Although protein can be used for energy in certain circumstances, fats and carbohydrates are the primary sources of energy for our bodies.

2. **F** There is no evidence that consuming amino acid supplements assists in building muscle tissue. Exercising muscles, specifically using weight training, is the stimulus needed to build muscle tissue.

3. **F** Excess protein is broken down and its component parts are either stored as fat or used for energy or tissue building and repair. Only the nitrogen component of protein is excreted in the urine.

4. **F** Vegetarian diets can meet and even exceed an individual's protein needs, assuming that adequate energy-yielding macronutrients, a variety of protein sources, and complementary protein sources are consumed.

5. **T** Most people in Canada consume 1.5 to 2 times more protein than they need.

Summary

- Unlike carbohydrates and fat, the structure of proteins is dictated by DNA, and proteins contain nitrogen.
- Amino acids are the building blocks of proteins; they are composed of an amine group, an acid group, a hydrogen atom, and a unique side chain called the R group.

- There are 20 different amino acids in our bodies: nine are essential amino acids, meaning that our bodies cannot produce them, and we must obtain them from food; 11 are non-essential, meaning our bodies can make them so they do not need to be consumed in the diet.

- Our genetic makeup determines the sequence of amino acids in our proteins. Gene expression refers to using a gene in a cell to make a protein.

- Protein turnover involves the synthesis of new proteins and the degradation of existing proteins.

- The three-dimensional shape of proteins determines their function in the body.

- When proteins are exposed to damaging substances such as heat, acids, bases, and alcohol, they are denatured, meaning they lose their shape and function.

- A limiting amino acid is one that is missing or in limited supply, preventing the synthesis of adequate proteins.

- Mutual supplementation is the process of combining two incomplete protein sources to make a complete protein. The two foods involved in this process are called complementary proteins.

- Most digestion of proteins occurs in the small intestine.

- Protein quality is determined by its amino acid content and digestibility. Higher-quality proteins contain more essential amino acids and are more digestible. Animal sources, soy protein, and legumes are highly digestible forms of protein.

- Proteins are needed to promote cell growth, repair, and maintenance. They act as enzymes and hormones; help maintain the balance of fluids, electrolytes, acids, and bases; and support healthy immune function. They are also critical for nutrient transport and storage.

- The RDA for protein for adults is 0.8 g of protein per kilogram of body weight per day; protein should make up 10% to 35% of total energy intake. Most people in Canada routinely eat 1.5 to 2 times the RDA for protein.

- High protein intakes may be harmful and can lead to increased blood cholesterol levels, and increased risk for kidney disease in people who are susceptible to kidney problems.

- There are many forms of vegetarianism: lacto-ovo-vegetarians eat plant foods plus eggs and dairy products; pescovegetarians consume plant foods and rely on fish as the only meat source; vegans consume only plant foods.

- Consuming a well-planned vegetarian diet may reduce the risk of obesity, heart disease, type 2 diabetes, and some forms of cancer.

- Vegans may need to supplement their diet with vitamins B_{12} and D, riboflavin, iron, calcium, and zinc.

- Marasmus and kwashiorkor are two forms of protein-energy malnutrition that result from grossly inadequate energy and protein intake.

- Phenylketonuria is a genetic disease in which the person cannot break down the amino acid phenylalanine. The buildup of phenylalanine and its by-products leads to brain damage.

- Sickle cell anemia is a genetic disorder of the red blood cells. Because of an alteration of one amino acid in hemoglobin, the red blood cells become sickle-shaped and cannot travel smoothly through blood vessels. This blocks the vessels, causing inadequate oxygenation of nearby tissues, organ damage, and anemia.

- Cystic fibrosis is a genetic disease that causes an alteration in chloride transport that leads to the production of thick, sticky mucous. This mucous causes serious respiratory and digestive problems, which leads to variable levels of debilitation and, in some cases, premature death.

Review Questions

1. The process of combining peanut butter and whole-wheat bread to make a complete protein is called
   a. deamination.
   b. vegetarianism.
   c. transamination.
   d. mutual supplementation.

2. Which of the following meals would be appropriate in a well-planned vegan diet?
   a. Rice, pinto beans, acorn squash, soy butter, and almond milk
   b. Veggie dog, bun, and a banana-yogourt milkshake
   c. Brown rice and green tea
   d. Egg salad on whole-wheat toast, broccoli, carrot sticks, and soy milk

3. The substance that breaks down polypeptides in the small intestine is called

   a. hydrochloric acid.   b. pepsin.
   c. protease.   d. ketones.

4. The portion of an amino acid that contains nitrogen is called the
   a. R group.   b. amine group.
   c. acid group.   d. nitrate cluster.

5. All proteins must contain
   a. carbon, oxygen, iron, and nitrogen.
   b. iron, oxygen, and hydrogen.
   c. carbon, oxygen, hydrogen, and nitrogen.
   d. carbon, oxygen, hydrogen, and sulphur.

6. Describe two methods of determining protein quality.

7. How do proteins differ from carbohydrates and lipids?

8. Explain the relationship between inadequate protein intake and the swollen bellies of children with kwashiorkor.

9. Explain the relationship between excessive protein intake and an increased risk for kidney disease.

10. You've always thought of your dad as a bit of a "health nut," so you're not surprised when you come home on spring break and he offers you a dinner of stir-fried vegetables and tofu. Over dinner, he announces that he is now a vegetarian and has joined an online vegetarian chat group. "But Dad," you protest, "you still eat meat, don't you?" "Sure I do," he answers, "but only once or twice a week. Lots of the other people in my chat group occasionally eat meat, too!" In your opinion, is your dad really a vegetarian? Defend your position.

11. Draw a sketch showing how amino acids bond to form proteins.

Web Links

www.dietitians.ca
Dietitians of Canada
Search for vegetarian diets to learn how to plan healthy meat-free meals.

www.hc-sc.gc.ca
Health Canada
Use the search function on this site to search for information about the listeria investigation and recall.

www.who.int/nut
World Health Organization Nutrition Site
Visit this site to find out more about the worldwide magnitude of protein-energy malnutrition and the diseases that can result from inadequate intakes of protein, energy-yielding carbohydrates, fats, and various additional nutrients.

www.inspection.gc.ca/english/toce.shtml
Canadian Food Inspection Agency
Visit this site to find out more about food recalls and allergy alerts.

MasteringNutrition®

www.masteringnutrition.pearson.com

Assignments
Animations: Deamination & Transamination • Fat Synthesis from Excess Protein • Nitrogen Balance • Protein Digestion • Protein Synthesis • Protein Absorption • The Building Blocks of Proteins

Study Area
Video: Understanding Proteins • Practice Tests • Diet Analysis • eText

References

1. Barr, S. I, and C. A. Rideout. 2004. Nutritional considerations for vegetarian athletes. *Nutrition* 20:696–703.
2. PBS. People and discoveries. *Banting and Best isolate insulin 1922.* Available online at www.pbs.org/wgbh/aso/databank/entries/dm22in.html (accessed June 10, 2010).
3. Humayun M. A., R. Elango, S. Moehn, R. O. Ball, and P. B. Pencharz. 2007. Application of the indicator amino acid oxidation technique for the determination of metabolic availability of sulfur amino acids from casein versus soy protein isolate in adult men. *J. Nutr.* 137:1874–1879.
4. Elango R., R. O. Ball, and P. B. Pencharz. 2008. Indicator amino acid oxidation: concept and application. *J. Nutr.* 138:243–246.
5. Kim K. I., I. McMillan, and H. S., Bayley. 1983. Determination of amino acid requirements of young pigs using an indicator amino acid. *Br. J. Nutr.* 50:369–382.
6. Elango, R., R. O. Ball, and P. B. Pencharz. 2008. Indicator amino acid oxidation: concept and application. *J. Nutr.* 138:243–246.
7. Zello, G. A., P. B. Pencharz, and R. O. Ball. 1993. Dietary lysine requirements of young adult males determined by oxidation of L-[1-13C] phenylalanine. *Am. J. Physiol.* 264:E677–E685.
8. Mager, D. R., L. J. Wykes, R. O. Ball, and P. B. Pencharz. 2003. Branched-chain amino acid requirements in school-aged children determined by indicator amino acid oxidation (IAAO). *J. Nutr.* 133:3540–3545.
9. Brunton, J. A., R. O. Ball, and P. B. Pencharz. 1998. Determination of amino acid requirements by indicator amino acid oxidation: applications in health and disease. *Curr. Opin. Clin. Nutr. Metab. Care* 1:449–453.
10. Humayun, M. A., R. Elango, S. Moehn, and R. O. Ball. 2007. Development of the indicator amino acid oxidation technique for

the determination of metabolic availability of sulfur amino acids from casein versus soy protein isolate in adult men. *J. Nutr.* 137:1874–1879.

11. Park, K. G., S. D. Heys, K. Blessing, P. Kelly, M. A. McNurlan, O. Eremin, and P. J. Garlick. 1992. Stimulation of human breast cancers by dietary L-arginine. *Clin. Sci.* 82:413–417.

12. Institute of Medicine, Food and Nutrition Board. 2002. *Dietary Reference Intakes for Energy, Carbohydrate, Fiber, Fat, Fatty Acids, Cholesterol, Protein, and Amino Acids (Macronutrients).* Washington, DC: National Academies Press.

13. Elango, R., M. A. Humayun, R. O. Ball, and P. B. Pencharz. 2010. Evidence that protein requirements have been significantly underestimated. *Curr. Opin. Clin. Nutr. Metab. Care* 13:52–57.

14. Health Canada. 2009. *Do Canadian Adults Meet Their Nutrient Requirements Through Food Intake Alone?* Available online at www.hc-sc.gc.ca/fnan/surveill/nutrition/commun/art-nutr-adult-eng.php (accessed June 10, 2010).

15. Johnson-Down, L., L. Jacobs-Starkey, and K. Gray-Donald. 2006. Primary sources of nutrients in the Canadian diet. *Can. J. Diet. Prac. Res.* 67:7–13.

16. Manore, M., and J. Thompson. 2000. *Sport Nutrition for Health and Performance.* Champaign, IL: Human Kinetics.

17. Fleming, R. M. 2000. The effect of high-protein diets on coronary blood flow. *Angiology* 51:817–826.

18. Leitzmann, C. 2005. Vegetarian diets: what are the advantages? *Forum Nutr.* 57:147–156.

19. Szeto, Y. T., T. C. Y. Kwok, and I. F. F. Benzie. 2004. Effects of a long-term vegetarian diet on biomarkers of antioxidant status and cardiovascular disease risk. *Nutrition* 20:863–866.

20. Munger, R. G., J. R. Cerhan, and B. C.-H. Chiu. 1999. Prospective study of dietary protein intake and risk of hip fracture in postmenopausal women. *Am. J. Clin. Nutr.* 69:147–152.

21. Alekel, D. L., A. St. Germain, C. T. Peterson, K. B. Hanson, J. W. Stewart, and T. Toda. 2000. Isoflavone-rich soy protein isolate attenuates bone loss in the lumbar spine of perimenopausal women. *Am. J. Clin. Nutr.* 72:844–852.

22. Kontessis, P., I. Bossinakou, L. Sarika, E. Iliopoulou, A. Papanto-niou, R. Trevisan, D. Roussi, K. Stipsanelli, S. Grigorakis, and A. Souvatzoglou. 1995. Renal, metabolic, and hormonal responses to proteins of different origin in normotensive, non-proteinuric type 1 diabetic patients. *Diabetes Care* 18:1233–1240.

23. Canadian Diabetes Association. 2008. Clinical practice guidelines for the prevention and management of diabetes in Canada. *Can. J. Diab.* 32:1–215.

24. Poortmans, J. R., and O. Dellalieux. 2000. Do regular high protein diets have potential health risks on kidney function in athletes? *Int. J. Sport Nutr.* 10:28–38.

25. Mukuddem-Peterson, J., W. Oosthuizen, and J. Jerling. 2005. A systematic review of the effects of nuts on blood lipid profiles in humans. *J. Nutr.* 135:2082–2089.

26. Banel, D., and F. Hu. 2009. Effects of walnut consumption on blood lipids and other cardiovascular risk factors: a meta-analysis and systematic review. *Am. J. Clin. Nutr.* 90:56–63.

27. Academy of Nutrition and Dietetics and Dietitians of Canada. 2003. Position of the Academy of Nutrition and Dietetics and Dietitians of Canada: vegetarian diets. *Can. J. Diet. Prac. Res.* 64:62–81.

28. Messina, M., and V. Messina. 1996. *The Dietitian's Guide to Vegetarian Diets.* Gaithersburg, MD: Aspen Publishers.

29. Messina, V. K., and K. I. Burke. 1997. Position of the Academy of Nutrition and Dietetics: vegetarian diets. *J. Am. Diet. Assoc.* 97:1317–1321.

30. O'Conner, M. A., S. W. Touyz, S. M. Dunn, and P. J. V. Beaumont. 1987. Vegetarianism in anorexia nervosa? A review of 116 consecutive cases. *Med. J. Aust.* 147:540–542.

31. CTV.ca. 2007. *Why Canada's greenhouse gas record stinks.* Available online at www.ctv.ca/servlet/ArticleNews/print/CTVNews/20070110gh (accessed June 17, 2010).

32. Food and Agriculture Organization. 2006. Livestock a major threat to environment: remedies urgently needed. *FAO Newsroom.* 29 November. www.fao.org/newsroom/en/news/2006/1000448/index.html (accessed March 2009.)

33. Eshel, G., and P. Martin. 2006. Diet, energy and global warming. *Earth Interactions* (March)10:1–17. http://geosci.uchicago.edu/~gidon/papers/nutri/nutri.html (accessed March 2009.)

34. Jowit, J. 2008. UN says eat less meat to curb global warming. *The Observer* (September 7). www.guardian.co.uk/environment/2008/sep/07/food.foodanddrink (accessed March 2009.)

35. National Cattlemen's Beef Association. November 2003. Beef industry "factoid" fighter. Available online at www.beef.org/documents/Factoid%20Fighter%20Revisions%2011-03-03.doc.

Meat Consumption and Global Warming: Tofu to the Rescue?

(a)

(b)

The difference in greenhouse gas emissions associated with meat-based (a) versus vegetarian (b) meals is similar to the difference between driving an SUV versus an average sedan.

When it comes to greenhouse gas emissions, Canada had the third-worst record of the countries who were members of the Organization for Economic Co-operation and Development (OECD) at the time of their study.[31]

Which causes more greenhouse gas emissions: livestock production or transportation? The answer may surprise you: according to the United Nations Food and Agriculture Organization (FAO), livestock production generates more of the gases responsible for global warming—18%—than transportation.[32] The FAO estimates that livestock production accounts for:

- 9% of all carbon dioxide (CO_2) production deriving from human activity
- 37% of all human-induced methane, a gas with 23 times the global warming potential (GWP) of CO_2
- 64% of ammonia, which contributes to acid rain

- 65% of human-related production of nitrous oxide, a gas with 296 times the GWP of CO_2

How does this compare to emissions generated from production of plant foods? A recent study from researchers at the University of Chicago concluded that an adult consuming an average daily number of calories from a typical mixed American diet causes the emission of 1485 kg of greenhouse gases *above* the emission associated with consuming the same number of calories from plant sources. Far from trivial, nationally this difference amounts to over 6% of the total U.S. greenhouse gas emissions.[33]

Livestock production is also a major source of land degradation, through both overgrazing and feed production. Livestock now use 30% of the earth's land surface for pasture or feed production. Aggressive deforestation, which has long been linked to global warming, is claiming more and more land for pasture; for example, in Latin

(a)

(b)

Livestock production (a) and aggressive deforestation (b) both contribute to increased greenhouse gas emissions.

America, about 70% of former forests in the Amazon have been cleared for grazing.[32] In addition, production of feed crops for livestock uses 33% of global arable land—acres that could be cultivated for crops for human consumption. Livestock's presence in vast tracts of land and its demand for feed crops also have contributed significantly to a reduction in biodiversity and decline in ecosystems.[32]

Water use can also be tremendous. It is estimated that in the United States, it takes 1630 L of water to produce 2.2 kg of pork. This is in contrast with the 572 L of water it takes to produce 2.2 kg of wheat. Water pollution is another concern: animal waste, antibiotics, hormones, and fertilizers and pesticides used on feed crops can run off into surrounding bodies of water, resulting in the pollution of neighbouring streams, rivers, and lakes, as well as nearby irrigation fields used to produce crops for human consumption.

Considering the damage that livestock production wreaks on the environment, should you adopt a vegetarian—or semi-vegetarian—diet? The world's leading authority on global warming thinks you should. In 2008, Dr. Rajendra Pachauri, chair of the United Nations Intergovernmental Panel on Climate Change, which earned a joint share of the Nobel Peace Prize in 2007, released a statement calling upon individuals to have one meat-free day a week if they want to make a personal and effective sacrifice that would help tackle climate change. He went on to advocate that people progressively reduce their meat consumption even further.[34] Pachauri noted that reducing meat consumption is an action that anyone can take immediately, and one that can have a significant impact on global warming in a short period of time.

But not everyone agrees. In response to many of the claims of environmental degradation due to livestock production, meat industry organizations have published information in defence of their practices. In a 2003 fact sheet, the National Cattlemen's Beef Association disputes many of the claims made by critics. It states:[35]

- The waste produced by cattle is very minor. In fact, the primary source of methane emissions is from landfills; only about 2% of the total methane production in the United States comes from domestic livestock.
- Much of the land used to raise livestock is not suitable for growing vegetable or grain crops.

- Although many countries have destroyed significant areas of rainforest to provide grazing land for domestic livestock, less than 1% of the total 2001 beef supply in the United States was imported from rainforest countries, and the largest fast food chains have policies in place that prohibit the purchase of beef from these same countries.
- Although it does take more water to produce a pound of beef than a pound of vegetables, the amount is much lower than claimed by many activists and is only 11% of the total amount of water used in the United States each year.

In addition, although some individuals choose vegetarianism to protect the environment, it is not practical or realistic to expect every human around the world to adopt this lifestyle. Animal products provide important nutrients for our bodies, and many people on the brink of starvation cannot survive without small amounts of milk and meat.

Still, if people were to significantly reduce their consumption of meat, it might be possible to return to the system of small family farming, which is more environmentally friendly. When animals are raised on smaller farms and/or allowed to range freely, they consume grass, crop wastes, and scraps recycled from the kitchen, which is an efficient means of utilizing food sources that humans do not consume. What's more, the waste produced by these animals can be used for fertilizer and fuel.

Using the Evidence

1. Are the data convincing that meat consumption increases global warming?

2. Given the accelerated pace of climate change, as well as land and water degradation, is adopting a vegetarian or semi-vegetarian diet our ethical responsibility as citizens of the earth?

3. Would such a diet be practical for you?

4. Whether or not you decide to eat less meat, what other actions could you take to reduce the "carbon footprint" of your diet?

Metabolism: From Food to Life

Test Yourself — True or False?

1. Every cell of the body is metabolically active. T *or* F

2. Certain vitamins are essential for producing energy in the body. T *or* F

3. All excess energy is stored as body fat. T *or* F

4. The fatty acids stored in adipose tissue are easily converted to glucose. T *or* F

5. During a period of extreme starvation, the body will use heart muscle for energy and to help maintain blood glucose levels. T *or* F

Test Yourself answers are located in the Chapter Review.

Chapter Objectives | *After reading this chapter, you will be able to:*

1. Distinguish between metabolism, catabolism, and anabolism, *pp. 238–239*.

2. Illustrate the following types of metabolic reactions: hydrolysis, condensation, oxidation–reduction, and phosphorylation, *pp. 240–243*.

3. Explain the role of enzymes, cofactors, and coenzymes during chemical reactions, *pp. 243–244*.

4. Describe in correct order the three stages by which energy is extracted from glucose, *pp. 244–249*.

5. Describe two conditions that are likely to increase ketone formation in the liver, *pp. 251–252*.

6. Explain how the catabolism of proteins differs from the catabolism of carbohydrates and lipids, *pp. 252–254*.

7. Delineate the process by which alcohol is metabolized, *pp. 254–257*.

8. Identify the body's mechanisms for storing excess glucose, triglycerides, and proteins, *pp. 258–259*.

9. Compare the processes of gluconeogenesis, lipogenesis, and amino acid synthesis, *pp. 259–261*.

10. Explain how the states of feasting and fasting affect metabolism, *pp. 263–265*.

Malia, just 12 hours old, was fussing in her father's arms when the hospital pediatrician and a neonatal nurse entered the room. While the nurse soothed Malia, the pediatrician broke the news: the results of a routine screening test had indicated that Malia was born with maple syrup urine disease (MSUD), a metabolic disorder, and further tests had confirmed the diagnosis. He explained that MSUD occurs when a baby lacks an enzyme necessary to break down certain amino acids. If the disorder is not treated, the unmetabolized amino acids quickly build up in the body's tissues, especially the brain, resulting in severe and sometimes fatal neurologic damage. Malia's parents had never heard of MSUD and immediately asked if their daughter would be okay. The pediatrician assured them that when the disease is detected and dietary treatment initiated in the first days of life, children with MSUD develop normally. He explained that Malia would not be able to breastfeed but would have to be fed a special formula low in the amino acids leucine, isoleucine, and valine. "Are you saying that the only thing we have to do to keep Malia healthy is switch her from breast milk to a special formula?" Malia's father asked. "For now, yes," the pediatrician replied. "But as she grows, you'll have to pay careful and consistent attention to her diet." He then scheduled them to meet with the hospital's registered dietitian that afternoon to discuss Malia's dietary needs.

Metabolic disorders such as MSUD, phenylketonuria (see Chapter 4), galactosemia (an error of carbohydrate metabolism), and others are rare, but because they interrupt the normal processes of metabolism, their consequences can be severe or fatal. Why is metabolism so critical to our health and life, and how does it occur? We explore these and other questions in this chapter.

The food we eat is converted to fuel and other necessary substances through metabolism.

Why Is Metabolism Essential for Life?

Although some people say they live to eat, we all have to eat to live. The food we eat each day provides the energy and nutrients the body needs to sustain life. **Metabolism** is the sum of all the chemical and physical processes by which the body breaks down and builds up molecules. When nutrition researchers burn food in a **calorimeter** to determine how much energy the food contains, carbon dioxide, water, and thermal energy (heat) are released. In a similar way, when the body uses food for fuel, carbon dioxide, water, and energy, both chemical and thermal, are released. Cells throughout the body require chemical energy to grow, reproduce, repair themselves, and maintain their functions. Indeed, every chemical reaction in the body either requires or releases energy. In addition, energy released as heat helps keep us warm. When cell metabolism functions properly, so too will the body.

Anabolism and Catabolism Require or Release Energy

As you learned in previous chapters, the end products of digestion are absorbed from the small intestine and then circulated to the body's cells. There they may be broken down even further for energy. Alternatively, the cells may use these small, basic molecules as building blocks to synthesize compounds such as glycogen, cholesterol, hormones, enzymes, or cell membranes, according to the body's needs. The process of making larger, chemically complex molecules from smaller, more basic ones is called **anabolism** (**Figure 7.1**). Because the process of anabolism supports the building of compounds, it is critical for growth, repairing and maintaining the body's tissues, and synthesizing the chemical products essential for human functioning. From a small subset of metabolic "building blocks" including glucose, amino acids, and fatty acids, the body is able to use anabolism to synthesize thousands of chemically complex substances.

Anabolic reactions require energy. If you've studied physics, you know that *energy* can be broadly defined as the capacity to perform work. Mechanical energy is necessary for movement, electrical energy sparks nerve impulses, and thermal energy maintains body temperature. The energy that fuels anabolic reactions is chemical energy. How exactly does the body generate this chemical energy?

metabolism The sum of all the chemical and physical changes that occur in body tissues when food is converted from large molecules to small molecules.

calorimeter A special instrument in which food can be burned and the amount of heat that is released can be measured; this process demonstrates the energy (caloric) content of the food.

anabolism The process of making new molecules from smaller ones.

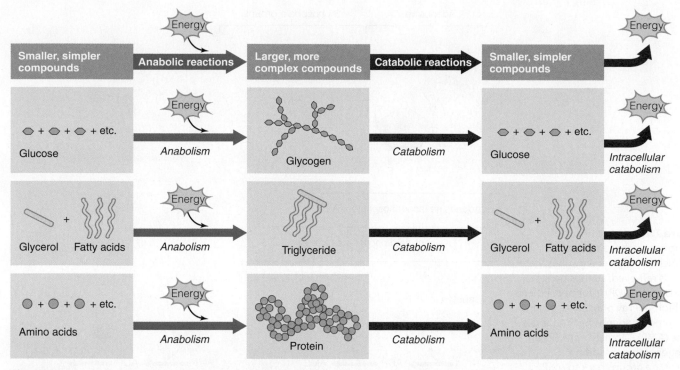

Figure 7.1 Anabolic reactions use energy to convert simple chemical compounds into larger, more complex structures. Catabolic reactions degrade complex compounds and produce energy.

Catabolism is the breakdown or degradation of larger, more complex molecules to smaller, more basic molecules (Figure 7.1). The opposite of anabolism, catabolism releases chemical energy. Catabolism of food begins with digestion, when chemical reactions break down the macronutrients we consume. The thousands of different proteins, lipids, and carbohydrates in the human diet are all broken down into the same small group of end products: amino acids, fatty acids, glycerol, and monosaccharides (usually glucose). After absorption, these basic components are transported to body cells. When a cell needs energy, it can catabolize these components into even smaller molecules. Energy is released as a by-product of this intracellular catabolism. Catabolism is also used to break down old cells or tissues that need to be repaired or replaced. The energy gained via catabolic reactions is used not only to fuel the body's work but also to build new compounds, cells, and tissues via anabolism. Thus, in response to our earlier question, the energy to fuel anabolic reactions comes from the body's catabolic reactions.

Overall, a balance between anabolism and catabolism maintains health and function. However, there are times when one of these two processes dominates. For example, fetal and childhood growth represents a net anabolic state, because more tissue is formed than broken down. However, disease is often dominated by catabolism, with more tissue being broken down than repaired. Of course, one goal of treatment is to stop or minimize these catabolic processes and allow the anabolic phase of recovery to begin.

Energy Stored in Adenosine Triphosphate Fuels the Work of All Body Cells

When cells catabolize nutrients such as glucose, they package the energy that is released during the reaction in a compound called **adenosine triphosphate (ATP)**. As you might guess from its name, a molecule of ATP includes an organic compound called adenosine and three phosphate groups (**Figure 7.2a**). The bonds between the phosphate groups store a significant amount of potential energy and are sometimes termed *high-energy phosphate*

catabolism The breakdown or degradation of larger molecules to smaller molecules.

adenosine triphosphate (ATP) A high-energy compound made up of the purine adenine, the simple sugar ribose, and three phosphate units; it is used by cells as a source of metabolic energy. Also, the common currency of energy for virtually all cells of the body.

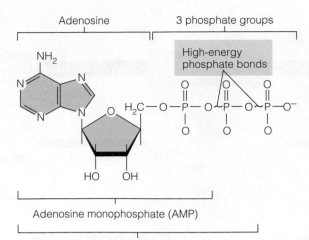

Figure 7.2 (a) Structure of adenosine triphosphate (ATP). (b) When one high-energy phosphate group is removed, adenosine diphosphate (ADP) is formed. When two high-energy phosphate groups are removed, adenosine monophosphate (AMP) is formed. (c) ATP can be regenerated by adding phosphate groups back to AMP and ADP through the process of phosphorylation.

(a) Structure of ATP

(b) Conversion of ATP to ADP and AMP

(c) Regeneration of ATP

bonds.[1] When these bonds are broken, their energy is released and can be used to do the work of the cell. This explains why ATP is often called the molecular "currency" of the cell: its phosphate bonds store energy to build new molecules, break down old molecules, and keep the cell functioning optimally.

When one high-energy phosphate bond is broken and a single phosphate group released, **adenosine diphosphate (ADP)** is produced (see Figure 7.2b). When two phosphates are removed, **adenosine monophosphate (AMP)** is produced. ATP can be regenerated by adding phosphate groups back to these molecules (see Figure 7.2c).

A small amount of ATP is stored in every cell for immediate use. When cells need more ATP, they can generate it via the catabolism of glucose, glycerol, fatty acids, and amino acids. Thus, the food we eat each day continues to help the body regenerate the ATP required by the cells.

Recap

All forms of life are dependent upon metabolic pathways for survival. A balance between anabolic and catabolic reactions helps the body achieve growth and repair and maintain health and functioning. The body uses and produces energy in the form of ATP.

adenosine diphosphate (ADP)
A metabolic intermediate that results from the removal of one phosphate group from ATP.

adenosine monophosphate (AMP)
A low-energy compound that results from the removal of two phosphate groups from ATP.

What Chemical Reactions Are Fundamental to Metabolism?

Metabolic pathways are clusters of chemical reactions that occur sequentially and achieve a particular goal, such as the breakdown of glucose for energy. Cells use different, yet related, metabolic pathways to release the energy in each of the major energy-containing nutrients—glucose, fatty acids, and amino acids. These pathways typically occur within a specific part of a cell. This is because many metabolic enzymes are restricted to one or a few

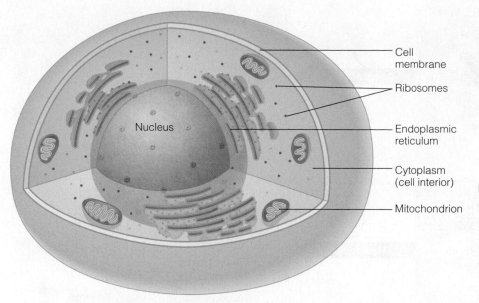

Cell membrane

Ribosomes

Nucleus

Endoplasmic reticulum

Cytoplasm (cell interior)

Mitochondrion

Figure 7.3 Structure of a typical cell. The cell membrane separates the cell from the extracellular fluid. The nucleus contains the genetic information. The cytoplasm contains the organelles, surrounded by a fluid called cytosol. Organelles include mitochondria, endoplasmic reticulum, and ribosomes.

locations within the cell. As an example, the process of glycolysis, to be discussed shortly, occurs in the cytosol, the liquid portion of the cytoplasm, because all of the enzymes needed for that process can be found in the cytosol. **Figure 7.3** shows the general structure of a cell and its components.

The cell's mitochondria, which might be compared to the furnace in your house, are the location of many other metabolic reactions. The mitochondria contain large numbers of metabolic enzymes and are the primary sites where chemical energy, in the form of ATP, is produced. Cells that lack mitochondria, such as red blood cells, are limited in their ability to produce energy. These cells must rely on less efficient energy-producing processes that can occur in their cytoplasm.

Metabolic pathways are not only limited to certain types of cells and certain cell structures, but they may also be limited to specific body organs or tissues. Glycogen stored in the liver can be catabolized and the resulting glucose released into the bloodstream, yet the catabolism of muscle glycogen does not allow for the release of glucose into the blood. Why the difference? Muscle lacks one enzyme that catalyzes one simple step in the metabolic pathway that is found in the liver.

Although all cells are metabolically active, many nutritional scientists view liver, muscle, and adipose cells as key locations for the integration of metabolic pathways. As this chapter unfolds, it will be possible to visualize the "networking" of metabolic pathways that occur between these and other body organs.

Before describing each of the unique metabolic pathways involving carbohydrates, fats, and proteins, we will review a few simple chemical reactions common to all of them.

In Condensation and Hydrolysis Reactions, Water Reacts with Molecules

Condensation and hydrolysis are chemical reactions involving water. **Condensation** is an anabolic process. It occurs when small, chemically simple units combine to produce a larger, more complex molecule. In the process, water is released as a by-product. Because the water produced is removed from the original molecules, this reaction is also called *dehydration synthesis*. The general formula for condensation reactions is written as follows:

$$A\text{—}OH + H\text{—}B \longrightarrow A\text{—}B + H_2O$$

Disaccharides are synthesized from individual monosaccharides via condensation. As discussed in Chapter 4, the formation of a chemical bond between two simple sugars

condensation An anabolic process by which smaller, chemically simple compounds are joined with the removal of water.

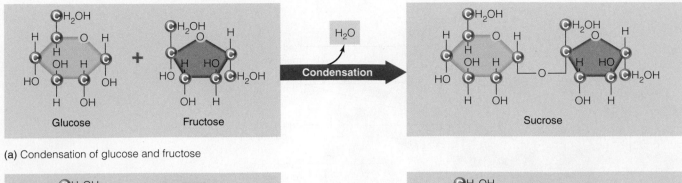

(a) Condensation of glucose and fructose

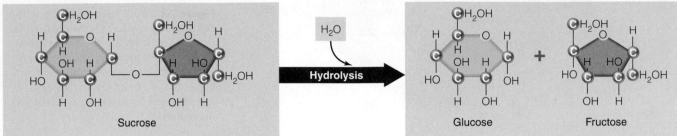

(b) Hydrolysis of sucrose

Figure 7.4 (a) Condensation of glucose and fructose. Glucose and fructose react and, with the release of water, combine through condensation to form sucrose. (b) Hydrolysis of sucrose. Sucrose undergoes hydrolysis, with the addition of water, to form glucose and fructose.

occurs when one monosaccharide donates a hydroxyl (OH) group and the other donates a hydrogen (H) group. The condensation of glucose and fructose is shown in **Figure 7.4a**.

Condensation is typically an anabolic process. Its opposite, termed *hydrolysis,* is usually catabolic. In hydrolysis, a large, chemically complex molecule is broken apart with the addition of water. Because the original molecule becomes hydrated, this reaction is also called a *hydration* reaction. Notice that the general formula for hydrolysis reactions is opposite that of condensation reactions:

$$A—B + H_2O \rightarrow A—OH + H—B$$

The disaccharide sucrose, for example, is broken down via hydrolysis to its smaller and chemically simpler components (glucose and fructose). This process is illustrated in Figure 7.4b.

In Phosphorylation Reactions, Molecules Exchange Phosphate

As mentioned, ATP is an energy reservoir within the cell because it contains two high-energy phosphate bonds. When these bonds are broken, energy is released and the inorganic phosphate (P_i) can be transferred to other molecules. The process by which phosphate is transferred is called **phosphorylation**. For example, glucose undergoes phosphorylation when it first enters a cell:

$$C_6H_{12}O_6 + A—P—P—P \rightarrow C_6H_{12}O_6—P + A—P—P$$

| Glucose | ATP | Glucose phosphate | ADP |

Once glucose is phosphorylated, it can either be stored as glycogen or oxidized for immediate energy (discussed shortly). Another example of phosphorylation is the synthesis of ATP from ADP plus a phosphate group (see Figure 7.2c). The energy required for this reaction comes from the oxidation of energy-containing substrates such as glucose. As you may have guessed, removal of phosphate groups, as in the breakdown of ATP (see Figure 7.2b), is called *dephosphorylation.*

phosphorylation The addition of one or more phosphate groups to a chemical compound.

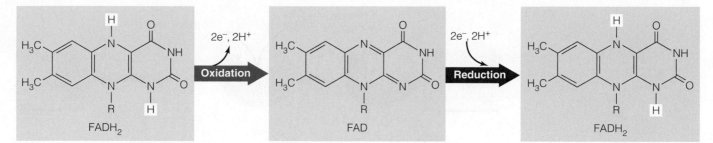

Figure 7.5 Oxidation and reduction of FAD and $FADH_2$. $FADH_2$ is easily oxidized to FAD, which can easily be reduced back to $FADH_2$.

In Oxidation–Reduction Reactions, Molecules Exchange Electrons

In **oxidation–reduction reactions**, the molecules involved exchange electrons, often in the form of hydrogen. These reactions always occur together, as electrons gained by one molecule must be donated by another. The molecule that gives up an electron is said to be *oxidized* because typically its electron has been removed by an oxygen atom. The molecule that has acquired an electron is said to be reduced because, in gaining an electron (e^-), it becomes more negatively charged. In the human body, the oxygen needed for oxidation reactions is obtained from the air we breathe. Because they involve the exchange of electrons, oxidation–reduction (or *redox*) reactions are classified as *exchange reactions*.

An example of a redox reaction important to metabolism involves **FAD (flavin adenine dinucleotide)** and $FADH_2$, two forms of riboflavin, one of the B-vitamins involved in energy metabolism. These compounds are required for the enzymes in energy reactions to function. $FADH_2$ is easily oxidized, losing electrons as hydrogen, and forming FAD (**Figure 7.5**). In contrast, FAD is easily reduced back to $FADH_2$ by the simple addition of hydrogen.

The production of energy from the energy-containing nutrients occurs through a series of oxidation–reduction reactions that ultimately yields carbon dioxide (CO_2) and water (H_2O). The oxidation of a fatty acid through this process is illustrated later in this chapter.

Enzymes Mediate Metabolic Reactions

As you know, chemical reactions in living cells are typically mediated by enzymes. During metabolism, one function of enzymes is to channel the energy-containing nutrients into useful pathways. For example, by increasing or decreasing the activity of an enzyme, the body can channel fatty acids toward breakdown for energy or toward storage as adipose tissue. Thus, enzymes are essential to the metabolism of the energy-containing nutrients.

In order to function, enzymes generally require substances called coenzymes and cofactors. **Coenzymes** are non-protein substances (**Figure 7.6**) that provide a functional group that either enhances or is necessary for the action of the enzyme, yet is smaller than the enzyme. Both FAD and $FADH_2$ function as coenzymes, as do forms of many other vitamins.[1,2] **Cofactors** are typically minerals, such as iron, magnesium, or zinc, that are required for enzyme activity. For example, they may help bind different parts of an enzyme together, or they may bind substrates or intermediates of the reaction, thereby helping to speed up the reaction.[1] In short, these non-energy-containing micronutrients are essential to ensure that energy can be extracted from food.

An example of an enzyme-driven metabolic reaction is the phosphorylation of glucose, mentioned earlier. The enzyme that activates this process is **glucokinase**. When glucose concentrations in the liver rise after a meal, the activity of this enzyme increases to handle the increased load, allowing for efficient metabolism of the glucose. Not every metabolic enzyme is as responsive, however. As discussed shortly, the liver enzyme that typically oxidizes alcohol does not increase in response to a sudden increase in alcohol consumption.

oxidation–reduction reactions Reactions in which electrons are lost by one compound (it is oxidized) and simultaneously gained by another compound (it is reduced).

FAD (flavin adenine dinucleotide) A coenzyme derived from the B-vitamin riboflavin; FAD readily accepts electrons (hydrogen) from various donors.

coenzymes A molecule that combines with an enzyme to activate it and help it do its job; many coenzymes are B-vitamins.

cofactor A small, chemically simple organic or inorganic substance that is required for enzyme activity; trace minerals such as iron, zinc, and copper function as cofactors.

glucokinase An enzyme that adds a phosphate group to a molecule of glucose.

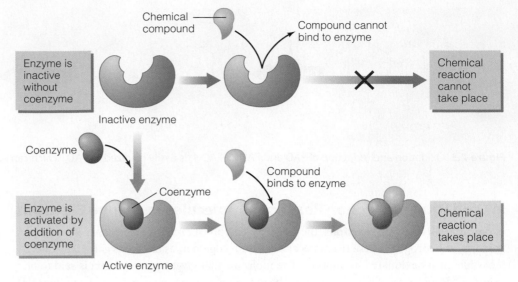

Figure 7.6 Coenzymes combine with enzymes to activate them, ensuring that the chemical reactions that depend upon these enzymes occur.

RECAP

Condensation and hydrolysis are chemical reactions involving water. The reaction in which phosphate is transferred is called phosphorylation. In oxidation–reduction reactions, the molecules involved exchange electrons. Enzymes, coenzymes, and cofactors increase the efficiency of metabolism.

How Is Energy Extracted from Carbohydrates?

As you learned in Chapter 4, most dietary carbohydrate is digested and absorbed as glucose. The glucose is then transported to the liver, where it has a number of metabolic fates:

- The glucose can be phosphorylated, as described earlier, and stored in the liver as glycogen.
- The glucose can be phosphorylated and then metabolized in the liver for energy or used to make other glucose-containing compounds.
- The glucose can be released into circulation for other cells of the body to take up and use as a fuel or, in the case of muscle tissue, store as glycogen.
- The glucose, if consumed in excess of total energy needs, can be converted to fatty acids and stored as triglycerides, primarily in the adipose tissue.

What happens to fructose and galactose, the other dietary monosaccharides? Although there are many other metabolic options for each, both can be (a) converted into glucose through a series of reactions or (b) channelled into the glycolysis pathway (discussed shortly) for energy production. For that reason, and because glucose is the dominant simple sugar in the human diet, this discussion will explore how the body uses glucose as an energy source.

The oxidation of glucose for the production of energy progresses through three distinct stages, each of which takes place in a different part of the cell. The three stages are (1) glycolysis, (2) the tricarboxylic acid (TCA) cycle, also known as the Krebs cycle, and (3) oxidative phosphorylation. Step by step, we will review these metabolic pathways.

In Glycolysis, Glucose Is Broken Down into Pyruvate

The metabolic pathway used by cells to produce energy from glucose begins with a sequence of reactions known as **glycolysis** (**Figure 7.7**). Because glycolysis occurs in the

Most dietary carbohydrate is digested and absorbed as glucose.

glycolysis A sequence of chemical reactions that converts glucose to pyruvate.

cytosol, even cells without mitochondria can extract energy from this pathway. Also, because the reactions of glycolysis are anaerobic (that is, do not require oxygen), this short pathway can be completed even when tissues are in an oxygen-deprived state.

During glycolysis, six-carbon glucose is converted into two molecules of three-carbon pyruvate. The first step of glycolysis is the phosphorylation of glucose, which, as described earlier, yields glucose 6-phosphate and ADP. The ATP that fuels this reaction is stored in the cell. Then, several enzyme-driven reactions result in the formation of pyruvate. (These reactions are omitted from Figure 7.7 but included in the complete figure in Appendix A.) Initially the process of glycolysis requires two ATP for the phosphorylation of glucose, but eventually this pathway produces a small amount (four molecules) of ATP, thus yielding a net of two ATP to be used as energy for the cell.

As shown in Figure 7.7, the process of glycolysis is one example of an oxidative pathway, because two hydrogen atoms (with their electrons) are released. These hydrogen atoms are picked up by the coenzyme **NAD (nicotinamide adenine dinucleotide)**, derived from the B-vitamin niacin, forming NADH, the reduced form of NAD. The metabolic fate of the newly formed NADH will be explained shortly.

If the pyruvate molecules generated by glycolysis are to be used for the production of energy, they must go through a number of further metabolic steps, which vary depending on whether oxygen is present (*aerobic* environment) or absent (*anaerobic* environment). If energy is not immediately needed by the cell, pyruvate can be used to resynthesize glucose, moving "back up" this stage of the metabolic pathway through a separate series of reactions (see Figure 7.7). This reverse process is known as gluconeogenesis and will be discussed later in this chapter.

In the Absence of Oxygen, Pyruvate Is Converted to Lactic Acid

In the absence of oxygen, the pyruvate produced through glycolysis is anaerobically converted to **lactate (or lactic acid)**. This one-step reaction involves a simple transfer of hydrogen. Both pyruvate and lactate are three-carbon compounds, so there is no loss or gain of carbon atoms. In a reversal of the hydrogen transfer that occurred in glycolysis (when NAD^+ accepted $2H^+ + 2e^-$ to form $NADH + H^+$), the conversion of pyruvate to lactate involves the transfer of $2e^- + 2H^+$ from NADH to lactate, leaving NAD^+ (**Figure 7.8a**). The production of lactate therefore regenerates the NAD^+ required for the continued functioning of the glycolysis pathway.

The anaerobic conversion of pyruvate to lactate occurs in cells with few or no mitochondria, such as the red blood cells and the lens and cornea of the eye. It also occurs in the muscle cells during high-intensity exercise, when oxygen delivery to the muscle is limited. Compared with the entire three-stage oxidation of glucose, the production of energy in this phase of anaerobic glycolysis is not very efficient. The short pathway from pyruvate to lactate does not yield any ATP; therefore, when one molecule of glucose is converted to lactate, the only ATP produced is the two (net) ATP units that were generated when the glucose was initially converted to pyruvate (see Figure 7.8). The anaerobic production of lactate is, however, a way of producing at least a small amount of energy when oxygen is absent or in those cells lacking mitochondria. The production of lactate, also known as lactic acid, also allows the regeneration of NAD^+ so that glycolysis can continue. During intense exercise, lactic acid and other acids and metabolic by-products can build up

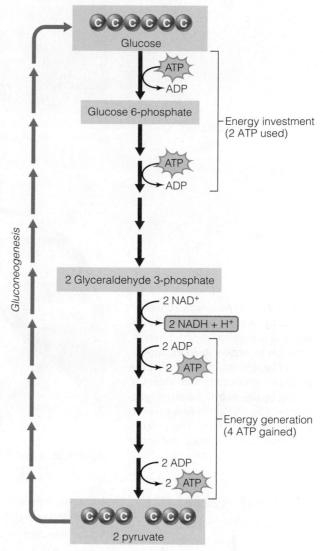

Figure 7.7 Overview of glycolysis. In the first stage of glucose oxidation, glucose is converted to pyruvate. A separate pathway provides for the regeneration of glucose via gluconeogenesis, which requires the input of ATP. Net production from glycolysis: two pyruvate molecules, two ATP, and two NADH + H+.

NAD (nicotinamide adenine dinucleotide) A coenzyme form of the B-vitamin niacin; NAD readily accepts electrons (hydrogen) from various donors.

lactate (or lactic acid) A three-carbon compound produced from pyruvate in oxygen-deprived conditions.

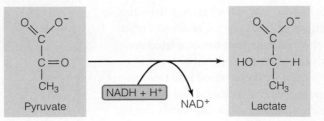

(a) Anaerobic conversion of pyruvate to lactate

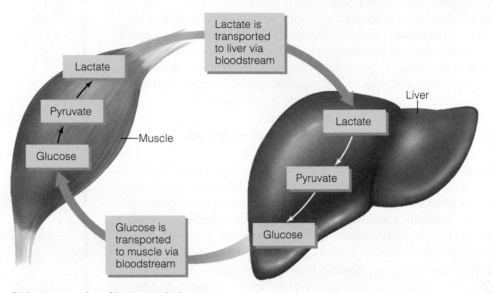

(b) Interconversion of lactate and glucose

Figure 7.8 (a) Anaerobic conversion of pyruvate to lactate. In the absence of oxygen, the body converts pyruvate to lactate. (b) Interconversion of lactate and glucose. After the anaerobic production and release of lactate by the muscle, when oxygen becomes available, the liver converts lactate back to glucose. This process, known as the Cori cycle, is discussed in more detail in Chapter 15.

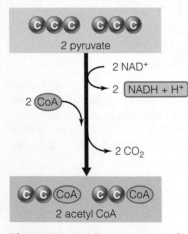

Figure 7.9 Aerobic conversion of pyruvate to acetyl CoA. In the presence of oxygen, the body converts pyruvate to acetyl CoA. This reaction links the first and second stages of glucose oxidation. The two pyruvate molecules were generated from glucose through glycolysis.

acetyl CoA (or acetyl coenzyme A) Coenzyme A is derived from the B-vitamin pantothenic acid; it readily reacts with two-carbon acetate to form the metabolic intermediate acetyl CoA.

in tissues, especially the muscle tissues, possibly contributing to fatigue and soreness (see Nutrition Myth or Fact? box in Chapter 15, page 551). This is one of the many reasons why individuals cannot sustain high-intensity exercise for long periods of time. After exercise, lactate can diffuse from the muscle cells into the blood, which transports it back to the liver. Then, when oxygen is readily available, it is reconverted to pyruvate, which can be used to synthesize glucose (Figure 7.8b). This cycle of glucose-to-lactate (during oxygen deprivation) followed by lactate-to-glucose (during oxygen availability) will be discussed in more detail in Chapter 15.

In the Presence of Oxygen, Pyruvate Is Converted to Acetyl CoA

In an aerobic environment where oxygen is plentiful, pyruvate is converted to a two-carbon compound known as **acetyl CoA** (**Figure 7.9**). This reaction occurs in the mitochondria and therefore does not occur in red blood cells or other cells that lack mitochondria. The "CoA" is shorthand for *Coenzyme A*, a coenzyme derived from the B-vitamin pantothenic acid. As with the conversion of glucose to pyruvate, the metabolic pathway taking pyruvate to acetyl CoA generates NADH + H$^+$ from the niacin-derived coenzyme NAD$^+$. Pyruvate is a three-carbon compound, whereas acetyl CoA is a two-carbon metabolite. What happens to the other carbon? It ends up within the gas carbon dioxide (CO_2), which the lungs exhale as a waste product.

Unlike the metabolic option to convert lactate to glucose, once pyruvate is metabolized to acetyl CoA there is no "going back" to glucose synthesis. In other words, there is no metabolic option for the conversion of acetyl CoA to glucose. Once acetyl CoA is produced, it can be further metabolized to produce energy (ATP) or, when the body has adequate ATP, redirected into fatty acid synthesis (discussed shortly).

The conversion of pyruvate to acetyl CoA is a critical step in the oxidation of glucose because it links stage 1 (glycolysis) to stage 2 (the TCA cycle). This reaction also marks the transition of cytosol-based pathways to mitochondria-based pathways. To begin this step, pyruvate moves from the cytosol into the mitochondria, where it is converted to acetyl CoA. Once acetyl CoA is produced in the mitochondria, it cannot be transferred back across the mitochondrial membrane without conversion to another compound called citrate. Thus, acetyl CoA is committed to the TCA cycle for energy production or the conversion to citrate, in which form it can move back out of the mitochondria for fat synthesis.

As this chapter proceeds, it will become clear that acetyl CoA is generated not only from glucose oxidation but also from fatty acid and amino acid catabolism (**Figure 7.10**). You may be familiar with the phrase "All roads lead to Rome." In metabolism, most "roads" (metabolic pathways) lead to acetyl CoA!

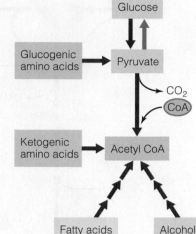

Figure 7.10 Metabolic crossroads. Acetyl CoA is generated as a result of carbohydrate, fatty acid, amino acid, and alcohol metabolism.

The Tricarboxylic Acid Cycle Begins with the Entry of Acetyl CoA

The process of glycolysis has a clear starting point (glucose) and a clear ending point (pyruvate). The linking step (pyruvate to acetyl CoA) also has distinct start and end points. In contrast, the **TCA cycle** is a continuous circle of eight metabolic reactions (**Figure 7.11**). The complete TCA cycle is illustrated in Appendix A, and a condensed version will be used here for simplicity.

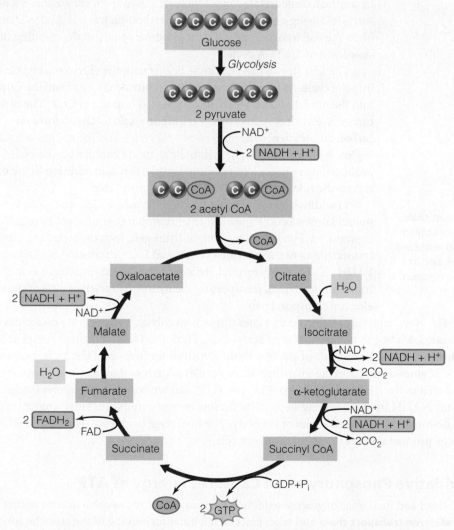

Figure 7.11 Overview of the TCA cycle. In the second stage of glucose oxidation, acetyl CoA enters the TCA cycle, resulting in the release of carbon dioxide, GTP (ATP), and reduced coenzymes NADH and FADH$_2$.

TCA cycle The tricarboxylic acid (TCA) cycle is a repetitive series of eight metabolic reactions, located in cell mitochondria, that metabolizes acetyl CoA for the production of carbon dioxide, high-energy GTP, and reduced coenzymes NADH and FADH$_2$.

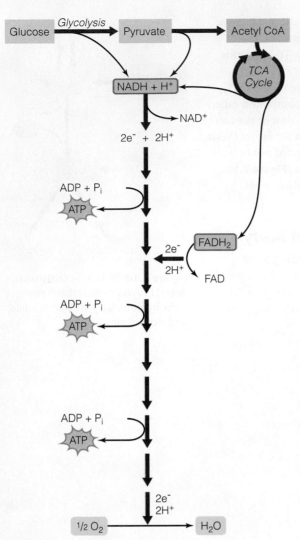

Figure 7.12 Overview of the electron transport chain. In the third and final stage of glucose oxidation, called *oxidative phosphorylation*, additional ATP and water are produced as electrons from NADH and FADH$_2$ and are passed from one carrier to the next along the electron transport chain.

The TCA cycle is located in the mitochondria of the cell, which is where all of the necessary metabolic enzymes can be found. The mitochondria are also the location of stage 3 of glucose oxidation (involving the electron transport chain) and ATP synthesis; thus, the transition between stages 2 and 3 is highly efficient.

We think of cycles as self-regenerative, but the acetyl CoA within the TCA cycle does not regenerate. As will be seen, the two carbons that form acetyl CoA end up within two molecules of carbon dioxide. In contrast, the fate of the four-carbon compound oxaloacetate does illustrate the cyclical nature of this stage of glucose oxidation: as shown in Figure 7.11, it is "used up" in the first step of the TCA cycle and is regenerated in the final step. Oxaloacetate and other metabolic intermediates within the TCA cycle are necessary for continued functioning of the TCA cycle; when these compounds are limited, the TCA cycle decreases in activity, and energy production sharply declines.[1]

Although oxaloacetate can be made from some amino acids, dietary carbohydrate is the primary source. The glucose that is derived from dietary carbohydrate can be converted to acetyl CoA (stage 1, Figure 7.11), which can enter the TCA cycle and be converted to oxaloacetate. In contrast, oxaloacetate cannot be synthesized from fatty acids. If a person is following a very-low-carbohydrate diet, such as the Atkins Diet, he or she will have limited ability to produce oxaloacetate, resulting in a slowdown of the TCA cycle.

The first step of the TCA cycle begins with the entry of acetyl CoA into the cycle. As previously explained, pyruvate crosses from the cytosol into the mitochondria, where it is converted into acetyl CoA. The two-carbon acetyl CoA reacts with four-carbon oxaloacetate to form six-carbon citrate (hence the term *citric acid cycle*), and the metabolic cycle begins. By the time all eight metabolic steps are completed, the cycle has produced two molecules of carbon dioxide; this is in addition to the one carbon dioxide produced in the earlier "linking" step.

In addition to the release of carbon dioxide, a high-energy compound known as GTP (guanosine triphosphate), equivalent to one ATP, is produced. Finally, a total of eight hydrogen, with their electrons, are transferred to two coenzymes: NAD$^+$ and FAD, producing NADH and FADH$_2$. These newly formed, hydrogen-rich coenzymes serve as the transition to stage 3, transporting the hydrogen and their electrons to the electron transport chain.

For every molecule of glucose that goes through glycolysis, two pyruvate molecules are generated, leading to two molecules of acetyl CoA. Thus, the TCA cycle must complete two "rotations" for each molecule of glucose. From glycolysis through the TCA cycle, one molecule of glucose produces the following: six molecules of carbon dioxide (including those produced in the "linking step"), two ATP, two GTP, and ten reduced coenzymes (including the NADH from the linking step). Note the low energy output: this small amount will not do much to fuel the activities of the body. The final stage of glucose oxidation is where energy production as ATP assumes a major role.

Oxidative Phosphorylation Captures Energy as ATP

The third and final stage of glucose oxidation, termed *oxidative phosphorylation,* occurs in the **electron transport chain** and takes place in the inner membrane of the mitochondria (**Figure 7.12**). The electron transport chain is a series of enzyme-driven reactions or couplings; various proteins, called electron carriers, alternately accept, then donate, electrons. The electrons come from the NADH and FADH$_2$ generated during glycolysis, the linking step,

electron transport chain A series of metabolic reactions that transports electrons from NADH or FADH$_2$ through a series of carriers, resulting in ATP production.

and the TCA cycle. As summarized in Figure 7.12, as the electrons are passed from one carrier to the next, energy is released. In this process, NADH and $FADH_2$ are oxidized and their electrons are donated to O_2, which is reduced to H_2O (water). The energy released from the reduction of O_2 to water is used to phosphorylate mitochondrial ADP to ATP, thereby capturing the metabolic energy in ATP's high-energy phosphate bonds. Once formed, the ATP can exit the mitochondria for use by all components of the cell.

As mentioned, the final step in the electron transport chain occurs when oxygen accepts the low-energy electrons, reacts with hydrogen, and forms water. If the cell lacks adequate oxygen for this final step, the entire electron transport chain comes to a halt. Oxygen is essential for cellular energy production; without oxygen, cell metabolism stops.

This brings the process of glucose oxidation to a close. The complete process started with glucose and ended with the production of carbon dioxide, water, and ATP. The carbon dioxide was produced in the linking step (pyruvate to acetyl CoA) and the TCA cycle. The water was produced in the final step of the electron transport chain. ATP was produced in various amounts during the three stages.

Finally, the amount of ATP produced by NADH and $FADH_2$ is not exact (about two to three ATP per NADH and one to two for $FADH_2$); thus, different researchers calculate different values. Many biochemistry textbooks report a net of 30 to 32 ATP produced by the complete oxidation of one glucose molecule. Other references (including Appendix A of this textbook) use the range of 36 to 38 ATP per glucose molecule. To the student, this may seem confusing, but the study of nutrient metabolism is rarely an exact science.

The first step in breaking down fats, such as fats in the meat and cheese of a taco, is lipolysis.

RECAP

Glucose oxidation occurs in three well-defined stages: glycolysis, the TCA cycle, and oxidative phosphorylation. The conversion of pyruvate to acetyl CoA is a critical link between glycolysis and the TCA cycle. In the absence of oxygen, the pyruvate is converted to lactate, which can then be "recycled" by liver cells back into glucose. The end products of glucose oxidation are carbon dioxide, water, and ATP.

How Is Energy Extracted from Fats?

The fatty acids used for cellular energy can come from the triglycerides circulating in serum lipoproteins, including the dietary fat in chylomicrons, or from the triglycerides stored in body tissues, including adipose tissue and muscle. Because the triglyceride molecule is more complex than that of glucose, there are more steps involved in converting it into energy. Of course, the first step requires that each fatty acid be removed from the glycerol backbone. Through a process called **lipolysis**, dietary and adipocyte triglycerides are broken down by lipases to yield glycerol and three fatty acids. Triglycerides in lipoproteins are broken down through the action of lipoprotein lipase, while triglycerides in adipose cells and other tissues are catabolized by the enzyme **hormone-sensitive lipase**. Whether the glycerol and fatty acids have come from dietary fat or stored body fat, they feed into the same metabolic pathways.

Glycerol Is Converted to Pyruvate

Glycerol, the small three-carbon backbone of triglycerides, does not produce much energy but does serve other important metabolic functions. The liver readily converts glycerol into pyruvate, another three-carbon compound (see **Figure 7.13**). As previously discussed, pyruvate can be converted into acetyl CoA for entry into the TCA cycle (see Figure 7.9) or it can be used for the regeneration of glucose (see Figure 7.7).

Fatty Acids Are Converted to Acetyl CoA

Fatty acids are attached to **albumin**, a blood protein, and transported to working cells in need of energy, such as muscle or liver cells. They are catabolized for energy through a

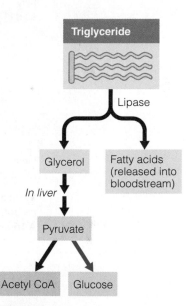

Figure 7.13 Conversion of glycerol to pyruvate. The glycerol derived from the catabolism of fatty acids is readily converted to pyruvate, which can be used for glucose synthesis or be converted to acetyl CoA.

lipolysis The enzyme-driven catabolism of triglycerides into free fatty acids and glycerol.

hormone-sensitive lipase The enzyme that breaks down the triglycerides stored in adipose and other body tissues.

albumin A serum protein, made in the liver, that transports free fatty acids from one body tissue to another.

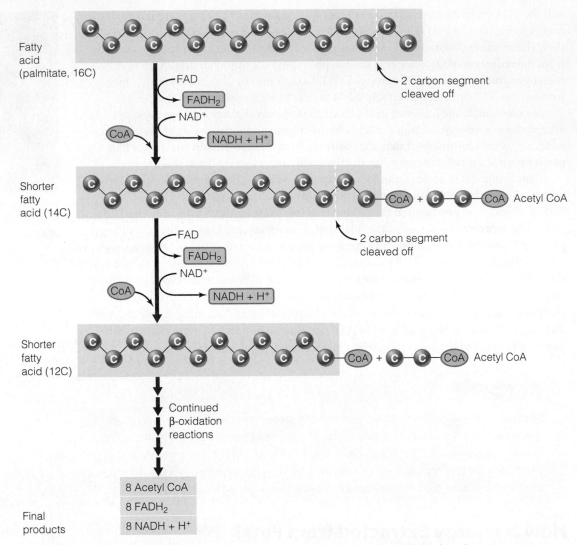

Figure 7.14 Overview of β-oxidation of fatty acids. Fatty acids are sequentially broken down into two-carbon segments that result in the formation of one additional acetyl CoA during each step of the process. A 16-carbon fatty acid yields 8 acetyl CoA units.

β-oxidation (or fatty acid oxidation) A series of metabolic reactions that oxidizes free fatty acids, leading to the end products of water, carbon dioxide, and ATP.

carnitine A small organic compound that transports free fatty acids from the cytosol into the mitochondria for oxidation.

process known as **β-oxidation** or **fatty acid oxidation**. This metabolic pathway takes place in the mitochondria, which means that fatty acids must move from the cytosol across the mitochondrial membrane. Before the fatty acids can be transported, however, they must be activated by the addition of Coenzyme A (CoA), the same coenzyme used in the synthesis of acetyl CoA from pyruvate. This reaction requires an "investment" of energy from ATP. The activated fatty acids are then shuttled across the mitochondrial membrane by a compound known as **carnitine**.

Once in the mitochondria, β-oxidation proceeds, systematically breaking down long-chain fatty acids into two-carbon segments that lead to the formation of acetyl-CoA units (**Figure 7.14**). Thus, a sixteen-carbon fatty acid is converted to eight acetyl-CoA units. As the two-carbon segments are cleaved off the fatty acid, high-energy electrons are transferred to the coenzymes NAD^+ and FAD, forming $NADH + H^+$ and $FADH_2$. As with glucose oxidation, the acetyl CoA generated from fatty acid oxidation feeds into the TCA cycle for the production of ATP. The electron-rich coenzymes produced in the TCA cycle feed into the electron transport chain and produce ATP. An overview of β-oxidation is provided in Figure 7.14; a more detailed illustration is provided in Appendix A.

As previously described, the glycerol component of triglycerides also feeds into the TCA cycle after its conversion to pyruvate and acetyl CoA. In summary, the process of extracting energy from triglycerides started with fatty acids and glycerol and ended with the production of carbon dioxide, water, and ATP (**Figure 7.15**). These are the same three compounds produced during the oxidation of glucose.

As previously noted, because fatty acids almost always have more carbons than the six found in glucose, more acetyl CoA and more ATP are produced during β-oxidation than during glucose catabolism. A single 18-carbon fatty acid yields nearly 3.5 times the ATP than that derived from one 6-carbon molecule of glucose. In addition, fatty acids have relatively few oxygen atoms compared with oxygen-rich glucose (**Figure 7.16**). Fatty acids offer numerous opportunities for oxidation, which results in a higher output of NADH and FADH₂, leading to greater production of ATP through the electron transport chain. The result is that fatty acids have a much higher energy potential compared with carbohydrates, approximately 9 kcal/g versus approximately 4 kcal/g.

Fatty Acids Cannot Be Converted to Glucose

Earlier, we noted that the liver is able to convert pyruvate to glucose and that glycerol can feed into glucose production via pyruvate. In contrast, there is no metabolic pathway to convert acetyl CoA into pyruvate for glucose synthesis. Because cells cannot convert acetyl CoA into glucose, it is impossible for fatty acids to feed into glucose production. Again, there is no metabolic pathway that allows for the conversion of fatty acids to glucose.

Ketones Are a By-product of Fat Catabolism

Recall that the acetyl CoA that enters the TCA cycle can come from glucose or fatty acid catabolism. But the TCA cycle functions only when there is adequate oxaloacetate, a carbohydrate derivative (see Figure 7.11). Thus, if a person is following a very-low-carbohydrate diet, which increases fat catabolism, or has too little functioning insulin to allow glucose to enter cells, oxaloacetate production falls and TCA cycle activity decreases. As fat catabolism continues during this carbohydrate-depleted state, acetyl CoA builds up, exceeding the ability of the TCA cycle to metabolize it, and begins to accumulate in the liver cells.

As the acetyl CoA builds up, liver cells divert it into an alternative metabolic pathway leading to the synthesis of **ketone bodies** (for example, acetoacetate, acetone, and

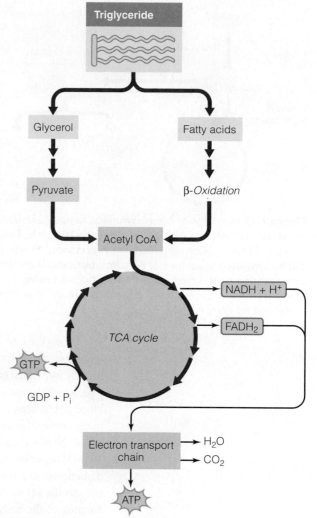

Figure 7.15 Extraction of energy from triglycerides. Glycerol and fatty acids can be metabolized to yield energy as ATP.

ketone bodies Three- and four-carbon compounds (acetoacetate, acetone, and β- or 3-hydroxybutyrate) derived when acetyl CoA levels become elevated.

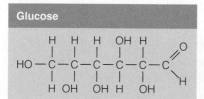

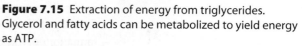

Figure 7.16 A comparison of glucose and fatty acid structures. In contrast with glucose, where each carbon is attached to an oxygen, there are many opportunities for oxidation of the carbon-to-hydrogen bonds of a fatty acid.

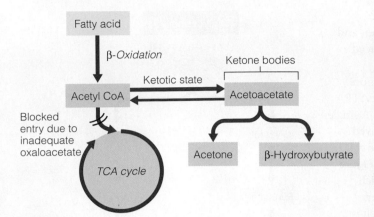

Figure 7.17 Overview of ketone synthesis. Ketones are produced when acetyl CoA is blocked from entering the TCA cycle. Two molecules of acetyl CoA combine to form acetoacetate, which can be converted to acetone or β-hydroxybutyrate. These three compounds are collectively called ketone bodies. Energy is later extracted from ketones when acetoacetate is reconverted back to acetyl CoA for entry into the TCA cycle.

β-hydroxybutyrate or 3-hydroxybutyrate) (**Figure 7.17**). The liver constantly produces low levels of ketone bodies; however, production increases dramatically during times of very low carbohydrate intake, whether from prolonged fasting, starvation, or very-low-carbohydrate diets, as well as in people with diabetes who do not produce any insulin or enough insulin for glucose transport into the cell. If someone with diabetes cannot obtain insulin, glucose cannot be transported into the cell, the body will be unable to maintain oxaloacetate production, the TCA cycle will slow down, and ketone production will increase. Ketone bodies are released from the liver into the bloodstream, where they can be taken up by the cells and used as an alternative fuel by the brain, certain kidney cells, and other body cells when their normal fuel source (glucose) is not available.

The production of energy from ketones is metabolically inefficient because the total number of ATP produced will be lower than what would have been produced through β-oxidation of fatty acids. A little energy, however, is better than none; thus, ketone synthesis provides a backup energy system for carbohydrate-deprived cells.

When the rate of ketone production increases above its use by cells, blood and urine ketone levels rise, a condition known as ketosis. Typical blood levels of ketones are <0.3 mmol/L in a healthy individual eating a mixed diet but can rise to 0.9 mmol/L in severe ketosis, as seen in a person with type 1 diabetes without insulin. Ketones are acidic and inappropriately lower blood pH (increasing its acidity); thus, the body attempts to eliminate them by excreting them in the urine. This process, however, also causes dehydration as fluid is lost in the urine. As the pH of the blood falls further and dehydration becomes more severe, ketoacidosis occurs. If allowed to persist unchecked, ketoacidosis can result in coma or death. A classic symptom of diabetic ketoacidosis is a fruity odour on the breath that results from increased production of the specific ketone body acetone. Although high amounts of ketone bodies are normally harmful to the body, some medical conditions are treated with ketogenic diets. These medically supervised diets are high in protein and fat and extremely low in carbohydrates (10–20 g/d). See the You Do the Math box on page 255 to get a better idea of the strict limitations of this medical ketogenic diet. One medical condition that seems to respond to a ketogenic diet is epilepsy, specifically childhood epilepsy that has not responded to other treatments. The ketones produced on this diet appear to reduce the number of severe seizures experienced. The exact mechanism by which the ketogenic diet exerts its antiseizure action is not yet fully understood.[3, 4]

RECaP

Triglycerides are broken down into glycerol and free fatty acids. Glycerol can be (a) converted to glucose via pyruvate or (b) oxidized for energy. Free fatty acids are oxidized to produce acetyl CoA and coenzymes, which can enter the TCA cycle and electron transport chain. The end products of fatty acid oxidation are carbon dioxide, water, and ATP. Fatty acids cannot be converted into glucose. With carbohydrate inadequacy, fat catabolism increases and the excess acetyl CoA is diverted to ketone formation, which if continued unchecked can result in ketoacidosis and consequently coma or death.

Dietary proteins are broken down into single amino acids or small peptides.

How Is Energy Extracted from Proteins?

As you read in Chapter 6, protein is the preferred substrate for building and repairing body tissues; however, small amounts of protein can be and are used for energy. The exact amount of protein used for energy will depend on the total energy in the diet and the amount of fat and carbohydrate consumed. The body preferentially uses fat and carbohydrate as fuel sources and prefers to save protein for metabolic functions that cannot be performed by other compounds. Proteins are used as fuel sources primarily when total energy or carbohydrate intake is low.

In Proteolysis, Proteins Are Broken Down to Amino Acids

During protein breakdown, called **proteolysis**, dietary proteins are digested into single amino acids or small peptides that are absorbed into the body; eventually, the small peptides are further catabolized into single amino acids. These amino acids are absorbed then transported to the liver, where they can be made into various proteins or released into the bloodstream for uptake by other cells for their unique building and repair functions. If protein is consumed in excess of what is needed by the cells, some of this protein can be used for energy or converted into fatty acids for storage as triglycerides. Additionally, if we don't eat enough total energy or carbohydrate, the tissues can break down some of the proteins in their cells for energy. This process is explained shortly.

In Deamination, the Amino Group Is Removed

Under conditions of starvation or extreme dieting, the body must turn to its own tissues for energy, including protein. Amino acids are unique from other energy-containing nutrients in that they contain nitrogen, which must be removed so the remaining carbon skeleton can be used for energy. Thus, the utilization of amino acids for energy begins with deamination of the amino acids, which removes their amine (NH_2), or nitrogen, group and leaves a **carbon skeleton** (**Figure 7.18**). The end products of deamination are **ammonia** (NH_3), derived from the amine group, and the remaining carbon skeleton, often classified as a **keto acid**. (Note: Even though the terms *ketone* and *keto acid* appear very similar, they are produced from completely different metabolic pathways and have very different metabolic roles. Be careful not to get the two terms confused!)

After Deamination, the Carbon Skeleton Feeds into Energy Production

The carbon skeleton produced through deamination can be channelled into glycolysis or the TCA pathway to produce energy (**Figure 7.19**). Each of the 20 amino acids identified in Chapter 6 has a different carbon skeleton and is classified into a number of different groups, many of which overlap. We will discuss only two of these groups here:

- The carbon skeletons of **glucogenic amino acids** are converted to pyruvate, which can then be used to synthesize glucose or converted to acetyl CoA for entry into the TCA cycle. The primary glucogenic amino acids are alanine, glycine, serine, cysteine, and tryptophan.
- The carbon skeletons of **ketogenic amino acids** are converted directly to acetyl CoA for entry into the TCA cycle or for use in synthesizing fatty acids. The only totally ketogenic amino acids are leucine and lysine.

Many of the amino acids can feed into the TCA cycle at various entry points. For example, some amino acids can have both ketogenic and gluconeogenic functions, such as tyrosine, phenylalanine, tryptophan, lysine, and leucine. Because amino acids can have multiple functions, it is difficult to easily fit them into groups. Appendix A shows how the carbon skeletons of the various amino acids can contribute to TCA cycle intermediates, glucose production, and/or ketone body production.

The amount of energy or ATP produced from the catabolism of amino acids depends on where in the metabolic pathway the carbon skeleton enters. The "higher up" the point of entry, such as conversion to pyruvate, the greater the ATP production. No amino acid, however, generates as much ATP as one molecule of glucose or one free fatty acid.

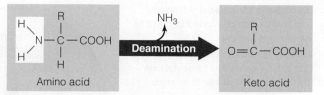

Figure 7.18 The process of deamination. Amino acids are deaminated when the amine group is removed; the remaining structure is known as a keto acid or carbon skeleton.

proteolysis The breakdown of dietary proteins into single amino acids or small peptides that are absorbed by the body.

carbon skeleton The unique "side group" that remains after deamination of an amino acid; also referred to as a keto acid.

ammonia A highly toxic compound released during the deamination of amino acids.

keto acid The chemical structure that remains after deamination of an amino acid.

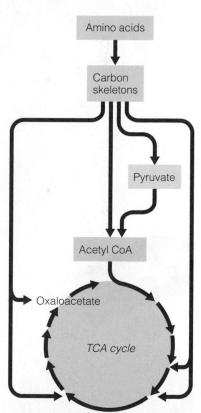

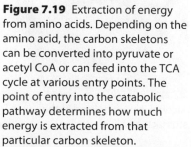

Figure 7.19 Extraction of energy from amino acids. Depending on the amino acid, the carbon skeletons can be converted into pyruvate or acetyl CoA or can feed into the TCA cycle at various entry points. The point of entry into the catabolic pathway determines how much energy is extracted from that particular carbon skeleton.

glucogenic amino acid An amino acid that can be converted to glucose via gluconeogenesis.

ketogenic amino acid An amino acid that can be converted to acetyl CoA for the synthesis of free fatty acids.

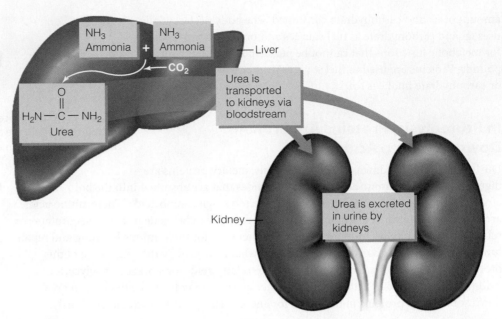

Figure 7.20 Overview of urea synthesis. The liver converts highly toxic ammonia, derived from deamination of amino acids, into urea. The urea is then released into the bloodstream for urinary excretion by the kidney.

Ammonia Is a By-product of Protein Catabolism

Whereas some ammonia is useful as a nitrogen source for the synthesis of non-essential amino acids, high levels of ammonia are toxic to the body. Thus, the ammonia generated as the result of the deamination of amino acids must be eliminated quickly. To protect against ammonia toxicity, liver cells combine two molecules of ammonia together with carbon dioxide to form urea, which is much less toxic. **Figure 7.20** illustrates a simplified pathway for urea synthesis; the complete metabolic pathway can be found in Appendix A. The urea produced from amino acid catabolism is released from the liver into the bloodstream, and then eliminated by the kidneys in the urine. When the body has to make and excrete a large amount of urea, as occurs with a very high protein intake, the kidney excretes a large volume of urine. This in turn increases the risk of dehydration unless the individual drinks a large amount of water or other fluids.

The processes by which energy is extracted from carbohydrates, triglycerides, and proteins are summarized in Table 7.1.

Alcohol is metabolized in the stomach and liver.

RECAP

After deamination, the carbon skeletons of amino acids can be used as sources of energy. Glucogenic amino acids are converted into pyruvate, whereas ketogenic amino acids are converted into acetyl CoA. Some amino acids feed into the TCA cycle as various metabolic intermediates. The amine group released as a result of deamination can be transferred onto a keto acid for the synthesis of non-essential amino acids or, via ammonia, converted to and excreted as urea.

How Is Alcohol Metabolized?

We're ready to explore how the body metabolizes alcohol. Are there ways to speed up the process? These and other topics are explored here.

Table 7.1 **Extraction of Energy from Carbohydrate, Triglycerides, Protein, and Alcohol**

Nutrient	Yields Energy as ATP?	Oxidative End Products?	Feeds into Glucose Production?	Feeds into Non-essential Amino Acid Production?	Feeds into Fatty Acid Production and Storage as Triglycerides?
Carbohydrate (Glucose)	Yes	CO_2, H_2O	Yes	Yes, if source of nitrogen is available	Yes, although process is inefficient
Triglycerides: Fatty acids	Yes	CO_2, H_2O	No	No	Yes
Triglycerides: Glycerol	Yes	CO_2, H_2O	Yes, if carbohydrate is unavailable to cells	Yes, if source of nitrogen is available	Yes
Protein (Amino acids)	Yes	CO_2, H_2O, N as urea	Yes, if carbohydrate is unavailable to cells	Yes	Yes
Alcohol	Yes	CO_2, H_2O	No	No	Yes

Alcohol Is Metabolized Through Oxidation

As with glucose and fatty acids, alcohol is metabolized in a stepwise fashion through a series of oxidation reactions. In people with low to moderate intakes, alcohol is oxidized first into acetaldehyde by the action of **alcohol dehydrogenase (ADH)**, and then the acetaldehyde is oxidized by **aldehyde dehydrogenase (ALDH)** into acetate (**Figure 7.21**). Last, acetate is readily converted into acetyl CoA. In people who chronically abuse alcohol, an alternative pathway, the **microsomal ethanol oxidizing system (MEOS)**, becomes important for oxidizing the increased levels of alcohol. Both the ADH and MEOS pathways result in the formation of acetyl CoA. As previously discussed (pages 246–248), acetyl CoA is the primary "fuel" for the TCA cycle and is also generated from the catabolism of carbohydrates, lipids, and amino acids. The oxidation of alcohol into acetaldehyde creates imbalances in

alcohol dehydrogenase (ADH) An enzyme that converts ethanol to acetaldehyde in the first step of alcohol oxidation.

aldehyde dehydrogenase (ALDH) An enzyme that oxidizes acetaldehyde to acetate.

microsomal ethanol oxidizing system (MEOS) A liver enzyme system that oxidizes ethanol to acetaldehyde; its activity predominates at higher levels of alcohol intake.

YOU DO THE MATH

Designing a Ketogenic Diet

As noted in our discussion on ketosis, some children with epilepsy are prescribed a ketogenic diet, in addition to their medication, to reduce the number or severity of their seizures. The benefits of the ketogenic diet for the reduction of epileptic seizures has been known for centuries; accounts of the beneficial effect of fasting on epilepsy are long-standing.[3, 4] Physicians have been using ketogenic diets to treat epilepsy for the past 80 years; however, we still do not know the specific mechanism of how ketones alter brain chemistry to reduce seizures. A medical ketogenic diet is very high in fat and low in both protein and carbohydrate. Although the diet should always be developed and monitored by a registered dietitian and/or physician, you can work through these calculations to get a general idea of the diet plan.

Most children are prescribed a diet providing 4 g of fat (36 kcal) for every 1 g of protein/carbohydrate (4 kcal). A child needing 1500 kcal/day would be fed 150 g of fat and about 38 g of protein/carbohydrate combined. Estimating the protein requirement at about 20 g per day, that means the child could eat 18 g of carbohydrates each day. In summary, the child's diet would be as follows:

	1500 kcal/day
150 g of fat	1350 fat kcal
20 g of protein	80 protein kcal
18 g of carbohydrate	72 carbohydrate kcal

Using the nutrient data from food composition tables, develop a one-day menu for this child. High-fat, low-protein/carbohydrate foods include cream, butter, bacon, oils, and so forth. Small amounts of fried chicken or fish would provide fat plus protein, as would nuts and peanut butter.

Obviously, children on a medical ketogenic diet eat very few fruits and vegetables, very little milk/dairy, and few grains/cereals. The dietitian develops a strict plan describing exactly how much of which foods are allowed; a nutrient supplement is also prescribed. Usually, the diet is tried for about three months to see how well it works. If there is little or no improvement, the dietitian will usually recommend a return to the normal diet.

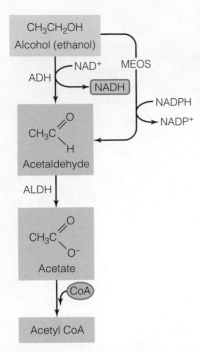

Figure 7.21 Pathways of alcohol metabolism. The primary metabolic by-product of alcohol oxidation is acetyl CoA.

two key pairs of coenzymes, NAD⁺/NADH and NADP⁺/NADPH, which contribute to some of the metabolic and health problems associated with chronic alcohol abuse.

The Oxidation of Alcohol Begins in the Stomach

While the oxidation of alcohol occurs primarily in the liver, a small but important amount of alcohol is actually oxidized in the stomach, before it is even absorbed into the bloodstream. This is known as *first-pass metabolism* and occurs via the ADH pathway. The action of gastric (stomach) ADH reduces, rather than simply delaying, the absorption of alcohol by as much as 20%. This enzyme is less active in young women than men; thus, women do not oxidize as much alcohol in their stomach, leaving more alcohol to be absorbed.[5] As a result of this biological difference, women absorb an average of 30% to 35% more alcohol than a similar-sized man consuming the same amount of alcohol. Gastric ADH activity decreases with age in men but apparently not in women, and there also appear to be genetic differences in the amount or activity of this enzyme.[6] Fasting for as little as one day prior to alcohol consumption lowers gastric ADH activity, increasing the amount of alcohol absorbed into the bloodstream.

The Oxidation of Alcohol Continues in the Liver

While a small amount is oxidized in the stomach, most of the alcohol consumed by an individual is rapidly absorbed into the bloodstream and transported to the liver, the primary site of alcohol oxidation. In the liver, the ADH pathway dominates at low to moderate intakes of alcohol while the MEOS pathway becomes more important as the amount of alcohol consumed increases. The liver typically oxidizes alcohol at a fairly constant rate, equivalent to approximately one drink per hour. This rate varies somewhat with the individual's genetic profile, state of health, body size, use of medication, and nutritional status. If a person drinks more alcohol than the liver can oxidize over the same period of time, the excess is released back into the bloodstream. The greater the disparity between rate of alcohol intake and rate of alcohol oxidation, the higher the blood alcohol level (**Figure 7.22**).

Despite popular theories, there are no practical interventions that will speed up the breakdown of alcohol: it doesn't help to walk around (skeletal muscles don't oxidize alcohol), consume coffee or caffeinated beverages (caffeine doesn't increase rates of ADH

PERCENT BLOOD ALCOHOL CONCENTRATION (% BAC)											
MEN						**WOMEN**					
Drinks	Body Weight in lbs (kg)					Drinks	Body Weight in lbs (kg)				
	165 (75)	180 (82)	195 (88)	210 (95)	225 (102)		100 (45)	115 (52)	130 (59)	145 (66)	160 (73)
2	.020	.016	.012	.009	.007	1	.019	.013	.008	.004	.001
3	.045	.039	.034	.029	.025	2	.068	.055	.045	.037	.031
4	.070	.062	.055	.049	.043	3	.117	.097	.083	.071	.062
5	.095	.085	.076	.068	.062	4	.165	.140	.120	.105	.092
6	.120	.108	.097	.088	.080	5	.214	.182	.158	.138	.123
7	.145	.130	.118	.108	.098	6	.263	.225	.195	.172	.153
8	.170	.153	.139	.127	.117	7	.312	.267	.233	.206	.184

For MEN: Impairment Begins at the level between 225 lb column (.025) rows; Legally Impaired for Driving begins lower.

For WOMEN: Impairment Begins; Legally Impaired for Driving.

One drink is considered 44 mL of spirits, 341 mL of beer, or 148 mL of wine.

Figure 7.22 Effect of alcohol intake on blood alcohol concentration two hours post consumption on the driving behaviour of men and women. It is a criminal offence for drivers in Canada to have a BAC over .08; if you're caught driving with a BAC in the .05–.08 range, in most provinces, police can impose a fine and suspend your licence up to 7 days.
(*Data from:* Adapted, with permission, from MADD Canada's "The ABC's of BAC's").

or ALDH activity), or use commercial herbal or nutrient supplements (no impact on rates of ADH or ALDH activity). The key to avoiding the behavioural and physiologic consequences of alcohol is to consume alcohol at the rate of about one drink per hour, which then allows the liver to keep up with intake.

Although alcohol itself is a cellular toxin, acetaldehyde also produces specific and damaging effects. The degree to which acetaldehyde accumulates depends on the relative activities of ADH and ALDH. In some ethnic groups, including certain Asian populations, the rate of ADH activity is normal or high and the activity of ALDH is relatively low. When a person with this genetic profile drinks alcohol, acetaldehyde accumulates. This causes a characteristic cluster of signs and symptoms, including facial flushing, headaches, nausea, tachycardia (rapid heartbeat), and hyperventilation (rapid breathing), which are often severe enough to inhibit future intake of alcohol. Researchers have long known that people with this type of enzyme imbalance are at low risk for alcohol abuse because the downside of alcohol intake typically outweighs any pleasurable effect, even at low levels of consumption. Acetaldehyde also contributes to metabolic abnormalities such as inhibition of protein synthesis, increases in harmful free-radical production, and increased lipid **peroxidation**.[5]

As an individual's alcohol intake increases over time, the liver's ADH pathway for alcohol oxidation becomes less efficient, and the MEOS pathway becomes more active. As a result of increased MEOS activity, the liver metabolizes alcohol more efficiently, and blood alcohol levels rise more slowly. This condition reflects a metabolic tolerance to alcohol. Compared with light or moderate drinkers, people who chronically abuse alcohol must consume increasingly larger amounts before reaching a state of intoxication. Over time, they may need to consume twice as much alcohol as when they first started to drink to reach the same state of euphoria.

People who chronically consume alcohol in more-than-moderate amounts are at significant risk of dangerous drug–alcohol interactions. Thus, a number of pain killers, antidepressants, and other drugs are clearly labelled "not to be consumed with alcohol." What accounts for this risk? The MEOS system is commonly used in the breakdown of many drugs. When an individual is consuming alcohol, however, the MEOS enzymes prioritize alcohol metabolism, leaving the drugs to accumulate. This "metabolic diversion" away from drug detoxification means the medication remains intact, continues to circulate in the blood, and leads to an exaggerated or intensified drug effect. The combination of drugs and alcohol can be fatal, and drug label warnings must be taken very seriously.

Although the majority of ingested alcohol is oxidized by enzymatic pathways in the stomach and liver, a small amount, typically less than 10% of intake, is excreted through the urine, breath, and sweat. Alcohol is distributed throughout all body fluids and water-based tissue spaces in roughly equivalent concentrations. Increases in blood alcohol concentration are paralleled by increases in breath vapour alcohol levels; this relationship forms the basis of the common Breathalyzer testing done by law enforcement agencies. Some people try to rid themselves of alcohol through saunas and steam rooms, but the amount of alcohol lost through the increased sweat is negligible.

Black coffee will not speed up the breakdown of alcohol.

ReCaP

The majority of ingested alcohol is oxidized in the stomach and liver by pathways involving ADH and ALDH. As an individual's alcohol intake increases over time, these pathways for alcohol oxidation become less efficient and the MEOS pathway becomes more active. The liver oxidizes alcohol at a steady rate of approximately one drink per hour; there is no effective way to speed up the liver's oxidation of alcohol.

peroxidation The oxidative deterioration of an organic compound, such as a lipid, resulting in the formation of a peroxide.

Did You Know?

Alcohol consumption is common among undergraduates. In a 2004 survey of over 6200 full-time students from 40 Canadian universities, 77% of students reported using alcohol in the previous month.[7] Only about one in ten identified themselves as being lifetime abstainers. More surprisingly, 32% of undergraduates reported hazardous or harmful patterns of drinking. This rate was significantly higher among men (38%) and those students attending university in Atlantic Canada (47%). Rates of hazardous or harmful drinking were significantly lower among students attending university in British Columbia (27%) and Quebec (27%). Just under half (44%) of the students reported at least one indicator of harmful drinking such as feeling guilty, experiencing memory loss or an injury, or having other concerns about their drinking. One-third reported at least one indicator of dependent drinking such as being unable to stop, failing to perform normal everyday activities, or needing a drink first thing in the morning. Are these behaviours unique to university students?

When 10 466 Canadian adults aged 18–76 years were asked about alcohol consumption, similar drinking patterns were revealed.[8] Men in the Maritime provinces reported consuming significantly more alcohol then men in other areas of the country (486 drinks/year compared to the Canadian average of 432 drinks/year). Women consume significantly less alcohol (average of 183 drinks/year) then men regardless of place of residence. When binge-drinking was considered, it was revealed that 64% of Canadian men but only 37% of women report engaging in this behaviour at least once a year.

How Is Energy Stored?

The body needs stored energy it can use during times of sleep, fasting, or exercise, when energy demands persist but food is not being consumed. The body typically stores extra energy as either fat, in the form of triglycerides, or carbohydrate, in the form of glycogen (discussed in the next section). Although humans appear to have an unlimited ability to store fat, only a limited amount of carbohydrate can be stored as glycogen (Table 7.2). The body has no storage mechanism for amino acids or nitrogen, and the pool of free amino acids in the blood is small. Thus, most of the body's amino acids are bound up in protein molecules. These factors make triglycerides the most useful form of stored energy.

The body needs stored energy during sleep.

The Energy of Dietary Glucose Is Stored as Muscle and Liver Glycogen

Recall from Chapter 4 that limited amounts of carbohydrate are stored in the body as glycogen, the storage form of glucose synthesized primarily in the liver and muscles. Glucose can easily be stored as glycogen within these tissues, and after an overnight fast, much of the carbohydrate consumed at breakfast is used to replenish the liver glycogen depleted during the night to maintain blood glucose levels.

Overall, the body stores approximately 250 to 500 kcal of carbohydrate as liver glycogen and approximately 800 to 2000 kcal as muscle glycogen.[9, 10] Of course, the amount of

Table 7.2 Body Energy Reserves of a Well-Nourished 70-kg Male

	Triglycerides	Glycogen	Protein
Weight	15 kg	0.2 kg	6 kg
Kilocalories	135 000	800	24 000

stored glycogen will depend on the adequacy of dietary carbohydrate and the size of the individual: people on a low-carbohydrate diet store very little glycogen, and larger individuals, assuming an adequate dietary carbohydrate intake, can store more glycogen because of the larger size of their muscle tissues and livers. But even in larger individuals, typical body stores of glycogen can be quickly depleted if dietary intake of carbohydrate is low and utilization of glucose as fuel is high. Individuals who participate in endurance exercise are heavy glycogen users. Therefore they need to make sure their glycogen stores are replenished after each workout or competitive event. Chapter 15 explores the process of carbohydrate loading for endurance athletes in detail.

The Energy of Dietary Triglycerides Is Stored as Adipose Tissue

Whenever we eat in excess of energy needs, the body uses the dietary carbohydrate for energy and preferentially stores the dietary fat as body fat. A number of factors contribute to this preference:

- The conversion of dietary fat to body fat is very efficient and requires little energy.
- Dietary fatty acids can be taken up by adipose tissue cells and converted into stored triglycerides without dramatic changes to the fatty acid structures from their original (dietary) form.
- The conversion of dietary carbohydrates to fatty acids that can be stored within the adipose cells requires a number of metabolic steps and is energy inefficient.
- When dietary carbohydrate is consumed in excess of the body's need, there is an increase in the oxidation of carbohydrate (glucose) over fat for energy, leaving more of the dietary fat available for storage in the adipose tissue.

Thus, when you overeat and consume a large meal, the fat within that meal will probably be converted to body fat and stored, whereas the carbohydrate in the meal will be preferentially used to fuel your body for the next four to five hours and to replenish glycogen stores.

The Energy of Dietary Proteins Is Found as Circulating Amino Acids

Although the body has no designated storage place for extra protein, some free amino acids circulating within the blood can be quickly broken down for energy if necessary. These free amino acids are either derived from dietary protein or are produced when tissue proteins are broken down. During protein catabolism, cells recycle as many of the amino acids as possible, using them to make new proteins or releasing them into the blood for uptake by other tissues. This process efficiently recycles many of the amino acids within the body, reducing our overall protein requirements from food.

RECAP

The body is able to convert glucose into muscle and liver glycogen, the body's storage form of carbohydrate. Free fatty acids and glycerol are readily reassembled into triglycerides for storage in the adipose tissue, the body's largest energy depot. Technically, there are no protein stores in the human body; a small circulating pool of free amino acids can be used for energy if needed.

How Are Macronutrients Synthesized?

During the process of anabolism, a relatively small number of chemically simple components, including glucose, fatty acids, and amino acids, are used to synthesize a very large number of more complex body proteins, lipids, carbohydrates, and other

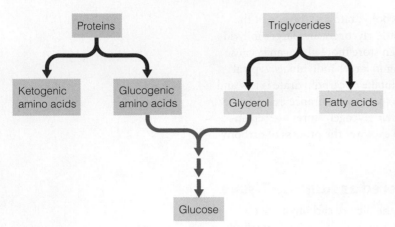

Figure 7.23 Overview of gluconeogenesis. In the absence of dietary carbohydrate and adequate glycogen stores, the body is able to convert glycerol and glucogenic amino acids into glucose.

compounds (recall Figure 7.1). The body also has the ability to synthesize glucose, fatty acids, and some amino acids. The following discussion will explore some of these common anabolic pathways.

Gluconeogenesis Is the Synthesis of Glucose

Glucose is the preferred source of energy for most body tissues and the sole or primary energy source for the brain and other nerve cells. If the supply of glucose is interrupted, loss of consciousness and even death may occur. In the absence of adequate dietary carbohydrate, liver glycogen can sustain blood glucose levels for several hours. Beyond that time, however, if dietary intake is not restored, the body must synthesize glucose from non-carbohydrate substances.

The process of making new glucose from non-carbohydrate substrates is called gluconeogenesis (**Figure 7.23**). The primary substrates for gluconeogenesis are the glucogenic amino acids derived from the catabolism of body proteins or free glucogenic amino acids circulating in the blood. A small amount of glucose can be produced from the glycerol found in triglycerides, although the body cannot make glucose from free fatty acids.

The body relies on gluconeogenesis to maintain blood glucose levels at night when we are sleeping and during times of fasting, trauma, and exercise. Normally, the amount of body protein used for gluconeogenesis is low, but it increases dramatically during times of illness, fasting, or starvation. Protein catabolism for glucose production can draw on vital tissue proteins, such as skeletal muscles, heart muscle, and organ proteins. The deadly consequences of this metabolic pathway are described in more detail in the section on starvation.

lipogenesis The synthesis of free fatty acids from non-lipid precursors such as ketogenic amino acids or ethanol.

de novo synthesis The process of synthesizing a compound "from scratch."

Lipogenesis Is the Synthesis of Fatty Acids

Lipogenesis is the production of fat from non-fat substances such as carbohydrates, ketogenic amino acids, and alcohol. This process is also called **de novo synthesis** of fatty acids, because it is the synthesis of new fatty acids from non-fat compounds. Lipogenesis typically occurs when individuals consume any energy-producing nutrient in excess of energy needs: excess dietary carbohydrate, protein, and alcohol all contribute to lipogenesis.

How does the body convert the six-carbon ring of glucose or the carbon skeleton of an amino acid to a long-chain fatty acid with many carbons? Not surprisingly, the process involves many steps. As shown in **Figure 7.24**, the two-carbon acetyl CoA units derived from glucose, amino acid, and alcohol metabolism are "reassembled" into fatty acid chains. Most lipogenesis occurs in liver cells. The newly synthesized fatty acids are then combined with glycerol to form triglycerides. The liver releases these triglycerides as VLDLs, which then circulate in the bloodstream. Eventually, the fatty acids are removed from the VLDLs, taken up into adipose tissue cells, and reassembled into triglycerides for storage as body fat.

The Synthesis of Amino Acids

As discussed in Chapter 6, the human body is capable of synthesizing as many as eleven non-essential amino acids (NEAAs). The body typically makes the carbon skeleton of NEAAs from carbohydrate- or fat-derived metabolites. The amine group can be provided through the process of transamination, where it is donated by one amino acid and accepted by a keto acid (**Figure 7.25**). When the keto acid accepts the donated amine group, it becomes a newly formed amino acid. The synthesis of non-essential amino acids occurs only when the body has enough energy and nitrogen to complete the necessary anabolic steps.

Consuming an excess amount of carbohydrate, protein, or alcohol will contribute to lipogenesis.

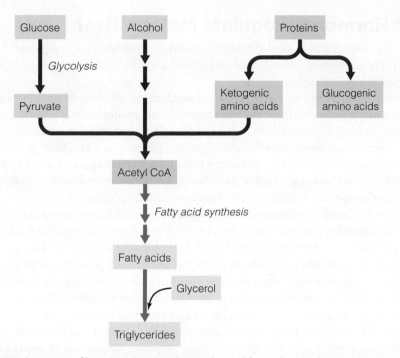

Figure 7.24 Overview of lipogenesis. Acetyl CoA, derived from glucose, ketogenic amino acids, or alcohol, can be converted into fatty acids for eventual storage as adipocyte triglycerides.

Essential amino acids (EAAs) are distinguished from NEAAs by their carbon skeletons. The carbon skeletons of EAAs cannot be derived from carbohydrate or fat metabolic intermediates; therefore, EAAs must be consumed in their existing form from dietary proteins. Essential amino acids can be degraded or catabolized through several metabolic reactions, but they cannot be synthesized by cellular pathways.

ReCaP

The dietary intake of carbohydrates, fats, and protein supplies the body with glucose, fatty acids, and amino acids. If intake is interrupted or inadequate, the body has the ability to endogenously (internally) synthesize glucose, almost all fatty acids, and eleven non-essential amino acids from readily available metabolic intermediates, including pyruvate and acetyl CoA.

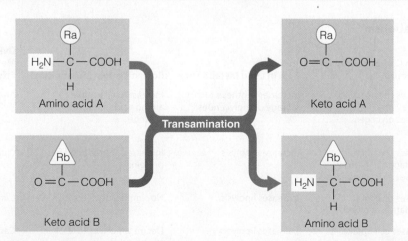
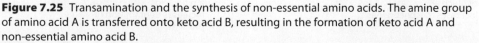

Figure 7.25 Transamination and the synthesis of non-essential amino acids. The amine group of amino acid A is transferred onto keto acid B, resulting in the formation of keto acid A and non-essential amino acid B.

What Hormones Regulate Metabolism?

To maintain homeostasis (balanced internal conditions), the body must regulate energy storage and breakdown as needed. A set of anabolic and catabolic hormones helps regulate metabolism (Table 7.3).

The primary anabolic hormone is insulin, which increases in the blood after a meal, especially when protein and carbohydrate are consumed. Insulin activates the storage enzymes of the body and signals the cells to take up glucose, fatty acids, and amino acids. These compounds are then converted into glycogen, triglycerides, and body protein. Thus, insulin favours substrate uptake, emphasizes macronutrient storage, and slows catabolic processes within the body (see Table 7.3). If endogenous insulin production is inhibited in any way, then exogenous insulin (insulin injections) must be provided.

Conversely, glucagon, **epinephrine**, and **cortisol** are catabolic hormones that trigger the breakdown of stored triglycerides, glycogen, and body proteins for energy. They also slow the anabolic pathways that store energy (see Table 7.3). As blood glucose drops, glucagon concentrations increase, prompting the body to release glucose from glycogen stored in the liver. During exercise, blood levels of epinephrine increase quickly, stimulating the breakdown of stored energy reserves. Cortisol rises during times of energy deprivation and physical stress such as injury or exercise and stimulates gluconeogenesis and lipolysis.

A rise in blood cortisol levels also occurs during times of emotional stress and is considered a hallmark of the primitive "fight-or-flight" response. Catabolism of stored energy prepares the body to either fight or flee from an enemy, two situations that typically demand high energy. In today's world, we do not typically physically fight or flee from our enemies, so the fatty acids and glucose that are dumped into the bloodstream in response to stress are not utilized as physiologically intended. When day-to-day stresses chronically trigger elevations in blood cortisol levels during physically inactive periods, these metabolically inappropriate responses can increase a person's risk of excessive abdominal fat storage and/or glucose intolerance, thereby increasing the risk of type 2 diabetes and cardiovascular diseases.

As you can see, a number of catabolic hormones regulate substrate breakdown, and insulin is the major anabolic hormone. Homeostasis requires a balance among these hormones. If one or more of them ceases to regulate properly, normal metabolic controls fail. For example, most people with type 2 diabetes make plenty of insulin, even too much. As described in Chapter 4, however, when the cells of people with type 2 diabetes become insensitive to insulin, they fail to take up glucose for fuel and must turn to glucogenic amino acids. Normally, insulin promotes amino acid uptake and protein synthesis; in people with type 2 diabetes, however, the ineffective insulin response triggers protein catabolism. Thus, normal metabolic controls are lost, and the balance between anabolism and catabolism is disrupted.

epinephrine A hormone produced mainly by the adrenal medulla that stimulates the release of glucose from liver glycogen and the release of free fatty acids from stored triglycerides.

cortisol A hormone produced by the adrenal cortex that increases rates of gluconeogenesis and lipolysis.

Table 7.3 Hormonal Regulation of Metabolism

Metabolic State	Hormone	Site of Secretion	Role in Carbohydrate Metabolism	Role in Lipid Metabolism	Role in Protein Metabolism	Overall Metabolic Effect
Fed	Insulin	Pancreatic beta cells	Increases cell uptake of glucose Increases glycogen synthesis	Increases synthesis and storage of triglycerides	Increases cell uptake of amino acids and protein synthesis	Anabolic
Fasted	Glucagon	Pancreatic alpha cells	Increases glycogen degradation to glucose Increases gluconeogenesis	Increases lipolysis	Increases degradation of proteins	Catabolic
Exercise	Epinephrine	Adrenal medulla	Increases glycogen degradation to glucose	Increases lipolysis	No significant effect	Catabolic
Stress	Cortisol	Adrenal cortex	Decreases cell uptake of glucose Increases gluconeogenesis	Increases lipolysis	Decreases cell uptake of amino acids Increases degradation of proteins	Catabolic

RECaP

To maintain homeostasis, the body must regulate energy storage and breakdown as needed. The primary anabolic hormone is insulin, whereas glucagon, epinephrine, and cortisol are catabolic hormones.

How Do Feeding and Fasting Affect Metabolism?

Although the need for energy is constant, most people eat or fuel their bodies on an intermittent basis. Every night, while we sleep, the body continues its metabolic processes, drawing upon stored energy. In the morning, when we "break our fast," the body receives an infusion of new energy sources. How does the body take advantage of energy when it is available, even if not needed at that moment? And how does it remain metabolically active even in the absence of food intake? The metabolic responses to the cycles of feeding and fasting are explored here.

Metabolic Responses to Feeding

For several hours after the consumption of a meal, food is digested and nutrients are absorbed. The bloodstream is enriched with glucose, fatty acids, and amino acids. Most cells are able to meet their immediate energy needs through glucose oxidation. Only if the meal was very low in carbohydrate would body cells break down fatty acids or amino acids for fuel.

The fed state is generally an anabolic state; after absorption, the end products of digestion are converted into larger, more chemically complex compounds. Glucose in excess of energy needs is converted to and stored as liver and muscle glycogen. Once glycogen stores are saturated, any remaining glucose is converted to fatty acids and eventually stored as triglycerides. Dietary fatty acids are combined with glycerol to form and be stored as triglycerides, largely in the adipose tissue. The liver takes up newly absorbed amino acids and converts some of them to needed proteins. The remaining amino acids are deaminated, and the carbon skeletons are converted to fatty acids for eventual storage as triglycerides. **Figure 7.26** summarizes the interrelated metabolic responses to feeding.

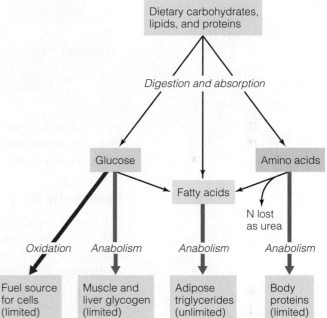

Figure 7.26 Overview of the fed state. Once the energy needs of cells have been met, a limited amount of glucose is converted to and stored as liver and muscle glycogen. Some amino acids are used to synthesize body proteins. Excess glucose and amino acids are converted to fatty acids, which then are used to synthesize triglycerides for storage in the adipose tissue.

Metabolic Responses to Short-Term Fasting

As the gap between meals lengthens beyond three hours or so, the body shifts from its previous anabolic state to a catabolic profile. Without a readily available supply of dietary carbohydrate, the body must turn inward to maintain normal blood glucose levels. **Figure 7.27** summarizes these metabolic responses.

Recall from Chapter 4 that muscle glycogen is "reserved" for muscle tissue alone and is not available for normalization of blood glucose levels. Liver glycogen is broken down and glucose is released into the bloodstream; however, the supply of liver glycogen is limited. Most body cells, including muscle cells, are able to switch to the use of fatty acids as fuel, conserving the remaining blood glucose for brain and other cells that rely very heavily on glucose as fuel. As the carbohydrate-deprived state continues, ketone bodies accumulate as fatty-acid-derived acetyl CoA units are blocked from entering the TCA cycle. As the fasted state becomes more prolonged, the process of gluconeogenesis increases in intensity: glucose is synthesized from glucogenic amino acids (drawn initially from free amino acids in

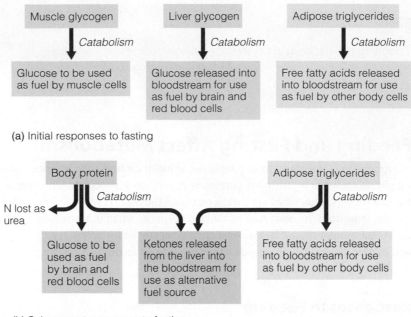

Figure 7.27 Metabolic responses to short-term fasting. **(a)** In the early stages of a fast, glycogen stores are depleted, and the body increases its use of fatty acids as fuel. **(b)** Subsequent responses to prolonged fasting: Glucogenic amino acids provide some glucose for brain and red blood cells. Ketones and free fatty acids are used as fuel by other body cells.

the blood, then largely from the breakdown of muscle protein) and glycerol. These short-term adaptations will provide the glucose and energy needed to meet the body's needs for a few days (see Figure 7.27b).

Metabolic Responses to Prolonged Starvation

After two to three days of fasting, the body senses an approaching crisis and responds with dramatic changes in its metabolic profile. Whether the starvation is the result of a voluntary action (for example, political protest, religious ritual, or self-defined act) or involuntary circumstances (for example, severe illness, famine, war, extreme poverty), the body shifts into survival mode. There are two overriding problems to be solved: the problem of meeting energy requirements and the problem of maintaining blood glucose levels in support of glucose-dependent cells such as brain and red blood cells. The body must solve these problems while maintaining the integrity of its essential functions, including preservation of skeletal and cardiac muscle, maintenance of the immune system, and continuation of brain function for as long as possible. How, then, does the body meet these challenges?

In response to continued starvation, the body initiates several energy-conserving tactics: as fatigue sets in, there is a sharp decline in voluntary physical activity, core body temperature drops, and resting metabolic rate declines. Overall, the energy needs of the body drop dramatically. To meet the remaining energy needs, most cells further increase their use of fatty acids as primary fuel, conserving the limited supply of glucose. Plasma levels of free fatty acids increase sharply as they move from adipose stores to the tissues and cells in need of energy. In addition, the brain shifts away from its normal reliance on glucose and uses ketone bodies for fuel. Plasma ketone levels increase to an even greater extent as they are released from the liver and circulate throughout the body. Yet, even with these adaptations, the need by brain cells for a certain amount of glucose remains.

There are very few options available for solving the body's glucose problem. As stored triglycerides are broken down to provide fatty acids for fuel, the glycerol component is used to provide small amounts of glucose. Glucogenic amino acids, however, remain the major source of glucose for use by the brain. Day after day, the body sacrifices muscle protein to maintain a small but essential supply of glucose.

Over time, from weeks to even months later, a new crisis arises: fat stores become depleted, depriving the body of its most efficient source of fuel. With no other option available, the body turns to its previously protected pools of protein: skeletal muscle, cardiac muscle, protein in organs such as the liver and kidney, and serum proteins such as immune factors and transport proteins. As discussed in Chapter 6, children with marasmus illustrate this final stage of depletion: they have no visible fat stores, their muscles are atrophied, and they lack the reserves to sustain immune, hair, skin, and other protein synthesis. At this final stage, many die of cardiac failure as the heart muscle becomes too wasted to properly function. Others die of infections, lacking normal immune responses.

How long can a person survive complete starvation? Obviously, the need for water is critical; a person will die of dehydration long before reaching these final stages of prolonged starvation. Prior health and nutritional status play an important role: if a person enters starvation with large stores of body fat, his or her survival will be prolonged. If a person has good muscle mass and adequate nutrient stores, he or she is also at a slight advantage. Older adults and young children are more susceptible to the effects of starvation. Most previously healthy adults can survive without food for one to three months, assuming no illness or trauma and an adequate supply of water. Extreme environmental conditions and increased physical activity shorten survival time.

RECaP

In the fed state, the body assumes an anabolic profile, converting newly absorbed glucose, fatty acids, and amino acids into stored glycogen and triglycerides, and synthesizing some proteins. During short-term fasts, the body mobilizes stored glycogen and triglycerides to meet its need for glucose and energy. If the fasted state persists, more extreme adaptations to glucose and energy deficits occur. The body relies heavily on fatty acids and ketones as fuel sources and catabolizes proteins for gluconeogenesis. Over time, body fat and protein stores are so depleted that death occurs.

CASE STUDY ▸ Pure Protein Power

Alejandro is on the varsity men's basketball team. Some of his teammates just finished reading a book called *Pure Protein Power* and are keen to incorporate its key messages into their training diet.

The author of the book stresses that "protein makes protein." So, if you eat a high-protein diet, with virtually no fat and no carbohydrates, you will gain muscle, but not fat. The author also claims that this approach will keep your blood sugar really low, even if you have diabetes, because protein "can't be used to make sugar."

Alejandro is keen to try the diet over the next few weeks so that he can be in top shape for next season. The next day he puts his plan into action:

Breakfast:	Omelette, made using cooking spray, with
	4 egg whites,
	75 g cooked lean ham

	60 mL mushrooms
	60 mL diced tomato
	15 mL diced onion
	250 mL black coffee
Snack:	125 mL low-fat cottage cheese mixed with 30 mL salsa
Lunch:	Tuna salad, made with
	250 mL romaine lettuce
	225 mL tuna packed in water
	125 mL diced tomato
	125 mL cucumber
	30 mL diced red onion
	355 mL diet cola
Dinner:	225 g lean roast beef with 30 mL fat-free gravy
	125 mL steamed broccoli
	125 mL steamed cauliflower
	125 mL steamed carrots
	Water
Snack:	175 mL 0% milk fat plain yogourt mixed with 45 mL blackberries
	355 mL soda water

Thinking Critically

1. Compare Alejandro's intake of protein, fat, and carbohydrate with the appropriate AMDR for each nutrient.
2. Are there any foods that are really "pure protein" with no dietary carbohydrate or fat?
3. Is it true that you can eat as much protein as you want without gaining fat? Why or why not?
4. Do you agree with the claim that protein can't be used to make sugar? Explain.
5. Describe Alejandro's metabolic response to the *Pure Protein Power* menu he planned above.

SEE FOR YOURSELF

Galactosemia

Galactosemia is a metabolic disorder that develops when one or more enzymes in the pathway to break down galactose are abnormal or missing. If left untreated, galactose builds up in the bloodstream and body tissues, leading to cataracts, enlarged liver, developmental disabilities, and early death. Luckily, strict limitation of dietary galactose lowers the risk of these health problems.

Galactose is one of the two monosaccharides that make up lactose, so greatly reducing dietary intake of lactose will lower galactose intake. Easy enough, you may think: just avoid milk, cheese, yogourt, ice cream, and other dairy products. You may be surprised, however, at the number of different foods that contain lactose or milk-based ingredients. Each of these foods represents a "hidden" source of galactose that would create problems for a person with galactosemia.

Next time you are at the supermarket, carefully look at the labels of foods such as bologna and other processed meats; cream soups or chowders; breaded frozen fish; and baked goods such as breads, cakes, and cookies. Look for the following milk or milk-based ingredients:

- Non-fat dry milk or milk solids
- Lactose
- Whey protein or whey solids
- Casein, caseinates, or hydrolyzed casein
- Milk chocolate

Every time you find a label with one of those ingredients, you have found a food that is forbidden or strictly limited in the diet of a person with galactosemia. Would you have trouble following this diet?

Chapter Review

7

Test Yourself | **Answers**

1. **T** All cells are metabolically active, but liver, muscle, and adipose cells are key locations for integration of metabolic pathways.

2. **T** Two vitamins that help produce energy from the macronutrients are riboflavin and niacin.

3. **F** Carbohydrate is stored in the liver or muscle as glycogen. We also store smaller amounts of glycogen in certain organs, such as the heart.

4. **F** There is no metabolic pathway by which fatty acids can be converted into glucose.

5. **T** During periods of starvation, body proteins are catabolized and their glucogenic amino acids used in gluconeogenesis.

Summary

- Metabolism is the sum of all the chemical and physical processes by which the body breaks down and builds up molecules.

- All forms of life maintain a balance between anabolic and catabolic reactions, which determines if the body achieves growth and repair or if it persists in a state of loss.

- Metabolic pathways are clusters of chemical reactions that occur sequentially and achieve a particular goal, such as the breakdown of glucose for energy. These pathways are carefully controlled, either favoured or slowed, by hormones released within the body.

- Condensation and hydrolysis are chemical reactions involving water, whereas phosphorylation is a chemical reaction in which phosphate is transferred. In oxidation–reduction reactions, the molecules involved exchange electrons.

- Enzymes, coenzymes, and cofactors increase the efficiency of metabolism.

- Glucose oxidation occurs in three well-defined stages: glycolysis, the TCA cycle, and oxidative phosphorylation via the electron transport chain. The end products of glucose oxidation are carbon dioxide, water, and ATP.

- During glycolysis, six-carbon glucose is converted into two molecules of three-carbon pyruvate. If glycolysis is anaerobic, this pyruvate is converted to lactic acid. If glycolysis is aerobic, this pyruvate is converted to acetyl CoA and enters the TCA cycle.

- During the TCA cycle, acetyl CoA coming from either carbohydrate, fat, or protein metabolism results in the production of GTP or ATP, NADH, and $FADH_2$. These two final compounds go through oxidative phosphorylation (as part of the electron transport chain) to produce energy.

- During oxidative phosphorylation, the NADH and the $FADH_2$ enter the electron transport chain where, through a series of reactions, ATP is produced.

- Triglycerides are broken down into glycerol and free fatty acids. Glycerol can be (a) converted to glucose or (b) oxidized for energy. Free fatty acids are oxidized for energy but cannot be converted into glucose. In a carbohydrate-depleted state, fatty acids are diverted to ketone formation. The end products of fatty acid oxidation are carbon dioxide, water, and ATP.

- After deamination, the carbon skeletons of amino acids can be oxidized for energy. The carbon skeletons of glucogenic amino acids are converted into pyruvate, whereas those of ketogenic amino acids are converted into acetyl CoA. Some amino acids feed into the TCA cycle as various metabolic intermediates. The end products of amino acid oxidation are carbon dioxide, water, ATP, and urea.

- The amine group released as a result of deamination can be transferred onto a keto acid for the synthesis of non-essential amino acids or, via ammonia, converted to and excreted as urea.

- Alcohol metabolism begins in the stomach, where up to 20% of the alcohol consumed is oxidized. The remainder is oxidized in the liver. At high intakes, some alcohol continues to circulate in the blood because the liver oxidizes alcohol at a steady rate of approximately one drink per hour.

- The body extracts energy from glucose, fatty acids, glycerol, and amino acids. Glycogen is the body's storage form of carbohydrate. Triglycerides in the adipose tissue form the body's largest energy depot. Technically, there are no protein stores in the human body.

- The dietary intake of carbohydrates, fats, and protein supplies the body with glucose, fatty acids, and amino acids. If intake is inadequate, the body synthesizes glucose, almost all fatty acids, and eleven non-essential amino acids from readily available metabolic intermediates.

- The primary substrates for gluconeogenesis are the glucogenic amino acids. A small amount of glucose can be produced from glycerol, but the body cannot make glucose from fatty acids.

- Excess dietary carbohydrate, protein, and alcohol all contribute to lipogenesis and triglyceride storage.

- The body can make the carbon skeleton of NEAAs from carbohydrate- or fat-derived metabolites. The amine group can be provided through the process of transamination. The carbon skeletons of EAAs cannot be derived from carbohydrate or fat metabolic intermediates; therefore, EAAs must be consumed in their existing form from dietary proteins.

- To maintain homeostasis, the body must regulate energy storage and breakdown as needed. The primary anabolic hormone is insulin, whereas glucagon, epinephrine, and cortisol are catabolic hormones.

- In the fed state, the body converts newly absorbed glucose, fatty acids, and amino acids into stored glycogen and triglycerides.

- During short-term fasts, the body uses stored glycogen and triglycerides for glucose and energy. If the fast persists, the body relies heavily on fatty acids and ketones for fuel and initiates gluconeogenesis from glycerol and glucogenic amino acid to meet its glucose requirements. Over time, body fat and protein stores are so depleted that death occurs.

Review Questions

1. One by-product of anaerobic glucose metabolism is
   a. lactic acid.
   b. acetyl CoA.
   c. oxaloacetate.
   d. six molecules of NADH.

2. Mitochondria are often called the cell's
   a. energy currency.
   b. power plant.
   c. fat producer.
   d. fat storage centre.

3. In which of the following types of chemical reactions is a molecule catabolized by the addition of a molecule of water?
   a. hydrolysis
   b. condensation
   c. oxidation
   d. phosphorylation

4. Anya skipped breakfast this morning. It is now mid-afternoon, and she has joined a friend for a late lunch. Although she rarely drinks alcohol, while waiting for her food to arrive, she enjoys a glass of wine. Which of the following statements best describes Anya's body's response to the alcohol?
   a. Gastric ADH oxidizes about 30% to 35% of the alcohol Anya consumes; the rest is absorbed into her bloodstream.
   b. When the alcohol enters Anya's bloodstream, her muscles quickly take it up for oxidation before her blood alcohol level increases.
   c. The microsomal ethanol oxidizing system breaks down about 20% of the alcohol Anya consumes before it is absorbed into her bloodstream.
   d. None of the above statements is true.

5. Glucagon, epinephrine, and cortisol are
   a. coenzymes.
   b. cofactors.
   c. anabolic hormones.
   d. catabolic hormones.

6. The typical human adult has glycogen reserves that are adequate for about one day. Describe three ways a starved body can obtain more glucose after the reserves have been depleted.

7. Discuss three possible fates of acetyl CoA in metabolism.

8. Explain the statement that, within the electron transport chain, energy is captured in ATP.

9. Describe the process of fatty acid oxidation.

10. An older adult patient who has type 1 diabetes is admitted to the hospital in a state of severe ketoacidosis. The patient is comatose, but an elderly friend tells the admitting staff that he thinks his companion is sick because recently she has not had enough money to buy insulin. Describe a possible series of physiologic events that might have led to her ketoacidosis.

11. Review the information you learned about phenylketonuria (PKU) in Chapter 4, and then describe the physiologic events likely to occur in a child with phenylketonuria who, unknown to his parents, goes off his diet every day at school and eats whatever his friends are eating.

12. Your Aunt Winifred has been overweight her entire life. Recently, she began a very strict semi-starvation diet because it promises that "all the weight you lose will be fat." What information could you share with her that would explain why her weight loss will include loss of body protein, not just body fat?

Web Links

www.nutritionandmetabolism.com
Nutrition and Metabolism
An online, peer-reviewed journal with articles concerning the integration of nutrition, exercise physiology, clinical investigations, and metabolism.

www.endo-metab.ca
Canadian Society of Endocrinology and Metabolism
The Canadian Society of Endocrinology and Metabolism (CSEM) is a professional organization that brings together clinical endocrinologists, educators, and researchers engaged in providing health care, training, and research in endocrinology.

www.canpku.org
The Canadian PKU and Allied Disorders
This site offers news, information, and support to families and professionals dealing with phenylketonuria and similar rare, inherited metabolic disorders.

www.liver.ca
Canadian Liver Foundation
Visit this site to learn more about research and education into the causes, diagnoses, prevention, and treatment of liver disease.

MasteringNutrition®

www.masteringnutrition.pearson.com

Assignments
Animations: Hydrolytic & Condensation Reactions • Energy Production from Triglycerides • Cori Cycle • TCA Cycle • Electron Transport Chain • The Energy Currency ATP • Glycolysis • Ketone Body Formation
Activities: NutriTools

Study Area
Video: Understanding Metabolism • Practice Tests • Diet Analysis • eText

References

1. Champe, P. C., R. A. Harvey, and D. R. Ferrier. 2008. *Lippincott's Illustrated Reviews: Biochemistry.* 4th ed. Philadelphia: Lippincott Williams & Wilkins.
2. *Stedman's Medical Dictionary.* 5th ed. 2005. Philadelphia: Lippincott Williams & Wilkins.
3. Zupec-Kania, B. A., and E. Spellman. 2008. An overview of the ketogenic diet for pediatric epilepsy. *Nutr. Clinic. Pract.* 23(6):589–596.
4. Freeman, J. M., E. H. Kossoff, and A. L. Hartman. 2007. The ketogenic diet: One decade later. *Pediatrics* 119(3):535–543.
5. Caballeria, J. 2003. Current concepts in alcohol metabolism. *Annals Hepatology* 2(2):60–68.
6. Suter, P. M. 2006. Alcohol: The role in health and nutrition. In: B. A. Bowman and R. M. Russell, eds. *Present Knowledge in Nutrition, Volume I.* 9th ed. Washington, DC: ILSI Press, pp. 138–156.
7. Adlaf, E. M., A. Demers, and L. Gliksman, (Eds.) 2005. *Canadian Campus Survey 2004.* Toronto, ON: Centre for Addiction and Mental Health.
8. Paradis, C., A. Demers, and E. Picard, 2010. Alcohol consumption: A different kind of Canadian mosaic. *Can. J. Pub. Health* 101:275–280.
9. Manore, M., N. Meyer, and J. Thompson. 2009. *Sport Nutrition for Health and Performance.* 2nd ed. Champaign, IL: Human Kinetics.
10. Kreider, R. G., A. L. Almada, J. Antonio, C. Broeder, C. Earnest, M. Greenwood, T. Incledon, D. S. Kalman, S. M. Kleiner, B. Leutholtz, L. M. Lowery, R. Mendel, J. R. Stout, D. S. Willoughby, and T. N. Ziegenfuss. 2004. ISSN exercise and sport nutrition review: research and recommendations. *J. Int. Soc. Sports Nutr.* 1(1):1–44.
11. Brass, E. P. 2004. Carnitine and sports medicine: use or abuse? *Ann. NY Acad. Sci.* 1033:67–78.
12. Villani R. G., J. Gannon, M. Self, and P. A. Rich. 2000. L-carnitine supplementation combined with aerobic training does not promote weight loss in moderately obese women. *Int. J. Sport Nutr. Exerc. Metab.* 10:199–207.
13. Stephens, F. B., D. Constantin-Teodosiu, and P. L. Greenhaff. 2007. New insights concerning the role of carnitine in the regulation of fuel metabolism in skeletal muscle. *J. Physiol.* 581(2):431–444.
14. Calvani, M., P. Benatti, A. Mancinelli, S. D'Iddio, V. Giordano, A. Koverech, A. Amato, and E. P. Brass. 2004. Carnitine replacement in end-stage renal disease and hemodialysis. *NY Ann. Acad. Sci.* 1033:52–66.

EVIDENCE-INFORMED DECISION MAKING

Are Carnitine Supplements Worthwhile?

Product labels, magazine advertisements, and TV infomercials practically shout the term "fat burner" in trying to convince consumers of the value of carnitine supplements; for years, carnitine has been included in many so-called weight-loss products.[10] The appeal of their claim is undeniable: use this product, and body fat will "melt" away.

As previously explained, carnitine shuttles fatty acids across the mitochondrial membrane. Fatty acids are oxidized along the inside of the mitochondrial membrane because that is where the enzymes of the β-oxidation pathway are found. If fatty acids can't get across the mitochondrial membrane, they will not be oxidized as a fuel and will accumulate. It seems logical, then, that carnitine supplements will increase fat oxidation and decrease body fat stores. But do they? There are two arguments often used in marketing carnitine supplements: (1) Many people are low in carnitine, and so would benefit from carnitine supplements, and (2) even healthy people with normal carnitine levels could lower their body fat by taking extra carnitine. How do these arguments hold up?

Looking at the first issue: are many people low in carnitine? Two important pieces of information are often left out of advertisements for carnitine supplements: (1) Carnitine is widely available from a large number of foods, and (2) humans synthesize carnitine in amounts that fully meet the needs of healthy people. Food sources of carnitine include meat, poultry, fish, and dairy products; healthy children and adults on a mixed diet get all the carnitine needed from their normal diet. What about vegetarians and vegans? It is true that they *eat* much less dietary carnitine than non-vegetarians, but the body can easily synthesize it from the amino acids lysine and methionine. Lysine is found in legumes, including soybeans, whereas methionine is plentiful in grains, nuts, and seeds. Vegetarians commonly consume these foods in abundant amounts. As long as their diets provide enough of these foods, as well as the iron, niacin, vitamin B_6, and vitamin C used as cofactors, healthy vegetarians and vegans can meet their need for carnitine through endogenous (internal) synthesis. So, well-nourished healthy people—vegetarians and vegans included—are rarely, if ever, low in carnitine.

What about the second claim? Do high doses of carnitine supplements benefit overweight or obese persons? Manufacturers promote carnitine supplements as "fat burners" by implying that high intakes will increase blood levels, then muscle levels, of carnitine. Once in the muscle, the advertisements suggest, the carnitine would trigger fat oxidation and "burn up" body fat. Most studies have shown that taking large doses of carnitine, for up to two weeks, does not increase muscle carnitine levels, and so would have no effect on body fat oxidation.[11] In addition, carnitine supplementation had no impact on weight loss in obese women.[12] Overall, well-controlled research has failed to support either of the claims made by those marketing carnitine supplements to healthy persons.

Are there any situations where carnitine supplements are useful? Yes, but they are limited to a small number of unusual situations. Persons with rare genetic metabolic defects must be provided with supplementary carnitine because they are unable to synthesize or utilize it;[13] patients with chronic kidney failure or those on dialysis treatment for kidney failure are often supplemented with carnitine as well.[14] In general, however, there is no evidence to support the claims that carnitine supplements increase the body's rate of fat oxidation or reduce body fat in healthy adults. The only "burning" you might experience when buying carnitine supplements is that of the money in your wallet!

Using the Evidence

1. What lessons can we learn from the marketing of carnitine supplements?

2. If a label or advertising claim seems logical, does that mean it's necessarily true? What's the difference?

3. Even if a substance is necessary for normal body functioning, does that mean consuming extra amounts of it will be beneficial? Why or why not?

4. Are supplement manufacturers the most reliable sources of information about human physiology? Why or why not? If not, who or what would be a better source?

Micronutrients, Phytochemicals, and Functional Foods

Chapter Objectives | *After reading this chapter, you will be able to:*

1. Describe how vitamins are classified and named, *pp. 275–277.*
2. Describe how minerals are classified, *pp. 278–280.*
3. Compare and contrast vitamin and mineral absorption, *pp. 280–281.*
4. Discuss the role of food versus supplements in providing micronutrients, and explain the role of supplements in disease prevention, *pp. 281–282.*
5. Define phytochemicals and explain their role in disease prevention, *pp. 284–286.*
6. Discuss the safety of functional foods, *p. 288.*
7. Define probiotics and prebiotics, and provide examples of each that are currently on the market, *pp. 289–290.*
8. Discuss the risks and benefits of at least three functional foods currently on the market, *pp. 289–291.*

Have you heard the one about the university student on the junk-food diet who developed scurvy, a disease caused by inadequate intake of vitamin C? This urban legend seems to circulate on most university campuses every year, but that might be because there's some truth behind it. Away from their families, many university students do adopt diets that are deficient in one or more food groups and hence one or more micronutrients. For instance, some students adopt a vegan diet with insufficient iron, others stop choosing foods rich in calcium and vitamin D, and some cut out almost all fruit and vegetables. Why is it important to consume adequate levels of the micronutrients, and exactly what is a micronutrient, anyway? How are phytochemicals different from micronutrients and what makes a food a functional food? This chapter provides an overview of micronutrients, including their discovery, classification and naming, and general impact on our health. Groups of micronutrients with common functions and specific vitamins and minerals will be explored in more depth in subsequent chapters. Here we also explore some of the reasons why the chemicals naturally occurring in plant foods, called phytochemicals, are thought to promote our health. We'll also examine the claims made for so-called functional foods such as yogourt, eggs, chocolate, and beverages that manufacturers say have health benefits beyond their basic nutritional function.

Discovering the "Hidden" Nutrients

As you recall, there are three general classes of nutrients. Fluids provide water, which is essential for our survival and helps regulate many body functions. Macronutrients, which include carbohydrates, fats, and proteins, provide energy; thus, we need to consume them in relatively large amounts. Micronutrients, which include vitamins and minerals, are needed in much smaller amounts. They assist body functions such as energy metabolism and the formation and maintenance of healthy cells and tissues.

Much of our knowledge of vitamins and minerals comes from accidental observations of animals and humans. For instance, in the 1890s, a Dutch physician by the name of C. Eijkman noticed that chickens fed polished rice developed paralysis, which could be reversed by feeding them whole-grain rice. Noting the high incidence of beriberi, which results in extensive nerve damage, among hospital patients fed polished rice, he hypothesized that a highly refined diet was the main cause of beriberi. We now know that whole-grain rice, with its nutrient-rich bran layer, contains the vitamin thiamine and that thiamine deficiency results in beriberi. Similarly, in the early 1900s, it was observed that Japanese children living in fishing villages rarely developed a type of blindness common among Japanese children who did not eat fish. Experiments soon showed that cod liver oil, chicken liver, and eel fat prevented the disorder. We now know that each of these foods contains vitamin A, which is essential for healthy vision.

Such observations were followed by years of laboratory research before nutritionists came to fully accept the idea that very small amounts of substances present in food were critical to good health. In 1906, the term *accessory factors* was coined by the English scientist F. G. Hopkins; we now categorize these accessory factors as vitamins and minerals.

RECAP

Micronutrients, which include vitamins and minerals, are needed in small amounts. They assist body functions such as energy metabolism and the formation and maintenance of healthy cells and tissues. Much of our knowledge about vitamins and minerals comes from accidental observation of animals and humans.

How Are Vitamins Classified?

Vitamins are carbon-containing compounds that regulate a wide range of body processes. Of the 13 vitamins recognized as essential, humans can synthesize only small amounts of vitamins D and K, so we must consume virtually all of the vitamins in our diets. Almost everyone who eats a varied and healthy diet can readily meet their vitamin needs from foods alone. The exceptions to this will be discussed shortly.

Fat-Soluble Vitamins

Vitamins A, D, E, and K are fat-soluble vitamins (Table 8.1). They are found in the fatty portions of foods (butterfat, cod liver oil, corn oil, and so on) and are absorbed along with dietary fat. Fat-containing meats, dairy products, nuts, seeds, vegetable oils, and avocados are all sources of one or more fat-soluble vitamins.

In general, the fat-soluble vitamins are readily stored in the body's adipose tissue; thus, we don't need to consume them every single day. While this may simplify day-to-day menu planning, there is also a disadvantage to our ability to store these nutrients. When we consume more of them than we can use, they build up in the adipose tissue, liver, and other tissues and can reach toxic levels. Symptoms of fat-soluble vitamin toxicity, described in Table 8.1, include damage to our hair, skin, bones, eyes, and nervous system. Overconsumption of vitamin supplements is the most common cause of vitamin toxicity in Canada; rarely do our dietary choices lead to toxicity. Of the four fat-soluble vitamins, vitamins A and D are the most toxic; **megadosing** with ten or more times the recommended intake of either can result in irreversible organ damage and even death.

megadosing Taking a dose of a nutrient that is 10 or more times greater than the recommended amount.

Table 8.1 Fat-Soluble Vitamins

Vitamin Name	Primary Functions	Recommended Intake*	Reliable Food Sources	Toxicity/Deficiency Symptoms
A (retinol, retinal, retinoic acid)	Required for ability of eyes to adjust to changes in light Protects colour vision Assists cell differentiation (e.g., epithelial tissues) Required for sperm production in men and fertilization in women Contributes to healthy bone Contributes to healthy immune system	RDA: Men = 900 μg/day Women = 700 μg/day UL = 3000 μg/day	Preformed retinol: Beef and chicken liver, egg yolks, milk Carotenoid precursors: Spinach, carrots, mango, apricots, cantaloupe, pumpkin, yams	*Toxicity:* Fatigue; bone and joint pain; spontaneous abortion and birth defects of fetuses in pregnant women; nausea and diarrhea; liver damage; nervous system damage; blurred vision; hair loss; skin disorders *Deficiency:* Night blindness, xerophthalmia; impaired growth, immunity, and reproductive function
D (cholecalciferol)	Regulates blood calcium levels Maintains bone health Assists cell differentiation	RDA (assumes that person does not get adequate sun exposure): Adult aged 19 to 50 = 15 μg/day Adult aged 50 to 70 = 15 μg/day Adult aged > 70 = 20 μg/day UL = 100 μg/day	Canned salmon and mackerel; fortified milk; fortified soy, almond, and rice milk; fortified cereals	*Toxicity:* Hypercalcemia *Deficiency:* Rickets in children; osteomalacia and/or osteoporosis in adults
E (tocopherol)	As a powerful antioxidant, protects cell membranes, polyunsaturated fatty acids, and vitamin A from oxidation Protects white blood cells Enhances immune function Improves absorption of vitamin A	RDA: Men = 15 mg/day Women = 15 mg/day UL = 1000 mg/day from synthetic forms only	Sunflower seeds, almonds, vegetable oils, fortified cereals	*Toxicity:* Rare; increased risk of haemorrhagic stroke with supplements *Deficiency:* Hemolytic anemia; impairment of nerve, muscle, and immune function
K (phylloquinone, menaquinone, menadione)	Serves as a coenzyme during production of specific proteins that assist in blood coagulation and bone metabolism	AI: Men = 120 μg/day Women = 90 μg/day	Kale, spinach, turnip greens, Brussels sprouts	*Toxicity:* None known *Deficiency:* Impaired blood clotting; possible effect on bone health

*Abbreviations: RDA, Recommended Dietary Allowance; UL, Upper Limit; AI, Adequate Intake.

Avocados are a source of fat-soluble vitamins.

Water-soluble vitamins can be found in a variety of foods.

Even though we can store the fat-soluble vitamins, deficiencies can occur, especially in people who have a disorder that reduces their ability to absorb dietary fat. In addition, people who are "fat phobic," or eat very small amounts of dietary fat, are at risk for a deficiency. The consequences of fat-soluble vitamin deficiencies, described in Table 8.1, include osteoporosis, the loss of night vision, and even death in the most severe cases.

Water-Soluble Vitamins

Vitamin C (ascorbic acid) and the B vitamins (thiamine, riboflavin, niacin, vitamin B_6, vitamin B_{12}, folate, pantothenic acid, and biotin) are all water-soluble vitamins (Table 8.2). They are found in a wide variety of foods, including whole grains, fruits, vegetables, meats, and dairy products. They are easily absorbed through the intestinal tract directly into the bloodstream, where they then travel to target cells.

With the exception of vitamin B_{12}, we do not store large amounts of water-soluble vitamins. Instead, our kidneys filter from our bloodstream any excess amounts, and they are excreted in urine. Because we do not store large amounts of these vitamins in our tissues, toxicity is rare. When it does occur, however, it is often from overuse of high-potency vitamin supplements. Toxicity can cause nerve damage and skin lesions.

Because most water-soluble vitamins are not stored in large amounts, they need to be consumed on a daily or weekly basis. Deficiency symptoms, including diseases or syndromes, can arise fairly quickly, especially during fetal development and in growing infants and children. The signs of water-soluble vitamin deficiency vary widely and are identified in Table 8.2.

Same Vitamin, Different Names and Forms

Food and supplement labels, magazine articles, and even nutrition textbooks such as this often use simplified alphabetic (A, D, E, K) names for the fat-soluble vitamins. The letters reflect their order of discovery: vitamin A was discovered in 1916, whereas vitamin K was not isolated until 1939. These lay terms, however, are more appropriately viewed as "umbrellas" that unify a small cluster of chemically related compounds. For example, the term *vitamin A* refers to the specific compounds retinol, retinal, and retinoic acid. Similarly, *vitamin E* occurs naturally in eight forms, known as tocopherols, of which the primary form is alpha-tocopherol. Compounds with *vitamin D* activity include cholecalciferol and ergocalciferol, and the *vitamin K* "umbrella" includes phylloquinone and menaquinone. As you can see, most of the individual compounds making up a fat-soluble vitamin cluster have similar chemical designations (tocopherols, calciferols, and so on). Table 8.1 lists both the alphabetic and chemical terms for the fat-soluble vitamins.

Similarly, there are both alphabetic and chemical designations for water-soluble vitamins. In some cases, such as *vitamin C* and *ascorbic acid*, you may be familiar with both terms. But few people would recognize *cobalamin* as designating the same micronutrient as *vitamin B_{12}*. Some of the water-soluble vitamins, such as niacin and vitamin B_6, mimic the "umbrella" clustering seen with vitamins A, E, D, and K: the term *vitamin B_6* includes pyridoxal, pyridoxine, and pyridoxamine. If you read any of these three terms on a supplement label, you'll know it refers to vitamin B_6.

Some vitamins exist in only one form. For example, thiamine is the only chemical compound known as *vitamin B_1*. There are no other related chemical compounds. Table 8.2 lists both the alphabetic and chemical terms for the water-soluble vitamins.

Table 8.2 Water-Soluble Vitamins

Vitamin Name	Primary Functions	Recommended Intake*	Reliable Food Sources	Toxicity/Deficiency Symptoms
Thiamine (vitamin B₁)	Required as enzyme cofactor for carbohydrate and amino acid metabolism	RDA: Men = 1.2 mg/day Women = 1.1 mg/day	Pork, fortified cereals, enriched rice and pasta, peas, tuna, legumes	*Toxicity:* None known *Deficiency:* Beriberi; fatigue, apathy, decreased memory, confusion, irritability, muscle weakness
Riboflavin (vitamin B₂)	Required as enzyme cofactor for carbohydrate and fat metabolism	RDA: Men = 1.3 mg/day Women = 1.1 mg/day	Beef liver, shrimp, milk and dairy foods, fortified cereals, enriched breads and grains	*Toxicity:* None known *Deficiency:* Ariboflavinosis; swollen mouth and throat; seborrheic dermatitis; anemia
Niacin, nicotin-amide, nicotinic acid	Required for carbohydrate and fat metabolism Plays role in DNA replication and repair and cell differentiation	RDA: Men = 16 mg/day Women = 14 mg/day UL = 35 mg/day from supplements of fortified foods only	Beef liver, most cuts of meat/fish/poultry, fortified cereals, enriched breads and grains, canned tomato products	*Toxicity:* Flushing, liver damage, glucose intolerance, blurred vision *Deficiency:* Pellagra (dermatitis, dementia, death); vomiting, constipation, or diarrhea; apathy
Pyridoxine, pyridoxal, pyridoxamine (vitamin B₆)	Required as enzyme cofactor for carbohydrate and amino acid metabolism Assists synthesis of blood cells	RDA: Men and women aged 19 to 50 = 1.3 mg/day Men aged >50 = 1.7 mg/day Women aged >50 = 1.5 mg/day UL = 100 mg/day	Chickpeas (garbanzo beans), most cuts of meat/fish/poultry, fortified cereals, white potatoes	*Toxicity:* Nerve damage, skin lesions *Deficiency:* Anemia; seborrheic dermatitis; depression, confusion, and convulsions
Folate (folic acid)	Required as enzyme cofactor for amino acid metabolism Required for DNA synthesis Involved in metabolism of homocysteine	RDA: Men = 400 µg/day Women = 400 µg/day UL = 1000 µg/day from supplements or fortified foods only	Fortified cereals, enriched breads and grains, spinach, legumes (lentils, chickpeas, pinto beans), greens (spinach, romaine lettuce), liver	*Toxicity:* Masks symptoms of vitamin B₁₂ deficiency, specifically signs of nerve damage *Deficiency:* Macrocytic anemia; neural tube defects in a developing fetus; elevated homocysteine levels
Cobalamin (vitamin B₁₂)	Assists with formation of blood Required for healthy nervous system function Involved as enzyme cofactor in metabolism of homocysteine	RDA: Men = 2.4 µg/day Women = 2.4 µg/day	Shellfish, all cuts of meat/fish/poultry, milk and dairy foods, fortified cereals	*Toxicity:* None known *Deficiency:* Pernicious anemia; tingling and numbness of extremities; nerve damage; memory loss, disorientation, and dementia
Pantothenic acid	Assists with fat metabolism	AI: Men = 5 mg/day Women = 5 mg/day	Meat/fish/poultry, shiitake mushrooms, fortified cereals, egg yolk	*Toxicity:* None known *Deficiency:* Rare
Biotin	Involved as enzyme cofactor in carbohydrate, fat, and protein metabolism	AI: Men = 30 µg/day Women = 30 µg/day	Nuts, egg yolk	*Toxicity:* None known *Deficiency:* Rare
Ascorbic acid (vitamin C)	Antioxidant in extracellular fluid and lungs Regenerates oxidized vitamin E Assists with collagen synthesis Enhances immune function Assists in synthesis of hormones, neurotransmitters, and DNA Enhances iron absorption	RDA: Men = 90 mg/day Women = 75 mg/day Smokers = 35 mg more per day than RDA UL = 2000 mg	Sweet peppers, citrus fruits and juices, broccoli, strawberries, kiwi	*Toxicity:* Nausea and diarrhea, nosebleeds, increased oxidative damage, increased formation of kidney stones in people with kidney disease *Deficiency:* Scurvy; bone pain and fractures, depression, and anemia

*Abbreviations: RDA, Recommended Dietary Allowance; UL, Upper Limit; AI, Adequate Intake.

Vitamins are carbon-containing compounds that regulate a wide range of body processes. Vitamins are classified as being fat soluble or water soluble. Fat-soluble vitamins are readily stored in adipose tissue; thus, we don't need to consume them every day. Water-soluble vitamins are not stored in large amounts and therefore must be consumed daily or weekly.

Plants absorb minerals from soil and water.

How Are Minerals Classified?

Minerals are naturally occurring inorganic (non-carbon-containing) substances such as calcium, iron, and zinc. All minerals are elements; that is, they are already in the simplest chemical form possible and are not digested or broken down prior to absorption. Furthermore, unlike vitamins, they cannot be synthesized in the laboratory or by any plant or animal, including humans. Minerals are the same wherever they are found, whether in soil, a car part, or the human body. The minerals in our foods ultimately come from the environment; for example, the selenium in soil and water is taken up into plants and then incorporated into the animals that eat the plants. Whether humans eat the plant foods directly or eat the animal products, all of the minerals in our food supply originate from Mother Earth!

Major Minerals

Major minerals are those that are required in amounts of at least 100 mg per day. In addition, these minerals are found in the human body in amounts of 5 g (5000 mg) or higher. There are seven major minerals: sodium, potassium, phosphorous, chloride, calcium, magnesium, and sulphur. Table 8.3 summarizes the primary functions, recommended intakes, food sources, and toxicity/deficiency symptoms of these minerals.

Table 8.3 Major Minerals

Mineral Name	Primary Functions	Recommended Intake*	Reliable Food Sources	Toxicity/Deficiency Symptoms
Sodium	Fluid balance Acid–base balance Transmission of nerve impulses Muscle contraction Glucose transport	AI: Adults = 1.5 g/day (1500 mg/day) UL 2300mg/d	Table salt, pickles, most canned soups, snack foods, cured luncheon meats, canned tomato products	*Toxicity:* Water retention, high blood pressure, loss of calcium in urine *Deficiency:* Muscle cramps, dizziness, fatigue, nausea, vomiting, mental confusion
Potassium	Fluid balance Transmission of nerve impulses Muscle contraction	AI: Adults = 4.7 g/day (4700 mg/day)	Most fresh fruits and vegetables: potatoes, bananas, tomato juice, orange juice, melons	*Toxicity:* Muscle weakness, vomiting, irregular heartbeat *Deficiency:* Muscle weakness, paralysis, mental confusion, irregular heartbeat
Phosphorous	Fluid balance Bone formation Component of ATP, which provides energy for our bodies	RDA: Adults = 700 mg/day UL 4g/d UL 19 to 70 = 4000 mg/day >70 = 3000 mg/day	Milk/cheese/yogourt, soy milk and tofu, legumes (lentils, black beans), nuts (almonds, peanuts and peanut butter), poultry	*Toxicity:* Muscle spasms, convulsions, low blood calcium *Deficiency:* Muscle weakness, muscle damage, bone pain, dizziness
Chloride	Fluid balance Transmission of nerve impulses Component of stomach acid (HCl) Antibacterial	AI: Adults = 2.3 g/day (2300 mg/day) 51 to 70 2.0 g/d males and 70+ 1.8g/d females 51 to 70 2.0g/d and 70+ 1.8g/d UL = 3.6 g/d (3600 mg/day)	Table salt	*Toxicity:* None known *Deficiency:* Dangerous blood acid–base imbalances, irregular heartbeat
Calcium	Primary component of bone Acid–base balance Transmission of nerve impulses Muscle contraction	RDA: Women 19 to 70 1000 mg/day Women >70 1200 mg/day Men 19 to 50 1000 mg/day Men >51 1200 mg/day UL 19 to 50 = 2500 mg/day 51 to 70 = 2000 mg/day	Milk/yogourt/cheese (best-absorbed form of calcium), sardines, collard greens and spinach, calcium-fortified juices	*Toxicity:* Mineral imbalances, shock, kidney failure, fatigue, mental confusion *Deficiency:* Osteoporosis, rickets, convulsions, heart failure
Magnesium	Component of bone Muscle contraction Assists more than 300 enzyme systems	RDA: Men aged 19 to 30 = 400 mg/day Men aged >30 = 420 mg/day Women aged 19 to 30 = 310 mg/day Women aged >30 = 320 mg/day UL = 350 mg/day from pharmacological agents only	Greens (spinach, kale, collard greens), whole grains, seeds, nuts, legumes (navy and black beans)	*Toxicity:* None known *Deficiency:* Low blood calcium, muscle spasms or seizures, nausea, weakness, increased risk of chronic diseases such as heart disease, hypertension, osteoporosis, and type 2 diabetes
Sulphur	Component of certain B-vitamins and amino acids Acid–base balance Detoxification in liver	No DRI	Protein-rich foods	*Toxicity:* None known *Deficiency:* None known

*Abbreviations: RDA, Recommended Dietary Allowance; UL, Upper Limit; AI, Adequate Intake; DRI, Dietary Reference Intake.

Trace Minerals

Trace minerals are those we need to consume in amounts of less than 100 mg per day. They are found in the human body in amounts of less than 5 g (5000 mg). Currently, the Dietary Reference Intake (DRI) Committee recognizes eight trace minerals as essential for human health: selenium, fluoride, iodine, chromium, manganese, iron, zinc, and copper.[1] Table 8.4 identifies the primary functions, recommended intakes, food sources, and toxicity/deficiency symptoms of these minerals.

Table 8.4 Trace Minerals

Mineral Name	Primary Functions	Recommended Intake*	Reliable Food Sources	Toxicity/Deficiency Symptoms
Selenium	Required for carbohydrate and fat metabolism	AI: Adults = 55 µg/day UL = 400 µg/day	Nuts, shellfish, meat/fish/poultry, whole grains	*Toxicity:* Brittle hair and nails, skin rashes, nausea and vomiting, weakness, liver disease *Deficiency:* Specific forms of heart disease and arthritis, impaired immune function, muscle pain and wasting, depression, hostility
Fluoride	Development and maintenance of healthy teeth and bones	AI: Men = 4 mg/day Women = 3 mg/day UL = 2.2 mg/day for children aged 4 to 8; 10 mg/day for everyone aged >8	Fish, seafood, legumes, whole grains, drinking water (variable)	*Toxicity:* Fluorosis of teeth and bones *Deficiency:* Dental caries, low bone density
Iodine	Synthesis of thyroid hormones Temperature regulation Reproduction and growth	RDA: Adults = 150 µg/day UL = 1100 µg/day	Iodized salt, saltwater seafood	*Toxicity:* Goiter *Deficiency:* Goiter, hypothyroidism, cretinism in infant of mother who is iodine deficient
Chromium	Glucose transport Metabolism of DNA and RNA Immune function and growth	AI: Men aged 19 to 50 = 35 µg/day Men aged >50 = 30 µg/day Women aged 19 to 50 = 25 µg/day Women aged >50 = 20 µg/day	Whole grains, brewers yeast	*Toxicity:* None known *Deficiency:* Elevated blood glucose and blood lipids, damage to brain and nervous system
Manganese	Assists many enzyme systems Synthesis of protein found in bone and cartilage	AI: Men = 2.3 mg/day Women = 1.8 mg/day UL = 11 mg/day for adults	Whole grains, nuts, leafy vegetables, tea	*Toxicity:* Impairment of neuromuscular system *Deficiency:* Impaired growth and reproductive function, reduced bone density, impaired glucose and lipid metabolism, skin rash
Iron	Component of hemoglobin in blood cells Component of myoglobin in muscle cells Assists many enzyme systems	RDA: Adult men = 8 mg/day Women aged 19 to 50 = 18 mg/day Women aged >50 = 8 mg/day UL 45mg/d	Meat/fish/poultry (best-absorbed form of iron), fortified cereals, legumes, spinach	*Toxicity:* Nausea, vomiting, and diarrhea; dizziness, confusion; rapid heart beat, organ damage, death *Deficiency:* Iron-deficiency microcytic (small red blood cells), hypochromic anemia, delayed psychomotor development in infants, impaired cognitive function
Zinc	Assists more than 100 enzyme systems Immune system function Growth and sexual maturation Gene regulation	RDA: Men = 11 mg/day Women = 8 mg/day UL = 40 mg/day	Meat/fish/poultry (best-absorbed form of zinc), fortified cereals, legumes	*Toxicity:* Nausea, vomiting, and diarrhea; headaches; depressed immune function; reduced absorption of copper *Deficiency:* Growth retardation, delayed sexual maturation, eye and skin lesions, hair loss, increased incidence of illness and infection
Copper	Assists many enzyme systems Iron transport	RDA: Adults = 900 µg/day UL = 10 mg/day	Shellfish, organ meats, nuts, legumes	*Toxicity:* Nausea, vomiting, and diarrhea; liver damage *Deficiency:* Anemia, reduced levels of white blood cells, osteoporosis in infants and growing children

*Abbreviations: RDA, Recommended Dietary Allowance; UL, Upper Limit; AI, Adequate Intake.

Same Mineral, Different Forms

Unlike most vitamins, which can be identified by either alphabetic designations or the more complicated chemical terms, minerals are known by one name only. Iron, calcium, sodium, and all other minerals are simply referred to by their chemical name. That said, minerals do often exist within different chemical compounds; for example, a supplement label might identify calcium as calcium lactate, calcium gluconate, or calcium citrate. As we will discuss shortly, these different chemical compounds, while all containing the same elemental mineral, may differ in their ability to be absorbed by the body.

The iron in foods is chemically identical to that in a wrought iron fence.

Foods high in oxalic acid, such as rhubarb, can decrease zinc and iron absorption.

Recap

Minerals are naturally occurring inorganic substances. Minerals are classified as major, required in amounts of at least 100 mg/day, or trace, needed to be consumed in amounts of less then 100 mg per day. Absorption of minerals depends on their chemical form.

How Do Our Bodies Use Micronutrients?

In Chapter 3, we investigated the truth behind the claim that "You are what you eat." We found out that the body has to change food to use it. This is also true for foods containing vitamins and minerals, because the micronutrients found in foods and supplements are not always in a chemical form that can be used by our cells. This discussion will highlight some of the ways in which our bodies modify the food forms of vitamins and minerals to maximize their absorption and utilization.

What We Eat Differs from What We Absorb

The most healthy diet is of no value to our bodies unless the nutrients can be absorbed and transported to the cells that need them. Unlike carbohydrates, fats, and proteins, which are efficiently absorbed (85%–99% of what is eaten makes it into the blood), some micronutrients are so poorly absorbed that only 3% to 10% of what is eaten ever arrives in the bloodstream. The absorption and utilization of a nutrient is called its bioavailability.

The absorption of many vitamins and minerals depends on their chemical form. Dietary iron, for example, can be in the form of **heme iron** (found only in meats, fish, and poultry) or **non-heme iron** (found in plant and animal foods as well as iron-fortified foods and supplements). Healthy adults absorb about 25% of heme iron but as little as 3% to 5% of non-heme iron.

In addition, the presence of other factors within the same food influences mineral absorption. For example, approximately 30% to 45% of the calcium found in milk and dairy products is absorbed, but the calcium in spinach, Swiss chard, seeds, and nuts is absorbed at a much lower rate because factors in these foods, such as oxalates, bind the calcium and prevent its absorption. Non-heme iron, zinc, vitamin E, and vitamin B$_6$ are other micronutrients whose absorption can be affected by various binding factors in foods.

The absorption of many vitamins and minerals is also influenced by other foods within the meal. For example, the fat-soluble vitamins are much better absorbed when the meal contains some dietary fat. Calcium absorption is increased by the presence of lactose, found in milk, and non-heme iron absorption can be doubled if the meal includes vitamin C–rich foods such as red peppers, oranges, or tomatoes. On the other hand, high-fibre foods such as whole grains and foods high in oxalic acid, such as tea, spinach, and rhubarb, can decrease the absorption of zinc and iron. It may seem an impossible task to correctly balance your food choices to optimize micronutrient absorption, but the best approach, as always, is to eat a variety of healthy foods every day.

heme iron Iron that is part of hemoglobin and myoglobin; found only in animal-based foods such as meat, fish, and poultry.

non-heme iron The form of iron that is not a part of hemoglobin or myoglobin; found in animal- and plant-based foods.

What We Eat Differs from What Our Cells Use

Many vitamins undergo one or more chemical transformations after they are eaten and absorbed into our bodies. For example, before they can go to work for our bodies, the B-complex vitamins must combine with other substances. For thiamine and vitamin B_6, a phosphate group is added. Vitamin D is another example: before cells can use it, the food form of vitamin D must have two hydroxyl ($-OH$) groups added to its structure. These transformations activate the vitamin; because the reactions don't occur randomly, but only when the active vitamin is needed, they help the body maintain control over its metabolic pathways.

While the basic nature of minerals does not, of course, change, they can undergo minor modifications that change their atomic structure. Iron (Fe) may alternate between Fe^{2+} (ferrous) and Fe^{3+} (ferric); copper (Cu) may exist as Cu^{1+} or Cu^{2+}. These are just two examples of how micronutrients can be modified from one form to another to help the body make the best use of dietary nutrients.

RECaP

The absorption of vitamins and minerals depends on their chemical form, the presence of other components in the same food, and the composition of the meal. Many vitamins undergo chemical transformations to activate the vitamin. Minerals can undergo minor modifications that change their atomic structure prior to their use in the body.

Controversies in Micronutrient Metabolism

The science of nutrition continues to evolve, and our current understanding of vitamins and minerals will no doubt change over the next several years or decades. While some people interpret the term *controversy* as negative, nutrition controversies are exciting developments, proof of new information, and a sign of continued growth in the field.

Are Supplements Healthy Sources of Micronutrients?

For millions of years, humans relied solely on natural foodstuffs as their source of nutrients. Only within the past 60 years or so has a second option become available: nutrient supplements, including those added to fortified foods. Are the micronutrients in supplements any better or worse than those in foods? Do our bodies use the nutrients from these two sources any differently? These are issues that nutrition scientists and consumers continue to discuss.

As previously noted, the availability or "usefulness" of micronutrients in foods depends in part on the food itself. The iron and calcium in spinach are poorly absorbed, whereas the iron in beef and the calcium in milk are absorbed efficiently. Because of these and other differences in the availability of micronutrients from different sources, it is difficult to generalize about the usefulness of supplements. Nevertheless, we can say a few things about this issue:

- In general, it is much easier to develop a toxic overload of nutrients from supplements than it is from foods. It is very difficult, if not impossible, to develop a vitamin or mineral toxicity through diet (food) alone.
- Some micronutrients consumed as supplements appear to be harmful to the health of certain subgroups of consumers. Although still controversial, some research has shown that use of high-potency supplements of vitamins A, C, and E may actually increase rates of death.[2] Earlier, it had been shown that high-potency beta-carotene supplements increased death rates among male smokers. Alcoholics are more susceptible to the potentially toxic effects of vitamin A supplements and should avoid their use unless specifically prescribed by a healthcare provider. There is also

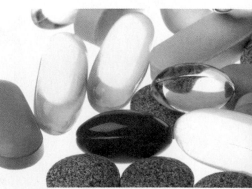

Thousands of supplements are marketed to consumers.

some evidence that a high intake of vitamin A, including supplement use, increases risk of osteoporosis and hip fracture in older adults.[3]

- Most minerals are better absorbed from animal food sources than they are from supplements. The one exception might be calcium citrate-malate, used in calcium-fortified juices. This form is used by the body as effectively as the calcium from milk or yogourt.
- Enriching a low-nutrient food with a few vitamins and/or minerals does not turn it into a healthier food. For example, water that has been fortified with selected micronutrients is still basically water.
- Eating a variety of healthy foods provides you with more nutrients, phytochemicals, and other dietary factors than supplements alone. Scientists are not even sure they have identified all essential nutrients; it is possible that the list of essential micronutrients may, in the future, expand. Supplements provide only those nutrients that the manufacturer puts in; foods provide nutrients that have been identified as well as yet-unknown factors.
- Foods often provide a balance of micronutrients and other factors that work in concert with one another. The whole food is healthier than its isolated individual nutrients, providing benefits not always seen with purified supplements or highly refined, highly enriched food products. As one science reporter recently suggested, "Eat food. Don't eat anything your great-great-grandmother wouldn't recognize as food."[4]
- A healthy diet, built from a wide variety of foods, offers social, emotional, and other benefits that are absent from supplements. Humans eat food, not nutrients.

In certain populations, micronutrient supplements can play an important role in promoting good health. These include pregnant women, children with poor eating habits, and people with certain illnesses. The relative benefits of supplements versus whole foods are discussed further in Chapter 11 (pages 402–405).

Can Micronutrients Really Prevent or Treat Disease?

Dietitians and other healthcare professionals clearly accept the role that dietary fat plays in the prevention and treatment of coronary heart disease. The relationship between total carbohydrate intake and the management of diabetes is also firmly established. Less clear, however, are the links between individual vitamins and minerals and certain chronic diseases.

A number of research studies have suggested, but not proven, links between the following vitamins and disease states. In each case, adequate intake of the nutrient has been associated with lower disease risk.

- Vitamin C and cataracts
- Vitamin D and colon cancer
- Vitamin E and complications of diabetes
- Vitamin K and osteoporosis

Other studies have examined relationships between minerals and chronic diseases. Again, in each case, the nutrient seems to be protective against the disease listed.

- Calcium and high blood pressure (hypertension)
- Chromium and type 2 diabetes in older adults
- Magnesium and muscle wasting (sarcopenia) in older adults
- Selenium and certain types of cancer

As consumers, it is important to critically evaluate any claim that might be made regarding the protective or disease-preventing ability of a specific vitamin or mineral. Supplements that provide megadoses of micronutrients are potentially harmful, and vitamin/mineral therapies should never replace more traditional, proven methods of disease treatment. Current, reputable information can provide updates as the research into micronutrients continues.

Eating a variety of fruits and vegetables provides you with more nutrients, phytochemicals and other dietary factors then supplements alone.

HIGHLIGHT

How Can We Protect Ourselves When Purchasing Supplements over the Internet?

Many supplements are sold today over the Internet. Dancho and Manore suggest six criteria that can be used to evaluate dietary supplement websites.[5] Keep these criteria in mind each time you consider buying a dietary supplement over the web:

1. What is the purpose of the site? Is the website trying to sell a product or educate the consumer? Keep in mind that the primary purpose of supplement companies is to make money. Look for sites that provide educational information about a specific nutrient or product and don't just focus on selling the products.

2. Does the site contain accurate information? Accuracy of the information on the website is the most difficult thing for a consumer to determine. Testimonials (claims by athletes or other famous people) are *not* reliable and accurate; claims supported by scientific research are most desirable. If what the company claims about its product sounds too good to be true, it probably is.

3. Does the site contain reputable references? References should be from articles published in peer-reviewed scientific journals. The reference should be complete and

Always research supplements and supplement manufacturers before purchasing.

contain author names, title of article, journal title, date, volume, and page numbers. This information allows the consumer to check original research for the validity of a company's claims about its product. Be cautious of sites that refer to claims that are "proven by research studies" but fail to provide a complete reference.

4. Who owns or sponsors the site? Full disclosure regarding sponsorship and possible sources of bias or conflict of interest should be included in the site's information.

5. Who wrote the information? Websites should clearly identify the author of the article and include the credentials of the author. Recognized experts include individuals with relevant health-related credentials such as RD, Ph.D., M.D., or M.S. Keep in mind that this person is responsible for the information posted in the article but may not be the creator of the website.

6. Is the information current and updated regularly? As information about supplements changes regularly, websites should be updated regularly, and the date should be clearly posted. All websites should also include contact information to allow consumers to ask questions about the information posted.

Do More Essential Micronutrients Exist?

Nutrition researchers continue to explore the potential of a variety of substances to qualify as essential micronutrients. Vitaminlike factors such as carnitine and trace minerals such as boron, nickel, and silicon seem to have beneficial roles in human health, yet additional information is needed to fully define their metabolic roles. Until more research is done, we cannot classify such substances as essential micronutrients.

Another subject of controversy is the question, "What is the appropriate intake of each micronutrient?" Contemporary research suggests that the answer to this question is to be found in each individual's genetic profile. As you learned in Chapter 1, the science of *nutrigenomics* blends the study of human nutrition with that of genetics. It is becoming clear that some individuals, for example, require much higher intakes of folate to achieve optimal health. Researchers have identified a specific genetic variation in a subset of the population that increases their need for dietary folate.[6] Future studies may identify other examples of how a person's genetic profile influences his or her individual need for vitamins and minerals.

As explained in Chapter 1, the DRI Committees rely on Adequate Intake (AI) guidelines to suggest appropriate nutrient intake levels when research has not clearly defined an Estimated Average Requirement (EAR). As the science of nutrition continues to evolve, the next 50 years will be an exciting time for micronutrient research. Who knows? Within a few decades, we all might have personalized micronutrient prescriptions matched to our gender, age, and DNA!

RECAP

Generally, vitamins and minerals consumed in food are more available, less likely to be consumed in toxic amounts, and are provided in balance with other micronutrients. Consuming food provides us with known micronutrients as well as other compounds that may have beneficial effects on our health.

Apricots contain carotenoids, a type of phytochemical.

Phytochemicals and Functional Foods

Imagine a patient seeing his physician for a minor problem: "sluggish" bowel movements. The physician asks him several questions and performs an exam. At the close of the visit, he hands the patient a prescription: *one apple, two servings of dark-green leafy vegetables, 250 mL yogourt, and 500 mL of green tea daily.* The patient accepts the prescription gratefully, assuring his physician as he says goodbye, "I'll stop at the market on my way home!"

Sound unreal? As researchers provide more and more evidence on the link between nutrition and health, it's possible that scenarios like this might become familiar.

What Are Phytochemicals?

Phyto- means plant, so phytochemicals are literally plant chemicals. These naturally occurring compounds are believed to protect plants from a variety of injurious agents, including insects, microbes, the oxygen they produce, and the UV light they capture and transform into the nutrients we need. Although more than 5000 different phytochemicals have already been identified, researchers believe there are thousands more.[7] Any one food can contain hundreds. **Figure 8.1** on page 285 shows some groups of only a few of the most common.

Phytochemicals are not considered nutrients, that is, substances necessary for sustaining life. Even for carotenoids, a well-studied class of phytochemicals, the Food and Nutrition Board of the Institute of Medicine concluded in 2000 that there was not enough evidence to establish a daily recommended intake.[8] So whereas a total lack of vitamin C or iron is incompatible with life, a total lack of lutein or allylic sulphur compounds is not known to be fatal. On the other hand, eating an abundance of phytochemical-rich foods has been shown to reduce the risk of cardiovascular disease, cancer, diabetes, Alzheimer's disease, cataracts, and age-related functional decline.[7, 9]

The evidence supporting this observation of a reduced disease risk stems mainly from large epidemiologic studies in which people report their usual food intake to researchers who then look for relationships between specific dietary patterns and common diseases. These large studies often find that the reduced disease risk from high intakes of plant foods cannot be attributed solely to differences in intake of macronutrients and micronutrients. This suggests that other compounds in plant foods may be reducing the risk for disease.

As we noted in Chapter 1, epidemiologic studies can only reveal *associations* between general patterns of food intake and health conditions; they cannot prove that a food or dietary pattern directly *causes* a health outcome. To better understand how phytochemicals influence health and disease, researchers have turned to biochemical, cellular, and animal studies.

How Do Phytochemicals Reduce Our Risk of Disease?

For decades, laboratory experiments have shown that, at least in the test tube, many phytochemicals have antioxidant properties. Antioxidants can neutralize free radicals,

Phytochemical	Health Claims	Food Source
Carotenoids: alpha-carotene, beta-carotene, lutein, lycopene, zeaxanthin, etc.	Diets with foods rich in these phytochemicals may reduce the risk of cardiovascular disease, certain cancers (e.g., prostate), and age-related eye diseases (cataracts, macular degeneration).	Red, orange, and deep-green vegetables and fruits such as carrots, cantaloupe, sweet potatoes, apricots, kale, spinach, pumpkin, and tomatoes 
Flavonoids:[1] flavones, flavonols (e.g., quercetin), catechins (e.g., epigallocatechin gallate or EGCG), anthocyanidins, isoflavonoids, etc.	Diets with foods rich in these phytochemicals are associated with lower risk of cardiovascular disease and cancer, possibly because of reduced inflammation, blood clotting, and blood pressure, and increased detoxification of carcinogens or reduction in replication of cancerous cells.	Berries, black and green tea, dark chocolate, purple grapes and juice, citrus fruits, olives, soybeans and soy products (soy milk, tofu, soy flour, textured vegetable protein), flaxseed, whole wheat 
Phenolic acids:[1] ellagic acid, ferulic acid, caffeic acid, curcumin, etc.	Similar benefits as flavonoids.	Coffee beans, fruits (apples, pears, berries, grapes, oranges, prunes, strawberries), potatoes, mustard, oats, soy 
Phytoestrogens:[2] genistein, diadzein, lignans	Foods rich in these phytochemicals may provide benefits to bones and reduce the risk of cardiovascular disease and cancers of reproductive tissues (e.g., breast, prostate).	Soybeans and soy products (soy milk, tofu, soy flour, textured vegetable protein), flaxseed, whole grains 
Organosulphur compounds: allylic sulphur compounds, indoles, isothiocyanates, etc.	Foods rich in these phytochemicals may protect against a wide variety of cancers.	Garlic, leeks, onions, chives, cruciferous vegetables (broccoli, cabbage, cauliflower), horseradish, mustard greens 

[1] Flavonoids, phenolic acids, and stilbenes are three groups of phytochemicals called phenolics. Resveratrol, the phytochemical discussed in the Highlight "Will a PB&J Keep the Doctor Away?" on page 287, is a stilbene. Flavonoids and phenolic acids are the most abundant phenolics in our diet.
[2] Phytoestrogens include phytochemicals that have mild or anti-estrogenic action in our body. They are grouped together based on this similarity in biologic function, but they also can be classified into other phytochemical groups, such as isoflavonoids.

Figure 8.1 Health claims and food sources of phytochemicals.

those unstable, highly reactive compounds that damage proteins, lipids, and DNA in our cells. Free radicals are an unavoidable by-product of normal metabolism, but are also produced in response to X-rays, air pollution, industrial chemicals, tobacco smoke, infections, and even intense exercise.

The health effects of this damage, also known as oxidative damage, typically don't arise until later in life. Many **diseases of aging**, such as cardiovascular disease, cancer, cataracts,

diseases of aging Conditions that typically occur later in life as a result of lifelong accumulated risk, such as exposure to high-fat diets, lack of physical activity, and excess sun exposure.

arthritis, and certain neurologic disorders, have been linked to oxidative damage that accumulates over years. It's no surprise, therefore, that antioxidant-rich foods would reduce the risk of these conditions.

Unfortunately, biology is not fully explained by a few simple chemical reactions. In fact, the latest research evidence on phytochemicals suggests that their health-promoting properties are largely unrelated to the antioxidant activity measured in the test tube.[10, 11] This is in part because phytochemicals can be modified during digestion and also after absorption so that cells are exposed to **metabolites** that are structurally different from the phytochemicals found in foods.[11] Clearly, the test tube cannot explain what is happening inside the body.

Fortunately, researchers have also employed cellular and animal studies, which have revealed that phytochemicals have many health-promoting functions independent of their antioxidant properties. These functions of phytochemicals include the following:

- Reduce inflammation,[12] which is linked to the development of Alzheimer's disease and cardiovascular disease and is symptomatic of arthritis.
- Enhance the activity of certain enzymes throughout the body that function to detoxify carcinogens.[13]
- Protect against cancer by slowing tumour cell growth and instructing cancer cells to die.[13]
- Protect against infections indirectly by enhancing our immune function and directly by acting as antibacterial and antiviral agents.[13]
- Reduce the risk of cardiovascular disease by lowering blood lipids, blood pressure, and blood clotting.[7]

Which of these roles is most important in reducing disease risk is not yet known. Many other issues are also not well understood yet, such as which phytochemicals are needed, in which combinations and how much.

Is There an RDA for Phytochemicals?

Most well-controlled studies in cells, animals, or people typically research only one phytochemical or food. When the results are published, we read about them in the popular press: one day we're advised to eat tomatoes, another day blueberries, then pomegranates. But these findings are only the tip of the iceberg that must be explored before we can make precise recommendations about phytochemicals and health. As scientists begin to "map" more and more phytochemical "icebergs," they're making the following discoveries:

- Phytochemicals interact with each other in the body to produce a synergistic effect that is greater than the sum of the effects of individual phytochemicals.[7] This may explain why whole tomatoes were found to reduce prostate cancer in rats, whereas a phytochemical called lycopene that is present in tomatoes, when given alone, did not.[14]
- Phytochemicals interact with macronutrients and vitamins and minerals. For example, the anticancer effect of garlic is enhanced by vitamin A, selenium, and certain fats.[15]
- Phytochemicals can act in different ways under different circumstances in the body. For example, phytoestrogens in soy appear to reduce the incidence of breast cancer in healthy women, but they may enhance cancer development especially when an estrogen receptor-positive form of breast cancer is already present.[16]

For these reasons, no RDA for phytochemicals can safely be established for any life stage group.

In addition, although epidemiological studies suggest that the more phytochemicals we consume, the better our health, this benefit appears to be limited to phytochemicals found in foods. That is, phytochemicals appear to be protective in the low doses commonly provided by foods, but may have very different effects as supplements. This may be due to their mode of action; scientists now believe that, instead of *protecting* our cells, phytochemicals might benefit our health by *stressing* our cells, causing them to boost their internal

Avoid phytochemical supplements in favour of whole foods.

metabolites The form that nutrients take when they have been used by the body. For example, lactate is a metabolite of carbohydrate that is produced when we use carbohydrate for energy.

defence systems.[10] Cells are very well equipped to deal with minor stresses, but not with excessive stress, which may explain why clinical trials with phytochemical supplements rarely show the same benefits as high intakes of plant foods.[10-17]

So are phytochemical supplements harmful? Generally speaking, taking high doses of anything is risky. A basic principle of toxicology is that any compound can be toxic if the dose is high enough. Dietary supplements are no exception to this rule. For example, clinical trials found that supplementing with 20 to 30 mg/day of beta-carotene for four to six years increased lung cancer risk by 16% to 28% in smokers.[18, 19] Based on these and other results, beta-carotene supplementation is not recommended.[20]

In short, whereas there is ample evidence to support the health benefits of diets rich in fruits, vegetables, legumes, whole grains, and nuts, no recommendation for precise amounts can be given, and phytochemical supplements should be avoided. The best advice for optimal health is to consume a plant-based diet consisting of as many whole foods as possible.

Recap

Phytochemicals are plant compounds that reduce the risk of chronic diseases independent of their antioxidant functions. Phytochemicals appear to interact with macronutrients, micronutrients, and one another; consequently, no RDA for phytochemicals can be established for any life stage group.

HIGHLIGHT

Will a PB&J Keep the Doctor Away?

Whole-grain bread, natural peanut butter, and grape jelly: how could a food that tastes so good be good for the body, too? We've known for decades about some of the healthy nutrients in peanut butter and jelly sandwiches, including the fibre and micronutrients in whole-grain bread and the plant protein, fibre, monounsaturated fat, and minerals in peanuts. But recently, research has revealed that the comforting PB&J also appears to be a good source of resveratrol, a phytochemical that is being studied in labs across the world because of its health-promoting potential.[21, 22]

A flavonoid found in the skins of dark grapes, resveratrol is plentiful both in the raw fruit, in dark grape juice, and in most red wines, which are fermented with the grape skins still in the vat. It is also present to a lesser extent in dark berries such as blueberries and cranberries. But fruits are not the only source: resveratrol just happens to also be plentiful in peanuts, including peanut butter.

But what does resveratrol do, and does a PB&J contain enough of the stuff to make a difference? Researchers have linked resveratrol to protective effects against cancer, heart disease, obesity, viral infections, and neurologic diseases such as Alzheimer's; however, so far, the effects have been demonstrated only in mice. What's more, no one yet knows what an effective "dose" of resveratrol looks like, nor whether the amounts in a peanut butter and jelly sandwich could possibly confer health benefits. More disturbingly, we don't yet know whether high doses, such as those found in supplements, could be harmful. Unfortunately, these facts have not stopped supplements manufacturers from marketing hundreds of different resveratrol supplements to humans.

If you do decide to add resveratrol to your diet, we hope you'll bypass supplements in favour of the humble PB&J. Although the jury is still out on the benefits of its resveratrol content, it still makes a highly nutritious meal or snack, doesn't need refrigeration, is inexpensive, and tastes great.

Grains enriched with iron and B-vitamins are an example of a functional food.

What Are Functional Foods?

Scientists generally define a **functional food** as a food or food component that provides a health benefit beyond basic nutrition. Examples include conventional foods, fortified, enriched, or enhanced foods, and dietary supplements.[23] Functional foods may contain naturally occurring phytochemicals, helpful bacteria required for production of the food, or a level of micronutrients higher than what would be provided by the same food in an unprocessed form.[24]

Most commonly, the health-promoting substances are added to an existing food. For example, iodine is added to salt, grains are enriched with iron and B-vitamins, orange juice is fortified with calcium, or milk is enriched with *extra* calcium and vitamin D. Alternatively, the health-promoting substances are caused to develop in a functional food by altering the way in which the food is produced. For example, eggs with higher levels of omega-3 fatty acids result from feeding chickens a diet rich in this nutrient. Also, tomatoes can be genetically engineered to contain higher levels of phytochemicals. These qualify as functional foods.

Labels are an important source of information for health-promoting foods.

Are Functional Foods Safe?

The Canadian Food Inspection Agency (CFIA), under regulations from Health Canada, is responsible for ensuring that all foods are safe and properly labelled.[23]

According to Health Canada "A functional food is similar in appearance to, or may be, a conventional food, is consumed as part of a usual diet, and is demonstrated to have physiological benefits and/or reduce the risk of chronic disease beyond basic nutritional functions." The type of food and related properties along with the evidence for the claim would determine what, if any, disease risk reduction or function claim it could carry. An example of a functional food would be a margarine containing added phytosterols that help in lowering blood cholesterol.

Functional foods are either foods or natural health products (NHPs), and both are regulated under the Food and Drugs Act (FDA). Products that are considered NHPs are regulated by the FDA as drugs, and by separate legislation called the National Health Products Regulations (NHPR). Products that are considered food are regulated by the FDA as food. A product that is both an NHP and a food would be regulated by the NHPR but not the FDA as it applies to food.[25] Since the NHPRs came into force in 2004, Health Canada has received several hundred product licence applications for products in a food format that carry health claims and have characteristics of both foods and natural health products. Examples include energy drinks, protein supplements, and nutritional supplements. The FDA requires that all health claims be truthful and not misleading or deceptive. Claims such as disease risk reduction or therapeutic claims are only allowed once a regulatory amendment specifying the conditions for their use has been completed.[23] See Chapter 2 for examples of disease risk reduction claims allowed in Canada.

Did You Know?

Canada produces many ingredients that are used in functional foods, for example, soluble fibre from oats, barley, and pulses; omega-3 fatty acids from fish and flax oil; unsaturated fatty acids from canola oil; plant sterols and stanols from vegetable oils; and protein from soy.

functional food A food that provides a health benefit beyond basic nutrition.

Are Functional Foods Effective?

Is there any research to support the claims of health benefits made by manufacturers of functional foods? That depends on the product. So if you're considering regular consumption of a functional food, do your homework. To give you some practice, let's consider a few currently on the market.

Designer Yogourts

People have been consuming yogourt and other fermented milk products for thousands of years. But interest in their health benefits began only about 100 years ago, when a Russian microbiologist named Ilya Metchnikov linked the long, healthy lives of Bulgarian peasants with their consumption of such foods. Subsequent research identified bacteria in fermented milk products as responsible for their healthy effects, and the probiotics industry was born.

Probiotics means "pro-life." Probiotics are live microorganisms found in, or added to, fermented dairy foods such as yogourt, buttermilk, sour cream, and kefir (a yogourt-style liquid beverage) and fermented vegetable foods such as sauerkraut, miso, and tempeh (fermented tofu). Probiotics are also available in supplement form.

Fermented foods such as tempeh contain probiotics.

Our intestines contain an amazing number and variety of bacteria and other microorganisms. Many of these are vital to maintaining our health and supporting digestive function, but some can be harmful. The correct balance between beneficial and harmful microbes can be disturbed by medications and illness. The main symptoms of an unbalanced microbial environment are digestive, such as diarrhea or constipation, but other conditions may also be related to unbalanced intestinal bacteria.

How do probiotics work? When a person consumes a product containing probiotics, these bacteria adhere to the intestinal wall for a few days. Once attached to the intestinal wall, the bacteria can exert their beneficial actions. The activity of these bacteria is short lived, and they probably need to be consumed on a daily basis to benefit human health. The exact mechanism of how probiotics work is currently being researched. It is believed that different types of bacteria provide benefits in different ways; some crowd out harmful bacterial, viral, and fungal species; some produce nutrients and other substances that influence nutrition and health; and others appear to influence our immune system.[26] Although there is still limited research on whether probiotics can really improve immune function and overall health in humans, there is promising evidence that probiotics may be beneficial in the following conditions:[26–28]

- Diarrhea caused by certain infectious microorganisms (rotavirus, *Clostridium difficile*, and so on) or associated with use of antibiotic medications
- Infections in infants and children in day care
- Irritable bowel syndrome and inflammatory bowel diseases
- Infection from *Helicobacter pylori*, the bacteria associated with peptic ulcers, gastritis, and gastric cancer
- Urinary and genital tract infections in women
- Atopic dermatitis (eczema) in children
- Lactose intolerance
- Reducing the risk of allergies in infants

It is important to remember that to be effective, foods must provide a minimum number of bacteria. While the exact number of bacteria is not known, it is estimated that a daily dose of at least 1 billion to 10 billion bacteria is needed to be effective.[29] Because these live cultures can survive only for a limited period of time, foods and supplements containing probiotics have a limited shelf life, and these products must be properly stored and consumed within a relatively brief period of time to receive maximal benefit.

probiotics Live beneficial microorganisms in foods that can colonize the intestine and optimize the intestinal bacterial environment. There is promising research suggesting various health benefits from consuming probiotics.

Consuming yogourt with probiotics may improve bowel function.

It is unclear whether eggs enriched with omega-3s are better for us, but there's no question that they are more expensive.

prebiotics Fibres that are preferentially fermented by the beneficial lactobacilli and bifidobacteria in gut flora and thus encourage their growth.

At this time, there are no national standards for identifying the level of active bacteria in foods or supplements in Canada.

Prebiotics are food components related to probiotics. These are types of fibre naturally found in fruits, vegetables, and whole grains that promote the growth of friendly bacteria. Inulin and oligofructose are the most widely studied. Prebiotics can be added to functional foods, typically to those that contain probiotics or high fibre cereals and bars, such as granola bars.

Some food manufacturers are employing researchers to find and cultivate strains of probiotic bacteria that have specific health benefits. For example, Activia, a yogourt recently introduced by Danone, contains a probiotic species called *Bifidus regularis.* The company states that this species promotes regular bowel movements by reducing the time stool stays in the colon. As you learned in Chapter 3, the longer fecal matter remains in the colon, the more water is removed from it, so reduced transit time means softer bowel movements. Is this claim valid?

If you check out the research cited on Danone's website (www.activia.ca), you'll discover that five studies on Activia and *Bifidus regularis* have been published in peer-reviewed journals. The studies found that consuming three 125 mL servings of Activia a day for 10 to 14 days sped up stool transit time by 10% to 40%. This effect was seen in men and women, and in both young (mid-20s) and older (up to 75 years) subjects. Although benefits were seen with just one 125 mL serving a day, the biggest benefits were seen with two or three daily servings. Convinced? If constipation were a problem for you, what further questions might you want to ask to determine whether or not this product would be worth purchasing?

Extraordinary Eggs

In Chapter 1, you learned that the diet fed to agouti mice could influence the constitution of their offspring. Similarly, the diet fed to hens can influence the nutrients present in their eggs. Feeding chickens a diet rich in omega-3 fatty acids, vitamin E, or lutein results in eggs that contain these substances. Such eggs can cost twice as much per dozen as conventional eggs. Are they worth the cost?

As you learned in Chapter 5, increased intake of omega-3 fatty acids may be important in reducing the risk of cardiovascular disease.[30–32] Typically, the positive effects are seen in clinical trials with a precisely controlled high omega-3 intake. Would the level of omega-3s in these eggs confer health benefits? We simply don't have the research to answer this question. Nevertheless, small doses of omega-3s via foods can certainly add up.

What about vitamin E? We know that diets with plenty of vitamin E–rich foods (nuts and dark-green leafy vegetables) are associated with better health, but research on vitamin E supplements has found no benefits at all and may actually be harmful.[10, 33] Thus, there is no evidence to support recommending vitamin E–enriched eggs for disease prevention.

Lutein is a phytochemical found in many green and yellow plants. Lutein and zeaxanthin are the only carotenoids found in the retina and lens of the eye. Epidemiological studies suggest that diets rich in lutein and zeaxanthin (providing about 6 mg/day) may help slow the development of age-related macular degeneration. However, it is not known whether consuming eggs with lutein has the same effect.[11]

Extra Dark Chocolate

You've just finished lunch when a friend offers you a piece of her extra dark chocolate bar. Should you, or shouldn't you? Recently, the results from a number of laboratory and clinical studies have suggested you *should*. Here's why.

Certain fruits, vegetables, tea, and red wine have long been associated with lower cardiovascular disease (CVD) risk. These foods are especially rich in a class of antioxidant phytochemicals called flavonoids. Cocoa has been found to have greater amounts of flavonoids per serving than teas and red wines, as well as many fruits and vegetables.[34] The darker the chocolate, the more flavonoids per serving. Thus, research interest in the potential effects of chocolate—especially dark chocolate—on CVD risk has grown.

Dozens of human feeding trials have been conducted since 2000. Most have shown that daily doses of cocoa have positive effects on one or more CVD risk factors, including improvements in blood lipids and blood pressure.[34] Several studies have shown benefits from consuming as little as 30 calories of dark chocolate daily.[35] In response, some chocolate manufacturers have produced specialty brands of "extra dark chocolate" with increased amounts of "antioxidant-rich cocoa."

So what's the hitch? One is that not all studies show the same effects. The variability in response is likely due to differences in the subjects' health and age and in the dose they consumed. And we can't ignore the fact that chocolate contains sugar and fat. Some studies have fed subjects about 100 grams of chocolate per day, which can deliver over 400 extra calories to the diet!

Which raises a question that chocolate lovers would probably prefer to ignore: to reduce our risk of CVD, do we need to eat chocolate at all? Why not apples, for example, which contain 50% more flavonoids than a comparable serving of dark chocolate, only about 60 calories each, and no fat?[34]

For now, it seems likely that cocoa has positive health effects mediated by phytochemicals. So when debating whether or not to indulge in a small dose of extra dark chocolate, consider your diet as a whole: do you consume a wide variety of unrefined plant foods each day? If you do, then a little chocolate might be a sensible indulgence.

Dark chocolate is high in flavonoids.

resveratrol A potent phenolic antioxidant found in red wines as well as grapes and nuts.

HIGHLIGHT

Benefits of Moderate Alcohol Intake

Those who choose to drink alcoholic beverages should do so in moderation—defined as the consumption of no more than two drinks per day most days and a maximum of 10 drinks per week for women and no more than three drinks a day most days and 15 drinks per week for men.

In most people, moderate alcohol intake offers some psychological benefits; it can reduce stress and anxiety while improving self-confidence. It can also have nutritional benefits: in the elderly, moderate use of alcohol can improve appetite and dietary intake.

In addition, moderate consumption of certain types of alcohol has been linked to lower rates of heart disease, especially in older adults and those already at risk for heart disease. Certain types of alcohol may increase levels of the "good" type of cholesterol (HDL) while lowering the concentration of "bad" cholesterol (LDL); it also reduces the risk of abnormal clot formation in the blood vessels. Recently, there has been a lot of interest in **resveratrol,** a phytochemical found in red wines and foods such as grapes and nuts.[36] Some researchers, based on experiments with mice, are proposing that resveratrol may be able to lower our risk for certain chronic diseases such as diabetes, heart disease, and liver disease. However, if resveratrol is found to be effective in promoting human health, the amount needed would be so high that it would have to be given as a purified supplement, not in the form of red wine.

What does one drink look like? A drink is equivalent to 45 mL of distilled spirits, 120 to 150 mL of wine, 300 mL of wine cooler, or 350 mL of beer.

For additional information what constitutes moderate alcohol intake in Canada see www.ccsa.ca/Eng/Priorities/Alcohol/Canada-Low-Risk-Alcohol-Drinking-Guidelines/Pages/default.aspx

Enviga claims to burn extra calories.

Calorie-Burning Beverages

Enviga is one of several so-called "calorie-burning beverages" brought onto the market in the United States. The manufacturers of these beverages claimed that they increased the consumer's metabolic rate, caused the body to burn additional calories, and that the effect lasted for several hours after consuming the beverage. Claims by the company state that a clinical trial it funded found that, on average, participants expended 106 more calories per day after consuming three servings of Enviga for three days. The study was conducted in 2004 and has now been published in a peer-reviewed journal.[37] Although the Enviga study has not been repeated, allowing it to be reviewed suggests it is sound.

Why, then, did the Center for Science in the Public Interest (CSPI), a consumer advocacy group, contend in a lawsuit that the claims made for Enviga are fraudulent?[38] Here are some of the claims challenged by the CSPI: Enviga is "much smarter than fads, quick-fixes, and crash diets." It keeps "those extra calories from building up," and there is a "calorie burning effect from a single can." The CSPI challenged these claims because not one of them was substantiated by the clinical trial.

Is a product like Enviga safe? Enviga contains caffeine and *epigallocatechin gallate* (*EGCG*), a phytochemical that occurs in green tea. No negative effects have been seen with EGCG. The ingredient of concern is caffeine. Three cans of Enviga provide 300 mg of caffeine, which is the caffeine equivalent of nine cans of Coke. This level of caffeine intake is generally not recommended.[39] (Caffeine is discussed in more detail in Chapter 15.)

Is Enviga worth the cost? The company claimed that three cans would boost one's metabolism by 60 to 100 calories per day. At an average cost of about $1.39 per 375 mL can, drinking the effective dose of Enviga would cost about $130 a month! In comparison, you could brew coffee containing the same amount of caffeine for less than $10 a month. Even better, you could burn more calories free of charge by running 1.5 km a day (about 106 calories for a 60 kg-pound person), and you'd get all of the other health benefits of exercise to boot! With sales of Enviga flagging in mid-2010, the company responsible for the product decided to remove it from the U.S. market.

Are You Ready to Choose Functional Foods?

As these examples show, when it comes to functional foods, "Let the buyer beware." If you're considering specific products, do you know enough about their safety and effectiveness to feel confident adding them to your daily diet? Do you support the introduction of foods like Enviga in Canada? How do you think food labels could be improved to assist you in identifying foods that might be beneficial for your specific health concerns? As the number of functional foods increases in the Canadian market, these are just some of the questions that consumers need to answer.

RECAP

Functional foods are foods that provide a health benefit beyond basic nutrition. Usually the health-promoting substances are added to the food, though they may be induced in the food through altered production or genetic engineering. In Canada, functional foods are regulated by Health Canada through the Food and Drugs Act (FDA) and Natural Health Products Regulations (NHPR). The FDA requires that all health claims be truthful and not misleading or deceptive. It is important for consumers to become informed about the safety and efficacy of functional foods before choosing to include them in their diet.

CASE STUDY Choosing Functional Foods

Chen was recently diagnosed with high blood cholesterol. His sister suggested that he should try eating this new type of healthy egg that she saw advertised on the internet. She said that the farmer feeds the hens some kind of seed that contains oil that's good for heart health, and that some of the fatty acids from the oil get into the eggs the hens lay.

Chen asked about the cost of the healthy eggs and found that they were more than twice the cost of regular eggs. He searched the internet and found this Nutrition Facts table for the healthy eggs:

Nutrition Facts Valeur nutritive Per 1 large egg (53 g) / pour 1 gros ceuf (53 g)		
Amount **Teneur**	**% Daily Value** **% valeur quotidienne**	
Calories / Calories 70		
Fat / Lipides 5 g	**8** %	
Saturated / saturés 1.5 g		
+ trans / trans 0 g	**8** %	
Cholesterol / Cholestérol 195 mg		
Sodium / Sodium 65 mg	**3** %	
Carbohydrate / Glucides 1 g	**1** %	
Fibre / Fibres 0 g	**0** %	
Sugars / Sucres 0 g		
Protein / Protéines 6 g		
Vitamin A / Vitamine A	10 %	
Vitamin C / Vitamine C	0 %	
Calcium / Calcium	2 %	
Iron / Fer	6 %	

Thinking Critically

1. What type of seeds do you think were added to the healthy eggs?
2. Do you think that the higher price is a reasonable cost for a functional food? Why or why not?
3. Examine the label for the healthy egg. How does the amount of omega-3 fatty acids compare to the DRI recommendation? What about the amount of omega-6 fatty acids?
4. Should Chen switch from his regular eggs to the new functional food eggs? Why or why not?
5. What else could Chen do to reduce his risk of heart disease?

SEE FOR YOURSELF

Is There a Place for Functional Foods in a Healthy Diet?

Go to your local grocery store and compile a list of ten examples of functional foods. Record the name of the food, the health-promoting substance, the purported health benefit, and the cost of the food. For each item, note whether you found the claim convincing enough to persuade you that the item would be part of a healthy diet.

Chapter Review

8

Test Yourself | Answers

1. **T** Taking megadoses of Vitamin A or D can result in irreversible organ damage and even death.

2. **T** Absorption of calcium, non-heme iron, zinc, vitamin E, and vitamin B_6 can be reduced by various binding factors in food. Conversely, some foods can increase absorption; for example, dietary fat can enhance absorption of vitamins A, D, E, and K.

3. **F** It is much easier to develop a toxic overload of nutrients from supplements than it is from food. Certain micronutrients in supplement form can increase risk of death for some populations.

4. **F** Phytochemicals appear to be protective in the low doses provided by foods, but may have different effects as supplements.

5. **T** The activity of probiotics is short lived, and they likely need to be consumed daily to benefit human health.

Summary

- Micronutrients, which include vitamins and minerals, are needed in small amounts. They assist body functions such as energy metabolism and the formation and maintenance of healthy cells and tissues.

- Much of our knowledge about vitamins and minerals comes from accidental observation of animals and humans. In the 1890s, C. Eijkman discovered that thiamine prevents beriberi in hospitalized patients fed polished rice.

- In the 1900s vitamin A was found to prevent blindness in Japanese children who didn't consume fish.

- Vitamins are carbon-containing compounds that regulate a wide range of body processes. Vitamins are classified as being fat soluble or water soluble.

- Fat-soluble vitamins are readily stored in adipose tissue; thus we don't need to consume them every day.

- Water-soluble vitamins are not stored in large amounts and therefore must be consumed daily or weekly.

- Minerals are naturally occurring inorganic substances. Minerals are classified as major, requiring amounts of at least 100 mg/day, or trace, needing to be consumed in amounts of less then 100 mg per day.

- The absorption of vitamins and minerals depends on their chemical form, the presence of other components in the same food, and the composition of the meal.

- Many vitamins undergo chemical transformations to activate the vitamin. Minerals can undergo minor modifications that change their atomic structure prior to their use in the body.

- Generally, vitamins and minerals consumed in food are more available, less likely to be consumed in toxic amounts, and are provided in balance with other micronutrients.

- A number of research studies have suggested a link between some vitamins (e.g., vitamin C, D, E, and K) and minerals (e.g., Ca, Cr, Mg, and Se) and the risk of chronic disease.

- Eating food provides us with known micronutrients, as well as other compounds that may have beneficial effects on our health. The composition of a supplement is based on our knowledge of current compounds.

- Phytochemicals are plant compounds that have either positive or negative effects on health. Many phytochemicals have the potential to reduce the risk of chronic diseases independent of their antioxidant functions. Phytochemicals appear to interact with macronutrients, micronutrients, and one another.

- Evidence exists for a health-promoting role for carotenoids, flavonoids, phenolic acids, phytoestogens, and organosulphur compounds.

- At present there is insufficient scientific evidence to set RDAs, AIs, or ULs for phytochemcials.

- Functional foods are foods that provide a health benefit beyond basic nutrition. Usually the health promoting substances are added to the food, though they may be induced in the food through altered production or genetic engineering.
- In Canada, functional foods are regulated by Health Canada through the Food and Drugs Act (FDA) and Natural Health Products Regulations (NHPR). The FDA requires that all health claims be truthful and not misleading or deceptive.
- It is important for consumers to become informed about the safety and efficacy of functional foods before choosing to include them in their diet.
- Designer yogurts, omega-3 fortified eggs, and dark chocolate are examples of functional foods available in Canada.

Review Questions

1. Overconsumption of _____ has the greatest potential for toxicity.
   a. thiamine
   b. riboflavin
   c. vitamin B$_{12}$
   d. vitamin A

2. A number of research studies suggest that calcium may be protective against which chronic disease?
   a. diabetes
   b. hypertension
   c. breast cancer
   d. cataracts

3. Which of the following vitamins has an RDA?
   a. biotin
   b. choline
   c. vitamin K
   d. pantothenic acid

4. Diets rich in these phytochemicals may reduce the risk of age-related eye diseases.
   a. lutein
   b. quercetin
   c. lignan
   d. isothiocyanates

5. It has been suggested that probiotics can
   a. increase infections in infants and children.
   b. promote flare up of inflammatory bowel disease.
   c. reduce the risk of allergies in infants.
   d. All of the above.

6. Discuss the factors that influence vitamin and mineral absorption.

7. Do you consider Canada's regulations around natural health products too restrictive? Why or why not?

8. Numerous studies have linked phytochemicals to the prevention of chronic diseases such as cancer; however, no DRIs have been established for any of these compounds. Explain.

9. Your roommate Amy doesn't like to cook; each evening she eats cereal and milk for supper. Her favourite cereal provides 100% of the DV of 15 different vitamins and minerals, so Amy feels that it really doesn't matter what else she eats throughout the day. Do you agree with Amy's assessment of her diet?

10. Functional foods are being touted for their ability to naturally promote health and reduce the potential of disease. What advice would you give to a friend who asks whether she should be eating probiotic yogourt?

Web Links

www.hc-sc.gc.ca/dhp-mps/prodnatur/index-eng.php
Health Canada—Natural Health Products
This Health Canada site contains information on natural health products.

www.hc-sc.gc.ca/fn-an/legislation/acts-lois/act-loi_reg-eng.php
Health Canada—Food and Drugs Act
Explore the regulations that govern the sale of foods in Canada.

www.rcffn.ca/home
Richardson Centre for Functional Foods and Nutraceuticals
Visit this site to find up-to-date and accurate information on functional foods.

MasteringNutrition®
www.masteringnutrition.pearson.com
Study Area
Practice Tests • Diet Analysis • eText

References

1. Institute of Medicine, Food and Nutrition Board. 2001. *Dietary Reference Intakes for Vitamin A, Vitamin K, Arsenic, Boron, Chromium, Copper, Iodine, Iron, Manganese, Molybdenum, Nickel, Silicon, Vanadium, and Zinc.* Washington, DC: National Academy Press.

2. Bjelakovic, G., D. Nikolova, L. L. Gluud, R. G. Simonetti, and C. Gluud. 2007. Mortality in randomized trials of antioxidant supplements for primary and secondary prevention. *J. Am. Med. Assoc.* 297:842–857.

3. Penniston, K. L., and S. A. Tanumihardjo. 2006. The acute and chronic toxic effects of vitamin A. *Am. J. Clin. Nutr.* 83:191–201.

4. Pollan, M. 2007. The age of nutritionism. *The New York Times Magazine,* January 28.

5. Dancho, C., and M. M. Manore. 2001. Dietary supplement information on the World Wide Web. Sorting fact from fiction. *ACSM's Health and Fitness Journal* 5:7–12.

6. Stover, P. J. 2006. Influence of human genetic variation on nutritional requirements. *Am. J. Clin. Nutr.* 83:436S–443S.

7. Liu, R. H. 2003. Health benefits of fruit and vegetables are from additive and synergistic combinations of phytochemicals. *Am. J. Clin. Nutr.* 78(suppl.):517S–520S.

8. Panel on Dietary Antioxidants and Related Compounds. Subcommittee on Upper Reference Levels of Nutrients and Interpretation and Uses of Dietary Reference Intakes. Standing Committee on the Scientific Evaluation of Dietary Reference Intakes. Food and Nutrition Board. Institute of Medicine. 2000. *Dietary Reference Intakes for Vitamin C, Vitamin E, Selenium, and Carotenoids.* Washington, DC: National Academies Press.

9. Chun, O. K., et al. 2007. Estimated dietary flavonoid intake and major food sources of US adults. *J. Nutr.* 137:1244–1252.

10. Melton, L. 2006. The antioxidant myth: a medical fairy tale. *New Sci.* 2563:40–43.

11. Linus Pauling Institute, Oregon State University. 2005. Micronutrient information center: flavonoids. Available at http://lpi.oregonstate.edu/infocenter/phytochemicals/flavonoids/ (accessed July 2007.)

12. Beauchamp, G. K., R. S. Keast, D. Morel, J. Lin, J. Pika, Q. Han, C. H. Lee, A. B. Smith, and P. A. Breslin. 2005. Ibuprofen-like activity in extra virgin olive oil. *Nature* 437:45–46.

13. Liu, R. H. 2004. Potential synergy of phytochemicals in cancer prevention: mechanism of action. *J. Nutr.* 134:3479S–3485S.

14. Boileau, T. W.-M., et al. 2003. Prostate carcinogenesis in N-methyl-N-nitrosurea (NMU)-testosterone-treated rats fed tomato powder, lycopene, and energy-restricted diets. *J. Natl. Cancer Inst.* 95:1578–1586.

15. Milner, J. A. 2001. A historical perspective on garlic and cancer. *J. Nutr.* 131:1027S–1031S.

16. Rice S., and S. A. Whitehead. 2006. Phytoestrogens and breast cancer—promoters or protectors? *Endocr. Relat. Cancer* 13(4):995–1015.

17. Meyskens, F. L., and E. Szabo. 2005. Diet and cancer: the disconnect between epidemiology and randomized clinical trials. *Cancer Epidemiol. Biomarkers Prev.* 14(6):1366–1369.

18. The Alpha-Tocopherol, Beta-Carotene Cancer Prevention Study Group. 1994. The effect of vitamin E and beta carotene on the incidence of lung cancer and other cancers in male smokers. *N. Engl. J. Med.* 330(15):1029–1035.

19. Omenn, G. S., et al. 1996. Risk factors for lung cancer and for intervention effects in CARET, the Beta-Carotene and Retinol Efficacy Trial. *J. Natl. Cancer Inst.* 88(21):1550–1559.

20. U.S. Preventive Services Task Force. 2003. Routine vitamin supplementation to prevent cancer and cardiovascular disease: recommendations and rationale. *Ann. Intern. Med.* 139(1):51–55.

21. Baur, J. A., et al. 2006. Resveratrol improves health and survival of mice on a high-calorie diet. *Nature* 444:337–342.

22. Lagouge, M., et al. 2006. Resveratrol improves mitochondrial function and protects against metabolic disease by activating SIRT1 and PGC-1alpha. *Cell* 27(6):1109–1122.

23. Health Canada. 2002. Nutraceuticals/Functional Foods and Health Claims on Foods. Available at www.hc-sc.gc.ca/fn-an/label-etiquet/claims-reclam/nutra-funct_foods-nutra-fonct_aliment-eng.php (accessed March 10, 2011).

24. Committee on Opportunities in the Nutrition and Food Sciences, Food and Nutrition Board, Institute of Medicine, Thomas, P. R., and R. Earl (eds.). 1994. *Opportunities in the Nutrition and Food Sciences: Research, Challenges and the Next Generation of Investigators.* Washington, DC: National Academies Press.

25. Health Canada. 2010. Classification of Products at the Food—Natural Health Product Interface: Products in Food Format. Available at www.hc-sc.gc.ca/dhp-mps/alt_formats/hpfb-dgpsa/pdf/prodnatur/food-nhp-aliments-psn-guide-eng.pdf (accessed March 14, 2011).

26. Saier, M. H., Jr., and N. M. Mansour. 2005. Probiotics and prebiotics in human health. *J. Mol. Microbiol. Biotechnol.* 10(1):22–25.

27. Doron, S., and S. L. Gorbach. 2006. Probiotics: their role in the treatment and prevention of diseases. *Expert Rev. Anti-Infect. Ther.* 4(2):261–275.

28. Ezendam, J., and H. van Loveren. 2006. Probiotics: immunomodulation and evaluation of safety and efficacy. *Nutr. Rev.* 64(1):1–14.

29. Sanders, M. E., D. C. Walker, K. M. Walker, K. Aoyama, and T. R. Klaenhammer. 1996. Performance of commercial cultures in fluid milk applications. *J. Dairy Sci.* 79:943–955.

30. American Heart Association. 2007. Fish and omega-3 fatty acids: AHA recommendation. Available at www.americanheart.org/presenter.jhtml?identifier=4632 (accessed July 2007.)

31. Center for Food Safety and Applied Nutrition. 2004. Questions and answers: qualified health claims for omega-3 fatty acids, eicosapentaenoic acid (EPA) and docosahexaenoic acid (DHA). CFSAN/Office of Nutritional Products, Labeling, and Dietary Supplements. Available at www.cfsan.fda.gov/~dms/labo3qa.html (accessed July 2007.)

32. National Heart, Lung, and Blood Institute, NIH, DHHS. 2005. Your guide to lowering cholesterol with therapeutic lifestyle changes (TLC). Available at www.nhlbi.nih.gov/health/public/heart/chol/chol_tlc.pdf (accessed July 2007.)

33. Friedrich, M. J. 2004. To "E" or not to "E," vitamin E's role in health and disease is the question. *JAMA* 292(6):671–673.

34. Ding, E. L., S. M. Hutfless, X. Ding, and S. Girotra. 2006. Chocolate and prevention of cardiovascular disease: a systematic review. *Nutr. Metab.* 3:2. Available at www.nutritionandmetabolism.com/content/3/1/2.

35. Taubert, D., et al. 2007. Effects of low habitual cocoa intake on blood pressure and bioactive nitric oxide: a randomized controlled trial. *JAMA* 298(1):49–60.

36. Wu, J. M, T-C Hseieh, and Z. Wang. 2011. Cardioprotection by resveratrol: a review of effects/targets in cultured cells and animal tissues. *Am. J. Cardiovasc. Dis.* 1:38–47.

37. Rudelle, S., et al. 2007. Effect of a thermogenic beverage on 24-hour energy metabolism in humans. *Obesity* 15(2):349–355.

38. Center for Science in the Public Interest. 2006. "Calorie burning" Enviga tea drink a fraud, group says. CSPI to sue Coke, Nestlé if weight loss claims persist. Press release: December 4, 2006. Available at www.cspinet.org/new/200612041.html (accessed July 2007.)

39. McGee, W. 2005. Caffeine in the diet. Medline Plus Medical Encyclopedia. Available at www.nlm.nih.gov/medlineplus/ency/article/002445.htm (accessed July 2007.)

40. Seeram, N. P., S. N. Henning, Y. Niu, R. Lee, H. S. Scheuller, and D. Herber. 2006. Catechin and caffeine content of green tea dietary supplements and correlation with antioxidant capacity. *J. Agric. Food Chem.* 80:1558–1564.

41. Jian, L, L. P. Xie, A. H. Lee, and C. W. Binns. 2004. Protective effect of green tea against prostate cancer: a case-control study in Southeast China. *Int. J. Cancer* 108:130–135.

42. Bettuzi, S., M. Brausi, R. Rizzi, G. Castagnetti, G. Peracchia, and A. Corti. 2006. Chemoprevention of human prostate cancer by oral administration of green tea catechins in volunteers with high-grade prostate intra-epithelial neoplasia: a preliminary report from a one-year proof-of-principle study. *Cancer Res.* 66:1234–1240.

43. Zhang, M., C. D'Arcy, J. Holman, J. P. Huang, and X. Xie. 2007. Green tea and the prevention of breast cancer: a case-control study in Southeast China. *Carcinogenesis* 28:1074–1078.

44. Sano, J., S. Inami, K. Seimiya, T. Ohba, S. Sakai, and T. Takano. 2004. Effects of green tea intake on the development of coronary artery disease. *Circ. J.* 68:665–670.

45. Yang, Y. C., F. H. Lu, J. S. Wu, C. H. Wu, and C. J. Chang. 2004. The protective effect of habitual tea consumption on hypertension. *Arch. Intern. Med.* 164:1534–1540.

46. Zheng, X-X, Y-L Xu, S-H Li, X-X Liu, R. Hui, and X-H Huang. 2011. Green tea intake lowers fasting serum total and LDL cholesterol in adults: a meta-analysis of 14 randomized controlled trials. *Am. J. Clin. Nutr.* 94:601–610.

47. Kao, Y. H., H. H. Chang, M. J. Lee, and C. L. Chen. 2006. Tea, obesity, and diabetes. *Mol. Nutr. Food Res.* 50:188–210.

Is Green Tea a Miracle Beverage?

Green tea comes from the plant *Camellia sinensis*. Unlike black tea, green tea has not undergone fermentation. Green tea contains numerous polyphenols: epigallocatechin gallate (EGCG), epicatechin gallate (ECG), and epicatechin (EC). Together, these make up approximately 30% of the weight of tea leaves.[40] EGCG is the primary catechin in green tea and is considered to be the main component responsible for its biological effects.

Regular green tea consumption has been suggested to have a number of health benefits, such as lowering the risk of developing some forms of cancer, cardiovascular disease, and type 2 diabetes. What evidence is there to support these claims?

Cancer

Case-control and cohort studies conducted primarily in Japan and China suggest that regular intake of green tea is associated with a decreased risk of developing prostate and breast cancer.[41–43]

Results of research using *in vitro* and animal models of prostate cancer are also promising; however, it is difficult to extrapolate these results into recommendations for human consumption. There are very few clinical studies examining prostate or breast cancer in human subjects, and those that have been published use variable forms of green tea or extracts as well as differing doses. The majority of epidemiological studies conducted in

North America examining the relationship between tea intake and risk of prostate and breast cancer produced mixed results and often don't differentiate between green and black tea. In one study, consumption of 200 mg of green tea catechin capsules for one year was associated with a lower incidence of cancer among men with pre-malignant lesions of the prostate.[42] Currently, there is insufficient evidence to conclude that green tea will protect against breast cancer.[43]

Cardiovascular Disease

Research examining the role of green tea in preventing cardiovascular disease suffers from many of the same limitations as described above. Epidemiological research suggests that the consumption of at least 750 mL of tea per day is associated with a small decrease in the risk of heart attack and hypertension.[44, 45] There is now consistent data indicating that tea and tea flavonoids can enhance nitric oxide status and improve endothelial function, which may be at least partly responsible for benefits on cardiovascular health.[46] However, clinical research is lacking and additional studies are needed before any concrete recommendations can be made.

Type 2 Diabetes

There is very little research on the effects of green tea on blood glucose levels among adults with type 2 diabetes,

Green tea comes in many forms, from traditional leaves to encapsulated extracts.

and the research that has been published produced mixed results.[47] There is some evidence that suggests benefits of green tea (flavonoids) on body weight and body fatness; however, data supporting reduced risk of type 2 diabetes remains inadequate to draw any conclusions.[46] Most of the studies use *in vitro* and animal models of diabetes; consequently, there is not enough evidence from human research to make concrete recommendations.

Safety

Most studies examining the protective effects of green tea consider regular consumption to be at least five cups a day. The size of a cup can vary considerably from study to study, as can the method of brewing the tea. Even at these doses, green tea is considered safe as it has been a part of Asian society for centuries. However, there are some reports of liver damage among individuals taking high doses of commercial supplements of green tea extracts in capsules and tablets.

Scientists are studying green tea for its health benefits.

Using the Evidence

1. Would you recommend that Canadians include green tea as part of a healthy diet? Why or why not?

2. Are supplements of green tea catechins a good substitute for individuals who don't like green tea? Justify your position.

3. What other sources of polyphenols can you choose to provide protection against some types of cancer, cardiovascular disease, and type 2 diabetes?

4. Why are results from human clinical trials needed to establish safety and efficacy of green tea?

9

Nutrients Involved in Energy Metabolism

Test Yourself **True** *or* **False?**

1. The B-vitamins are an important source of energy for our bodies.
   T *or* F

2. A severe deficiency of certain B-vitamins active in energy metabolism can be fatal. T *or* F

3. B-vitamins are water soluble, so there is no risk of toxicity. T *or* F

4. Chromium supplementation reduces body fat and enhances muscle mass.
   T *or* F

5. In Canada, if we use table salt, we consume adequate iodine. T *or* F

Test Yourself answers are located in the Chapter Review.

Chapter Objectives | *After reading this chapter, you will be able to:*

1. Describe how coenzymes enhance the activities of enzymes, *p. 302*.
2. Name the B-vitamins that are primarily involved in energy metabolism and describe their function, *pp. 303–315*.
3. Describe the actions of at least two minerals that function as cofactors in energy metabolism, *pp. 315–320*.
4. Identify the deficiency disorders associated with thiamine, niacin, and riboflavin, *pp. 320–322*.
5. Describe the toxic effects of high doses of niacin and vitamin B$_6$, *pp. 310–313*.
6. Identify the deficiency disorders associated with poor iodine intake, *pp. 316–317*.
7. Explain how researchers determine the minimum amount of a vitamin we need to consume for good health, *p. 321*.
8. Explain why poor B-vitamin intake decreases the ability to do physical activity, *p. 322*.

n southern Africa, the months of September through December, the season when the rains begin, are known as "the hungry period."[1] In many areas, food stores have been depleted: meat is a rare luxury, and the variety and quantity of fruits and vegetables are extremely limited. The one staple typically available, including through food-aid programs, is maize.[1] It is during the hungry period that physicians begin to see patients suffering from the same constellation of symptoms: a skin rash, diarrhea, depression, apathy, loss of memory, and fatigue. These people suffer from pellagra, a deficiency disease we described in Chapter 1. As you may recall, pellagra is caused by an extreme shortage of niacin, which is not available from maize.

In this chapter, we explore the reasons why certain B-vitamins, including niacin, are essential to the body's breakdown and use of the macronutrients and why severe deficiency of these vitamins is incompatible with life. We also discuss the role of the minerals iodine, chromium, manganese, and sulphur in energy metabolism; and we conclude the chapter with a look at the impact of low B-vitamin intake on our ability to work, play, and exercise.

How Does the Body Regulate Energy Metabolism?

We explored the digestion and metabolism of carbohydrates, lipids, proteins, and alcohol in Chapters 3 through 7 of this text. In those chapters, you learned that the regulation of energy metabolism is a complex process involving numerous biological substances and chemical pathways. Here, we describe how certain micronutrients we consume in our diet assist us in generating energy from the carbohydrates, lipids, and proteins we eat along with them.

The Body Requires Vitamins and Minerals to Produce Energy

Although vitamins and minerals do not contain kilocalories and thus do not directly provide energy, the body is unable to generate energy from the macronutrients without them. The B-vitamins are particularly important in assisting energy metabolism and include thiamine, riboflavin, vitamin B_6, niacin, folate, vitamin B_{12}, pantothenic acid, and biotin. Except for vitamin B_{12}, these water-soluble vitamins need to be consumed regularly, because the body has no storage reservoir for them. Conversely, excess amounts of these vitamins, either from food or supplementation, are easily lost in the urine.

The primary role of the B-vitamins is to act as coenzymes in a number of metabolic processes. As you learned in Chapter 7 (see page 243), a coenzyme is a molecule that combines with an enzyme to activate it and help it do its job. Six of them (thiamine, riboflavin, vitamin B_6, niacin, pantothenic acid, and biotin) function primarily in energy metabolism, whereas the other two (folate and vitamin B_{12}) function primarily in cell regeneration and the synthesis of red blood cells. Although folate and vitamin B_{12} have minor roles in energy metabolism, we discuss them in Chapter 13 with the other blood nutrients.

Figure 9.1 provides a simple overview of how some of the B-vitamins act as coenzymes to promote energy metabolism, and **Figure 9.2** on page 304 shows how these coenzymes participate in the energy metabolism pathways. For instance, thiamine is part of the coenzyme thiamine pyrophosphate, or TPP, which is required for the breakdown of glucose. Riboflavin is a part of two coenzymes, flavin mononucleotide (FMN) and flavin adenine dinucleotide (FAD), which help break down glucose and fatty acids. The specific functions of each B-vitamin primarily involved in energy metabolism are described in detail shortly.

Some Micronutrients Assist with Nutrient Transport and Hormone Production

Some micronutrients promote energy metabolism by facilitating the transport of nutrients into the cells. For instance, the mineral chromium helps improve glucose uptake into cells. Other micronutrients assist in the production of hormones that regulate metabolic processes; the mineral iodine, for example, is necessary for synthesis of thyroid hormones,

Vitamins do not provide energy directly, but the B-vitamins help the body create the energy that it needs from the foods we eat.

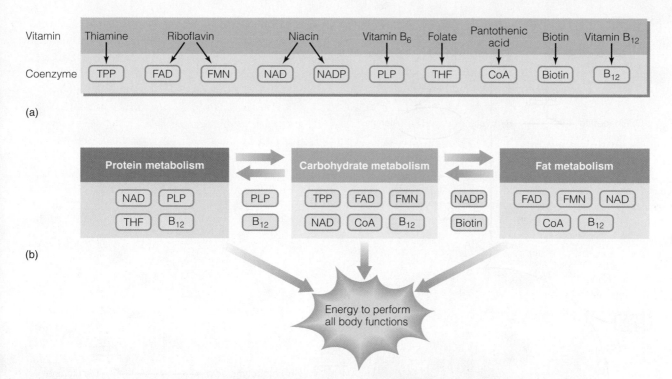

Figure 9.1 The B-vitamins play many important roles in the reactions involved in energy metabolism. (a) B-vitamins and the coenzymes of which they are a part. (b) This chart illustrates many of the coenzymes essential for various metabolic functions; however, this is only a small sample of the thousands of roles that the B-vitamins serve in our bodies. TPP, thiamine pyrophosphate; FAD, flavin adenine dinucleotide; FMN, flavin mononucleotide; NAD, nicotinamide adenine dinucleotide; NADP, nicotinamide adenine dinucleotide phosphate; PLP, pyridoxal phosphate; CoA, coenzyme A.

which regulate our metabolic rate and promote growth and development. The details of these processes and their related nutrients are discussed in the following section.

RECAP

Vitamins and minerals are not direct sources of energy, but they help extract the energy from carbohydrates, fats, proteins, and alcohol. Acting as coenzymes and cofactors, micronutrients such as the B-vitamins assist enzymes in metabolizing macronutrients to produce energy. Minerals such as chromium and iodine assist with nutrient uptake into the cells and with regulating energy production and cell growth.

A Profile of Nutrients Involved in Energy Metabolism

As we have stated, the primary function of the B-vitamins, except for folate and B_{12}, is to facilitate the production of energy in the body. Other nutrients involved in energy metabolism include a vitaminlike substance called choline and the minerals iodine, chromium, manganese, and sulphur. In this section, we discuss the functions, recommended intakes, toxicity, and deficiency symptoms for these nutrients. A summary of the B vitamins involved in energy metabolism is provided in Table 9.1.

Thiamine (Vitamin B_1)

Thiamine was the first B-vitamin discovered, hence its designation as vitamin B_1. Because this compound was recognized as vital to health and has a functional amine group, it was

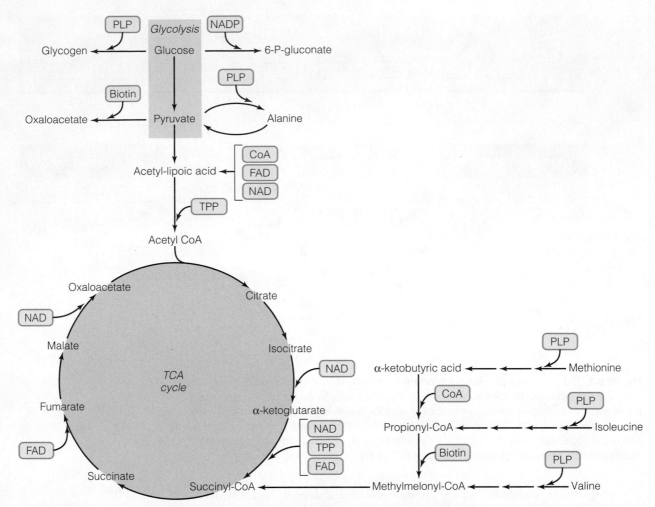

Figure 9.2 Example of some metabolic pathways that require B-vitamins for energy production.

initially called "vitamine."[2] Later, this term was applied to several other non-mineral compounds that are essential for health, and the spelling was changed to *vitamin*. Thiamine was given a new name reflecting both its thiazole and amine groups. Thiamine is required for the formation of its coenzyme thiamine pyrophosphate, or TPP. The structures of thiamine and TPP are shown in **Figure 9.3**. Dietary thiamine is converted to TPP by the body.

Functions of Thiamine

Thiamine is important in a number of energy-producing metabolic pathways within the body. As a part of TPP, thiamine plays a critical role in the breakdown of glucose for energy. For example, TPP is required for pyruvate dehydrogenase, the enzyme responsible for the conversion of pyruvate to acetyl-CoA (see Figure 9.2). This is a critical step in the conversion of glucose into a smaller molecule that can enter the TCA cycle for energy production. Thus, when dietary thiamine is inadequate, the body's ability to metabolize carbohydrate is diminished.

Another primary role of TPP is to act as a coenzyme in the metabolism of the branched-chain amino acids, which include leucine, isoleucine, and valine. TPP is a coenzyme for two α-keto acid dehydrogenase complexes. One of these enzyme complexes helps convert the carbon skeletons of the branched-chain amino acids into products that can enter the TCA cycle, whereas the other converts

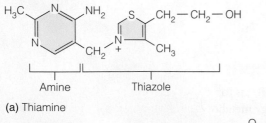

(a) Thiamine

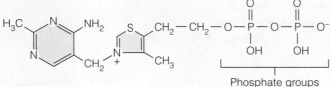

(b) Thiamine pyrophosphate

Figure 9.3 Structure of (a) thiamine and (b) thiamine pyrophosphate (TPP).

α-ketoglutarate to succinate in the TCA cycle (see Figure 9.2). The highest concentrations of the branched-chain amino acids are found in the muscle, where they make up approximately 25% of the content of the average protein. Thus, these amino acids play a significant role in providing fuel for the working muscle, especially during high-intensity exercise.[3]

TPP also assists in the production of DNA and RNA, making it important for cell regeneration and protein synthesis. Finally, it plays a role in the synthesis of neurotransmitters—chemicals that transmit messages throughout the central nervous system.

How Much Thiamine Should We Consume?

The RDA for thiamine for adults aged 19 years and older is 1.2 mg/day for men and 1.1 mg/day for women. Based on the Canadian Community Health Survey (CCHS) data collected in Canada between January 2004 and January 2005, the average dietary intake of thiamine for men and women 19 years and older was approximately 2 mg/day and 1.5 mg/day, respectively.[4] Thus, it appears that the average adult in Canada gets adequate amounts of thiamine in the diet.

Those at greatest risk of poor thiamine status are older adults, who typically have reduced total energy intakes, and anyone with malabsorption syndrome or on renal dialysis, as thiamine is easily cleared by the kidney.

Physically active individuals, especially those who consume high amounts of carbohydrate, may be at risk for poor B-vitamin status, including thiamine. Research indicates that depletion of the B-vitamins can reduce the ability to perform physical activity. This is discussed in more detail at the end of the chapter.

Table 9.1 Overview of Nutrients Involved in Energy Metabolism

Nutrient	Recommended Intake
Thiamine (Vitamin B$_1$)	RDA for 19 years and older: Women = 1.1 mg/day Men = 1.2 mg/day
Riboflavin (Vitamin B$_2$)	RDA for 19 years and older: Women = 1.1 mg/day Men = 1.3 mg/day
Niacin (nicotinamide and nicotinic acid)	RDA for 19 years and older: Women = 14 mg/day Men = 16 mg/day
Vitamin B$_6$ (pyridoxine)	RDA for 19 to 50 years of age: Women and men = 1.3 mg/day RDA for 51 years and older: Women = 1.5 mg/day Men = 1.7 mg/day
Folate (folic acid)	RDA for 19 years and older: Women and men = 400 μg/day
Vitamin B$_{12}$ (cobalamin)	RDA for 19 years and older: Women and men = 2.4 μg/day
Pantothenic acid	AI for 19 years and older: Women and men = 5 mg/day
Biotin	AI for 19 years and older: Women and men = 30 μg/day
Choline	AI for 19 years and older: Women = 425 mg/day Men = 550 mg/day

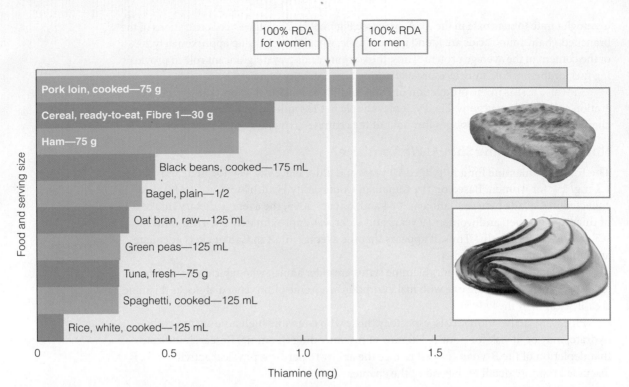

Figure 9.4 shows a horizontal bar chart of Thiamine (mg) content.

100% RDA for women

100% RDA for men

Food and serving size:
- Pork loin, cooked—75 g
- Cereal, ready-to-eat, Fibre 1—30 g
- Ham—75 g
- Black beans, cooked—175 mL
- Bagel, plain—1/2
- Oat bran, raw—125 mL
- Green peas—125 mL
- Tuna, fresh—75 g
- Spaghetti, cooked—125 mL
- Rice, white, cooked—125 mL

Thiamine (mg): 0, 0.5, 1.0, 1.5

Figure 9.4 Common food sources of thiamine. The RDA for thiamine is 1.2 mg/day for men and 1.1 mg/day for women 19 years and older.
Data from: The Canadian Nutrient File. Health Canada, 2012. Reproduced with the permission of the Minister of Health, 2012.

Food Sources of Thiamine

Thiamine is found abundantly in ham and other pork products (**Figure 9.4**). Sunflower seeds, beans, oat bran, mixed dishes that contain whole or enriched grains and meat, tuna fish, soy milk, and soy-based meat substitutes are also good sources. Enriched and whole-grain foods, including fortified ready-to-eat cereals, are rich in several B-vitamins, including thiamine. **Figure 9.5** identifies the B-vitamin content of one popular fortified cereal.

What Happens If We Consume Too Much Thiamine?

Excess thiamine is readily cleared by the kidneys, and to date there have been no reports of adverse effects from consuming high amounts of thiamine from either food or supplements. Thus, the Institute of Medicine (IOM) has not been able to set a tolerable upper intake level (UL) for thiamine.[5]

Figure 9.5 Many enriched ready-to-eat cereals, like the one in this example, are a consistently good source of B-vitamins.
Data from: The Canadian Nutrient File. Health Canada, 2012. Reproduced with the permission of the Minister of Health, 2012.

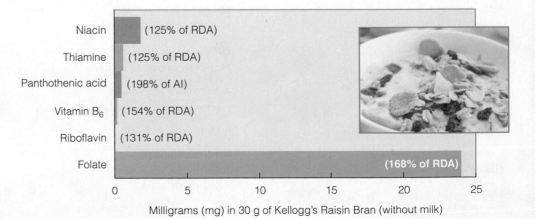

Figure 9.5 bar chart:
- Niacin (125% of RDA)
- Thiamine (125% of RDA)
- Panthothenic acid (198% of AI)
- Vitamin B$_6$ (154% of RDA)
- Riboflavin (131% of RDA)
- Folate (168% of RDA)

Milligrams (mg) in 30 g of Kellogg's Raisin Bran (without milk): 0, 5, 10, 15, 20, 25

What Happens If We Don't Consume Enough Thiamine?

As the B-vitamins are involved in most energy-generating processes, the deficiency symptoms include a combination of fatigue, apathy, muscle weakness, and reduced cognitive function. As you learned in Chapter 1, thiamine-deficiency disease is called **beriberi**. There are two forms of beriberi, wet beriberi and dry beriberi. In dry beriberi the body's inability to metabolize energy leads to muscle wasting and nerve damage; in later stages, patients may be unable to move at all. In wet beriberi the heart muscle may be affected, and the patient may die of heart failure. Beriberi is seen in countries in which unenriched, processed grains are a primary food source; for instance, beriberi was widespread in China when rice was processed and refined, and it still occurs in refugee camps and other settlements dependent on poor-quality food supplies.

Thiamine deficiency is also seen in industrialized countries in people with chronic heavy alcohol consumption and limited food intake. This alcohol-related thiamine deficiency is called Wernicke–Korsakoff syndrome. High alcohol intake contributes to thiamine deficiency in three ways: it is generally accompanied by a diet low in thiamine; at the same time, it increases the need for thiamine to metabolize the alcohol; and it reduces thiamine absorption. Together, these factors contribute to thiamine deficiency.[6] The symptoms of Wernicke–Korsakoff syndrome are tremors, confusion, and impairment of memory.[6]

Riboflavin (Vitamin B₂)

Riboflavin was the second B-vitamin discovered, thus, its designation as vitamin B₂. The term *riboflavin* reflects its structure; *ribo* refers to the carbon-rich ribityl side chain, and *flavin* is associated with the ring-structure portion of the vitamin (**Figure 9.6a**). Riboflavin is water soluble and has a yellow colour. It is relatively heat stable but sensitive to light: when exposed to light, the ribityl side chain is cleaved off and the vitamin loses its activity.

beriberi A disease caused by thiamine deficiency.

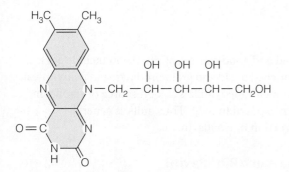

(a) Riboflavin

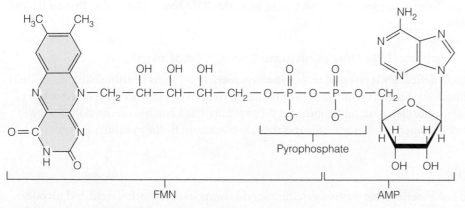

(b) Flavin adenine dinucleotide (FAD) (coenzyme)

Figure 9.6 Structure of (a) riboflavin. (b) Its coenzyme forms flavin mononucleotide (FMN) and flavin adenine dinucleotide (FAD).

Functions of Riboflavin

Riboflavin is an important component of two coenzymes that are involved in oxidation–reduction reactions occurring within the energy-producing metabolic pathways, including the electron transport chain. These coenzymes, flavin mononucleotide (FMN) and flavin adenine dinucleotide (FAD), are involved in the metabolism of carbohydrates, fatty acids, and amino acids for energy. (The structures of FMN and FAD are shown in Figure 9.6b.) FAD and FMN function as electron acceptors in the electron transport chain, which eventually results in the production of ATP. FAD is also a part of the α-ketoglutarate dehydrogenase complex, which converts α-ketoglutarate to succinate in one step of the TCA cycle (see Figure 9.2). It is also a coenzyme for succinate dehydrogenase, the enzyme involved in the conversion of succinate to fumarate in the next step of the TCA cycle. Finally, riboflavin is a part of the coenzyme required by glutathione peroxidase, which assists in the fight against oxidative damage. Antioxidants are discussed in detail in Chapter 11.

How Much Riboflavin Should We Consume?

The RDA for riboflavin for adults aged 19 years and older is 1.3 mg/day for men and 1.1 mg/day for women. Based on the CCHS survey data, the average dietary intake of riboflavin from food for men 19 years and older was 2.2 mg/day and for women of the same age the average intake was approximately 1.7 mg/day.[4] Thus, it appears that, on average, adults in Canada get adequate amounts of riboflavin in their diet.

As with thiamine, those at greatest risk of low riboflavin intakes are older adults, who may have reduced total energy intake; individuals who make poor food selections; those with malabsorption problems; and patients on renal dialysis.[7] People who eliminate milk and milk products from their diet may also be at risk. Approximately one-third of the RDA for riboflavin is supplied in the Canadian diet by milk and milk products; thus, it is easy to see how individuals who do not consume these foods could have a lower riboflavin intake.[6, 7]

Food Sources of Riboflavin

In addition to dairy products, foods considered good sources of riboflavin include eggs; meats, including organ meats; broccoli; enriched bread and grain products; and ready-to-eat cereals (see Figure 9.5 and **Figure 9.7**). As mentioned, milk is a good source of riboflavin; however, riboflavin is destroyed when it is exposed to light. Thus, milk is generally stored in opaque containers to prevent the destruction of riboflavin.

What Happens If We Consume Too Much Riboflavin?

As with thiamine, there are no reports of adverse effects from consuming high amounts of riboflavin from either food or supplements; thus, the IOM has not been able to set a UL for riboflavin.[5]

What Happens If We Don't Consume Enough Riboflavin?

Riboflavin deficiency is referred to as **ariboflavinosis**. Symptoms of ariboflavinosis include sore throat; swelling of the mucous membranes in the mouth and throat; lips that are dry and scaly; a purple-coloured tongue; and inflamed, irritated patches on the skin. Severe riboflavin deficiency can impair the metabolism of vitamin B$_6$ (or pyridoxine) and niacin.

Niacin

Niacin is a generic name for two specific vitamin compounds, nicotinic acid and nicotinamide, which are shown in **Figure 9.8**. This B-vitamin was previously designated as vitamin B$_3$, a name you will sometimes still see on vitamin supplement labels. Niacin was first established as an essential nutrient in the treatment of pellagra in 1937.

Milk is a good source of riboflavin and is stored in opaque containers to prevent the destruction of riboflavin by light.

ariboflavinosis A condition caused by riboflavin deficiency.

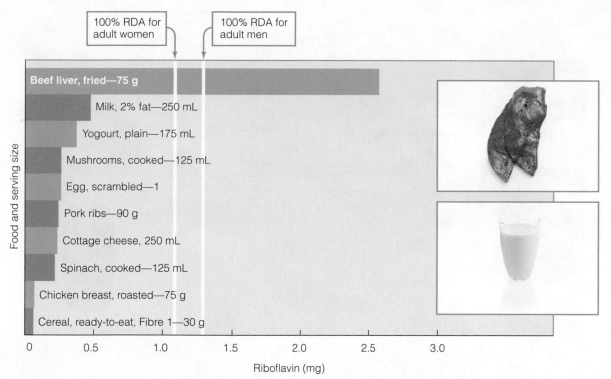

Figure showing bar chart with labels: 100% RDA for adult women, 100% RDA for adult men. Y-axis: Food and serving size. Bars for: Beef liver, fried—75 g; Milk, 2% fat—250 mL; Yogourt, plain—175 mL; Mushrooms, cooked—125 mL; Egg, scrambled—1; Pork ribs—90 g; Cottage cheese, 250 mL; Spinach, cooked—125 mL; Chicken breast, roasted—75 g; Cereal, ready-to-eat, Fibre 1—30 g. X-axis: Riboflavin (mg), 0, 0.5, 1.0, 1.5, 2.0, 2.5, 3.0.

Figure 9.7 Common food sources of riboflavin. The RDA for riboflavin is 1.3 mg/day for men and 1.1 mg/day for women.
Data from: The Canadian Nutrient File. Health Canada, 2012. Reproduced with the permission of the Minister of Health, 2012.

Functions of Niacin

The two forms of niacin, nicotinic acid and nicotinamide, are essential for the formation of the two coenzymes nicotinamide adenine dinucleotide (NAD) and nicotinamide adenine dinucleotide phosphate (NADP). These coenzymes, like those formed from riboflavin and thiamine, are required for the oxidation–reduction reactions involved in the catabolism of carbohydrate, fat, and protein for energy. For example, NADP-dependent dehydrogenase enzymes catalyze steps in the β-oxidation of fatty acids, the oxidation of ketone bodies, the degradation of carbohydrates, and the catabolism of amino acids.[6] Some metabolic pathways in which niacin functions are illustrated in Figure 9.2. Niacin is also an important coenzyme in DNA replication and repair and in the process of cell differentiation.

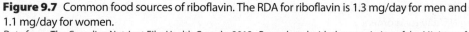

(a) Nicotinic acid   (b) Nicotinamide

Figure 9.8 Forms of niacin. (a) Structure of nicotinic acid. (b) Structure of nicotinamide. The generic term *niacin* is used to refer to these two compounds.

How Much Niacin Should We Consume?

Niacin is a unique vitamin in that the body can synthesize a limited amount from the amino acid tryptophan. However, the ratio reflecting the conversion of tryptophan to niacin is 60:1; thus, the body relies on the diet to provide the majority of niacin necessary for functioning. The term *niacin equivalents (NE)* is used to express niacin intake recommendations, and reflects the amount of niacin in our diet and the amount synthesized from tryptophan within the body.

The RDA for niacin for adults aged 19 and older is 16 mg/day of NE for men and 14 mg/day of NE for women. Based on the CCHS data, the average dietary intake of niacin from food for men and women older than 19 was approximately 46 mg/day and 34 mg/day, respectively.[4]

Food Sources of Niacin

Good food sources of niacin include meat, fish, poultry, enriched bread products, and ready-to-eat cereals; however, the availability of this niacin for absorption differs. For example, the niacin in cereal grains is bound to other substances and is only 30% available for absorption, whereas the niacin found in meats is much more available.[5] To calculate the

Fish is a good source of niacin.

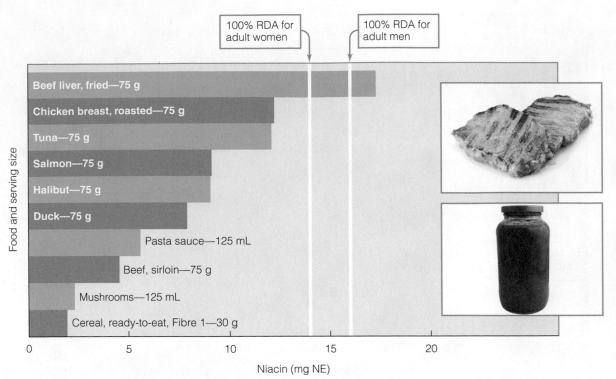

Figure 9.9 Common food sources of niacin. The RDA for niacin is 16 mg NE/day for men and 14 mg NE/day for women.
Data from: The Canadian Nutrient File. Health Canada, 2012. Reproduced with the permission of the Minister of Health, 2012.

NE in your own diet, see You Do the Math below. See **Figure 9.9** for the niacin content of commonly consumed foods.

What Happens If We Consume Too Much Niacin?

There seem to be no adverse effects from the consumption of naturally occurring niacin in foods; however, niacin can cause toxicity symptoms when taken in supplement form.[5] These symptoms include *flushing,* which is defined as burning, tingling, and itching sensations accompanied by a reddened flush primarily on the face, arms, and chest. Liver damage, glucose intolerance, blurred vision, and edema of the eyes can be seen with very large doses of niacin taken over long periods of time. Consequently, the UL for niacin is 35 mg/day from supplements and was determined based on the level of niacin below which flushing is typically not observed.

YOU DO THE MATH

Calculating Niacin Equivalents

When you analyze your diet using food composition tables or dietary analysis software, you will notice they report total niacin equivalents (NE). How is this calculation done?

To calculate NE, you first need to determine the amount of two components of your diet: (1) total niacin intake from food in mg/day; (2) total intake of tryptophan in mg/day. Now you are ready to do the calculation, using the following formula. Just keep in mind that 1 NE = either 60 mg of tryptophan or 1 mg of niacin.

$$\text{Total NE} = \text{niacin intake from food} + (\text{tryptophan intake}/60)$$

Now calculate the NE intake of an adult male who consumes 18.9 mg/day of niacin and 630 mg/day of tryptophan. What percentage of his total NE intake is coming from tryptophan? Is this person meeting his RDA?

What Happens If We Don't Consume Enough Niacin?

Pellagra results from severe niacin deficiency. It commonly occurred in the United States and parts of Europe in the early 20th century in areas where corn, maize, or sorghum was the dietary staple. These foods are low in both niacin and the amino acid tryptophan. Although traditional diets in South America are also high in corn, these diets do not cause pellagra, a fact attributed to the cooking of the corn in lime powder (that is, calcium oxide), which makes niacin more available. At the present time, pellagra is rarely seen in industrialized countries, except in cases of chronic alcoholism. Pellagra is still found in India, China, and Africa. (For more information on this disease, see the Highlight box, "Solving the Mystery of Pellagra," on page 5 in Chapter 1.)

Initial symptoms of pellagra include functional changes in the gastrointestinal tract that decrease the amount of HCl produced and the absorption of nutrients, and lesions in the central nervous system causing weakness, fatigue, and anorexia. These initial symptoms are followed by what have been identified as the classic "three Ds"—dermatitis, diarrhea, and dementia.[6] The name *pellagra* literally means "rough skin": dermatitis occurs on parts of the body more exposed to the elements, such as the face, neck, hands, and feet (see the photograph on page 5). The diarrhea and dementia develop as the disease worsens and further affects the gastrointestinal tract and central nervous system.

Vitamin B₆ (Pyridoxine)

Vitamin B_6 is actually a group of three related compounds: pyridoxine (PN), pyridoxal (PL), pyridoxamine (PM), and their phosphate forms, which include pyridoxine phosphate (PNP), pyridoxal phosphate (PLP), and pyridoxamine phosphate (PMP), respectively. The structures of these compounds are shown in **Figure 9.10**.

Functions of Vitamin B₆

Some of the metabolic pathways in which vitamin B_6 functions are illustrated in Figure 9.2. In the form of PLP, vitamin B_6 is a coenzyme for more than 100 enzymes involved in the metabolism of amino acids. It plays a critical role in transamination, which is the key process in making non-essential amino acids; without adequate vitamin B_6, all amino acids become essential, as the body cannot make them in sufficient quantities. In addition, PLP is required for synthesis of glycogen phosphorylase, the enzyme responsible for releasing glucose from stored glycogen. Vitamin B_6 is also essential for gluconeogenesis and assists in several steps of glucose metabolism.

Vitamin B_6 is also important, along with folate and vitamin B_{12}, for the metabolism of the amino acid homocysteine, which is described in more detail in Chapter 13. It also plays a role in the synthesis of hemoglobin and in oxygen transport.

pellagra A disease that results from severe niacin deficiency.

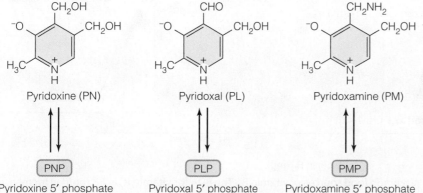

Figure 9.10 Structure of the vitamin B₆ compounds and their interconversions to the phosphorylated forms.

How Much Vitamin B₆ Should We Consume?

The RDA for vitamin B₆ for adult men and women aged 19 to 50 years is 1.3 mg/day. For adults 51 years of age and older, the RDA increases to 1.7 mg/day for men and 1.5 mg/day for women. The increased requirement with aging is based on data indicating that more vitamin B₆ is required to maintain normal vitamin B₆ status, using blood PLP concentrations as a status indicator, in older individuals. Based on CCHS data, the average dietary intake of vitamin B₆ from food for men and women older than 19 years was approximately 2.2 mg/day and 1.6 mg/day, respectively.[4]

Because of the role vitamin B₆ plays in protein metabolism, it has been proposed that the requirement for vitamin B₆ be based on protein intake. Although the RDAs do not define vitamin B₆ intake in terms of protein intake, we do know that as protein intake increases, more vitamin B₆ is required.[5] Fortunately, nature has combined vitamin B₆ and protein in many of the same foods so that food sources high in protein are also typically high in vitamin B₆.

Food Sources of Vitamin B₆

Good sources of vitamin B₆ include meat, fish (especially tuna), poultry, and organ meats, which are also high in protein (**Figure 9.11**). Thus, protein and vitamin B₆ are provided together in the same food, which ensures adequate protein metabolism. Besides meat and fish, good food sources of vitamin B₆ include enriched ready-to-eat cereals, potatoes and other starchy vegetables, bananas, and fortified soy-based meat substitutes. In the typical Canadian diet, approximately 40% of the dietary vitamin B₆ comes from animal sources, while 60% comes from plants.[4] For this reason, individuals who eliminate animal foods from their diet need to make sure they select plant foods high in vitamin B₆.

What Happens If We Consume Too Much Vitamin B₆?

As with the other B-vitamins discussed earlier, there are no adverse effects associated with high intakes of vitamin B₆ from food sources. Vitamin B₆ supplements have been used to

Tuna is a very good source of vitamin B₆.

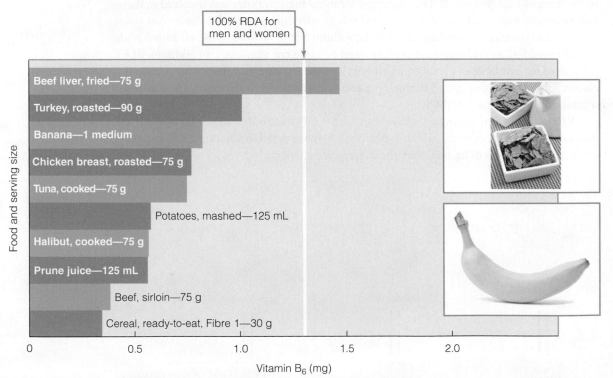

100% RDA for men and women

Food and serving size:
- Beef liver, fried—75 g
- Turkey, roasted—90 g
- Banana—1 medium
- Chicken breast, roasted—75 g
- Tuna, cooked—75 g
- Potatoes, mashed—125 mL
- Halibut, cooked—75 g
- Prune juice—125 mL
- Beef, sirloin—75 g
- Cereal, ready-to-eat, Fibre 1—30 g

Vitamin B₆ (mg): 0, 0.5, 1.0, 1.5, 2.0

Figure 9.11 Common food sources of vitamin B₆. The RDA for vitamin B₆ is 1.3 mg/day for men and women aged 19 to 50 years.
Data from: The Canadian Nutrient File. Health Canada, 2012. Reproduced with the permission of the Minister of Health, 2012.

treat conditions such as premenstrual syndrome and carpal tunnel syndrome. Caution is required, however, when using such supplements and they should be taken only under the supervision of a qualified health professional. High doses of supplemental vitamin B_6 have been associated with sensory neuropathy and dermatological lesions.[5] Thus, the UL for supplemental vitamin B_6 is set at 100 mg/day. See the Evidence-informed Decision Making feature following this chapter for more discussion of high intakes of vitamin B_6 and premenstrual syndrome.

What Happens If We Don't Consume Enough Vitamin B_6?

A number of conditions appear to increase the need for vitamin B_6. These include alcoholism, certain prescription medications, intense physical activity, and chronic diseases such as arthritis and vascular disease.[5, 8, 9] If we don't get enough vitamin B_6 in the diet, the symptoms of vitamin B_6 deficiency can develop. These include anemia, convulsions, depression, confusion, and inflamed, irritated patches on the skin. Notice that the symptoms associated with vitamin B_6 deficiency involve three tissues: skin, blood, and nervous system. This fact reflects the role of vitamin B_6 in protein metabolism, red blood cell development, and the synthesis of neurotransmitters.

As you will read in Chapter 13, vitamin B_6, folate, and vitamin B_{12} are important for the metabolism of the amino acid methionine. If the intakes of any of these three vitamins are low, blood levels of homocysteine increase because of incomplete metabolism of methionine. High blood homocysteine concentrations may be related to cardiovascular disease. There is no specific disease that is solely attributed to vitamin B_6 deficiency.

Pantothenic Acid

Pantothenic acid is an essential vitamin that is metabolized into two major coenzymes: coenzyme A (CoA) and acyl carrier protein (ACP), which are shown in **Figure 9.12**. Both are essential in the synthesis of fatty acids, while CoA is essential for fatty acid oxidation, ketone metabolism, and the metabolism of carbohydrate and protein.[10] For example, in the conversion of pyruvate to acetyl CoA, the enzyme pyruvate dehydrogenase requires CoA.

Shiitake mushrooms contain 10 to 20 times more pantothenic acid than other types of mushrooms.

(a) Coenzyme A (CoA)

(b) Acyl carrier protein (ACP)

Figure 9.12 Structure of coenzymes containing pantothenic acid. (a) Coenzyme A (CoA). (b) Acyl carrier protein (ACP).

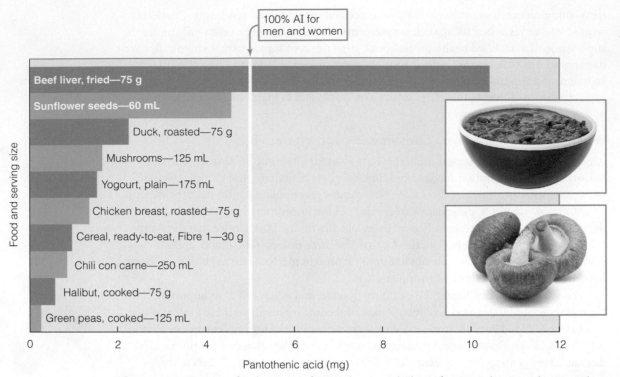

Figure 9.13 Common food sources of pantothenic acid. The AI for pantothenic acid is 5 mg/day for men and women.
Data from: The Canadian Nutrient File. Health Canada, 2012. Reproduced with the permission of the Minister of Health, 2012.

Many of the metabolic reactions that require pantothenic acid for energy production are illustrated in Figure 9.2. Besides its role in energy metabolism, pantothenic acid is required in the synthesis of cholesterol and steroids and in the detoxification of drugs.

The AI for pantothenic acid for adult men and women aged 19 years and older is 5 mg/day. Pantothenic acid is widely distributed in foods, with the average daily intake at approximately 5 mg/day and usual intakes ranging from 3 to 7 mg/day.[11, 12] Thus, the AI for pantothenic acid and the average dietary intake are similar. As mentioned, pantothenic acid is available from a variety of foods, including chicken, beef, egg yolk, potatoes, oat cereals, tomato products, whole grains, and organ meats (**Figure 9.13**). There are no known adverse effects from consuming excess amounts of pantothenic acid, and deficiencies of pantothenic acid are very rare.

Biotin

Biotin is a component of four carboxylase enzymes that are present in humans. These enzymes serve as the CO_2 (carbon dioxide) carrier and the carboxyl donor for substrates.[10] **Figure 9.14** shows the structure of biotin.

The enzymes that require biotin as a coenzyme are involved in fatty acid synthesis (for example, lipogenesis), gluconeogenesis, and carbohydrate, fat, and protein metabolism. For example, pyruvate carboxylase catalyzes the synthesis of oxaloacetate from pyruvate in the TCA cycle. Many of the enzyme reactions that require biotin for energy production are illustrated in Figure 9.2.

The AI for biotin for adult men and women aged 19 and older is 30 µg/day. The biotin content has been determined for very few foods, and these values are not reported in food composition tables or dietary analysis programs. In food, biotin exists as free biotin or bound to protein as biocytin, both of which appear

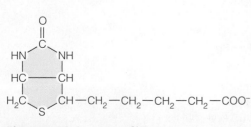

Figure 9.14 Structure of biotin.

to be widespread in foods. The free form of biotin is shown in Figure 9.14; the structure of biocytin is similar to free biotin but has an amino acid attached to the carboxyl end.

There are no known adverse effects from consuming excess amounts of biotin. Biotin deficiencies are typically seen only in people who consume a large number of raw egg whites over long periods of time. This is because raw egg whites contain a protein that binds with biotin and prevents its absorption. Biotin deficiencies are also seen in people fed total parenteral nutrition (nutrients administered by a route other than the GI tract) that is not supplemented with biotin. Symptoms include thinning of hair; loss of hair colour; development of a red, scaly rash around the eyes, nose, and mouth; depression; lethargy; and hallucinations.

RECaP

The B-vitamins include thiamine, riboflavin, niacin, vitamin B_6 (pyridoxine), folate, vitamin B_{12} (cobalamin), pantothenic acid, and biotin. The primary action of the B-vitamins, except for folate and B_{12}, is to assist in the metabolism of carbohydrates, fats, protein, and alcohol. They are commonly found in whole grains, enriched breads, ready-to-eat cereals, meats, dairy products, and some fruits and vegetables. B-vitamin toxicity is rare unless a person consumes large doses as supplements. Thiamine deficiency causes beriberi, and niacin deficiency causes pellagra.

Did You Know?

In 2006, researchers at the University of British Columbia were the first to demonstrate choline deficiency in children with cystic fibrosis (CF).[13] They analyzed the plasma from 35 children with CF and 15 healthy controls, and found that children with CF had significantly lower plasma choline concentrations. The researchers had previously shown higher fecal loses of choline in CF patients likely due to the reduced digestion and impaired absorption characteristic of this disease. They suggested that poor choline status may contribute to or exacerbate some of the complications associated with CF.

Choline

Choline is a vitaminlike substance that is important for metabolism, the structural integrity of cell membranes, and neurotransmission. It is typically grouped with the B-vitamins because of its role in fat digestion and transport and homocysteine metabolism.

Specifically, choline plays an important role in the metabolism and transport of fats and cholesterol. High amounts of the choline-containing compound phosphatidylcholine are found in bile, which aids fat digestion, and in the formation of lipoproteins, which transport endogenous and dietary fat and cholesterol in the blood to the cells. Choline is also necessary for the synthesis of phospholipids and other components of cell membranes; thus, choline plays a critical role in the structural integrity of cell membranes. Finally, choline accelerates the synthesis and release of **acetylcholine**, a neurotransmitter that is involved in many functions, including muscle movement and memory storage.

Although small amounts of choline can be synthesized within the body, the amount made is insufficient for our needs; thus, choline is considered an essential dietary nutrient. Choline has an AI of 550 mg/day for men aged 19 and older and an AI of 425 mg/day for

Choline is widespread in foods and can be found in eggs and milk.

acetylcholine A neurotransmitter that is involved in many functions, including muscle movement and memory storage.

women aged 19 and older. There are limited data on the choline intake of North Americans, because choline intake is not reported in the NHANES or other large surveys done in the United States or Canada. In addition, it is not reported in major nutrient databases. However, it is estimated that choline intakes in the United States and Canada range from 730 to 1040 mg/day,[5] based on the typical choline content of foods.

Choline is widespread in foods, typically in the form of phosphatidylcholine (see Figure 5.6 on page 169) in the cell membranes of the food. Foods that are high in choline include milk, liver, eggs, and peanuts.[5] Lecithin (another term for phosphatidylcholine) is added to foods during processing as an emulsifying agent, which also increases choline intakes in the diet. Inadequate intakes of choline can lead to increased fat accumulation in the liver, which eventually leads to liver damage. Excessive intake of supplemental choline results in various toxicity symptoms, including a fishy body odour, vomiting, excess salivation, sweating, diarrhea, and low blood pressure. The UL for choline from food, water, and supplements for adults 19 years of age and older is 3.5 g/day.

Iodine

Iodine is the heaviest trace element required for human health and a necessary component of the thyroid hormones, which help regulate human metabolism. In nature, this element is found primarily as inorganic salts in rocks, soil, plants, animals, and water as either iodine or iodide, but once it enters the GI tract, it is broken down to iodide, which is the negative ion of iodine, designated I⁻. Upon absorption, the majority of this iodide is taken up by the thyroid gland.[14]

Functions of Iodine

As just noted, iodine is responsible for a single function within the body: the synthesis of thyroid hormones.[15] Although iodine's function is singular, the multiple actions of thyroid hormones mean that it affects the whole body. Thyroid hormones regulate key metabolic reactions associated with body temperature, resting metabolic rate, macronutrient metabolism, and reproduction and growth.[15]

The structure of the thyroid hormones, thyroxine (T_4) and 3, 5, 3′-triiodothyronine (T_3), illustrates the placement of iodine (I) in these two hormones (**Figure 9.15**). Both are derived from the iodination of the amino acid tyrosine, shown in Figure 9.15c. Notice that thyroxine has four iodine molecules as part of its structure, whereas triiodothyronine has three—thus, the abbreviated designations T_4 and T_3. Thyroxine (T_4) is the primary circulating thyroid hormone. The removal of one iodine group is required to generate the active form of T_3.[15]

How Much Iodine Should We Consume?

The body needs relatively little iodine to maintain health. The RDA for adults 19 years of age and older is 150 µg/day. It is estimated that the iodine intake from food in Canada is approximately 200 to 300 µg/day for men and 190 to 210 µg/day for women.[16]

Very few foods are reliable sources of iodine, because the amount of iodine in foods varies according to the soil, irrigation, and fertilizers used. Saltwater foods, both fish and plants, tend to have higher amounts because marine species concentrate iodine from seawater. Good food sources include saltwater fish, shrimp, seaweed, iodized salt, and white and whole-wheat breads made with iodized salt and bread conditioners. In addition, iodine is added to dairy cattle feed and used in sanitizing solutions in the dairy industry, making dairy foods an important source of iodine.

Adding iodine to salt in Canada has been mandatory since 1949 to combat iodine deficiency resulting from the poor iodine content of soils in this country.

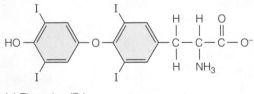

(a) Thyroxine (T_4)

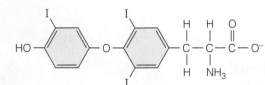

(b) 3, 5, 3′–Triiodothyronine (T_3)

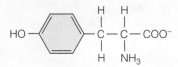

(c) Tyrosine

Figure 9.15 Thyroid hormones contain iodine (I). (a) Structure of the thyroid hormone T_4. (b) Structure of the thyroid hormone T_3. Both are derived from the iodination of (c) tyrosine, an amino acid.

For many people, iodized salt is their primary source of iodine, and approximately one-half a teaspoon of iodized salt meets the entire adult RDA for iodine. Kosher, pickling, and sea salt are a source of natural iodine but do not contain as much as iodized table salt.

Excess iodine intakes can cause a number of health-related problems, especially related to thyroid gland function. Too much iodine causes the thyroid gland to attempt to produce more hormones, consequently it may enlarge, a condition known as **goiter** (**Figure 9.16**). Goiter refers to the enlargement of the thyroid gland, regardless of its cause. Iodine toxicity generally occurs as a result of excessive supplementation. Thus, the UL for iodine is 1100 µg/day.

A number of deficiency disorders are associated with low iodine intakes. Paradoxically, goiter is also the most classic disorder of iodine deficiency. An insufficient supply of iodine means there is less iodine for the production of thyroid hormones. The body responds by stimulating the thyroid gland, including increasing the size of the gland, in an attempt to capture more iodine from the blood.

The development of a goiter is only one of many symptoms that result when iodine is insufficient in the diet. A broader term applied to the disorders associated with poor iodine intakes is *iodine deficiency disorders,* or *IDDs,* which include cretinism, growth and developmental disorders, mental deficiencies, neurologic disorders, decreased fertility, congenital abnormalities, and prenatal and infant death.[15–17] The World Health Organization (WHO) considers iodine deficiency to be the "greatest single cause of preventable brain damage and mental retardation" in the world.[17] If a woman experiences iodine deficiency during pregnancy, her infant has a high risk of being born with a unique form of mental retardation referred to as **cretinism**. In addition to mental retardation, these infants may suffer from stunted growth, deafness, and muteness. Among pregnant women, iodine deficiency may also increase the occurrence of spontaneous abortion, stillbirths and congenital abnormalities, and infant mortality.[15] The impact of mild iodine deficiency on the development of the brain and neurologic system of a child is more difficult to determine. Iodine deficiency can also cause **hypothyroidism** (low blood levels of thyroid hormone), which is characterized by decreased body temperature, inability to tolerate cold environmental temperatures, weight gain, fatigue, and sluggishness.

According to the International Council for the Control of IDDs (ICCIDD), 2.2 billion people live in areas of iodine deficiency and are at increased risk for its health complications and consequences.[18] In Canada and the United States, large areas of crop-producing lands are low in iodine, and thus foods grown on these lands are low in iodine. At the beginning of the 20th century, IDDs and goiter were considered endemic in North America. However, the problem was not fully addressed until World War I, when many conscripted men were barred from military service because they had goiters. At this time, treatment of goiters with sodium iodine was shown to be effective, and the search was on for a method of increasing iodine in the food supply from either fortification of processed foods, increasing the level of iodine in the soil through fertilizers, or adding iodine to the feed of animals. After much debate, it was determined that the fortification of salt with iodine was the best solution. This action has reduced the incidence of goiter to <2.8% of individuals in developed countries.[15, 17]

Hyperthyroidism (high blood levels of thyroid hormone) is most commonly caused by Graves' disease, which is an autoimmune disease that causes an overproduction of thyroid hormones. The symptoms include weight loss, increased heat production, muscular tremors, nervousness, racing heart beat, and protrusion of the eyes.

Chromium

Chromium is a trace mineral that plays an important role in carbohydrate metabolism. You may be interested to learn that the chromium in the body is the same metal used in the chrome plating for cars. Chromium enhances the ability of insulin to transport glucose from the bloodstream into cells.[16] Chromium also plays important roles in the metabolism of RNA and DNA, in immune function, and in growth.

Figure 9.16 Goiter, or enlargement of the thyroid gland, occurs with both iodine toxicity and deficiency.

Saltwater fish, fresh or canned, contain iodine.

goiter Enlargement of the thyroid gland; can be caused by iodine toxicity or deficiency.

cretinism A unique form of mental retardation that occurs in infants when the mother experiences iodine deficiency during pregnancy.

hypothyroidism A condition characterized by low blood levels of thyroid hormone.

hyperthyroidism A condition characterized by high blood levels of thyroid hormone.

Our bodies contain very little chromium. Asparagus is a good dietary source of this trace mineral.

Chromium supplements are marketed to reduce body fat and enhance muscle mass and have become popular with bodybuilders and other athletes interested in improving their body composition. The Nutrition Myth or Fact? box below investigates whether taking supplemental chromium is effective in improving body composition.

The body needs only small amounts of chromium. The AI for adults aged 19 to 50 years is 35 µg/day for men and 25 µg/day for women. For adults 51 years of age and older, the AI decreases to 30 µg/day and 20 µg/day for men and women, respectively.[16] The AI for individuals over 50 years was based on the energy intake of older adults, which is typically lower than that of younger individuals.

The question of whether or not the average diet provides adequate chromium is controversial: chromium is widely distributed in foods, but concentrations in any particular food are not typically high. In addition, determining the chromium content of food is difficult because contamination can easily occur during the laboratory analysis. Thus, we cannot determine average chromium intake from any currently existing nutrient database.

Foods identified as good sources of chromium include mushrooms, prunes, dark chocolate, nuts, whole grains, cereals, asparagus, brewer's yeast, some beers, red wine, and

NUTRITION MYTH OR FACT?

Can Chromium Supplements Enhance Body Composition?

Chromium supplements, predominantly in the form of chromium picolinate, are popular with bodybuilders and weight lifters. This popularity stems from claims that chromium increases muscle mass and muscle strength and decreases body fat. But are these claims myth or fact?

An early study of chromium supplementation was promising, in that chromium use in both untrained men and football players was found to decrease body fat and increase muscle mass.[19] These findings caused a surge in the popularity of chromium supplements and motivated many scientists to test the reproducibility of these early findings. The next study of chromium supplementation found no effects of chromium on muscle mass, body fat, or muscle strength.[20]

These contradictory reports led experts to closely examine the two studies. When they did so, they found a number of flaws in the methodology of both. One major concern with the first study was that the chromium status of the research participants prior to the study was not measured or controlled.[19] It was possible that the participants were deficient in chromium; this deficiency could cause a more positive reaction to chromium than would be expected in people with normal chromium status. Thus, subsequent studies were designed to control for participants' pre-study chromium status.

A second major concern was that body composition was measured in these studies using the skinfold technique, in which calipers are used to measure the thickness of the skin and fat at various sites on the body. Although this method gives a good general estimate of body fat in young, lean, healthy people, it is not sensitive to small changes in muscle mass. Thus, subsequent studies of chromium used more sophisticated methods of measuring body composition.

The results of research studies conducted over the past 10 years consistently show that chromium supplementation has no effect on muscle mass, body fat, or muscle strength in a variety of groups, including untrained university males and females, overweight and obese females, collegiate wrestlers, and older men and women.[21–27] Neither have scientists found an effect of chromium on body composition when different types of experimental designs have been used, with varying energy intakes and exercise expenditure.[28, 29] Despite this overwhelming evidence to the contrary, many supplement companies still claim that chromium supplements enhance strength and muscle mass and reduce body fat. These claims result in millions of dollars of sales of supplements to consumers each year. Before you decide to purchase chromium supplements, read some of the studies cited here. The information they provide may help you avoid being one of the many consumers fooled by this costly nutrition myth.

meats, especially processed meats. Dairy products are typically poor sources of chromium. Food-processing methods can also add chromium to foods, especially if the food is processed in stainless steel containers. For example, it is assumed that wine and beer derive some of their chromium content from processing.[16]

There appears to be no toxicity related to consuming chromium in the diet, but there are insufficient data to establish a UL for chromium. Because chromium supplements are widely used in the United States and Canada, the Institute of Medicine (IOM) has recommended more research to determine the safety of high-dose chromium supplements. Until this research is available, supplementation with high amounts of chromium is discouraged. Chromium deficiency appears to be uncommon in North America. When chromium deficiency is induced in a research setting, glucose uptake into the cells is inhibited, causing a rise in blood glucose and insulin levels. Chromium deficiency can also result in elevated blood lipid levels and in damage to the brain and nervous system.[16]

Manganese

A trace mineral, manganese is a cofactor involved in protein, fat, and carbohydrate metabolism, gluconeogenesis, cholesterol synthesis, and the formation of urea, the primary component of urine.[30] It also assists in the synthesis of the protein matrix found in bone tissue and in building cartilage, a tissue supporting joints. Manganese is also an integral component of superoxide dismutase, an antioxidant enzyme. Thus, it assists in the conversion of free radicals to less damaging substances, protecting the body from oxidative damage (see Chapter 11).

The AI for manganese for adults 19 years of age and older is 2.3 mg/day for men and 1.8 mg/day for women. Manganese requirements are easily met, as this mineral is widespread in foods and is readily available in a varied diet. Whole-grain foods such as oat bran, wheat flour, whole-wheat spaghetti, and brown rice are good sources of manganese (**Figure 9.17**). Other sources include pineapple, pine nuts, okra, spinach, and raspberries. Overall, grain products contribute approximately 37% of dietary manganese, and vegetables and beverages, primarily tea, contribute another 18% to 20%.[16]

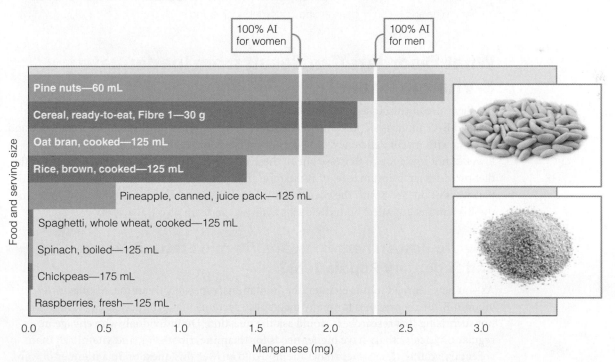

Figure 9.17 Common food sources of manganese. The AI for manganese is 2.3 mg/day for men and 1.8 mg/day for women.
Data from: The Canadian Nutrient File. Health Canada, 2012. Reproduced with the permission of the Minister of Health, 2012.

Okra is one of the many foods that contain manganese.

Manganese toxicity can occur in occupational environments in which people inhale manganese dust. It can also result from drinking water high in manganese. Toxicity results in impairment of the neuromuscular system, causing symptoms similar to those seen in Parkinson's disease, such as muscle spasms and tremors. Elevated blood manganese concentrations and neurotoxicity were the criteria used to determine the UL for manganese, which is 11 mg/day for adults 19 years of age and older.[16]

Manganese deficiency is rare in humans. Symptoms include impaired growth and reproductive function, reduced bone density and impaired skeletal growth, impaired glucose and lipid metabolism, and skin rash.

Sulphur

Sulphur is a major mineral and a component of the B-vitamins thiamine and biotin. As such, it is essential for macronutrient metabolism. In addition, as part of the amino acids methionine and cysteine, sulphur helps stabilize the three-dimensional shapes of proteins in the body. The liver requires sulphur to assist in the detoxification of alcohol and various drugs, and sulphur assists in maintaining acid–base balance.

The body is able to obtain ample sulphur from protein-containing foods; as a result, there is no DRI specifically for sulphur. There are no known toxicity or deficiency symptoms associated with sulphur.

Recap

Choline is a vitaminlike substance that is required for the production of phosphatidylcholine. Iodine is necessary for the synthesis of thyroid hormones, which regulate metabolic rate and body temperature. Chromium assists the transport of glucose into the cell, the metabolism of RNA and DNA, and immune function and growth. Manganese is involved in energy metabolism, the formation of urea, the synthesis of bone protein matrix and cartilage, and protection against free radicals. Sulphur is part of the B-vitamins thiamine and biotin and the amino acids methionine and cysteine.

What Disorders Can Result from Inadequate B-Vitamin Intake?

We have already discussed the classic deficiency diseases that can result when intake of selected B-vitamins is significantly inadequate, such as beriberi with thiamine deficiency and pellagra with niacin deficiency. However, what happens when intake of the B-vitamins is low, but not low enough to cause one of these deficiency diseases? What happens when the diet provides a minimum level of B-vitamins, but not enough to fully supply the metabolic pathways of the body with the coenzymes they need? Here, we discuss how a low intake of the B-vitamins can affect an individual's ability to perform physical activity.

How Do Researchers Compare Vitamin Status in Active and Sedentary Populations?

As you have learned in this chapter, the B-vitamins, especially thiamine, riboflavin, and vitamin B_6, are coenzymes for many metabolic reactions that produce energy. Thus, it is not surprising that researchers would ask the question: Do individuals who engage in regular physical activity have higher needs for thiamine, riboflavin, and vitamin B_6 than sedentary adults? Researchers have attempted to answer this question in a number of ways.

First, researchers have designed studies in which they identify individuals with poor B-vitamin status and then determine the impact of the low status on the individuals' ability to perform exercise. They can then compare the average performance of low-status individuals to the average performance of individuals with good B-vitamin status.

Second, they have performed controlled metabolic diet studies to determine if athletes need higher levels of B-vitamins than sedentary adults to maintain their vitamin status. For more information on this type of study, see the accompanying Highlight: How Do Scientists Determine Vitamin Requirements?

HIGHLIGHT

How Do Scientists Determine Vitamin Requirements?

Throughout this book, we identify the precise amounts of the different vitamins you need to consume each day to maintain good health. But have you ever wondered how researchers determine these recommendations? Of the several methods used, one of the most rigorous is the metabolic diet study.

The goal of a metabolic diet study is to determine how vitamin assessment parameters in the blood, urine, and feces change as the dietary intake of a nutrient, such as vitamin B_6, is closely controlled. In a metabolic diet study, which may last for weeks or months, all foods eaten by study participants are carefully prepared, weighed to within 0.1 g, and recorded. Subjects are usually required to either live at the research facility (where all physical activity is monitored) or come to the research facility for all of their meals. Depending on the nutrient being studied, all fluids, even water, may also be provided to the participant. Throughout the study, each participant's body weight is measured daily to prevent any increase or decrease in weight. If weight does change, energy intake is altered so that the subject returns to the baseline weight. This must be done without altering the intake of the vitamin being studied. Because many of the vitamins we talked about in this chapter help to metabolize protein, fat, and/or carbohydrate, it is important that the body stores of these macronutrients do not change during the metabolic study. This is why monitoring weight and physical activity is so important. At different times during the study, vitamin assessment parameters will be measured in the blood, urine, and feces. This may require that the subject collect all urine and feces throughout the study.

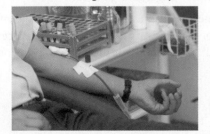

For example, let's say you want to determine whether active and sedentary men have different requirements for vitamin B_6. You know that during physical activity, carbohydrate is burned for fuel, and that protein is necessary for the building and repair of muscle tissue. You also know that vitamin B_6 is very important for glucose and protein metabolism; thus, physical activity might increase the body's need for this B-vitamin.

To compare vitamin B_6 requirements, you might design a study as follows. First you would recruit active young men between the ages of 20 and 35 years (all of equal fitness levels and exercising the same number of hours/week), as well as sedentary males of the same age. You would then feed the participants a succession of three different diets, each lasting three weeks, and each providing a different level of vitamin B_6. The diets would be

1. Vitamin B_6 below the RDA (1.0 mg/day);
2. Vitamin B_6 at the level of the RDA (1.3 mg/day); and
3. Vitamin B_6 above the RDA (1.6 mg/day).

Ideally, you would randomly assign these diets so that one individual might be fed diet number 1 while another individual is on diet number 2, and another is on diet number 3. By randomly assigning the diets, you ensure that you do not dictate the order in which they are fed. Because you don't want the effect of one diet to carry over to the next diet you are feeding, you would need to include a "washout" period between diets. How long this washout period lasted would depend on the vitamin you are researching, but for our example, six weeks should be long enough because vitamin B_6 is a water-soluble vitamin. During the washout period, all participants would be fed a diet providing the RDA for vitamin B_6 for normal healthy men.

During the study period, you would need to ensure that subjects do not eat any foods except what you feed them. In addition, study participants must be monitored to *make sure they eat all the food.* Throughout the study, the amount of vitamin B_6 in the foods would need to be determined via chemical analysis in a lab, as would the amount of vitamin B_6 in the participants' blood, urine, and fecal samples. You would also need to make sure all subjects maintained baseline body weights.

You would then determine nutritional status for the men when they were on each of the three test diets to determine which diet was able to keep assessment parameters within normal range. You would also compare vitamin status between groups for each of the diets. If the active men have poor status on 1.3 mg/day of vitamin B_6, while the sedentary subjects have adequate status on this level, you would conclude that the RDA is not adequate for the active individuals and they would need more vitamin B_6 to maintain good status.

Third, researchers have conducted cross-sectional studies that compare the nutritional status of trained athletes to sedentary individuals to determine the frequency of poor B-vitamin status in each group. A drawback of cross-sectional studies is that the two groups of people they compare may have other differences besides their fitness level that contribute to their differences in nutritional status. Cross-sectional studies help determine whether or not differences exist between two groups, but more detailed studies are needed to determine if those differences were due to level of physical activity alone.

The ideal study of the effect of physical activity on B-vitamin status would be longitudinal, controlling B-vitamin intake over several months in a study group of athletes, while varying their activity level from low to high. Researchers would then be able to monitor any changes in nutritional status and determine whether these changes affect an individual's ability to perform physical activity. Unfortunately, such studies are difficult and expensive to conduct.

What Evidence Links Exercise Performance and B-Vitamin Status?

Because of the role B-vitamins play in energy production during exercise, researchers generally assume that individuals with poor B-vitamin status will have a reduced ability to perform physical activity. This hypothesis has been supported in classic studies examining the effect of thiamine, riboflavin, and vitamin B_6 deficiency on work performance.[31–32]

For example, a team of Dutch researchers depleted 24 healthy active men of thiamine, riboflavin, and vitamin B_6 over an 11-week period by feeding them a diet high in processed foods (see the diet below).[31] Specifically, the diet contained only 50% of the RDA for thiamine, riboflavin, and vitamin B_6. Researchers then examined the effect of this B-vitamin deficiency on the men's ability to perform physical activity. They found that B-vitamin depletion significantly decreased the ability to perform maximal work by 7% to 12%, depending on the testing method used. Thus, it took only 11 weeks of eating a low-B-vitamin diet before these men were unable to exercise at the same intensity and duration as they had when they were consuming adequate amounts of these vitamins. Exercise may increase the need for B-vitamins; however, this need should easily be met by the increases in food intake required to meet the increased energy needs and supplements are not required.

What Types of Diets Are Low in B-Vitamins?

Diets high in unenriched processed foods would provide inadequate levels of the B-vitamins. In the Dutch study just described, feeding a diet high in processed foods produced poor vitamin status in just 11 weeks.[31, 32] The diet used in this study included rolls, cakes, and cookies made with unenriched white flour.

- Breakfast: white rolls, margarine, cheese, jam
- Lunch: white rolls, margarine, cheese, beef, jam, peanut butter
- Dinner: white rice, carrots, green peas, beans, margarine, applesauce, beef, cream, peaches
- Snacks: soft drinks, honey cake, cookies, tea, coffee, sugar, margarine

In 1976 Health Canada mandated the enrichment of refined flour sold in Canada with thiamine, riboflavin, niacin, and iron. Thus, most of the nutrients lost in the milling process are replaced by the enrichment process. Further, all processed foods made with white flour must be made from enriched white flour.

In Canada, all foods made from white flour must be made from enriched white flour.

RECAP

The hypothesis that individuals with poor B-vitamin status will have a reduced ability to perform physical activity has been supported in studies examining the effect of thiamine, riboflavin, and vitamin B_6 deficiency on work performance. Consuming a diet high in whole grains, fruits, vegetables, and lean meats and dairy will ensure that your body has adequate B-vitamins to fuel physical activity. In Canada, most of the nutrients lost in the milling of grains are replaced by the enrichment process.

SEE FOR YOURSELF

Meeting Your RDA for Vitamin B₆

Open up your cupboard and take a look inside. How many processed foods providing B-vitamins do you consume on a typical day? Pull out all such foods, including breads, ready-to-eat cereals, pasta, energy bars, meal replacement drinks, and so forth. Then, if you take any supplements, including vitamins, protein powders, weight loss supplements, and so forth, line those up, too.

Now, let's see if we can determine whether you are meeting or exceeding your RDA for vitamin B₆. We'll limit our analysis to B₆ because it is one of the B-vitamins with a UL. Use the template provided below to document

your vitamin B₆ intake for a typical day. On food labels, the amount of the vitamin will be given as a percentage of the daily value (%DV). Thus, you will first have to write down the %DV for each serving. Be sure to look at the serving size! If you eat two servings, you will need to multiply this value by two, and so on. Finally, convert the %DV to the amount that you ate. For vitamin B₆, 100% of the DV is 1.8 mg. The You Do the Math box on page 51 in Chapter 2 will also help you with this activity. Notice that we have filled in one line of the template as an example.

Meal	Food	%DV for B₆	Servings	%DV per serving	B₆ consumed (mg)
Breakfast	Mini-Wheats	20%	2	40%	0.7 mg
Lunch					
Snack					
Dinner					
Supplements					
Total mg B₆/day:					

How much vitamin B₆ did you get each day from processed foods and supplements alone? How much additional vitamin B₆ would you estimate you get in whole foods, such as meat, fish, poultry, starchy vegetables, and bananas? Are

you close to the UL for vitamin B₆ (100 mg for adults age 19–70)? Although this assignment was designed to look at vitamin B₆, you could look at other micronutrients in your diet that have a UL.

CASE STUDY — Energizing B-Vitamins

Emily is a 32-year-old mother of three young boys who is feeling tired and run down. She has been extremely busy lately and knows that she hasn't been eating as well as she should. Her friend Isra, who works at a health food store, suggests that she should start taking a new supplement that they carry called PEP. It is designed to boost energy.

After taking PEP for about a week, Emily sees a documentary on healthy eating that cautions against taking vitamin supplements because they can be toxic. She brings the bottle to you and asks for your advice.

PEP - Pure Energy Power	
Each capsule contains:	
Thiamine	20 mg
Riboflavin	20 mg
Niacin	30 mg
Vitamin B_6	35 mg
Pantothenic acid	10 mg
Folic acid	100 µg
Vitamin B_{12}	10 µg
Biotin	10 µg
Choline	500 mg

Directions: Take 3 capsules daily

Thinking Critically

1. **Are all of the components of this supplement considered essential vitamins?**
2. **Create a table comparing the amount of each ingredient in a daily dose of this supplement to the RDA or AI and the UL.**
3. **Do any of the ingredients in this supplement pose a risk of toxicity at this dosage? If yes, explain the health risk.**
4. **Would you recommend that Emily continue taking this product? Why or why not?**

Chapter Review

9

Test Yourself | Answers

1. **F** B-vitamins do not directly provide energy. However, they play critical roles in ensuring that the body is able to generate energy from carbohydrates, fats, and proteins.
2. **T** A severe niacin deficiency can cause pellagra, which once killed thousands of people in North America each year; and thiamine deficiency causes beriberi, which can result in heart failure.
3. **F** The IOM has set ULs for both niacin and vitamin B_6. High intakes of these nutrients can cause adverse effects.
4. **F** Research studies have failed to show any consistent effects of chromium supplements on reducing body fat or enhancing muscle mass.
5. **T** Canada has mandatory iodization of table salt.

Summary

- The B-vitamins include thiamine, riboflavin, vitamin B_6, niacin, folate, vitamin B_{12}, pantothenic acid, and biotin.

- The primary role of thiamine, riboflavin, niacin, pantothenic acid, and biotin is to act as coenzymes. In this role, they activate enzymes and assist them in the metabolism of carbohydrates, fats, amino acids, and alcohol for energy; the synthesis of fatty acids and cholesterol; and gluconeogenesis.

- Food sources of the B-vitamins include whole grains, enriched breads, ready-to-eat cereals, meats, dairy products, and some fruits and vegetables.

- A deficiency of thiamine can cause beriberi, and a deficiency of niacin can cause pellagra.

- Toxicity is possible with megadoses of some B-vitamins from supplements.

- Choline is a vitaminlike substance that assists with homocysteine metabolism. Choline also accelerates the synthesis and release of acetylcholine, a neurotransmitter.

- Iodine is a trace mineral needed for the synthesis of thyroid hormones. Thyroid hormones are integral to the regulation of body temperature, maintenance of resting metabolic rate, and healthy reproduction and growth.

- Chromium is a trace mineral that enhances the ability of insulin to transport glucose from the bloodstream into the cell. Chromium is also necessary for the metabolism of RNA and DNA and supports normal growth and immune function.

- Manganese is a trace mineral that acts as a cofactor in energy metabolism and in the formation of urea. Manganese also assists in the synthesis of bone and cartilage and is a component of the superoxide dismutase antioxidant enzyme system.

- Sulphur is a major mineral that is a component of thiamine and biotin and the amino acids methionine and cysteine. Sulphur helps stabilize the three-dimensional shapes of proteins and helps the liver detoxify alcohol and various drugs.

- Inadequate levels of the B-vitamins can reduce an individual's ability to perform physical activity.

Review Questions

1. The B-vitamins include
   a. niacin, folate, and iodine.
   b. cobalamin, iodine, and chromium.
   c. manganese, riboflavin, and pyridoxine.
   d. thiamine, pantothenic acid, and biotin.

2. Which of the following statements about choline is true?
   a. Choline is found exclusively in foods of animal origin.
   b. Choline is a B-vitamin that assists in homocysteine metabolism.
   c. Choline is a neurotransmitter that is involved in muscle movement and memory storage.
   d. Choline is necessary for the synthesis of phospholipids and other components of cell membranes.

3. According to the World Health Organization (WHO), the greatest single cause of preventable brain damage and mental retardation in the world is
   a. iodine deficiency.
   b. chromium deficiency.
   c. manganese deficiency.
   d. sulphur deficiency.

4. Which of the following lunches provides the highest levels of thiamine, riboflavin, niacin, and vitamin B_6?
   a. cheeseburger on a white bun, French fries, applesauce, diet soda
   b. tuna sandwich on whole-wheat bread, green peas, banana, 1 cup of low-fat milk

   c. yogourt parfait (made with plain low-fat yogourt, canned peaches, and raw, unprocessed oats) and fresh-squeezed orange juice
   d. green salad with olive oil and vinegar dressing, low-fat cottage cheese, a slice of sourdough bread with butter, and water

5. Which of the following statements is true of riboflavin?
   a. It is sensitive to heat.
   b. It is a component of CoA.
   c. It is associated primarily with protein metabolism.
   d. It is water soluble.

6. Kyle has been abusing alcohol for over 20 years. He has recently been diagnosed with Wernicke-Korsakoff syndrome and has been told that it is related to a thiamine deficiency. Explain why a high alcohol intake contributes to thiamine deficiency.

7. Colin is a bodybuilder who consumes an eggnog drink containing six raw eggs daily. Explain to Colin why this might lead to a biotin deficiency.

8. Would you expect goiter to be more common in coastal regions or inland? Explain your answer.

9. Explain the statement that, without vitamin B_6, all amino acids become essential.

10. Aaron eats only whole, unprocessed foods and beverages. He asserts that "we would all be better off if we ate foods fresh off the farm" instead of allowing our food industry to "spray"

foods with factory-produced vitamins and minerals. Do you agree with Aaron's position? Why or why not?

11. Your great-aunt is on renal dialysis. Explain the implications, if any, for her B-vitamin status.

12. Sally is 35 years old and has always been energetic; however, lately she has been feeling exhausted. She can hardly get out of bed in the morning even after eight hours of sleep. She has attributed this fatigue to the fact that she has been dieting for weight loss for the last six months and is using a low-sodium, low-calorie vegan diet (1000 kcal/day) that she also hopes will help reduce her blood pressure. She is eating lots of fruits and vegetables, but little else. Although she knows it is important to exercise for weight loss, she is too tired. What do you think might be contributing to Sally's fatigue? Of the micronutrients discussed in this chapter, which ones might be low in her diet? How might they contribute to fatigue?

Web Links

www.bbc.co.uk/health/treatments/healthy_living/nutrition/
BBC Healthy Living: Nutrition
Click on one of the vitamin or mineral links under "Dietary Requirements" to find information on vitamins and minerals, signs of deficiency, therapeutic uses, and food sources.

www.unicef.org/nutrition/index.html
UNICEF: Nutrition
This site provides information about micronutrient deficiencies in developing countries and UNICEF's efforts and programs to combat them.

www.who.int/nutrition/topics/micronutrients/en/
World Health Organization (WHO): Nutrition
This site provides information on nutrient deficiencies throughout the world, including iodine deficiency disorders (IDDs).

http://ods.od.nih.gov
National Institutes of Health (NIH) Office of Dietary Supplements
This site provides information on vitamins and minerals, safe use of supplements, and the research available on the treatment of health problems and disease with various supplements.

www.hc-sc.gc.ca/fn-an/nutrition/fiche-nutri-data/index-eng.php
Canadian Nutrient File
The Canadian Nutrient File is an online, searchable database that allows Canadians to search the nutrient values for over 5800 foods.

www.micronutrient.org/english/view.asp?x=1
The Micronutrient Initiative
The Micronutrient Initiative (MI) is the leading organization working exclusively to eliminate vitamin and mineral deficiencies in the world's most vulnerable populations.

www.acdi-cida.gc.ca/acdi-cida/ACDI-CIDA.nsf/En/FRA-4422402-563
Canadian International Development Agency (CIDA)
Explore this site to see Canada's response to preventing micronutrient deficiencies in developing countries around the world.

MasteringNutrition®

www.masteringnutrition.pearson.com

Study Area
Video: Introduction to the Functional Approach & Understanding Energy Metabolism • Practice Tests • Diet Analysis • eText

References

1. James, N. 2002. Malnutrition data, food security and the geography of food in a communal area of North West Zimbabwe. *Global Built Environment Review* 2(3):42–53. Available online at www.edgehill.account.uk/gber/pdf/vol2/issue3.

2. Tanphaichiter, V. 1999. Thiamine. In: M. E. Shils, J. A. Olson, M. Shire, and A. C. Ross, eds. *Modern Nutrition in Health and Disease*, 9th ed. Philadelphia: Lippincott Williams & Wilkins, pp. 381–389.

3. Smith, C., A. D. Marks, and M. Lieberman. 2005. *Mark's Basic Medical Biochemistry: A Clinical Approach*. 2nd ed. Philadelphia: Lippincott Williams & Wilkins.

4. Health Canada and Statistics Canada. 2009. Canadian Community Health Survey, Cycle 2.2, Nutrition (2004)—Nutrient Intakes from Food: Provincial, Regional and National Data Tables Volumes 1, 2, & 3 Disk. Ottawa: Health Canada publications.

5. Institute of Medicine, Food and Nutrition Board. 1998. *Dietary Reference Intakes for Thiamine, Riboflavin, Niacin, Vitamin B_6, Folate, Vitamin B_{12}, Pantothenic Acid, Biotin, and Choline*. Washington, DC: National Academy Press.

6. McCormick, D. B. 2000. Niacin, riboflavin, and thiamine. In: M. H. Stipanuk, ed. *Biochemical and Physiological Aspects*

of Human Nutrition. Philadelphia: W. B. Saunders, pp. 458–482.

7. Powers, H. J. 2003. Riboflavin (vitamin B₂) and health. *Am. J. Clin. Nutr.* 77:1352–1360.

8. Manore, M. M. 2000. Effect of physical activity on thiamine, riboflavin, and vitamin B₆ requirements. *Am. J. Clin. Nutr.* 72:598S–606S.

9. Woolf, K., and M. M. Manore. 1999. Nutrition, exercise and rheumatoid arthritis. *Topics Clin. Nutr.* 14(3):30–42.

10. Sweetman, L. 2000. Pantothenic acid and biotin. In: M. H. Stipanuk, ed. *Biochemical and Physiological Aspects of Human Nutrition*. Philadelphia: W. B. Saunders, pp. 519–540.

11. Taylor, J., L. Van Til, and D. MacLellan. 2002. *Prince Edward Island Nutrition Survey*. Charlottetown, PEI: University of Prince Edward Island Family and Nutritional Sciences and Prince Edward Island Department of Health and Social Services.

12. Sante-Quebec. 1995. Les Québécoises et les Québécois-Mangent-ils mieux? Rapport de l'enquête Québécoise sur la nutrition, 1990. Montréal: Ministère se la Santé et des Services Sociaux, Gouvernement du Québec.

13. Innis, S. M., and D. Hasman. 2006. Evidence of Choline Depletion and reduced betaine and dimethylglycine with increased homocysteine in plasma of children with cystic fibrosis. *J. Nutr.* 136:2226–2231.

14. Dunn, J. T. 2006. Iodine. In: M. E. Shils, M. Shike, A. C. Ross, B. Caballero, and R. Cousins, eds. *Modern Nutrition in Health and Disease*. 10th ed. Philadelphia: Lippincott Williams & Wilkins, pp. 300–311.

15. Freake, H. C. 2000. Iodine. In: M. H. Stipanuk, ed. *Biochemical and Physiological Aspects of Human Nutrition*. Philadelphia: W. B. Saunders, pp. 761–781.

16. Institute of Medicine, Food and Nutrition Board. 2001. *Dietary Reference Intakes for Vitamin A, Vitamin K, Arsenic, Boron, Chromium, Copper, Iodine, Iron, Manganese, Molybdenum, Nickel, Silicon, Vanadium, and Zinc*. Washington, DC: National Academy Press.

17. World Health Organization. 2004. Nutrition. Micronutrient deficiencies. International Council of Control of Iodine Deficiency Disorders. Available online at www.who.dk/eprise/main/WHO/Progs/NUT/Deficiency.

18. International Council for the Control of Iodine Deficiency Disorders (ICCIDD). Iodine deficiency. www.iccidd.org/pages/iodine-deficiency.php (accessed February 2009.)

19. Evans, G. W. 1989. The effect of chromium picolinate on insulin controlled parameters in humans. *Int. J. Biosoc. Med. Res.* 11:163–180.

20. Hasten, D. L., E. P. Rome, D. B. Franks, and M. Hegsted. 1992. Effects of chromium picolinate on beginning weight training students. *Int. J. Sports Nutr.* 2:343–350.

21. Lukaski, H. C., W. W. Bolonchuk, W. A. Siders, and D. B. Milne. 1996. Chromium supplementation and resistance training: effects on body composition, strength, and trace element status of men. *Am. J. Clin. Nutr.* 63:954–965.

22. Hallmark, M. A., T. H. Reynolds, C. A. DeSouza, C. O. Dotson, R. A. Anderson, and M. A. Rogers. 1996. Effects of chromium and resistive training on muscle strength and body composition. *Med. Sci. Sports Exerc.* 28:139–144.

23. Pasman, W. J., M. S. Westerterp-Plantenga, and W. H. Saris. 1997. The effectiveness of long-term supplementation of carbohydrate, chromium, fiber and caffeine on weight maintenance. *Int. J. Obes. Relat. Metab. Disord.* 21:1143–1151.

24. Walker, L. S., M. G. Bemben, D. A. Bemben, and A. W. Knehans. 1998. Chromium picolinate effects on body composition and muscular performance in wrestlers. *Med. Sci. Sports Exerc.* 30:1730–1737.

25. Campbell, W. W., L. J. Joseph, S. L. Davey, D. Cyr-Campbell, R. A. Anderson, and W. J. Evans. 1999. Effects of resistance training and chromium picolinate on body composition and skeletal muscle in older men. *J. Appl. Physiol.* 86:29–39.

26. Volpe, S. L., H. W. Huang, K. Larpadisorn, and I. I. Lesser. 2001. Effect of chromium supplementation and exercise on body composition, resting metabolic rate and selected biochemical parameters in moderately obese women following an exercise program. *J. Am. Coll. Nutr.* 20:293–306.

27. Campbell, W. W., L. J. O. Joseph, R. A. Anderson, S. L. Davey, J. Hinton, and W. J. Evans. 2002. Effects of resistive training and chromium picolinate on body composition and skeletal muscle size in older women. *Int. J. Sports Nutr. Exerc. Metab.* 12:125–135.

28. Diaz, L. D., B. A. Watkin, Y. Li, R. A. Anderson, and W. W. Campbell. 2008. Chromium picolinate and conjugated linoleic acid do not synergistically influence diet- and exercise-induced changes in body composition and health indexes in overweight women. *J Nutr. Biochemistry* 19:61–68.

29. Lukaski, H. C., W. A. Siders, and J. G. Penland. 2007. Chromium picolinate supplementation in women: effects on body weight, composition and iron status. *Nutr.* 23:187–195.

30. Fleet, J. C. 2000. Zinc, copper and manganese. In: M. H. Stipanuk, ed. *Biochemical and Physiological Aspects of Human Nutrition*. Philadelphia: W.B. Saunders, pp. 741–761.

31. van der Beek, E. J., W. van Dokkum, J. Schrijver, M. Wedel, A. W. K. Gaillard, A. Wesstra, H. van de Weerd, and R. J. J. Hermus. 1988. Thiamine, riboflavin, and vitamins B₆ and C: impact of combined restricted intake on functional performance in man. *Am. J. Clin. Nutr.* 48:1451–1462.

32. van der Beek, E. J., W. van Dokkum, M. Wedel, J. Schrijver, and H. van den Berg. 1994. Thiamine, riboflavin and vitamin B₆: impact of restricted intake on physical performance in man. *J. Am. Coll. Nutr.* 13:629–640.

33. Wyatt, K. M., P. W. Dimmock, P. W. Jones, and P. M. Shaughn O'Brien. 1999. Efficacy of vitamin B₆ in the treatment of premenstrual syndrome: systemic review. *Br. J. Med.* 318:1375–1381.

34. Freeman, E. W. 2003. Premenstrual syndrome and premenstrual dysphoric disorder: definitions and diagnosis. *Psychoneuroendocrinology* 28:25–37.

35. Rapkin, A. 2003. The review of treatment of premenstrual syndrome & premenstrual dysphoric disorder. *Psychoneuroendocrinology* 28:39–53.

36. Thys-Jacobs, S. 2000. Micronutrients and the premenstrual syndrome: the case for calcium. *J. Am. Coll. Nutr.* 19:220–227.

37. Bendich, A. 2000. The potential for dietary supplements to reduce premenstrual syndrome (PMS) symptoms. *J. Am. Coll. Nutr.* 29(1):3–12.

38. Schaumburg, H., J. Kaplan, A. Winderbank, N. Vick, S. Rasmus, D. Pleasure, and M. J. Brown. 1983. Sensory neuropathy from pyridoxine abuse: a new megavitamin syndrome. *N. Engl. J. Med.* 309:445–448.

39. Wyatt, K.M., Dimmock, P.W., Jones, P.W. and S. O'Brien. 1999. Efficacy of vitamin B-6 in the treatment of premenstrual syndrome: systematic review. *BMJ* 318:1375–1381.

40. Fugh-Berman, A., and F. Kronenbertg. 2003. Complementary and alternative medicine (CAM) in reproductive-age women: a review of randomized controlled trials. *Reproductive Toxicology* 17:137–152.

Treating Premenstrual Syndrome with Vitamin B$_6$: Does It Work? Is It Risky?

Perform an internet search for treatments for premenstrual syndrome (PMS) and you are likely to find many recommendations for supplementing with high doses of vitamin B$_6$. In addition, almost any PMS supplement sold in a pharmacy or health food store will contain 50 to 200 mg of vitamin B$_6$ per capsule or tablet, with the recommendation that the consumer take at least two capsules per day. As you learned in this chapter, the UL of vitamin B$_6$ is 100 mg/day, and high doses of vitamin B$_6$ over an extended period of time can cause neurologic disorders. Is there research to support recommending high levels of vitamin B$_6$ for PMS? Do the benefits of supplementing outweigh the risk of toxicity?

What Is PMS?

PMS is a disorder characterized by a cluster of symptoms triggered by hormonal changes that occur one to two weeks prior to the start of menstruation. These symptoms typically fall into the three general categories in the following bulleted list.[33–35] These categories are also used by the American College of Obstetricians and Gynecologists in the diagnosis of PMS.

- Physical symptoms: Fluid retention leading to bloating, breast tenderness, weight gain, abdominal discomfort and pain, and headache pain
- Behavioural symptoms: Appetite changes, especially cravings for sweets, dairy products, and alcohol; sleep disturbances; poor concentration; and social withdrawal
- Mood symptoms: Depression and anxiety, including irritability, tension, feeling out of control, crying without reason, rapid mood changes, and/or aggression

For a woman to be diagnosed with PMS, she typically has to complain of at least one moderate to severe mood symptom and one physical symptom.[35] It is estimated that 90% of menstruating women experience at least a mild form of one or more of these symptoms, 30% to 50% experience troublesome symptoms, and 5% have severe symptoms that impact their work and health.[36]

Currently, there is no universally accepted medical treatment for PMS. Not surprisingly, given the diversity of associated symptoms, a wide variety of therapies have been promoted, including megadoses of vitamins (vitamin B$_6$ and vitamin E), minerals (calcium,

Headaches, anxiety, irritability, tension, and depression are common symptoms of PMS.

magnesium), amino acid supplements (L-tryptophan), and herbs (St. John's wort, kava-kava, chaste tree fruit, and *dong quai*).[35, 37] Unfortunately, some of these remedies, such as vitamin B$_6$, have the potential for negative health consequences if taken in excess.

Vitamin B$_6$ Toxicity

In 1983, the *New England Journal of Medicine* first reported the development of sensory neuropathy (a disorder affecting the sensory nerves) in individuals taking high doses of pyridoxine, the most common form of vitamin B$_6$ in supplements.[38] In this report, the researchers described seven individuals, ranging from 20 to 43 years of age, with serious neurotoxicity associated with megadoses of pyridoxine.

Five of the individuals began with 50 to 100 mg/day of vitamin B$_6$ before steadily increasing their dose in an attempt to derive a benefit. In one case, a 27-year-old woman began taking 500 mg/day of vitamin B$_6$ to treat premenstrual edema. Over the course of a year, she gradually increased her dose to 5000 mg/day (5 g/day), which is 50 times higher than the UL for vitamin B$_6$. She reported a tingling sensation in her neck, legs, and feet; numbness in her hands and feet; impaired walking; and impairment in handling small objects. She also noticed changes in the feeling in her lips and tongue. Within two months of stopping her supplement, she began to see improvement in her gait and sensation, but it was seven months before she could walk without a cane. At the time the report was written, the numbness in her legs and hands had still not improved.

A total of four of the seven individuals became so severely disabled they could not walk or could walk only with a cane. The other individuals experienced less severe symptoms, including "lightninglike" pains in their calves and shins, especially after exercise. Unfortunately, none of the individuals reported that the supplements had improved their premenstrual edema, made them feel better, or improved their mood, the reasons they gave for taking the supplement in the first place.

In summary, four of the seven individuals began feeling better within six months after stopping supplementation but still had diminished sensory perception. Two individuals did not experience recovery until two to three years after supplementation stopped.

Does Research Support the Treatment of PMS with Vitamin B$_6$?

Does a review of the research literature support the use of high doses of vitamin B$_6$ for the treatment of PMS? To date, there have been nine randomized clinical trials testing whether vitamin B$_6$ supplementation improves PMS symptoms. These nine trials, including 940 subjects, were systematically reviewed by researchers in the United Kingdom to determine if there was enough evidence to recommend using vitamin B$_6$ as a treatment for PMS.[39] Unfortunately, none of the clinical trials met the highest criteria set for research quality. The results show that about half of the studies reported some positive effects of vitamin B$_6$ supplements on PMS symptoms when compared with the placebo group, but frequently the improvement was only for some of the symptoms. The authors concluded that "there was insufficient evidence of high enough quality to give a confident recommendation for using vitamin B$_6$ in the treatment of PMS."[39]

Some of the problems observed when reviewing these studies reveal why the authors could not give definitive

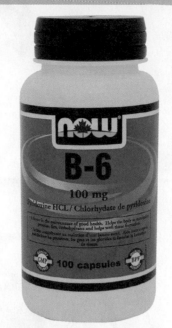

Vitamin B$_6$: Do the potential benefits outweigh the risk of toxicity?

recommendations. For example, one study showed that 58% of the individuals taking vitamin B$_6$ felt better, but then so did 59% of the individuals taking the placebo; thus, there were no differences between the groups. Many of the studies showed improvement in only some of the symptoms of PMS, such as anxiety and food cravings, but not headaches and depression. Finally, the level of treatment varied in the studies from 50 to 600 mg/day of vitamin B$_6$. Thus, although some studies suggest a benefit, the evidence for efficacy of treating PMS with vitamin B$_6$ is not convincing and further research is needed.[35, 37, 39, 40]

Using the Evidence

1. Do you think the limited benefits of treating PMS with vitamin B$_6$ outweigh the risks of vitamin B$_6$ toxicity?

2. What would you do if a friend told you she was taking 100 mg/day of vitamin B$_6$ for PMS?

3. What if she told you she was taking twice that amount and had been doing so for several months?

10

Nutrients Involved in Fluid and Electrolyte Balance

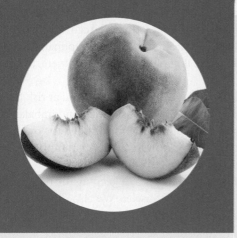

Test Yourself | True or False?

1. About 50% to 70% of body weight is made up of fluid. **T** *or* F

2. Sodium is an unhealthy nutrient, and we should avoid consuming it in our diets. **T** *or* F

3. Drinking until we are no longer thirsty always ensures that we are properly hydrated. **T** *or* F

4. Although more expensive than tap water, bottled water provides additional health and nutritional benefits. **T** *or* F

5. Eating a high-sodium diet causes high blood pressure in most individuals. **T** *or* F

Test Yourself answers are located in the Chapter Review.

Chapter Objectives | *After reading this chapter, you will be able to:*

1. Distinguish between extracellular fluid, intracellular fluid, interstitial fluid, and intravascular fluid, *pp. 332–333*.
2. Identify at least four nutrients that function as electrolytes in our bodies, *pp. 333–334*.
3. Discuss how the kidneys regulate blood pressure and blood volume, *p. 334*.
4. List at least three functions of water in our bodies, *pp. 334–335*.
5. Describe how electrolytes assist in the regulation of healthy fluid balance, *pp. 335–337*.
6. Discuss the physical changes that occur to trigger the thirst mechanism, *pp. 338–339*.
7. Describe the avenues of fluid intake and excretion in our bodies, *pp. 339–340*.
8. Define hyponatremia and identify factors that can cause this condition, *p. 347*.
9. Identify four symptoms of dehydration, *pp. 352–353*.
10. Define hypertension and list three lifestyle changes that can reduce it, *pp. 353–356*.

n April 2002, Cynthia Lucero, a healthy 28-year-old woman who had just completed her doctoral dissertation, was running the Boston Marathon. Although not a professional athlete, Cynthia was running in her second marathon and had trained carefully. While her parents, who had travelled from Ecuador, waited at the finish line, friends in the crowd watched as Cynthia steadily completed kilometre after kilometre, drinking large amounts of water as she progressed through the course. They described her as looking strong until she began to jog up Heartbreak Hill, about 10 kilometres from the finish. She drank more fluid, but a few minutes later began to visibly falter. One of her friends ran to her side and asked if she was okay. Cynthia replied that she felt dehydrated and rubber-legged, and then she fell to the pavement. She was rushed to nearby Brigham and Women's Hospital, but by the time she got there, she was in an irreversible coma. The official cause of her death was hyponatremia, commonly called "low blood sodium." According to a study involving the 488 runners in that 2002 Boston Marathon, 13% had hyponatremia by the end of the race. Hyponatremia continues to cause illness and death in runners, triathletes, and even hikers.[1]

What is hyponatremia, and how does it differ from dehydration? Are you at risk for either condition? Do sports beverages confer any protection against these fluid imbalances? If at the start of football practice on a hot, humid afternoon, a friend confided to you that he had been on a drinking binge the night before and had vomited twice that morning, what would you say to him? Would you urge him to tell his coach, and if so, why?

In this chapter, we explore the role of fluids and electrolytes in keeping the body properly hydrated and maintaining the functions of nerves and muscles. We also discuss how blood pressure is maintained and take a look at some disorders that occur when fluids and electrolytes are out of balance.

What Are Fluids and Electrolytes, and What Are Their Functions?

Of course you know that orange juice, blood, and shampoo are all fluids, but what makes them so? A **fluid** is characterized by its ability to move freely and changeably, adapting to the shape of the container that holds it. This might not seem very important, but as you'll learn in this chapter, the fluid composition of cells and tissues is critical to the body's ability to function.

Body Fluid Is the Liquid Portion of Cells and Tissues

Between about 50% and 70% of a healthy adult's body weight is fluid. When we cut a finger, we can see some of this fluid dripping out as blood, but the fluid in the bloodstream can't account for such a large percentage of one's total body weight. So where is all this fluid hiding?

About two-thirds of the body's fluid is held within the walls of cells and is therefore called **intracellular fluid** (**Figure 10.1a**). Every cell in the body contains fluid. When cells lose their fluid, they quickly shrink and die. On the other hand, when cells take in too much fluid, they swell and burst apart. This is why appropriate fluid balance—which we'll discuss throughout this chapter—is so critical to life.

The remaining third of the body's fluid is referred to as **extracellular fluid** because it flows outside of the cells (see Figure 10.1a). There are two types of extracellular fluid:

1. **Interstitial fluid** flows between the cells that make up a particular tissue or organ, such as muscle fibres or the liver (Figure 10.1b).
2. **Intravascular fluid** is the water in the bloodstream and lymph. *Plasma* is specifically the extracellular fluid portion of blood that transports blood cells within the body's arteries, veins, and capillaries (Figure 10.1c).

Not every tissue in the body contains the same amount of fluid. Lean tissues, such as muscle, are more than 70% fluid, whereas fat tissue is only between 10% and 20% fluid.

fluid A substance composed of molecules that move past one another freely. Fluids are characterized by their ability to conform to the shape of whatever container holds them.

intracellular fluid The fluid held at any given time within the walls of the body's cells.

extracellular fluid The fluid outside of the body's cells, either in the body's tissues (interstitial fluid) or as the liquid portion of the blood or lymph (intravascular fluid).

interstitial fluid The fluid that flows between the cells that make up a particular tissue or organ, such as muscle fibres or the liver.

intravascular fluid The fluid in the bloodstream and lymph.

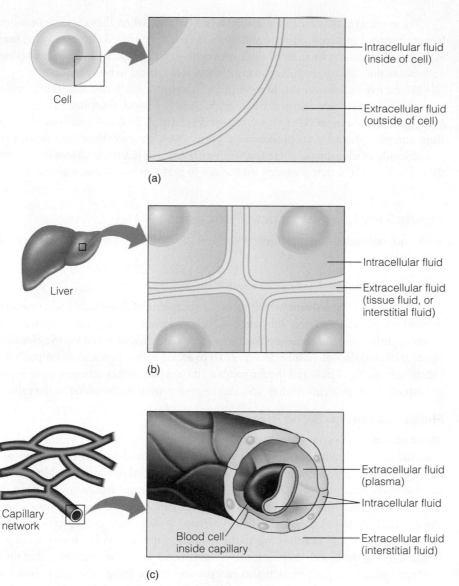

Cell

(a)

Intracellular fluid
(inside of cell)

Extracellular fluid
(outside of cell)

Liver

(b)

Intracellular fluid

Extracellular fluid
(tissue fluid, or
interstitial fluid)

Capillary
network

Blood cell
inside capillary

(c)

Extracellular fluid
(plasma)

Intracellular fluid

Extracellular fluid
(interstitial fluid)

Figure 10.1 The components of body fluid. (a) Intracellular fluid is contained within the cells that make up our body tissues. Extracellular fluid is external to cells. (b) Interstitial fluid is external to tissue cells, and (c) plasma is external to blood cells.

This is not surprising considering the hydrophobic nature of lipid cells, which was discussed in Chapter 5.

Body fluid levels also vary according to gender and age. Males have more lean tissue and thus a higher percentage of body weight as fluid than females. The amount of body fluid as a percentage of total weight decreases with age. About 75% of an infant's body weight is water, whereas the total body water of an older person is generally less than 50% of body weight. This decrease in total body water is, in part, a result of the loss of lean tissue that can occur as people age.

Body Fluid Is Composed of Water and Dissolved Substances Called Electrolytes

Water is made up of molecules consisting of two hydrogen atoms bound to one oxygen atom (H_2O). Although water is essential to maintain life, we would quickly die if our cell and tissue fluids contained only water. Instead, within the body fluids are a variety of dissolved substances (called *solutes*) critical to life. These include major minerals such as sodium, calcium, potassium, chloride, and phosphorous. We consume these minerals in compounds called *salts,* including table salt, which is made of sodium and chloride.

As we age, our body water content decreases: approximately 75% of an infant's body weight is composed of water, whereas an older adult's is only 50% (or less).

These mineral salts are called **electrolytes**, because when they dissolve in water the two component minerals separate and form electrically charged particles called **ions**. This electrical charge, which can be positive or negative, is the "spark" that stimulates nerves and causes muscles to contract, making electrolytes critical to body function.

Of the five major minerals just mentioned, sodium (Na^+), calcium (Ca^{2+}), and potassium (K^+) are positively charged, whereas chloride (Cl^-) and phosphorous (in the form of hydrogen phosphate, or HPO_4^{2-}) are negatively charged. In the intracellular fluid, potassium and phosphate are the predominant electrolytes. In the extracellular fluid, sodium and chloride predominate. There is a slight difference in electrical charge on either side of the cell's membrane that is needed for the cell to perform its normal functions.

Fluids Serve Many Critical Functions

Water not only quenches our thirst; it performs a number of functions that are critical to support life.

Fluids Dissolve and Transport Substances

Water is an excellent **solvent**, which means it is capable of dissolving a wide variety of substances. All water-soluble substances—such as amino acids, glucose, the water-soluble vitamins, minerals, and some medications—are readily transported via the bloodstream. In contrast, fats do not dissolve in water. To overcome this chemical incompatibility, fatty substances such as lipids and the fat-soluble vitamins are either attached to or surrounded by water-soluble proteins so they, too, can be transported in the blood to the cells.

Fluids Account for Blood Volume

Blood volume is the amount of fluid in blood; thus, appropriate body fluid levels are essential to maintaining healthy blood volume. When blood volume rises inappropriately, blood pressure increases; when blood volume decreases inappropriately, blood pressure decreases. As you know, high blood pressure is an important risk factor for heart disease and stroke, whereas low blood pressure can cause people to feel tired, confused, or dizzy. We discuss high blood pressure (called *hypertension*) later in this chapter.

The kidneys play a central role in the regulation of blood volume and blood pressure. While filtering the blood, they reabsorb (retain) water and other nutrients that the body needs and excrete waste products and excess water in the urine. Changes in blood volume, blood pressure, and concentration of solutes in the blood signal the kidneys to adjust the volume and concentration of urine.

Imagine that you have just finished working out for an hour, during which time you did not drink any fluids, but you lost fluid through sweat. In response to the increased concentration of solutes in your blood, **antidiuretic hormone (ADH)** is released from the pituitary gland (**Figure 10.2**). The action of ADH is appropriately described by its name: it has an antidiuretic effect, stimulating the kidneys to reabsorb water and to reduce the production of urine.

Simultaneously, your reduced blood volume has resulted in a decrease in blood pressure. This drop in blood pressure stimulates pressure receptors in the kidney, which signal the kidney to secrete the enzyme **renin**. Renin then activates a blood protein called angiotensinogen, which is produced in the liver. Angiotensinogen is the precursor of another blood protein, angiotensin I. Angiotensin I is converted to **angiotensin II**, which is a powerful vasoconstrictor; this means it works to constrict the diameter of blood vessels, which results in an increase in blood pressure.

Angiotensin II also signals the release of the hormone **aldosterone** from the adrenal glands. Aldosterone signals the kidneys to retain sodium and chloride. Because water travels with these two minerals, this results in water retention, which increases blood pressure and decreases urine output. These responses help regulate fluid balance and blood pressure.

electrolyte A substance that disassociates in solution into positively and negatively charged ions and is thus capable of carrying an electrical current.

ion Any electrically charged particle, either positively or negatively charged.

solvent A substance that is capable of mixing with and breaking apart a variety of compounds. Water is an excellent solvent.

blood volume The amount of fluid in blood.

antidiuretic hormone (ADH) A hormone released from the pituitary gland in response to an increase in blood solute concentration. ADH stimulates the kidneys to reabsorb water and to reduce the production of urine.

renin An enzyme secreted by the kidneys in response to a decrease in blood pressure. Renin converts the blood protein angiotensinogen to angiotensin I, which eventually results in an increase in sodium reabsorption.

angiotensin II A potent vasoconstrictor that constricts the diameter of blood vessels and increases blood pressure; it also signals the release of the hormone aldosterone from the adrenal glands.

aldosterone A hormone released from the adrenal glands that signals the kidneys to retain sodium and chloride, which in turn results in the retention of water.

Fluids Help Maintain Body Temperature

Just as overheating is disastrous to a car engine, a high internal temperature can cause the body to stop functioning. Fluids are vital to the body's ability to maintain its temperature within a safe range. Two factors account for the cooling power of fluids. First, water has a high capacity for heat: it takes a lot of energy to raise its temperature. Because the body contains a lot of water, only sustained high heat can increase body temperature.

Second, body fluids are our primary coolant. When heat needs to be released from the body, there is an increase in the flow of blood from the warm body core to the vessels lying just under the skin. This action transports heat out to the body periphery, where it can be released from the skin. When we are hot, the sweat glands secrete more sweat from the skin. As this sweat evaporates off of the skin's surface, heat is released and the skin and underlying blood are cooled (**Figure 10.3**). This cooler blood flows back to the body's core and reduces internal body temperature.

Fluids Protect and Lubricate the Tissues

Water is a major part of the fluids that protect and lubricate tissues. The cerebrospinal fluid that surrounds the brain and spinal column protects these vital tissues from damage, and a fetus in a mother's womb is protected by amniotic fluid. Synovial fluid lubricates joints, and tears cleanse and lubricate the eyes. Saliva moistens the food we eat, and the mucous lining the walls of the GI tract helps it move smoothly along. Finally, the pleural fluid covering the lungs allows their friction-free expansion and retraction behind the chest wall.

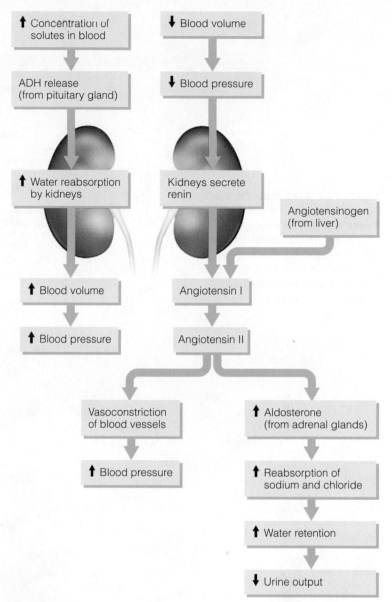

Figure 10.2 Regulation of blood volume and blood pressure by the kidneys.

RECAP

Body fluid consists of water plus a variety of dissolved substances, including electrically charged minerals called electrolytes. Water serves many important functions, including dissolving and transporting substances, accounting for blood volume, regulating body temperature, and cushioning and lubricating body tissues.

Electrolytes Support Many Body Functions

Now that you know why fluid is so essential to the body's functioning, we're ready to explore the critical role of the minerals within it.

Electrolytes Help Regulate Fluid Balance

Cell membranes are *permeable* to water. This means that water flows easily through them. Cells cannot voluntarily regulate this flow of water and thus have no active control over the

To prevent illness, hikers need to adjust their fluid intake according to the humidity level and temperature of their environment.

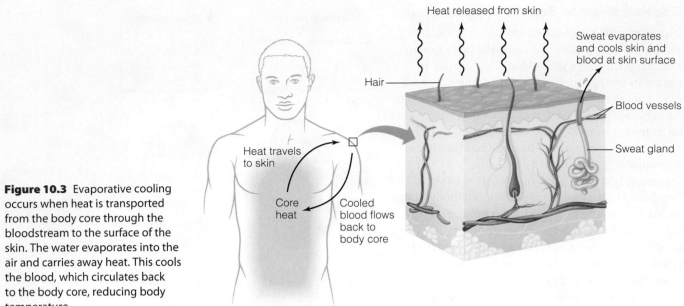

Figure 10.3 Evaporative cooling occurs when heat is transported from the body core through the bloodstream to the surface of the skin. The water evaporates into the air and carries away heat. This cools the blood, which circulates back to the body core, reducing body temperature.

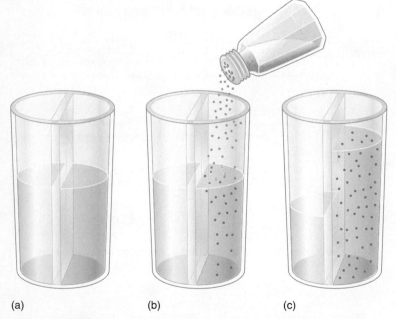

Figure 10.4 Osmosis. (a) A filter that is freely permeable to water is placed in a glass of pure water. (b) Salt is added to only one side of the glass. (c) Drawn by the high concentration of electrolytes, pure water flows to the "salt water" side of the filter. This flow of water into the concentrated solution will continue until the concentration of electrolytes on both sides of the membrane is equal.

osmosis The movement of water (or any solvent) through a semi-permeable membrane from an area where solutes are less concentrated to areas where they are highly concentrated.

osmotic pressure The pressure that is needed to keep the particles in a solution from drawing liquid toward them across a semi-permeable membrane.

balance of fluid between the intracellular and extracellular compartments. In contrast, cell membranes are *not* freely permeable to electrolytes. Sodium, potassium, and the other electrolytes stay where they are, either inside or outside of a cell, unless they are actively transported elsewhere by special proteins. So how do electrolytes help the cells maintain their fluid balance? To answer this question, we need to review a bit of chemistry.

Imagine that you have a special filter that has the same properties as cell membranes; in other words, this filter is freely permeable to water but not permeable to electrolytes. Now imagine that you insert this filter into a glass of pure distilled water to divide the glass into two separate chambers (**Figure 10.4a**). The level of water on either side of the filter would of course be identical, because the filter is freely permeable to water. Now imagine that you add a teaspoon of salt (which contains the electrolytes sodium and chloride) to the water on one side of the filter only (Figure 10.4b). You would see the water on the "pure water" side of the glass suddenly begin to flow through the filter to the "salt water" side of the glass (Figure 10.4c). Why would this mysterious movement of water occur? The answer is that water always moves from areas where solutes such as sodium and chloride are in low concentrations to areas where they are highly concentrated. This movement is referred to as **osmosis**. To put it another way, electrolytes attract water toward areas where they are concentrated. This movement of water toward solutes continues until the concentration of solutes is equal on both sides of the cell membrane.

Water follows the movement of electrolytes; this action provides a means to control movement of water into and out of the cells. The pressure that is needed to keep the particles in a solution from drawing liquid toward them across a semi-permeable membrane is referred to as **osmotic pressure**. Cells can regulate the osmotic pressure, and thus the balance of fluids between their internal and extracellular environments, by using special

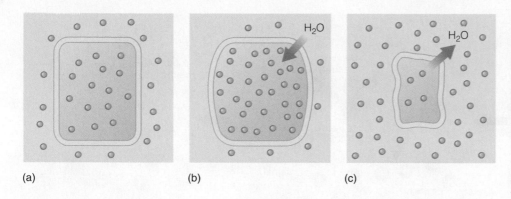

(a)   (b)   (c)

Figure 10.5 The health of our body's cells depends on maintaining the proper balance of fluids and electrolytes on either side of the cell membrane. (a) The concentration of electrolytes is the same on either side of the cell membrane. (b) The concentration of electrolytes is much greater inside the cell, drawing water into the cell and making it swell. (c) The concentration of electrolytes is much greater outside the cell, drawing water out of the cell and making it shrink.

transport proteins to actively pump electrolytes across their membranes. An example of how transport proteins pump sodium and potassium across the cell membrane was illustrated in Chapter 6 (see Figure 6.12 on page 215).

By maintaining the appropriate movement of electrolytes into and out of the cell, the proper balance of fluid and electrolytes is maintained between the intracellular and extracellular compartments (**Figure 10.5a**). If the concentration of electrolytes is much higher inside of the cells as compared with outside, water will flow into the cells in such large amounts that the cells can burst (Figure 10.5b). On the other hand, if the extracellular environment contains too high a concentration of electrolytes, water flows out of the cells, and they can dry up (Figure 10.5c).

Certain illnesses can threaten the delicate balance of fluid inside and outside of the cells. You may have heard of someone being hospitalized because of excessive diarrhea and vomiting. When this happens, the body loses a great deal of fluid from the intestinal tract and extracellular compartment. This heavy fluid loss causes the extracellular electrolyte concentration to become very high. In response, a great deal of intracellular fluid leaves the cells to try to balance this extracellular fluid loss. This imbalance in fluid and electrolytes changes the flow of electrical impulses through the heart, causing an irregular heart rate that can be fatal if left untreated. Food poisoning and eating disorders involving repeated vomiting and diarrhea can also result in death from life-threatening fluid and electrolyte imbalances.

Electrolytes Enable Nerves to Respond to Stimuli

In addition to their role in maintaining fluid balance, electrolytes are critical in enabling nerves to respond to stimuli. Nerve impulses are initiated at the membrane of a nerve cell in response to a change in the degree of electrical charge across the membrane. An influx of sodium into a nerve cell causes the cell to become slightly less negatively charged. This is called *depolarization* (**Figure 10.6**). If enough sodium enters the cell, the change in electrical charge triggers an *action potential*, an electrical signal that is then propagated along the length of the cell. Once the signal is transmitted, that portion of cell membrane returns to its normal electrical state through the release of potassium to the outside of the cell. This return of the cell to its initial electrical state is termed *repolarization*. Thus, both sodium and potassium play critical roles in ensuring that nerve impulses are generated, transmitted, and completed.

Electrolytes Signal Muscles to Contract

Muscles contract because of a series of complex physiologic changes that we will not describe in detail here. Simply stated, muscles are stimulated to contract in response to stimulation of nerve cells. As described earlier, sodium and potassium play a key role in the generation of nerve impulses, or electrical signals. When a muscle fibre is stimulated by an electrical signal, changes occur in the cell membrane that lead to an increased flow of calcium into the muscle from the extracellular fluid. This release of calcium into the muscle stimulates muscle contraction. The muscles can relax after a contraction once the electrical signal is complete and calcium has been pumped out of the muscle cell.

By sprinkling salt on a slice of tomato, you can see for yourself the effects of osmotic pressure.

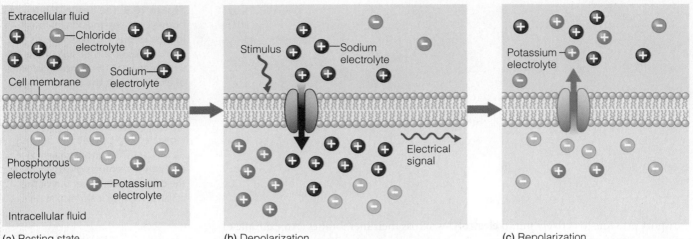

(a) Resting state

(b) Depolarization

(c) Repolarization

Figure 10.6 The role of electrolytes in conduction of a nerve impulse. (a) In the resting state, the intracellular fluid has slightly more electrolytes with a negative charge. (b) A stimulus causes changes to occur that prompt the influx of sodium into the interior of the cell. Sodium has a positive charge, so when this happens, the charge inside the cell becomes slightly positive. This is called depolarization. If enough sodium enters the cell, an action potential is transmitted to adjacent regions of the cell membrane. (c) Release of potassium to the exterior of the cell allows the first portion of the membrane almost immediately to return to the resting state. This is called repolarization.

RECAP

Electrolytes help regulate fluid balance by controlling the movement of fluid into and out of cells. Electrolytes, specifically sodium and potassium, play a key role in generating nerve impulses in response to stimuli. Calcium is an electrolyte that stimulates muscle contraction.

How Does the Body Maintain Fluid Balance?

The proper balance of fluid is maintained in the body by a series of mechanisms that prompt us to drink and retain fluid when we are dehydrated and to excrete fluid as urine when we consume more than we need.

The Thirst Mechanism Prompts Us to Drink Fluids

Imagine that, at lunch, you ate a ham sandwich and a bag of salted potato chips. Now it's almost time for your afternoon seminar to end and you are very thirsty. The last 5 minutes of class are a torment, and when the instructor ends the session you dash to the nearest drinking fountain. What prompted you to suddenly feel so thirsty?

The body's command centre for fluid intake is a cluster of nerve cells in the same part of the brain we studied in relation to food intake; that is, the *hypothalamus*. Within the hypothalamus is a group of cells, collectively referred to as the **thirst mechanism**, that causes you to consciously desire fluids. The thirst mechanism prompts us to feel thirsty when it is stimulated by:

* Increased concentration of salt and other dissolved substances in the blood. Remember that ham sandwich and those potato chips? Both of these foods are salty, and eating them increased the blood's sodium concentration.
* A reduction in blood volume and blood pressure. This can occur when fluids are lost through profuse sweating, blood loss, vomiting, diarrhea, or simply when fluid intake is too low.
* Dryness in the tissues of the mouth and throat. Tissue dryness reflects a lower amount of fluid in the bloodstream, which causes a reduced production of saliva.

thirst mechanism A cluster of nerve cells in the hypothalamus that stimulates our conscious desire to drink fluids in response to an increase in the concentration of salt in our blood or a decrease in blood pressure and blood volume.

Once the hypothalamus detects such changes, it stimulates the release of ADH to signal the kidneys to reduce urine flow and return more water to the bloodstream. As previously discussed, the kidneys also secrete renin, which eventually results in the production of angiotensin II and the retention of water. Water is drawn out of the salivary glands in the mouth in an attempt to further dilute the concentration of substances in the blood; this causes the mouth and throat to become even drier. Together, these mechanisms prevent a further loss of body fluid and help avoid dehydration.

Although the thirst mechanism can trigger an increase in fluid intake, this mechanism alone is not always sufficient: people tend to drink until they are no longer thirsty, but the amount of fluid consumed may not be enough to achieve fluid balance. This is particularly true when body water is rapidly lost, such as during intense exercise in the heat or high humidity. Because the thirst mechanism has some limitations, it is important that you drink regularly throughout the day and not wait to drink until you become thirsty, especially if you are active.

Fruits and vegetables are delicious sources of water.

We Gain Fluids by Consuming Beverages and Foods and Through Metabolism

The fluid needed each day is obtained from three primary sources: beverages, foods, and the production of metabolic water by the body. Of course you know that beverages are mostly water, but it isn't as easy to see the water content in foods. For example, iceberg lettuce is almost 96% water, and even almonds contain a small amount of water (**Figure 10.7**).

Metabolic water is the water formed from the body's metabolic reactions. In the breakdown of fat, carbohydrate, and protein, adenosine triphosphate (ATP), carbon dioxide, and water are produced. The water that is formed during metabolic reactions contributes about 10% to 14% of the water the body needs each day.

We Lose Fluids Through Urine, Sweat, Evaporation, Exhalation, and Feces

Water loss that is noticeable, such as through urine output and sweating, is referred to as **sensible water loss**. Most of the water we consume is excreted through the kidneys in the form of urine. When we consume more water than we need, the kidneys process and excrete it in the form of dilute urine.

metabolic water The water formed as a by-product of the body's metabolic reactions.

sensible water loss Water loss that is noticed by a person, such as through urine output and sweating.

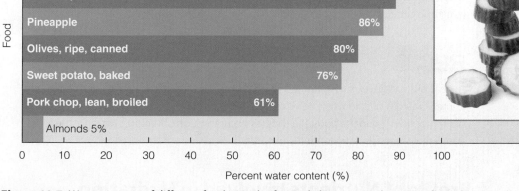

Food	Percent water content (%)
Lettuce, iceberg	96%
Cucumbers, with peel, raw	95%
Peaches, raw	89%
Pineapple	86%
Olives, ripe, canned	80%
Sweet potato, baked	76%
Pork chop, lean, broiled	61%
Almonds	5%

Figure 10.7 Water content of different foods. Much of your daily water intake comes from the foods you eat.
Data from: The Canadian Nutrient File. Health Canada, 2012. Reproduced with the permission of the Minister of Health, 2012.

The second type of sensible water loss is via sweat. The sweat glands produce more sweat during exercise or when a person is in a hot environment. The evaporation of sweat from the skin releases heat, which cools the skin and reduces the body's core temperature.

Water is continuously evaporated from the skin even when a person is not consciously sweating, and water is also continuously exhaled from the lungs. Water loss through these avenues is referred to as **insensible water loss**, as it is not perceived by the person. Under normal resting conditions, insensible water loss is less than 1 litre (L) of fluid each day; during heavy exercise or in hot weather, a person can lose up to 2 L of water per hour from insensible water loss.

Under normal conditions, only about 150 to 200 mL of water is lost each day in the feces. The gastrointestinal tract typically reabsorbs much of the large amounts of fluids that pass through it each day. However, when someone suffers from extreme diarrhea due to illness or from consuming excess laxatives, water loss in the feces can be as high as several litres per day.

In addition to these five avenues of regular fluid loss, certain situations can cause a significant loss of fluid from the body:

- Illnesses that involve fever, coughing, vomiting, diarrhea, and a runny nose significantly increase fluid loss. This is why doctors advise people to drink plenty of fluids when they are ill.
- Traumatic injury, internal hemorrhaging, blood donation, and surgery also increase loss of fluid because of the blood loss involved.
- Exercise increases fluid loss via sweat and respiration; although urine production typically decreases during exercise, fluid losses increase through the skin and lungs.
- Environmental conditions that increase fluid loss include high altitudes, cold and hot temperatures, and low humidity such as in a desert or on an airplane. Because the water content of these environments is low, water from the body readily evaporates into the atmosphere. We also breathe faster at higher altitudes because of the lower oxygen pressure; this results in greater fluid loss via the lungs. We sweat more in the heat, thus losing more water. Cold temperatures can trigger hormonal changes that result in an increased fluid loss.
- Pregnancy increases fluid loss for the mother because fluids are continually diverted to the fetus and amniotic fluid.
- Breastfeeding requires a tremendous increase in fluid intake to make up for the loss of fluid.
- Consumption of **diuretics**—substances that increase fluid loss via the urine—can result in dangerously excessive fluid loss. Diuretics include certain prescription medications and alcohol. Many over-the-counter weight-loss remedies are really just diuretics. In the past, it was believed that the caffeine in beverages such as coffee, tea, and cola could cause serious dehydration, but research now suggests that caffeinated drinks do not have a significant impact on the hydration status of adults, especially those that habitually consume caffeine.[2, 3]

Drinking alcoholic beverages causes an increase in water loss because alcohol is a diuretic.

insensible water loss The loss of water not noticeable by a person, such as through evaporation from the skin and exhalation from the lungs during breathing.

diuretic A substance that increases fluid loss via the urine. Common diuretics include alcohol as well as prescription medications for high blood pressure and other disorders.

RECAP

A healthy fluid level is maintained in the body by balancing intake with excretion. Primary sources of fluids include water and other beverages, foods, and the production of metabolic water in the body. Fluid losses occur through urination, sweating, the feces, and evaporation from the lungs.

A Profile of Nutrients Involved in Hydration and Neuromuscular Function

Nutrients that assist in maintaining hydration and neuromuscular function include water and the minerals sodium, potassium, chloride, and phosphorous (see Table 10.1).

Table 10.1 Overview of Nutrients Involved in Hydration and Neuromuscular Function

To see the full profile of nutrients involved in hydration and neuromusclar function, turn to Chapter 8.

Nutrient	Recommended Intake for Adults
Sodium	1.5 g/day*
Potassium	4.7 g/day *
Chloride	2.3 g/day*
Phosphorous	700 mg/day†

*Adequate Intake (AI)
†RDA

As discussed in Chapter 1, these minerals are classified as *major minerals,* as the body needs more than 100 mg of each per day.

Calcium and magnesium also function as electrolytes and influence the body's fluid balance and neuromuscular function. However, because of their critical importance to bone health, they are discussed in Chapter 12.

Water

Water is essential for life. Although we can live for weeks without food, we can survive only a few days without water, depending on environmental temperature. We do not have the capacity to store water, so we must continuously replace the water lost each day.

How Much Water Should We Drink?

The need for water varies greatly depending on age, body size, health status, physical activity level, and exposure to environmental conditions. It is important to pay attention to how much the need for water changes under various conditions so that dehydration can be avoided.

Recommended Intake Fluid requirements are very individualized. For example, a highly active male athlete training in a hot environment may require up to 10 L of fluid per day to maintain healthy fluid balance, whereas an inactive, petite woman who lives in a mild climate and works in a temperature-controlled office building may only require about 3 L of fluid per day. The DRI for adult men aged 19 to 50 years is 3.7 L of total water per day. This includes approximately 3.0 L (or 13 cups) as total water, other beverages, and food.[4] The DRI for adult women aged 19 to 50 is 2.7 L of total water per day. This includes about 2.2 (or 9 cups) as total water, other beverages, and food.[4]

Figure 10.8 shows the amount and sources of water intake and output for a woman expending 2500 kcal per day. Based on current recommendations, this woman needs about 3000 mL of water per day. As illustrated:

Vigorous exercise causes significant water loss that must be replenished to optimize performance and health.

- Water from metabolism provides 300 mL of water.
- The foods she eats provides her with an additional 500 mL of water each day.
- The beverages she drinks provide the remainder of water needed, which is equal to 2200 mL.

Fluids are an important source of energy for Canadians, especially for children. For children (aged 4 to 18) and adults (aged 19 to 30), about 20% of their total daily energy intake comes from fluids. Water is the major source of this fluid but, after water, fluid choices vary by age group. As they get older, children drink less milk and fruit juice and more soft drinks and fruit-flavoured drinks. Up to the age of 30, milk is the most commonly consumed fluid after water. However, after the age of 50, milk is replaced by coffee.[5]

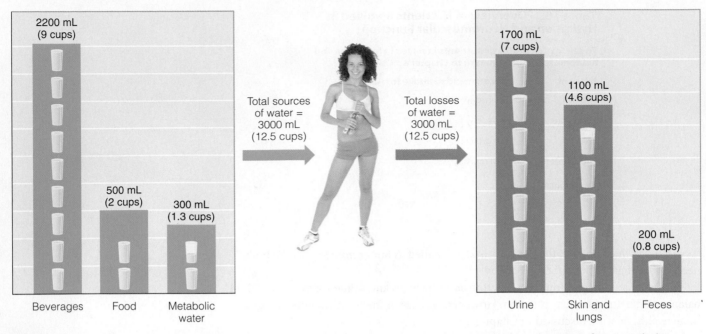

Figure 10.8 Amounts and categories of water sources and losses for a woman expending 2500 kcal per day. Water from metabolism provides 300 mL. The foods she eats provide her with an additional 500 mL. The beverages she drinks, including water, provide the remainder of water she needs, about 2200 mL. The total of 3000 mL matches her water losses.

Athletes or people who are active, especially those working in very hot environments, may require more fluid than the current recommendations. The amount of sweat lost during exercise is very individualized and depends on body size, exercise intensity, level of fitness, environmental temperature, and humidity. We do know that some people can lose as much as 1.8 kg of fluid per hour as sweat![6] Thus, these individuals need to drink more to replace the fluid they lose. Sodium is the major electrolyte lost in sweat; we also lose some potassium and small amounts of minerals such as iron and calcium in sweat.[7]

Because of these fluid and electrolyte losses during exercise, some athletes drink sports beverages instead of plain water to help them maintain fluid balance. Recently, sports beverages have also become popular with recreationally active people and non-athletes. Is it really necessary for people to consume these beverages? The answer to this question is probably no. See Chapter 15 for guidelines for fluid replacement during different types of activity.

Sources of Drinking Water   So many types of drinking water are available in Canada, how can we distinguish among them? Carbonated water contains carbon dioxide gas that either occurs naturally or is added to the water. Mineral water contains 250 to 500 parts per million (ppm) of minerals. Many people prefer the unique taste of mineral water; however, a number of brands contain high amounts of sodium and so should be avoided by people who are trying to reduce their sodium intake. Distilled water is processed in such a way that all dissolved minerals are removed; this type of water is often used in steam irons, as it will not clog the iron with mineral buildup, but it has a flat taste. Purified water has been treated so that all dissolved minerals and contaminants are removed, making this type of water useful in research and medical procedures. Of course, we can also drink the tap water found in our homes and in public places.

One of the major changes in the beverage industry during the past 20 years is the marketing of bottled water.[8] Canadians now consume about 60 litres of bottled water per person, per year. This meteoric rise in bottled water production and consumption is most likely because of the convenience of drinking bottled water, the health messages related to drinking more water, and the public's fears related to the safety of tap water. Recent environmental concerns related to disposal of water bottles, however, has blunted the use

YOU DO THE MATH

Calculating Fluid Intake

You may have read or heard that drinking eight glasses of fluid a day is recommended for most people. But what does this mean? What is a "glass"? Does "fluid" mean water or do other types of beverages count? How do you know how much fluid you need to drink each day to meet your requirements?

You have just learned that the DRI for adult men (19 to 50 years) is 3.7 L of total water per day while adult women require 2.7 L per day. This requirement includes water from metabolism as well as water found in the foods we eat. This makes it a little challenging to determine how much fluid you need to drink since you can only estimate the amount from metabolism and food.

A quick way to estimate the amount of fluid you need to drink is to determine your energy requirement. For each kcal you expend, you require 1 mL of fluid.

1. Let's say your energy expenditure is 2000 kcal/day. How much fluid would you require?

2. Calculate the amount of fluid provided by the following beverages:
   250 mL orange juice
   1000 mL regular soft drink
   500 mL black coffee

3. Would you be meeting your fluid requirement with these beverages?

4. 250 mL of a regular soft drink provides 100 kcal. How many kcalories would you be consuming from soft drinks alone? If your total daily energy intake is 2000 kcal, what percentage of your total daily energy intake would this represent?

5. Instead of the regular soft drink and black coffee, what other beverages could you choose that might be smarter choices for you?

of bottled water.[9] Is bottled water safer or healthier than tap water? Refer to the Nutrition Myth or Fact? box on page 345 on bottled water to find the answer.

What Happens If We Drink Too Much Water?

Drinking too much water and becoming overhydrated is very rare. Even individuals who regularly consume large quantities of water do not develop major health problems because healthy kidneys are able to process the excess water.

Certain illnesses can cause excessive reabsorption or retention of water by the kidneys. When this occurs, overhydration and dilution of blood sodium result. Also, as described in the introductory story on Cynthia Lucero, marathon runners and other endurance athletes can overhydrate and dangerously dilute their serum sodium concentration. This condition, called *hyponatremia*, is discussed in more detail in the next section.

What Happens If We Don't Drink Enough Water?

Dehydration results when we do not drink enough water or are unable to retain the water we drink. It is one of the leading causes of death around the world. Because an understanding of the physiology of dehydration requires familiarity with the roles and requirements for the major electrolytes, we discuss this condition, along with a related illness called *heat stroke*, later in this chapter.

Sodium

Virtually all of the dietary sodium consumed is absorbed by the body. Most dietary sodium is absorbed from the small intestine, although some can be absorbed in the large intestine. As discussed earlier in this chapter, the kidneys reabsorb sodium when it needs to be retained by the body and excrete excess sodium in the urine.

Over the past 20 years, researchers have linked high sodium intake to an increased risk for high blood pressure especially among individuals with salt sensitivity, a disorder where there is an abnormally large change in blood pressure in response to changes in sodium levels. Because of this link, many people have come to believe that sodium is harmful to the body. That oversimplification, however, is just not true; sodium is a valuable nutrient that is essential for survival.

Functions of Sodium

Sodium has a variety of functions. As discussed earlier in this chapter, it is the major positively charged electrolyte in the extracellular fluid. Its exchange with potassium across cell membranes allows cells to maintain proper fluid balance; it also helps regulate blood pressure and acid–base balance.

Sodium also assists with the transmission of nerve signals and aids in muscle contraction and relaxation. Finally, sodium assists in the absorption of glucose from the small intestine. Glucose is absorbed via active transport that involves sodium-dependent glucose transporters.

How Much Sodium Should We Consume?

Many people are concerned with consuming too much sodium in the diet, as they believe it causes high blood pressure and bloating. Although this concern may be valid for certain individuals, sodium is an important nutrient that is necessary for maintaining health. Therefore, it should not be completely eliminated from the diet.

Recommended Dietary Intake for Sodium The AI for sodium is 1.5 g/day (or 1500 mg/day) for adult men and women aged 19 to 50 years, which is equivalent to just over half a teaspoon of salt.[4] The AI drops to 1.3 g/day for those 51 to 70 years of age and 1.2 g/day for persons over the age of 70 years. The tolerable upper intake level (UL) for sodium is 2300 mg/day. Most people in Canada greatly exceed this guideline.

Food Sources of Sodium Sodium is found naturally in many common foods, and many processed foods contain large amounts of added sodium. Thus, it is easy to consume excess amounts in our daily diets. Try to guess which of the following foods contains the most sodium: 250 mL of store bought tomato juice, 30 g of potato chips, or 4 saltine crackers? Now look at Table 10.2 to find the answer. This table shows foods that are high in sodium and gives lower-sodium alternatives. Are you surprised to find out that of all of these food items, the tomato juice has the most sodium? When eating processed foods, such as lunch meats, canned soups and beans, vegetable juices, and prepackaged rice and pasta dishes, look for labels with the words "low-sodium" or "no added salt," as these foods are lower in sodium than the original versions.

What Happens If We Consume Too Much Sodium?

High blood pressure is more common in people who consume high-sodium diets. This strong relationship has prompted many health organizations to recommend lowering sodium intakes. Whether high-sodium diets actually cause high blood pressure is the subject of some controversy (see page 354). Also controversial is the effect of high sodium intake on bone loss: consuming excessive sodium has been shown to cause increased urinary

Many popular snack foods are high in sodium.

Table 10.2 High-Sodium Foods and Lower-Sodium Alternatives

High-Sodium Food	Sodium (mg)	Lower-Sodium Food	Sodium (mg)
Dill pickle (1 large, 10 cm)	1181	Low-sodium dill pickle (1 large, 10 cm)	13
Ham, cured, roasted (75 g)	1039	Pork, loin roast (75 g)	44
Beef, cured, dried (35 g)	976	Beef chuck roast, cooked (35 g)	21
Tomato juice, regular (250 mL)	691	Tomato juice, lower sodium (250 mL)	26
Tomato sauce, canned (125 mL)	678	Fresh tomato (1 medium)	14
Canned cream corn (250 mL)	771	Cooked corn, fresh (250 mL)	2
Tomato soup, canned (250 mL)	701	Lower-sodium tomato soup, canned (250 mL)	57
Saltine crackers (4 each)	132	Saltine crackers, unsalted (4 each)	76
Potato chips, salted (10 chips/20 g)	105	Baked potato, unsalted (1 medium)	12

Data from: The Canadian Nutrient File. Health Canada, 2012. Reproduced with the permission of the Minister of Health, 2012.

NUTRITION MYTH OR FACT?

Is Bottled Water Safer or Healthier than Tap Water?

Bottled water has become increasingly popular during the past 20 years. It is estimated that the annual per capita consumption of bottled water in Canada increased from 28.4 L in 1998 to 66 L in 2006.[10] Many people prefer the taste of bottled water to that of tap water. They also believe that bottled water is safer and better for them. Is this true?

The water we drink in Canada generally comes from two sources: surface water and groundwater. *Surface water* comes from lakes, rivers, and reservoirs. Common contaminants of surface water include runoff from highways, pesticides, and animal and industrial wastes. Many of the cities across Canada obtain their water from surface water sources. *Groundwater* comes from underground rock formations called *aquifers*. People who live in rural areas generally pump groundwater from a well as their water source. Hazardous substances leaking from waste sites, dumps, landfills, and oil and gas pipelines can contaminate groundwater. Groundwater can also be contaminated by naturally occurring substances such as arsenic or high levels of lead.

Water treatment plants treat and purify community water supplies, typically with either chlorine or ozone. These chemicals are effective in killing many contaminants. Water treatment plants routinely check our water supplies for hazardous chemicals, minerals, and other contaminants. Because of these efforts, Canada has one of the safest water systems in the world.

In Canada, all levels of government play a role to make sure our water supplies are safe. The federal government's primary mandate is to protect the health of all Canadians by developing the Guidelines for Canadian Drinking Water Quality in partnership with the provinces and territories. The provincial and territorial governments are generally in charge of making sure our water supplies are safe by implementing these guidelines. Municipal governments usually oversee the day-to-day operations of the treatment facilities. Unfortunately, breakdowns can occur in the system leading to illness and death. Such was the case in Walkerton, Ontario, in 2000 where 2300 people became ill and seven died after drinking contaminated water. The inquiry that followed concluded that this crisis could have been prevented by the proper chlorination of the drinking water, highlighting the importance of ongoing monitoring of the system.[11]

Bottled water is regulated as a food in Canada and therefore is covered by the Food and Drug Regulations. All bottled water must be safe for people to drink and companies that bottle water must comply with quality standards, good manufacturing practices, and labelling requirements set by Health Canada and the Canadian Food Inspection Agency.[12] Health Canada is responsible for establishing health and safety standards for bottled water and develops labelling policies related to health and nutrition. The Canadian Food Inspection Agency is responsible for developing standards related to the packaging, labelling, and advertising of bottled water, in addition to all inspection and enforcement duties. Labels must indicate how the water has been treated (e.g., carbonated, demineralized, distilled, filtered, etc.) and must state the location and source of the water.

Is bottled water healthier than tap water? While some brands may contain more minerals than tap water, bottled water has no other nutritional advantages over tap water. In fact, some bottled waters (with the exception of mineral or spring water) may actually be from a municipal water tap!

As the popularity of bottled water has increased, there are growing concerns about the potential burden drinking bottled water can have on the environment.[13] Specifically, many people have become concerned that the world will be inundated with billions of plastic bottles if people throw them away in landfills

Numerous varieties of bottled water are available to consumers.

instead of recycling them. Although plastic bottles can be reused, they do not last forever and bacterial growth becomes a concern with repeated use. On the other hand, many environmentally conscious consumers using refillable plastic (polycarbonate) water bottles have been faced with recent concerns over the use of BPA (bisphenol A) in certain brands of reusable water bottles. Not all bottle manufacturers have removed BPA from their products so it is important that those who opt for reusable water bottles versus commercial bottled water purchase stainless steel or BPA-free plastic reusable bottles.

Should you spend money on bottled water? Before you decide, consider this simple calculation: Let's say you purchase one bottle five days a week from the vending machine at the gym after you finish your workout. It costs you $1.50 per bottle. Over the course of a single year, you will have spent $390, and have added 260 bottles to recycling centres or landfills!

If, after reading this discussion, you still choose to drink bottled water, Health Canada has the following advice for you:

- Do not refill old bottles
- Do not share bottles
- Clean the bottle top or cap before drinking or pouring from them
- Keep the opened bottle clean and refrigerated

For additional information on bottled water in Canada go to www.inspection.gc.ca/english/fssa/labeti/inform/wateaue.shtml.

excretion of calcium in some people, which in turn may increase the risk for bone loss. Studies have shown that a reduction in sodium intake improves bone status,[14] yet the extent to which excess sodium intake affects bone health remains under study.

Hypernatremia refers to an abnormally high blood sodium concentration. It is usually caused by a rapid intake of high amounts of sodium, such as when a shipwrecked sailor drinks seawater. Eating a high-sodium diet does not usually cause hypernatremia in a healthy person, as the kidneys are able to excrete excess sodium in the urine. But people with congestive heart failure or kidney disease are not able to excrete sodium effectively, making them more prone to the condition. Hypernatremia is dangerous because it causes an abnormally high blood volume, leading to edema (swelling) of tissues and raising blood pressure to unhealthy levels.

Did You Know?

In 2007, Canada's Minister of Health established a Sodium Working Group to develop a population health strategy for reducing sodium intake among Canadians. This group consisted of 25 members from various sectors (food manufacturing, food industry, nongovernmental organizations, scientists, consumers, health professional organizations, and government). Three years later, in July 2010, they released their report, the *Sodium Reduction Strategy for Canada*.[15] This report makes targeted recommendations in four different areas that include a voluntary reduction in sodium levels in processed foods and foods sold in restaurants, an education and awareness campaign, research, and monitoring and evaluation. The ultimate goal is to reduce sodium intakes so that most Canadians have a daily intake below the UL of 2300 mg per day. It was recognized that this will be a significant challenge given that the average daily sodium intake is 3098 mg in Canada,[16] and very few Canadians understand what is meant by a healthy amount of sodium.[15] About 77% of the sodium in our diets comes from processed foods; only about 11% comes from salt added during cooking or at the table.[17] Thus, to achieve the goal of reducing sodium intakes to the UL, it will be necessary for industry to commit to lowering the sodium content of processed foods. Health Canada disbanded the Sodium Working Group in 2011. For more information about the Sodium Working Group and the *Sodium Reduction Strategy for Canada,* visit www.hc-sc.gc.ca/fn-an/nutrition/sodium/sodium-intake-apport-reduction/working-group-travail/sodium-working-travail-group-eng.php.

hypernatremia A condition in which blood sodium levels are dangerously high.

What Happens If We Don't Consume Enough Sodium?

Because dietary sodium intake is so high in Canada, deficiencies are extremely rare, except in individuals who sweat heavily or consume little or no sodium in the diet. Nevertheless, certain conditions can cause dangerously low blood sodium levels. **Hyponatremia**, abnormally low blood sodium concentration, can occur in active people who drink large volumes of water and fail to replace sodium. This was the subject of the chapter-opening vignette and is also discussed in the Highlight box on page 348. Severe diarrhea, vomiting, or excessive prolonged sweating can also cause hyponatremia.

Symptoms of hyponatremia include headaches, dizziness, fatigue, nausea, vomiting, and muscle cramps. If hyponatremia is left untreated, it can lead to seizures, coma, and death. Treatment for hyponatremia includes the ingestion of liquids and foods high in sodium and may even require the administration of electrolyte-rich solutions intravenously if the person has lost consciousness or is not able to consume beverages and foods by mouth.[18–21]

RecaP

Sodium is the primary positively charged electrolyte in the extracellular fluid. It works to maintain fluid balance and blood pressure, assists in acid–base balance and transmission of nerve signals, aids muscle contraction, and assists in the absorption of some nutrients. The AI for sodium is 1.5 g per day; however, most people have sodium intakes above the UL of 2300 mg/d. Deficiencies are rare, because the typical Canadian diet is high in sodium. Excessive sodium intake has been related to high blood pressure and loss of bone density in some, but not all, studies.

Tomato juice is an excellent source of potassium.

Potassium

As we discussed previously, potassium is the major positively charged electrolyte in the intracellular fluid. It is a major constituent of all living cells and is found in both plants and animals. About 85% of dietary potassium is absorbed, and as with sodium, the kidneys regulate reabsorption and urinary excretion of potassium.

Functions of Potassium

Potassium and sodium work together to maintain proper fluid balance and to regulate the contraction of muscles and transmission of nerve impulses. Potassium also assists in maintaining blood pressure. In contrast with a high-sodium diet, eating a diet high in potassium actually helps maintain a lower blood pressure.

How Much Potassium Should We Consume?

We can reduce our risk for high blood pressure by consuming adequate potassium in our diet. The AI for potassium for adult men and women aged 19 to 50 years is 4.7 g/day (or 4700 mg/day).[4]

Potassium is found in abundance in many fresh foods, particularly fresh fruits and vegetables. **Figure 10.9** identifies foods that are high in potassium. Processing foods generally increases their amount of sodium and decreases their amount of potassium. Thus, you can optimize your potassium intake and reduce your sodium intake by avoiding processed foods and eating more fresh fruits, vegetables, legumes, and whole grains.

What Happens If We Consume Too Much Potassium?

People with healthy kidneys are able to excrete excess potassium effectively. However, people with kidney disease are not able to regulate their blood potassium levels. **Hyperkalemia**, or high blood potassium concentration, occurs when potassium is not efficiently excreted from

hyponatremia A condition in which blood sodium levels are dangerously low.

hyperkalemia A condition in which blood potassium levels are dangerously high.

Potato, whole, baked – 1 medium

Tomato juice – 250 mL

Banana, raw, slices – 250 mL

Yogourt, non-fat, plain – 250 mL

Orange juice, from concentrate – 250 mL

Milk, 1% MF, chocolate – 250 mL

Cantaloupe, raw, diced – 250 mL

Halibut, cooked – 75 g

Spinach, raw – 250 mL

Food and serving size

Potassium (mg)

0   200   400   600   800   1000

Figure 10.9 Common food sources of potassium. The AI for potassium is 4.7 g/day.
Data from: The Canadian Nutrient File. Health Canada, 2012. Reproduced with the permission of the Minister of Health, 2012.

HIGHLIGHT

Can Water Be Too Much of a Good Thing? Hyponatremia in Marathon Runners

At the beginning of this chapter, we described the death of Boston Marathon runner Cynthia Lucero. Her case is only one of several that have gained attention in recent years. How can seemingly healthy, highly fit individuals competing in marathons collapse and even die during or after a race? One common challenge faced by these athletes is maintaining a proper balance of fluid and electrolytes during the race.

It is well known that people participating in distance events such as marathons (42.2 km) need to drink enough fluid to ensure proper fluid balance. But how much is enough? The winner of the women's marathon in the Athens Olympics, running in 36-degree Celsius heat, drank for just 30 seconds of the entire race. Surprisingly, recent research has suggested that runners, particularly novice runners, may be at greater risk from drinking too much water than from drinking too little.

Two recent studies examined exercise-associated hyponatremia among marathon runners after a race.[1, 19] The major contributing factors appeared to be longer race time and drinking large amounts of fluid during the race. Experts observe that elite runners complete a race more quickly and drink as they run; thus, they simply don't have time to overdo the fluids. In contrast, less experienced athletes run

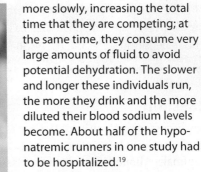

more slowly, increasing the total time that they are competing; at the same time, they consume very large amounts of fluid to avoid potential dehydration. The slower and longer these individuals run, the more they drink and the more diluted their blood sodium levels become. About half of the hyponatremic runners in one study had to be hospitalized.[19]

Hyponatremia is a dangerous and potentially fatal condition, but it can be prevented. Recently, a group of international experts on exercise physiology and fluid balance developed guidelines for the prevention and treatment of exercise-associated hyponatremia.[20]

The fear of hyponatremia should not cause athletes to avoid drinking adequate fluids during long-distance activities, as dehydration and subsequent heat illness are as important to prevent as hyponatremia. The key to staying safe during competitive events is to match fluid and sodium intake with sweat loss.[21] Athletes should weigh themselves regularly before and after training to determine average sweat loss and then consume enough fluid to minimize loss of body weight but not enough to cause weight gain. Drinking sports beverages, which contain electrolytes (particularly sodium), and moderating fluid intake during marathons and other long-distance events can help prevent hyponatremia.

the body. Because of potassium's role in cardiac muscle contraction, severe hyperkalemia can alter the normal rhythm of the heart, resulting in heart attack and death. People with kidney disease must monitor their potassium intake very carefully, and should avoid consuming salt substitutes, as these products are high in potassium.

What Happens If We Don't Consume Enough Potassium?

Because potassium is widespread in many foods, a dietary potassium deficiency is rare. However, potassium deficiency is not uncommon among people who have serious medical disorders. Kidney disease, diabetic ketoacidosis, and other illnesses can lead to potassium deficiency.

In addition, people with high blood pressure who are prescribed certain diuretic medications to treat their disease are at risk for potassium deficiency. As we noted earlier, diuretics promote the excretion of fluid as urine through the kidneys. Some diuretics also increase the body's urinary excretion of potassium. People who are taking diuretic medications should have their blood potassium monitored regularly and should eat foods that are high in potassium to prevent **hypokalemia**, or low blood potassium concentration. This is not a universal recommendation, however, because some diuretics are specially formulated to spare or retain potassium; therefore, people taking diuretics should consult their physician regarding dietary potassium intake.

Extreme dehydration, vomiting, and diarrhea can also cause hypokalemia, as can long-term consumption of natural licorice, which contains glycyrrhizic acid (GZA), a substance that increases urinary excretion of potassium. Because the majority of foods that contain licorice flavouring in Canada do not contain GZA, licorice-induced hypokalemia is rarely seen here. People who abuse alcohol or laxatives can suffer from hypokalemia. Symptoms include confusion, loss of appetite, and muscle weakness. Severe cases of hypokalemia result in fatal changes in heart rate; many deaths attributed to extreme dehydration or an eating disorder are caused by abnormal heart rhythms due to hypokalemia.

Recap

Potassium is the major positively charged electrolyte inside of the cell. It regulates fluid balance, blood pressure, and muscle contraction, and it helps in the transmission of nerve impulses. The AI for potassium is 4.7 g per day. Potassium is found in abundance in fresh foods, particularly fruits and vegetables. Both hyperkalemia and hypokalemia can result in heart failure and death.

Chloride

Chloride is a negatively charged ion that is obtained almost exclusively from sodium chloride or table salt. It should not be confused with *chlorine,* which is a poisonous gas used to kill germs in our water supply. As with sodium, the majority of dietary chloride is absorbed in the small intestine. The kidneys regulate urinary excretion of chloride.

Functions of Chloride

Coupled with sodium in the extracellular fluid, chloride assists with the maintenance of fluid balance. Chloride is also a part of hydrochloric acid (HCl) in the stomach, which aids in preparing food for further digestion (see Chapter 3). Chloride also works with the white blood cells during an immune response to help kill bacteria, and it assists in the transmission of nerve impulses.

How Much Chloride Should We Consume?

The AI for chloride for adult men and women aged 19 to 50 years is 2.3 g/day (or 2300 mg/day).[4] As chloride is coupled with sodium to form table salt, our primary dietary source of

Almost all chloride is consumed through table salt.

hypokalemia A condition in which blood potassium levels are dangerously low.

chloride is salt in our foods. Chloride is also found in some fruits and vegetables. Keep in mind that salt is composed of about 60% chloride; thus, you can calculate the content of chloride in processed foods by multiplying its salt content by 0.60 (or 60%). For instance, a food that contains 500 mg of salt would contain 300 mg of chloride (or 500 mg × 0.60 = 300 mg).

What Happens If We Consume Too Much Chloride?

Because we consume virtually all of our dietary chloride in the form of sodium chloride, there is no known toxicity symptom for chloride alone. As noted earlier, consuming excess amounts of sodium chloride over a prolonged period leads to hypertension in salt-sensitive individuals.

What Happens If We Don't Consume Enough Chloride?

Because of our relatively high dietary salt intake in Canada, most people consume more than enough chloride. Even when a person consumes a low-sodium diet, chloride intake is usually adequate. A chloride deficiency can occur, however, during conditions of severe dehydration and frequent vomiting. This is sometimes seen in people with eating disorders who regularly vomit to rid their bodies of unwanted energy.

ReCaP

Chloride is the major negatively charged electrolyte outside of the cell. It assists with fluid balance, digestion, immune responses, and the transmission of nerve impulses. The AI for chloride is 2.3 g per day. Our main dietary source of chloride is sodium chloride. There is no known toxicity for chloride alone. Chloride deficiencies are rare but can occur during severe dehydration and frequent vomiting.

Milk is a good source of phosphorous.

Phosphorous

Phosphorous is the major intracellular negatively charged electrolyte. In the body, phosphorous is most commonly found combined with oxygen in the form of phosphate, PO_4^{-3}. Phosphorous is an essential constituent of all cells and is found in both plants and animals. Adults absorb about 55% to 70% of dietary phosphorous, primarily in the small intestine. The active form of vitamin D (1,25-dihydroxyvitamin D or calcitriol) facilitates the absorption of phosphorous, whereas consumption of aluminum-containing antacids and high doses of calcium carbonate reduce its absorption. The kidneys regulate reabsorption and urinary excretion of phosphorous.

Functions of Phosphorous

Phosphorous works with potassium inside of the cell to maintain proper fluid balance. It also plays a critical role in bone formation, as it is a part of the mineral complex of bone (see Chapter 12). In fact, about 85% of the body's phosphorous is stored in the bones.

As a primary component of ATP, phosphorous plays a key role in creating energy for the body through the reactions in glycolysis and oxidative phosphorylation. It also helps regulate many biochemical reactions by activating and deactivating enzymes during phosphorylation. Phosphorous is a part of both DNA and RNA, and it is a component of cell membranes (as phospholipids) and of lipoproteins.

How Much Phosphorous Should We Consume?

The RDA for phosphorous is 700 mg per day.[22] The average Canadian adult consumes about twice this amount each day, thus phosphorous deficiencies are rare. Phosphorous is widespread in many foods and is found in high amounts in foods that contain protein. Milk, meats, and eggs are good sources of phosphorous (**Figure 10.10**).

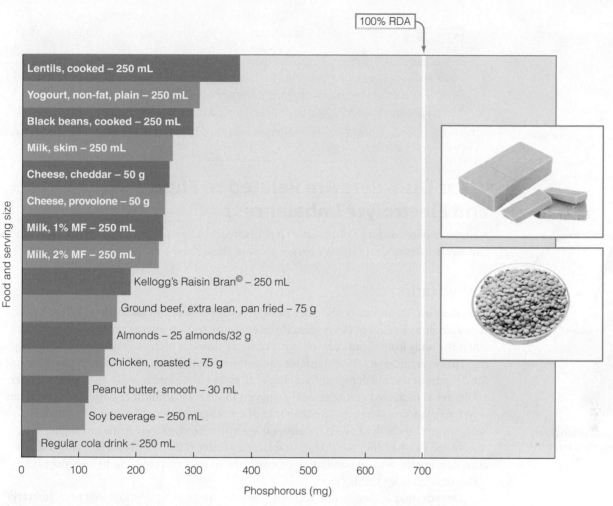

Figure 10.10 Common food sources of phosphorous. The RDA for phosphorous is 700 mg/day.
Data from: The Canadian Nutrient File. Health Canada, 2012. Reproduced with the permission of the Minister of Health, 2012.

It is important to note that phosphorous from animal sources is absorbed more readily than phosphorous from plant sources. Much of the phosphorous in plant foods such as beans, whole-grain cereals, and nuts is found in the form of **phytic acid**, a plant storage form of phosphorous. Our bodies do not produce enzymes that can break down phytic acid, but we are still able to absorb up to 50% of the phosphorous found in plant foods because the bacteria in the large intestine can break down phytic acid. Soft drinks are another common source of phosphorous in the diet; refer to Chapter 12 to learn how heavy consumption of soft drinks may be detrimental to bone health.

What Happens If We Consume Too Much Phosphorous?

People suffering from kidney disease and people taking too many vitamin D supplements or too many phosphorous-containing antacids can suffer from high blood phosphorous levels. Severely high levels of blood phosphorous cause muscle spasms and convulsions.

What Happens If We Don't Consume Enough Phosphorous?

As mentioned previously, deficiencies of phosphorous are rare. People who may suffer from low blood phosphorous levels include premature infants, older people with poor diets, and people who abuse alcohol. People with vitamin D deficiency, hyperparathyroidism (oversecretion of parathyroid hormone), and those who overuse antacids that bind with phosphorous may also have low blood phosphorous levels.

phytic acid The form of phosphorous stored in plants.

What Disorders Are Related to Fluid and Electrolyte Imbalances?

A number of serious, and potentially fatal, disorders can result from an imbalance of fluid and electrolytes in the body. We review some of these here.

Dehydration

Dehydration is a serious health problem that results when fluid losses exceed fluid intake. It can occur as a result of heavy exercise or exposure to high environmental temperatures, when the body loses significant amounts of water through increased sweating and breathing. However, older adults and infants can get dehydrated even when inactive, as their risk for dehydration is much higher than that of healthy young and middle-aged adults. Older adults are at increased risk because they have a lower total amount of body water and their thirst mechanism is less effective than that of a younger person; they are therefore less likely to meet their fluid needs. Infants, on the other hand, excrete urine at a higher rate, cannot tell us when they are thirsty, and have a greater ratio of body surface area to body core, causing them to respond more dramatically to heat and cold and to lose more body water than an older child.

Dehydration is classified in terms of the percentage of weight loss that is exclusively due to the loss of fluid. As indicated in Table 10.3, relatively small losses in body water result in symptoms such as thirst, discomfort, and loss of appetite. More severe water losses result in symptoms that include sleepiness, nausea, flushed skin, and problems with mental concentration. Severe losses of body water can result in delirium, coma, cardiac arrest, and death.

We discussed earlier the importance of fluid replacement when you are exercising. How can you tell whether you are drinking enough fluid before, during, and after your exercise sessions? First, you can measure your body weight before and after each session. If you weighed in at 73 kg before basketball practice, and immediately afterward you weigh 72 kg, then you have lost 1 kg of body weight. This is equal to 1.3% of your body weight prior to practice. As you can see in Table 10.3, you are most likely feeling strong thirst, diminished appetite, and you may even feel generally uncomfortable. Your goal is to consume enough

Dehydration occurs when fluid excretion exceeds fluid intake.

dehydration Depletion of body fluid that results when fluid excretion exceeds fluid intake.

Table 10.3 Percentages of Body Fluid Loss Correlated with Weight Loss and Symptoms

% Body Water Loss	Weight Lost If You Weigh 73 kg	Weight Lost If You Weigh 59 kg	Symptoms
1–2	0.7 kg–1.5 kg	0.6 kg–1.2 kg	Strong thirst, loss of appetite, feeling uncomfortable
3–5	2.2 kg–3.6 kg	1.8 kg–3.0 kg	Dry mouth, reduced urine output, greater difficulty working and concentrating, flushed skin, tingling extremities, impatience, sleepiness, nausea, emotional instability
6–8	4.4 kg–5.8 kg	3.5 kg–4.7 kg	Increased body temperature that doesn't decrease, increased heart rate and breathing rate, dizziness, difficulty breathing, slurred speech, mental confusion, muscle weakness, blue lips
9–11	6.5 kg–8 kg	5.3 kg–6.5 kg	Muscle spasms, delirium, swollen tongue, poor balance and circulation, kidney failure, decreased blood volume and blood pressure

water and other fluids to bring your body weight back to 73 kg prior to your next exercise session. This would require drinking about 1500 mL of fluid, as 0.9 kg of body weight is equal to just less than 1 L, however, an extra 500 mL is required to compensate for urinary excretion.

A simpler method of monitoring your fluid levels is to observe the colour of your urine (**Figure 10.11**). If you are properly hydrated, your urine should be clear to pale yellow in colour, similar to diluted lemonade. Urine that is medium to dark yellow in colour, similar to apple juice, indicates an inadequate fluid intake. Very dark or brown-coloured urine, such as the colour of a cola beverage, is a sign of severe dehydration and indicates potential muscle breakdown and kidney damage. People should strive to maintain a urine colour that is clear or pale yellow.

Heat Stroke

Heat stroke is a potentially fatal heat illness characterized by failure of the body's heat-regulating mechanisms. Symptoms include rapid pulse; hot, dry skin; high temperature; and loss of consciousness.

Athletes who work out in hot, humid weather are particularly vulnerable to heat stroke. In August 2001, 27-year-old National Football League all-star player Korey Stringer died of complications from heat stroke after working out in a hot and humid environment.[23] Despite having access to ample fluids and excellent medical assistance, Stringer's temperature rose to 42°C. In addition to heat, humidity, and dehydration, Stringer's tightly fitting polyester uniform and helmet, which trapped warm air close to his body, were factors in his death. Stringer's large body size (193 cm, 150 kg) also contributed: our ability to dissipate body heat via sweat is extremely limited in a humid environment, and large individuals with a great deal of muscle mass produce a lot of body heat. In addition, excess body fat adds an extra layer of insulation that makes it even more difficult to dissipate body heat.

Similar deaths have occurred in the past with collegiate and high-school football players in the United States. These deaths prompted national attention and resulted in strict guidelines encouraging regular fluid breaks and cancellation of events or changing the time of the event to avoid high heat and humidity. In addition, people who are active in a hot environment should stop exercising if they feel dizzy, light-headed, disoriented, or nauseated. Heat illnesses can be avoided by following established guidelines for fluid intake before, during, and after exercise (See Chapter 15 for information on fluid requirements during exercise).

Water Intoxication

Is it possible to drink too much water? **Overhydration**, or *water intoxication,* can occur but it is rare. It generally only occurs in people with health problems that cause the kidneys to retain too much water, causing overhydration and hyponatremia, which were discussed earlier. However, there are also documented cases of deaths due to overhydration among college and university students participating in hazing rituals. In these examples, people were forced to consume very large amounts of water in a short period of time while being prevented from going to the bathroom, resulting in fatalities. Thus, the overconsumption of water can be deadly and should never be thought of as a prank or a joke.

Hypertension

One of the major chronic diseases in Canada is high blood pressure, which healthcare professionals refer to as **hypertension**. A person with hypertension is unable to maintain blood pressure in a healthy range. It is estimated that nearly one-fifth (19%) of adult Canadians have hypertension; another 20% have a condition termed pre-hypertension. The prevalence of hypertension is about the same in men (19.7%) and women (19.0%) and increases sharply with age.[24] However, recent research suggests that Canadian children are also at risk. A study of 1913 Ontario students in grades 6 to 8 revealed that 6.5% to 8% had

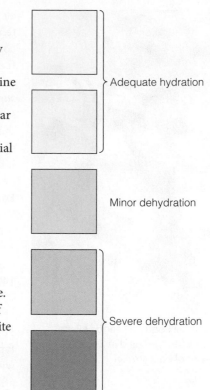

Figure 10.11 Urine colour chart. Colour variations indicate levels of hydration.

Adequate hydration

Minor dehydration

Severe dehydration

heat stroke A potentially fatal response to high temperature characterized by failure of the body's heat-regulating mechanisms. Symptoms include rapid pulse, reduced sweating, hot and dry skin, high temperature, headache, weakness, and sudden loss of consciousness. Commonly called sunstroke.

overhydration Dilution of electrolytes in the body fluid. It results when water intake or retention is excessive.

hypertension A chronic condition characterized by above-average blood pressure readings; specifically, systolic blood pressure over 140 mm Hg or diastolic blood pressure over 90 mm Hg.

National Football League all-star Korey Stringer died in 2001 as a result of heat stroke.

elevated blood pressure, with 1.5% to 4% having serious hypertension.[25] Although hypertension itself is often without symptoms, it increases a person's risk for many other serious conditions, including heart disease, stroke, and kidney disease; it can also reduce brain function, impair physical mobility, and cause death.

Blood pressure is measured in two phases: systolic and diastolic. *Systolic blood pressure* represents the pressure exerted in the arteries at the moment that the heart contracts, sending blood into the blood vessels. *Diastolic blood pressure* represents the pressure in the arteries between contractions, when the heart is relaxed. You can also think of diastolic blood pressure as the resistance in the arteries that the heart must pump against every time it beats. Blood pressure is measured in millimetres of mercury (mm Hg). When your blood pressure is measured, the systolic pressure is given first, followed by the diastolic pressure. For example, your reading might be given as "115 (systolic) over 75 (diastolic)."

Optimal systolic blood pressure is *less than* 120 mm Hg, whereas optimal diastolic blood pressure is *less than* 80 mm Hg. Pre-hypertension is defined as a systolic blood pressure between 120 and 139 mm Hg, or a diastolic blood pressure between 80 and 89 mm Hg. You would be diagnosed with hypertension if your systolic blood pressure were greater than or equal to 140 mm Hg or your diastolic blood pressure were greater than or equal to 90 mm Hg.

What Causes Hypertension?

For about 90% to 95% of people who have it, the causes of hypertension are unknown. This type is referred to as *primary* or *essential hypertension*. For the other 5% to 10% of people with hypertension, causes may include kidney disease, sleep apnea (a sleep disorder that affects breathing), or chronic alcohol abuse. It is estimated that over half of all adults with hypertension have a condition known as **salt sensitivity**. These people respond to a high salt intake by experiencing an increase in blood pressure; they also experience a decrease in blood pressure when salt intake is low. People who do not experience changes in blood pressure with changes in salt intake are referred to as **salt resistant**.

Five Lifestyle Changes That Can Reduce Hypertension

Although we do not know what causes most cases of hypertension, there are five primary lifestyle changes that can help reduce it. These changes include:

Hypertension is a major chronic disease in Canada, affecting more than 50% of adults over 65 years of age.

salt sensitivity A condition in which certain people respond to a high salt intake by experiencing an increase in blood pressure; these people also experience a decrease in blood pressure when salt intake is low.

salt resistance A condition in which certain people do not experience changes in blood pressure with changes in salt intake.

- Achieving and maintaining a healthy weight. Systolic blood pressure values have been shown to decrease 5 to 20 points in people who were overweight or obese and lost an average of 10 kg of body weight.[26]
- Increasing physical activity. The amount and intensity of exercise needed to improve blood pressure are easily achievable for most people. Regular physical activity, such as brisk walking, lasting at least 30 minutes per day, most days of the week, can help lower blood pressure.[26]
- Reducing alcohol intake. Because alcohol consumption can worsen high blood pressure, it is suggested that people with this disease abstain from drinking alcohol or limit their intake to no more than one (women) or two (men) drinks per day.[26]
- Reducing sodium intake in salt-sensitive individuals. Even people who are not salt sensitive will benefit from eating lower-sodium diets and everyone should strive for sodium intakes below the UL.[26, 27]
- Eating more whole grains, fruits, vegetables, and low-fat dairy foods.[26, 27]

Among nutrition and healthcare professionals, one area of controversy is the impact that sodium intake has on our blood pressure. For years it was believed that the high sodium intakes of the typical North American diet led to hypertension. This is because people who live in countries in which sodium intake is high have greater rates of hypertension than people from countries in which sodium intake is low. We have recently learned, however, that not everyone with hypertension is sensitive to sodium. Unfortunately, it is impossible to know who is sensitive to sodium, as there is no definitive test for the condition. Because lowering sodium intake does not reduce blood pressure in all people with hypertension, there is significant debate over whether everyone can benefit from eating a lower-sodium diet. Despite this debate, Health Canada continues to support a reduction in dietary sodium (see the Did You Know? box on page 346 for more information).

The Role of the DASH Diet Plan

The **DASH diet** plan resulted from a large research study funded by the National Institutes of Health (NIH).[28, 29] DASH stands for "Dietary Approaches to Stop Hypertension" pressure. Table 10.4 shows the DASH eating plan for a 2000-kcal diet. This plan is similar to the goals of *Eating Well with Canada's Food Guide* in that it is low in fat and high in fibre. The DASH diet also emphasizes foods that are rich in potassium, calcium, and magnesium, including 10 servings of fruits and vegetables each day along with whole-grain foods and low-fat or non-fat milk and dairy products. The sodium content of the DASH diet is about 3 g (or 3000 mg) of sodium, which is slightly less than the average sodium intake in Canada.

Over the past several years, many research studies have convincingly illustrated that eating the DASH diet has a positive impact on blood pressure. The 1997 DASH trial was a randomized, controlled trial that showed that hypertensive patients who followed the DASH diet were able to significantly reduce their blood pressure when compared to hypertensive patients following a control diet (typical North American diet low in calcium, potassium, and magnesium).[30] The DASH-Sodium trial found that blood pressure continues to decrease if sodium intake is reduced below 3000 mg per day.[27] Participants ate a DASH diet that provided either 3500 mg, 2400 mg, or 1500 mg of sodium each day. After one month on this diet, all people eating the DASH diet saw a significant decrease in their blood pressure; however, those who ate the lowest sodium version of the diet experienced

Losing weight and increasing physical activity can help fight hypertension.

Table 10.4 The DASH Diet Plan

Food Group	Daily Servings	Serving Size
Grains and grain products	7–8	1 slice bread 250 mL ready-to-eat cereal* 125 mL cooked rice, pasta, or cereal
Vegetables	4–5	250 mL raw leafy vegetables 125 mL cooked vegetable 188 mL vegetable juice
Fruits	4–5	1 medium fruit 62.5 mL dried fruit 125 mL fresh, frozen, or canned fruit 188 mL fruit juice
Low-fat or fat-free dairy foods	2–3	250 mL milk 250 mL yogourt 43 g cheese
Lean meats, poultry, and fish	2 or less	85 g cooked lean meats, skinless poultry, or fish
Nuts, seeds, and dry beans	4–5 per week	83 mL nuts 15 mL seeds 125 mL cooked dry beans
Fats and oils[†]	2–3	5 mL soft margarine 15 mL low-fat mayonnaise 30 mL light salad dressing 5 mL vegetable oil
Sweets	5 per week	15 mL sugar 15 mL jelly or jam 14 g jelly beans 250 mL lemonade

Note: The plan is based on 2000 kcal per day. The number of servings in a food group may differ from the number listed, depending on your own energy needs.
*Serving sizes vary between 125 and 312 mL. Check the product's nutrition label.
[†]Fat content changes serving counts for fats and oils: for example, 15 mL of regular salad dressing equals 1 serving; 15 mL of a low-fat dressing equals 1/2 serving; 15 mL of a fat-free dressing equals 0 servings.
Data from: National Institutes of Health. Healthier Eating with DASH. Available at www.nhlbi.nih.gov/health/public/heart/hbp/dash/new_dash.pdf.

DASH diet Term for the Dietary Approach to Stop Hypertension, this diet plan emphasizes fruits and vegetables, whole grains, low/no-fat milk and dairy, and lean meats.

the largest decrease. The most recent guidelines from the Canadian Hypertension Education Program recommend that both hypertensive and normotensive individuals (those with normal blood pressure) follow the DASH diet to treat and prevent hypertension.[31]

In addition to its beneficial effects in reducing blood pressure, the DASH diet has also been shown to lower risk for coronary heart disease and stroke among women[32] as well as the risk for metabolic syndrome.[33] Finally, the DASH diet has been shown to be particularly beneficial in hypertensive African Americans, a population group at very high risk for the disease and its complications.[34]

CASE STUDY ▸ Following the DASH Diet

Carter is a 45-year-old man who has recently been diagnosed with essential hypertension. He has had an ongoing battle with his weight since he was a teenager and is currently considered to be obese. Carter works as a web designer with a large company and finds his job very stressful. He gets very little physical activity during the week but tries to go for walks with his dogs on the weekend. Carter's favourite foods are deep fried chicken wings, potato chips, and molasses cookies. His doctor sent him to a dietitian to teach him about the DASH diet. The dietitian conducts a usual food intake recall and finds out that Carter does not eat any breakfast. He drinks five to six cups of coffee with cream and sugar throughout the day. At lunch, he usually eats a toasted chicken salad sandwich on white bread with mayonnaise and pickles, and French fries with extra salt and ketchup. Dinner is usually about 300 g of red meat with 375 mL mashed potatoes, a can (341 mL) of vegetables, and two large glasses (500 mL) of whole milk.

Thinking Critically

1. **What risk factors for hypertension does Carter have that are modifiable? Which are non-modifiable?**
2. **What are the sources of sodium and potassium in Carter's usual food recall?**
3. **Estimate how many servings Carter is getting from each food group in *Eating Well with Canada's Food Guide* and compare them to the recommendations for a man of his age.**
4. **Using Table 10.4, identify how many servings Carter needs from each food group if he follows the DASH diet.**
5. **What other dietary and/or lifestyle advice would you give to Carter to help lower his blood pressure if you were his dietitian?**

The DASH diet emphasizes fruits and vegetables, whole grains, low-fat or non-fat dairy, and lean protein sources.

seizures Uncontrollable muscle spasms caused by increased nervous system excitability that can result from electrolyte imbalances or a chronic disease such as epilepsy.

Medications

For some individuals, lifestyle changes are not completely effective in normalizing hypertension. When this is the case, a variety of medications can bring a person's blood pressure into the normal range. Individuals taking medications to control blood pressure should also continue to practise the healthy lifestyle changes identified earlier, as these changes will continue to benefit their long-term health.

Hypertension is called "the silent killer," because often there are no obvious symptoms of this disease. For this reason, it is important that people get their blood pressure checked on a regular basis. Tragically, many people with hypertension fail to take their prescribed medication because they do not feel sick. Some of these people eventually suffer the consequences of their actions by experiencing a heart attack or stroke.

Neuromuscular Disorders

Because nerves synapse with muscles, electrolyte imbalances that alter nervous system function will in turn disturb muscle function. For example, **seizures** are uncontrollable muscle spasms that may be localized to one area of the body, such as the face, or can affect a person's entire body. **Muscle cramps** are involuntary, spasmodic, and painful muscle contractions that last for many seconds or even minutes. Hypernatremia that occurs with dehydration is known to cause cramps, as are other electrolyte imbalances. Muscle weakness and paralysis can also occur with severe electrolyte imbalances such as hypokalemia, hyperkalemia, and low blood phosphorous levels.

RECAP

Dehydration, heat stroke, and even death can occur when water loss exceeds water intake. Because the thirst mechanism is not always sufficient, it is important to drink water throughout the day to promote adequate fluid intake. Hypertension is a major chronic illness in Canada; it can often be controlled by losing weight if overweight, increasing physical activity, decreasing alcohol intake, and making specific dietary changes such as those in the DASH diet. Electrolyte imbalances can also lead to neuromuscular disorders.

muscle cramps Involuntary, spasmodic, and painful muscle contractions that last for many seconds or even minutes; electrolyte imbalances are often the cause of muscle cramps.

SEE FOR YOURSELF

How Pure Is Your Favourite Bottled Water?

Next time you reach for your favourite brand of bottled water, check the label. To find out how pure it is, consider the following factors:

1. Find out where it comes from. If no location is identified, even a bottle labelled "spring water" may actually contain tap water with minerals added to improve the taste. What you're looking for are the words "Bottled at the source." Water that comes from a protected groundwater source is less likely to have contaminants such as disease-causing microbes. If the label doesn't identify the water's source, it should at least provide contact information such as a phone number or website of the bottled water company so that you can track down the source.

2. Find out how the water in the bottle has been treated. There are several ways of treating water, but what you're looking for are either of the following two methods, which have been proven to be effective against the most common waterborne disease-causing micro-organisms:

   ■ *Micron filtration* is a process whereby water is filtered through screens with various-sized microscopic holes. High-quality micron filtration can eliminate most chemical contaminants and microbes.

   ■ *Reverse osmosis* is a process often referred to as *ultrafiltration* because it uses a membrane with microscopic openings that allow water to pass through but not larger compounds. Reverse-osmosis membranes also utilize electrical charges to reject harmful chemicals.

   If the label on your bottle of water says that the water was purified using any of the following methods,

Can you tell where the water in each bottle comes from?

you might want to consider switching brands: filtered, carbon-filtered, particle-filtered, ozonated or ozone-treated, ultraviolet light, ion exchange, and deionized. These methods have not been proven to be effective against the most common waterborne disease-causing micro-organisms.

3. Check the nutrient content on the label. Ideally, water should be high in magnesium (at least 20 mg/250 mL serving) and calcium, but low in sodium (less than 5 mg/250 mL serving). Avoid bottled waters with sweeteners, as their "empty calories" can contribute significantly to your energy intake. These products are often promoted as healthy beverage choices, with names including words such as *vitamins, herbs, nature,* and *life*, but they are essentially "liquid candy." Check the Nutrition Facts table and don't be fooled!

Chapter Review

Test Yourself | Answers

1. **T** Between approximately 50% and 70% of our body weight consists of fluid.

2. **F** Sodium is a nutrient necessary for health, but we should not consume more than recommended amounts.

3. **F** Our thirst mechanism signals that we need to replenish fluids, but it is not always sufficient to ensure we are completely hydrated.

4. **F** There is no evidence that bottled water consistently offers any additional health or nutrition benefits compared to tap water.

5. **F** We do not know the cause of high blood pressure in most people. A high-sodium diet can cause high blood pressure in a subset of people who are sensitive to sodium.

Summary

- Approximately 50% to 70% of a healthy adult's body weight is fluid. Two-thirds of this fluid is intracellular fluid, and the remainder is extracellular fluid.

- Electrolytes are electrically charged particles found in body fluid that assist in maintaining fluid balance and the normal functioning of cells and the nervous system.

- Water acts as a solvent, provides protection and lubrication for organs and tissues, and acts to maintain blood volume, blood pressure, and body temperature.

- The three primary sources of fluid intake are beverages, foods, and metabolic water produced by chemical reactions during metabolism.

- The primary avenues of fluid excretion are sensible water loss (urine and sweat), insensible water loss (via evaporation and exhalation), and feces.

- Conditions that significantly increase water loss from our bodies include fever, vomiting, diarrhea, hemorrhage, blood donation, heavy exercise, and exposure to heat, cold, and altitude.

- Fluid intake needs are highly variable and depend on body size, age, physical activity, health status, and environmental conditions.

- Drinking too much water can lead to overhydration and hyponatremia, or dilution of blood sodium, whereas drinking too little water leads to dehydration, one of the leading causes of death around the world.

- Sodium assists in maintaining fluid balance, blood pressure, nervous function, and muscle contraction.

- Consuming excess sodium can cause high blood pressure or hypernatremia. Sodium deficiencies are rare, but hyponatremia can occur when excessive fluid intake is not accompanied by adequate sodium intake.

- Potassium assists in maintaining fluid balance, healthy blood pressure, transmission of nerve impulses, and muscle function.

- Hyperkalemia is excess blood potassium, which occurs because of kidney disease or malfunction. Hypokalemia is low blood potassium and can occur as a result of kidney disease, diabetic acidosis, and through the use of some diuretic medications.

- Chloride assists in maintaining fluid balance, normal nerve transmission, and the digestion of food via the action of HCl.

- Phosphorous assists in maintaining fluid balance and transferring energy via ATP. It is also a component of bone, phospholipids, genetic material, and lipoproteins.

- Dehydration occurs when water excretion exceeds water intake. Individuals at risk include older adults, infants, people exercising heavily for prolonged periods in the heat, and individuals suffering from prolonged vomiting and diarrhea.

- Heat stroke can lead to death if left untreated.

- Overhydration, or water intoxication, is caused by consuming too much water. Hyponatremia can also result from water intoxication.

- Hypertension, or high blood pressure, increases the risk for heart disease, stroke, and kidney disease. Consuming excess sodium is associated with hypertension in some, but not all, people.

- Lifestyle changes such as normalization of body weight, regular physical activity, reduction in alcohol intake, and dietary modifications such as the DASH diet are effective and low-risk approaches that reduce a person's risk for hypertension.

Review Questions

1. Which of the following is a characteristic of potassium?
   a. It is the major positively charged electrolyte in the extracellular fluid.
   b. It can be found in fresh fruits and vegetables.
   c. It is a critical component of the mineral complex of bone.
   d. It is the major negatively charged electrolyte in the extracellular fluid.

2. Which of the following people probably has the greatest percentage of body fluid?
   a. A female adult who is slightly overweight and vomits nightly after eating dinner
   b. An older adult male of average weight who has low blood pressure
   c. An overweight football player who has just completed a practice session in high heat
   d. A healthy infant of average weight

3. Plasma is one example of
   a. extracellular fluid.
   b. intracellular fluid.
   c. tissue fluid.
   d. metabolic water.

4. Which of the following is true of the cell membrane?
   a. It is freely permeable to water and many solutes.
   b. It is freely permeable only to water.
   c. It is freely permeable only to water and fats.
   d. It is freely permeable only to water and proteins.

5. Which of the following lifestyle changes has been shown to reduce hypertension in all people with high blood pressure?
   a. Consuming a low-sodium diet
   b. Normalizing body weight
   c. Getting at least eight hours of sleep nightly
   d. Consuming one to two glasses of red wine daily

6. Explain why people with kidney disease must monitor their potassium intake very carefully and avoid using salt substitutes.

7. Compare and contrast the dietary guidelines promoted by *Eating Well with Canada's Food Guide* and the DASH diet plan.

8. Explain why severe diarrhea in a young child can lead to death from heart failure.

9. After winning a cross-country relay race, you and your teammates celebrate with a trip to the local tavern for a few beers. That evening, you feel shaky and disoriented, and you have a "pins and needles" feeling in your hands and feet. What could be going on that is contributing to these feelings?

10. For lunch today, your choices include (a) chicken soup, a ham sandwich, and a can of tomato juice; or (b) potato salad, a tuna-fish sandwich, and a bottle of mineral water. You have hockey practice in mid-afternoon. Which lunch should you choose, and why?

11. Your cousin, who is breastfeeding her 3-month-old daughter, confesses to you that she has resorted to taking over-the-counter weight-loss pills to help her lose the weight she gained during pregnancy. What concerns might this raise?

12. While visiting your grandmother over the holidays, you notice that she avoids drinking any beverage with her evening meal or in the hours prior to bedtime. You ask her about it, and she explains that she avoids fluids so that she won't have to get up and go to the bathroom during the night. "Though I still don't get a good night's sleep," she sighs. "Many nights I wake up with cramps in my legs and have to get up and walk around anyway!" Is there a link here? If so, explain.

Web Links

www.bottledwater.org
International Bottled Water Association
Find current information about bottled water from this trade association that represents the bottled water industry.

www.nlm.nih.gov/medlineplus
MEDLINE Plus Health Information
Search for "dehydration" and "heat stroke" to obtain additional resources and the latest news about the dangers of these heat-related illnesses.

www.nih.gov
National Institutes of Health (NIH)
Search this site to learn more about the DASH diet (Dietary Approaches to Stop Hypertension).

www.heartandstroke.com
Heart & Stroke Foundation of Canada
Go to this site to find out more about heart disease, including how to prevent high blood pressure or hypertension.

www.phac-aspc.gc.ca
Public Health Agency of Canada
Go to this site to learn more about the Canadian Heart Health Strategy and hypertension initiatives and programs.

www.hc-sc.gc.ca
Health Canada
Find out more about Health Canada's role in making sure our water supply is safe and the Guidelines for Canadian Drinking Water Quality.

www.hypertension.ca
Hypertension Canada
This website provides tools and resources for health professionals and the public related to the prevention and control of hypertension.

MasteringNutrition®

www.masteringnutrition.pearson.com

Assignments
Animations: Role of Electrolytes in Water Balance • Intracellular & Extracellular Fluid • Water Balance

Study Area
Video: Using the Functional Approach to Understand Fluid & Electrolyte Balance • Practice Tests • Diet Analysis • eText

References

1. Almond, C. S. D., A. Y. Shin, E. B. Fortescue, R. C. Mannix, D. Wypij, B. A. Binstadt, C. N. Duncan, D. P. Olson, A. E. Salerno, J. W. Newburger, and D. S. Greenes. 2005. Hyponatremia among runners in the Boston Marathon. *N. Engl. J. Med.* 352:1150–1156.
2. Maughan R. J., and J. Griffin. 2003. Caffeine ingestion and fluid balance: a review. *J. Hum. Nutr. Diet.* 16:411–420.
3. Armstrong, L. E. 2002. Caffeine, body fluid-electrolyte balance, and exercise performance. *International Journal of Sport Nutrition and Exercise Metabolism* 12(2):189–206.
4. Institute of Medicine. 2004. *Dietary Reference Intakes for Water, Potassium, Sodium, Chloride, and Sulfate.* Washington, DC: The National Academies Press.
5. Statistics Canada. 2008. *Study: Beverage consumption by children and adults.* Available at www.statcan.gc.ca/daily-quotidien/ 081119/dq081119c-eng.htm (accessed January 30, 2011).
6. American College of Sports Medicine (ACSM). 1996. Exercise and fluid replacement. *Med. Sci. Sports Exerc.* 28:i–vii.
7. Coyle, E. F. 2004. Fluid and fuel intake during exercise. *J. Sports Sciences* 22:39–55.
8. Bottled water continues as number 2 in 2007. Available at www. bottledwater.org/public/marketin.htm (accessed April 2009).
9. Napier, G. L., and C. M. Kodner. 2008. Health risks and benefits of bottled water. *Prim. Care Clin. Office Pract.* 35:789–802.
10. Agriculture and Agri-Foods Canada. 2009. *The Canadian Bottled Water Industry.* Available at www4.agr.gc.ca/AAFC-AAC/ display-afficher.do?id=1171644581795 (accessed November 21, 2010).
11. CBC News. 2010. *Highlights of the Walkerton Inquiry Report.* Available at www.cbc.ca/canada/story/2010/05/10/f-walkerton-report.html (accessed January 30, 2011).
12. Health Canada. 2009. *It's Your Health: The safety of bottled water.* Available at www.hc-sc.gc.ca/hl-vs/alt_formats/pacrb-dgapcr/ pdf/iyh-vsv/food-aliment/bottled-embouteillee-eng.pdf (accessed November 2, 2010).
13. Marsh, B. 2007. A battle between the bottle and the faucet. *The New York Times,* July 15.
14. Lin, P. H., F. Ginty, L. J. Appel, M. Aickin, A. Bohannon, P. Garnero, D. Barclay, and L. P. Svetkey. 2003. The DASH diet and sodium reduction improve markers of bone turnover and calcium metabolism in adults. *J. Nutr.* 133:3130–3136.
15. Health Canada. 2010. *Sodium reduction strategy for Canada: Recommendations of the Sodium Working Group.* Available at www.hc-sc.gc.ca/fn-an/alt_formats/pdf/nutrition/sodium/ strateg/index-eng.pdf (accessed November 21, 2010).
16. Fischer, P. W. F., M. Vigneault, R. Huang, K. Arvanti, and P. Roach. 2009. Sodium food sources in the Canadian diet. *Appl. Physiol. Nutr. Metab.* 34:884–892.
17. International Food Information Council Foundation. 2010. *Sodium in food and health.* Available at www.ific.org (accessed February 12, 2011).
18. Kolata, G. 2005. Study cautions runners to limit intake of water. *New York Times* 14 April:A1, A20.
19. Davis D. P., J. S. Videen, A. Marino, G. M. Vilke, J. V. Dunford, S. P. Van Camp, and L. G. Maharam. 2001. Exercise-associated

hyponatremia in marathon runners: a two-year experience. *J. Emerg. Med.* 21:47–57.

20. Exercise-Associated Hyponatremia (EAH) Consensus Panel. 2005. Consensus statement of the 1st International Exercise-Associated Hyponatremia Consensus Development Conference, Cape Town, South Africa, 2005. *Clin. J. Sport Med.* 15:208–213.

21. Noakes, T. 2003. Fluid replacement during marathon running. *Clin. J. Sport Med.* 13(5):309–318.

22. Institute of Medicine. Food and Nutrition Board. 1999. *Dietary Reference Intakes for Calcium, Phosphorus, Magnesium, Vitamin D, and Fluoride.* Washington, DC: National Academies Press.

23. George, T. 2001. Pro football. Heat kills a pro football player. N.F.L. orders a training review. *New York Times,* 2 August. Available at www.nytimes.com/2001/08/02/sports/pro-football-heat-kills-a-pro-football-player-nfl-orders-a-training-review.html?scp=1&sq=korey%20stringer%20death&st=cse (accessed April 2009.)

24. Statistics Canada. 2010. *Canadian Health Measures Survey: Blood Pressure in Canadian Adults.* Available at www.statcan.gc.ca/daily-quotidien/100217/dq100217b-eng.htm (accessed November 2, 2010).

25. Mullins, K. J. 2010. Study: Up to 8 percent of Canadian children have hypertension. *Digital Journal.* Available at www.digitaljournal.com/print/article/300636 (accessed January 30, 2011).

26. U.S. Department of Health and Human Services. 2004. *The Seventh Report of the Joint National Committee on Prevention, Detection, Evaluation, and Treatment of High Blood Pressure.* NIH Publication No. 04-5230. Washington, DC: U.S. Government Printing Office.

27. Bray, G. A., W. M. Vollmer, F. M. Sacks, E. Obarzanek, L. P. Svetkey, and L. J. Appel. 2004. A further subgroup analysis of the effects of the DASH diet and three dietary sodium levels on blood pressure: results of the DASH-sodium trial. *Am. J. Card.* 94:222–227.

28. Appel L. J., T. J. Moore, E. Obarzanek, W. M. Vollmer, L. P. Svetkey, F. M. Sacks, G. A. Bray, T. M. Vogt, J. A. Cutler, M. M. Windhauser, P. H. Lin, and N. Karanja. 1997. A clinical trial of the effects of dietary patterns on blood pressure. *N. Engl. J. Med.* 336:1117–1124.

29. Sacks F. M., L. P. Svetkey, W. M. Vollmer, L. J. Appel, G. A. Bray, D. Harsha, E. Obarzanek, P. R. Conlin, E. R. Miller III, D. G. Simons-Morton, N. Karanja, and P. H. Lin. 2001. Effects on blood pressure of reduced dietary sodium and the Dietary Approaches to Stop Hypertension (DASH) diet. *N. Engl. J. Med.* 344:3–10.

30. Appel, L. J., T. J. Moore, E. Obarzanek, W. M. Vollmer, L. P. Svetkey, F. M. Sacks, G. A. Bray, T. M. Vogt, J. A. Cutler, M. M. Windhauser, P-H Lin, N. Karanja, D. Simons-Morton, M. McCullough, J. Swain, P. Steele, M. A. Evans, E. R. Miller, and D. W. Harsha. 1997. Dietary patterns and blood pressure. DASH Collaborative Research Group. *N. Engl. J. Med.* 337:637–638.

31. Hackam, D., N. A. Khan, B. R. Hemmelgarn, S. W. Rabkin, R. M. Touyz, N. R. Campbell, R. Padwal, T. S. Campbell, M. P. Lindsay, M. D. Hill, R. R. Quinn, J. L. Mahon, R. J. Herman, E. L. Schiffrin, M. Ruzicka, P. Larochelle, R. D. Feldman, M. Lebel, L. Poirier, J. M. Arnold, G. W. Moe, J. G. Howlett, L. Trudeau, S. L. Bacon, R. J. Petrella, A. Milot, J. A. Stone, D. Drouin, J. M. Boulanger,

M. Sharma, P. Hamet, G. Fodor, G. K. Dresser, S. G. Carruthers, G. Pylypchuk, E. D. Burgess, K. D. Burns, M. Vallee, G. V. Prasad, R. E. Gilbert, L.A. Leiter, C. Jones, R. I. Ogilvie, V. Woo, P. A. McFarlane, R. A. Hegele, and S. W. Tobe. 2010. The 2010 Canadian Hypertension Education Program recommendations for the management of hypertension: part 2—therapy. *Can. J. Cardiol.* 26:249–258.

32. Fung T. T., S. E. Chiuve, M. L. McCullough, K. M. Rexrode, G. Logroscino, and F. B. Hu. 2008. Adherence to a DASH-style diet and risk of coronary heart disease and stroke in women. *Archives of Internal Medicine* 168(7):713–720.

33. Azadbakht L., P. Mirmiran, A. Esmaillzadeh, T. Azizi, and F. Azizi. 2005. Beneficial effects of dietary approaches to stop hypertension eating plan on features of the metabolic syndrome. *Diabetes Care* 28:2823–2831.

34. Reusser, M. E., and D. A. McCarron. 2006. Reducing hypertensive cardiovascular disease risk of African Americans with diet: focus on the facts. *J. Nutr.* 136:1099–1102.

35. Global News. 2010. *Health Canada to Investigate Energy Drinks.* Available at www.globalregina.com/Health+Canada+Investigate+Energy+Drinks/3765459/story.html (accessed February 13, 2011).

36. Globe and Mail. 2010. *Energy drinks pose serious health risk to kids: Canadian Medical Journal.* Available at www.theglobeandmail.com/life/health/energy-drinks-pose-serious-health-risk-to-kids-canadian-medical-journal/article1652080 (accessed February 13, 2011).

37. Agriculture and Agri-Food Canada. 2008. *Market Brief: The Canadian Energy Drink Market.* Available at www.ats.agr.gc.ca/can/4469-eng.htm (accessed February 13, 2011).

38. Dietitians of Canada. 2010. *Energy Drinks—What You Need to Know.* Available at www.dietitians.ca/Nutrition-Resources-A-Z/Fact-Sheet-Pages%28HTML%29/Miscellaneous/Energy-Drinks.aspx (accessed August 3, 2011).

39. Health Canada. 2010. *It's Your Health: Safe Use of Energy Drinks.* Available at www.hc-sc.gc.ca/hl-vs/iyh-vsv/food-aliment/boissons-energ-drinks-eng (accessed February 13, 2011).

40. MacDonald, N., M. Stanbrook, and P. C. Hebert. 2010. "Caffeinating" children and youth. *Can. Med. Assoc. J.* 182(15):1597.

41. Health Canada. 2006. *It's Your Health: Caffeine.* Available at www.hc-sc.gc.ca/hl-vs/iyh-vsv/food-aliment/caffeine-eng.php#he (accessed February 13, 2011).

42. Battram, D. S., R. Arthur, A. Weekes, and T. E. Graham. 2006. The glucose intolerance induced by caffeinated coffee ingestion is less pronounced than that due to alkaloid caffeine in men. *J. Nutr.* 136:1276–1280.

43. Noordzij, M., C. S. Uiterwaal, L. R. Arends, F. J. Kok, D. W. Grobbee, and J. M. Geleijnse. 2005. Blood pressure response to chronic intake of coffee and caffeine: a meta-analysis of randomized controlled trials. *J. Hypertension* 23(5):921–928.

44. Food and Nutrition Board. Institute of Medicine.2004. *Dietary Reference Intakes for Thiamine, Riboflavin, Niacin, Vitamin B_6, Folate, Vitamin B_{12}, Pantothenic Acid, Biotine, and Choline.* Washington, DC: The National Academies Press.

45. Malinauskas, B. M., V. G. Aeby, R. F. Overton, T. Aeby-Carpenter, and K. Barber-Heidal. 2007. A survey of energy drink consumption patterns among college students. *J. Nutr.* 6:35. DO:10.1186/1475-2891-6-35.

46. Reissig, C. J., E. C. Strain, and R. C. Griffiths. 2009. Caffeinated energy drinks—a growing problem. *Drug Alcohol Depend.* 99:1–10.

Energy Drinks: Should They Be Banned?

In 2008, a 15-year-old Canadian boy died from an irregular heartbeat after drinking a Red Bull® energy drink. His father claimed that the drink contributed to his son's death.[35] In July 2010, Health Canada's Director-General of the Marketed Health Products Directorate, Chris Turner, stated that his department had received several dozen reports of adverse reactions related to the consumption of energy drinks. Fifteen of those adverse reactions were cardiac events.[36] In 2006, per capita spending on energy drinks in Canada reached $8.70 per person, up from $6.90 in 2001.[37] According to Agriculture and Agri-Food Canada, the sales of energy drinks are expected to lead the beverage sector in growth through 2011.[37] This surge in popularity and the growing concerns about their use by Canadian children leads us to ask two important questions:

- Are these energy drinks dangerous?
- Should energy drinks be banned in Canada?

Energy drinks are a category of beverages that claim to stimulate and energize the user.[38] They are regulated as natural health products under the Natural Health Product (NHP) regulations because of their ingredients and the claims that are made about them.[39] Consumers can identify whether or not an energy drink is approved for sale in Canada by looking for the eight digit Natural Product Number (NPN) on the label. As of July 2010, Health Canada had approved 18 energy drinks as natural health products.[36] Energy drinks are not the same as sports drinks. Sports drinks are specially formulated to rehydrate the body, provide carbohydrate for energy, and replace electrolytes. Energy drinks, on the other hand, should not be used to as a fluid replacement.[39]

The main ingredient in energy drinks is usually caffeine or a combination of caffeine plus glucose. The caffeine found in these drinks may be in the form of pure caffeine or as guarana or yerba mate.[38] Typically, the dose is about 80 mg per 250 mL; however, some energy drinks have been found to contain as much as 500 mg per can.[40] Health Canada recommends that intakes of caffeine not exceed 2.5 mg/kg/day for children aged 4 through 12. Based on average body weights, this translates into a daily caffeine intake of less than 45 mg for children aged 4 to 6, 62.5 mg for children aged 7 to 9, and 85 mg for children aged 10 to 12.[41] There was not enough data to set recommendations for adolescents (aged 13 years and older). However, similar to the recommendations for younger children, Health Canada recommends that intakes do not exceed 2.5 mg/kg/day in this age group.

Recent studies have suggested that the effects of pure caffeine added to energy drinks may be different from the effects associated with other caffeinated beverages. Battram and colleagues found that the ingestion of pure caffeine resulted in impaired glucose tolerance while chronic coffee consumption reduced the risk of type 2 diabetes.[42] A meta-analysis of randomized controlled trials of the effect of coffee or caffeine on blood pressure concluded that while regular caffeine intake increases blood pressure, the effect of coffee consumption was small.[43] These authors hypothesized that the difference may be due to non-caffeine–containing chemicals in coffee that may inhibit the actions of caffeine.[42, 43]

Other substances that may be added to energy drinks include taurine, vitamins, and glucuronolactone. Taurine is a conditionally essential amino acid that is usually found in energy drinks in doses of 1 gram per 250 mL.[38] This exceeds the amount that would be found in a typical Canadian diet. Product advertising often suggests that taurine is responsible for the mental stimulatory effects of energy drinks, however there is no research evidence to support this claim.[38] B-vitamins, particularly niacin, are found in many energy drinks because of their role in energy metabolism. In some cases, the amount of niacin may exceed the upper limit (UL) of 35 mg/day set by the Institute of Medicine and increase the risk of flushing, itching, and redness of the skin.[44] Glucuronolactone is a carbohydrate that is purported to improve energy, mental alertness, and cognitive function. There is no evidence to support this claim.[38]

Health Canada has expressed concern about how energy drinks are marketed and does encourage Canadians to report any adverse effects they experience after consumption of an energy drink. They advise Canadians to:

- Read the labels of all energy drinks and follow label instructions
- Consume energy drinks in moderation
- Not mix energy drinks with alcohol
- Drink water instead of energy drinks if engaging in physical activity

They also advise that energy drinks not be consumed by children or pregnant or breastfeeding women.[39] Many health professionals have stated that this is not enough. An editorial in the *Canadian Medical Association Journal* in 2010 called for stricter regulations. Currently, there are no regulations prohibiting the sale of energy drinks to children and research has shown that 40% or more of children and adolescents consume energy drinks.[38]

Further, a survey of energy drink consumption among college and university students showed that many mixed alcohol with these drinks and were four times more likely to drink and drive while under the influence of these beverages.[45] Another concern relates to the long-term effects of drinking large amounts of energy drinks on a regular basis. There is some evidence to suggest that high intakes of energy drinks are related to increased blood pressure, abnormal heart rhythm, orthostatic intolerance (fainting and dizziness upon standing), and seizures.[46]

Using the Evidence

1. Why do you think energy drinks are so popular among young people?

2. Do you think that energy drinks are dangerous? Why or why not?

3. Should Health Canada ban the sale of energy drinks in Canada? Why or why not?

Nutrients Involved in Antioxidant Function

Chapter Objectives | *After reading this chapter, you will be able to:*

1. Define free radicals and discuss how they can damage cells, *pp. 366–367.*

2. Describe how antioxidants protect cells from the oxidative damage caused by free radicals, *pp. 367–368.*

3. List three antioxidant enzyme systems and describe how these systems help fight oxidative damage, *p. 368.*

4. List three vitamins that have antioxidant properties, *p. 368.*

5. Describe how vitamin A works to ensure healthy vision, *pp. 380–381.*

6. Identify food sources that are high in nutrients with antioxidant properties, *pp. 368–386.*

7. Describe the relationship between antioxidant nutrients and the risk for cancer, *pp. 388–393.*

8. Discuss how consuming foods with antioxidant nutrients can reduce the risk for cardiovascular disease, *pp. 394–395.*

9. Compare and contrast macular degeneration and cataracts, and discuss how antioxidants may affect these two disorders, *pp. 395–396.*

Mika, a first-year student at a university hundreds of kilometres from home, just opened another care package from her mom. As usual, it contained an assortment of healthy snacks, a box of chamomile tea, and several types of supplements: echinacea extract to ward off colds, powdered papaya for good digestion, and antioxidant vitamins. "Wow, Mika!" her roommate laughed. "Can you let your mom know I'm available for adoption?"

"I guess she just wants me to stay healthy," Mika sighed. She wondered what her mother would think if she ever found out how much junk food Mika had been eating since she'd started university, or that she'd been binge-drinking every weekend, or that she'd been smoking since high school. "Still," Mika reminded herself, "at least I take the vitamins she sends."

What do you think of Mika's current lifestyle? Can a poor diet, binge-drinking, and smoking cause cancer or other health problems, and can the use of dietary supplements provide some protection? What are antioxidant vitamins, and why do you think Mika's mom included a bottle of these in her care package? If your health food store was promoting an antioxidant supplement, would you buy it?

It isn't easy to sort fact from fiction when it comes to antioxidants—especially when they're in the form of supplements. Internet ads and articles in fitness and health magazines tout their benefits, yet some researchers claim that they don't protect us from diseases and in some cases may even be harmful. In this chapter, you'll learn what antioxidants are and how they work in the body. We'll also profile the antioxidant nutrients and discuss their relationship to health. Finally, you'll learn about the role antioxidants may play in preventing cancer and heart disease and in slowing the aging process.

What Are Antioxidants, and How Does the Body Use Them?

Antioxidants are compounds that protect cells from the damage caused by oxidation. *Anti* means "against," and antioxidants work *against,* or *prevent* oxidation. Before we can go further in our discussion of antioxidants, we need to review what oxidation is and how it damages cells.

Oxidation Is a Chemical Reaction in Which Atoms Lose Electrons

As you recall from Chapter 7, during metabolic reactions, atoms may lose electrons (**Figure 11.1a**). This loss of electrons is called **oxidation**, because it is fueled by oxygen. Atoms are also capable of gaining electrons, through a complementary process called *reduction* (Figure 11.1b). Because oxidation–reduction reactions typically result in an even exchange of electrons, scientists call them *exchange reactions*.

Stable atoms have an even number of electrons orbiting in pairs at successive distances (called *shells* or *rings*) from the nucleus. When a stable atom loses an electron during oxidation, it is left with an odd number of electrons in its outermost shell. In other words, it now has an *unpaired electron.* In most exchange reactions, two atoms with unpaired electrons immediately pair up, making newly stabilized molecules, but in rare cases, atoms with unpaired electrons in their outermost shell remain unpaired. Such atoms are highly unstable and

antioxidant A compound that has the ability to prevent or repair the damage caused by oxidation.

oxidation A chemical reaction in which molecules of a substance are broken down into their component atoms. During oxidation, the atoms involved lose electrons.

(a) Oxidation   (b) Reduction

Figure 11.1 The exchange reaction. Exchange reactions consist of two parts. (a) During oxidation, molecules *lose* electrons. (b) In the second part of the reaction, molecules *gain* electrons, which is called reduction.

are called **free radicals**. When an oxygen molecule becomes a free radical, it is specifically referred to as a **reactive oxygen species (ROS)**.

As you learned in Chapter 7, the body uses oxygen and hydrogen to generate energy (ATP). The process of metabolism sometimes results in the release of single electrons. Occasionally, oxygen accepts one of these single electrons. When it does so, the newly unstable oxygen atom becomes a free radical because of the added unpaired electron. This type of free-radical production is common during metabolism. Free radicals are also formed from other metabolic processes, such as when our immune systems fight infections. Environmental factors that cause free-radical formation include exposure to pollution, excessive sunlight, toxic substances, radiation, tobacco smoke, and asbestos. Continual exposure to these factors leads to uncontrollable free-radical formation and increases the individual's risk for chronic disease, as discussed next.

Free Radicals Can Destabilize Other Molecules and Damage Cells

Why are we concerned with the formation of free radicals? Simply put, it is because of their destabilizing power. If you were to think of paired electrons as a married couple, a free radical would be an extremely seductive outsider. Its unpaired electron exerts a powerful attraction toward all stable molecules around it. In an attempt to stabilize itself, a free radical will "steal" an electron from stable compounds, in turn generating more unstable free radicals. This is a dangerous chain reaction, because the free radicals generated can damage or destroy cells.

One of the most significant sites of free-radical damage is the cell membrane. As shown in **Figure 11.2a**, free radicals that form within the phospholipid bilayer of cell membranes steal electrons from their stable lipid molecules. When the lipid molecules, which are hydrophobic, are destroyed, they no longer repel water. With the cell membrane's integrity lost, the ability to regulate the movement of fluids and nutrients into and out of the cell is also lost. This loss of cell integrity causes damage to the cell and to all systems affected by this cell.

Other sites of free-radical damage include low-density lipoproteins (LDLs), cell proteins, and DNA. Damage to these sites disrupts the transport of substances into and out of cells, alters protein function, and can disrupt cell function because of defective DNA. These changes may increase our risk for chronic diseases such as heart disease, various cancers, type 2 diabetes, cataracts, Alzheimer's disease, and Parkinson's disease.

Antioxidants Work by Stabilizing Free Radicals or Opposing Oxidation

How does the body fight free radicals and repair the damage they cause? Antioxidant vitamins, minerals, and other compounds accomplish these functions in a variety of ways:

1. Antioxidant *vitamins* work independently by donating their electrons or hydrogen molecules to free radicals to stabilize them and reduce the damage caused by oxidation (see Figure 11.2b).

Exposure to pollution from car exhaust and industrial waste increases our production of free radicals.

free radical A highly unstable atom with an unpaired electron in its outermost shell.

reactive oxygen species (ROS) A specific term used to describe an oxygen molecule that has become a free radical.

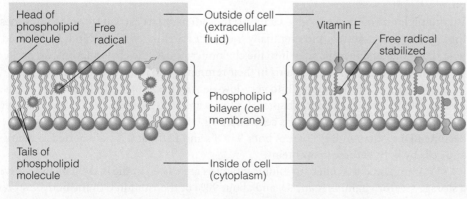

(a)   (b)

Head of phospholipid molecule — Free radical — Outside of cell (extracellular fluid) — Vitamin E — Free radical stabilized — Phospholipid bilayer (cell membrane) — Tails of phospholipid molecule — Inside of cell (cytoplasm)

Figure 11.2 (a) The formation of free radicals in the lipid portion of our cell membranes can cause a dangerous chain reaction that damages the integrity of the membrane and can cause cell death. (b) Vitamin E is stored in the lipid portion of our cell membranes. By donating an electron to free radicals, it protects the lipid molecules in our cell membranes from being oxidized and stops the chain reaction of oxidative damage.

2. Antioxidant *minerals*, including selenium, copper, iron, zinc, and manganese, act as cofactors within complex antioxidant enzyme systems that convert free radicals to less damaging substances that are excreted by the body. They also work to break down fatty acids that have become oxidized, thereby destroying the free radicals associated with them. Antioxidant enzyme systems also make more vitamin antioxidants available to fight other free radicals. Examples of antioxidant enzyme systems include the following:
   - Superoxide dismutase converts free radicals to less damaging substances, such as hydrogen peroxide.
   - Catalase removes hydrogen peroxide from the body by converting it to water and oxygen.
   - Glutathione peroxidase also removes hydrogen peroxide from the body and stops the production of free radicals in lipids.
3. Other compounds such as *beta-carotene* and other *phytochemicals* help stabilize free radicals and prevent damage to cells and tissues.

In summary, free-radical formation is generally kept safely under control by certain vitamins, minerals working within antioxidant systems, and phytochemicals. Next, we take a look at the specific vitamins and minerals involved. Phytochemicals were discussed in Chapter 8.

RECaP

Free radicals are formed when a stable atom loses or gains an electron and this electron remains unpaired. They can be produced during the formation of ATP, when our immune system fights infections, and when we are exposed to radiation or toxic substances. Free radicals can damage our cell membranes, low-density lipoproteins (LDLs), cell proteins, and DNA and are associated with many chronic diseases, including heart disease, various cancers, and type 2 diabetes. Antioxidant vitamins donate electrons or hydrogen atoms to free radicals to stabilize them. Antioxidant minerals function as part of antioxidant enzyme systems that convert free radicals to less damaging substances. Some phytochemicals also have antioxidant properties.

A Profile of Nutrients That Function as Antioxidants

To maintain optimal health, we must consume antioxidants in our diet. Nutrients that appear to have antioxidant properties or are part of our protective antioxidant enzyme systems include vitamins E, C, and A; beta-carotene (a precursor to vitamin A); and the mineral selenium (see Table 11.1, page 370). The minerals copper, iron, zinc, and manganese play a peripheral role in fighting oxidation and are only mentioned in this chapter. Let's review each of these nutrients now and learn more about their functions in the body.

Vitamin E

Vitamin E is one of the fat-soluble vitamins; thus, dietary fats carry it from the intestines through the lymph system and eventually transport it to the cells. Vitamin E is absorbed with dietary fat and incorporated into the chylomicrons. As the chylomicrons are broken down, most of the vitamin E remains in their remnants and is transported to the liver. There, vitamin E is incorporated into very-low-density lipoproteins (VLDLs) and released into the blood. As described in Chapter 5, VLDLs are transport vehicles that ferry triglycerides from their source to the body's cells. After VLDLs release their triglyceride load, they become LDLs. Vitamin E is a part of both VLDLs and LDLs and is transported to the tissues and cells by both of these lipoproteins.

Vitamin E and the other fat-soluble vitamins are stored in the body. The liver serves as a storage site for vitamins A and D, and about 90% of the vitamin E in the body is stored in our adipose tissue. The remaining vitamin E is found in cell membranes.

Vegetable oils, nuts, seeds, and avocados are good sources of vitamin E.

Forms of Vitamin E

Vitamin E is actually two separate families of compounds, **tocotrienols** and **tocopherols**. None of the four different tocotrienol compounds—alpha, beta, gamma, and delta—appears to play an active role in the body. The tocopherol compounds are the biologically active forms. Four different tocopherol compounds have been discovered; as with tocotrienol, these have been designated alpha, beta, gamma, and delta. Of these, the most active, or potent, vitamin E compound found in food and supplements is *alpha-tocopherol* (**Figure 11.3**). The RDA for vitamin E is expressed as alpha-tocopherol in milligrams per day (α-tocopherol, mg per day). Food labels and vitamin and mineral supplements may express vitamin E in units of alpha-tocopherol equivalents (α-TE), milligrams, and as International Units (IU). For conversion purposes:

- In food, 1α-TE is equal to 1 mg of active vitamin E.
- In supplements containing natural sources of vitamin E, 1 IU is equal to 0.67 mg α-TE.
- In supplements containing synthetic sources of vitamin E, 1 IU is equal to 0.45 mg α-TE.

Functions of Vitamin E

The primary function of vitamin E is as an antioxidant: it donates an electron to free radicals, stabilizing them and preventing them from destabilizing other molecules. Once vitamin E is oxidized, it is either excreted from the body or recycled back into active vitamin E through the help of other antioxidant nutrients, such as vitamin C.

Because vitamin E is prevalent in adipose tissue and cell membranes, its action specifically protects *polyunsaturated fatty acids* (PUFAs) and other fatty components of our cells and cell membranes from being oxidized (see Figure 11.2b). Vitamin E also protects LDLs from being oxidized, thereby lowering the risk for heart disease.[1,2] (The relationship between antioxidants and heart disease is reviewed later in this chapter.) In addition to protecting PUFAs and LDLs, vitamin E protects the membranes of red blood cells from oxidation and plays a critical role in protecting the cells of our lungs, which are constantly exposed to oxygen and the potentially damaging effects of oxidation. Vitamin E's role in protecting PUFAs and other fatty components also explains why it is added to many oil-based foods and skincare products—by preventing oxidation in these products, it reduces rancidity and spoilage.

Vitamin E serves many other roles essential to human health. It is critical for normal fetal and early childhood development of red blood cells, nerves and muscles, as well as for maintenance of their functions. It enhances immune function by protecting white blood cells and other components of the immune system, thereby helping the body to defend against illness and disease. It also improves the absorption of vitamin A if the dietary intake of vitamin A is low.

How Much Vitamin E Should We Consume?

Considering the importance of vitamin E to our health, you might think that you need to consume a huge amount daily. In fact, the RDA is modest and the food sources are plentiful.

Recommended Dietary Allowance for Vitamin E   The RDA for vitamin E for men and women is 15 mg alpha-tocopherol per day. This is the amount determined to be sufficient to prevent **erythrocyte hemolysis**, or the rupturing (*lysis*) of red blood cells (*erythrocytes*). The tolerable upper intake level (UL) is 1000 mg alpha-tocopherol per day. Remember that one of the primary roles of vitamin E is to protect PUFAs from oxidation. Thus, our need for vitamin E increases as we eat more oils and other foods that contain PUFAs. Fortunately, these foods also contain vitamin E, so we typically consume enough vitamin E within them to protect their PUFAs from oxidation.

Good Food Sources of Vitamin E   Vitamin E is widespread in foods. Much of the vitamin E that we consume comes from vegetable oils and the products made from them

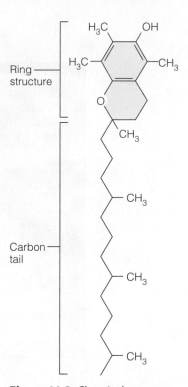

Figure 11.3 Chemical structure of α-tocopherol. Note that α-tocopherol is composed of a ring structure and a long carbon tail. Variations in the spatial orientation of the carbon atoms in this tail and in the composition of the tail itself are what result in forming the different tocopherol and tocotrienol compounds.

tocotrienols A second family of vitamin E that does not play an important biological role in our bodies.

tocopherols A family of vitamin E that is the active form in our bodies.

erythrocyte hemolysis The rupturing or breakdown of red blood cells, or erythrocytes.

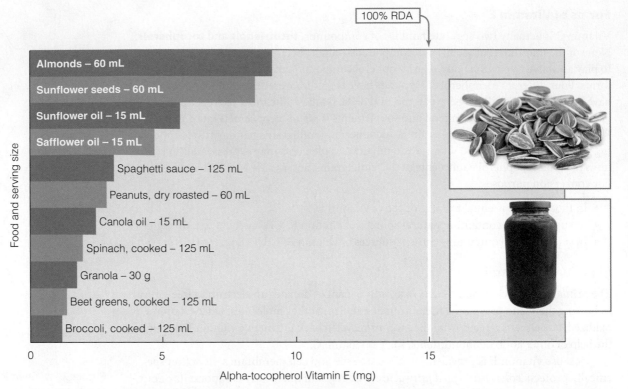

Figure 11.4 Common food sources of vitamin E. The RDA for vitamin E is 15 mg α-tocopherol per day for men and women.
Data from: The Canadian Nutrient File. Health Canada, 2012. Reproduced with the permission of the Minister of Health, 2012.

(**Figure 11.4**). Safflower oil, sunflower oil, canola oil, and soybean oil are good sources. Mayonnaise and salad dressings made from these oils also contain vitamin E. Nuts, seeds, and some vegetables also contribute vitamin E to our diet. Although no single fruit or vegetable contains very high amounts of vitamin E, eating the recommended amounts of fruits and vegetables each day will help ensure adequate intake of this nutrient. Grain products contribute modest amounts to our diet; wheat germ and soybeans are also good sources of vitamin E. Animal and dairy products are poor sources.

Vitamin E is destroyed by exposure to oxygen, metals, ultraviolet light, and heat. Although raw (uncooked) vegetable oils contain vitamin E, heating these oils destroys vitamin E. Thus, foods that are deep-fried and processed contain little vitamin E. This includes most fast foods and convenience foods.

What Happens If We Consume Too Much Vitamin E?

Until recently, standard supplemental doses (1 to 18 times the RDA) of vitamin E were not associated with any adverse health effects. However, among adults 55 years of age or older with vascular disease or diabetes, a daily intake of 268 mg of vitamin E per day (about 18 times the RDA) for approximately seven years resulted in a significant increase in heart failure.[3] However, these results have not been confirmed by additional research studies. At this time, it is unclear whether these adverse effects are an anomaly or if high supplemental doses of vitamin E may be harmful for certain individuals.

Some individuals report side effects such as nausea, intestinal distress, and diarrhea with vitamin E supplementation. In addition, certain medications interact negatively with vitamin E. The most important of these are the *anticoagulants,* substances that stop blood from clotting excessively. Aspirin is an anticoagulant, as is the prescription drug Coumadin. Vitamin E supplements can augment the action of these substances, causing uncontrollable bleeding. In addition, new evidence suggests that in some people, long-term use of standard

Table 11.1 Overview of Nutrients Involved in Antioxidant Function

Nutrient	Recommended Intake
Vitamin E (fat soluble)	RDA: Women and men = 15 mg alpha-tocopheral
Vitamin C (water soluble)	RDA: Women = 75 mg Men = 90 mg Smokers = 35 mg more per day than RDA
Beta-carotene (fat-soluble provitamin for vitamin A)	None at this time
Vitamin A (fat soluble)	RDA: Women: 700 µg Men: 900 µg
Selenium (trace mineral)	RDA: Women and men = 55 µg

vitamin E supplements may cause hemorrhaging in the brain, leading to a type of stroke called *hemorrhagic stroke*.[4]

What Happens If We Don't Consume Enough Vitamin E?

True vitamin E deficiencies are uncommon in humans. This is primarily because vitamin E is fat soluble, so we typically store adequate amounts in our fatty tissues even when our diets are low in this nutrient. However, it is considered common for people in North America to consume suboptimal amounts of vitamin E. Assessment of vitamin E intake in the diets of Canadians is complicated by incomplete vitamin E data in the Canadian Nutrient File, which provides data on α-tocopherols only.[5]

Despite the rarity of true vitamin E deficiencies, they do occur. One vitamin E deficiency symptom is *erythrocyte hemolysis*. This rupturing of red blood cells leads to *anemia*, a condition in which the red blood cells cannot carry and transport enough oxygen to the tissues, leading to fatigue, weakness, and a diminished ability to perform physical and mental work. We discuss anemia in more detail in Chapter 13. Premature babies can suffer from vitamin E–deficiency anemia; if born too early, the infant does not receive vitamin E from its mother, as the transfer of this vitamin from mother to baby occurs during the last few weeks of the pregnancy.

Other symptoms of vitamin E deficiency include loss of muscle coordination and reflexes, leading to impairments in vision, speech, and movement. As you might expect, vitamin E deficiency can also impair immune function, especially if accompanied by low body stores of the mineral selenium.

In adults, vitamin E deficiencies are usually caused by diseases, particularly diseases that cause malabsorption of fat, such as those that affect the small intestine, liver, gallbladder, and pancreas. As reviewed in Chapter 3, the liver makes bile, which is necessary for the absorption of fat. The gallbladder delivers the bile into our intestines, where it facilitates digestion of fat. The pancreas makes fat-digesting enzymes. Thus, when the liver, gallbladder, or pancreas are not functioning properly, fat and the fat-soluble vitamins, including vitamin E, cannot be absorbed, leading to their deficiency.

RECAP

Vitamin E protects cell membranes from oxidation, enhances immune function, and improves the absorption of vitamin A if dietary intake is low. The RDA for vitamin E is 15 mg alpha-tocopherol per day for men and women. Vitamin E is found primarily in vegetable oils and nuts. Toxicity is uncommon, but taking very high doses can cause excessive bleeding. A genuine deficiency is rare, but symptoms include anemia and impaired vision, speech, and movement.

Vitamin C

Vitamin C is a water-soluble vitamin. We must therefore consume it on a regular basis, as any excess is excreted (primarily in the urine) rather than stored. There are two active forms of vitamin C: ascorbic acid and dehydroascorbic acid (**Figure 11.5**). Interestingly, most animals can make their own vitamin C from glucose. Humans and guinea pigs are two groups that cannot synthesize their own vitamin C and must consume it in the diet.

At low concentrations, vitamin C is absorbed in the intestines via active transport; at high concentrations, it is absorbed via simple diffusion. Between consumptions of 30 to 80 mg/day, about 70% to 90% of dietary vitamin C is absorbed, but absorption falls to less than 50% when more than 1 g per day is consumed.[6] The kidneys regulate excretion of vitamin C, with increased excretion occurring during periods of high dietary intake and decreased excretion when dietary intakes are low.

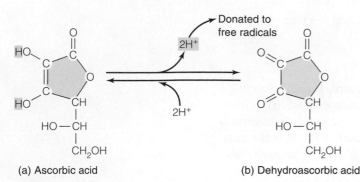

Figure 11.5 Chemical structures of ascorbic acid and dehydro-ascorbic acid. (a) By donating two of its hydrogens to free radicals, ascorbic acid protects against oxidative damage and becomes (b) dehydroascorbic acid. In turn, dehydroascorbic acid can accept two hydrogens to become ascorbic acid.

(a) Ascorbic acid

(b) Dehydroascorbic acid

Many fruits, like these yellow tomatoes, are high in vitamin C.

glutathione (GSH) A tripeptide composed of glycine, cysteine, and glutamic acid that assists in regenerating vitamin C into its antioxidant form.

Functions of Vitamin C

Vitamin C is probably most well known for its role in preventing scurvy, a disease that ravaged sailors on long sea voyages centuries ago. In fact, the derivation of the term *ascorbic acid* means "a" (without) "scorbic" (having scurvy). Scurvy was characterized by bleeding tissues, especially of the gums, and is thought to have caused more than half of the deaths that occurred at sea. During these long voyages, the crew ate all of the fruits and vegetables early in the trip then had only grain and animal products available until they reached land to resupply. In 1740 in England, Dr. James Lind discovered that citrus fruits could prevent scurvy. This is due to their high vitamin C content. Fifty years after the discovery of the link between citrus fruits and prevention of scurvy, the British Navy finally required all ships to provide daily lemon juice rations for each sailor to prevent the onset of scurvy. A century later, sailors were given lime juice rations, earning them the nickname "limeys." It wasn't until 1930 that vitamin C was discovered and identified as a nutrient.

One reason that vitamin C prevents scurvy is that it assists in the synthesis of collagen. Collagen, a protein, is a critical component of all connective tissues in the body, including bone, teeth, skin, tendons, and blood vessels. Collagen assists in preventing bruises, and it ensures proper wound healing, as it is a part of scar tissue and a component of the tissue that mends broken bones. Without adequate vitamin C, the body cannot form collagen, and tissue hemorrhage, or bleeding, occurs. Vitamin C may also be involved in the synthesis of other components of connective tissues, such as elastin and bone matrix.

In addition to connective tissues, vitamin C assists in the synthesis of DNA, bile, neurotransmitters such as serotonin (which helps regulate mood), and carnitine, which transports long-chain fatty acids from the cytosol into the mitochondria for energy production. Vitamin C also helps ensure that appropriate levels of thyroxine, a hormone produced by the thyroid gland, are produced to support basal metabolic rate and to maintain body temperature. Other hormones that are synthesized with assistance from vitamin C include epinephrine, norepinephrine, and steroid hormones.

Vitamin C also acts as an antioxidant. Because it is water soluble, it is an important antioxidant in the extracellular fluid. Like vitamin E, it donates electrons to free radicals, thus preventing the damage of cells and tissues (see Figure 11.5a). It also protects LDL-cholesterol from oxidation, which may reduce the risk for cardiovascular disease. Vitamin C acts as an important antioxidant in the lungs, helping to protect us from the damage caused by ozone and cigarette smoke.[1] It also enhances immune function by protecting the white blood cells from the oxidative damage that occurs in response to fighting illness and infection. But contrary to popular belief, it is not a miracle cure (see the accompanying Nutrition Myth or Fact? box on vitamin C). In the stomach, vitamin C reduces the formation of *nitrosamines,* cancer-causing agents found in foods such as cured and processed meats. We discuss the role of vitamin C and other antioxidants in preventing some forms of cancer later in this chapter (pages 388–393).

Vitamin C also regenerates vitamin E after it has been oxidized. This occurs when ascorbic acid donates electrons to vitamin E radicals, becoming dehydroascorbic acid (**Figure 11.6**). The regenerated vitamin E can now continue to protect cell membranes and other tissues. In turn, dehydroascorbic acid is regenerated as an antioxidant by gaining an electron from the reduced form of **glutathione (GSH)**, which is a tripeptide composed of glycine, cysteine, and glutamic acid. Glutathione is then restored to its antioxidant form by the enzyme *glutathione reductase,* in a reaction (not shown in Figure 11.6) that is dependent on the mineral selenium, which is discussed later in this chapter.

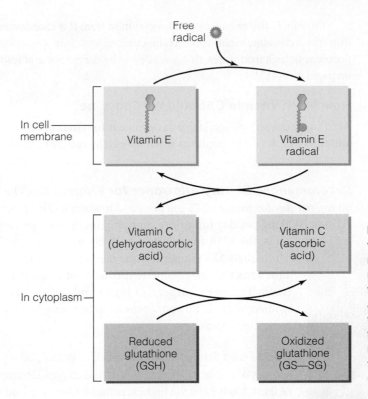

Figure 11.6 Regeneration of vitamin E by vitamin C. Vitamin E neutralizes free radicals in the cell membrane, and vitamin C (in the form of ascorbic acid) regenerates vitamin E from the resulting vitamin E radical. Vitamin C (in the form of dehydroascorbic acid) is regenerated to ascorbic acid by the reduced form of glutathione (GSH).

NUTRITION MYTH OR FACT?

Can Vitamin C Prevent the Common Cold?

What do you do when you feel a cold coming on? If you are like many people, you drink a lot of orange juice or take vitamin C supplements to ward it off. Do these tactics really help prevent a cold?

It is well known that vitamin C is important for a healthy immune system. A deficiency of vitamin C can seriously weaken the immune cells' ability to detect and destroy invading microbes, increasing susceptibility to many diseases and illnesses—including the common cold. Many people have taken vitamin C supplements to prevent the common cold, basing their behaviour on its actions of enhancing our immune function. Interestingly, scientific studies do not support this action. A recent review of many of the studies of vitamin C and the common cold found that people taking vitamin C regularly in an attempt to ward off the common cold experienced as many colds as people who took a placebo. However, the *duration* of their colds was significantly reduced—by 8% in adults and 13.6% in children.[7] Timing

appears to be important, though: taking vitamin C after the onset of cold symptoms did not reduce either the duration or severity of the cold. Interestingly, taking vitamin C supplements regularly did reduce the number of colds experienced in marathon runners, skiers, and soldiers participating in exercises done under extreme environmental conditions.

The amount of vitamin C taken in these studies was at least 200 mg per day, with many using doses as high as 4000 mg per day (more than 40 times the RDA), with no harmful effects noted in those studies that reported adverse events.

In summary, it appears that, for most people, taking vitamin C supplements regularly will not prevent colds, but may reduce their duration. Consuming a healthy diet that includes excellent sources of vitamin C will also help you maintain a strong immune system. Taking vitamin C after the onset of cold symptoms does not appear to help, so next time you feel a cold coming on, you may want to think twice before taking extra vitamin C.

Vitamin C also enhances the absorption of iron. It is recommended that people with low iron stores consume vitamin C–rich foods along with iron sources to improve absorption. For people with high iron stores, this practice can be dangerous and lead to iron toxicity (discussed on pages 452–453).

How Much Vitamin C Should We Consume?

Although popular opinion suggests our needs for vitamin C are high, we really only require amounts that are easily obtained when we eat the recommended amounts of fruits and vegetables daily.

Recommended Dietary Allowance for Vitamin C   The RDA for vitamin C is 90 mg per day for men and 75 mg per day for women. The Tolerable Upper Intake Level (UL) is 2000 mg per day for adults. Smoking increases a person's need for vitamin C. Thus, the RDA for smokers is 35 mg more per day than for non-smokers. This equals 125 mg per day for men and 110 mg per day for women. Other situations that may increase the need for vitamin C include healing from a traumatic injury, surgery, or burns and the use of oral contraceptives among women; there is no consensus as to how much extra vitamin C is needed in these circumstances.

Good Food Sources of Vitamin C   Fruits and vegetables are the best sources of vitamin C. Because heat and oxygen destroy vitamin C, fresh sources of these foods have the highest content. Cooking foods, especially boiling them, leaches their vitamin C, which is then lost when we strain them. Forms of cooking that are least likely to compromise the vitamin C content of foods include steaming, microwaving, and stir-frying.

As indicated in **Figure 11.7**, many fruits and vegetables are high in vitamin C. Citrus fruits (such as oranges, lemons, and limes), potatoes, strawberries, tomatoes, kiwi fruit, broccoli, spinach and other leafy greens, cabbage, green and red peppers, and cauliflower are excellent sources of vitamin C. Fortified beverages and cereals are also good sources. Dairy foods, meats, and non-fortified cereals and grains provide little or no vitamin C. By eating the recommended amounts of fruits and vegetables daily, we can easily meet the body's requirement for vitamin C. Remember that a serving of vegetables is 125 mL of cooked or 250 mL of leafy green vegetables or 125 mL of vegetable juice, and a serving of fruit is one medium fruit, 125 mL of chopped or canned fruit, or 125 mL of fruit juice.

Fresh vegetables are good sources of vitamin C and beta-carotene.

What Happens If We Consume Too Much Vitamin C?

Because vitamin C is water soluble, we usually excrete any excess. Consuming excess amounts in food sources does not lead to toxicity, and only supplements can lead to toxic doses. Taking megadoses of vitamin C is not fatally harmful. However, side effects of doses exceeding 2000 mg per day for a prolonged period include nausea, diarrhea, nosebleeds, and abdominal cramps.

There are rare instances in which consuming even moderately excessive doses of vitamin C can be harmful. As mentioned earlier, vitamin C enhances the absorption of iron. This action is beneficial to people who need to increase iron absorption. It can be harmful, however, to people with a disease called *hemochromatosis,* which causes an excess accumulation of iron in the body. Such iron toxicity can damage tissues and lead to a heart attack. In people who have preexisting kidney disease, taking excess vitamin C can lead to the formation of kidney stones. This does not appear to occur in healthy individuals. Critics of vitamin C supplementation claim that taking the supplemental form of the vitamin is "unbalanced" nutrition and leads vitamin C to act as a prooxidant. A **prooxidant**, as you might guess, is a nutrient that promotes oxidation. It does this by pushing the balance

prooxidant   A nutrient that promotes oxidation and oxidative cell and tissue damage.

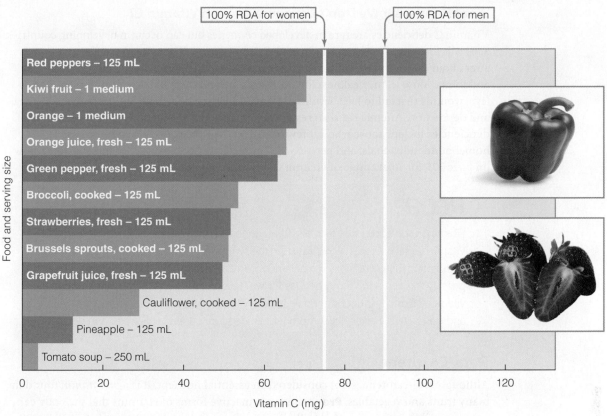

100% RDA for women   100% RDA for men

Food and serving size

Red peppers – 125 mL

Kiwi fruit – 1 medium

Orange – 1 medium

Orange juice, fresh – 125 mL

Green pepper, fresh – 125 mL

Broccoli, cooked – 125 mL

Strawberries, fresh – 125 mL

Brussels sprouts, cooked – 125 mL

Grapefruit juice, fresh – 125 mL

Cauliflower, cooked – 125 mL

Pineapple – 125 mL

Tomato soup – 250 mL

0   20   40   60   80   100   120

Vitamin C (mg)

Figure 11.7 Common food sources of vitamin C. The RDA for vitamin C is 90 mg per day for men and 75 mg per day for women.
Data from: The Canadian Nutrient File. Health Canada, 2012. Reproduced with the permission of the Minister of Health, 2012.

of exchange reactions toward oxidation, which promotes the production of free radicals. Although the results of a few studies have suggested that vitamin C acts as a prooxidant, these studies were found to be flawed or irrelevant for humans. At the present time, there appears to be no strong scientific evidence that vitamin C, either from food or dietary supplements, acts as a prooxidant in humans.

Did You Know?

In 2009, researchers at the University of Toronto studied a cross-sectional sample of 979 non-smoking men and women aged 20–29 years.[8] They assessed dietary intake over the previous month with a 196-item food frequency questionnaire and measured fasting serum ascorbic acid concentrations. Results showed that 53% of subjects had adequate, 33% had suboptimal, and 14% had deficient levels of serum ascorbic acid. Further, the subjects with serum ascorbic acid that was considered deficient had a higher waist circumference, blood pressure, and concentration of C-reactive protein, a marker of inflammation, than did subjects with adequate levels. The researchers concluded that 1 in 7 young adults had serum ascorbic acid deficiency that may have long-term health consequences.

What Happens If We Don't Consume Enough Vitamin C?

Vitamin C deficiencies are rare in developed countries but can occur in developing countries. Scurvy is the most common vitamin C–deficiency disease. The symptoms of scurvy appear after about one month of a vitamin C–deficient diet. Symptoms include bleeding gums and joints, loose teeth, weakness, hemorrhages around the hair follicles of the arms and legs, wounds that fail to heal, swollen ankles and wrists, bone pain and fractures, diarrhea, and depression. Anemia can also result from vitamin C deficiency. People most at risk of deficiencies include those who eat few fruits and vegetables, including impoverished or homebound individuals, and people who abuse alcohol and drugs. See the Did you Know on page 375 for an example of vitamin C in university students.

RECaP

Vitamin C scavenges free radicals and regenerates vitamin E after it has been oxidized. Vitamin C prevents scurvy and assists in the synthesis of collagen, hormones, neurotransmitters, and DNA. Vitamin C also enhances iron absorption. The RDA for vitamin C is 90 mg per day for men and 75 mg per day for women. Many fruits and vegetables are high in vitamin C. Toxicity is uncommon with dietary intake; symptoms include nausea, diarrhea, and nosebleeds. Deficiency symptoms include scurvy, anemia, diarrhea, and depression.

Beta-Carotene

Although beta-carotene is not considered an essential nutrient, it is a *provitamin* found in many fruits and vegetables. **Provitamins** are inactive forms of vitamins that the body cannot use until they are converted to their active form. Our bodies convert beta-carotene to an active form of vitamin A, or *retinol*; thus, beta-carotene is a precursor of retinol.

Beta-carotene is a phytochemical classified as a **carotenoid**, one of a group of plant pigments that are the basis for the red, orange, and deep-yellow colours of many fruits and vegetables. (Even dark-green leafy vegetables contain plenty of carotenoids, but the green pigment, chlorophyll, masks their colour!) Although there are more than 600 carotenoids found in nature, only about 50 are found in the typical human diet. The six most common carotenoids found in human blood are alpha-carotene, beta-carotene, beta-cryptoxanthin, lutein, lycopene, and zeaxanthin. Of these, the body can convert only alpha-carotene, beta-carotene, and beta-cryptoxanthin to retinol. These are referred to as *provitamin A carotenoids*. We are just beginning to learn more about how carotenoids function in our bodies and how they may affect our health (see the Nutrition Myth or Fact? box, next page). Most of our discussion will focus on beta-carotene, as the majority of research on carotenoids to date has focused on this substance.

One molecule of beta-carotene can be split to form two molecules of active vitamin A (**Figure 11.8**). So why are 12 g of beta-carotene considered equivalent to just 1 g of vitamin A?

provitamin An inactive form of a vitamin that the body can convert to an active form. An example is beta-carotene.

carotenoids Fat-soluble plant pigments that the body stores in the liver and adipose tissues. The body is able to convert certain carotenoids to vitamin A.

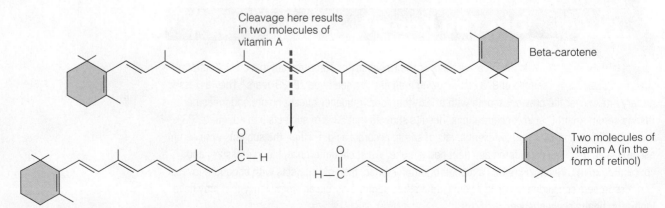

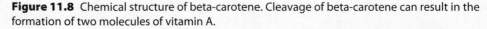

Figure 11.8 Chemical structure of beta-carotene. Cleavage of beta-carotene can result in the formation of two molecules of vitamin A.

Several factors account for this. Sometimes a beta-carotene molecule is cleaved in such a way that only one molecule of vitamin A is produced. In addition, not all of the dietary beta-carotene that is consumed is converted to vitamin A, and the absorption of beta-carotene from the intestines is not as efficient as our absorption of vitamin A. Nutritionists express the units of beta-carotene in a food as Retinol Activity Equivalents, or RAE. This measurement indicates how much active vitamin A is available to the body after it has converted the beta-carotene in the food.

Functions of Beta-Carotene

Beta-carotene and some other carotenoids are nutrients recognized to have antioxidant properties.[9] Like vitamin E, they are fat-soluble and fight the harmful effects of oxidation in the lipid portions of the cell membranes and in LDLs; but, compared with vitamin E, beta-carotene is a relatively weak antioxidant. In fact, other carotenoids, such as lycopene and lutein, may be stronger antioxidants than beta-carotene. Research is currently being conducted to elucidate how many carotenoids are found in foods and which ones are effective antioxidants.

Carotenoids play other important roles in the body through their antioxidant actions. Specifically, they:

- Enhance the immune system and boost the body's ability to fight illness and disease.
- Protect skin from the damage caused by the sun's ultraviolet rays.
- Protect our eyes, preventing or delaying age-related vision impairment.

Carotenoids are also associated with a decreased risk of certain types of cancer. We discuss the roles of carotenoids and other antioxidants in cancer later in this chapter.

NUTRITION MYTH OR FACT?

Can Beta-Carotene Supplements Cause Cancer?

Beta-carotene is one of many carotenoids known to have antioxidant properties. Because there is substantial evidence that people eating foods high in antioxidants have lower rates of cancer, large-scale studies are being conducted to determine whether taking antioxidant supplements can decrease our risk for cancer. In particular, the Alpha-Tocopherol Beta-Carotene (ATBC) Cancer Prevention Study and the Beta-Carotene and Retinol Efficacy Trial (CARET) have shown surprising results.[10, 11]

The ATBC Cancer Prevention Study was conducted in Finland from 1985 to 1993 with the purpose of determining the effects of beta-carotene and vitamin E supplements on the rates of lung cancer and other forms of cancer among male smokers between the ages of 50 and 69 years. Almost 30 000 men participated in the study for an average of six years. The participants were given a daily beta-carotene supplement, a vitamin E supplement, a supplement containing both beta-carotene and vitamin E, or a placebo.

Contrary to what was expected, the male smokers who took beta-carotene supplements experienced an *increased* number of deaths during the study. More men in this group died of lung cancer, heart disease, and stroke. There was also a trend in this group for higher rates of prostate and stomach cancers. This negative effect appeared to be particularly strong in men who had a higher alcohol intake.[10]

CARET began as a pilot study in the United States in 1985 and included more than 18 000 men and women who were smokers, former smokers, or workers who were exposed to asbestos. The participants were randomly assigned to take daily supplements of beta-carotene and retinol (vitamin A) or a placebo. After a four-year follow-up period, the incidence of lung cancer was 28% higher among those taking the beta-carotene and retinol supplement. This significant finding, in addition to the results from the ATBC Cancer Prevention Study, prompted researchers to end the CARET study early and recommend that participants discontinue the supplements.[11]

The reasons why beta-carotene increased lung cancer risk in this population are not clear. It is possible that the supplementation period was too brief to benefit these high-risk individuals, although studies of shorter duration have found beneficial effects. There may be other components besides beta-carotene in whole foods that are protective against cancer, making supplementation with an isolated nutrient ineffective. In any case, the results of these studies suggest that for certain people, supplementation with beta-carotene may be harmful. There is still much to learn about how people of differing risk levels respond to antioxidant supplementation.

Foods that are high in carotenoids are easy to recognize by their bright colours.

How Much Beta-Carotene Should We Consume?

Nutritional scientists do not consider beta-carotene and other carotenoids to be essential nutrients, as they play no known essential roles in our body and are not associated with any deficiency symptoms. Thus, no RDA for these compounds has been established. It has been suggested that consuming 6 to 10 mg of beta-carotene per day from food sources can increase the beta-carotene levels in the blood to amounts that may reduce the risks for some diseases, such as cancer and heart disease.[9] Supplements containing beta-carotene have become very popular, and supplementation studies have prescribed doses of 15 to 30 mg of beta-carotene. Refer to the Nutrition Myth or Fact? box on beta-carotene to learn more about how supplementation with this compound may affect the risk for cancer.

Fruits and vegetables that are red, orange, yellow, and deep green are generally high in beta-carotene and other carotenoids such as lutein and lycopene. Eating the recommended amounts of fruits and vegetables each day ensures an adequate intake of carotenoids. Because of its colour, beta-carotene is used as a natural colouring agent for many foods, including margarine, yellow cheddar cheese, cereal, cake mixes, gelatins, and soft drinks. However, these foods are not significant sources of beta-carotene. **Figure 11.9** identifies common foods that are high in beta-carotene.

We generally absorb only between 20% and 40% of the carotenoids present in the foods we eat. In contrast to vitamins E and C, carotenoids are absorbed better from cooked foods. Carotenoids are bound in the cells of plants, and the process of lightly cooking these plants breaks chemical bonds and can rupture cell walls, which humans don't digest. These actions result in more of the carotenoids being released from the plant. For instance, 250 mL of raw carrots contains approximately 9 mg of beta-carotene, whereas the same amount of cooked frozen carrots contains approximately 12 mg.[12]

What Happens If We Consume Too Much Beta-Carotene?

Consuming large amounts of beta-carotene or other carotenoids in foods does not appear to cause toxic symptoms. However, your skin can turn yellow or orange if you consume large amounts of foods that are high in beta-carotene. This condition is referred to as

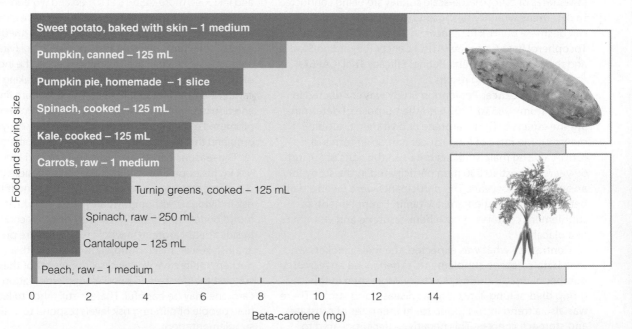

Figure 11.9 Common food sources of beta-carotene. There is no RDA for beta-carotene.
Data from: The Canadian Nutrient File. Health Canada, 2012. Reproduced with the permission of the Minister of Health, 2012.

carotenosis or *carotenodermia,* and it appears to be both reversible and harmless. Taking beta-carotene supplements is not generally recommended, because we can get adequate amounts of this nutrient by eating more fruits and vegetables.

What Happens If We Don't Consume Enough Beta-Carotene?

There are no known deficiency symptoms of beta-carotene or other carotenoids apart from beta-carotene's function as a precursor for vitamin A.

> ## Recap
>
> Beta-carotene is a carotenoid and a provitamin of vitamin A. It protects the lipid portions of cell membranes and LDL-cholesterol from oxidative damage. It also enhances immune function and protects vision. There is no RDA for beta-carotene. Orange, red, and deep-green fruits and vegetables are good sources of beta-carotene. There are no known toxicity or deficiency symptoms, but yellowing of the skin can occur if too much beta-carotene is consumed.

Vitamin A: Much More Than an Antioxidant Nutrient

Vitamin A, a fat-soluble vitamin, plays a number of significant roles in the body. Limited research suggests that it has antioxidant properties; thus, it is discussed in this chapter. More important, vitamin A is critical to vision and the growth and differentiation of cells.

There are three active forms of vitamin A in the body. **Retinol** is also called preformed vitamin A and is the alcohol form. At the cellular level, retinol can be metabolized to **retinal** the aldehyde form. Retinal can be further metabolized to **retinoic acid** the acid form. These three forms are collectively referred to as the *retinoids* (**Figure 11.10**). Remember from the previous section that beta-carotene is a precursor to vitamin A: the beta-carotene in foods is converted to retinol in the wall of the small intestine. Preformed vitamin A is present in foods in the form of retinol and also as *retinyl ester-compounds,* in which retinol is attached to a fatty acid. These retinyl ester-compounds are hydrolyzed in the small intestine, leaving retinol in its free form. Free retinol is then absorbed into the wall of the small intestine, where a fatty acid is attached to form new retinyl ester-compounds. These compounds are then packaged into chylomicrons and enter into the lymph system. The chylomicrons transport vitamin A to the cells as needed or into the liver for storage. About 90% of the vitamin A we absorb is stored in the liver; the remainder is stored in adipose tissue, the kidneys, and the lungs.

Because fat-soluble vitamins cannot dissolve in the blood, they require proteins that can bind with and transport them from their storage sites through the bloodstream to

retinol An active, alcohol form of vitamin A that plays an important role in healthy vision and immune function.

retinal An active, aldehyde form of vitamin A that plays an important role in healthy vision and immune function.

retinoic acid An active, acid form of vitamin A that plays an important role in cell growth and immune function.

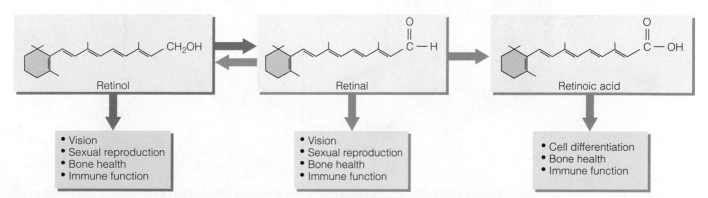

Figure 11.10 The three active forms of vitamin A in our bodies are retinol, retinal, and retinoic acid. Retinol and retinal can be converted interchangeably; retinoic acid is formed from retinal, and this process is irreversible. Each form of vitamin A contributes to many of our bodily processes.

target tissues and cells. *Retinol-binding protein* is one such carrier protein for vitamin A. Retinol-binding protein carries retinol from the liver to the cells that require it.

The unit of expression for vitamin A is Retinol Activity Equivalents (RAE). You may still see the expression Retinol Equivalents (RE) or International Units (IU) for vitamin A on food labels or dietary supplements. The conversions to RAE from various forms of retinol and from the units IU and RE are as follows:

- 1 RAE = 1 microgram (μg) retinol
- 1 RAE = 12 μg beta-carotene
- 1 RAE = 24 μg alpha-carotene or beta-cryptoxanthin
- 1 RAE = 1 RE
- 1 RAE = 3.3 IU

Functions of Vitamin A

The known functions of vitamin A are numerous, and researchers speculate that many are still to be discovered.

Vitamin A Acts as an Antioxidant   Limited research indicates that vitamin A may act as an antioxidant.[13, 14] Like vitamins E and C, it appears to scavenge free radicals and protect LDLs from oxidation. As you might expect, adequate vitamin A levels in the blood are associated with lower risks of some forms of cancer and heart disease. However, the role of vitamin A as an antioxidant is not strongly established and is still under investigation.

Vitamin A Is Essential to Sight   A critical role of vitamin A in the body is certainly in the maintenance of healthy vision. Specifically, vitamin A affects our sight in two ways: it enables us to react to changes in the brightness of light, and it enables us to distinguish between different wavelengths of light; in other words, to see different colours. Let's take a closer look at this process.

Light enters the eyes through the cornea, travels through the lens, and then hits the **retina**, which is a delicate membrane lining the back of the inner eyeball (see **Figure 11.11**).

retina The delicate, light-sensitive membrane lining the inner eyeball and connected to the optic nerve. It contains retinal.

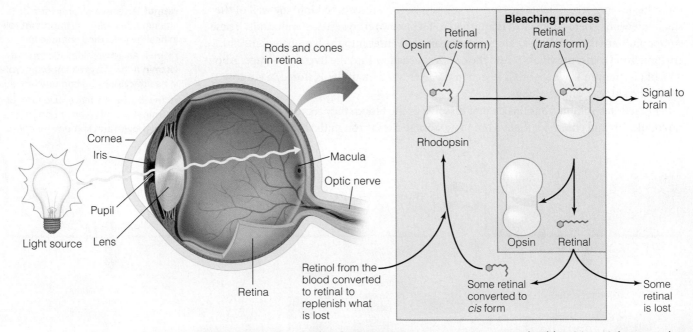

Figure 11.11 The visual cycle. Vitamin A is necessary to maintain healthy vision. Light enters the eye through the cornea, travels through the lens, and hits the retina located in the back of the eye. The light reacts with the retinal stored in the rod cells of the retina, thereby allowing us to see black-and-white images. A similar reaction occurring in the cone cells allows for colour vision.

You might already have guessed how *retinal* got its name: it is found in—and integral to—the retina. In the retina, retinal combines with a protein called **opsin** to form **rhodopsin**, a light-sensitive pigment. Rhodopsin is found in the **rod cells**, which are cells that react to dim light and interpret black-and-white images.

When light hits the retina, the rod cells go through a **bleaching process**. In this reaction, rhodopsin is split into retinal and opsin and the rod cells lose their colour. The retinal component also changes spatial orientation from a *cis* configuration, which is bent, into a *trans* configuration, which is straight. The opsin component also changes shape. These changes in retinal and opsin during the bleaching process generate a nerve impulse that travels to the brain, resulting in the perception of a black-and-white image. Most of the retinal is converted back to its original *cis* form and binds with opsin to regenerate rhodopsin, allowing the visual cycle to begin again. However, some of the retinal is lost with each cycle and must be replaced by retinol from the bloodstream. This visual cycle goes on continually, allowing our eyes to adjust moment-to-moment to subtle changes in our surroundings or in the level of light.

When levels of vitamin A are deficient, people suffer from a condition referred to as night blindness. **Night blindness** results in the inability of the eyes to adjust to dim light. It can also result in the failure to regain sight quickly after a bright flash of light (**Figure 11.12**).

At the same time that we are interpreting black-and-white images, the **cone cells** of the retina, which are only effective in bright light, use retinal to interpret different wavelengths of light as different colours. The pigment involved in colour vision is **iodopsin**. Iodopsin experiences similar changes during the colour vision cycle as rhodopsin does during the black-and-white vision cycle. As with the rod cells, the cone cells can also be affected by a deficiency of vitamin A, resulting in colour blindness.

In summary, the abilities to adjust to dim light, recover from a bright flash of light, and see in colour are all critically dependent on adequate levels of retinal in the eyes.

opsin A protein that combines with retinal in the retina to form rhodopsin.

rhodopsin A light-sensitive pigment found in the rod cells that is formed by retinal and opsin.

rod cells Light-sensitive cells found in the retina that contain rhodopsin and react to dim light and interpret black-and-white images.

bleaching process A reaction in which the rod cells in the retina lose their colour when rhodopsin is split into retinal and opsin.

night blindness A vitamin A–deficiency disorder that results in loss of the ability to see in dim light.

cone cells Light-sensitive cells found in the retina that contain the pigment iodopsin and react to bright light and interpret colour images.

iodopsin A colour-sensitive pigment found in the cone cells of the retina.

(a) Normal night vision　　　**Poor night vision**

(b) Normal light adjustment　　　**Slow light adjustment**

Figure 11.12 A deficiency of vitamin A can result in poor night vision and difficulty adjusting from bright light to dim light.

Vitamin A Contributes to Cell Differentiation

Another important role of vitamin A is its contribution to **cell differentiation**, the process by which stem cells mature into highly specialized cells that perform unique functions. The retinoic acid form of vitamin A interacts with the receptor sites on a cell's DNA. This interaction influences gene expression and the determination of the type of cells that the stem cells eventually become. Obviously, this process is critical to the development of healthy organs and effectively functioning body systems.

An example of cell differentiation is the development of epithelial cells such as skin cells and mucous-producing cells of the protective linings of the lungs, vagina, intestines, stomach, bladder, urinary tract, and eyes. The mucus that epithelial cells produce lubricates the tissue and helps to propel microbes, dust particles, foods, and fluids out of the body tissues (for example, when we cough up secretions or empty the bladder). When vitamin A levels are insufficient, the epithelial cells fail to differentiate appropriately and we lose these protective barriers against infectious microbes and irritants.

Vitamin A is also critical to the differentiation of specialized immune cells called *T-lymphocytes,* or *T-cells.* T-cells assist in fighting infections. You can therefore see why vitamin A deficiency can lead to a breakdown of immune responses and to infections and other disorders of the lungs and respiratory tract, urinary tract, vagina, and eyes.

Other Functions of Vitamin A

Vitamin A is involved in reproduction. Although its exact role is unclear, it appears necessary for sperm production in men and for fertilization to occur in women. It also contributes to healthy bone growth by assisting in breaking down old bone so that new, longer, and stronger bone can develop. As a result of a vitamin A deficiency, children suffer from stunted growth and wasting.

Two popular treatments for acne contain derivatives of vitamin A. Retin-A, or tretinoin, is a treatment applied to the skin. Accutane, or isotretinoin, is taken orally. These medications should be used carefully and only under the supervision of a licensed physician. Both medications increase a person's sensitivity to the sun, and it is recommended that exposure to sunlight be limited while using them. They also can cause birth defects in infants if used while a woman is pregnant and can lead to other toxicity problems, depression, and suicide in some individuals. Interestingly, vitamin A itself has no effect on acne; thus, vitamin A supplements are not recommended in its treatment.

How Much Vitamin A Should We Consume?

Vitamin A toxicity can occur readily because it is a fat-soluble vitamin, so it is important to consume only the amount recommended for your gender and age range.

Recommended Dietary Intake for Vitamin A

The RDA for vitamin A is 900 µg per day for men and 700 µg per day for women. The UL is 3000 µg per day of preformed vitamin A in women (including those pregnant and lactating) and men.

Good Food Sources of Vitamin A

Vitamin A is present in both animal and plant sources. To calculate the total RAE in a person's diet, you must take into consideration both the amount of retinol and the amount of provitamin A carotenoids that are present in the foods eaten. Remember that 12 g of beta-carotene yields 1 g of RAE, and 24 g of alpha-carotene or beta-cryptoxanthin yields 1 g of RAE. Thus, if a person consumes 400 g retinol, 1200 g beta-carotene, and 3000 g alpha-carotene, the total RAE is equal to 400 g + (1200 g ÷ 12) + (3000 g ÷ 24), or 625 g RAE.

The most common sources of dietary preformed vitamin A are animal foods such as beef liver, chicken liver, eggs, and whole-fat dairy products. Vitamin A is also found in fortified reduced-fat milks and margarine (**Figure 11.13**). The other half of the vitamin A

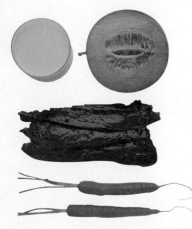

Liver contains vitamin A, and carrots and cantaloupe contain carotenoids that can be converted to vitamin A.

cell differentiation The process by which immature, undifferentiated stem cells develop into highly specialized functional cells of discrete organs and tissues.

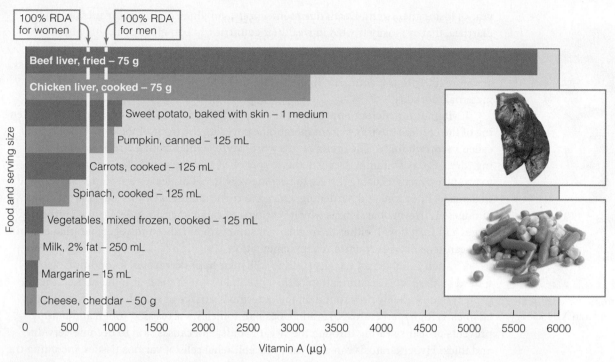

Figure 11.13 Common food sources of vitamin A. The RDA for vitamin A is 900 μg per day for men and 700 μg per day for women.
Data from: The Canadian Nutrient File. Health Canada, 2012. Reproduced with the permission of the Minister of Health, 2012.

we consume comes from foods high in beta-carotene and other carotenoids that can be converted to vitamin A. As discussed earlier in this chapter, dark-green, orange, and deep-yellow fruits and vegetables are good sources of beta-carotene and thus of provitamin A. Carrots, spinach, mango, cantaloupe, and tomato juice are excellent sources of provitamin A because they contain beta-carotene.

What Happens If We Consume Too Much Vitamin A?

Vitamin A is highly toxic, and toxicity symptoms develop after consuming only three to four times the RDA. Toxicity rarely results from food sources, but vitamin A supplements are known to have caused severe illness and even death. Consuming excess vitamin A while pregnant can cause serious birth defects and spontaneous abortion. Other toxicity symptoms include fatigue, loss of appetite, blurred vision, hair loss, skin disorders, bone and joint pain, abdominal pain, nausea, diarrhea, and damage to the liver and nervous system. If caught in time, many of these symptoms are reversible once vitamin A supplementation is stopped. However, permanent damage can occur to the liver, eyes, and other organs. Because liver contains such a high amount of vitamin A, children and pregnant women should not consume liver on a daily or weekly basis. Importantly, the UL only applies to the preformed vitamin A and the toxicity symptoms listed here do not apply to beta-carotene or other carotenoids.

What Happens If We Don't Consume Enough Vitamin A?

As discussed earlier, night blindness and colour blindness can result from vitamin A deficiency. How severe a problem is night blindness? Although less common among people of developed nations, vitamin A deficiency is a severe public health concern in developing nations. According to the World Health Organization, approximately 250 million preschool children suffer from vitamin A deficiency.[15] Of the children affected, 250 000 to 500 000 become permanently blinded every year. At least half of these children will die within one

Eating plenty of fruits and vegetables will help prevent vitamin A deficiency.

year of losing their sight. Death due to infections and illnesses, including measles and diarrhea, that are easily treated in wealthier countries, is also more common with a vitamin A deficiency as the immune system is impaired. Vitamin A deficiency is also a tragedy for pregnant women in these countries. These women suffer from night blindness, are more likely to transmit HIV to their child if HIV-positive, and run a greater risk of maternal mortality.

If vitamin A deficiency progresses, it can result in irreversible blindness due to hardening of the cornea (the transparent membrane covering the front of the eye), a condition called **xerophthalmia**. The prefix of this word, *xero-*, comes from a Greek word meaning "dry." Lack of vitamin A causes the epithelial cells of the cornea to lose their ability to produce mucus, causing the eye to become very dry. This leaves the cornea susceptible to damage, infection, and hardening. Once the cornea hardens in this way, the resulting blindness is irreversible. This is why it is critical to catch vitamin A deficiency in its early stages and treat it with either the regular consumption of fruits and vegetables that contain beta-carotene or with vitamin A supplementation.

Vitamin A deficiency can also lead to follicular **hyperkeratosis**, a condition characterized by the excess accumulation of the protein keratin in the hair follicles. Keratin is a protein that is usually only found on the outermost surface of skin, hair, nails, and tooth enamel. With hyperkeratosis, keratin clogs hair follicles, makes skin rough and bumpy, prevents proper sweating through the sweat glands, and causes skin to become very dry and thick. Hyperkeratosis can also affect the epithelial cells of various tissues, including the mouth, urinary tract, vagina, and eyes, reducing the production of mucus by these tissues and leading to an increased risk of infection. Hyperkeratosis can be reversed with vitamin A supplementation.

Other deficiency symptoms include impaired immunity, increased risk of illness and infections, reproductive system disorders, and failure of normal growth. Individuals who are at risk for vitamin A deficiency include older adults with poor diets, newborn or premature infants (because of low liver stores of vitamin A), young children with inadequate vegetable and fruit intakes, and alcoholics. Any condition that results in fat malabsorption can also lead to vitamin A deficiency. Children with cystic fibrosis and individuals with Crohn's disease, celiac disease, and diseases of the liver, pancreas, or gallbladder are at risk for vitamin A deficiency.

ReCaP

The role of vitamin A as an antioxidant is still under investigation. Vitamin A is critical for maintaining our vision. It is also necessary for cell differentiation, reproduction, and growth. The RDA for vitamin A is 900 µg per day for men and 700 µg per day for women. Animal liver, dairy products, and eggs are good animal sources of preformed vitamin A; fruits and vegetables are high in beta-carotene, which provide provitamin A that can be converted to vitamin A. Supplementation can be dangerous, as toxicity is reached at levels of only three to four times the RDA. Toxicity symptoms include birth defects, spontaneous abortion, blurred vision, and liver damage. Deficiency symptoms include night blindness, impaired immune function, and growth failure.

xerophthalmia An irreversible blindness due to hardening of the cornea and drying of the mucous membranes of the eye.

hyperkeratosis A condition resulting in the excess accumulation of the protein keratin in the follicles of the skin; this condition can also impair the ability of epithelial tissues to produce mucus.

Selenium

Selenium is a trace mineral, and it is found in varying amounts in soil and thus in the food grown there. Keep in mind that although we need only minute amounts of trace minerals, they are just as important to our health as the vitamins and the major minerals. Selenium is efficiently absorbed, with about 50% to 90% of dietary selenium absorbed from the small intestine.[6]

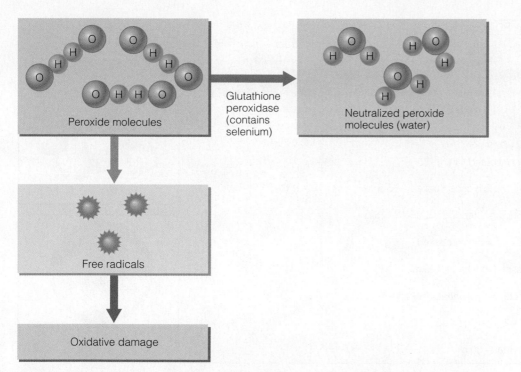

Figure 11.14 Selenium is part of glutathione peroxidase, which neutralizes peroxide molecules that are formed by the body so they cannot form free radicals; this decrease in the number of free radicals spares vitamin E and prevents oxidative damage.

Functions of Selenium

It is only recently that we have learned about the critical role of selenium as a nutrient in human health. In 1979, Chinese scientists reported an association between a heart disorder called **Keshan disease** and selenium deficiency. This disease occurs in children in the Keshan province of China, where the soil is depleted of selenium. The scientists found that Keshan disease can be prevented with selenium supplementation.

The selenium in our bodies is contained in amino acids. Two amino acid derivatives contain the majority of selenium in our bodies: **selenomethionine** is the storage form for selenium, and **selenocysteine** is the active form of selenium. Selenocysteine is a critical component of the glutathione peroxidase enzyme system mentioned earlier (page 368). As shown in **Figure 11.14**, glutathione peroxidase breaks down the peroxides (such as hydrogen peroxide) that are formed by the body so they cannot form free radicals; this decrease in the number of free radicals spares vitamin E. Thus, selenium and vitamin E work together to prevent oxidative damage to lipids and decrease damage to cell membranes.

Like vitamin C, selenium is needed for the production of *thyroxine,* or thyroid hormone. By this action, selenium is involved in the maintenance of basal metabolism and body temperature. Selenium appears to play a role in immune function, and poor selenium status is associated with higher rates of some forms of cancer.

How Much Selenium Should We Consume?

The content of selenium in foods is highly variable. As it is a trace mineral, we need only minute amounts to maintain health. The RDA for selenium is 55 µg per day for both men and women. The UL is 400 µg per day.

Selenium is present in both plant and animal food sources but in variable amounts. Because it is stored in the tissues of animals, selenium is found in reliably consistent amounts in animal foods. Organ meats, such as liver and kidney, as well as pork and seafood, are particularly good sources (see **Figure 11.15**).

Wheat is a rich source of selenium.

Keshan disease A heart disorder caused by selenium deficiency. It was first identified in children in the Keshan province of China.

selenomethionine An amino acid derivative that is the storage form for selenium in the body.

selenocysteine An amino acid derivative that is the active form of selenium in the body.

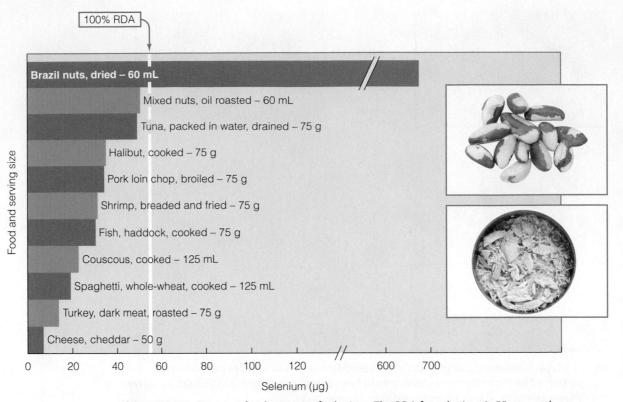

Figure 11.15 Common food sources of selenium. The RDA for selenium is 55 µg per day.
Data from: The Canadian Nutrient File. Health Canada, 2012. Reproduced with the permission of the Minister of Health, 2012.

In contrast, the amount of selenium in plants is dependent on the selenium content of the soil in which the plant is grown. Many companies marketing selenium supplements warn that the agricultural soils in North America are depleted of selenium and inform us that we need to take selenium supplements. In reality, the selenium content of soil varies greatly across North America, and because we obtain our food from a variety of geographic locations, few people in Canada suffer from selenium deficiency. This is especially true for people who eat even small quantities of meat or seafood.

What Happens If We Consume Too Much Selenium?

Selenium toxicity does not result from eating foods high in selenium. However, supplementation can cause toxicity. Toxicity symptoms include brittle hair and nails that can eventually break and fall off. Other symptoms include skin rashes, nausea, vomiting, weakness, and cirrhosis of the liver.

What Happens If We Don't Consume Enough Selenium?

As discussed previously, selenium deficiency is associated with a form of heart disease called Keshan disease. Selenium deficiency does not cause the disease, but selenium is necessary to help the immune system effectively fight the viral infection or exposure to chemicals that prompt it.[6] Selenium supplements significantly reduce the incidence of Keshan disease, but they cannot reduce the damage to the heart muscle once it occurs.

Another deficiency disease is *Kashin-Beck disease,* a disease of the cartilage that results in deforming arthritis (**Figure 11.16**). Kashin-Beck disease is also found in selenium-depleted areas in China and in Tibet. Other deficiency symptoms include impaired immune responses, infertility, depression, impaired cognitive function, and muscle pain and wasting. Deficiencies of both selenium and iodine in pregnant women can cause a form of *cretinism* in the infant. Cretinism was discussed in detail in Chapter 9.

Figure 11.16 Selenium deficiency can lead to a form of deforming arthritis called Kashin-Beck disease.

Copper, Iron, Zinc, and Manganese Play a Peripheral Role in Antioxidant Function

As discussed earlier, there are numerous antioxidant enzyme systems in our bodies. Copper, zinc, and manganese are a part of the superoxide dismutase enzyme complex. Iron is part of the structure of catalase. In addition to their role in protecting against oxidative damage, these minerals play major roles in the optimal functioning of many other enzymes in the body. Copper, iron, and zinc help maintain the health of our blood, and manganese is an important cofactor in carbohydrate metabolism. The functions, requirements, food sources, and deficiency and toxicity symptoms of these nutrients are discussed in detail in Chapter 13, which focuses on the nutrients involved in blood health and immunity.

RECAP

Selenium is part of the glutathione peroxidase enzyme system. It indirectly spares vitamin E from oxidative damage, and it assists with immune function and the production of thyroid hormone. Organ meats, pork, and seafood are good sources of selenium, as are Brazil nuts. The selenium content of plants is dependent on the amount of selenium in the soil in which they are grown. Toxicity symptoms include brittle hair and nails, nausea, vomiting, and liver cirrhosis. Deficiency can result in Keshan disease, Kashin-Beck disease, impaired immune function, infertility, and muscle wasting. Copper, zinc, and manganese are cofactors for the superoxide dismutase antioxidant enzyme system. Iron is a cofactor for the catalase antioxidant enzyme. These minerals play critical roles in blood health and energy metabolism.

What Disorders Are Related to Free-Radical Damage?

You've probably encountered many health claims related to the functions of antioxidants—for instance, that they slow the effects of aging or prevent heart disease and cancer. In opposition to these claims, there is some evidence that taking antioxidant supplements may be harmful for certain people (refer back to the Nutrition Myth or Fact? box on beta-carotene, page 377).

In this section, we will review what is currently known about the role of antioxidant nutrients in cancer, heart disease, and aging.

Cancer

Before we explore how antioxidants affect the risk for cancer, let's take a closer look at precisely what cancer is and how it spreads. **Cancer** is actually a group of diseases that are all characterized by cells that grow "out of control." By this we mean that cancer cells reproduce spontaneously and independently, and they are not inhibited by the boundaries of tissues and organs. Thus, they can aggressively invade tissues and organs far away from those in which they originally formed.

cancer A group of diseases characterized by cells that reproduce spontaneously and independently and may invade other tissues and organs.

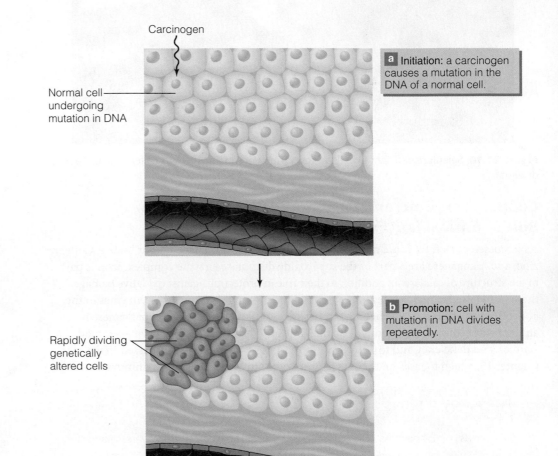

Carcinogen

a Initiation: a carcinogen causes a mutation in the DNA of a normal cell.

Normal cell undergoing mutation in DNA

b Promotion: cell with mutation in DNA divides repeatedly.

Rapidly dividing genetically altered cells

c Progression: cancer cells invade surrounding tissues and spread to other sites in body.

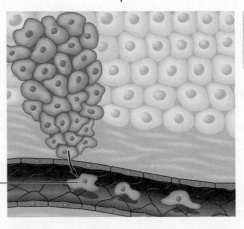

Cancer cell transported in blood vessel

Figure 11.17 (a) Cancer cells develop as a result of a genetic mutation in the DNA of a normal cell. (b) The mutated cell replicates uncontrollably, eventually resulting in a tumour. (c) If not destroyed or removed, the cancerous tumour metastasizes (spreads) to other parts of the body.

Most forms of cancer result in one or more **tumours**, which are newly formed masses of undifferentiated cells that are immature and have no physiologic function. Although the word *tumour* sounds frightening, it is important to note that not every tumour is *malignant,* or cancerous. Many are *benign* (not harmful to us) and are made up of cells that will not spread widely.

Figure 11.17 shows how changes to normal cells prompt a series of other changes that can progress into cancer. There are three primary steps of cancer development: initiation, promotion, and progression. These steps occur as follows:

1. **Initiation:** The initiation of cancer occurs when a cell's DNA is *mutated* (or changed). This mutation causes permanent changes in the cell.
2. **Promotion:** During this phase, the genetically altered cell is stimulated to repeatedly divide. The mutated DNA is locked into each new cell's genetic instructions. Because the enzymes that normally work to repair damaged cells cannot detect alterations in the DNA, the cells can continue to divide uninhibited.
3. **Progression:** During this phase, the cancerous cells grow out of control and invade surrounding tissues. These cells then *metastasize* (spread) to other sites of the body. In the early stages of progression, the immune system can sometimes detect these cancerous cells and destroy them. However, if the cells continue to grow, they develop into malignant tumours, and cancer results.

Heredity, Lifestyle Choices, and Infectious and Environmental Agents Can Increase Cancer Risk

Cancer is the leading cause of death in Canada, and researchers estimate that about half of all men and one-third of all women will develop cancer during their lifetime.[16] But what factors cause cancer? Are you and your loved ones at risk? The answer depends on several factors, including your family history of cancer, your exposure to environmental agents, and various lifestyle choices.

Heredity can play a role in the development of cancer, because inherited "cancer genes," such as the BRCA genes for breast cancer, increase the risk that an individual with those genes will develop cancer. However, it is important to bear in mind that a family history of cancer does not guarantee you will get cancer, too. It just means that you are at an increased risk and should take all preventive actions available to you. While some risk factors are out of your control, others are modifiable, which means that you can take positive steps to reduce your risk.

The Canadian Cancer Society identifies several modifiable risk factors that have been shown to impact an individual's cancer risk; each is discussed below.[17]

Smoking and Tobacco Cigarette smoke contains over 4000 chemicals and poisons, including 50 that are known to cause cancer. Using tobacco increases the risk for cancers of the lung, larynx, mouth, and esophagus and can also cause heart disease, stroke, and emphysema (**Figure 11.18**). (See Highlight box on disorders linked to tobacco use, page 390). It is estimated that smoking is responsible for 30% of all cancer deaths and is related to more than 85% of lung cancer cases in Canada.[17] The positive news is that tobacco use is a modifiable risk factor. If you smoke or use smokeless tobacco, you can reduce your risk for cancer considerably by quitting. Within 10 years of quitting, the overall risk of an ex-smoker dying from lung cancer is cut in half.[18, 19]

Nutrition and Fitness Up to 35% of all cancers can be prevented by being active, eating well, and maintaining a healthy body weight.[17] After not smoking, maintaining a healthy body weight is one of the best things you can do to reduce your risk of getting cancer.

Consumption of substances such as alcohol, unhealthy dietary fats, and compounds found in cured and charbroiled meats can increase the risk for cancer (see the Highlight on page 393). Nutritional factors that are protective against cancer include antioxidants,

Using tobacco is a risk factor for cancer.

Figure 11.18 Cigarette smoking significantly increases our risk for lung and other types of cancer. The risk of lung cancer is 22.4 times higher in men who smoke and 12 times higher in women who smoke. (a) A normal, healthy lung; (b) the lung of a smoker. Notice the deposits of tar as well as the areas of tumour growth.

tumour Any newly formed mass of undifferentiated cells.

HIGHLIGHT

Disorders Linked to Tobacco Use

Many people smoke cigarettes or cigars, or use smokeless tobacco. The use of these products can lead to serious health consequences that together reduce life expectancy by more than 13 years in males and 14 years in females.[18] Tobacco use is a risk factor in development of all of the following diseases and health concerns:

1. Cancers:
   - ■ Lung
   - ■ Larynx
   - ■ Mouth (**Figure 11.19a**)
   - ■ Pharynx
   - ■ Esophagus
   - ■ Bladder
   - ■ Pancreas
   - ■ Uterus
   - ■ Kidney
   - ■ Stomach
   - ■ Some leukemias
2. Heart disease
3. Bronchitis
4. Emphysema
5. Stroke
6. Erectile dysfunction
7. Conditions related to maternal smoking:
   - ■ Miscarriage
   - ■ Preterm delivery
   - ■ Stillbirth
   - ■ Infant death
   - ■ Low birth weight

In addition, smoking causes a variety of other problems, such as the premature wrinkling and coarsening of the skin shown in Figure 11.19b. Smoking also causes bad breath, yellowing of the fingernails and hair, and bad-smelling clothes, hair, and living quarters. Second-hand smoke is another concern, especially for those who live or work with smokers. Non-smokers who are exposed to smoke at home or work increase their risk of developing heart disease by 25% to 30% and increase their risk of developing lung cancer by 20% to 30%. Research indicates that there is no risk-free level of exposure to second-hand smoke.[19]

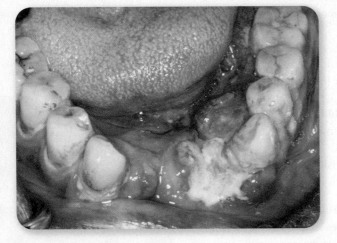

(a)

(b)

Figure 11.19 Effects of tobacco use. In addition to increasing your risk for lung cancer and cardiovascular disease, **(a)** using tobacco increases your risk of mouth cancer, and **(b)** smoking results in premature wrinkling of the skin, especially around the mouth.

fibre, and phytochemicals. Diets high in saturated fats and low in fruits and vegetables increase the risk of cancers of the esophagus, colon, breast, and prostate. Increasing your intake of whole grains, fruits, and vegetables, and decreasing your intake of red meats and fatty meats are keys to cancer prevention.[20]

Research shows that regular physical activity can help protect against certain types of cancer such as colorectal, breast, and uterine cancer.[20] A recent review of several studies has found that moderately intense and vigorous physical activity are associated with a 20% to 30% reduction in our overall risk for cancer.[21] Being active also keeps your heart healthy, makes your bones and muscles stronger, and helps you feel better about yourself.

Alcohol   Drinking alcohol can increase the risk of developing several types of cancer including cancer of the breast, colon and rectum, esophagus, larynx, liver, mouth, and pharynx. The less alcohol you drink, the more you reduce your risk.[20]

Vitamin D   There is growing evidence that vitamin D may reduce the risk of some types of cancer, particularly colorectal and breast cancers. Experts are now concerned that many people are not getting enough vitamin D.[17] You can get vitamin D from exposure to sunlight, in your diet (especially if you eat foods fortified with vitamin D), or by taking vitamin supplements. Because of our northern latitude and because the sun's rays are weak in the fall and winter, the Canadian Cancer Society recommends that Canadian adults consider taking a vitamin D supplement of 1000 international units (IU) a day during fall and winter months.

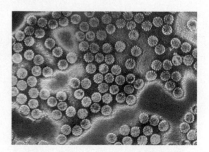

Figure 11.20 Human papillomavirus (HPV) is an infectious agent that can cause cancer.

Viruses and Bacteria   Infectious agents account for 18% of cancers worldwide. For example, infection of the female cervix with the sexually transmitted virus *Human papillomavirus* is linked to cervical cancer (**Figure 11.20**), and infection with the bacterium *Helicobacter pylori* is linked not only to ulcers but also to stomach cancer. As microbial research advances, it is thought that more cancers will be linked to infectious agents.[17]

Sun and UV   No one is completely safe from the sun. In Canada, sunlight is strong enough to cause skin cancer and premature aging of the skin. The risk of skin cancer today is much greater than it was 20 years ago and continues to increase. We are exposed to more ultraviolet (UV) rays as the protective layer of ozone around the earth becomes thinner due to the effects of pollution and chemicals.[17] UV rays damage the DNA of immature skin cells, which then reproduce uncontrollably. Research has shown that a person's risk for skin cancer doubles if he or she has had five or more sunburns; however, your risk for skin cancer still increases with UV exposure even if you do not get sunburned.[22] Exposure to tanning beds before age 35 increases your risk of developing the most invasive form of skin cancer by 75%.[23]

Arctic explorers wear special clothing to protect themselves from the cold as well as the high levels of ultraviolet rays from the sun.

Skin cancer includes the non-melanoma cancers (basal and squamous cell cancers), which are not typically invasive, and malignant melanoma, which is one of the most deadly of all types of cancer (**Figure 11.21**). Limiting exposure to sunlight to not more than 20 minutes between 11 a.m. and 4 p.m. can help reduce your risk for skin cancer while allowing your body to synthesize adequate vitamin D.[17] After that, wear sunscreen with at least a 15 SPF (sun protection factor) rating and protective clothing.

Antioxidants Play a Role in Preventing Cancer

There is a large and growing body of evidence that antioxidants play an important role in cancer prevention. But how? Some proposed mechanisms include:

- Enhancing the immune system, which assists in the destruction and removal of precancerous cells from the body
- Inhibiting the growth of cancer cells and tumours
- Preventing oxidative damage to the cells' DNA by scavenging free radicals and stopping the formation and subsequent chain reaction of oxidized molecules

Eating whole foods that are high in antioxidants—especially fruits, vegetables, and whole grains—is consistently shown to be associated with decreased cancer risk.[24] In addition, populations eating diets low in antioxidant nutrients have a higher risk for cancer. These studies show a strong association between level of dietary antioxidants and cancer risk, but they do not prove cause and effect. Nutrition experts agree that there are important interactions between antioxidant nutrients and other substances in foods, such as fibre and phytochemicals, which work together to reduce the risk for many types of cancers. Studies

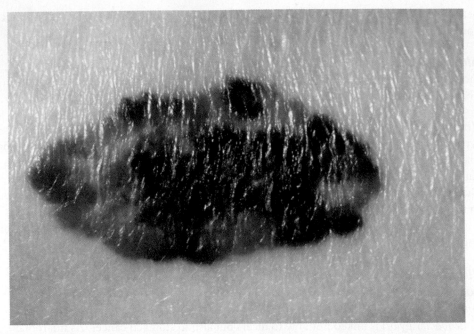

Figure 11.21 A lesion associated with malignant melanoma is characterized by asymmetry, uneven or blurred borders, mixed shades of tan, brown, black, and sometimes red or blue, and a diameter larger than a pencil eraser (6 mm).

Staying physically active may help reduce our risk for some cancers.

are now being conducted to determine whether eating foods high in antioxidants directly causes lower rates of cancer.

The link between taking antioxidant supplements and reducing cancer risk is not clear. Laboratory animal and test tube studies show that the individual nutrients reviewed in this chapter act as antioxidants in various situations. However, supplementation studies in humans do not consistently show benefits of taking antioxidant supplements in the prevention of cancer and other diseases. For example:

- In the Alpha-Tocopherol Beta-Carotene Cancer Prevention Study discussed earlier, supplementation with vitamin E resulted in a lower risk for cancers of the prostate, colon, and rectum but was related to more cancers of the stomach.[10] In this same study, beta-carotene supplements increased risk for cancers of the lung, prostate, and stomach in current and former smokers.[25]
- In the Nutritional Prevention of Cancer Trial, selenium supplementation was found to reduce the risk of prostate, colon, and lung cancers, but it did not reduce the risk of non-melanoma skin cancers.[26]
- The Linxian intervention trials, named for the region of China where the studies were conducted, found that a supplement containing beta-carotene, vitamin E, and selenium reduced mortality from overall cancer, specifically reducing the risk for cancers of the esophagus and stomach.[27]
- More recent trials such as the Physician's Health Study II,[28] the SELECT trial,[29] and the Women's Health Study[30] have shown that taking vitamin C, vitamin E, and selenium supplements does not reduce the risk for total cancer or the risk for many site-specific cancers such as prostate, breast, colorectal, and lung.

Why do antioxidant supplements appear to work in some studies and for some cancers but not in others? The human body is very complex, as is the development and progression of the numerous forms of cancer. People differ substantially in their susceptibility and response to carcinogens, as well as to protective factors. These complexities cloud the relationship between nutrition and cancer. In any research study, it is impossible to control all factors that may increase the risk for cancer. Thus, many unknown factors can

HIGHLIGHT

Nutritional Factors That Influence Our Risk for Cancer[20]

Nutritional factors that may increase our cancer risk include the following:

- Heterocyclic amines in cooked meat: carcinogenic chemicals formed when meat is cooked at high temperatures, such as during broiling, barbecuing, and frying.
- Nitrates in drinking water: a carcinogenic chemical found in fertilizers that is proven to increase the risk of non-Hodgkin's lymphoma. People drinking contaminated tap water in agricultural areas may be at risk.
- Nitrites and nitrates in cured meats: compounds found in some sausages, hams, bacon, and lunch meats. These compounds bind with amino acids to form nitrosamines, which are potent carcinogens.
- Obesity: appears to increase the risk of cancers of the breast, colon, prostate, endometrium (the lining of the uterus), cervix, ovary, kidney, gallbladder, liver, pancreas, rectum, and esophagus. The exact link between obesity and increased cancer risk is not clear but may be linked with hormonal changes that occur in people with excess body fat.
- High-saturated-fat diet: diets high in saturated fat have been associated with increased risk of many cancers, including prostate and breast. However, not all studies support this association.
- Alcohol: excessive use is linked with an increased risk of cancers of the esophagus, pharynx, and mouth. May also increase the risk for cancers of the liver, breast, colon, and rectum. Alcohol may impair cells' ability to repair damaged DNA, increasing the possibility of cancer initiation.

Factors that may protect against cancer include the following:

- Antioxidant-rich foods: includes vitamins E, C, A, beta-carotene, and other carotenoids and minerals such as

These vegetables provide antioxidant nutrients, fibre, and phytochemicals, all of which reduce the risk of some cancers.

selenium. Supplementation with individual antioxidants does not show consistent benefits.
- Dietary fibre: some studies show reduced risks for breast, colon, and rectal cancer with increased fibre intake, although findings are not consistent.
- Phytoestrogens: compounds found in soy-based foods and some vegetables and grains that may decrease the risk for breast, endometrial, and prostate cancers.
- Omega-3 fatty acids: includes alpha-linolenic acid, eicosapentaenoic acid (EPA), and docosahexaenoic acid (DHA). These fatty acids are found in fish and fish oils. Consuming foods high in omega-3 fatty acids is associated with reduced rates of breast, colon, and rectal cancers.
- Vitamin D: there is growing evidence that vitamin D may reduce the risk of some types of cancer, particularly colorectal and breast cancers.

Factors falsely claimed to cause cancer include the following:

- Artificial sweeteners: there are claims that aspartame (brand name Nutrasweet) is carcinogenic. There is no evidence to support these claims; however, they continue to resurface on the internet.
- Coffee: no studies support the claim that drinking coffee increases the risk for cancer. Some of the chemicals used to make decaffeinated coffee are known to be carcinogenic; most companies now use safer chemicals for this process.
- Fluoridated water: studies conducted over the past 40 years show no association between drinking fluoridated water and increased cancer risk.
- Food additives: it is estimated that more than 15 000 substances are added to our foods during growth, processing, and packaging. To date, there is no evidence that food additives contribute significantly to cancer risk.

affect study outcomes. It has also been speculated that antioxidants taken in supplemental form may act as prooxidants in some situations, whereas antioxidants consumed in foods may be more balanced. Many studies currently being conducted are examining the impact of whole foods and antioxidant supplements on the risk for various forms of cancer. The results of these studies will provide important insights into the link between whole foods, individual nutrients, and cancer.

> **CASE STUDY** ▶ Preventing Colon Cancer
>
> Mia, a busy mother to two teenage daughters, is 46 years of age. She works as an accountant for a downtown firm. Between her job, her family, and her volunteer work with her daughter's swim team, she doesn't have a lot of time for herself.
>
> Last year, her 52-year-old sister was diagnosed with colon cancer and is currently in remission. This has Mia thinking about her own health. She drinks occasionally, doesn't smoke, goes walking on Saturdays when her daughters have swim practice, and tries to eat healthily. She eats red meat only two or three times a week, always has at least one vegetable with dinner, and tries to snack on fruit in the evenings. With a BMI of 27, her weight has been stable over the past five years.
>
> Mia wonders whether she is doing everything she can to prevent developing cancer.
>
> **Thinking Critically**
>
> 1. **Explain what dietary changes Mia should make to decrease her risk of developing colon cancer.**
> 2. **What lifestyle changes can Mia make to decrease her risk of developing colon cancer?**
> 3. **Mia read that antioxidants such as vitamins C and E and selenium can play a role in preventing cancer. Should she start taking supplements of these? Why or why not?**
> 4. **Mia saw an ad in the local paper encouraging men and women over the age of 50 to get screened for colon cancer. Would you recommend that Mia be screened? Why or why not?**

Cardiovascular Disease

The details of *cardiovascular disease* (CVD) and its relationship to cholesterol and lipoproteins were presented in Chapter 5. A brief review of CVD is presented in this section, which focuses on the question of how antioxidants may reduce the risk for CVD.

CVD is the second leading cause of death for adults in Canada. CVD encompasses all diseases of the heart and blood vessels, including coronary heart disease, hypertension (or high blood pressure), and atherosclerosis (or hardening of the arteries). The two primary manifestations of CVD are heart attack and stroke. Almost 70 000 people die each year from CVD, and it is estimated that CVD costs Canada $22.2 billion in healthcare costs and lost work revenue.[31]

Remember that the major risks for CVD are smoking, hypertension (high blood pressure), high blood levels of LDL-cholesterol, obesity, and a sedentary lifestyle. Other risk factors include a low level of high-density lipoprotein (HDL) cholesterol, diabetes, family history (CVD in males younger than 55 years of age and females younger than 65 years of age), being a male older than 45 years of age, and being a postmenopausal woman. Although we cannot alter our gender, family history, or age, we can change our nutrition and physical activity habits to reduce our risk for CVD.

Research has recently identified a risk factor for CVD that may be even more important than elevated cholesterol levels. This risk factor is a condition called *low-grade inflammation*.[32] This condition weakens the plaque in the blood vessels, making it more fragile. You may remember from Chapter 5 that plaque is the fatty material that builds up on the lining of arteries and causes atherosclerosis. As the plaque becomes more fragile, it is more likely to burst, breaking away from the arterial lining and travelling freely in the bloodstream. It may then lodge in the blood vessels of the heart or brain, closing them off and leading to a heart attack or stroke, respectively.

In laboratory blood tests, the marker that indicates the degree of inflammation is C-reactive protein. Having higher levels of C-reactive protein increases the risk for a heart attack even if people do not have elevated cholesterol levels. For people with high levels of C-reactive protein and cholesterol, the risk of a heart attack is almost nine times higher than that of someone with normal cholesterol and C-reactive protein levels. These findings have prompted the medical community to develop standards for measuring C-reactive protein along with cholesterol as a test for CVD risk.

How can antioxidants decrease the risk for CVD? There is growing evidence that certain antioxidants, specifically vitamin E and lycopene, work in a variety of ways that reduce the damage to the vessels, which in turn reduces the risk for a heart attack or stroke. Some of the ways these nutrients decrease the risk for CVD include scavenging free radicals, reducing low-grade inflammation, and reducing blood coagulation and the formation of blood clots.

As with the research conducted on cancer, the studies of antioxidants and CVD show inconsistent results. Two large-scale surveys conducted in the United States show that men and women who eat more fruits and vegetables have a significantly reduced risk of CVD.[33, 34] However, few intervention studies have been conducted to determine the effect of antioxidant supplements on risk for CVD. Vitamin E was found to lower the number of heart disease deaths in smokers in the Alpha-Tocopherol Beta-Carotene Cancer Prevention Study, but had no overall effect on the risk of stroke.[35] In the HOPE study, vitamin E had no impact on the risk for CVD in people who are at high risk for heart attack and stroke.[3] Recently published results of large intervention studies in the United States indicate no reductions in major cardiovascular events in men and women taking vitamins E or C.[4, 30] Thus, there is growing evidence that antioxidant supplements do not reduce our risk for CVD. Furthermore, there is evidence that high intakes of vitamin E supplements can increase the risk of haemorrhagic strokes.

It is important to note that other compounds (besides antioxidants) found in fruits, vegetables, and whole grains can reduce our risk for CVD. For instance, soluble fibre has been shown to reduce elevated LDL-cholesterol and total cholesterol. The most successful effects have been found in people eating oatmeal and oat-bran cereals. Dietary fibre in general has been shown to reduce blood pressure, lower total cholesterol levels, and improve blood glucose and insulin levels. Folate, a B-vitamin, is found in fortified cereals, green leafy vegetables, bananas, legumes, and orange juice. Folate is known to reduce homocysteine levels in the blood, and a high concentration of homocysteine in the blood may be linked to CVD. Unfortunately, as you will learn in Chapter 13, research has shown that folic acid supplementation does not reduce cardiovascular disease risk. A recent study from the Netherlands showed that individuals who drank more than three cups of black tea (which is high in flavonoids) per day had a lower rate of heart attacks than non–tea drinkers.[36] Thus, it appears that there are many nutrients and other components in fruits, vegetables, and whole-grain foods that may be protective against CVD.

The flavonoids in black tea might reduce the risk of CVD.

Age-Related Vision Impairment

Some diseases associated with aging may be preventable by consuming antioxidants. Two of these diseases are macular degeneration and cataracts, both of which impair vision in older adults.

Macular degeneration is the leading cause of blindness of adults 55 years and older in Canada. The macula is the central part of the retina, and it is responsible for our central vision and our ability to see details. A person with macular degeneration loses the ability to see details, such as small print, small objects, and facial features. Objects seem to fade or disappear, straight lines or edges appear wavy, and the ability to read standard printed material is lost (**Figure 11.22a**). Macular degeneration does not affect peripheral vision. There is no known cure for macular degeneration. The causes of this disease are unknown.

A **cataract** is a damaged portion of the eye's lens, the portion of the eye through which we focus entering light. Cataracts cause cloudiness in the lens that impairs vision (Figure 11.22b). People with cataracts have a very difficult time seeing in bright light; for instance,

macular degeneration A vision disorder caused by deterioration of the central portion of the retina and marked by loss or distortion of the central field of vision.

cataract A damaged portion of the eye's lens, which causes cloudiness that impairs vision.

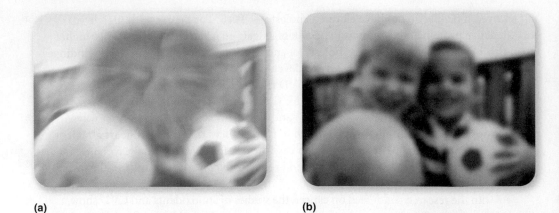

(a)   **(b)**

Figure 11.22 These photos simulate two forms of vision loss common in older adults. **(a)** Macular degeneration results in a loss of central vision. **(b)** Cataracts impair vision across the visual field. *Data from:* National Eye Institute, National Institutes of Health. November 2003. Photos, Images, and Videos. Ref. no. EDS05. Available at www.nei.nih.gov/photo/search/keyword.asp?keyword=macular; and National Eye Institute, National Institutes of Health. November 2003. Photos, Images, and Videos. Ref. no. EDS03. Available at www.nei.nih. gov/photo/search/keyword.asp?keyword=cataract.

they see halos around lights, glare, and scattering of light. Having cataracts also impairs a person's ability to adjust from dark to bright light. It is estimated that more than one-half of all people over the age of 65 years in Canada have some cataract development. Cataracts can be treated with surgery. As with macular degeneration, the causes of cataracts are unknown.

Current research findings are showing some promise of reducing the risk for macular degeneration and cataracts through the use of antioxidant supplements. A recent study conducted with individuals who had early signs of macular degeneration found that consuming a supplement containing vitamins C and E, beta-carotene, and zinc reduced the progression of this disease.[37] Earlier studies have also shown that higher blood levels of antioxidants and consuming more antioxidants in the diet are associated with a lower risk of macular degeneration.[38, 39] The effects of antioxidant supplements and cataracts are mixed, with some studies showing a reduced rate of cataract development in people taking vitamin C and E and beta-carotene supplements or having higher blood levels of antioxidants, but other studies show no benefit of antioxidants.[40–42] At this time, it is not possible to reach a conclusion regarding the effectiveness of antioxidant supplements to prevent these two diseases of aging. However, there is enough evidence that consuming a healthy diet that includes fruits, vegetables, and whole grains is associated with improved quality of life as we age.

RECAP

Cancer is a group of diseases in which genetically mutated cells grow out of control. Tobacco use, nutritional factors, environmental exposures, UV radiation, and low physical activity levels are related to a higher risk for some cancers. Eating foods high in antioxidants is associated with lower rates of cancer, but studies of antioxidant supplements and cancer are equivocal. Cardiovascular disease (CVD) is the second leading cause of death in Canada. Antioxidants may help reduce the risk by preventing oxidative damage to LDL-cholesterol, reducing inflammation in the vessels, and reducing the formation of blood clots. Macular degeneration and cataracts are two diseases of vision that are associated with aging. Antioxidant nutrients have been found to reduce the risk of diseases in some studies.

SEE FOR YOURSELF

What Is Your Cancer Risk?

A risk factor is something that increases a person's chances of developing cancer. Nobody knows the exact causes of cancer. But with research, we are learning more about the risk factors for the disease and how you can reduce your risk. Some risk factors cannot be changed, such as your age, sex, or the genes you inherited from your parents (family genetics).[17]

Take the following quiz and see for yourself!
Do you…

- Eat a variety of colourful fruits and vegetables daily?
- Choose whole grains over refined grains?
- Limit your consumption of saturated and trans fats?
- Eat meatless meals several times a week?
- Rarely eat cured meats containing nitrates and nitrites?
- Rarely eat broiled, fried, or barbequed meats?
- Maintain a healthy weight?
- Not smoke?
- Limit your exposure to second-hand smoke?
- Drink no more than one alcoholic beverage per day for women and two alcoholic beverages per day for men?
- Limit your sun exposure to less than 20 minutes per day?
- Engage in moderate or vigorous physical activity for at least 30 minutes, 5 days a week?

Every time you answered yes to the questions listed above you were taking steps to lower your risk of developing cancer!

Chapter Review

11

Summary

- Antioxidants are compounds that protect our cells from oxidative damage.

- Free radicals are produced under many situations, including when the body generates ATP, when the immune system fights infection, and when we are exposed to environmental toxins such as pollution, overexposure to sunlight, radiation, and tobacco smoke.

- Free radicals are dangerous because they can damage the lipid portion of our cell membranes, destroying the integrity of our cell membranes. Free radicals also damage LDLs, cell proteins, and DNA.

- Antioxidant vitamins donate their electrons or hydrogen molecules to free radicals to neutralize them. Antioxidant minerals are cofactors in antioxidant enzyme systems, which convert free radicals to less damaging substances that our bodies excrete.

- Vitamin E is an antioxidant that protects the fatty components of cell membranes from oxidation. It also protects LDLs, vitamin A, and our lungs from oxidative damage. Other functions of vitamin E are the development of nerves and muscles, enhancement of the immune function, and improvement of the absorption of vitamin A if intake of vitamin A is low.

- Vitamin C is an antioxidant that is oxidized by free radicals and prevents the damage of cells and tissues. Vitamin C also regenerates vitamin E after it has been oxidized. Other functions of vitamin C include helping the synthesis of collagen, carnitine, various hormones, neurotransmitters, and DNA; enhancing immune function; and increasing the absorption of iron.

- Beta-carotene is one of about 600 carotenoids identified to date. Beta-carotene is a provitamin, or precursor, to vitamin A, meaning it is an inactive form of vitamin A that is converted to vitamin A in the body.

- Beta-carotene protects the lipid portions of our membranes and the LDL-cholesterol from oxidative damage. Other functions of beta-carotene include enhancing our immune systems, protecting our skin from sun damage, and protecting our eyes from oxidative damage. The carotenoids may help reduce our risk for some forms of cancer.

- Vitamin A is a fat-soluble vitamin. The three active forms of vitamin A are retinol, retinal, and retinoic acid. Beta-carotene is converted to vitamin A in the small intestine.

- Vitamin A is extremely important for healthy vision. It ensures our ability to adjust to changes in the brightness of light, and it also helps us maintain colour vision. Vitamin A may also act as an antioxidant, as it protects LDL-cholesterol from oxidative damage. Other functions of vitamin A include assistance in cell differentiation, maintaining healthy immune function, sexual reproduction, and proper bone growth.

- Selenium is a trace mineral that is part of the structure of glutathione peroxidases, a family of antioxidant enzymes. Other functions of selenium include assisting in the production of thyroid hormone and enhancing immune function.

- Copper, iron, zinc, and manganese are minerals that act as cofactors for antioxidant enzyme systems. Copper, zinc, and manganese are part of the superoxide dismutase complex, whereas iron is part of catalase. These minerals also play critical roles in energy metabolism and blood formation.

- Antioxidants play a role in cancer prevention. Eating foods high in antioxidants results in lower rates of some cancers, but supplementing with antioxidants can increase the risk of cancer in some situations.

- Antioxidants may help reduce our risk for CVD by scavenging free radicals and preventing oxidative damage to LDL-cholesterol, reducing low-grade inflammation (which, in turn, prevents the rupture of plaque in our blood vessels), and preventing the formation of blood clots.

- Antioxidants found in foods may help prevent two age-related diseases of vision: macular degeneration and cataracts. Antioxidant supplements may reduce the risk of macular degeneration, which causes us to lose the ability to see details, small print, and facial features. A cataract is a damaged portion of the eye's lens that causes cloudiness and impairs vision. Cataracts impair our ability to adjust from dark to bright light.

Review Questions

1. Which of the following is a characteristic of vitamin E?
   a. It enhances the absorption of iron.
   b. It can be manufactured from beta-carotene.
   c. It is a critical component of the glutathione peroxidase system.
   d. It is destroyed by exposure to high heat.

2. Oxidation is best described as a process in which
   a. a carcinogen causes a mutation in a stem cell's DNA.
   b. an atom loses an electron.
   c. an element loses an atom of oxygen.
   d. a compound loses a molecule of water.

3. Which of the following disorders is linked with the production of free radicals?
   a. cardiovascular disease
   b. carotenosis
   c. ulcers
   d. malaria

4. Which of the following are known carcinogens?
   a. phytochemicals
   b. antioxidants
   c. carotenoids
   d. nitrates

5. Taking daily doses of three to four times the RDA of which of the following nutrients may cause death?
   a. vitamin A
   b. vitamin C
   c. vitamin E
   d. selenium

6. Your friend Allysa is taking 4000 mg of vitamin C a day, hoping to avoid getting a cold before exam time. What would you tell Allysa about vitamin C's role in preventing the common cold?

7. Explain what happens if you consume too much beta-carotene and why beta-carotene supplements are generally not recommended.

8. Explain how free radicals damage cell membranes and lead to cell death.

9. Describe the process by which cancer occurs, beginning with initiation and ending with metastasis of the cancer to widespread body tissues.

10. Explain how vitamin E reduces our risk for heart disease.

11. Discuss the contribution of trace minerals such as selenium to the prevention of oxidation.

12. Your mother has a heart condition that requires her to take the prescription drug Coumadin, an anticoagulant. While chatting with you over lunch one day, she mentions that she has started taking an antioxidant supplement that is supposed to "boost cardiovascular health." You ask to see the supplement and note that it contains 500 mg vitamin E as alpha-tocopherol, 500 mg of vitamin C, and 100 µg of selenium. Should you be concerned? Why or why not?

Web Links

www.unicef.org/nutrition/index.html
UNICEF: Nutrition
This site provides information about micronutrient deficiencies in developing countries and UNICEF's efforts and programs to provide nutrition programming aimed at fulfilling every child's right to adequate nutrition.

www.who.int/nutrition/topics/micronutrients/en/
World Health Organization (WHO)
This site provides information on nutrient deficiencies throughout the world, including iodine, vitamin A, and iron deficiency disorders.

www.hc-sc.gc.ca/ahc-asc/branch-dirgen/hpfb-dgpsa/ nhpd-dpsn/index-eng.php
Natural Health Products Directorate
See this site for up-to-date information on natural health products regulations in Canada.

www.eyesite.ca/english/index.htm
The Canadian Ophthalmological Society
See this site for information on age-related macular degeneration diagnosis and treatment.

MasteringNutrition®

www.masteringnutrition.pearson.com

Assignments

Animations: Free Radical Formation • Vitamin A and Epithelial Tissue • Vitamin A and the Visual Cycle

Study Area

Video: Using the Functional Approach to Understand Fluid & Electrolyte Balance • Practice Tests • Diet Analysis • eText

References

1. Yeomans, V. C., J. Linseisen, and G. Wolfram. 2005. Interactive effects of polyphenols, tocopherol, and ascorbic acid on the Cu2+-mediated oxidative modification of human low density lipoproteins. *Eur. J. Nutr.* (April 15), Epub DO: 10.1007/s00394-005-0546-y.

2. Winklhofer-Roob, B. M., A. Meinitzer, M. Maritschnegg, J. M. Roob, G. Khoschsorur, J. Fibalta, I. Sundl, S. Wuga, W. Wonisch, B. Tiran, and E. Rock. 2004. Effects of vitamin E depletion/repletion on biomarkers of oxidative stress in healthy aging. *Ann. N.Y. Acad. Sci.* 1031:361–364.

3. The HOPE and HOPE-TOO Trial Investigators. 2005. Effects of long-term vitamin E supplementation on cardiovascular events and cancer. A randomized controlled trial. *JAMA* 293:1338–1347.

4. Sesso, H. D., J. E. Buring, W. G. Christen, T. Kurth, C. Belanger, J. MacFadyen, V. Bubes, J. E. Manson, R. J. Glynn, and J. M. Gaziano. 2008. Vitamins E and C in the prevention of cardiovascular disease in men: the Physicians' Health Study II randomized controlled trial. *JAMA* 300(18):2123–2133.

5. Health Canada, Canadian Nutrient File, 2007b version. Available at www.healthcanada.ca/cnf (accessed November 18, 2010).

6. Institute of Medicine, Food and Nutrition Board. 2000. *Dietary Reference Intakes for Vitamin C, Vitamin E, Selenium, and Carotenoids.* Washington, DC: The National Academy of Sciences.

7. Hemilä, H., E. Chalker, B. Treacy, and B. Douglas. 2007. Vitamin C for preventing and treating the common cold. *Cochrane Database of Systematic Reviews.* Issue 3. Art. No. CD000980. DOI: 10.1002/14651858.CD000980.pub3.

8. Cahill, L., P. N. Corey, and A. El-Sohemy. 2009. Vitamin C deficiency in a population of young Canadian adults. *Am. J. Epidemiol.* 170:464–471.

9. Burri, B. J. 1997. Beta-carotene and human health: a review of current research. *Nutr. Res.* 17:547–580.

10. Albanes D., O. P. Heinonen, J. K. Huttunen, P. R. Taylor, J. Virtamo, B. K. Edwards, J. Haapakoski, M. Rautalahti, A. M. Hartman, J. Palmgren, and P. Greenwald. 1995. Effects of α-tocopherol and β-carotene supplements on cancer incidence in the Alpha-Tocopherol Beta-Carotene Cancer Prevention Study. *Am. J. Clin. Nutr.* 62(suppl.):1427S–1430S.

11. Omenn G. S., G. E. Goodman, M. D. Thornquist, J. Balmes, M. R. Cullen, A. Glass, J. P. Keogh, F. L. Meyskens Jr., B. Valanis, J. H. Williams Jr., S. Barnhart, and S. Hammar. 1996. Effects of a combination of beta carotene and vitamin A on lung cancer and cardiovascular disease. *N. Engl. J. Med.* 334:1150–1155.

12. U.S. Department of Agriculture (USDA), Agricultural Research Service. 2008. USDA National Nutrient Database for Standard Reference, Release 21. Available at www.ars.usda.gov/ba/bhnrc/ndl.

13. Livrea, M. A., L. Tesoriere, A. Bongiorno, A. M. Pintaudi, M. Ciaccio, and A. Riccio. 1995. Contribution of vitamin A to the oxidation resistance of human low density lipoproteins. *Free Radic. Biol. Med.* 18:401–409.

14. Gutteridge, J. M. C., and B. Halliwell. 1994. *Antioxidants in Nutrition, Health, and Disease.* Oxford, UK: Oxford University Press.

15. World Health Organization (WHO). 2009. Micronutrient deficiencies. Vitamin A deficiency. Available at www.who.int/nutrition/topics/vad/en/.

16. Statistics Canada. 2008. Ranking and number of deaths for 10 leading causes, Canada, 2008. Available www.statcan.gc.ca/daily-quotidien/111101/t111101b1-eng.htm (accessed July 28, 2012).

17. Canadian Cancer Society. 2010. *Prevention.* Available at www.cancer.ca/Canada-wide/Prevention.aspx?sc_lang=en (accessed November 25, 2010).

18. American Cancer Society. 2009. ACS guide to quitting smoking. Available at www.cancer.org/docroot/PED/content/PED_10_13X_Guide_for_Quitting_Smoking.asp?sitearea=PED.

19. U.S. Department of Health and Human Services (USDHHS). 2004. *The Health Consequences of Smoking: A Report of the Surgeon General.* Washington, DC: U.S. Department of Health and Human Services, Centers for Disease Control and Prevention, National Center for Chronic Disease Prevention and Health Promotion, Office on Smoking and Health.

20. World Cancer Research Fund/American Institute for Cancer Research. 2007. *Food, Nutrition, Physical Activity, and the Prevention of Cancer: A Global Perspective.* Washington DC: AICR.

21. Thune, I., and A. S. Furberg. 2001. Physical activity and cancer risk: dose-response and cancer, all sites and site-specific. *Med. Sci. Sports Exerc.* 33(suppl.):S530–S550.

22. Pfahlberg, A., K. F. Kolmel, and O. Gefeller. 2002. Adult vs. childhood susceptibility to melanoma. Is there a difference? *Arch. Dermatol.* 138:1234–1235.

23. Heinonen, O. P., D. Albanes, J. Virtamo, P. R. Taylor, J. K. Huttunen, A. M. Hartman, J. Haapakoski, N. Malila, M. Rautalahti, S. Ripatti, H. Maepaa, and International Agency for Research on Cancer (IARC). 2007. The association of use of sunbeds with cutaneous malignant melanoma and other skin cancers: a systematic review. *Intl. J. Cancer* 120:1116–1122.

24. Greenwald P., C. K. Clifford, and J. A. Milner. 2001. Diet and cancer prevention. *Eur. J. Cancer* 37:948–965.

25. Heinonen O. P., D. Albanes, J. Virtamo, P. R. Taylor, J. K. Huttunen, A. M. Hartman, J. Haapakoski, N. Malila, M. Rautalahti, S. Ripatti, H. Maepaa, L. Teerenhovi, L. Koss, M. Virolainen, and B. K. Edwards. 1998. Prostate cancer and supplementation with α-tocopherol and β-carotene: incidence and mortality in a controlled trial. *J. Natl. Cancer Inst.* 90:440–446.

26. Clark, L. C., B. Dalkin, A. Krongrad, G. F. Combs Jr., B. W. Turnbull, E. H. Slate, R. Witherington, J. H. Herlong, E. Janosko, D. Carpenter, C. Borosso, S. Falk, and J. Rounder. 1998. Decreased incidence of prostate cancer with selenium supplementation: results of a double-blind cancer prevention trial. *Br. J. Urol.* 81:730–734.

27. Blot, W. J., J.-Y. Li, P. R. Taylor, W. Guo, S. M. Dawsey, and B. Li. 1995. The Linxian trials: mortality rates by vitamin-mineral intervention group. *Am. J. Clin. Nutr.* 62(suppl.):1424S–1426S.

28. Gaziano, J. M., R. J. Glynn, W. G. Christen, T. Kurth, C. Belanger, J. MacFadyen, V. Bubes, J. E. Manson, H. D. Sesso, and J. E. Buring. 2009. Vitamins E and C in the prevention of prostate and total cancer in men: the Physicians' Health Study II Randomized Controlled Trial. *JAMA* 301(1):52–62.

29. Lippman, S. M., E. A. Klein, P. J. Goodman, M. S. Lucia, I. M. Thompson, L. G. Ford, H. L. Parnes, L. M. Minasian, J. M. Gaziano, J. A. Hartline, J. Kellogg Parsons, J. D. Bearden III, E. D. Crawford, G. E. Goodman, J. Claudio, E. Winquist, E. D. Cook, D. D. Karp, P. Walther, M. M. Lieber, A. R. Kristal, A. K. Darke, K. B. Arnold, P. A. Ganz, R. M. Santella, D. Albanes, P. R. Taylor, J. L. Probstfield, T. J. Jagpal, J. J. Crowley, F. L. Meyskens Jr., L. H. Baker, and C. A. Coltman Jr. 2009. Effect of selenium and vitamin E on risk of prostate cancer and other cancers: the Selenium and Vitamin E Cancer Prevention Trial (SELECT). *JAMA* 301(1):39–51.

30. Lee, I. M., N. R. Cook, J. M. Gaziano, D. Gordon, P. M. Ridker, J. E. Manson, C. H. Hennekens, and J. E. Buring. 2005. Vitamin E in the primary prevention of cardiovascular disease and cancer: the Women's Health Study: a randomized controlled trial. *JAMA* 294(1):56–65.

31. Heart and Stroke Foundation. 2006. *Statistics.* Available at www.heartandstroke.com/site/c.ikIQLcMWJtE/b.3483991/k.34A8/Statistics.htm (accessed November 25, 2010).

32. de Ferranti S., and N. Rifai. 2002. C-reactive protein and cardiovascular disease: a review of risk prediction and interventions. *Clinica Chimica Acta* 317:1–15.

33. Joshipura, K. J., F. B. Hu, J. E. Manson, M. J. Stampfer, E. B. Rimm, F. E. Speizer, G. Colditz, A. Ascherio, B. Rosner, D. Spiegelman, and W. C. Willett. 2001. The effect of fruit and vegetable intake on risk for coronary heart disease. *Ann. Intern. Med.* 134:1106–1114.

34. Liu, S., I.-M. Lee, U. Ajani, S. R. Cole, J. E. Buring, and J. E. Manson. 2001. Intake of vegetables rich in carotenoids and risk of coronary heart disease in men: the Physicians' Health Study. *Intl. J. Epidemiol.* 30:130–135.

35. The Alpha-Tocopherol, Beta-Carotene Cancer Prevention Study Group (The ATBC Study Group). 1994. The effect of vitamin E and beta carotene on the incidence of lung cancer and other cancers in male smokers. *N. Engl. J. Med.* 330:1029–1035.

36. Geleijnse, J. M., L. J. Launer, D. A. M. van der Kuip, A. Hofman, and J. C. M. Witteman. 2002. Inverse association of tea and flavonoid intakes with incident myocardial infarction: the Rotterdam Study. *Am. J. Clin. Nutr.* 75:880–886.

37. Age-Related Eye Disease Study Research Group. 2001. A randomized, placebo-controlled, clinical trial of high-dose supplementation with vitamins C and E, beta-carotene, and zinc for age-related macular degeneration and vision loss: AREDS Report No. 8. *Arch. Ophthalmol.* 119:1417–1436.

38. Delcourt C., J. P. Cristol, F. Tessier, C. L. Léger, B. Descomps, and L. Papoz. 1999. Age-related macular degeneration and antioxidant status in the POLA study. POLA Study Group. Pathologies Oculaires Liées à l'Age. *Arch. Ophthalmol.* 117:1384–1390.

39. West S., S. Vitale, J. Hallfrisch, B. Munoz, D. Muller, S. Bressler, and N. M. Bressler. 1994. Are antioxidants or supplements protective for age-related macular degeneration? *Arch. Ophthalmol.* 112:222–227.

40. Chylack, L. T. Jr., N. P. Brown, A. Bron, M. Hurst, W. Kopcke, U. Thien, and W. Schalch. 2002. The Roche European American Cataract Trial (REACT): a randomized clinical trial to investigate the efficacy of an oral antioxidant micronutrient mixture to slow progression of age-related cataract. *Ophthalmic Epidemiol.* 9:49–80.

41. Gale, C. R., N. F. Hall, D. I. Phillips, and C. N. Martyn. 2001. Plasma antioxidant vitamins and carotenoids and age-related cataract. *Ophthalmology* 108:1992–1998.

42. Age-Related Eye Disease Study Research Group. 2001. A randomized, placebo-controlled, clinical trial of high-dose supplementation with vitamins C and E and beta-carotene for age-related cataract and vision loss: AREDS Report No. 9. *Arch. Ophthalmol.* 119:1439–1452.

43. Nutrition Business Journal. 2006. *NBJ's Supplement Business Report 2006.* ©Penton Media, Inc.

44. Blendon, R. J., C. M. DesRoches, J. M. Benson, M. Brodie, and D. E. Altman. 2001. Americans' views on the use and regulation of dietary supplements. *Arch. Intern. Med.* 26:805–810.

45. Health Canada. 2010. *Natural Health Products.* Available at www.hc-sc.gc.ca/dhp-mps/prodnatur/index-eng.php (accessed November 26, 2010).

46. Fife, J., S. Raniga, P. N. Hider, and F. A. Frizelle. 2011. Folic acid supplementation and colorectal cancer risk: a meta-analysis. *Colorectal Dis.* 13:132–137.

47. Dietitians of Canada. 2010. *Vitamin and Mineral Supplementation.* Available at www.dietitians.ca/Dietitians-View/VitaminMineral-Supplementation.aspx (accessed May 16, 2011).

Vitamin and Mineral Supplementation: Necessity or Waste?

Marcus has type 2 diabetes and high blood cholesterol and is worried about his health. He attended a nutrition seminar in which the health benefits of various vitamin and mineral supplements were touted. After hearing the speaker, Marcus was convinced that he needed to take a series of supplements that contain more than 200% of the RDA for many vitamins and minerals. After a few months of taking these supplements on a daily basis, Marcus started to experience headaches, nausea, diarrhea, and tingling in his hands and feet. Although Marcus was not an expert in nutrition, he suspected that he might be experiencing side effects related to nutrient toxicity. He decided to talk to his doctor about the supplements he was taking to determine whether they could be causing his symptoms.

Marcus's story is not unique. The use of dietary supplements in North America has skyrocketed in recent years. One industry source cites annual sales of supplements in the United States at $21.3 billion.[43] With a population one-tenth of the United States, it has been suggested that the Canadian market is valued at approximately $2 billion. A recent survey shows that 71% of Canadians regularly take vitamins and minerals, herbal products, homeopathic medicines, and the like. However, they are unlikely to report their use to their physicians because they feel they have little knowledge of the products and may harbour a bias toward their use.[44] Interestingly, many supplement users stated that they would continue to use these products even if scientific studies found them to be ineffective!

Why do so many people take dietary supplements? Many people believe they cannot consume adequate nutrients in their diet, and they take a supplement as extra nutritional insurance. Others have been advised by their healthcare provider to take a supplement to address a given health concern. There are people, like Marcus, who believe that they can use certain supplements to treat their disease. There are also people who believe supplements are necessary to enhance their appearance or athletic performance.

Are such uses wise? Who should be taking supplements? These questions are not easy to answer. Before deciding whether you might benefit from taking dietary supplements, read on.

Dietary Supplements Include Vitamins, Minerals, and Other Products

According to Health Canada, natural health products (NHPs) are defined as vitamins and minerals, herbal remedies, homeopathic medicines, traditional medicines such as traditional Chinese medicines, probiotics, and other products such as amino acids and essential fatty acids.[45] These supplements come in many forms, including tablets, capsules, liquids, and powders.

How Are Dietary Supplements Regulated?

As of January 1, 2004, all natural health products sold in Canada require a product licence.[45] Obtaining a licence requires submitting detailed information on the product to Health Canada, including medicinal ingredients, source, potency, non-medicinal ingredients, and recommended use(s). Once a product has been assessed and granted market authorization by Health Canada, the product label will bear an eight-digit product licence number preceded by the distinct letters NPN (which stand for Natural Product Number), or, in the case of a homeopathic medicine, by the letters DIN-HM (which stand for Homeopathic Medicine Number). This number on the label will inform consumers that the product has been reviewed and approved by Health Canada for safety, efficacy, and quality. It is important to note that many products on the market when the new regulations came into effect received a temporary exemption. These products are designated with an EN (which stands for Exemption Number) and can remain on the market while they undergo the detailed review process. The regulations as they pertain to functional foods can be found on page 288.

How Can We Protect Ourselves from Fraudulent or Dangerous Supplements?

Although many of the supplement products sold today are safe, some are not. In addition, some companies are less than forthright about the true content of ingredients in

Supplements can be powders, tablets, capsules, or liquid.

their supplements. How can you avoid purchasing fraudulent or dangerous supplements? Health Canada suggests that consumers can do the following to protect themselves from fraudulent or dangerous supplements:[45]

1. Look for the NPN on the label. This notation indicates that the manufacturer followed the standards established by Health Canada for drugs for features such as safety, efficacy, and quality.
2. Consider buying recognized brands of supplements. Although not guaranteed, products made by nationally recognized companies more likely have well-established manufacturing standards.
3. Do not assume that the word "natural" on the label means that the product is safe. Arsenic, lead, and mercury are all natural substances that can kill you if consumed in large enough quantities.
4. Do not hesitate to question a company about how it makes its products. Reputable companies have nothing to hide and are more than happy to inform their customers about the safety and quality of their products.

Dietary Supplements Can Be Both Helpful and Harmful

Contrary to what some people believe, the Canadian food supply is not void of nutrients, and all people do not need to supplement all of the time. In fact, we now know that foods contain a diverse combination of compounds that are critical to our health, and vitamin and mineral supplements do not contain the same amount or variety of substances found in foods. Thus, dietary supplements are not substitutes for whole foods. However, our nutritional needs change throughout our lifespan, and some of us may need to take supplements at certain times for certain reasons. For instance, some athletes can benefit from consuming foods or beverages formulated to provide carbohydrate and other nutrients necessary to support intense exercise. Dietary supplements include hundreds of thousands of products sold for many purposes, and it is impossible to discuss here all of the various situations in which their use may be advisable. So to simplify this discussion, let's focus on identifying the groups of people who may or may not benefit from taking vitamin and mineral supplements.

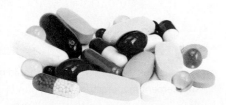

Always research supplements and supplement manufacturers before purchasing.

Who Might Benefit from Taking Vitamin and Mineral Supplements?

Table 11.2 lists groups of people who may benefit from supplementation. But even if you fall within one of these groups, it's still important to analyze your total diet to determine whether you might need to take the vitamin or mineral supplement indicated. It is also a good idea to check with your healthcare provider or a registered dietitian before taking any supplements, as supplements can interfere with some prescription and over-the-counter medications.

When Can Taking a Vitamin and Mineral Supplement Be Harmful?

There are many people who can benefit from taking vitamin and mineral supplements in certain situations. There are also many people who do not need to take supplements but do so anyway. Instances in which taking vitamin and mineral supplements are unnecessary or harmful include:

1. Providing fluoride supplements to children who already drink fluoridated water.
2. Taking supplements in the belief that they will cure a disease such as cancer, diabetes, or heart disease.
3. Taking supplements with certain medications. For instance, people who take the blood-thinning drug Coumadin should not take vitamin E supplements, as this can cause excessive bleeding. People who take Aspirin daily should check with their physician before taking vitamin E supplements, as Aspirin also thins the blood.
4. Taking non-prescribed supplements if you have liver or kidney diseases. Physicians may prescribe vitamin and mineral supplements for their patients because many nutrients are lost during treatment for these diseases. However, these individuals cannot properly metabolize certain supplements and should not take any that are not prescribed by their physicians because of a high risk for toxicity.
5. Taking beta-carotene supplements if you are a smoker. As already mentioned, there is evidence that beta-carotene supplementation increases the risk of lung and other cancers in smokers.
6. Taking folic acid, the supplemental form of folate. Although study results are controversial, high folic acid intakes achieved through folic acid supplementation may increase the risk of certain chronic diseases such as colorectal cancer.[46]
7. Taking vitamins and minerals in an attempt to improve physical appearance or athletic performance. There is no evidence that vitamin and mineral

Table 11.2 Individuals Who May Benefit from Dietary Supplementation

Type of Individual	Specific Supplements That May Help
Newborns	Routinely given a single dose of vitamin K at birth
Infants	Depends on age and nutrition; may need iron, vitamin D, or other nutrients
Children not drinking fluoridated water	Fluoride supplements
Children on strict vegetarian diets	Vitamin B_{12}, iron, zinc, vitamin D (if not exposed to sunlight)
Children with poor eating habits or overweight children on an energy-restricted diet	Multivitamin/multimineral supplement that does not exceed the RDA for the nutrients it contains
Pregnant teenagers	Iron and folic acid; other nutrients may be necessary if diet is very poor
Women who may become pregnant	Multivitamin or multivitamin/multimineral supplement that contains 0.4 mg of folic acid
Pregnant or lactating women	Multivitamin/multimineral supplement that contains iron, folic acid, zinc, copper, calcium, vitamin B_6, vitamin C, vitamin D
People on prolonged weight-reduction diets	Multivitamin/multimineral supplement
People recovering from serious illness or surgery	Multivitamin/multimineral supplement
People with HIV/AIDS or other wasting diseases; people addicted to drugs or alcohol	Multivitamin/multimineral supplement or single-nutrient supplements
People who do not consume adequate calcium	Calcium supplements: for example, women need to consume 1000 to 1300 mg of dietary calcium per day; thus, supplements may be necessary
People whose exposure to sunlight is inadequate to allow synthesis of adequate vitamin D	Vitamin D
People eating a vegan diet	Vitamin B_{12}, riboflavin, calcium, vitamin D, iron, and zinc
People who have had portions of the intestinal tract removed; people who have a malabsorptive disease	Depends on the exact condition; may include various fat-soluble and/or water-soluble vitamins and other nutrients
People with lactose intolerance	Calcium supplements
Older adults	Multivitamin/multimineral supplement, vitamin B_{12}
People over the age of 50	Eating Well with Canada's Food Guide recommends 10 µg vitamin D daily

supplements enhance appearance or athletic performance in healthy adults who consume a varied diet with adequate energy.

8. Taking supplements to increase your energy level. Vitamin and mineral supplements do not provide energy, because they do not contain fat, carbohydrate, or protein (sources of kilocalories). Although many vitamins and minerals are necessary for us to produce energy, taking dietary supplements in place of eating food will not provide us with the energy necessary to live a healthy and productive life.

9. Taking single-nutrient supplements, unless a qualified healthcare practitioner prescribes a single-nutrient supplement for a diagnosed medical condition (for example, prescribing iron supplements for someone with anemia). These products contain very high amounts of the given nutrient, and taking these types of products can quickly lead to toxicity.

Dietitians of Canada advises that the ideal nutritional strategy for optimizing health is to eat a healthy diet that contains a variety of whole foods.[47] This way, you will not need to take vitamin and mineral supplements. And, if you do use a supplement, select one that contains no more than 100% of the recommended levels for the nutrients it contains. Avoid taking single-nutrient supplements unless advised to do so by your healthcare practitioner. Finally, avoid taking supplements that contain substances that are known to cause illness or injuries. Some of these substances are listed in Table 11.3.

Using the Evidence

1. Do you think that Health Canada should more closely regulate supplement manufacturers? If so, how?

2. Have you decided whether or not taking a supplement is right for you? Why or why not?

Table 11.3 Ingredients Found in Supplements That Are Associated with Illnesses and Injuries

Ingredient	Potential Risks
Herbal Ingredients	
Chaparral	Liver disease
Kava (also known as kava kava)	Severe liver toxicity
Comfrey	Obstruction of blood flow to liver, possible death
Slimming/dieter's teas	Nausea, diarrhea, vomiting, stomach cramps, constipation, fainting, possible death
Ephedra (also known as ma huang, Chinese ephedra, and epitonin)	High blood pressure, irregular heartbeat, nerve damage, insomnia, tremors, headaches, seizures, heart attack, stroke, possible death
Germander	Liver disease, possible death
Lobelia	Breathing problems, excessive sweating, rapid heartbeat, low blood pressure, coma, possible death
Magnolia-Stephania preparation	Kidney disease, can lead to permanent kidney failure
Willow bark	Reyes syndrome (a potentially fatal disease that may occur when children take Aspirin), allergic reaction in adults
Wormwood	Numbness of legs and arms, loss of intellectual processing, delirium, paralysis
Vitamins and Essential Minerals	
Vitamin A (when taking 25 000 IU or more per day)	Birth defects, bone abnormalities, severe liver disease
Vitamin B_6 (when taking more than 100 mg per day)	Loss of balance, injuries to nerves that alter touch sensation
Niacin (when taking slow-release doses of 500 mg or more per day, or when taking immediate-release doses of 750 mg or more per day)	Stomach pain, nausea, vomiting, bloating, cramping, diarrhea, liver disease, damage to the muscles, eyes, and heart
Selenium (when taking 800 to 1000 μg per day)	Tissue damage
Other Ingredients	
Germanium (a non-essential mineral)	Kidney damage
L-tryptophan (an amino acid)	Eosinophilia-myalgia syndrome (a potentially fatal blood disorder that causes high fever)

Health Canada publishes advisories, warnings, and recalls of products available in the Canadian marketplace. They also advise consumers of health risks related to foreign products not authorized for sale in Canada but which may have entered the country through personal importation or purchase over the internet. You can access these though Health Canada at www.hc-sc.gc.ca/index-eng.php.

12

Nutrients Involved in Bone Health

Test Yourself   True *or* False?

1. Most people are unable to consume enough calcium in their diets; therefore, they must take calcium supplements.   T *or* F

2. Osteoporosis is a disease that affects only older adult women.   T *or* F

3. We are capable of making vitamin D within our bodies by using energy obtained from exposure to sunlight.   T *or* F

4. Dairy products must be consumed to meet the current dietary recommendations for calcium.   T *or* F

5. Being overweight or obese may increase a person's risk for osteoporosis.   T *or* F

Test Yourself answers are located in the Chapter Review.

Chapter Objectives | *After reading this chapter, you will be able to:*

1. Discuss the processes of bone growth, modelling, and remodelling, *pp. 409–411*.
2. Describe three methods used to measure bone density, *pp. 411–412*.
3. List and describe the functions of two vitamins and three minerals that play important roles in maintaining bone health, *pp. 412–430*.
4. Identify foods that are good sources of calcium, *pp. 415–416*.
5. Delineate the process by which the body synthesizes vitamin D from exposure to sunlight, and explain why the geographic region where people live affects their ability to do so, *pp. 419–420*.
6. Describe how vitamin D assists in regulating blood calcium levels, *pp. 413, 419*.
7. Explain why consumption of soft drinks may be detrimental to bone health, *p. 426*.
8. Define osteoporosis, discuss how it affects a person's health, and list three reasons women are at greater risk than men for this disease, *pp. 430–434*.

As a young woman, Erika Goodman leapt across the stage in leading roles with the Joffrey Ballet, one of the premier dance companies in the world. But at the age of 59, she died after falling in her Manhattan apartment. Goodman had a disease called *osteoporosis*, which means "porous bone." As you might suspect, the less dense the bone, the more likely it is to break; indeed, osteoporosis can cause bones to break during even minor weight-bearing activities, such as carrying groceries. In advanced cases, bones in the hip and spine fracture spontaneously, merely from the effort of holding the body erect.

If you are age 20 or older, your bones are already at or close to their peak density. But just how dense are your bones, and what changes can you make right now, no matter what your age, to keep them as strong as possible? What foods build bone? Are there foods that accelerate its breakdown? In this chapter, we discuss the nutrients and lifestyle factors that play a critical role in maintaining bone health.

How Does the Body Maintain Bone Health?

Contrary to what most people think, the skeleton is not an inactive collection of bones that simply holds the body together. Bones are living organs that contain several tissues, including bone tissue, nerves, cartilage, and connective tissue. Blood vessels supply nutrients to bone to support its activities. Bones have many important functions in the body, some of which might surprise you (Table 12.1). For instance, did you know that most blood cells are formed deep within the bones?

Given the importance of bones, it is critical that we maintain their health. Bone health is achieved through complex interactions among nutrients, hormones, and environmental factors. To better understand these interactions, we first need to learn about bone structure and the constant activity of bone cells.

The Composition of Bone Provides Strength and Flexibility

We tend to think of bones as totally rigid, but if they were, how could we play basketball or even carry an armload of books up a flight of stairs? Bones need to be both strong and flexible so they can resist the compression, stretching, and twisting that occur throughout our daily activities. Fortunately, the composition of bone is ideally suited for its complex job: about 65% of bone tissue is made up of an assortment of minerals (mostly calcium and phosphorous) that provide hardness, but the remaining 35% is a mixture of organic substances that provide strength, durability, and flexibility. The most important of these substances is a fibrous protein called **collagen**. You might be surprised to learn that collagen fibres are actually stronger than steel fibres of similar size. Within bones, the minerals form tiny crystals (called *hydroxyapatite*) that cluster around the collagen fibres. This design enables bones to bear weight while responding to demands for movement.

Bone strength and flexibility are also affected by its structure. If you examine a bone very closely, you will notice two distinct types of tissue (**Figure 12.1**): cortical bone and

collagen A protein that forms strong fibres in bone and connective tissue.

Table 12.1 Functions of Bone in the Human Body

Functions Related to Structure and Support	Functions Related to Metabolic Processes
Bones provide physical support for our organs and body segments.	Bone tissue acts as a storage reservoir for many minerals, including calcium, phosphorous, and fluoride. The body draws upon such deposits when these minerals are needed for various body processes; however, this can reduce bone mass.
Bones protect our vital organs; for example, the rib cage protects our lungs, the skull protects our brains, and the vertebrae in the spine protect the spinal cord.	
Bones provide support for muscles that allow movement—muscles attach to bones via tendons, and we are able to move all of our joints because of the connections between our muscles and our bones.	Most of the blood cells needed by our bodies are produced in the marrow of our bones.

trabecular bone. **Cortical bone**, which is also called *compact bone*, is very dense. It comprises approximately 80% of the skeleton. The outer surface of all bones is cortical; plus many small bones of the body are made entirely of cortical bone. Although cortical bone looks solid to the naked eye, it actually contains many microscopic openings that serve as passageways for blood vessels and nerves.

In contrast, **trabecular bone** makes up only 20% of the skeleton. It is found within the ends of the long bones (such as the bones of the arms and legs), and inside the spinal vertebrae, the breastbone, ribs, most bones of the skull, and the bones of the pelvis. Trabecular bone is sometimes referred to as *spongy bone* because to the naked eye it looks like a sponge, with no clear organization. The microscope reveals that trabecular bone is in fact aligned in a precise network of columns that protects the bone from stress. You can think of trabecular bone as the scaffolding of the inside of the bone that supports the outer cortical bone.

Cortical and trabecular bone also differ in their rate of turnover—that is, in how quickly the bone tissue is broken down and replenished. Trabecular bone has a faster turnover rate than cortical bone. This makes trabecular bone more sensitive to changes in hormones and nutritional deficiencies. It also accounts for the much higher rate of age-related fractures in the spine and pelvis (including the hip)—all of which contain a significant amount of trabecular bone. Let's now investigate how bone turnover, or the constant activity of bone, influences bone health.

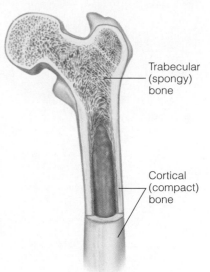

Figure 12.1 The structure of bone. Notice the difference in density between the trabecular (spongy) bone and the cortical (compact) bone.

Labels: Trabecular (spongy) bone; Cortical (compact) bone

The Constant Activity of Bone Tissue Promotes Bone Health

Bones develop through a series of three processes: bone growth, bone modelling, and bone remodelling (**Figure 12.2**). Bone growth and modelling begin during the early months of fetal life when the skeleton is forming and continue until early adulthood. Bone remodelling predominates during adulthood; this process helps to maintain a healthy skeleton as one ages.

Bone Growth and Modelling Determine the Size and Shape of Our Bones

Through the process of *bone growth,* the size of bones increases. The first period of rapid bone growth is from birth to age 2, but growth continues in spurts throughout childhood and into adolescence. Most girls reach their adult height by age 14, and boys generally reach adult height by age 17.[1] In the later decades of life, some loss in height usually occurs because of decreased bone density in the spine, as will be discussed shortly.

Bone modelling is the process by which the shape of bones is determined, from the round "pebble" bones that make up the wrists, to the uniquely shaped bones of the face, to the long bones of the arms and legs. Even after bones stop growing in length, they can still increase in thickness if they are stressed by repetitive exercise such as weight training or by being overweight or obese.

cortical bone (compact bone) A dense bone tissue that makes up the outer surface of all bones, as well as the entirety of most small bones of the body.

trabecular bone (spongy bone) A porous bone tissue that makes up only 20% of the skeleton and is found within the ends of the long bones, inside the spinal vertebrae, inside the flat bones (breastbone, ribs, and most bones of the skull), and inside the bones of the pelvis.

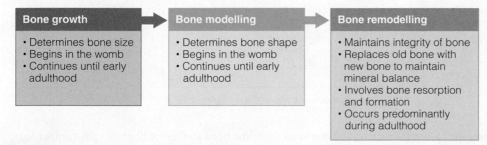

Bone growth	**Bone modelling**	**Bone remodelling**
• Determines bone size • Begins in the womb • Continues until early adulthood	• Determines bone shape • Begins in the womb • Continues until early adulthood	• Maintains integrity of bone • Replaces old bone with new bone to maintain mineral balance • Involves bone resorption and formation • Occurs predominantly during adulthood

Figure 12.2 Bone develops through three processes: bone growth, bone modelling, and bone remodelling.

Bone Remodelling Maintains a Balance Between Breakdown and Repair

Although the shape and size of bones do not significantly change after puberty, **bone density**, or the compactness of bones, continues to develop into early adulthood. *Peak bone density* is the point at which bones are strongest because they are at their highest density. Factors associated with a lower peak bone density include late pubertal age in boys and late onset of menstruation in girls; inadequate calcium and vitamin D intakes; low body weight; and physical inactivity during the pubertal years.[2–4] About 90% of a woman's bone density is built by 17 years of age, whereas the majority of a man's bone density is built during his twenties. However, male or female, before we reach the age of 30 years, our bodies have reached peak bone mass, and we can no longer significantly add to our bone density. In our thirties, our bone density remains relatively stable, but by age 40, it begins its irreversible decline.

Although bones cannot increase in density after our twenties without medication, bone cells remain very active throughout adulthood, balancing the breakdown of older bone tissue and the formation of new bone tissue. This bone recycling process is called **remodelling**. Remodelling is also used to repair fractures and to strengthen bone regions that are exposed to higher physical stress. The process of remodelling involves two steps: resorption and formation.

Bone is broken down through a process referred to as **resorption** (**Figure 12.3a**). During resorption, cells called **osteoclasts** erode the bone surface by secreting enzymes and acids that dig grooves into the bone matrix. Their ruffled surface also acts somewhat like a scrubbing brush to assist in the erosion process. One of the primary reasons the body regularly breaks down bone is to release calcium into the bloodstream. As discussed in more detail later in this chapter, calcium is critical for many physiologic processes, and bone is an important calcium reservoir. The body also breaks down bone that is fractured and needs to be repaired. Resorption at the injury site smooths the rough edges created by the break. Bone may also be broken down in areas away from the fracture site to obtain the minerals that are needed to repair the damage. Regardless of the reason, once bone is broken down, the resulting products are transported into the bloodstream and utilized for various body functions.

New bone is formed through the action of cells called **osteoblasts**, or "bone builders" (see Figure 12.3b). These cells work to synthesize new bone matrix by laying down the collagen-containing organic component of bone. Within this substance, the hydroxyapatite crystallizes and packs together to create new bone where it is needed.

In young healthy adults, the processes of bone resorption and formation are equal, so that just as much bone is broken down as is built, resulting in bone mass being maintained. Around 40 years of age, bone resorption begins to occur more rapidly than bone formation, and this imbalance results in an overall loss in bone density. Because this affects the vertebrae of the spine, people tend to lose height as they age. As discussed shortly, achieving

bone density The degree of compactness of bone tissue, reflecting the strength of the bones. Peak bone density is the point at which a bone is strongest.

remodelling The two-step process by which bone tissue is recycled; includes the breakdown of existing bone and the formation of new bone.

resorption The process by which the surface of bone is broken down by cells called osteoclasts.

osteoclasts Cells that erode the surface of bones by secreting enzymes and acids that dig grooves into the bone matrix.

osteoblasts Cells that prompt the formation of new bone matrix by laying down the collagen-containing component of bone that is then mineralized.

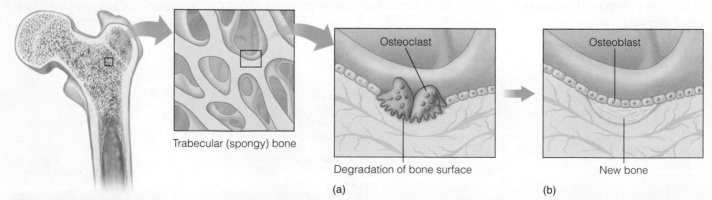

Trabecular (spongy) bone

Osteoclast

Degradation of bone surface

(a)

Osteoblast

New bone

(b)

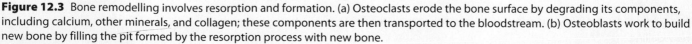

Figure 12.3 Bone remodelling involves resorption and formation. (a) Osteoclasts erode the bone surface by degrading its components, including calcium, other minerals, and collagen; these components are then transported to the bloodstream. (b) Osteoblasts work to build new bone by filling the pit formed by the resorption process with new bone.

a high peak bone mass through proper nutrition and exercise when one is young provides for a stronger skeleton before the loss of bone begins, and it can be protective against the debilitating effects of osteoporosis.

ReCaP

Bones are organs that contain metabolically active tissues composed primarily of minerals and a fibrous protein called collagen. Of the two types of bone, cortical bone is more dense and trabecular bone is more porous. Trabecular bone is also more sensitive to hormonal and nutritional factors and turns over more rapidly than cortical bone. The three types of bone activity are growth, modelling, and remodelling. Bones reach their peak bone mass by the late teenage years into the twenties; bone mass begins to decline around age 40.

How Do We Assess Bone Health?

Over the past 30 years, technological advancements have led to the development of a number of affordable methods for measuring bone health. **Dual energy X-ray absorptiometry**, also referred to as DXA (or DEXA), is considered the most accurate assessment tool for measuring bone density. This method can measure the density of the bone mass over the entire body.

The DXA procedure is simple, painless, non-invasive, and considered to be of minimal risk to humans. It takes only 15 to 30 minutes to complete. The person participating in the test remains fully clothed but must remove all jewellery or other metal objects. The participant lies quietly on a table, and bone density is assessed through the use of a very low level of X-ray (**Figure 12.4**).

DXA is a very important tool to determine a person's risk for osteoporosis. It generates a bone density score that is compared to the average peak bone density of a 30-year-old

dual energy X-ray absorptiometry (DXA or DEXA) Currently the most accurate tool for measuring bone density.

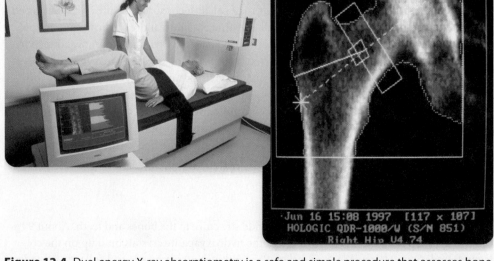

k = 1.208 d0 = 114.8(1.000H)

Jun 16 15:08 1997 [117 x 107]
HOLOGIC QDR-1000/W (S/N 851)
Right Hip U4.74

Figure 12.4 Dual energy X-ray absorptiometry is a safe and simple procedure that assesses bone density.

healthy adult. Doctors use this comparison, which is known as the **T-score**, to assess the risk of fracture and determine whether or not the person has osteoporosis. If bone density is normal, the T-score will range between +1 and −1 of the value for a 30-year-old healthy adult. A negative T-score between −1 and −2.5 indicates low bone mass and an increased risk for fractures. If the T-score is more negative than −2.5, the person has osteoporosis.

DXA tests are generally recommended for postmenopausal women because they are at highest risk for osteoporosis and fracture. Men and younger women may also be recommended for a DXA test if they have significant risk factors for osteoporosis (see pages 431–434).

Other technologies have been developed to measure bone density. The quantitative ultrasound technique uses sound waves to measure the density of bone in the heel, shin, and kneecap. Peripheral dual energy X-ray absorptiometry, or pDXA, is a form of DXA that measures bone density in the peripheral regions of our bodies, including the wrist, heel, or finger. Single energy X-ray absorptiometry is a method that measures bone density at the wrist or heel. These technologies are frequently used at health fairs because the machines are portable and provide scores faster than the traditional DXA.

ReCaP

Dual energy X-ray absorptiometry (DXA or DEXA) is the gold-standard measurement of bone mass. It is a simple, painless, and minimal-risk procedure. The results of a DXA include a T-score, which is a comparison of the person's bone density with that of a 30-year-old healthy adult. A T-score between +1 and −1 is normal; a score between −1 and −2.5 indicates poor bone density; and a score more negative than −2.5 indicates osteoporosis. Quantitative ultrasound, peripheral dual energy X-ray absorptiometry, and single energy X-ray absorptiometry are additional methods that can be used to measure bone density.

A Profile of Nutrients That Maintain Bone Health

Calcium is the most recognized nutrient associated with bone health; however, vitamins D and K, phosphorous, magnesium, and fluoride are also essential for strong bones, and the roles of other vitamins, minerals, and phytochemicals are currently being researched.

Calcium

Dietary calcium is absorbed in the intestines via active transport and passive diffusion across the intestinal mucosal membrane. The majority of calcium consumed in the diet is absorbed from the duodenum, as this area of the small intestine is slightly more acidic than the more distal regions, and calcium absorption is enhanced in an acidic environment. Active transport of calcium is dependent upon the active form of vitamin D, or 1,25-dihydroxyvitamin D; most of the absorption of calcium at low to moderate intake levels is accounted for by this vitamin D–enhanced active transport. Passive diffusion of calcium across the intestinal mucosal membrane is a function of the calcium concentration gradient in the intestines, and this mechanism becomes a more important means of calcium absorption at high calcium intakes.[5]

Calcium is by far the most abundant major mineral in the body, comprising about 2% of our entire body weight! Not surprisingly, it plays many critical roles in maintaining overall function and health.

Functions of Calcium

One of the primary roles of calcium is to provide structure to the bones and teeth. About 99% of the calcium found in the body is stored in the hydroxyapatite crystals built up on the collagen foundation of bone. As noted earlier, the combination of crystals and collagen provides both the characteristic hardness of bone and the flexibility needed to support various activities.

One major role of calcium is to form and maintain bones and teeth.

T-score A comparison of an individual's bone density to the average peak bone density of a 30-year-old healthy adult.

The remaining 1% of calcium in the body is found in the blood and soft tissues. Calcium is alkaline, or basic, and plays a critical role in assisting with acid–base balance. We cannot survive for long if our blood calcium level rises above or falls below a very narrow range; therefore, the body maintains the appropriate blood calcium level at all costs.

Figure 12.5 illustrates how various organ systems and hormones work together to maintain blood calcium levels. When blood calcium levels fall (Figure 12.5a), the parathyroid glands are stimulated to produce **parathyroid hormone (PTH)**. Also known as parathormone, PTH stimulates the activation of vitamin D. Together, PTH and vitamin D stimulate the kidneys to reabsorb calcium. They also stimulate osteoclasts to break down bone, releasing more calcium into the bloodstream. In addition, vitamin D increases the absorption of calcium from the intestines. Through these three mechanisms, blood calcium levels increase.

When blood calcium levels are too high, the thyroid gland secretes a hormone called **calcitonin**, which inhibits the actions of vitamin D (Figure 12.5b). Thus, calcitonin prevents reabsorption of calcium in the kidneys, limits calcium absorption in the intestines, and inhibits the osteoclasts from breaking down bone.

As just noted, the body must maintain blood calcium levels within a very narrow range. Thus, when an individual does not consume or absorb enough calcium from the diet, osteoclasts erode bone so that calcium can be released into the blood. To maintain healthy bone density, we need to consume and absorb enough calcium to balance the calcium taken from our bones.

Calcium is also critical for the normal transmission of nerve impulses. Calcium flows into nerve cells and stimulates the release of molecules called neurotransmitters, which transfer the nerve impulses from one nerve cell (neuron) to another. Without adequate calcium, the nerves' ability to transmit messages is inhibited. Not surprisingly, when blood calcium levels fall dangerously low, a person can experience convulsions.

parathyroid hormone (PTH) A hormone secreted by the parathyroid gland when blood calcium levels fall. It is also known as parathormone, and it increases blood calcium levels by stimulating the activation of vitamin D, increasing reabsorption of calcium from the kidneys, and stimulating osteoclasts to break down bone, which releases more calcium into the bloodstream.

calcitonin A hormone secreted by the thyroid gland when blood calcium levels are too high. Calcitonin inhibits the actions of vitamin D, preventing reabsorption of calcium in the kidneys, limiting calcium absorption in the intestines, and inhibiting the osteoclasts from breaking down bone.

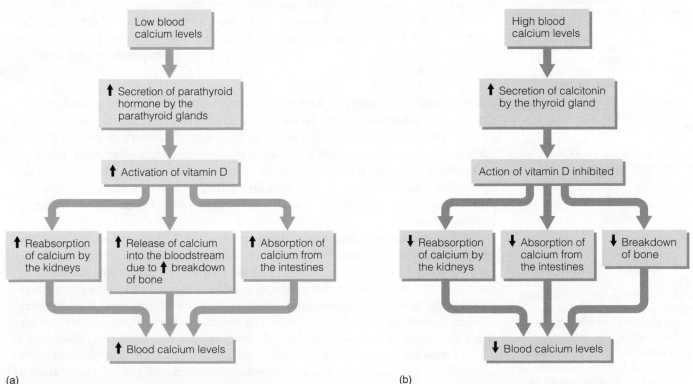

(a)

(b)

Figure 12.5 Regulation of blood calcium levels by various organs and hormones. (a) Low blood calcium levels stimulate the production of parathyroid hormone and activation of vitamin D, which in turn causes an increase in blood calcium levels. (b) High blood calcium levels stimulate the secretion of calcitonin, which in turn causes a decrease in blood calcium levels.

Data from: Whitney, E., and Rolfs, E. Understanding Nutrition, 10/e, p. 414. © 2005. Reprinted with permission of Brooks/Cole, a division of Thomson Learning.

Table 12.2 Overview of Nutrients Essential to Bone Health

To see the full profile of nutrients essential to bone health, turn to Chapter 8.

Nutrient	Recommended Intake
Calcium (major mineral)	Recommended Dietary Allowance (RDA): Women aged 19–50 = 1000 mg/day Women aged >50 = 1200 mg/day Men aged 19–70 = 1000 mg/day Men aged >70 = 1200 mg/day
Vitamin D (fat-soluble vitamin)	RDA:* Women and men aged 19 to 70 years = 15 µg/day Women and men aged >70 years = 20 µg/day
Vitamin K (fat-soluble vitamin)	AI: Women: 90 µg/day Men: 120 µg/day
Phosphorous (major mineral)	RDA: Women and men = 700 mg/day
Magnesium (major mineral)	RDA: Women aged 19 to 30 years = 310 mg/day Women aged >30 years = 320 mg/day Men aged 19 to 30 years = 400 mg/day Men aged >30 years = 420 mg/day
Fluoride (trace mineral)	AI: Women: 3 mg/day Men: 4 mg/day

Based on the assumption that a person does not get adequate sun exposure.

calcium tetany A condition in which muscles experience twitching and spasms due to inadequate blood calcium levels.

calcium rigour A failure of muscles to relax, which leads to a hardening or stiffening of the muscles; caused by high levels of blood calcium.

bioavailability The degree to which our bodies can absorb and utilize any given nutrient.

A fourth role of calcium is to assist in muscle contraction. Muscles are relaxed when calcium levels in the muscle are low. Contraction is stimulated by calcium flowing into the muscle cell; conversely, muscles relax when calcium is pumped back outside of the muscle cell. If calcium levels are inadequate, normal muscle contraction and relaxation is inhibited, and the person may suffer from twitching and spasms. This is referred to as **calcium tetany**. High levels of blood calcium can cause **calcium rigour**, which results in a failure of muscles to relax and leads to a hardening or stiffening of the muscles. These problems affect the function not only of skeletal muscles but also of heart muscle and can cause heart failure.

A 2004 research study suggested that a weight loss diet high in calcium-rich foods may help people lose more weight than if they reduce their energy intake but do not consume enough dietary calcium.[6] In contrast, Bowen and colleagues published a study in 2005 that failed to replicate these findings.[7] Since then, several researchers have explored the relationship between calcium and weight loss and most have found that increasing intakes of calcium or dairy products does not increase weight or fat loss during caloric restriction among overweight or obese adults.[8, 9] However, many of these studies had small sample sizes and were not specifically designed to explore the effects of calcium supplementation among those with varying levels of intake. Until more research is published on this topic, the question of whether dietary calcium can enhance weight loss in people who are dieting remains unanswered.

Other roles of calcium include the maintenance of healthy blood pressure, the initiation of blood clotting, and the regulation of various hormones and enzymes.

How Much Calcium Should We Consume?

Calcium requirements, and thus recommended intakes, vary according to age and gender (Table 12.2). There is a concern that Canadian adults may not be meeting their needs for calcium. Previously, it had not been possible to conclude anything about the prevalence of inadequacy of calcium because of the limited usefulness of the AI in assessing the usual nutrient intakes of groups. However, Canadian Community Health Survey data did show that median calcium intakes of Canadian adults are below their AIs for all age and gender groups except for males between the ages of 19 and 30.[10] Now that an EAR and RDA have been set for calcium intakes (see below), it will be possible to determine the probability of adequate intake in the future.

Recommended Dietary Intake for Calcium In 2011, the Institute of Medicine of the National Academies updated the dietary reference intakes for calcium and vitamin D. For the first time, EARs and RDAs were set for these nutrients.[11] For calcium, the RDA for adult men and women aged 19 to 50 years is 1000 mg of calcium per day. After the age of 50, the RDA for women increases to 1200 mg day. For men, the RDA remains at 1000 mg per day until age 70. After age 70, the RDA for calcium for men increases to 1200 mg per day. At 1300 mg per day, the RDA for boys and girls aged 14 to 18 years is even higher, reflecting their developing bone mass.

The term **bioavailability** refers to the degree to which the body can absorb and utilize any given nutrient. The bioavailability of calcium depends in part on a person's age and his or her need for calcium. For example, infants, children, and adolescents can absorb more than 60% of the calcium they consume, as calcium needs are very high during these stages of life. In addition, pregnant and lactating women can absorb about 50% of dietary calcium. In contrast, healthy young adults only absorb about 30% of the calcium consumed in the diet. When calcium needs are high, the body can generally increase its absorption of calcium from the small intestine. Although older adults have a high need for calcium, their ability to absorb calcium from the small intestine diminishes with age and can be as low as 25%. These variations in bioavailability and absorption capacity were taken into account when calcium recommendations were determined.

The bioavailability of calcium also depends on how much calcium is consumed throughout the day or at any one time. When diets are generally high in calcium, absorption of calcium is reduced. In addition, the body cannot absorb more than 500 mg of calcium at any one time, and as the amount of calcium in a single meal or supplement goes up, the fraction that is absorbed goes down. This explains why it is critical to consume calcium-rich foods throughout the day rather than relying on a single high-dose supplement. Conversely, when dietary intake of calcium is low, the absorption of calcium is increased.

Dietary factors can also affect the absorption of calcium. Binding factors such as phytates and oxalates occur naturally in some calcium-rich seeds, nuts, grains, and vegetables such as spinach and Swiss chard. Such factors bind to the calcium in these foods and prevent its absorption from the intestine. Additionally, consuming calcium at the same time as iron, zinc, magnesium, or phosphorous has the potential to interfere with the absorption and utilization of all of these minerals. Despite these potential interactions, the Institute of Medicine concluded that at the present time, there is not sufficient evidence to suggest that these interactions cause deficiencies of calcium or other minerals in healthy individuals.[5] However, there are people who are vulnerable to mineral deficiencies, such as older adults or people consuming very low mineral intakes, and more research needs to be done in these populations to determine the health risks associated with interactions between calcium and other minerals.

Finally, because vitamin D is necessary for the absorption of calcium, lack of vitamin D severely limits the bioavailability of calcium. We discuss this and other contributions of vitamin D to bone health shortly.

Although spinach contains high levels of calcium, binding factors in the plant prevent much of its absorption.

Kale is a good source of calcium.

Food Sources of Calcium   Dairy products are among the most common sources of calcium in the Canadian diet. Skim milk, low-fat cheeses, and non-fat yogourt are excellent sources of calcium, and they are low in fat and kilocalories (**Figure 12.6**). Ice cream, regular cheese, and whole milk also contain a relatively high amount of calcium, but these foods should be eaten in moderation because of their high saturated fat and energy content.

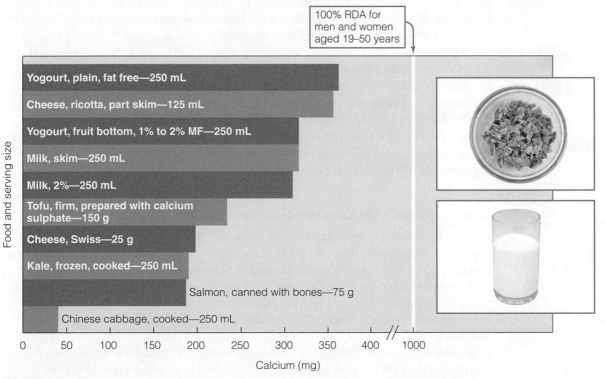

Figure 12.6 Common food sources of calcium. The RDA for adult men and women aged 19 to 50 years is 1000 mg of calcium per day. After the age of 50, the RDA for women increases to 1200 mg day while for men, the RDA remains at 1000 mg per day until age 70. After age 70, the RDA for calcium for men increases to 1200 mg per day.
Data from: The Canadian Nutrient File. Health Canada, 2012. Reproduced with the permission of the Minister of Health, 2012.

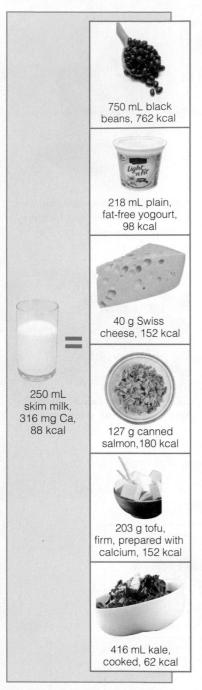

750 mL black beans, 762 kcal

218 mL plain, fat-free yogourt, 98 kcal

40 g Swiss cheese, 152 kcal

250 mL skim milk, 316 mg Ca, 88 kcal

127 g canned salmon, 180 kcal

203 g tofu, firm, prepared with calcium, 152 kcal

416 mL kale, cooked, 62 kcal

Figure 12.7 Serving sizes and energy content of various foods that contain the same amount of calcium as a 250 mL glass of skim milk.

Cottage cheese is one dairy product that is a relatively poor source of calcium, as the processing of this food removes a great deal of the calcium. One cup of low-fat cottage cheese contains approximately 150 mg of calcium, whereas the same serving of low-fat milk contains almost 300 mg. However, calcium-fortified cottage cheese has recently become available. One cup of calcium-fortified cottage cheese contains 400 mg of calcium.

Other good sources of calcium are green leafy vegetables such as kale, turnip greens, broccoli, cauliflower, green cabbage, Brussels sprouts, and Chinese cabbage (bok choy). The bioavailability of the calcium in these vegetables is relatively high compared with spinach, as they contain low levels of oxalates. Many packaged foods are now available fortified with calcium. For example, you can buy calcium-fortified orange juice, soy milk, rice milk, and tofu processed with calcium. Some dairies have even boosted the amount of calcium in their brand of milk!

Figure 12.7 illustrates serving sizes of various calcium-rich foods that contain the equivalent amount of calcium as one glass (250 mL) of skim milk. As you can see from this figure, a wide variety of foods can be consumed each day to contribute to adequate calcium intakes. When you are selecting foods that are good sources of calcium, it is important to remember that we do not absorb 100% of the calcium contained in our foods.[12] For example, although a serving of milk contains approximately 300 mg of calcium, we do not actually absorb this entire amount into our bodies. To learn more about how calcium absorption rates vary for select foods, see the Nutrition Label Activity.

In general, meats and fish are not good sources of calcium. An exception is canned fish with bones (for example, sardines or salmon), providing you eat the bones. Fruits (except dried figs) and non-fortified grain products are also poor sources of calcium.

Although many foods in the Canadian diet are good sources of calcium, many Canadians do not have adequate intakes because they consume very few dairy-based foods and calcium-rich vegetables. There is a concern that Canadian adolescents may not be meeting their needs for calcium.[13] A study conducted by Veugelers and colleagues in Nova Scotia found that 42.3% of children in grade five did not meet recommendations for milk products, and average intakes of calcium were below recommended levels.[14]

There are now quick, simple tools available to assist individuals in determining their daily calcium intake. Most of these tools are designed to estimate a calcium intake score or to calculate calcium intake based on the types and amounts of calcium-rich foods a person consumes. To estimate your calcium intake, go to "Calculate My Calcium" at http://www.osteoporosis.ca/index.php/ci_id/5355/la_id/1.htm.

If you are unable to consume enough calcium because of dietary constraints, you will probably benefit from taking calcium supplements. Refer to the Highlight, "Calcium Supplements: Which Ones Are Best?" on page 418 to learn how to choose a calcium supplement that is right for you.

What Happens If We Consume Too Much Calcium?

In general, consuming too much calcium in the diet does not lead to significant toxicity symptoms in healthy individuals. Much of the excess calcium is simply excreted in feces. However, excessive intake of calcium from supplements can lead to health problems.[15] As mentioned earlier, one concern with consuming too much calcium is that it can lead to various mineral imbalances because calcium interferes with the absorption of other minerals, including iron, zinc, and magnesium. This interference may only be of major concern in individuals vulnerable to mineral imbalance, such as older adults and people who consume very low amounts of minerals in their diets. Data from the Women's Health Initiative (WHI) trial suggested that high intakes of supplemental calcium (1000 mg/day) resulted in an increased incidence of kidney stones among post-menopausal women, ages 50 to 79 years.[16] The UL for calcium for adults is thus based on the risk for the formation of kidney stones. For adults aged 19 to 50, the UL has been set at 2500 mg per day (from food and supplements). This decreases to 2000 mg per day for adults over the age of 50, as research has shown that older men and women are at greater risk for the

NUTRITION LABEL ACTIVITY

How Much Calcium Am I Really Consuming?

As you have learned in this chapter, we do not absorb 100% of the calcium contained in our foods. This is particularly true for individuals who eat a diet predominated by foods that are high in fibre, oxalates, and phytates, such as whole grain breads and cereals and certain vegetables. Thus, it is important to understand how the rate of calcium absorption differs for various foods as you design an eating plan that contains adequate calcium to optimize bone health.

How do you determine the amount of calcium you are absorbing from various foods? Unfortunately, the absorption rate of calcium has not been determined for most foods. However, estimates have been established for a variety of common foods that are considered good sources of calcium. The table below shows some of these foods and their calcium absorption rate. As you can see, many dairy products have a similar calcium absorption rate, just over 30%. Interestingly, many green leafy vegetables have a higher absorption rate of around 60%; however, because a typical serving of these foods contains less

calcium than dairy foods, you would have to eat more vegetables to get the same calcium as you would from a standard serving of dairy foods (see Figure 12.7 on page 416). Note the relatively low calcium absorption rate for spinach, even though it contains a high amount of calcium. This is due to the high levels of oxalates in spinach, which bind with calcium and reduce its bioavailability.

You Do the Math

1. **Find out how much calcium is in the identified serving of each food using the Canadian Nutrient File online search tool at www.hc-sc.gc.ca/fn-an/nutrition/fiche-nutri-data/index-eng.php.**

2. **Estimate the amount of calcium that will be absorbed for each food by multiplying the calcium per serving by the absorption rate.**

3. **Which food will provide you with the most amount of calcium?**

Food	Serving Size	Calcium per Serving (mg)	Absorption Rate (%)	Estimated Amount of Ca Absorbed (mg)
Yogourt, plain, fat-free	250 mL		32	
Milk, skim	250 mL		32	
Milk, 2%	250 mL		32	
Kale, frozen, cooked	250 mL		59	
Broccoli, boiled	250 mL		61	
Cauliflower, boiled	250 mL		69	
Spinach, frozen, cooked	250 mL		5	

Data from: Weaver, C. M., W. R. Proulx, R. Heaney. 1999. Choices for achieving adequate dietary calcium with a vegetarian diet. *Am. J. Clin. Nutr.* 70(suppl):543S–548S; Weaver C. M., K. L. Plawecki. 1994. Dietary calcium: adequacy of a vegetarian diet. *Am. J. Clin. Nutr.* 59(suppl):1238S–1241S.

development of kidney stones.[17] For children aged 9 through 18 years, the UL for calcium is 3000 mg per day.

Various diseases and metabolic disorders can alter the body's ability to regulate blood calcium. **Hypercalcemia** is a condition in which blood calcium levels reach abnormally high concentrations. Hypercalcemia can be caused by cancer and also by the overproduction of PTH. As discussed earlier on page 413, PTH stimulates the osteoclasts to break down bone and release more calcium into the bloodstream. Symptoms of hypercalcemia include fatigue, loss of appetite, constipation, and mental confusion and can lead to coma and possibly death. Hypercalcemia can also lead to an accumulation of calcium deposits in the soft tissues such as the liver and kidneys, causing failure of these organs.

hypercalcemia A condition marked by an abnormally high concentration of calcium in the blood.

What Happens If We Don't Consume Enough Calcium?

There are no short-term symptoms associated with consuming too little calcium. Even when a person does not consume enough dietary calcium, the body continues to tightly regulate blood calcium levels by taking the calcium from bone. A long-term repercussion of inadequate calcium intake is osteoporosis or rickets in children. But because other nutrients may be involved, we discuss this disease later in the chapter.

Hypocalcemia is a term that describes an abnormally low level of calcium in the blood. Hypocalcemia does not result from consuming too little dietary calcium but is caused by various diseases. Some of the causes of hypocalcemia include kidney disease, vitamin D deficiency, and diseases that inhibit the production of PTH. Symptoms of hypocalcemia include muscle spasms and convulsions.

hypocalcemia A condition characterized by an abnormally low concentration of calcium in the blood.

HIGHLIGHT

Calcium Supplements: Which Ones Are Best?

We know that calcium is a critical nutrient for bone health. Now that so many products are fortified with calcium, from cereals and energy bars to orange juice and soy milk, it is not difficult for many people, even vegans, to get sufficient calcium from the diet. Still, small or inactive people who eat less to maintain a healthy weight may not be able to consume enough food to provide adequate calcium, and older adults may need more calcium than they can obtain in their normal diets. In these circumstances, calcium supplements may be warranted.

Numerous calcium supplements are available to consumers, but which are best? Most supplements come in the form of calcium carbonate, calcium citrate, calcium lactate, or calcium phosphate. Our bodies are able to absorb about 30% of the calcium from these various forms. Calcium citrate malate, which is the form of calcium used in fortified juices, is slightly more absorbable at 35%. Many antacids are also good sources of calcium, and it appears these are safe to take as long as you only consume enough to get the recommended level of calcium.

What is the most cost-effective form of calcium? In general, supplements that contain calcium carbonate tend to have more calcium per pill than other types. Thus, you are getting more calcium for your money when you buy this type. However, be sure to read the label of any calcium supplement you are considering taking to determine just how much calcium it contains.

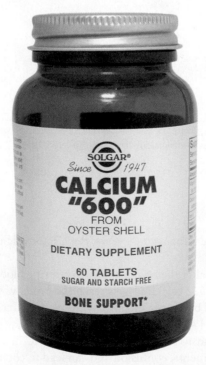

Some very expensive calcium supplements do not contain a lot of calcium per pill, and you could be wasting your money.

The lead content of calcium supplements is an important public health concern. Those made from "natural" sources such as oyster shell, bone meal, and dolomite are known to be higher in lead, and some of these products can contain dangerously high levels. One study of 22 calcium supplements found that 8 (or 36%) of the supplements tested were unacceptably high in lead, including both oyster shell supplements and refined calcium carbonate.[15] Shockingly, the supplement with the highest lead content was a popular, nationally recognized brand-name supplement! To be sure that a supplement has passed safety regulations, look for one of these groups of initials: DIN, NPN, GP, USP.

Research has shown that women taking calcium supplements have a 31% greater risk of having a heart attack compared to women not taking supplements. The reason for this increase is not known, but it may be due to increased calcification or hardening of the arteries.[18] Osteoporosis Canada, in a statement released by the members of their Scientific Advisory Council in April 2011, recommended that post-menopausal women (who are at higher risk of heart disease and osteoporosis) should not take high doses (1000 mg or more) of calcium supplements. Further, it is recommended that total calcium intake from diet and supplements be assessed and if total intake is equal to the RDA, further supplementation is not advised.[19]

If you decide to use a calcium supplement, how should you take it? Remember that the body cannot absorb more than 500 mg of calcium at any given time. Thus, taking a supplement that contains 1000 mg of calcium will be no more effective than taking one that contains 500 mg of calcium. If at all possible, try to consume calcium supplements in small doses throughout the day. In addition, calcium is absorbed better with meals, as the calcium stays in the intestinal tract longer during a meal and more calcium can be absorbed.

By consuming foods high in calcium throughout the day, you can avoid the need for calcium supplements. But if you cannot consume enough calcium in your diet, many inexpensive, safe, and effective supplements are available. The best supplement for you is the one that you can tolerate, is affordable, is lead-free, and is readily available when you need it.

RECaP

Calcium is the most abundant mineral in the body and a significant component of bones. It is also necessary for normal nerve and muscle function. Blood calcium is maintained within a very narrow range, and bone calcium is used to maintain normal blood calcium if dietary intake is inadequate. The RDA for adult men and women aged 19 to 50 years is 1000 mg of calcium per day. After age 50, the RDA for women increases to 1200 mg per day. For men, the RDA remains at 1000 mg until age 70. After age 70, the RDA for men increases to 1200 mg per day. The RDA for boys and girls aged 14 to 18 years is even higher at 1300 mg per day. Dairy products, canned fish with bones, and some green leafy vegetables are good sources of calcium. The most common long-term effect of inadequate calcium consumption is osteoporosis.

Vitamin D

Vitamin D is like other fat-soluble vitamins in that excess amounts are stored in the liver and adipose tissue. But vitamin D is different from other nutrients in two ways. First, vitamin D does not always need to come from the diet. This is because the body can synthesize vitamin D from exposure to sunlight. However, when we do not get enough sunlight, we must consume vitamin D in our diet. Second, in addition to being a nutrient, vitamin D is considered a *hormone* because it is made in one part of the body, yet regulates various activities in other parts of the body.

Figure 12.8 illustrates how the body makes vitamin D. When the ultraviolet rays of the sun hit the skin, they react with 7-dehydrocholesterol. This cholesterol compound is converted into a precursor of vitamin D, cholecalciferol, which is also called provitamin D_3. This inactive form is then converted to calcidiol in the liver, where it is stored. When needed, calcidiol travels to the kidneys where it is converted into **calcitriol**, which is considered the primary active form of vitamin D in the body. Calcitriol then circulates to various parts of the body, performing its many functions. Excess calcitriol can also be stored in adipose tissue for later use.

Functions of Vitamin D

As discussed on page 413, vitamin D, PTH, and calcitonin all work together continuously to regulate blood calcium levels, which in turn maintains bone health. They do this by regulating the absorption of calcium and phosphorous from the small intestine, causing more to be absorbed when the need for them is higher and less when the need is lower. They also decrease or increase blood calcium levels by signalling the kidneys to excrete more or less calcium in the urine. Finally, vitamin D works with PTH to stimulate osteoclasts to break down bone when calcium is needed elsewhere in the body.

Vitamin D is also necessary for the normal calcification of bone; this means it assists the process by which minerals such as calcium and phosphorous are crystallized. Vitamin D may also play a role in decreasing the formation of some cancerous tumours, as it can

calcitriol The primary active form of vitamin D in the body.

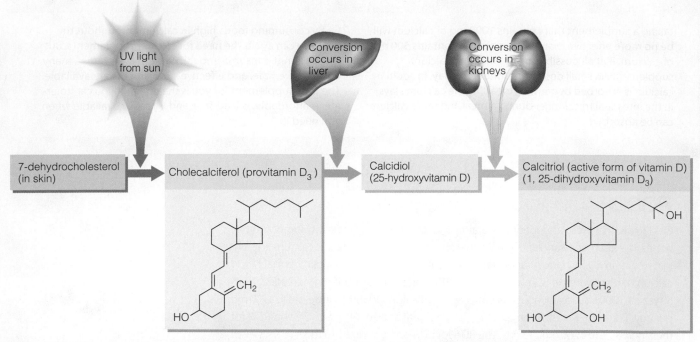

Figure 12.8 The process of converting sunlight into vitamin D in our skin. When the ultraviolet rays of the sun hit the skin, they react with 7-dehydrocholesterol. This compound is converted to cholecalciferol, an inactive form of vitamin D that is also called provitamin D_3. Cholecalciferol is then converted to calcidiol in the liver. Calcidiol travels to the kidneys, where it is converted into calcitriol, which is considered the primary active form of vitamin D in our bodies.
Data from: Nelson et al. Lehninger Principles of Biochemistry, 3/e, © 2000 W. H. Freeman. Used with permission.

Vitamin D synthesis from the sun is not possible during most of the winter months for people living in high latitudes. Therefore, many people around the world, such as the Inuit, need to consume vitamin D in their diets, particularly during the winter.

prevent certain types of cells from growing out of control. Similar to vitamin A, vitamin D appears to play a role in cell differentiation in various tissues.

How Much Vitamin D Should We Consume?

If your exposure to the sun is adequate, then you do not need to consume any vitamin D in your diet. But how do you know whether or not you are getting enough sun?

Recommended Dietary Intake for Vitamin D

As with calcium, the Institute of Medicine revised the DRIs for vitamin D in 2011. The EAR is based on the assumption of minimal sun exposure. Of the many factors that affect the ability to synthesize vitamin D from sunlight, latitude and time of year are most significant (Table 12.3). Individuals living in very sunny climates relatively close to the equator, such as the southern United States and Mexico, may synthesize enough vitamin D from the sun to meet their needs throughout the year—as long as they spend time outdoors. However, most Canadians are at risk for seasonal vitamin D–deficiency since in winter, above 35°N latitude, the sun does not provide enough ultraviolet radiation for the production of vitamin D.[20] Further, the use of sunscreen with an SPF greater than 8 lowers the rate of vitamin D synthesis;[21] however, the Canadian Cancer Society cautions Canadians about spending too much unprotected time in the sun.[22]

Other factors influencing vitamin D synthesis include time of day, skin colour, age, and obesity status:

- More vitamin D can be synthesized during the time of day when the sun's rays are strongest, generally between 9 a.m. and 3 p.m. Vitamin D synthesis is severely limited or may be non-existent on overcast days.
- Darker skin contains more melanin pigment, which reduces the penetration of sunlight. Thus, people with dark skin have a more difficult time synthesizing vitamin D from the sun than do light-skinned people.

Table 12.3 Factors Affecting Sunlight-Mediated Synthesis of Vitamin D in the Skin

Factors That Enhance Synthesis of Vitamin D	Factors That Inhibit Synthesis of Vitamin D
Season—Most vitamin D is produced during summer months, particularly June and July	Season—Winter months (October through February) result in little or no vitamin D production
Latitude—Locations closer to the equator get more sunlight throughout the year	Latitude—Regions that are north of 35°N and south of 35°S get inadequate sun
Time of day—Generally the hours between 9:00 a.m. and 3:00 p.m. (depending on latitude and time of year)	Time of day—Early morning, late afternoon, and evening hours
Age—Younger	Age—Older, due to reduced skin thickness with age
Limited or no use of sunscreen	Use of sunscreen with SPF 8 or greater
Sunny weather	Cloudy weather
Exposed skin	Protective clothing
Lighter skin pigmentation	Darker skin pigmentation
	Glass and plastics—Windows or other barriers made of glass or plastic (such as Plexiglas) block the sun's rays
	Obesity—May negatively affect metabolism and storage of vitamin D

- People 65 years of age or older experience a fourfold decrease in their capacity to synthesize vitamin D from the sun.[23, 24]
- Obesity is associated with lower levels of circulating vitamin D, possibly because of lower bioavailability of cholecalciferol from adipose tissue, decreased exposure to sunlight due to limited mobility or time spent outdoors with skin exposed, and alterations in vitamin D metabolism in the liver.[25, 26]

The current EAR for vitamin D (400 IU or 10 µg per day) for adults 19 through 70 years of age was based on the amount of vitamin D required to achieve serum 25-hydroxyvitamin D (also known as 25 OHD or calcidiol) concentrations of 40 nmol/L. It is widely accepted that the measurement of serum 25 OHD is a marker of vitamin D status in humans.[11] An intake of 600 IU or 15 µg per day was set as the RDA. The RDA increases to 800 IU or 20 µg per day for adults over the age of 70 years. *Eating Well with Canada's Food Guide* recommends that all adults over the age of 50 years take a vitamin D supplement of 10 µg/day in addition to following the food guide to ensure that these recommendations are met.[27] The UL for vitamin D is 100 µg/day for all age groups. The controversy surrounding the recommendations for vitamin D are discussed in more detail in the Evidence-informed Decision Making feature at the end of this chapter.

When reading labels, you will see the amount of vitamin D expressed on food and supplement labels in units of either µg or IU. For conversion purposes, 1 µg of vitamin D is equal to 40 IU of vitamin D.

Food Sources of Vitamin D
There are many forms of vitamin D, but only two are active in the body. These two forms are vitamin D_2, also called **ergocalciferol**, and vitamin D_3, or **cholecalciferol**. Vitamin D_2 is found exclusively in plant foods and may also be used in vitamin D supplements, whereas vitamin D_3 is found in animal foods and is also the form of vitamin D we synthesize from the sun.

Most foods naturally contain very little vitamin D, and those foods that do, such as cod liver oil and canned mackerel, are not typically consumed in the Canadian diet. Thus, the primary source of vitamin D in the diet is from fortified foods such as milk (**Figure 12.9**). In Canada, fluid milk is fortified with 2.5 µg of vitamin D per 250 mL serving. Other milk products that require vitamin D fortification are evaporated milk, powdered milk, and goat's milk. Calcium-fortified plant-based milks (such as rice milk) also need to be fortified with vitamin D. The only other food that is allowed to be fortified with vitamin D in Canada are margarines, which provide 13.25 µg (530 IU) per 100 g.[28]

ergocalciferol Vitamin D_2, a form of vitamin D found exclusively in plant foods.

cholecalciferol Vitamin D_3, a form of vitamin D found in animal foods and the form we synthesize from the sun.

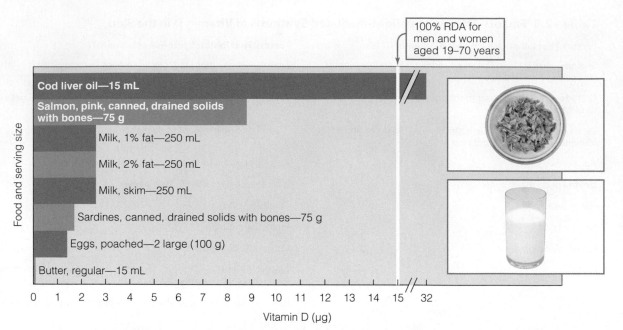

100% RDA for men and women aged 19–70 years

Food and serving size

Cod liver oil—15 mL

Salmon, pink, canned, drained solids with bones—75 g

Milk, 1% fat—250 mL

Milk, 2% fat—250 mL

Milk, skim—250 mL

Sardines, canned, drained solids with bones—75 g

Eggs, poached—2 large (100 g)

Butter, regular—15 mL

0 1 2 3 4 5 6 7 8 9 10 11 12 13 14 15 32

Vitamin D (µg)

Figure 12.9 Common food sources of vitamin D. For men and women aged 19 to 70 years, the RDA for vitamin D is 15 µg per day. The RDA for vitamin D for men and women over the age of 70 years is 20 µg per day.
Data from: The Canadian Nutrient File. Health Canada, 2012. Reproduced with the permission of the Minister of Health, 2012.

Fatty fish contain vitamin D.

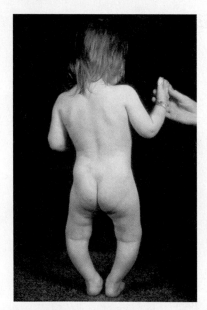

Figure 12.10 A vitamin D deficiency causes a bone-deforming disease in children called rickets.

Other foods that contain high amounts of vitamin D include cod liver oil, fatty fish (such as salmon, mackerel, and sardines), and certain fortified cereals. Eggs, butter, some margarines, and liver contain small amounts of vitamin D, but one would have to eat very large amounts of these foods to consume enough vitamin D. In addition, because plants contain very little vitamin D, vegetarians who consume no dairy products need to obtain their vitamin D from sun exposure, fortified soy or cereal products, or supplements.

What Happens If We Consume Too Much Vitamin D?

A person cannot get too much vitamin D from sun exposure, as the skin has the ability to limit its production. In addition, foods contain little natural vitamin D. Thus, the only way a person can consume too much vitamin D is through supplementation.

Consuming too much vitamin D causes hypercalcemia, or high blood calcium concentrations. As discussed in the section on calcium, symptoms of hypercalcemia include weakness, loss of appetite, diarrhea, mental confusion, vomiting, excessive urine output, and extreme thirst. Hypercalcemia also leads to the formation of calcium deposits in soft tissues such as the kidney, liver, and heart. In addition, toxic levels of vitamin D lead to increased bone loss because calcium is then pulled from the bones and excreted more readily from the kidneys.

What Happens If We Don't Consume Enough Vitamin D?

The primary deficiency associated with inadequate vitamin D is loss of bone mass. In fact, when vitamin D levels are inadequate, the intestines can only absorb 10% to 15% of the calcium consumed. Vitamin D deficiencies occur most often in individuals who have diseases that cause intestinal malabsorption of fat and thus the fat-soluble vitamins. People with liver disease, kidney disease, Crohn's disease, celiac disease, cystic fibrosis, or Whipple disease suffer from vitamin D deficiencies and require supplements.

Vitamin D–deficiency disease in children, called **rickets**, results in inadequate mineralization or demineralization of the skeleton. The symptoms of rickets include deformities of the skeleton such as bowed legs, knocked knees, and an enlarged head and rib cage (**Figure 12.10**). In Canada, fluid dairy products are fortified with vitamin D[29], and

Health Canada, Dietitians of Canada, and the Canadian Paediatric Society recommend that infants and children receive 10 μg (400 IU) of vitamin D per day through either diet or supplementation.[30] Despite these efforts, rickets continues to persist in this country. A recent study reported an overall incidence rate of 2.9 cases per 100 000 infants and children; children residing in the north and infants with darker skin who are breastfed without supplementation are at particular risk.[31]

Vitamin D–deficiency disease in adults is called **osteomalacia**, a term meaning "soft bones." With osteomalacia, bones become weak and prone to malformations and fractures. Osteoporosis, discussed in detail later in this chapter, can also result from a vitamin D deficiency.

Vitamin D deficiencies have recently been found to be more common among Canadian adults than previously thought. This may be partly due to jobs and lifestyle choices that keep people indoors for most of the day. Not surprisingly, the population at greatest risk is older institutionalized individuals who get little or no sun exposure.

Various medications can also alter the metabolism and activity of vitamin D. For instance, glucocorticoids, which are medications used to reduce inflammation, can cause bone loss by inhibiting the ability to absorb calcium through the actions of vitamin D. Antiseizure medications such as phenobarbital and Dilantin alter vitamin D metabolism. Thus, people who are taking such medications may need to increase their vitamin D intake.

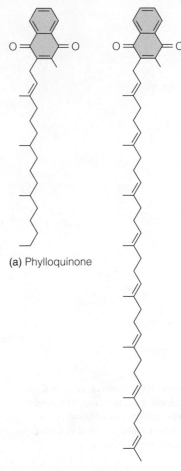

(a) Phylloquinone

(b) Menaquinone

Figure 12.11 The chemical structure of (a) phylloquinone, the plant form of vitamin K, and (b) menaquinone, the animal form of vitamin K.

RECAP

Vitamin D is a fat-soluble vitamin and a hormone. It can be made in the skin using energy from sunlight. Vitamin D regulates blood calcium levels and maintains bone health. The RDA for vitamin D is 15 μg per day for adult men and women aged 19 to 50 years; the RDA increases to 20 μg per day for adults over the age of 70 years. Foods contain little vitamin D, with fortified milk being the primary source. Vitamin D toxicity causes hypercalcemia. Vitamin D deficiency can result in osteoporosis; rickets is caused by vitamin D deficiency in children, whereas osteomalacia results from a vitamin D deficiency in adults.

Vitamin K

Vitamin K, a fat-soluble vitamin stored primarily in the liver, is actually a family of compounds known as quinones. **Phylloquinone**, which is the primary dietary form of vitamin K, is also the form found in plants; **menaquinone** is the animal form of vitamin K produced by bacteria in the large intestine (**Figure 12.11**).

The absorption of phylloquinone occurs in the jejunum and ileum of the small intestine, and its absorption is dependent upon the normal flow of bile and pancreatic juice. Dietary fat enhances its absorption. The absorption of phylloquinone has been reported to be as low as 10% from boiled spinach eaten with butter to as high as 80% when given in its free form.[32] It is transported through the lymph as a component of chylomicrons, and it circulates to the liver, where most of the vitamin K in the body is stored. Small amounts of vitamin K are also stored in adipose tissue and bone.[32] The absorption of menaquinone is not well understood, and its contribution to the maintenance of vitamin K status has been difficult to assess.[33]

Functions of Vitamin K

The primary function of vitamin K is to serve as a coenzyme during the production of specific proteins that play important roles in the coagulation of blood and in bone metabolism. Refer to Chapter 13 for an in-depth description of the role of vitamin K in maintaining blood health.

Here, we limit our discussion to vitamin K's role in the production of two bone proteins, referred to as "Gla" proteins: **Osteocalcin** is a Gla protein that is secreted by osteoblasts and is

rickets Vitamin D–deficiency disease in children. Symptoms include deformities of the skeleton such as bowed legs and knocked knees.

osteomalacia Vitamin D–deficiency disease in adults, in which bones become weak and prone to fractures.

phylloquinone The form of vitamin K found in plants.

menaquinone The form of vitamin K produced by bacteria in the large intestine.

osteocalcin A vitamin K–dependent protein that is secreted by osteoblasts and is associated with bone turnover.

associated with bone remodelling. **Matrix Gla protein** is located in the protein matrix of bone and is also found in cartilage, blood vessel walls, and other soft tissues.[32] The specific role of vitamin K in maintaining bone health is still under study, but there is growing evidence that vitamin K supplementation may increase bone density in people with osteoporosis and that diets rich in vitamin K are associated with reduced fracture rates.[34] Matrix Gla protein also appears to play a role in preventing the calcification of arteries, which may reduce the risk for cardiovascular disease.[35]

How Much Vitamin K Should We Consume?

We can obtain vitamin K from our diets, and we also absorb the vitamin K produced by bacteria in the large intestine. These two sources of vitamin K usually provide adequate amounts of this nutrient to maintain health, and there is no RDA for vitamin K. AI recommendations for adult men and adult women are 120 µg per day and 90 µg per day, respectively. No UL has been set.

Only a few foods contribute substantially to our dietary intake of vitamin K. Green leafy vegetables including kale, spinach, turnip greens, and lettuce are good sources, as are broccoli, Brussels sprouts, and cabbage. Vegetable oils, such as soybean oil and canola oil, are also good sources. **Figure 12.12** identifies the micrograms per serving for these foods. The action of vitamin K is inhibited in laboratory animals given large doses of vitamin A and vitamin E; however, these vitamins do not appear to have the same effect on vitamin K in healthy humans.[33]

What Happens If We Consume Too Much Vitamin K?

Based on our current knowledge, for healthy individuals there appear to be no side effects associated with consuming large amounts of vitamin K.[33] This seems to be true for both supplements and food sources. In the past, a synthetic form of vitamin K was used for therapeutic purposes and was shown to cause liver damage; thus, this form is no longer used.

matrix Gla protein A vitamin K–dependent protein that is located in the protein matrix of bone and also found in cartilage, blood vessel walls, and other soft tissues.

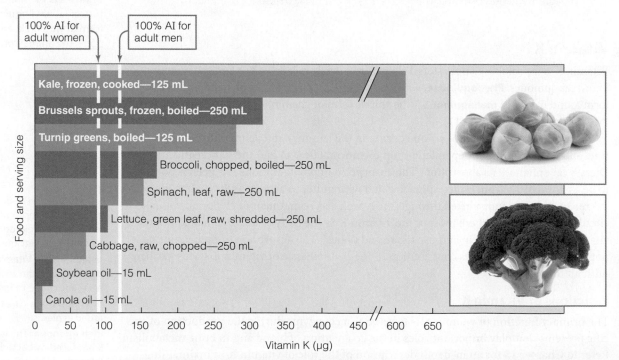

Figure 12.12 Common food sources of vitamin K. The AIs for adult men and adult women are 120 µg per day and 90 µg per day, respectively.
Data from: The Canadian Nutrient File. Health Canada, 2012. Reproduced with the permission of the Minister of Health, 2012.

What Happens If We Don't Consume Enough Vitamin K?

Vitamin K deficiency is associated with a reduced ability to form blood clots, leading to excessive bleeding; however, primary vitamin K deficiency is rare in humans. People with diseases that cause malabsorption of fat, such as celiac disease, Crohn's disease, and cystic fibrosis, can suffer secondarily from a deficiency of vitamin K. Long-term use of antibiotics, which typically reduce bacterial populations in the colon, combined with limited dietary intake of vitamin K–rich food sources can also lead to vitamin K deficiency. Newborns are typically given an injection of vitamin K at birth, as they lack the intestinal bacteria necessary to produce this nutrient.

The impact of vitamin K deficiency on bone health is controversial. A recent study of vitamin K intake and risk of hip fractures found that women who consumed the least amount of vitamin K had a higher risk of bone fractures than women who consumed relatively more vitamin K.[36] Despite the results of this study, there is not enough scientific evidence to support the contention that vitamin K deficiency directly causes osteoporosis.[33] In fact, there is no significant impact on overall bone density in people who take anticoagulant medications that result in a relative state of vitamin K deficiency.

(a)

Recap

Vitamin K is a fat-soluble vitamin and coenzyme that is important for blood clotting and bone metabolism. We obtain vitamin K largely from bacteria in the large intestine. The AIs for adult men and adult women are 120 µg per day and 90 µg per day, respectively. Green leafy vegetables and vegetable oils contain vitamin K. There are no known toxicity symptoms for vitamin K in healthy individuals. Vitamin K deficiency is rare and may lead to excessive bleeding.

(b)
Green leafy vegetables, including Brussels sprouts and turnip greens, are good sources of vitamin K.

Phosphorous

As discussed in Chapter 10, phosphorous is the major intracellular negatively charged electrolyte. In the body, phosphorous is most commonly found combined with oxygen in the form of phosphate (or PO_4^{3-}). Phosphorous is an essential constituent of all cells and is found in both plants and animals.

Functions of Phosphorous

Phosphorous plays a critical role in bone formation, as it is a part of the mineral complex of bone. As discussed earlier in this chapter, calcium and phosphorous crystallize to form hydroxyapatite crystals, which provide the hardness of bone. About 85% of the body's phosphorous is stored in bones, with the rest stored in soft tissues such as muscles and organs.

The role of phosphorous in maintaining proper fluid balance was discussed in detail in Chapter 10. Phosphorous is also a primary component of several energy molecules including adenosine triphosphate (ATP). It helps activate and deactivate enzymes, is a component of the genetic material in the nuclei of the cells (including both DNA and RNA), and is a component of cell membranes and lipoproteins.

How Much Phosphorous Should We Consume?

The details of phosphorous recommendations, food sources, and deficiency and toxicity symptoms were discussed in Chapter 10 (pages 350–351). In general, phosphorous is widespread in many foods and is found in high amounts in foods that contain protein. Milk, meats, and eggs are good sources. Refer to Figure 10.10 (page 351) for a review of the phosphorous content of various foods.

Phosphorous is found in many processed foods as a food additive, where it enhances smoothness, binding, and moisture retention. In the form of phosphoric acid, it is also a major component of soft drinks. Phosphoric acid is added to soft drinks to give them a

Phosphorous, in the form of phosphoric acid, is a major component of soft drinks.

sharper, or more tart, flavour and to slow the growth of moulds and bacteria. Our society has increased its consumption of processed foods and soft drinks substantially during the past 20 years, resulting in an estimated 10% to 15% increase in phosphorous consumption.[5]

Nutrition and medical professionals have become increasingly concerned that the heavy consumption of soft drinks may be detrimental to bone health. Studies have shown that consuming soft drinks is associated with reduced bone mass or an increased risk of fractures in both youth and adults.[37–39] Researchers have proposed three theories to explain why consumption of soft drinks may be detrimental to bone health. These include the following:

- consuming soft drinks in place of calcium-containing beverages, such as milk, leads to a deficient intake of calcium;
- the acidic properties and high phosphorous content of soft drinks cause an increased loss of calcium because calcium is drawn from bone into the blood to neutralize the excess acid; and
- the caffeine found in many soft drinks causes increased calcium loss through the urine.

A recent study of this problem tried to tease out which component of soft drinks may be detrimental to bone health.[40] Four different carbonated soft drinks were tested: two that contained phosphoric acid and two that contained citric acid. Two of these drinks also contained caffeine and two did not. Calcium loss was measured as the amount of calcium excreted in the participants' urine. Interestingly, the results showed that the contents of soft drinks had little effect on calcium status. Although the two beverages that contained caffeine caused some loss of calcium during the five-hour testing period, this effect of caffeine on calcium tends to taper off throughout the day and night, leading to no overall impact on calcium status over a 24-hour period. The researchers concluded that the most likely explanation for the link between soft drink consumption and poor bone health is the *milk-displacement effect;* that is, soft drinks take the place of milk in our diets, depriving us of calcium and vitamin D. Additional nutritional and lifestyle factors that affect bone health are discussed later in this chapter.

What Happens If We Consume Too Much Phosphorous?

As discussed in Chapter 10, people with kidney disease and those who take too many vitamin D supplements or too many phosphorous-containing antacids can suffer from high blood phosphorous levels; severely high levels of blood phosphorous can cause muscle spasms and convulsions.

What Happens If We Don't Consume Enough Phosphorous?

Phosphorous deficiencies are rare but can occur in people who abuse alcohol, in premature infants, and in older adults with poor diets. People with vitamin D deficiency, hyperparathyroidism (oversecretion of parathyroid hormone), and those who overuse antacids that bind with phosphorous may also have low blood phosphorous levels.

ReCaP

Phosphorous is the major negatively charged electrolyte inside of the cell. It helps maintain fluid balance and bone health. It also assists in regulating chemical reactions, and it is a primary component of ATP, DNA, and RNA. Phosphorous is commonly found in high-protein foods. Excess phosphorous can lead to muscle spasms and convulsion, whereas phosphorous deficiencies are rare.

Magnesium

Magnesium is a major mineral. Approximately 50% of dietary magnesium is absorbed via both passive and active transport mechanisms; maximal absorption of magnesium occurs in the distal jejunum and ileum of the small intestine. The absorption of magnesium decreases with higher dietary intakes. The kidneys are responsible for the regulation of blood magnesium levels. Two forms of vitamin D, 25-hydroxyvitamin D and 1,25-dihydroxyvitamin D, can enhance the intestinal absorption of magnesium to a limited extent. Excessive alcohol intake can cause magnesium depletion, and some diuretic medications can lead to increased excretion of magnesium in the urine. Dietary fibre and phytates decrease intestinal absorption of magnesium.

Total body magnesium content is approximately 25 g. About 50% to 60% of the magnesium in the body is found in bones, with the rest located in soft tissues.

Functions of Magnesium

Magnesium is one of the minerals that make up the structure of bone. It is also important in the regulation of bone and mineral status. Specifically, magnesium influences the formation of hydroxyapatite crystals through its regulation of calcium balance and its interactions with vitamin D and parathyroid hormone.

Magnesium is a critical cofactor for more than 300 enzyme systems. Magnesium is necessary for the production of ATP, and it plays an important role in DNA and protein synthesis and repair. Magnesium supplementation has been shown to improve insulin sensitivity, and there is epidemiological evidence that a high magnesium intake is associated with a decrease in the risk for colorectal cancer.[41, 42] Magnesium supports normal vitamin D metabolism and action and is necessary for normal muscle contraction and blood clotting.

How Much Magnesium Should We Consume?

As magnesium is found in a wide variety of foods, people who are adequately nourished generally consume adequate magnesium in their diets. The RDA for magnesium changes across age groups and genders. For adult men 19 to 30 years of age, the RDA for magnesium is 400 mg per day; the RDA increases to 420 mg per day for men 31 years of age and older. For adult women 19 to 30 years of age, the RDA for magnesium is 310 mg per day; this value increases to 320 mg per day for women 31 years of age and older. There is no UL for magnesium for food and water; the UL for magnesium from pharmacologic sources is 350 mg per day.

Magnesium is found in green leafy vegetables such as spinach. It is also found in whole grains, seeds, and nuts. Other good food sources of magnesium include seafood, beans, and some dairy products. Refined and processed foods are low in magnesium. **Figure 12.13** shows many foods that are good sources of magnesium.

The magnesium content of drinking water varies considerably. The "harder" the water, the higher its content of magnesium. This large variability in the magnesium content of water makes it impossible to estimate how much our drinking water may contribute to the magnesium content of our diets.

The ability of the small intestine to absorb magnesium is reduced when one consumes a diet that is extremely high in fibre and phytates, because these substances bind with magnesium. Even though seeds and nuts are relatively high in fibre, they are excellent sources of absorbable magnesium. Overall, our absorption of magnesium should be sufficient if we consume the recommended amount of fibre each day (20 to 35 g per day). In contrast, higher dietary protein intakes enhance the absorption and retention of magnesium.

Trail mix with chocolate chips, nuts, and seeds is one common food source of magnesium.

What Happens If We Consume Too Much Magnesium?

There are no known toxicity symptoms related to consuming excess magnesium in the diet. The toxicity symptoms that result from pharmacologic use of magnesium include diarrhea, nausea, and abdominal cramps. In extreme cases, large doses can result in acid–base imbalances, massive dehydration, cardiac arrest, and death. High blood magnesium, or **hypermagnesemia**, occurs in individuals with impaired kidney function who consume large amounts of non-dietary magnesium, such as antacids. Side effects include impairment of nerve, muscle, and heart function.

hypermagnesemia A condition marked by an abnormally high concentration of magnesium in the blood.

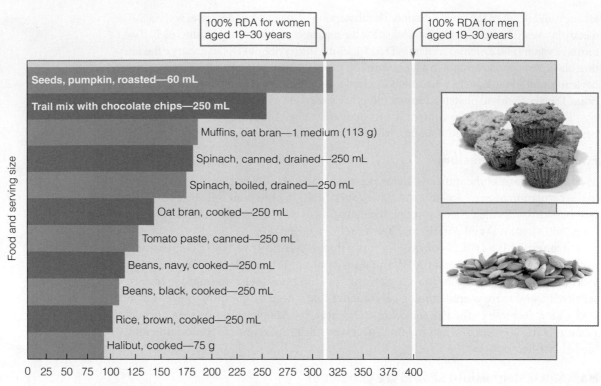

100% RDA for women aged 19–30 years

100% RDA for men aged 19–30 years

Food and serving size

Seeds, pumpkin, roasted—60 mL

Trail mix with chocolate chips—250 mL

Muffins, oat bran—1 medium (113 g)

Spinach, canned, drained—250 mL

Spinach, boiled, drained—250 mL

Oat bran, cooked—250 mL

Tomato paste, canned—250 mL

Beans, navy, cooked—250 mL

Beans, black, cooked—250 mL

Rice, brown, cooked—250 mL

Halibut, cooked—75 g

0   25   50   75   100   125   150   175   200   225   250   275   300   325   350   375   400

Magnesium (mg)

Figure 12.13 Common food sources of magnesium. For adult men 19 to 30 years of age, the RDA for magnesium is 400 mg per day; the RDA increases to 420 mg per day for men 31 years of age and older. For adult women 19 to 30 years of age, the RDA for magnesium is 310 mg per day; this value increases to 320 mg per day for women 31 years of age and older.
Data from: The Canadian Nutrient File. Health Canada, 2012. Reproduced with the permission of the Minister of Health, 2012.

What Happens If We Don't Consume Enough Magnesium?

Hypomagnesemia, or low blood magnesium, results from magnesium deficiency. This condition may result from kidney disease, chronic diarrhea, or chronic alcohol abuse. Older adults seem to be at particularly high risk of low dietary intakes of magnesium because they have a reduced appetite and blunted senses of taste and smell. In addition, older adults face challenges related to shopping and preparing meals that contain foods high in magnesium, and their ability to absorb magnesium is reduced.

Low blood calcium levels are a side effect of hypomagnesemia. Other symptoms of magnesium deficiency include muscle cramps, spasms or seizures, nausea, weakness, irritability, and confusion. Considering magnesium's role in bone formation, it is not surprising that long-term magnesium deficiency is associated with osteoporosis. Magnesium deficiency is also associated with many other chronic diseases, including heart disease, high blood pressure, and type 2 diabetes.[5]

hypomagnesemia A condition characterized by an abnormally low concentration of magnesium in the blood.

RECAP

Magnesium is a major mineral found in fresh foods, including spinach, nuts, seeds, whole grains, and meats. Magnesium is important for bone health, energy production, and muscle function. The RDA for magnesium is a function of age and gender. Hypermagnesemia can result in diarrhea, muscle cramps, and cardiac arrest. Hypomagnesemia causes hypocalcemia, muscle cramps, spasms, and weakness. Magnesium deficiencies are also associated with osteoporosis, heart disease, high blood pressure, and type 2 diabetes.

Fluoride

Fluoride is the ionic form of the element fluorine, and it is also a trace mineral. About 99% of the fluoride in the body is stored in teeth and bones.

Functions of Fluoride

Fluoride assists in the development and maintenance of teeth and bones. During the development of both baby teeth and permanent teeth, fluoride combines with calcium and phosphorous to form **fluorohydroxyapatite**, which is more resistant to destruction by acids and bacteria than hydroxyapatite. Even after all of our permanent teeth are in, treating them with fluoride, whether at the dentist's office or by using fluoridated toothpaste, gives them more protection against dental caries (cavities) than teeth that have not been treated. That's because fluoride enhances tooth mineralization, decreases and reverses tooth demineralization, and inhibits the metabolism of acid-producing bacteria that cause tooth decay.

Fluoride also stimulates new bone growth, and it is currently being researched as a potential treatment for osteoporosis both alone and in combination with other medications.[43-45] While early results are promising, more research needs to be conducted to determine if fluoride is an effective treatment for osteoporosis.[46]

How Much Fluoride Should We Consume?

Our need for fluoride is relatively small. There is no RDA for fluoride. The AI for children aged 4 to 8 years is 1 mg per day; this value increases to 2 mg per day for boys and girls aged 9 to 13 years. The AI for boys and girls aged 14 to 18 years is 3 mg per day. The AI for adults is 4 mg per day for adult men and 3 mg per day for adult women. The UL for fluoride is 2.2 mg per day for children aged 4 to 8 years; the UL for everyone older than 8 years of age is 10 mg per day.

Fluoride is readily available in many communities in Canada through fluoridated water and dental products. Fluoride is absorbed directly in the mouth into the teeth and gums and can also be absorbed from the gastrointestinal tract once it is ingested. In the early 1990s, there was considerable concern that our intake of fluoride was too high due to the consumption of fluoridated water and fluoride-containing toothpastes and mouthwashes; it was speculated that this high intake of fluoride could be contributing to an increased risk for cancer, bone fractures, kidney and other organ damage, infertility, and Alzheimer's disease. Health Canada convened an expert panel to review the health effects of exposure to fluoride in drinking water in 2007 and concluded that the current Maximum Acceptable Concentration (MAC) of 1.5 mg/L of fluoride in drinking water is unlikely to cause adverse health effects.[47]

Currently, there are concerns that individuals who consume bottled water exclusively may be consuming too little fluoride and increasing their risk for dental caries, as most bottled waters do not contain fluoride. However, these individuals may still consume fluoride through other beverages that contain fluoridated water and through fluoridated dental products. Toothpastes and mouthwashes that contain fluoride are widely marketed and used by the majority of consumers in Canada, and these products can contribute as much if not more fluoride to our diets than fluoridated water. Fluoride supplements are available only by prescription, and these are generally only given to children who do not have access to fluoridated water. Incidentally, tea is a good source of fluoride: one 250 mL cup provides about 20% to 25% of the AI.

What Happens If We Consume Too Much Fluoride?

Consuming too much fluoride increases the protein content of tooth enamel, resulting in a condition called **fluorosis**. Because increased protein makes the enamel more porous, the teeth become stained and pitted (**Figure 12.14**). Teeth seem to be at highest risk for fluorosis during the first eight years of life, when the permanent teeth are developing. To reduce the risk of fluorosis, children should not swallow oral care products that are

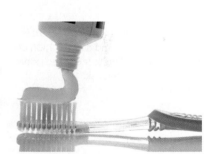

Fluoride is readily available in many communities in Canada through fluoridated water and dental products.

fluorohydroxyapatite A mineral compound in human teeth that contains fluoride, calcium, and phosphorous and is more resistant to destruction by acids and bacteria than hydroxyapatite.

fluorosis A condition marked by staining and pitting of the teeth; caused by an abnormally high intake of fluoride.

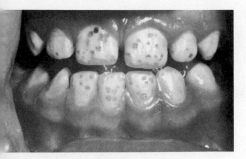

Figure 12.14 Consuming too much fluoride causes fluorosis, leading to staining and pitting of the teeth.

meant for topical use only, and children under the age of six years should be supervised while using fluoride-containing products.[46] Mild fluorosis generally causes white patches on the teeth, and it has no effect on tooth function. Although moderate and severe fluorosis causes greater discoloration of the teeth, there appears to be no adverse effect on tooth function.[5]

Excess consumption of fluoride can also cause fluorosis of the skeleton. Mild skeletal fluorosis results in an increased bone mass and stiffness and pain in the joints. This may occur at about 10 mg/day after 10 or more years of exposure.[47]

What Happens If We Don't Consume Enough Fluoride?

The primary result of fluoride deficiency is dental caries. Adequate fluoride intake appears necessary at an early age and throughout adult life to reduce the risk for tooth decay. Inadequate fluoride intake may also be associated with lower bone density, but there is not enough research currently available to support the widespread use of fluoride to prevent osteoporosis. Studies are currently being done to determine the role fluoride might play in reducing the risk for osteoporosis and fractures.

RECaP

Fluoride is a trace mineral whose primary function is to support the health of teeth and bones. The AI for fluoride is 4 and 3 mg per day for adult men and women, respectively. Primary sources of fluoride are fluoridated dental products and fluoridated water. Fluoride toxicity causes fluorosis of the teeth and skeleton, and fluoride deficiency causes an increase in tooth decay.

Osteoporosis Is the Most Prevalent Disorder Affecting Bone Health

osteoporosis A disease characterized by low bone mass and deterioration of bone tissue, leading to increased bone fragility and fracture risk.

Of the many disorders associated with poor bone health, the most prevalent in Canada is osteoporosis. **Osteoporosis** is a disease characterized by low bone mass and deterioration of bone tissue, leading to enhanced bone fragility and increase in fracture risk. The bone tissue of a person with osteoporosis is more porous and thinner than that of a person with healthy bone. These structural changes weaken the bone, leading to a significantly reduced ability of the bone to bear weight (**Figure 12.15**).

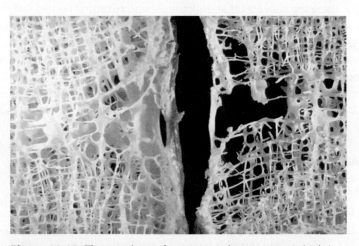

Figure 12.15 The vertebrae of a person with osteoporosis (right) are thinner and more collapsed than the vertebrae of a healthy person, in which the bone is more dense and uniform (left).

As mentioned earlier in this chapter, the hip and the vertebrae of the spinal column are common sites of osteoporosis; thus, it is not surprising that osteoporosis is the single most important cause of fractures of the hip and spine in older adults. These fractures are extremely painful and can be debilitating, with many individuals requiring nursing home care. In addition, they cause an increased risk of infection and other related illnesses that can lead to premature death. In fact, about 20% of older adults who suffer a hip fracture die within one year after the fracture occurs, and death rates are higher for men than for women.[48] Osteoporosis of the spine also causes a generalized loss of height and can be disfiguring. Gradual compression fractures in the vertebrae of the upper back lead to a shortening and hunching of the spine called *kyphosis,* commonly referred to as *dowager's hump* (**Figure 12.16**).

Osteoporosis is a common disease: At least one in three women and one in five men will suffer from an osteoporotic fracture during their lifetime in Canada.[49] Factors that influence the risk for fracture as a result of osteoporosis include age, gender, genetics, nutrition, and physical activity (Table 12.4). Let's review these factors and identify lifestyle changes that reduce the risk for osteoporosis.

The Impact of Aging on Osteoporosis Risk

Because bone density declines with age, low bone mass and osteoporosis are significant health concerns for both older men and women. The prevalence of osteoporosis and low bone mass are predicted to increase in Canada during the next 20 years, primarily because of increased longevity; as the population ages, more people will live long enough to suffer from osteoporosis.

Figure 12.16 Osteoporosis of the spine causes kyphosis, a shortening and hunching of the spine.

Table 12.4 Risk Factors for Osteoporosis

Age 65 or older
Vertebral compression fracture
Fracture with minimal trauma after age 40
Family history of osteoporotic fracture (especially parental hip fracture)
Long-term (more than 3 months continuously) use of glucocorticoid therapy such as prednisone
Medical conditions (such as celiac disease, Crohn's disease) that inhibit absorption of nutrients
Primary hyperparathyroidism
Tendency to fall
Spinal fracture apparent on X-ray
Hypogonadism (low testosterone in men, loss of menstrual periods in younger women)
Early menopause (before age 45)
Rheumatoid arthritis
Hyperthyroidism
Low body weight (<60 kg)
If your present weight is more than 10% below your weight at age 25
Low calcium intake
Excess alcohol (consistently more than two drinks a day)
Smoking
Low bone mineral density (BMD)

Risk factors are additive. The more risk factors you have the greater your risk of developing osteoporosis.
Data adapted from: Checklist for Risk of Broken Bones and Osteoporosis. http://www.osteoporosis.ca/index.php/ci_id/10408/la_id/1.htm. (Accessed March 1, 2012). Courtesy of Osteoporosis Canada. www.osteoporosis.ca.

Hormonal changes that occur with aging have a significant impact on bone loss. Average bone loss approximates 0.3% to 0.5% per year after 30 years of age; however, during menopause in women, levels of the hormone estrogen decrease dramatically and cause bone loss to increase to about 3% per year during the first five years of menopause. Both estrogen and testosterone play important roles in promoting the deposition of new bone and limiting the activity of osteoclasts. Thus, men can also suffer from osteoporosis caused by age-related decreases in testosterone. In addition, reduced levels of physical activity in older people and a decreased ability to metabolize vitamin D with age exacerbate the hormone-related bone loss.

Gender and Genetics Affect Osteoporosis Risk

Approximately one in four women over the age of 50 have osteoporosis. There are three primary reasons for this:

- Adult women have a lower absolute bone density than men. From birth through puberty, bone mass is the same in girls as in boys. But during puberty, bone mass increases more in boys, probably because of their prolonged period of accelerated growth. This means that when bone loss begins around age 40, women have less bone stored in their skeleton than men; thus, the loss of bone that occurs with aging causes osteoporosis sooner and to a greater extent in women than in men.
- The hormonal changes that occur in men as they age do not have as dramatic an effect on bone density as those in women.
- On average, women live longer than men, and because risk increases with age, more older adult women suffer from this disease.

A secondary factor that is gender-specific is social pressure on girls to be thin. Extreme dieting is particularly harmful in adolescence, when bone mass is building and adequate consumption of calcium and other nutrients is critical. In many girls, weight loss causes both a loss of estrogen and reduced weight-bearing stress on the bones. In contrast, men experience pressure to "bulk up," typically by lifting weights. This puts healthy stress on the bones, resulting in increased density.

Some individuals have a family history of osteoporosis, which increases their risk for this disease. Particularly at risk are Caucasian women of low body weight who have a first-degree relative (mother or sister) with osteoporosis. Asian women are also at higher risk than other non-Caucasian groups. Although we cannot change our gender or genetics, we can modify various lifestyle factors that affect our risk for osteoporosis.

Did You Know?

A team of researchers, led by Canada Research Chair in Bone and Muscle Development Dr. Wendy Ward, at the University of Toronto, is investigating the role of food components in the regulation of bone metabolism. One interesting area of their research involves the role of soy isoflavones in bone health. Epidemiological studies have shown that Asian women have a significantly lower incidence of osteoporosis-related fractures than women from North America. However, once these women adopt a Western diet, this health advantage disappears.[50] In a study published in the *Journal of Nutrition* in 2010, Ward and colleagues found that short-term neonatal exposure to isoflavones provided protection against the deterioration of bone tissue in female mice.[51] Further research is needed to determine the mechanism of action and the effects of soy infant formula on bone metabolism in adulthood.

Smoking and Poor Nutrition Increase Osteoporosis Risk

Cigarette smoking is known to decrease bone density because of its effects on hormones that influence bone formation and resorption; thus, cigarette smoking increases the risk for osteoporosis and resulting fractures.

Smoking increases our risk for osteoporosis and resulting fractures.

Chronic alcoholism is detrimental to bone health and is associated with high rates of fractures. In contrast, numerous research studies have shown that bone density is higher in people who are *moderate* drinkers.[36, 52-55] Despite the fact that moderate alcohol intake may be protective for bone, the dangers of alcohol abuse on overall health warrant caution in making any dietary recommendations. As is consistent with the alcohol recommendations related to heart disease, it is recommended that people should not start drinking if they are non-drinkers, and people who do drink should do so in moderation. That means no more than two drinks per day for men and one drink per day for women.

Some researchers consider excess caffeine consumption to be detrimental to bone health. Caffeine is known to increase calcium loss in the urine, at least over a brief period of time. Younger people are able to compensate for this calcium loss by increasing absorption of calcium from the intestine. However, older people are not always capable of compensating to the same degree. Although the findings have been inconsistent, recent research now indicates that the relative amounts of caffeine and calcium consumed are critical factors affecting bone health. In general, older adult women do not appear to be at risk for increased bone loss if they consume adequate amounts of calcium and moderate amounts of caffeine (equal to less than two cups (500 mL) of coffee, four cups (1000 mL) of tea, or six 375 mL cans of caffeine-containing soft drinks per day).[56] Older adult women who consume high levels of caffeine (more than three cups of coffee per day) have much higher rates of bone loss than women with low intakes.[57] Thus, it appears important to bone health that we moderate our caffeine intake and ensure adequate consumption of calcium in the diet. However, this has become more challenging since Health Canada authorized the broader use of caffeine as a food additive in 2010. Manufacturers are now allowed to add synthetic caffeine to non-cola soft drinks in concentrations less than 150 parts per million. This amount is considered to pose no health risk to consumers if they follow Health Canada's guidelines for the maximum daily caffeine intake of 400 mg per day.[58] Unfortunately, manufacturers are only required to identify caffeine in the list of ingredients and do not have to provide the total amount of caffeine in the product, making it difficult for consumers to know how much caffeine they are actually ingesting.

The excretion of sodium and calcium by the kidneys are linked; thus, higher intakes of sodium are known to increase the excretion of calcium in the urine. One study found an association between high urinary sodium excretion and increased bone loss from the hip in postmenopausal women.[59] However, there is no direct evidence that a high-sodium diet causes osteoporosis. At this time, the Institute of Medicine states that there is insufficient evidence to warrant different calcium recommendations based on dietary salt intake.[5]

The effect of high dietary protein intake on bone health is controversial. Whereas it is well established that high protein intakes increase calcium loss, protein is a critical component of bone tissue and is necessary for bone health. High protein intakes have been shown to have both a negative and positive impact on bone health. Similar to caffeine, the key to this mystery appears to be adequate calcium intake. Older adults taking calcium and vitamin D supplements and eating higher-protein diets were able to significantly increase bone mass over a three-year period, whereas those eating more protein and not taking supplements lost bone mass over this same time period.[60] Low protein intakes are also associated with bone loss and increased risk for osteoporosis and fractures in older adults. Thus, there appears to be an interaction between dietary calcium and protein, in that adequate amounts of each nutrient are needed together to support bone health.

Of the many nutrients that help maintain bone health, calcium and vitamin D have received the most attention for their role in the prevention of osteoporosis. Research studies conducted with older individuals have shown that these individuals reduce their bone loss and fracture risk by taking calcium and vitamin D supplements. We know that if people do not consume enough of these two nutrients over a prolonged period of time, their bone density is lower and they have a higher risk of bone fractures. Because bones reach peak density when people are young, it is very important that children and adolescents consume a high-quality diet that contains the proper balance of calcium, vitamin D, protein, and other nutrients to allow for optimal bone growth. Young adults also require a proper balance of these nutrients to maintain bone mass. In older adults, diets rich in calcium and vitamin D can help minimize bone loss.

In addition to their role in reducing the risk for heart disease and cancer, diets high in fruits and vegetables are also associated with improved bone health.[61, 62] This is most likely due to the fact that fruits and vegetables are good sources of nutrients that play a role in bone and collagen health, including magnesium, vitamin C, and vitamin K.

The Impact of Physical Activity on Osteoporosis Risk

Regular exercise is highly protective against bone loss and osteoporosis. Athletes are consistently shown to have more dense bones than non-athletes, and regular participation in weight-bearing exercises such as walking, jogging, tennis, and strength training can help increase and maintain bone mass. When we exercise, our muscles contract and pull on our bones; this stresses bone tissue in a healthy way that stimulates increases in bone density. In addition, carrying weight during activities such as walking and jogging stresses the bones of the legs, hips, and lower back, resulting in a healthier bone mass in these areas. It appears that people of all ages can improve and maintain bone health by consistent physical activity.

Can exercise ever be detrimental to bone health? Yes, when the body is not receiving the nutrients it needs to rebuild the hydroxyapatite and collagen broken down in response to physical activity. Thus, active people who are chronically malnourished, including people who are impoverished and those who suffer from eating disorders, are at increased fracture risk. Research has confirmed this association between nutrition, physical activity, and bone loss in the female athlete triad, a condition characterized by the coexistence of three (or a *triad* of) clinical conditions in some physically active females: low energy availability (with or without eating disorders), amenorrhea, and osteoporosis. In the female athlete triad, inadequate food intake and regular strenuous exercise together result in a state of severe energy drain that causes a multitude of hormonal changes, including a reduction in

Regular weight-bearing exercises such as jogging can help us increase and maintain our bone mass.

CASE STUDY   Osteoporosis Prevention

Antonia, a 68-year-old woman, recently fell and broke her hip. She has a family history of osteoporosis; her mother fell and broke her hip when she was in her 70s and died fairly soon after that. Antonia has always watched her weight. She currently weighs 55 kg. When she was 25 she weighed 70 kg. Antonia does a little gardening in the summer and tries to get out for walks occasionally in the winter, but most of her day is spent reading or visiting with friends. She does not drink milk, preferring to drink coffee and diet cola. In a typical day, Antonia would drink approximately eight cups of coffee and two or three bottles of diet cola.

Thinking Critically

1. **Using Table 12.4, identify the risk factors that apply to Antonia.**
2. **Why should Antonia be concerned about the amount of caffeinated beverages that she is drinking?**
3. **What nutrition and lifestyle changes would you recommend at this time?**
4. **How much calcium and vitamin D should Antonia be consuming at this stage of her life?**
5. **Would you suggest that Antonia ask her physician for a DXA test? Why or why not?**

estrogen production. These hormonal changes can result in the complete loss of menstrual function, called *amenorrhea*. Estrogen is important to maintaining healthy bone in women, so the loss of estrogen leads to osteoporosis in young women. The female athlete triad is discussed in Chapter 15 on page 563.

Treatments for Osteoporosis

Although there is no cure for osteoporosis, a variety of treatments can slow and even reverse bone loss. First, individuals with osteoporosis are encouraged to consume adequate calcium and vitamin D and to exercise regularly. Studies have shown that the most effective exercise programs include weight-bearing exercises such as jogging, stair climbing, and resistance training.[63]

In addition, several medications are available:

- Bisphosphonates, such as alendronate (brand name Fosamax), which decrease bone loss and can increase bone density and reduce the risk of spinal and non-spinal fractures
- Selective estrogen receptor modulators, such as raloxifene (brand name Evista), which have an estrogenlike effect on bone tissue, slowing the rate of bone loss and prompting some increase in bone mass
- Calcitonin (brand name Calcimar or Miacalcin), a pharmacologic preparation of the same thyroid hormone mentioned earlier, which can reduce the rate of bone loss
- Hormone replacement therapy (HRT), which combines estrogen with a hormone called progestin, and can reduce bone loss, increase bone density, and reduce the risk of hip and spinal fractures

All of these drugs can prompt side effects. For example, bisphosphonates are associated with several gastrointestinal side effects, including abdominal pain, constipation, diarrhea, heartburn, irritation of the esophagus, and difficulty swallowing. Side effects of HRT include breast tenderness, changes in mood, vaginal bleeding, and an increased risk for gallbladder disease.

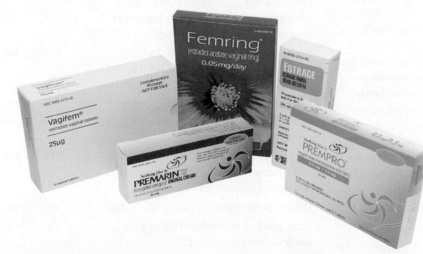

Hormone replacement medications come in a variety of forms.

Until recently, it was believed that HRT protected women against heart disease. A recent study found that one type of HRT actually increases a woman's risk for heart disease, stroke, and breast cancer.[64] As a result, hundreds of thousands of women in the United States have stopped taking HRT as a means to prevent or treat osteoporosis. However, despite the associated risks, it is recognized that HRT is still an effective treatment and prevention option for osteoporosis. It also reduces risk of colorectal cancer. Thus, women should work with their physicians to weigh these benefits against the increased risks of breast cancer and heart disease when considering HRT as a treatment option for osteoporosis.

A healthy diet and regular physical activity can reduce your risk of osteoporosis.

RECAP

Osteoporosis is a major disease of concern for older adult men and women in Canada. Osteoporosis increases the risk for fractures and premature death from subsequent illness. Factors that increase the risk for osteoporosis include genetics, being female, being of the Caucasian or Asian race, low levels of estrogen, cigarette smoking, alcohol abuse, sedentary lifestyle, and diets low in calcium and vitamin D. Medications are available for the prevention and treatment of osteoporosis.

SEE FOR YOURSELF

Calculate Your Risk for Osteoporosis

As many as 2 million Canadians have osteoporosis and the cost of treating osteoporosis and the resulting fractures it causes is estimated to be approximately $1.9 billion a year.[49] But if you know you are at risk, you can take the steps identified in this chapter, such as increasing the amount of weight-bearing exercise you do and making sure you get enough calcium and vitamin D, to maintain the maximum amount of bone mass possible. That's why it's important to assess your risk. Below is a Checklist for Risk of Broken Bones and Osteoporosis adapted from Osteoporosis Canada. The more "yes" answers you have, the greater the likelihood that you're in a higher risk group than the general population.

The questions in this Checklist relate to the major risk factors for the disease (see Table 12.4). Answering yes to any of these questions does not mean you have osteoporosis, but the more positive answers you have, the more likely you are to develop osteoporosis. Osteoporosis Canada recommends that people over the age of 50 who answer yes to one or more of the questions should talk to their doctor to see if they need a bone mineral density test and about doing a more comprehensive assessment.

Are you 65 or older?	Yes	No
Have you ever broken a bone from a simple fall or bump (after age 40)?	Yes	No
Has either your mother or father had a hip fracture?	Yes	No
Do you smoke?	Yes	No
Do you regularly drink three or more alcoholic drinks per day?	Yes	No
Do you have a condition that requires you to use a glucocorticoid medication such as prednisone?	Yes	No
Do you take any other medication that can cause osteoporosis (i.e., aromatase inhibitor for breast cancer or hormonal treatment for prostate cancer)?	Yes	No
Do you have a medical condition that can cause bone loss or fractures (i.e., rheumatoid arthritis, celiac disease)?	Yes	No
Have your periods stopped for several months or more (other than for pregnancy or menopause)?	Yes	No
Have you ever suffered from impotence, lack of sexual desire, or other symptoms related to low testosterone levels?	Yes	No
Do you currently weigh less than 60 kg?	Yes	No
Have you lost more than 10% of your body weight since age 25?	Yes	No
Have you recently had an X-ray that showed a spinal fracture?	Yes	No
Has a recent X-ray suggested you have low bone density?	Yes	No

Data from: Checklist for Risk of Broken Bones and Osteoporosis. http://www.osteoporosis.ca/index.php/ci_id/5465/la_id/1.htm (Accessed November 22, 2010). Courtesy of Osteoporosis Canada. www.osteoporosis.ca.

Chapter Review

12

Test Yourself | Answers

1. **F** By selecting foods that are good sources of calcium each day, most people can consume enough calcium in their diets to meet the RDA. People at risk for low calcium intakes include older adults, people who do not consume enough minerals in their diets, and people who do not consume enough food to maintain a healthy weight.

2. **F** Osteoporosis is more common among older women, but older men are also at increased risk for osteoporosis. Young women who suffer from an eating disorder and menstrual cycle irregularity, referred to as the female athlete triad, may also have osteoporosis.

3. **T** When exposed to sunlight, our bodies can convert a cholesterol compound in our skin to vitamin D.

4. **F** There are many good sources of calcium besides dairy foods, including calcium-fortified juices and soy/rice beverages and green leafy vegetables such as kale, broccoli, and Brussels sprouts.

5. **T** Recent studies indicate that overweight and obese people are more likely to have poor vitamin D status than people of normal weight. Poor vitamin D status increases the risk for osteoporosis.

Summary

- Bone develops through three processes: growth, modelling, and remodelling. Bone size is determined during growth, bone shape is determined during modelling and remodelling, and bone remodelling also affects the density of bone.

- Dual energy X-ray absorptiometry (DXA or DEXA) is the most accurate tool for measuring bone density.

- Calcium is a major mineral that is an integral component of bones and teeth. Calcium levels are maintained in the blood at all times; calcium is also necessary for normal nerve transmission, muscle contraction, healthy blood pressure, and blood clotting.

- The RDA for calcium is 1000 mg per day for adult women aged 19 to 50 years. For men aged 19 to 70 years the RDA is 1000 mg per day. The RDA is 1200 mg for women older than 50 years of age and for men older than 70 years of age.

- Consuming excess calcium leads to mineral imbalance, and consuming inadequate calcium increases the risk for osteoporosis.

- Vitamin D is a fat-soluble vitamin that can be produced from a cholesterol compound in skin using energy from sunlight. Vitamin D regulates blood calcium levels, regulates absorption of calcium and phosphorous from the intestines, and helps maintain bone health.

- The RDA for vitamin D is 15 μg per day for men and women aged 19 to 70 years and 20 μg per day for adults over the age of 70.

- Hypercalcemia results from consuming too much vitamin D, causing weakness, loss of appetite, diarrhea, vomiting, and formation of calcium deposits in soft tissues. Vitamin D deficiency leads to loss of bone mass, causing rickets in children or osteomalacia and osteoporosis in adults.

- Vitamin K is a fat-soluble vitamin that is obtained in the diet and is also produced in the large intestine by normal bacteria. Vitamin K serves as a coenzyme for blood clotting and bone metabolism.

- Phosphorous is a major mineral that is an important part of the structure of bone; phosphorous is also a component of ATP, DNA, RNA, cell membranes, and lipoproteins.

- Magnesium is a major mineral that is part of the structure of bone, influences the formation of hydroxyapatite crystals and bone health through its regulation of calcium balance and the actions of vitamin D and parathyroid hormone, and is a cofactor for more than 300 enzyme systems.

- Fluoride is a trace mineral that strengthens teeth and bones and reduces the risk for dental caries.

- Osteoporosis is a major bone disease in Canada, affecting one in four women over the age of 50.

- Osteoporosis leads to increased risk of bone fractures and premature disability and death due to subsequent illness.

- Factors that increase the risk for osteoporosis include increased age, being female, being of the Caucasian or Asian race, cigarette smoking, alcohol abuse, low calcium and vitamin D intakes, and a sedentary lifestyle.

Review Questions

1. Hydroxyapatite crystals are predominantly made up of
   a. calcium and phosphorous.
   b. hydrogen, oxygen, and titanium.
   c. calcium and vitamin D.
   d. calcium and magnesium.

2. On a DXA test, a T-score of +1.0 indicates that the patient
   a. has osteoporosis.
   b. is at greater risk of fractures than an average, healthy person of the same age.
   c. has normal bone density as compared with an average, healthy 30-year-old.
   d. has slightly lower bone density than an average, healthy person of the same age.

3. Which of the following statements about trabecular bone is true?
   a. It accounts for about 80% of the skeleton.
   b. It forms the core of all bones of the skeleton.
   c. It is also called compact bone.
   d. It provides the scaffolding for cortical bone.

4. Calcium is necessary for several body functions, including
   a. demineralization of bone, nerve transmission, and immune responses.
   b. cartilage structure, nerve transmission, and muscle contraction.
   c. structure of bone, nerve, and muscle tissue, immune responses, and muscle contraction.
   d. structure of bone, nerve transmission, and muscle contraction.

5. Explain the roles of the osteoclasts and osteoblasts in the process of bone remodelling.

6. What are the factors that affect the bioavailability of calcium?

7. Explain why consuming too much vitamin D can lead to hypercalcemia, or high blood calcium.

8. Explain why the consumption of soft drinks may be detrimental to your bone health.

9. Explain why people with diseases that cause a malabsorption of fat may suffer from deficiency of vitamins D and K.

10. Most people reach their peak height by the end of adolescence, maintain that height for several decades, and then start to lose height in their later years. Describe the two processes behind this phenomenon.

11. The morning after reading this chapter, you are eating your usual breakfast cereal when you notice that the Nutrition Facts table on the box states that one serving contains 100% of the Daily Value for calcium. In addition, you're eating the cereal with about 1/2 cup of skim milk. Does this meal ensure that your calcium needs for the day are met? Why or why not?

12. Bert has light skin and lives in Toronto, Ontario. How much time does Bert need to spend out of doors with exposed skin on winter days to avoid the need for consuming vitamin D in his diet or from supplements?

Web Links

www.osteoporosis.ca
Osteoporosis Canada
Learn more about the causes, prevention, detection, and treatment of osteoporosis.

www.aboutkidshealth.ca
The Hospital for Sick Children
Search for "rickets" or "osteopenia" to learn more about these vitamin D–deficiency diseases.

www.cda-adc.ca
Canadian Dental Association
Look under "Frequently Asked Questions" to learn more about fluoride, dental fluorosis, and the fluoridation of community water supplies.

www.osteofound.org
International Osteoporosis Foundation
Find out more about this foundation and its mission to increase awareness and understanding of osteoporosis worldwide.

www.phac-aspc.gc.ca
Public Health Agency of Canada
Access this site for additional resources and information on osteoporosis and seniors.

www.centre4activeliving.ca
Alberta Centre for Active Living
Search this site for evidence-based information on bone health and osteoporosis.

MasteringNutrition®

www.masteringnutrition.pearson.com

Assignments
Animations: Activation of Vitamin D • Calcium Metabolism
Study Area
Video: Using the Functional Approach to Understand Antioxidant Function • Practice Tests • Diet Analysis • eText

References

1. Ball, J. W., and R. C. Bindler. 2003. *Pediatric Nursing: Caring for Children.* Upper Saddle River, NJ: Pearson Education.
2. Ho, A. Y. Y., and A. W. C. Kung. 2005. Determinants of peak bone mineral density and bone area in young women. *J. Bone Miner. Metab.* 23:470–475.
3. Chevalley, T., R. Rizzoli, D. Hans, S. Ferrari, and J. P. Bonjour. 2005. Interaction between calcium intake and menarcheal age on bone mass gain: an eight-year follow-up study from prepuberty to postmenarche. *J. Clin. Endocrinol. Metab.* 90:44–51.
4. Kindblom, J. M., M. Lorentzon, E. Norjavaara, A. Hellqvist, S. Nilsson, D. Mellström, and C. Ohlsson. 2006. Pubertal timing predicts previous fractures and BMD in young adult men: the GOOD study. *J. Bone Min. Res.* 21:790–795.
5. Institute of Medicine, Food and Nutrition Board. 1997. *Dietary Reference Intakes for Calcium, Phosphorus, Magnesium, Vitamin D, and Fluoride.* Washington, DC: National Academy Press.
6. Zemel, M. B., W. Thompson, A. Milstead, K. Morris, and P. Campbell. 2004. Calcium and dairy acceleration of weight and fat loss during energy restriction in obese adults. *Obes. Res.* 12:582–590.
7. Bowen J., M. Noakes, and P. M. Clifton. 2005. Effect of calcium and dairy foods in high protein, energy-restricted diets on weight loss and metabolic parameters in overweight adults. *Int. J. Obes.* 29:957–965.
8. Wagner, G., S. Kindrick, S. Hertzler, and R. A. DiSilvestro. 2007. Effects of various forms of calcium on body weight and bone turnover markers in women participating in a weight loss program. *J. Am. Coll. Nutr.* 26:456–461.
9. Teegarden, D., and C. W. Gunther. 2008. Can the controversial relationship between dietary calcium and body weight be mechanistically explained by alterations in appetite and food intake? *Nutr. Rev.* 66:601–605.
10. Health Canada. 2009. Do Canadian Adults Meet Their Nutritional Requirements Through Food Intake Alone? Available at www.hc-sc.gc.ca/fn-an/surveill/nutrition/commun/art-nutr-adult-eng.php (accessed October 24, 2010).
11. Institute of Medicine. 2011. Dietary reference intakes: calcium vitamin D. Washington, DC: The National Academies Press.
12. Keller, J. L., A. J. Lanou, and N. D. Barnard. 2002. The consumer cost of calcium from food and supplements. *J. Am. Diet. Assoc.* 102:1669–1671.
13. Health Canada. 2009. Do Canadian Adolescents Meet Their Nutritional Requirements through Food Intake Alone? Available at www.hc-sc.gc.ca/fn-an/alt_formats/pdf/surveill/nutrition/commun/art-nutr-adol-eng.pdf (accessed October 24, 2010).
14. Veugelers P. J., A. L. Fitzgerald, and E. Johnston. 2005. Dietary intake and risk factors for poor diet quality among children in Nova Scotia. *Can. J. Pub. Health* 96:212–216.
15. Ross, E. A., N. J. Szabo, and I. R. Tebbett. 2000. Lead content of calcium supplements. *JAMA* 284:1425–1433.
16. Jackson, R. D., et al. 2006. Calcium plus vitamin D supplementation and the risk of fractures. *N. Engl. J. Med.* 354(7):669–683.
17. Curhan, G. C., W. C. Willett, E. G. Rimm, and M. J. Stampfer. 1993. A prospective study of dietary calcium and other nutrients and the risk of symptomatic kidney stones. *N. Engl. J. Med.* 328:833–838.
18. Bolland M. J., A. Avenell, J. A. Baron, A. Grey, G. S. MacLennan, G. D. Gamble, and I. R. Reid. 2010. Effect of calcium supplements on risk of myocardial infarction and cardiovascular events: meta analysis. *Br. Med. J.* 341:c3691 DOI:10.1136/bmj.c3691.
19. Osteoporosis Canada. 2009. Calcium intake statement. Available at www.osteoporosis.ca/index.php/ci_id/6872/la_id/1.htm (accessed May 5, 2011).
20. Hanley, D. A., A. Cranney, G. Jones, S. J. Whiting, W. D. Leslie, D. E. C. Cole, S. A. Atkinson, R. G. Josse, S. Feldman, G. A. Kline, and C. Rosen. 2010. Vitamin D in adult health and disease: a review and guideline statement from Osteoporosis Canada. *Can. Med. Assoc. J.* 182:E610–E618.
21. Matsuoka, L. Y., J. Wortsman, and B. W. Hollis. 1990. Use of topical sunscreen for the evaluation of regional synthesis of vitamin D. *J. Am. Acad. Dermatol.* 22:772–775.
22. Canadian Cancer Society. 2008. Media Backgrounder: Canadian Cancer Society's SunSense Guidelines. Available at www.cancer.ca/Canada-wide/About%20us/Media%20centre/CW-Media%20releases/CW-2008/Media%20Backgrounder%20-%20Canadian%20Cancer%20Societys%20SunSense%20guidelines.aspx?sc_lang=en (accessed October 24, 2010).
23. Holick, M. F., L. Y. Matsuoka, and J. Wortsman. 1989. Age, vitamin D, and solar ultraviolet. *Lancet* 2:1104–1105.
24. Need, A. G., H. A. Morris, M. Horowitz, and C. Nordin. 1993. Effects of skin thickness, age, body fat, and sunlight on serum 25-hydroxyvitamin D. *Am. J. Clin. Nutr.* 58:882–885.
25. Florez, H., R. Martinez, W. Chacra, N. Strickman-Stein, and S. Levis. 2007. Outdoor exercise reduces the risk of hypovitaminosis D in the obese. *J. Steroid Biochem. Mol. Biol.* 103:679–681.

26. Holick, M. F. 2005. The vitamin D epidemic and its health consequences. *J. Nutr.* 135:2739S–2748S.

27. Health Canada. 2007. Vitamin D Supplement for People Over 50. Available at www.hc-sc.gc.ca/fn-an/food-guide-aliment/context/evid-fond-eng.php (accessed October 24, 2010).

28. Calvo, M. S., S. J. Whiting, and C. N. Barton. 2004. Vitamin D fortification in the United States and Canada: current status and data needs. *Am. J. Clin. Nutr.* 80(suppl):1710S–1716S.

29. Institute of Medicine Food and Nutrition Board. 2003. Standing Committee on the Use of Dietary Reference Intakes in Nutrition Labelling. *Overview of food fortification in the United States and Canada.* In: *Dietary reference intakes: guiding principles for nutrition labeling and fortification.* Washington, DC: National Academies Press.

30. Statement of the Joint Working Group: Canadian Paediatric Society, Dietitians of Canada, Health Canada. 2010. *Nutrition for Healthy Term Infants.* Ottawa: Minister of Public Works and Government Services Canada. Available at www.hc-sc.gc.ca/fn-an/pubs/infant-nourrisson/nut_infant_nourrisson_term-eng.php (accessed November 21, 2010).

31. Ward, L. M., I. Gaboury, M. Ladhani, and S. Zlotkin. 2007. Vitamin D-deficiency rickets among children in Canada. *Can. Med. Assoc. J.* 177:161–166.

32. FAO and WHO. 2002. Vitamin K. In: Human vitamin and mineral requirements. Report of a joint FAO/WHO expert consultation. Available at www.micronutrient.org/idpas/pdf/846.10-CHAPTER10.pdf.

33. Institute of Medicine, Food and Nutrition Board. 2002. *Dietary Reference Intakes for Vitamin A, Vitamin K, Arsenic, Boron, Chromium, Copper, Iodine, Iron, Manganese, Molybdenum, Nickel, Silicon, Vanadium, and Zinc.* Washington, DC: National Academy Press.

34. Weber, P. 2001. Vitamin K and bone health. *Nutrition* 17:880–887.

35. Shearer, M. J. 2000. Role of vitamin K and Gla proteins in the pathophysiology of osteoporosis and vascular calcification. *Curr. Opin. Clin. Nutr. Metab. Care* 3:433–438.

36. Feskanich, D., S. A. Korrick, S. L. Greenspan, H. N. Rosen, and G. A. Colditz. 1999. Moderate alcohol consumption and bone density among post-menopausal women. *J. Women's Health* 8:65–73.

37. Wyshak, G., R. E. Frisch, T. E. Albright, N. L. Albright, I. Schiff, and J. Witschi. 1989. Nonalcoholic carbonated beverage consumption and bone fractures among women former college athletes. *J. Orthop. Res.* 7:91–99.

38. Wyshak, G., and R. E. Frisch. 1994. Carbonated beverages, dietary calcium, the dietary calcium/phosphorus ratio, and bone fractures in girls and boys. *J. Adolesc. Health* 15:210–215.

39. Wyshak, G. 2000. Teenaged girls, carbonated beverage consumption, and bone fractures. *Arch. Pediatr. Adolesc. Med.* 154:610–613.

40. Heaney, R. P., and K. Rafferty. 2001. Carbonated beverages and urinary calcium excretion. *Am. J. Clin. Nutr.* 74:343–347.

41. Paolisso G., S. Sgambato, A. Gambardella, G. Pizza, P. Tesauro, M. Varricchio, and F. D'Onofrio. 1992. Daily magnesium supplements improve glucose handling in elderly subjects. *Am. J. Clin. Nutr.* 55:1161–1167.

42. Larsson, S. C., L. Bergkvist, and A. Wolk. 2005. Magnesium intake in relation to risk of colorectal cancer in women. *JAMA* 293:86–89.

43. Pak, C. Y., K. Sakhaee, B. Adams-Huet, V. Piziak, R. D. Peterson, and J. R. Poindexter. 1995. Treatment of postmenopausal osteoporosis with slow-release sodium fluoride. Final report of a randomized controlled trial. *Ann. Int. Med.* 123:401–408.

44. Reginster, J. Y., D. Felsenberg, I. Pavo, J. Stepan, J. Payer, H. Resch, C. C. Glüer, D. Mühlenbacher, D. Quail, H. Schmitt, and T. Nickelsen. 2003. Effect of raloxifene combined with mono-fluorophosphate as compared with monofluorophosphate alone in postmenopausal women with low bone mass: a randomized, controlled trial. *Osteoporosis Int.* 14:741–749.

45. Ringe, J. D., A. Dorst, H. Faber, C. Kipshoven, L. C. Rovati, and I. Setnikar. 2005. Efficacy of etidronate and sequential mono-fluorophosphate in severe postmenopausal osteoporosis: a pilot study. *Rheumatol. Int.* 25:296–300.

46. Academy of Nutrition and Dietetics. 2005. Position of the Academy of Nutrition and Dietetics: the impact of fluoride on health. *J. Am. Diet. Assoc.* 105:1620–1628.

47. Health Canada. 2008. Findings and recommendations of the Fluoride Expert Panel (January 2007). Available at www.hc-sc.gc.ca/ewh-semt/pubs/water-eau/2008-fluoride-fluorure/index-eng.php (accessed November 21, 2010).

48. International Osteoporosis Foundation. 2007. Facts and statistics about osteoporosis and its impact. Available at www.iofbone-health.org/facts-and-statistics.html.

49. Osteoporosis Canada. Osteoporosis at-a-glance. Available at www.osteoporosis.ca/index.php/ci_id/5526/la_id/1.htm (accessed November 22, 2010).

50. Greendale, G. A., G. FitzGerald, M.-H. Huang, B. Sternfeld, E. Gold, T. Seeman, S. Sherman, and M. Sowers. 2002. Dietary soy isoflavones and bone mineral density: results from the study of women's health across the nation. *Am. J. Epidemiol.* 155:746–754.

51. Ward, W. E., and J. Kaludjerovi. 2010. Neonatal administration of isoflavones attenuates deterioration of bone tissue in female but not male mice. *J. Nutr.* 140:766–772.

52. Laitinen, K., M. Valimaki, and P. Keto. 1991. Bone mineral density measured by dual-energy x-ray absorptiometry in healthy Finnish women. *Calcif. Tissue Int.* 48:224–231.

53. Holbrook, T. L., and E. Barrett-Connor. 1993. A prospective study of alcohol consumption and bone mineral density. *BMJ* 306:1506–1509.

54. Felson, D. T., Y. Zhang, M. T. Hannan, W. B. Kannel, and D. P. Kiel. 1995. Alcohol intake and bone mineral density in elderly men and women. The Framingham Study. *Am. J. Epidemiol.* 142:485–492.

55. Rapuri, P. B., J. C. Gallagher, K. E. Balhorn, and K. L. Ryschon. 2000. Alcohol intake and bone metabolism in elderly women. *Am. J. Clin. Nutr.* 72:1206–1213.

56. Massey, L. K. 2001. Is caffeine a risk factor for bone loss in the elderly? *Am. J. Clin. Nutr.* 74:569–570.

57. Rapuri, P. B., J. C. Gallagher, H. K. Kinyamu, and K. L. Ryschon. 2001. Caffeine intake increases the rate of bone loss in elderly women and interacts with vitamin D receptor genotypes. *Am. J. Clin. Nutr.* 74:694–700.

58. Health Canada. 2010. News Release. Health Canada completes safety assessment of caffeine use in non-cola beverages. Available at www.hc-sc.gc.ca/ahc-asc/media/nr-ca/2010/2010_41-eng.php (accessed May 5, 2011).

59. Devine A., R. A. Criddle, I. M. Dick, D. A. Kerr, and R. L. Prince. 1995. A longitudinal study of the effect of sodium and calcium

intakes on regional bone density in post-menopausal women. *Am. J. Clin. Nutr.* 62:740–745.

60. Dawson-Hughes, B., and S. S. Harris. 2002. Calcium intake influences the association of protein intake with rates of bone loss in elderly men and women. *Am. J. Clin. Nutr.* 75:773–779.

61. Tucker, K. L., M. T. Hannan, H. Chen, L. A. Cupples, P. W. F. Wilson, and D. P. Kiel. 1999. Potassium, magnesium, and fruit and vegetable intakes are associated with greater bone mineral density in elderly men and women. *Am. J. Clin. Nutr.* 69:727–736.

62. Tucker, K. L., H. Chen, M. T. Hannan, L. A. Cupples, P. W. F. Wilson, D. Felson, and D. P. Kiel. 2002. Bone mineral density and dietary patterns in older adults: the Framingham Osteoporosis Study. *Am. J. Clin. Nutr.* 76:245–252.

63. South-Pal, J. E. 2001. Osteoporosis: part II. Nonpharmacologic and pharmacologic treatment. *Am. Fam. Physician* 63:1121–1128.

64. Writing Group for the Women's Health Initiative Investigators. 2002. Risks and benefits of estrogen plus progestin in healthy postmenopausal women. Principal results from the Women's Health Initiative randomized control trial. *JAMA* 288:321–332.

65. Weaver, C. M. and J. C. Fleet. 2004. Vitamin D requirements: current and future. *Am. J. Clin. Nutr.* 80(suppl):1735S–1739S.

66. Jackson, R. D., A. Z. LaCroix, M. Gass, R. B. Wallace, J. Robbins, C. E. Lewis, T. Bassford, S. A. A. Beresford, H. R. Black, P. Blanchette, D. E. Bonds, R. L. Brunner, R. G. Brzyski, B. Caan, J. A. Cauley, R. T. Chlebowski, S. R. Cummings, I. Granek, J. Hays, G. Heiss, S. L. Hendrix, B. V. Howard, J. Hsia, F. A. Hubbell, K. C. Johnson, H. Judd, J. Morley Kotchen, L. H. Kuller, R. D. Langer, N. L. Lasser, M. C. Limacher, S. Ludlam, J. E. Manson, K. L. Margolis, J. McGowan, J. K. Ockene, M. J. O'Sullivan, L. Phillips, R. L. Prentice, G. E. Sarto, M. L. Stefanick, L. Van Horn, J. Wactawski-Wende, E. Whitlock, G. L. Anderson, A. R. Assaf, and D. Barad. 2006. Calcium plus vitamin D supplementation and the risk of fractures. *N. Engl. J. Med.* 354:669–683.

67. Stolzenberg-Solomon, R. Z., R. Vieth, A. Azad, P. Pietinen, P. R. Taylor, J. Virtamo, and D. Albanes. 2006. A prospective nested case-control study of vitamin D status and pancreatic cancer risk in male smokers. *Cancer Res.* 66:10213–10219.

Vitamin D Recommendations: How Much Do We Need?

No doubt about it; unless you live at a latitude within 40° of the equator and spend time outdoors without sunscreen, it's tough to get enough vitamin D. That's because, as you learned in this chapter, there are very few natural food sources of vitamin D, and even fortified food sources are limited to milk and a handful of other products. But there seems to be conflicting views on how much vitamin D is needed and how much is too much. In part, this is due to the challenges associated with determining vitamin D requirements.

As you know, vitamin D is an essential nutrient but it is also synthesized in the skin through sun exposure. However, concerns about skin cancer preclude the possibility of including vitamin D synthesis in estimating requirements. There does not appear to be a threshold for sun exposure below which people do not increase their risk for skin cancer. At the same time, numerous factors affect a person's ability to produce vitamin D from exposure to sunlight. Thus, it is not possible to recommend a uniform amount of sunlight exposure for the general population. Further, it is often difficult to distinguish the health outcomes associated with vitamin D from those of calcium since they are metabolically interrelated. An individual's vitamin D status is best assessed by determining circulating levels of serum 25-hydroxyvitamin D (25-OHD). It reflects the amount of vitamin D produced in the skin as well as that from food and supplements. However, it is unclear to what extent 25-OHD levels relate to health outcomes.

In 2011, the Institute of Medicine (IOM) released updated recommendations for vitamin D intake, setting a new RDA of 15 µg (600 IU) daily for children and adults aged 9 through 70 years.[11] After age 70, the RDA increases to 20 µg (800 IU) daily. The previous AI was 5 µg (200 IU) daily for adults aged 19 to 50 years, 10 µg (400 IU) daily for adults aged 50 to 70 years, and 15 µg (600 IU) daily for adults over the age of 70. In setting the new DRIs, the IOM expert committee gathered background information on the metabolism and physiology of vitamin D and reviewed research related to a number of health outcomes that could potentially be related to vitamin D status. They determined that the relationships between vitamin D and cancer, cardiovascular disease, hypertension, diabetes and metabolic syndrome, falls and physical performance, immune functioning and autoimmune disorders, infections, neuropsychological functioning, and preeclampsia were inconclusive. They stated that the research results were often conflicting and did not demonstrate a cause-and-effect relationship. Further, there was some evidence

that for some cancers there appears to be an increase in incidence associated with higher serum 25-OHD concentrations or higher vitamin D intakes. Given the conflicting nature of the available evidence, the IOM set the new DRIs solely based on vitamin D's role in bone health, indicating that the potential roles of vitamin D in other disease states ". . . are currently best described as hypotheses of emerging interest".[65]

Osteoporosis Canada released a review and guideline statement regarding vitamin D's role in adult health and disease in 2010.[20] It identified several key points:

- Adequate vitamin D is essential in the prevention of osteoporosis.
- 20 µg (800 IU) is the lowest dose of vitamin D that has consistently been associated with reduced risk of fractures, especially for institutionalized older individuals.
- Vitamin D may reduce falls by improving muscle strength and functioning of the lower extremeties. However, studies have shown conflicting results, possibly due to differences in the populations studied, the dose used, and the method of determining data on falls.
- Dietary intake of vitamin D has a minimal influence on vitamin D status. Most circulating vitamin D is synthesized from sun exposure.
- There is no convincing evidence that there are any adverse effects of daily doses of vitamin D up to 125 µg (5000 IU). However, individuals taking vitamin D supplements at this level should be monitored.

Osteoporosis Canada's conclusion was that more research is needed to identify the minimum daily required dose of vitamin D and the tolerable upper limit given the inconclusive nature of the evidence. However, based on its review, it recommended an intake of 25 µg (1000 IU) as a minimum daily dose for Canadian adults.

There are valid concerns about increasing vitamin D recommendations. Recall that vitamin D is fat soluble, so the body readily stores it. Thus, excess amounts can build up in adipose and other tissues. Increasing recommendations could therefore increase the population's risk for vitamin D toxicity and its damaging side effects, such as hypercalcemia, increased bone loss, kidney stones, and calcification of other soft tissues such as the heart and liver. Although some evidence suggests that people can tolerate up to 250 µg (10 000 IU) per day of vitamin D, recent studies have indicated kidney stones with modest supplementation of 10 µg (400 IU) vitamin D_3 and 1000 mg calcium daily.[66] Also, smokers with relatively high circulating levels of vitamin D have a threefold increased risk of pancreatic cancer compared to smokers with lower levels.[67]

Using the Evidence

1. Now that you've read about what is presently known about vitamin D and its role in our health, do you believe that the new DRIs are appropriate, or should the RDA for adults be increased to 25 μg daily as recommended by Osteoporosis Canada?

2. Do you think you would benefit from vitamin D supplementation? Why or why not?

3. If you think you need to improve your vitamin D status, what method(s) would you choose?

4. Would you prefer to try to increase your circulating levels of vitamin D through natural foods, fortified foods, supplements, or increased sun exposure?

5. What are your reasons for your preference(s)?

13

Nutrients Involved in Blood Health and Immunity

Test Yourself | True or False?

1. Iron deficiency is the most common nutrient deficiency in the world.
   T *or* F

2. To reduce their risk of having a baby with a serious central nervous system defect, women should begin taking folate supplements when they are planning a pregnancy or as soon as they learn they are pregnant.
   T *or* F

3. People consuming a vegan diet are at greater risk for micronutrient deficiencies than are people who eat foods of animal origin. T *or* F

4. *Anemia* is the clinical term for iron deficiency. T *or* F

5. Fever, vomiting, and diarrhea all play a role in protecting the body from infectious disease. T *or* F

Test Yourself answers are located in the Chapter Review.

Chapter Objectives | *After reading this chapter, you will be able to:*

1. Describe the four components of blood, *p. 446*.
2. Discuss the role that iron plays in oxygen transport, *pp. 447–448*.
3. Discuss the functions of zinc and copper and the contributions of these minerals to blood health, *pp. 456–461*.
4. Compare and contrast the functions of two B-vitamins associated with blood health, *pp. 463–468*.
5. Describe the association of folate and vitamin B$_{12}$ with vascular disease, *pp. 469–470*.
6. Distinguish between microcytic anemia, pernicious anemia, and macrocytic anemia, *pp. 470–471*.
7. Discuss common malfunctions of the immune system, *p. 474*.
8. Describe how nutrient deficiencies affect immunity, *pp. 474–476*.

D r. Leslie Bernstein looked in astonishment at the 80-year-old man in his office. A leading gastroenterologist and professor of medicine at Albert Einstein College of Medicine in New York City, he had admired Pop Katz for years as one of his most healthy patients, a strict vegetarian and athlete who just weeks before had been going on 5 Km runs as if he were 40 years younger. Now, he could barely stand. He was confused, cried easily, was wandering away from the house partially clothed, and had lost control of his bladder. Tests showed that he was not suffering from Alzheimer's disease, had not had a stroke, did not have a tumour or infection, and had no evidence of exposure to pesticides, metals, drugs, or other toxins. Blood tests were normal except for one important clue: his red blood cells were slightly enlarged. Bernstein consulted with a neurologist, who diagnosed "rapidly progressive dementia of unknown origin."

Bernstein was unconvinced: "In a matter of weeks, a man who hadn't been sick for eighty years suddenly became demented. . . . 'Holy smoke!,' I thought, 'I'm an idiot! The man's been a vegetarian for thirty-eight years. No meat. No fish. No eggs. No milk. He hasn't had any animal protein for decades. He has to be vitamin B_{12} deficient!'"[1]

Bernstein immediately tested Katz's blood, then gave him an injection of vitamin B_{12}. The blood test confirmed Bernstein's hunch: the level of vitamin B_{12} in Katz's blood was too low to measure. The morning after his injection, Katz could sit up without help. Within a week of continuing treatment, he could read, play card games, and hold his own in conversations. Unfortunately, the delay in diagnosis left some permanent neurologic damage, including alterations in his personality and an inability to concentrate. Bernstein notes, "A diet free of animal protein can be healthy and safe, but it should be supplemented periodically with vitamin B_{12} by mouth or by injection."[1]

It was not until 1906, when English biochemist F. G. Hopkins discovered what he called *accessory factors,* that scientists began to appreciate the many critical roles of micronutrients in maintaining human health. Vitamin B_{12}, for instance, was not even isolated until 1948! In Chapters 8 through 12 we explored several key roles of vitamins and minerals, including energy metabolism, the regulation of fluids and nerve-impulse transmission, protection against the damage caused by oxidation, and maintenance of healthy bones. In this chapter, we conclude our exploration of the micronutrients with a discussion of two final roles: their contributions to the formation and maintenance of blood and to the production of the cells and chemicals of the immune system.

What Is the Role of Blood in Maintaining Health?

Blood transports to body cells virtually all the components necessary for life. No matter how much carbohydrate, fat, and protein we eat, we could not survive without healthy blood to transport these nutrients, and the oxygen to metabolize them, to our cells. In addition to transporting nutrients and oxygen, blood removes the waste products generated from metabolism so that they can be properly excreted. Our health and our ability to perform daily activities are compromised if the quantity and quality of our blood is diminished.

Blood is actually a tissue, the only fluid tissue in the body. It is composed of four components (**Figure 13.1**). **Erythrocytes**, or red blood cells, are the cells that transport oxygen. **Leukocytes**, or white blood cells, are the key to our immune function and protect us from infection and illness. **Platelets** are cell fragments that assist in the formation of blood clots and help stop bleeding. **Plasma** is the fluid portion of the blood, and it is needed to maintain adequate blood volume so that blood can flow easily throughout the body.

Certain micronutrients play important roles in the maintenance of blood health through their actions as coenzymes and cofactors and as regulators of oxygen transport. These nutrients are discussed in detail in the following section.

A Profile of Nutrients That Maintain Healthy Blood

The nutrients recognized as playing a critical role in maintaining blood health include iron, zinc, copper, vitamin K, folate, and vitamin B_{12} (Table 13.1). Because blood is a tissue,

erythrocytes Red blood cells; they transport oxygen in the blood.

leukocytes White blood cells; they protect the body from infection and illness.

platelets Cell fragments that assist in the formation of blood clots and help stop bleeding.

plasma The fluid portion of the blood; it is needed to maintain adequate blood volume so that the blood can flow easily throughout the body.

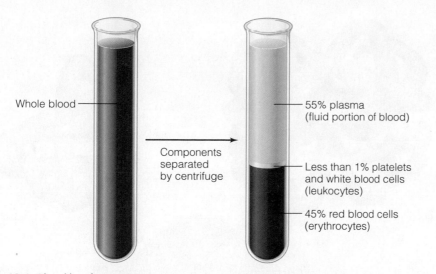

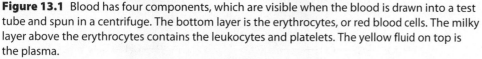

Whole blood

55% plasma (fluid portion of blood)

Components separated by centrifuge

Less than 1% platelets and white blood cells (leukocytes)

45% red blood cells (erythrocytes)

Figure 13.1 Blood has four components, which are visible when the blood is drawn into a test tube and spun in a centrifuge. The bottom layer is the erythrocytes, or red blood cells. The milky layer above the erythrocytes contains the leukocytes and platelets. The yellow fluid on top is the plasma.

Table 13.1 Overview of Nutrients Essential to Blood Health

To see the full profile of nutrients essential to blood health, turn to Chapter 8.

Nutrient	Recommended Intake (RDA or AI and UL)
Iron	RDA: Women aged 19 to 50 years = 18 mg/day Men aged 19 to 50 years = 8 mg/day UL = 45 mg/day
Zinc	RDA: Women aged 19 to 50 years = 8 mg/day Men aged 19 to 50 years = 11 mg/day UL = 40 mg/day
Copper	RDA for all people 19–50 years = 900 µg/day UL = 10 000 µg/day
Vitamin K	AI: Women 19–50 years = 90 µg/day Men 19–50 years = 120 µg/day UL = none determined
Folate (folic acid)	RDA for all people 19–50 years = 400 µg/day UL = 1000 µg/day
Vitamin B$_{12}$ (cyanocobalamin)	RDA for all people 19–50 years = 2.4 µg/day UL = not determined (ND)

adequate protein intake is also important for good blood health (see Chapter 6 for more on protein and its requirements).

Iron

Iron (Fe) is a trace mineral found in very small amounts in the body. Despite our relatively small need for iron, the World Health Organization lists iron deficiency as the most common nutrient deficiency in the world, including industrialized countries.[2] Iron is a unique mineral with a positive charge that can easily give up and/or gain an electron, thereby changing its state from ferrous iron (Fe^{+2}) to ferric iron (Fe^{+3}) and back again. Although other forms of iron exist, ferrous and ferric iron are the two most common forms in our diet. Iron also binds easily to negatively charged elements such as oxygen, nitrogen, and sulphur, a capacity that is important for the various functions iron plays in the body. We will discuss more about the various oxidative states of iron shortly.

Functions of Iron

Iron is a component of numerous proteins in the body, including enzymes and other proteins involved in energy production and both hemoglobin and myoglobin, the proteins involved in the transport and metabolism of oxygen. **Hemoglobin** is the oxygen-carrying protein found in the erythrocytes. It transports oxygen to tissues and accounts for almost two-thirds of all of the body's iron. Every day, within the bone marrow, the body produces approximately 200 billion erythrocytes that require more than 24 mg of iron.[3] Thus, it is easy to see that hemoglobin synthesis for the formation of red blood cells is a primary factor in iron homeostasis. **Myoglobin**, another oxygen-carrying protein that is similar to hemoglobin, transports and stores oxygen within the muscles, accounting for approximately 10% of total iron in the body.

We cannot survive for more than a few minutes without oxygen; thus, hemoglobin's ability to transport oxygen throughout the body is absolutely critical to life. To carry oxygen, hemoglobin depends on the iron in its **heme** groups. As shown in **Figure 13.2**, the hemoglobin molecule consists of four polypeptide chains studded with four iron-containing heme groups. Iron is able to bind with and release oxygen easily. It does this by transferring electrons to and from the other atoms as it moves between various oxidation states. In the bloodstream, iron acts as a shuttle, picking up oxygen from the

hemoglobin The oxygen-carrying protein found in red blood cells; almost two-thirds of all of the iron in the body is found in hemoglobin.

myoglobin An iron-containing protein similar to hemoglobin except that it is found in muscle cells.

heme The iron-containing molecule found in hemoglobin.

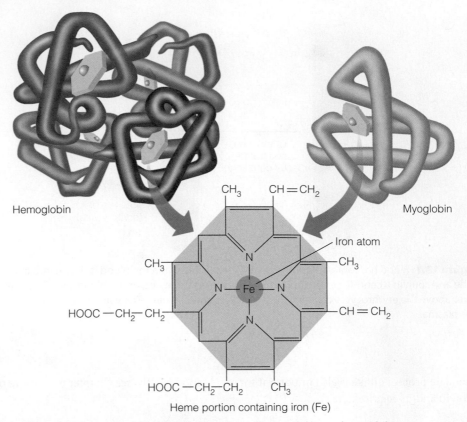

Figure 13.2 Iron is contained in the heme portion of hemoglobin and myoglobin.
Data from: Hemoglobin illustration, Irving Geis. Rights owned by Howard Hughes Medical Institute. Not to be reproduced without permission.

environment, binding it during its transport in the bloodstream, and then dropping it off again in our tissues.

As just noted, iron is also important in energy metabolism. It is a component of the cytochromes, electron carriers within the metabolic pathways that result in the production of energy from carbohydrates, fats, and protein. Cytochromes contain heme and thus require iron. If iron is not available to form them, the production of energy is limited, especially during times of high energy demand, such as during physical activity. Iron is also involved in some of the key enzymes in the tricarboxylic acid (TCA) cycle and for enzymes required in amino acid and lipid metabolism. As presented in Chapter 11, iron is a part of the antioxidant enzyme system that assists in fighting free radicals. Interestingly, excess iron can also act as a prooxidant and promote the production of free radicals. Finally, iron is necessary for enzymes involved in DNA synthesis and plays an important role in cognitive development and immune health (discussed later in this chapter).[3, 4]

How Does the Body Regulate Iron Homeostasis?

As mentioned earlier, the body contains relatively little iron; men have less than 4 g of iron in their bodies, and women have just over 2 g. Iron is necessary for life, yet too much iron is toxic; therefore, the body maintains iron homeostasis primarily through regulating iron digestion, absorption, transport, storage, and excretion. **Figure 13.3** provides an overview of iron digestion, absorption, and transport.

Iron Digestion and Absorption The body's ability to digest and absorb dietary iron is influenced by a number of factors. The most important of these are the individual's iron status, the level of dietary iron consumption, the type of iron present in the foods consumed, the amount of stomach acid present to digest the foods, and the presence of dietary factors that can either enhance or inhibit the absorption of iron.

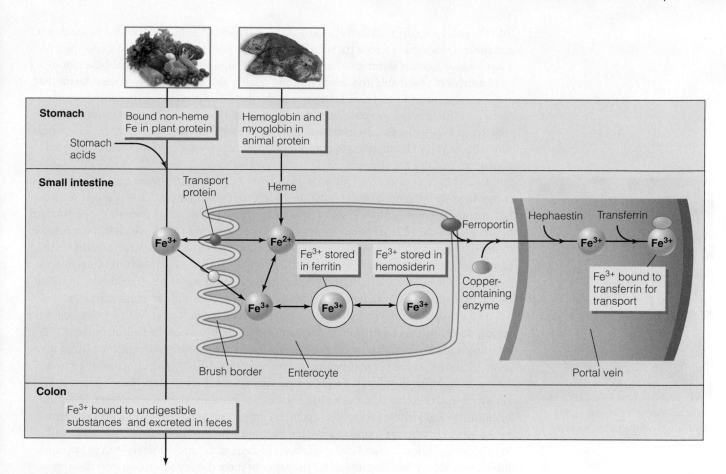

Figure 13.3 Overview of iron digestion, absorption, and transport.
Data adapted from: BLAKE, JOAN SALGE; MUNOZ, KATHY D.; VOLPE, STELLA, NUTRITION: FROM SCIENCE TO YOU, 1st Ed., © 2010. Reprinted and Electronically reproduced by permission of Pearson Education, Inc., Upper Saddle River, New Jersey.

Typically, the amount of iron absorbed from the diet is low, from 14% to 18% depending on the way iron absorption is measured; however, if iron status is poor, absorption can increase to as high as 40%.[3, 4] Thus, people with poor iron status, such as those with iron deficiency, pregnant women, or people who have recently experienced blood loss (including menstruation), generally have the highest iron absorption rates. The typical Western diet of 2000 kcal/day would contain about 12 mg of iron. In an individual with good iron status, only about 1.9 mg of this would be absorbed. However, in an individual with poor iron status, a maximum of 4.8 mg would be absorbed. By altering absorption rate, the body can improve iron status without dramatic increases in dietary iron intake.

Similarly, the total amount of iron consumed in the diet influences an individual's iron absorption rate. People who consume low levels of dietary iron absorb more iron from their foods than those with higher dietary iron intakes. If the gut mucosal cells have a high iron pool, less iron is absorbed from the next meal.

The type of iron in foods is a major factor influencing iron absorption. There are two types:

- Heme iron is a part of hemoglobin and myoglobin and is found only in animal-based foods such as meat, fish, and poultry.
- Non-heme iron is the form of iron that is not a part of hemoglobin or myoglobin. It is found in both plant-based and animal-based foods.

Heme iron is more absorbable than non-heme iron. Once heme, which contains the ferrous form (Fe^{2+}) of iron, is released from either hemoglobin or myoglobin in the small intestine, it is rapidly bound to a specific receptor on the intestinal lumen and is taken into the enterocyte by endocytosis. Within the enterocyte, the heme group is broken down, and the iron released becomes part of a common iron pool within the cell. Because the iron in animal-based foods is about 40% heme iron and 60% non-heme iron, animal-based foods are good sources of absorbable iron. Meat, fish, and poultry also contain a special **meat factor** that enhances the absorption of non-heme iron in the diet.[3] The protein component of muscle tissue binds to iron to form complexes that are more bioavailable. The meat factor is most effective in improving the absorption of iron from cereals and legumes, likely because it prevents the iron from binding to phytates and phenolic compounds, which form compounds that are unavailable for absorption.[5]

In contrast, all of the iron found in plant-based foods is non-heme iron. Its absorption is significantly influenced by the individual's level of stomach acid. During digestion, non-heme iron–containing foods enter the stomach, where gastric juices containing pepsin and hydrochloric acid reduce the ferric iron (Fe^{3+}) to ferrous iron (Fe^{2+}), which is more soluble in the alkaline environment (higher pH) of the small intestine. Thus, adequate amounts of stomach acid are necessary for iron absorption. People with low levels of stomach acid, including many older adults, have a decreased ability to absorb iron. In addition, individuals who use medications that reduce stomach acid may reduce their iron absorption.

Once iron enters the duodenum, it is taken up by the enterocytes, with ferrous iron more rapidly absorbed than ferric iron. In addition, the solubility of non-heme iron in the small intestine is greatly modified by the presence of enhancing and inhibitory factors within the meal. Vitamin C enhances non-heme absorption from the gut by reducing dietary ferric to ferrous iron, which then forms a soluble iron–ascorbic acid complex in the stomach.[4] Conversely, iron absorption is impaired by phytates, polyphenols, vegetable proteins, fibre, and calcium. Typically, these substances bind to the ferric iron and form complexes that cannot be digested. Phytates are found in legumes, rice, and whole grains; polyphenols are found in oregano, red wine, tea, and coffee. Soybean protein, fibre, and minerals such as calcium inhibit iron absorption. Because of the influence of these dietary factors on iron absorption, it is estimated that the bioavailability of iron from a vegan diet is approximately 10%, compared with the 14% to 18% absorption of the typical Western diet.

To optimize absorption of the non-heme iron in plant foods, consume these foods either with foods rich in heme iron or in combination with foods high in vitamin C. For instance, eating meat with beans or vegetables enhances the absorption of the non-heme iron found in the beans and vegetables. Drinking a glass of orange juice with breakfast cereal will increase the absorption of the non-heme iron in the cereal. Avoid taking zinc or calcium supplements or drinking milk when eating iron-rich foods, as iron absorption will be impaired.

Finally, cooking foods in cast-iron pans will significantly increase the iron content of any meal. That's because the iron in the pan is released and combines with food during the cooking process.

Iron Transport
Regardless of the form, iron taken into the enterocytes becomes part of the total iron pool. From this pool the iron can be stored within the enterocytes or it can be transported across the membrane of the enterocytes by **ferroportin** into the interstitial fluid, from which it can enter the circulation. Ferroportin is an iron transporter that helps regulate intestinal iron absorption and release.[6] Iron crossing into the interstitial fluid is in the ferrous form (Fe^{2+}) but it is quickly converted to ferric iron (Fe^{3+}) by either **hephaestin** in the intestinal basal cell membrane (see Figure 13.3) or **ceruloplasmin** in the blood, two copper-containing plasma proteins capable of oxidizing iron. This Fe^{3+} is rapidly bound to **transferrin**, the primary iron-transport protein in the blood, which transports the Fe^{3+} to cells of the body. Transferrin receptors on the cells increase and decrease in number depending on the cells' need for iron. In this way, cells can regulate the amount of iron they take in from the blood.

Iron Storage
The body is capable of storing small amounts of iron in two storage forms: **ferritin** and **hemosiderin**. These storage forms of iron provide us with iron when

Cooking foods in cast-iron pans significantly increases their iron content.

meat factor A special factor found in meat, fish, and poultry that enhances the absorption of non-heme iron.

ferroportin An iron transporter that helps regulate intestinal iron absorption and the release of iron from the enterocyte into the general circulation.

hephaestin A copper-containing protein that oxidizes Fe^{2+} to Fe^{3+} once iron is transported across the basolateral membrane by ferroportin.

ceruloplasmin A copper-containing protein that transports copper in the body. It also plays a role in oxidizing ferric to ferrous iron (Fe^{2+} to Fe^{3+}).

transferrin The transport protein for iron.

ferritin A storage form of iron found primarily in the intestinal mucosa, spleen, bone marrow, and liver.

hemosiderin A storage form of iron found primarily in the intestinal mucosa, spleen, bone marrow, and liver.

our diets are inadequate or when our needs are high. Both ferritin and hemosiderin can be mobilized if the body needs iron.

Figure 13.3 shows iron storage in the enterocytes as ferritin or hemosiderin. Other common areas of iron storage are the liver, bone marrow, and spleen. Ferritin is the normal storage form, whereas hemosiderin storage occurs predominately in conditions of iron overload. However, if an iron overload occurs, and excess iron is stored as hemosiderin in the heart and liver, organ damage can occur.

The amount of iron stored can vary dramatically between men and women, with women at greater risk for having low iron stores (from 300 to 1000 mg). Average iron stores for men are estimated to be 500 to 1500 mg. Women of childbearing age have one of the highest rates of iron deficiency, which is attributed to increased iron losses in menstrual blood, poor intakes of iron, and the additional iron requirements that accompany pregnancy. The iron "cost" of pregnancy is high; thus, a woman of childbearing age should have good iron stores prior to pregnancy and consume iron-rich foods during pregnancy. Iron supplements are routinely prescribed during the last two trimesters to ensure that there is adequate iron for the woman and her developing fetus. The iron needs of pregnancy are covered in more detail in Chapter 16.

Regulation of Total Body Iron   The body regulates iron balance and homeostasis through three mechanisms:

- *Iron absorption.* As discussed earlier, the change in iron absorption rate is based on the amount of iron consumed, the amount needed by the body, and the dietary factors that affect absorption.
- *Iron losses.* One of the major routes of iron loss is through the turnover of the gut enterocytes. Every three to six days, the gut cells are shed and lost into the lumen of the intestine. In this way, the iron stored as ferritin within the enterocytes is returned to the lumen, from which it is lost in the feces. The regulation of iron absorption in this way dramatically reduces the possibility of too much iron entering the system, regardless of the iron source. Iron can also be lost in blood (menses, blood donations, injury), sweat, semen, and passively from cells that are shed from the skin and urinary tract. Depending on body size, iron losses range from 0.75 to 1 mg of iron/day in non-menstruating women and in men.[4] Active individuals can also have increased iron losses due to iron lost in urine, sweat, and increased red blood cell turnover.[4] Iron deficiency has been shown to be prevalent in 29% to 36% and 4% to 6% of recreationally active women and men, respectively.[7]
- *Storage and recycling of iron.* Stored iron gives the body access to iron to maintain health when intakes of dietary iron are low or losses are great. Conversely, once iron balance has been restored, the body will gradually increase the amount of iron stored so that reserves are again available in times of need. The body is also efficient at recycling iron already within the system. The majority of the body's iron is bound to hemoglobin within the red blood cells, which have a life of 120 days. To prevent the body from losing this valuable source of iron, as old red cells are broken down, the iron is recycled and returned to the body's iron pool. The iron supplied through recycling is approximately 20 times greater than the amount of iron absorbed from the diet.[6] Thus, the ability of the body to recycle iron is extremely important in maintaining iron homeostasis.

Athletes may have an increased need for iron.

How Much Iron Should We Consume?

In determining the RDA for iron, researchers took into account the bioavailability of iron from food and absorption rates.[4, 8]

Recommended Dietary Intakes for Iron   The RDA for iron for men aged 19 years and older is 8 mg/day. The RDA for iron for women aged 19 to 50 years is 18 mg/day and decreases to 8 mg/day for women 51 years of age and older. The higher iron requirement

Table 13.2 Special Circumstances Affecting Iron Status

Circumstances That Improve Iron Status	Circumstances That Diminish Iron Status
Use of oral contraceptives—reduces menstrual blood loss in women.	**Use of hormone replacement therapy**—can cause uterine bleeding.
Breastfeeding—delays resumption of menstruation in new mothers and thereby reduces blood loss. It is therefore an important health measure, especially in developing nations.	**Eating a vegetarian diet**—reduces or eliminates sources of heme iron.
Consumption of iron-containing foods and supplements	**Intestinal parasite infection**—causes intestinal bleeding. Iron-deficiency anemia is common in people with intestinal parasite infection.
	Blood donation—reduces iron stores; people who donate frequently, particularly premenopausal women, may require iron supplementation.
	Intense endurance exercise training—appears to increase the risk for poor iron status because of many factors, including inflammation, suboptimal iron intake, and increased iron loss due to rupture of red blood cells and increased fecal losses.

Data from: Institute of Medicine, Food and Nutrition Board. 2000. *Dietary Reference Intakes for Vitamin A, Vitamin K, Arsenic, Boron, Chromium, Copper, Iodine, Iron, Manganese, Molybdenum, Nickel, Silicon, Vanadium, and Zinc*. Washington, DC: National Academies Press. © 2000 by the National Academy of Sciences.

for younger women is due to the excess iron and blood lost during menstruation. Because of the decreased bioavailability of iron from vegetarian diets, the recommended iron intake for vegetarians is 1.8 times that of non-vegetarians.[9] Pregnancy is a time of very high iron needs, and the RDA for pregnant women is 27 mg/day. The UL for iron for adults aged 19 and older is 45 mg/day. Although it is difficult to get too much iron from whole foods, it is easy to get high doses of iron from supplements and/or the use of highly fortified processed foods such as meal-replacement drinks, energy bars, and protein powders. Special circumstances that significantly affect iron status and may increase requirements are identified in Table 13.2.

Good Food Sources of Iron   Good food sources of heme iron include meats, poultry, and fish (**Figure 13.4**). Clams, oysters, and beef liver are particularly good sources of iron. Many breakfast cereals and breads are enriched or fortified with iron; although this iron is the non-heme type and less absorbable, it is still significant because these foods are a major part of the Western diet. Some vegetables and legumes are also good sources of iron, and the absorption of their non-heme iron can be enhanced by eating them with animal foods that contain the meat factor and heme iron or with vitamin C–rich foods. People who avoid animal products need to pay special attention to their diet to ensure adequate iron intake, because heme iron sources are eliminated.

What Happens If We Consume Too Much Iron?

According to a survey of five Canadian Poison Control Centres, iron is one of the top 10 products covered by the Food and Drugs Act that causes the largest number of calls for poisonings in children under the age of five.[10] It is important for parents to take the same precautions with dietary supplements as they would with other drugs, keeping them in a locked cabinet or well out of reach of children. Symptoms of iron toxicity include nausea, vomiting, diarrhea, dizziness, confusion, and rapid heart beat. If iron toxicity is not treated quickly, significant damage to the heart, central nervous system, liver, and kidneys can result in death.

Many adults who take iron supplements, even at prescribed doses, commonly experience constipation and gastrointestinal distress.[4] High doses of iron supplements can also cause nausea, vomiting, and diarrhea. Taking iron supplements with food can reduce these adverse effects in most, but not all, people.

As mentioned in Chapter 11, some individuals suffer from a hereditary disorder called hemochromatosis. This disorder affects between 1 in 200 and 1 in 400 individuals of northern European descent.[11] Hemochromatosis is characterized by excessive absorption of dietary iron and altered iron storage. In this disease, the transport of iron from the enterocytes into the circulation is not regulated appropriately and iron transport continues even when it is not needed.[6] Because the body has no homeostatic mechanism for eliminating

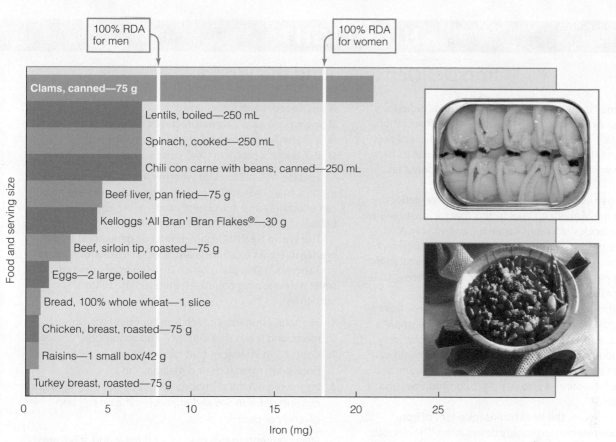

Figure 13.4 Common food sources of iron. The RDA for iron is 8 mg/day for men and 18 mg/day for women aged 19 to 50 years.
Data from: The Canadian Nutrient File. Health Canada, 2012. Reproduced with the permission of the Minister of Health, 2012.

high amounts of iron from the system, iron accumulates in body tissues over many years, causing organ damage and other disease. Treatment includes reducing dietary intake of iron, avoiding high intakes of vitamin C, and blood removal, a process similar to the donation of blood, except the blood is not reused.

What Happens If We Don't Consume Enough Iron?

Iron deficiency is the most common nutrient deficiency in the world and can have a number of health consequences that will be discussed here. People at particularly high risk for iron deficiency include infants and young children, adolescent girls, premenopausal women, and pregnant women. In Canada, 16% to 19% of women aged 19 to 50 have been found to have iron intakes from food intake alone that are below the EAR.[12] However, there is a low prevalence of inadequate intake among Canadian children (ages 1 to 8) with fewer than 5% having intakes below the EAR.[13] Refer to the Highlight box to learn more about the impact of iron deficiency on people around the world.

Many Factors Contribute to Iron Deficiency For some individuals, iron deficiency is simply due to poor dietary intakes of iron. Other factors can include high iron losses in blood and sweat, diets high in fibre or phytates that bind iron, low stomach acid, or poor iron absorption due to poor gut health or the consumption of dietary supplements containing high levels of minerals such as calcium that compete with iron-absorption binding sites. Significant blood losses through blood donations, surgery, or heavy menstrual periods can contribute to poor iron status. For example, the typical menstruating female loses approximately 14 mg of iron per menstrual cycle.[4] Thus, the causes of iron deficiency and/or depletion can be numerous and may involve a number of issues that need to be addressed before iron status can be improved.

HIGHLIGHT

Iron Deficiency Around the World

Iron deficiency is the most common nutritional deficiency in the world. According to the World Health Organization, approximately 4 to 5 billion people, or 66% to 80% of the world's population, are iron deficient.[14] Because of its high prevalence worldwide, iron deficiency is considered an epidemic.

As you have learned in this chapter, severe iron deficiency results in a type of anemia. Other factors that can cause anemia include deficiencies of folate, vitamin B$_{12}$, and vitamin A, as well as diseases that cause inflammation and infections such as hookworm and malarial parasites. In fact, it is estimated that 2 billion people worldwide suffer from worm infections, while 300 to 500 million people suffer from malaria.

Those who are particularly susceptible to iron deficiency include people living in developing countries, pregnant women, and young children. But iron deficiency not only hurts individuals. Because it results in increased healthcare needs, premature death, resultant family breakdown, and lost work productivity, it also damages communities and entire nations.

Among children, the health consequences of iron-deficiency anemia are particularly devastating. They include:

- Premature birth
- Low birth weight
- Increased risk of infections
- Increased risk of premature death
- Impaired cognitive and physical development
- Behavioural problems and poor school performance

To date, it is still unclear whether iron supplementation in children already suffering from iron-deficiency anemia can effectively and consistently reverse the cognitive and behavioural damage that has occurred.[15]

The World Health Organization has developed a comprehensive plan to address all aspects of iron deficiency and anemia.[14] This plan, which is being implemented in several developing countries, involves the following initiatives:

1. Increasing iron intake with iron supplements, iron-rich foods, and foods that enhance iron absorption;
2. Controlling infections that cause anemia, including hookworm infections and malaria; and
3. Improving overall nutritional status by controlling major nutrient deficiencies and improving the quality and diversity of people's diets.

By implementing this plan around the world, it is hoped that the devastating effects of iron deficiency can be reduced and potentially even eliminated.

Iron Deficiency Progresses Through Three Stages   As shown in **Figure 13.5**, **stage I** of iron deficiency is called **iron depletion**.[16] It is caused by a decrease in iron *stores,* resulting in reduced levels of circulating ferritin in the blood. As discussed earlier, ferritin is one form of stored iron. Small amounts of ferritin circulate in the blood, and these concentrations are highly correlated with iron stores.

During iron depletion, there are generally no physical symptoms because hemoglobin levels are not yet affected. However, when iron stores are low, the amount of iron available to mitochondrial proteins and enzymes appears to be depleted. This reduces the individual's ability to produce energy during periods of high demand. For example, research has shown that when sedentary women with poor ferritin levels participated in an exercise-training program, they did not experience the same improvements in fitness compared with women who had adequate ferritin levels.[17]

The second stage of iron deficiency causes a decrease in the *transport* of iron and is called **iron-deficiency erythropoiesis (stage II)**. This stage is manifested by a reduction in the saturation of transferrin with iron. Transferrin, the transport protein for iron, has the ability to bind two iron molecules and transport them to the cells of the body. During this stage, the iron binding sites on transferrin are left empty, because there is no iron available for binding. This results in transferrin having an increased ability to bind iron, which is called *total iron binding capacity (TIBC)*. Overall, then, individuals with iron-deficiency erythropoiesis will have low serum ferritin and iron concentrations, a low level of iron saturation, and a high TIBC. The production of heme and the ability to make new red

iron depletion (stage I) The first phase of iron deficiency characterized by a decrease in stored iron, which results in a decrease in blood ferritin levels.

iron-deficiency erythropoiesis (stage II) The second stage of iron deficiency, which causes a decrease in the transport of iron and leads to a decline in the ability to produce heme and make new red blood cells.

blood cells (for example, erythropoiesis) starts to decline during this stage, leading to symptoms of reduced work capacity, because fewer red blood cells are being made.

During the third and final stage of iron deficiency, **iron-deficiency anemia (stage III)** results. In iron-deficiency anemia, the production of normal, healthy red blood cells has decreased, the size of the red blood cells decreases as much as a third, and hemoglobin levels are inadequate. Thus, too few red blood cells are made, and those that are made cannot bind and transport oxygen adequately. Individuals with stage III iron-deficiency anemia will still have abnormal values for all the assessment parameters measured in stages I and II. The symptoms of iron-deficiency anemia are discussed in detail on page 470 under "Microcytic Anemias."

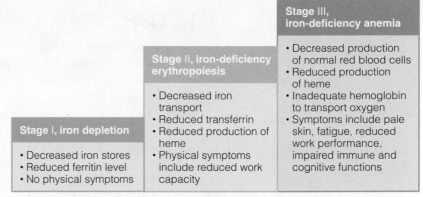

Stage III, iron-deficiency anemia
- Decreased production of normal red blood cells
- Reduced production of heme
- Inadequate hemoglobin to transport oxygen
- Symptoms include pale skin, fatigue, reduced work performance, impaired immune and cognitive functions

Stage II, iron-deficiency erythropoiesis
- Decreased iron transport
- Reduced transferrin
- Reduced production of heme
- Physical symptoms include reduced work capacity

Stage I, iron depletion
- Decreased iron stores
- Reduced ferritin level
- No physical symptoms

Figure 13.5 Iron deficiency passes through three stages. The first stage is identified by decreased iron stores and reduced ferritin levels. The second stage is identified by decreased iron transport and a reduction in transferrin. The final stage is iron-deficiency anemia, which is identified by decreased production of normal, healthy red blood cells and inadequate hemoglobin levels.

When Are Iron Supplements Needed?   Iron-deficiency anemia (stage III) cannot be treated by diet alone. Iron supplements are needed to restore deficient iron levels to normal within a reasonable time period. Supplemental iron is available in two forms: ferrous and ferric. Ferrous iron salts (ferrous fumarate, ferrous sulphate, and ferrous gluconate) are the most bioavailable forms of iron supplements. The amount of elemental iron (the amount of iron in a supplement that is available for absorption) is approximately 33% in ferrous fumarate supplements, 20% in ferrous sulphate supplements, and 12% in ferrous gluconate supplements.[18] If you are taking the ferric form of iron as a supplement, having a source of vitamin C along with the supplement will improve its absorption. Since the amount of iron absorbed decreases as the dose increases, the Centers for Disease Control in the United States recommends that most people take 50 mg to 60 mg of oral elemental iron twice daily for three months for the treatment of iron-deficiency anemia.[19] However, it is important to check with your physician as your individual needs may vary. Iron supplements are only available behind the counter in Canadian pharmacies because of the risk of adverse effects.

Liquid iron supplements are available for the treatment of iron-deficiency anemia in infants, however these solutions could stain a child's teeth. If they are used, it is recommended that they be administered using a dropper to the back of the mouth and that the mouth be rinsed with water after the dose is given.

Did You Know?

A team of researchers, led by Dr. Stanley Zlotkin at the Hospital for Sick Children in Toronto, have developed microencapsulated ferrous fumarate sprinkles with added vitamin C that can be added to any food to prevent iron-deficiency anemia in infants and young children. These sprinkles help alleviate the unpleasant side effects associated with liquid iron supplements and improve compliance with treatment.[20] In 2001, Dr. Zlotkin received the H. J. Heinz Humanitarian Award for his international efforts related to micronutrient deficiencies.

iron-deficiency anemia (stage III) A form of anemia that results from severe iron deficiency.

Recap

Iron is a trace mineral that, as part of the hemoglobin and myoglobin proteins, plays a major role in the transport of oxygen in the body. Iron is also a coenzyme in many metabolic pathways involved in energy production. The RDA for adult men aged 19 years and older is 8 mg/day. The RDA for adult women aged 19 to 50 years is 18 mg/day. Meat, fish, and poultry are good sources of heme iron, which is more absorbable than non-heme iron. Toxicity symptoms for iron range from nausea and vomiting to organ damage and potentially death. If left untreated, iron depletion can eventually lead to iron-deficiency anemia.

Zinc

Zinc (Zn^{2+}) is a positively charged trace mineral that, like iron, is found in very small amounts within the body (1.5–2.5 g). Most of the zinc found in the body is concentrated in the muscles and bone. However, in contrast with iron and other minerals, zinc has no dedicated storage sites within the body. Instead a small, exchangeable pool of zinc is found within the bone, liver, and blood.[16] Loss of zinc from this pool, if not replaced, leads to zinc deficiency.

Functions of Zinc

Zinc has multiple functions within nearly every body system. As a component of various enzymes, zinc helps to maintain the structural integrity of proteins and assists in the regulation of gene expression.[4] Without zinc, the body cannot grow, develop, or function properly. It is easiest to review the many roles of zinc within the body by dividing them into three categories: enzymatic, structural, and regulatory.

Enzymatic Functions It is estimated that more than one hundred different enzymes within the body require zinc for their functioning.[4] If zinc is not present, these enzymes cannot function properly and lose their activity. For example, we require zinc to metabolize alcohol, digest our food, help form bone, provide the body with energy through glycolysis, and synthesize the heme structure in hemoglobin. Thus, zinc, like iron, is required to make the oxygen-carrying component of hemoglobin. In this way, zinc contributes to the maintenance of blood health.

Structural Functions Zinc helps maintain the structural integrity and shape of proteins. If proteins lose their shape, they lose their function, much like a plastic spoon that has melted into a ball. Zinc helps stabilize the structure of certain DNA-binding proteins, called *zinc fingers*, which help regulate gene expression by facilitating the folding of proteins into biologically active molecules used in gene regulation.[16] Zinc fingers also help stabilize vitamin A receptors in the retina of the eye, thereby facilitating night vision. Other functions associated with zinc fingers include the sequencing of hormone receptors for vitamin D and thyroid hormone.

Zinc's ability to help maintain protein structures also includes maintaining the integrity of some enzymes. For example, zinc helps to maintain the integrity of copper–zinc superoxide dismutase, which is important in helping to prevent oxidative damage caused by free radicals. Zinc also helps to maintain the integrity of enzymes involved in the development and activation of certain immune cells (discussed on page 476). In fact, zinc has received so much attention for its contribution to immune system health that zinc lozenges have been formulated to fight the common cold. The Evidence-informed Decision Making feature at the end of this chapter explores the question of whether or not these lozenges are effective in combating the common cold.

Regulatory Functions   As a regulator of gene expression, zinc helps to turn genes "on" and "off," thus regulating the body functions these genes control. For example, in humans, if zinc is not available to activate certain genes related to cellular growth during the development of the fetus and after the child is born, growth is stunted. Zinc also plays a role in cell signalling. For example, zinc helps maintain blood glucose levels by interacting with insulin and influencing the way fat cells take up glucose. Zinc also helps regulate the activity of a number of other hormones, such as human growth hormone, sex hormones, and corticosteroids.[16]

A number of biological actions require zinc in all three of the functions just covered. The major example of this is in reproduction. Zinc is critical for cell replication and normal growth. In fact, zinc deficiency was discovered in the early 1960s when researchers were trying to determine the cause of severe growth retardation, anemia, and poorly developed testicles in a group of Middle Eastern men. These symptoms of zinc deficiency illustrate its critical role in normal growth and sexual maturation.

What Factors Alter Zinc Digestion, Absorption, and Balance?

Overall, zinc absorption is similar to that of iron, ranging from 10% to 35% of dietary zinc. People with poor zinc status absorb more zinc than individuals with optimal zinc status, and zinc absorption increases during times of growth, sexual development, and pregnancy. See **Figure 13.6** for an overview of zinc digestion, absorption, and transport.

Zinc is absorbed from the lumen of the intestine into the enterocytes through both active transport by carriers and simple diffusion, with the efficiency of absorption decreasing as the amount of zinc in the diet increases. Once inside the enterocytes, zinc can be released into the interstitial fluid (as discussed shortly) or bound to a protein called **metallothionein**, which prevents zinc from moving out of the enterocyte into the system. In this way, the body can regulate the amount of absorbed zinc that actually enters the total zinc pool of the body. When the enterocytes are sloughed off into the intestine, the zinc bound to metallothionein is lost in the feces. In this way, the body can maintain total zinc homeostasis.

metallothionein A zinc-containing protein within the enterocyte; it assists in the regulation of zinc homeostasis.

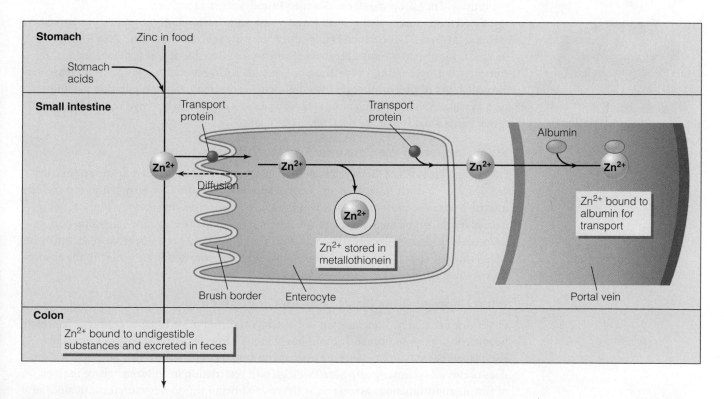

Figure 13.6 Overview of zinc digestion, absorption, and transport.
Data adapted from: BLAKE, JOAN SALGE; MUNOZ, KATHY D.; VOLPE, STELLA, NUTRITION: FROM SCIENCE TO YOU, 1st Ed., © 2010. Reprinted and Electronically reproduced by permission of Pearson Education, Inc., Upper Saddle River, New Jersey.

Several dietary factors influence zinc absorption. High non-heme iron intakes can inhibit zinc absorption, which is a primary concern with iron supplementation, particularly during pregnancy and lactation. (Iron supplements contain non-heme iron.) High intakes of heme iron, however, appear to have no effect on zinc absorption. Although calcium is known to inhibit zinc absorption in animals, this effect has not been demonstrated in humans. The phytates and fibre found in whole grains and beans strongly inhibit zinc absorption. In contrast, dietary protein enhances zinc absorption, with animal-based proteins increasing the absorption of zinc to a much greater extent than plant-based proteins. It's not surprising, then, that the primary cause of the zinc deficiency in the Middle Eastern men just mentioned was their low consumption of meat and high consumption of beans and unleavened breads (also called *flat breads*). In leavening bread, the baker adds yeast to the dough. This not only makes the bread rise but also helps reduce the phytate content of the bread.

How Is Zinc Transported in the Body?

Zinc is absorbed from the lumen of the intestine and moves into the enterocyte. It then crosses the basolateral enterocyte membrane via a process of active transport using both a zinc transporter and energy (ATP). Upon reaching the interstitial fluid, zinc is picked up by albumin, a transport protein in the plasma, and carried via the portal vein to the liver. Once in the liver, some of the zinc is repackaged and released back into the blood, bound to either albumin (about 60%) or other transport proteins (about 40%). The bound zinc can then be delivered to the cells, where it is taken up by energy-dependent carriers.

How Much Zinc Should We Consume?

As with iron, our need for zinc is relatively small, but our dietary intakes and level of absorption are variable. Absorption factors were considered when the RDA for zinc was set.[4] The RDA values for zinc for adult men and women aged 19 and older are 11 mg/day and 8 mg/day, respectively. The UL for zinc for adults aged 19 and older is 40 mg/day.

Good food sources of zinc include red meats, some seafood, whole grains, and enriched grains and cereals. The dark meat of poultry has a higher content of zinc than white meat. As zinc is significantly more absorbable from animal-based foods, zinc deficiency is a concern for people eating a vegetarian or vegan diet. However, it is possible to increase the bioavailability of zinc from vegetarian diets with appropriate food preparation techniques such as soaking and sprouting beans, grains, and seeds, and using leavened bread.[9] **Figure 13.7** shows various foods that are relatively high in zinc.

Zinc can be found in pork and beans.

What Happens If We Consume Too Much Zinc?

Eating high amounts of dietary zinc does not appear to lead to toxicity; however, toxicity can occur from consuming high amounts of supplemental zinc. Toxicity symptoms include intestinal pain and cramps, nausea, vomiting, loss of appetite, diarrhea, and headaches. Excessive zinc supplementation has also been shown to depress immune function and decrease high-density lipoprotein concentrations. High intakes of zinc (five to six times the RDA) can also reduce copper and iron status, as zinc absorption interferes with the absorption of these minerals.[4]

What Happens If We Don't Consume Enough Zinc?

Overt zinc deficiency is uncommon in Canada, occurring more often in countries in which people consume predominantly grain-based foods. However, 10% to 35% of Canadian adults have been found to consume inadequate amounts of zinc.[12] When zinc deficiency does occur, it is primarily associated with growth retardation in children, where the lack of zinc disrupts functions associated with growth hormone.[21] Other symptoms of zinc deficiency include diarrhea, delayed sexual maturation and impotence, eye and skin lesions, hair loss, and impaired appetite. As zinc is critical to a healthy immune system, zinc deficiency results in increased incidence of infections and illnesses.

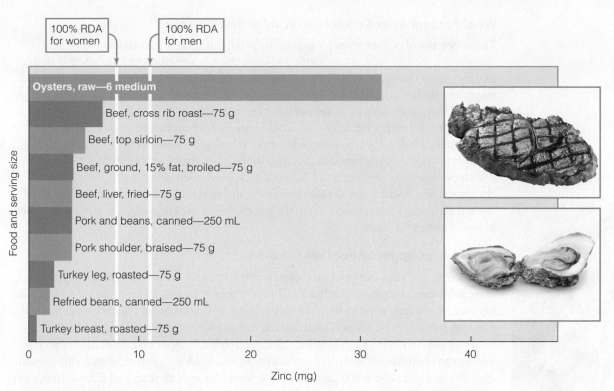

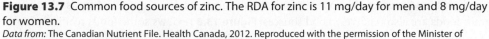

100% RDA for women

100% RDA for men

Oysters, raw—6 medium

Beef, cross rib roast—75 g

Beef, top sirloin—75 g

Beef, ground, 15% fat, broiled—75 g

Beef, liver, fried—75 g

Pork and beans, canned—250 mL

Pork shoulder, braised—75 g

Turkey leg, roasted—75 g

Refried beans, canned—250 mL

Turkey breast, roasted—75 g

Food and serving size

0   10   20   30   40

Zinc (mg)

Figure 13.7 Common food sources of zinc. The RDA for zinc is 11 mg/day for men and 8 mg/day for women.
Data from: The Canadian Nutrient File. Health Canada, 2012. Reproduced with the permission of the Minister of Health, 2012.

Because we do not have good assessment parameters for zinc, we have no way of recognizing poor zinc status until deficiency symptoms occur. In developed countries, those at greatest risk of zinc deficiencies are individuals with malabsorption syndromes and adults and children who eliminate high-zinc foods from their diet while consuming diets high in fibre. For example, recent research has shown that low-income Hispanic children who were in lower growth percentiles than predicted respond to zinc supplementation by growing closer to the predicted rate.[21]

Copper

Copper is a trace mineral that is required for a number of enzymes that have oxidative functions. Fortunately, copper is widely distributed in foods and deficiency is rare.

Functions of Copper

In the body, copper is primarily found as a component of ceruloplasmin, a protein that is critical for its transport. Indeed, an individual's copper status is typically assessed by measuring plasma levels of ceruloplasmin. As we mentioned in the discussion of iron, ceruloplasmin is important for the oxidation of ferrous to ferric iron ($Fe^{2+} \rightarrow Fe^{3+}$), which is necessary before iron can bind to transferrin and be transported in the plasma.[4] Because of ceruloplasmin's role in iron metabolism, it is also called ferroxidase I. When ceruloplasmin is inadequate, the transport of iron for heme formation is impaired and anemia can result. Because iron cannot be transported properly, iron accumulates in the tissues, causing symptoms similar to those described with the genetic disorder hemochromatosis (page 452).

Copper also functions as a cofactor in the metabolic pathways that produce energy, in the production of the connective tissues collagen and elastin, and as part of the superoxide dismutase enzyme system that fights the damage caused by free radicals. Copper is also necessary for the regulation of certain neurotransmitters, especially serotonin, important to brain function.

What Factors Alter Copper Absorption and Balance?

The major site of copper absorption is in the small intestine, with small amounts also absorbed in the stomach. As with zinc and iron, the amount of copper absorbed is related to the amount of copper in the diet, with absorption decreasing on high-copper diets and increasing on low-copper diets. Thus, regulation of copper absorption is one of the primary ways the body maintains good copper balance.

Copper is transported across the enterocytes by both carrier-mediated transport and simple diffusion.[21] Once absorbed, copper is bound to albumin (as with zinc), then transported in the portal blood to the liver. In the liver, about 60% to 95% of the copper is incorporated into ceruloplasmin, where it is then released into the plasma for general circulation and distribution to other tissues.[16] Copper is lost from the system in the feces when enterocytes are sloughed off into the lumen. When the copper in bile is not reabsorbed, it, too, is lost in the feces.

How Much Copper Should We Consume?

As with iron and zinc, our need for copper is small; but, our dietary intakes are variable and, as we have seen, absorption is influenced by a number of factors. People who eat a varied diet can easily meet their requirements for copper. High zinc intakes can reduce copper absorption and, subsequently, copper status. In fact, zinc supplementation is used as a treatment for a rare genetic disorder called Wilson disease, in which copper toxicity occurs. High iron intakes can also interfere with copper absorption. The RDA for copper for men and women aged 19 years and older is 900 μg/day. The UL for adults ages 19 years and older is 10 mg/day.

Good food sources of copper include organ meats, seafood, nuts, and seeds. Whole-grain foods are also relatively good sources. **Figure 13.8** reviews some foods relatively high in copper.

Lobster is a food that contains copper.

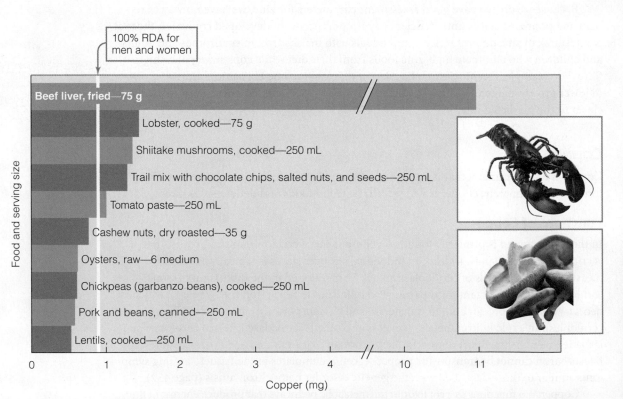

Figure 13.8 Common food sources of copper. The RDA for copper is 900 μg/day for men and women.
Data from: The Canadian Nutrient File. Health Canada, 2012. Reproduced with the permission of the Minister of Health, 2012.

What Happens If We Consume Too Much Copper?

The long-term effects of copper toxicity are not well studied in humans. However, accidental copper toxicity has occurred by drinking beverages that have come into contact with copper.[16] Toxicity symptoms include abdominal pain and cramps, nausea, diarrhea, and vomiting. Liver damage occurs in the extreme cases of copper toxicity that occur with Wilson disease and other health conditions associated with excessive copper levels. In Wilson disease, the copper accumulates in the liver because the liver cells cannot incorporate the copper into ceruloplasmin or eliminate it in the bile.[16]

What Happens If We Don't Consume Enough Copper?

Copper deficiency is rare but can occur in premature infants fed milk-based formulas and in adults fed prolonged formulated diets that are deficient in copper. Deficiency symptoms include anemia, reduced levels of white blood cells, and osteoporosis in infants and growing children, in whom the lack of copper contributes to bone demineralization.

Recap

Zinc is a trace mineral that is a part of almost one hundred enzymes that affect virtually every body system. It plays a critical role in hemoglobin synthesis, physical growth and sexual maturation, and immune function, and assists in fighting the oxidative damage caused by free radicals. For adults, the RDA for zinc is 8 mg/day. Copper is a component of ceruloplasmin, a protein that is critical for the proper transport of iron. This trace mineral is also a cofactor in the metabolic pathways that produce energy, in the production of the connective tissues collagen and elastin, and as part of the superoxide dismutase enzyme system that fights the damage caused by free radicals. For adults, the RDA for copper is 900 µg/day.

Vitamin K

Vitamin K is a fat-soluble vitamin important for both bone and blood health. Although a number of compounds exhibit vitamin K activity, the primary forms are phylloquinones and menaquinones. Phylloquinones are the form of vitamin K found in green plants and the primary form of vitamin K in our diet, whereas menaquinones are synthesized in the intestine from bacteria. The role of vitamin K in the synthesis of proteins involved in maintaining bone density was discussed in detail on pages 423–424 in Chapter 12. In this section, we focus primarily on its role in blood health.

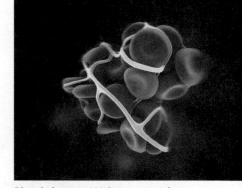

Blood clotting. Without enough vitamin K, the blood will not clot properly.

Functions of Vitamin K

Vitamin K acts as a coenzyme that assists in the synthesis of a number of proteins that are involved in the coagulation of blood, including *prothrombin* and the *procoagulants, factors VII, IX,* and *X.* Without adequate vitamin K, the blood does not clot properly: clotting time can be delayed or clotting may even fail to occur. The failure of the blood to clot can lead to increased bleeding from even minor wounds, as well as internal hemorrhaging.

What Factors Alter Vitamin K Absorption and Balance?

Vitamin K is not only found in food but also is synthesized in the intestine; thus, the amount of vitamin K needed from the diet will depend on intestinal health. Factors that reduce the ability of the gastrointestinal bacteria to produce vitamin K will also reduce our total vitamin K status.

Because vitamin K is a fat-soluble vitamin, it is absorbed into the enterocyte, incorporated into chylomicrons, and then released into the lymphatic system with other dietary fats and fat-soluble vitamins. Any factors, either dietary or intestinal, that disrupt fat absorption will also disrupt vitamin K absorption.

Vitamin K is found in all the circulating lipoproteins, and assessment of plasma phylloquinone is a good measure of recent vitamin K intake.[22] Although both forms of vitamin K are found in the liver, the phylloquinones are rapidly turned over and lost in the urine and bile. The liver does not store vitamin K as it does other fat-soluble vitamins.

How Much Vitamin K Should We Consume?

Our needs for vitamin K are relatively small, but intakes of this nutrient in Canada are thought to be highly variable because vitamin K is found in relatively few foods.[4, 23] A Canadian study found that a minimum of six days of diet records are needed to assess usual vitamin K intake in older adults.[24] Healthy intestinal bacteria produce vitamin K in the large intestine, providing us with an important non-dietary source. The AI for vitamin K for adults 19 years of age and older is 120 µg/day and 90 µg/day for men and women, respectively. There is no UL established for vitamin K at this time.[4]

In general, green, leafy vegetables are the major sources of vitamin K in our diets. Good sources include kale, spinach, broccoli, Brussels sprouts, and cabbage. Soybean and canola oils are also good sources. Refer to Figure 12.12 on page 424 for other common food sources of vitamin K.

What Happens If We Consume Too Much Vitamin K?

There are no known side effects associated with consuming large amounts of vitamin K from supplements or from food.[4] In the past, a synthetic form of vitamin K was used for therapeutic purposes and was shown to cause liver damage; this form is no longer used.

Blood thinning medications, such as warfarin, act by interfering with the conversion of vitamin K to its reduced form, which is needed for the regulation of blood coagulation. High vitamin K intakes can increase the effectiveness of warfarin and thus increase the risk for bleeding. Those using warfarin are advised to consume an adequate, but not excessive, intake of vitamin K and to tell their physician about any dietary changes (i.e., supplement use) so that adjustments to their warfarin dose can be made, if needed.[25]

What Happens If We Don't Consume Enough Vitamin K?

Vitamin K deficiency inhibits the blood's ability to clot, resulting in excessive bleeding and even severe hemorrhaging in some cases. Fortunately, vitamin K deficiency is rare in humans. However, little data exists on the prevalence of adequate vitamin K intake in Canada. One study found that the mean vitamin K intake of adults (aged 67 to 84 years) was 70 µg/day, suggesting that some Canadians may have inadequate intakes.[24] People with diseases that cause malabsorption of fat, such as celiac disease, Crohn's disease, and cystic fibrosis, can suffer secondarily from a deficiency of vitamin K. Newborns are typically given an injection of vitamin K at birth, as they lack the intestinal bacteria necessary to produce this nutrient.

As discussed in Chapter 12, the impact of vitamin K deficiency on bone health is controversial. Although a recent study found that low intakes of vitamin K were associated with a higher risk of bone fractures in women, there is not enough scientific evidence to indicate that vitamin K deficiency causes osteoporosis.[4, 26]

Green, leafy vegetables are a good source of vitamin K.

ReCaP

Vitamin K is a fat-soluble vitamin and coenzyme that is important for blood clotting and bone metabolism. Bacteria manufacture vitamin K in the large intestine. The AIs for adult men and adult women are 120 µg per day and 90 µg per day, respectively.

Folate

Folate is a water-soluble vitamin and one of the B-vitamins introduced in Chapter 9. The generic term *folate* is used for all the various forms of food folate that demonstrate biological activity. Folic acid (pteroylglutamate; see **Figure 13.9**) is the form of folate found in most supplements and used in the enrichment and fortification of foods. Folate was originally identified as a growth factor in green, leafy vegetables (foliage), and hence the name.[27]

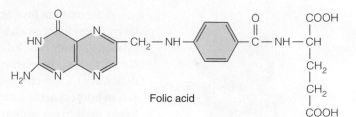

Folic acid

Figure 13.9 Structure of folic acid.

Functions of Folate and Folic Acid

Within the body, folate functions primarily in association with folate-dependent coenzymes that act as acceptors and donors of one-carbon units. These enzymes are critical for DNA synthesis, cell differentiation, and amino acid metabolism, which occur within the cytosol, nucleus, and mitochondria of the cells. Folate's role in assisting with cell division makes it a critical nutrient during the first few weeks of pregnancy when the combined sperm–egg cell multiplies rapidly to form the primitive tissues and structures of the human body. Without adequate folate, the embryo cannot develop properly. Folate is also essential in the synthesis of new cells, such as the red blood cells, and for the repair of damaged cells.

Folate, vitamin B_{12}, and vitamin B_6 are closely interrelated in some metabolic functions, including the metabolism of methionine, an essential amino acid. If these nutrients are not available, methionine cannot be metabolized completely, and a compound called **homocysteine** builds up in the body. High levels of homocysteine have been associated with an increased risk of cardiovascular disease and as a measure of poor intakes of folate, vitamin B_{12}, and vitamin B_6 in the diet. In this chapter, we will focus on the roles of vitamin B_{12} and folate in the metabolism of homocysteine.

What Factors Alter Folate Digestion, Absorption, and Balance?

Dietary folates are hydrolyzed by the brush border of the lumen and then absorbed into the enterocytes. This process is typically achieved through a carrier-mediated process, but some folates can cross the mucosal cell membrane by diffusion. Folates are then released from the enterocytes into the portal circulation, in which they are transported to the liver.[27]

The bioavailability of folate varies depending on its source. When folic acid is given as a supplement or in a fortified food, such as breakfast cereal, the amount absorbed is high—nearly 85% to 100%.[28] However, the bioavailability of food folate is less than 50%.[27] When large doses of folic acid are given as supplements, they are well absorbed; but, the body has no mechanism for retaining this folate, so it is easily lost in the urine.

Because dietary folate is only half as bioavailable as synthetic folic acid, the amount of food folate in the diet is expressed as dietary folate equivalents, or DFE. To calculate the amount of DFE, you need to know that 1 μg of food folate is equal to 0.5 μg of folic acid taken on an empty stomach or 0.6 μg of folic acid taken with a meal.[28] Thus, to calculate the total DFEs in an individual's diet, use the following equation:

$$\mu g \text{ of DFE provided in diet} = \mu g \text{ of food folate per day}$$
$$+ (1.7 \times \mu g \text{ of synthetic folic acid/day})$$

Because this calculation can be time consuming, most nutrient databases (such as the Canadian Nutrient File) calculate the DFEs automatically so that the total micrograms per day of folate provided in the nutrient analysis printout has already taken into account the bioavailability of the different types of folate in the diet.

Much of the folate circulating in the blood is attached to transport proteins, especially albumin, for transport to cells of the body. The red blood cells also contain folate attached to hemoglobin. Because this folate is not transferred out of the red blood cell to other tissues, it may be a good measure of folate status over the past three months—the life of the red blood cell.[27] If red blood cell folate levels begin to drop, this indicates that when the red blood cells were being formed, folate was inadequate in the body.

homocysteine An amino acid that requires adequate levels of folate, vitamin B_6, and vitamin B_{12} for its metabolism. High levels of homocysteine in the blood are associated with an increased risk for vascular diseases such as cardiovascular disease.

Ready-to-eat grain products, such as pasta, are often fortified with folic acid.

negative folate balance (stage I) The first stage of folate depletion, in which the body has less folate available to it and serum levels of folate begin to decline.

folate depletion (stage II) The second stage of folate depletion in which both serum and red blood cell folate are low.

folate-deficiency erythropoiesis (stage III) The third stage of folate depletion in which body levels of folate are so low that the ability to make new red blood cells is impaired.

folate-deficiency anemia (stage IV) The stage of folate deficiency in which the number of red blood cells has declined due to lack of folate, and macrocytic anemia develops.

Alterations in total body folate status mimic those seen with iron.[16, 29] As the body has less and less folate available to it, the serum levels of folate begin to decline. This level of folate deficiency is called **negative folate balance (stage I)**. If folate is not increased in the diet or through supplementation, then **folate depletion (stage II)** occurs. This stage of folate deficiency is characterized by both low serum and red blood cell folate, with slightly elevated serum homocysteine concentrations. In **folate-deficiency erythropoiesis (stage III)**, the folate levels in the body are low enough that the ability to synthesize new red blood cells is inhibited. Finally, in **folate-deficiency anemia (stage IV)**, the number of red blood cells has declined because folate is not available for DNA synthesis, and macrocytic anemia develops. This condition is discussed in more detail later in this chapter.

How Much Folate Should We Consume?

Folate is so important for good health and the prevention of birth defects that in 1998, Health Canada mandated the fortification of white flour and enriched grain products with folic acid. Because folic acid is highly available for absorption, the goal of this fortification was to increase folate intake in all Canadians and thus decrease the risk of birth defects and chronic diseases associated with low folate intakes.

The RDA for folate for adult men and women aged 19 years and older is 400 μg/day, with 600 μg/day required for pregnant women.[28] These higher levels of folate were set to minimize the risk of birth defects. The UL for folate is 1000 μg/day.

Ready-to-eat cereals, bread, and other grain products are among the primary sources of folate in Canada; folic acid is added to all white flour, enriched pasta, and cornmeal products. Other good food sources include liver, spinach, lentils, oatmeal, asparagus, and romaine lettuce. **Figure 13.10** shows some foods relatively high in folate. Losses of folate can occur when food is heated or when folate leaches out of cooked foods and the liquid from these foods is discarded. For this reason, cook green vegetables in a minimal amount of water and limit the time foods are exposed to high temperatures. These actions will help preserve the folate in the food.

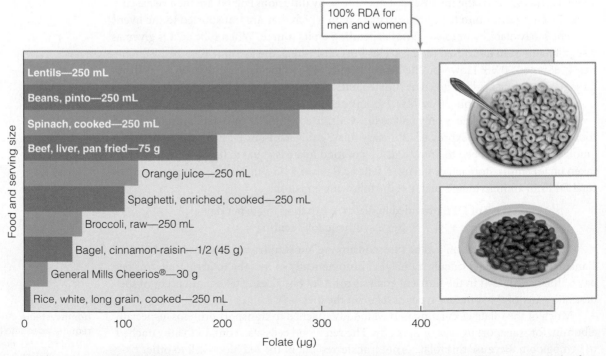

Figure 13.10 Common food sources of folate and folic acid. The RDA for folate is 400 μg/day for men and women.
Data from: The Canadian Nutrient File. Health Canada, 2012. Reproduced with the permission of the Minister of Health, 2012.

What Happens If We Consume Too Much Folate?

There have been no studies suggesting toxic effects of consuming high amounts of folate in food; however, toxicity can occur with high amounts of folic acid.[27] One especially frustrating problem with folate toxicity is that it can mask a simultaneous vitamin B_{12} deficiency. This often results in failure to detect the B_{12} deficiency and, as described in the chapter-opening case, a delay in diagnosis of B_{12} deficiency can contribute to severe damage to the nervous system. There do not appear to be any clear symptoms of folate toxicity independent from its interaction with vitamin B_{12} deficiency.

What Happens If We Consume Too Little Folate?

A folate deficiency can cause many adverse health effects, including *macrocytic anemia*. Folate and vitamin B_{12} deficiencies can cause elevated levels of homocysteine in the blood, a condition that is associated with heart disease. When folate intake is inadequate in pregnant women, *neural tube defects* (major malformations of the central nervous system that occur during the growth and development of the fetus) can occur. All of these conditions are discussed in more detail later in this chapter.

Recap

Folate is a water-soluble vitamin and coenzyme critical for the synthesis of DNA, cell differentiation, and amino acid metabolism. Because folate is essential in the synthesis of new cells, such as red blood cells, anemia can develop if folate is deficient. Folate is also important for normal development of the central nervous system of the fetus and, thus, the prevention of neural tube defects. In addition to plant foods, ready-to-eat cereals, breads, and many other grain products are good sources of folate or folic acid. The RDA for folate for adult men and women aged 19 years and older is 400 µg, with 600 µg/day required for pregnant women. The UL for supplemental folic acid is 1000 µg/day.

Vitamin B_{12} (Cyanocobalamin)

As with folate, the generic terms *vitamin B_{12}* or *cyanocobalamin* are used to describe a number of compounds that exhibit vitamin B_{12} biological activity. These compounds have cobalt in their centre and are surrounded by ring structures. See **Figure 13.11** for a diagram of the structure of cyanocobalamin, which is derived when vitamin B_{12} is purified from natural sources.[27] As you can see, vitamin B_{12} is a complex molecule, and the Nobel Prize was awarded for the delineation of its structure.

Functions of Vitamin B_{12}

Vitamin B_{12} is part of the coenzymes that assist with DNA synthesis, which is necessary for the proper formation of red blood cells.[16] As described in the chapter-opening scenario, vitamin B_{12} is essential for healthy functioning of the nervous system. Vitamin B_{12} helps maintain the myelin sheath that coats nerve fibres; when this sheath is damaged or absent, the conduction of nerve signals is altered, causing numerous neurologic problems.

Adequate levels of vitamin B_{12} and folate, as well as B_6, are also necessary for the metabolism of the amino acid homocysteine, which we discussed earlier. We discuss the relationship between homocysteine and heart disease in more detail on pages 469–470.

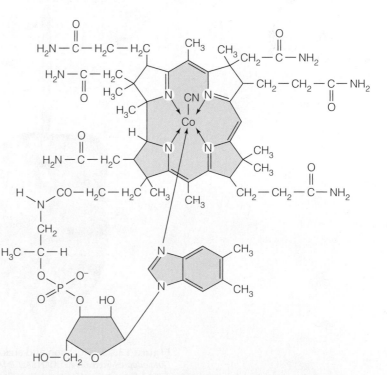

Figure 13.11 Structure of vitamin B_{12} (cyanocobalamin).

What Factors Alter Vitamin B_{12} Absorption, Metabolism, and Balance?

Vitamin B_{12} is synthesized almost entirely by bacteria in animals. For this reason, plant sources generally do not contain vitamin B_{12}. Thus, the vitamin B_{12} in our diet comes almost exclusively from meat, eggs, dairy products, and some seafood, and is approximately 50% bioavailable.[27]

The absorption of vitamin B_{12} is complex (**Figure 13.12**). In food, vitamin B_{12} is bound to protein. It is released from this protein in the acidic environment of the stomach, where it is then attached to another group of proteins called R-binders. The stomach also secretes **intrinsic factor**, a protein necessary for vitamin B_{12} absorption in the small intestine. The intrinsic factor and vitamin B_{12}–R-binder complexes formed in the stomach pass into the small intestine, where the R-binder protein is hydrolyzed by pancreatic proteolytic enzymes, after which free vitamin B_{12} binds to the intrinsic factor. The vitamin B_{12}–intrinsic factor complexes are then recognized by receptors on the enterocytes and internalized. These receptors do not recognize vitamin B_{12} alone but only when it is bound to intrinsic factor. Within the enterocytes, vitamin B_{12} is released into the cytosol. The vitamin B_{12} is then released from the enterocyte, bound to a protein called transcobalamin II, and then transported to the cells of the body. The body stores vitamin B_{12} in the liver, approximately 2 to 3 mg, which means we can probably survive for months without vitamin B_{12} in our diet.[28] Vitamin B_{12} is lost from the system in the urine and the bile.

Alterations in total body vitamin B_{12} status mimic those seen with iron and folate, with states of deficiency developing as the amount of vitamin B_{12} decreases in the body.[16] The states of vitamin B_{12} deficiency are as follows:

- *Stage I or negative vitamin B_{12} balance.* A decline in the blood level of cobalamin attached to its transport protein. This occurs as vitamin B_{12} absorption declines, decreasing the amount of total vitamin B_{12} available to the body.
- *Stage II or vitamin B_{12} depletion.* If vitamin B_{12} absorption is not increased or B_{12} supplementation provided, then blood levels of cobalamin attached to its transport protein continue to decline, resulting in a decreased saturation of the transport protein with cobalamin.

intrinsic factor A protein secreted by cells of the stomach that binds to vitamin B_{12} and aids its absorption in the small intestine.

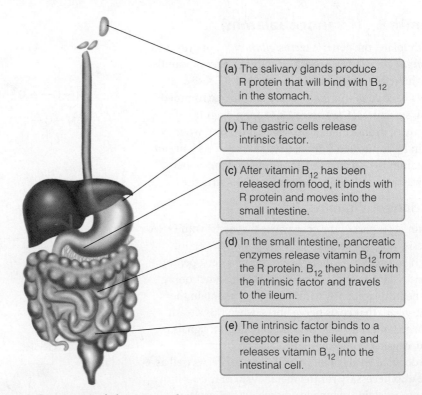

(a) The salivary glands produce R protein that will bind with B_{12} in the stomach.

(b) The gastric cells release intrinsic factor.

(c) After vitamin B_{12} has been released from food, it binds with R protein and moves into the small intestine.

(d) In the small intestine, pancreatic enzymes release vitamin B_{12} from the R protein. B_{12} then binds with the intrinsic factor and travels to the ileum.

(e) The intrinsic factor binds to a receptor site in the ileum and releases vitamin B_{12} into the intestinal cell.

Figure 13.12 Digestion and absorption of vitamin B_{12}.
Data adapted from: BLAKE, JOAN SALGE; MUNOZ, KATHY D.; VOLPE, STELLA, NUTRITION: FROM SCIENCE TO YOU, 1st Ed.,
© 2010. Reprinted and Electronically reproduced by permission of Pearson Education, Inc., Upper Saddle River, New Jersey.

- *Stage III or vitamin B$_{12}$–deficiency erythropoiesis.* The body's level of vitamin B$_{12}$ is so low that the ability to synthesize new red blood cells is inhibited.
- *Stage IV, called vitamin B$_{12}$–deficiency anemia.* The number of red blood cells has declined because vitamin B$_{12}$ is not available for DNA synthesis, and macrocytic anemia develops.

How Much Vitamin B$_{12}$ Should We Consume?

Vitamin B$_{12}$ has two unique features. First, it is found almost exclusively in animal foods; thus, the elimination of animal foods from the diet increases the risk of deficiency. Second, it is a water-soluble vitamin that is stored in the liver. This storage is important for anyone consuming very little vitamin B$_{12}$ in the diet.

The RDA for vitamin B$_{12}$ for adult men and women aged 19 and older is 2.4 µg/day. Vitamin B$_{12}$ is found primarily in dairy products, eggs, meats, and poultry. **Figure 13.13** reviews some foods relatively high in vitamin B$_{12}$. Individuals consuming a vegan diet need to eat vegetable-based foods that are fortified with vitamin B$_{12}$ or take vitamin B$_{12}$ supplements or injections to ensure that they maintain adequate blood levels of this nutrient.

As we age, our sources of vitamin B$_{12}$ may need to change. Non-vegan individuals younger than 51 years are generally able to meet the RDA for vitamin B$_{12}$ by consuming it in foods. However, it is estimated that about 10% to 30% of adults older than 50 years have a condition referred to as **atrophic gastritis**, which results in low stomach-acid secretion. Because stomach acid separates food-bound vitamin B$_{12}$ from dietary proteins, if the acid content of the stomach is inadequate, then we cannot free up enough vitamin B$_{12}$ from food sources alone.[28] Because atrophic gastritis can affect almost one-third of the older adult population, it is recommended that people older than 50 years of age consume foods fortified with vitamin B$_{12}$, take a vitamin B$_{12}$–containing supplement, or have periodic vitamin B$_{12}$ injections.

What Happens If We Consume Too Much Vitamin B$_{12}$?

There are no known adverse effects from consuming excess amounts of vitamin B$_{12}$ from food. Data are not available on the effects of excess amounts of vitamin B$_{12}$ from supplements.

Turkey contains vitamin B$_{12}$.

atrophic gastritis A condition, frequently seen in individuals over the age of 50 years, in which stomach acid secretion is low, resulting in decreased production of mucus, HCl, pepsin, and intrinsic factor.

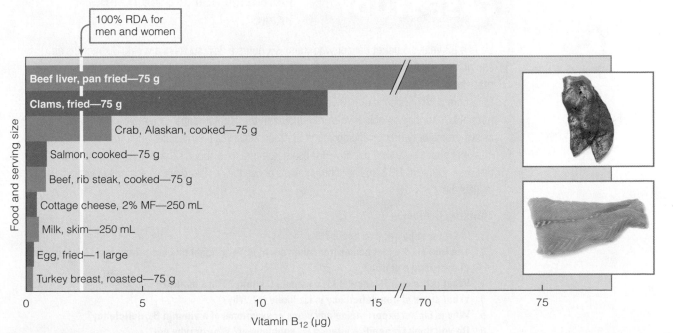

Figure 13.13 Common food sources of vitamin B$_{12}$. The RDA for vitamin B$_{12}$ is 2.4 µg/day for men and women.
Data from: The Canadian Nutrient File. Health Canada, 2012. Reproduced with the permission of the Minister of Health, 2012.

What Happens If We Consume Too Little Vitamin B$_{12}$?

Vitamin B$_{12}$ deficiency is rare but is generally associated with either dietary insufficiency or reduced absorption. Deficiency symptoms generally include those associated with anemia, as well as gastrointestinal and neurologic effects.[16] The symptoms of anemia include pale skin, diminished energy and exercise tolerance, fatigue, and shortness of breath. Gastrointestinal symptoms include loss of appetite, constipation, excessive gas, and changes in the tongue.[16] Neurologic symptoms include tingling and numbness of extremities, abnormal gait, memory loss, dementia, disorientation, visual disturbances, insomnia, and impaired bladder and bowel control.

As just noted, an important cause of vitamin B$_{12}$ deficiency is reduced absorption. A common culprit in reduced absorption is a condition called pernicious anemia, which is caused by inadequate secretion of intrinsic factor by parietal cells of the stomach. Pernicious anemia is discussed in more detail in the following section.

Anyone diagnosed with a vitamin B$_{12}$ deficiency needs to take a vitamin B$_{12}$ supplement. The type of supplement used depends on the cause of the deficiency. An oral supplement can be chosen for a deficiency caused by poor dietary intake. For those individuals with an intrinsic factor deficiency, vitamin B$_{12}$ is typically given by injection; although studies have shown that oral vitamin B$_{12}$ in doses of 1000 to 2000 µg/day is as effective.[30]

RECAP

Vitamin B$_{12}$ is a water-soluble vitamin and functions as a coenzyme for enzymes involved with DNA synthesis, which is necessary for formation of red blood cells. Vitamin B$_{12}$ is found exclusively in animal foods or foods fortified with vitamin B$_{12}$. The RDA for vitamin B$_{12}$ for adult men and women aged 19 years and older is 2.4 µg/day. There is no UL for vitamin B$_{12}$. Vitamin B$_{12}$ deficiency causes a form of macrocytic anemia and neurologic symptoms due to damage to nerve cells.

CASE STUDY — Increasing Iron and Vitamin B$_{12}$ Intake

Liz is a 23-year-old ballet dancer who trains six hours a day, six days a week. Six months ago she decided to try a vegetarian diet to help her maintain her weight. Her parents are concerned that she is not eating enough iron-rich foods and encourage her to go to her family physician for a complete physical exam. Blood values indicate that her serum transferrin levels are below normal but her hemoglobin levels are still within the normal range. There are no other signs or symptoms of nutrient deficiencies. A dietitian assesses her diet and finds that Liz's energy intake is about 1600 kcal per day. Her usual iron intake is about 12 mg/day. Her vitamin C intake is above the RDA and her fibre intake is above the AI. There are no sources of vitamin B$_{12}$ in Liz's diet.

Thinking Critically

1. **Is Liz meeting her iron needs?**
2. **The iron in Liz's diet comes from plant sources. Why might this contribute to an inadequate dietary intake of iron?**
3. **What is the significance of Liz's vitamin C intake? Fibre intake?**
4. **What stage of iron deficiency is Liz likely in? Why?**
5. **Why is Liz not experiencing any signs or symptoms of a vitamin B$_{12}$ deficiency?**
6. **Do you think Liz needs a vitamin B$_{12}$ supplement? Why or why not?**
7. **What advice would you give Liz to help her improve her diet?**

What Disorders Can Result from Inadequate Intakes of Nutrients Involved in Blood Health?

We have mentioned a number of illnesses and disorders that can occur if our intake of the nutrients related to blood health is inadequate. Following is a more detailed discussion of some of these disorders.

Neural Tube Defects

A woman's requirement for folate substantially increases during pregnancy. This is because of the high rates of cell development needed for enlargement of the uterus, development of the placenta, expansion of the mother's red blood cells, and growth of the fetus. Inadequate folate intake during pregnancy can not only cause macrocytic anemia but is also associated with major malformations in the fetus that are classified as neural tube defects.

Neural tube defects are the most common malformations of the central nervous system that occur during fetal development. The neural tube, which is formed by the fourth week of pregnancy, is a primitive structure that eventually develops into the brain and the spinal cord of the fetus. In a folate-deficient environment, the tube will fail to fold and close properly. The resultant defect in the newborn depends on the degree of failure and can range from protrusion of the spinal cord outside of the vertebral column to an absence of brain tissue. Some neural tube defects are minor and can be surgically repaired; others result in paralysis, and still others are fatal. In Canada (excluding Quebec), the prevalence of neural tube defects was 0.77 per 1000 live births in 1996.[31] After mandatory folic acid fortification was implemented, it has been estimated that this rate has decreased by 46%.[32] Neural tube defects are described in more detail in Chapter 16 and shown in Figure 16.7.

The nutritional challenge with neural tube defects is that they occur very early in a woman's pregnancy, almost always before a woman knows she is pregnant. Thus, adequate folate intake is extremely important for all sexually active women of childbearing age, whether or not they intend to become pregnant. To prevent neural tube defects, it is recommended that all women capable of becoming pregnant consume 400 μg of folic acid daily from supplements, fortified foods, or both in addition to the folate they consume in their standard diet.[28]

neural tube defects The most common malformations of the central nervous system that occur during fetal development. A folate deficiency can cause neural tube defects.

Vascular Disease and Homocysteine

Folate and vitamin B_{12} are necessary for the metabolism of the amino acid methionine. Vitamin B_6 is also involved, but we will focus only on vitamin B_{12} and folate here. If intakes of these nutrients are insufficient, methionine cannot be metabolized properly, and blood levels of homocysteine, a by-product of incomplete methionine metabolism, begin to increase (**Figure 13.14**). A systematic review of the research on this topic showed that elevated levels of homocysteine are associated with a 1.5 to 2 times greater risk for cardiovascular, cerebrovascular, and peripheral vascular diseases.[33] These diseases substantially increase a person's risk for a heart attack or stroke.

The exact mechanism by which elevated homocysteine levels increase the risk for vascular diseases is currently unknown. It has been speculated that homocysteine may damage the lining of blood vessels and stimulate the accumulation of plaque, which can lead to hardening of the arteries.[34] Homocysteine also increases blood clotting, which could lead to an increased risk of blocked arteries. Unfortunately, although supplementation with vitamins B_{12}, B_6, and folic acid has been shown to lower blood homocysteine levels, several high-quality clinical trials have concluded that these vitamins do not reduce

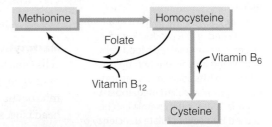

Figure 13.14 The metabolism of methionine, an essential amino acid, to homocysteine. Homocysteine can then be converted back to methionine through a vitamin B_{12}– and folate-dependent reaction or to cysteine through a vitamin B_6–dependent reaction. Cysteine is a non-essential amino acid important for making other biological compounds. Without these B-vitamins, blood levels of homocysteine can increase. High levels of homocysteine are a risk factor for cardiovascular disease.

cardiovascular disease risk or progression.[35] Thus, although eating foods that contain ample amounts of folate, vitamin B_6, and vitamin B_{12} is important, the current evidence does not support the use of supplements to decrease our risk for a heart attack or stroke. Further, the evidence suggests that it is not useful to measure homocysteine levels in the prevention and treatment of cardiovascular disease. However, most of the patients in the studies that have been conducted in this area had normal baseline plasma homocysteine levels. Future research needs to explore whether patients with elevated homocysteine levels might benefit from B-vitamin supplements.[36]

Anemia

The term *anemia* literally means "without blood"; it is used to refer to any condition in which hemoglobin levels are low, regardless of the cause. Some anemias are caused by genetic problems. For instance, you've probably heard of *sickle cell anemia,* a genetic disorder in which the red blood cells have a sickle shape. Another inherited anemia is *thalassemia,* a condition characterized by red blood cells that are small and short-lived. Here, we discuss anemias due to deficiencies of iron, vitamin B_6, vitamin B_{12}, or folate.

Microcytic Anemias

Microcytic anemias are a group of anemias characterized by red blood cells that are smaller than normal (*micro-* means small, and *–cyte* means cell). Red blood cells that are synthesized in an iron-deficient environment will be microcytic, and will not contain enough hemoglobin to transport adequate oxygen or to allow the proper transfer of electrons to produce energy. Microcytic anemia is sometimes referred to as *microcytic hypochromic anemia,* because reduced levels of hemoglobin deprive the cells of their bright-red colour (*hypo-* means low and *–chromic* refers to colour). As normal red blood cell death occurs over time, more and more healthy red blood cells are replaced by these abnormally small cells. At the same time, fewer total red blood cells are made. These changes prompt classic symptoms of oxygen and energy deprivation, including general fatigue, pale skin, depressed immune function, and impaired cognitive and nerve function, work performance, and memory. Pregnant women with severe anemia are at higher risk for low-birth-weight infants, premature delivery, and increased infant mortality.

Although we associate microcytic anemia with iron deficiency, a deficiency in vitamin B_6 can also cause it. Vitamin B_6 is required for the formation of the porphyrin rings that surround iron (see the gold area in Figure 13.2) and comprise an integral part of the heme complex. Without vitamin B_6, heme synthesis is impaired, just as it is with iron deficiency. Thus, either iron or vitamin B_6 deficiency can cause microcytic hypochromic anemia; however, iron deficiency is the more common cause.

Macrocytic Anemias

Macrocytic anemias are characterized by the production of larger-than-normal red blood cells (macrocytes) containing insufficient hemoglobin, thus inhibiting adequate transport of oxygen. Symptoms of macrocytic anemia are similar to the symptoms that occur with microcytic anemias, and include weakness, fatigue, difficulty concentrating, irritability, headache, shortness of breath, and reduced work tolerance. Deficiencies of two micronutrients are associated with macrocytic anemias: vitamin B_{12} and folate.

Pernicious anemia is classified as a type of macrocytic anemia and is associated with vitamin B_{12} deficiency. Pernicious anemia occurs at the end stage of an **autoimmune** disorder that causes the loss of various cells in the stomach, including the parietal cells that produce intrinsic factor. As you know, intrinsic factor binds to vitamin B_{12} in the small intestine and aids its absorption into the enterocyte. Without intrinsic factor, vitamin B_{12} cannot be absorbed from the gut. It is estimated that approximately 3% of older adults test positive for intrinsic factor antibodies, suggesting that they do not make intrinsic factor.[27]

microcytic anemia A form of anemia manifested as the production of smaller-than-normal red blood cells containing insufficient hemoglobin, which reduces the ability of the red blood cell to transport oxygen; it can result from iron deficiency or vitamin B_6 deficiency.

macrocytic anemia A form of anemia manifested as the production of larger-than-normal red blood cells containing insufficient hemoglobin, which inhibits adequate transport of oxygen; also called megaloblastic anemia. Macrocytic anemia can be caused by a severe folate deficiency or by vitamin B_{12} deficiency.

pernicious anemia A special form of macrocytic anemia that is the primary cause of a vitamin B_{12} deficiency; occurs at the end stage of an autoimmune disorder that causes the loss of various cells in the stomach.

autoimmune A destructive immune response directed toward the individual's own tissues.

Macrocytic anemia can also occur in people who consume little or no vitamin B_{12} in their diets, such as people following a vegan diet. It is also commonly seen in people with malabsorption disorders, such as people with tapeworm infestation of the gut, as the worms take up the vitamin B_{12} before it can be absorbed by the intestines.

In addition to the symptoms associated with all anemias—such as pale skin, reduced energy and exercise tolerance, fatigue, and shortness of breath—lack of B_{12} also causes the destruction of nerve cells. Thus, patients lose the ability to perform coordinated movements and to maintain body positioning. Central nervous system involvement can lead to irritability, confusion, depression, and even paranoia. As we saw in the case of Mr. Katz in the chapter opener, after onset of central nervous system–involved symptoms, even prompt intramuscular injections of vitamin B_{12} can only partially reverse the deficits.

A severe folate deficiency is another common cause of macrocytic anemia. Folate deficiency impairs DNA synthesis, which impairs the normal production of red blood cells. Because a deficiency of folate or vitamin B_{12} causes similar symptoms, it is important to determine if the macrocytic anemia observed is due to a folate or a vitamin B_{12} deficiency. As mentioned earlier, high doses of folate supplements can mask the physical symptoms of vitamin B_{12} deficiency so that this deficiency progresses unchecked and causes neurologic damage.[28] Thus, before treatment for macrocytic anemia can occur, the cause must be identified.

RECAP

Neural tube defects are potentially serious and even fatal malformations of the central nervous system in a developing fetus that can result from folate deficiency in the first few weeks of pregnancy. Low intakes of folate, vitamin B_6, or vitamin B_{12} are associated with elevated blood homocysteine levels, which increase the risk of cardiovascular, cerebrovascular, and peripheral vascular disease. Anemia refers to any condition in which hemoglobin levels are low. Inadequate intake of iron or vitamin B_6 can lead to microcytic anemia, whereas deficiency of either vitamin B_{12} or folate causes macrocytic anemia.

What Is the Immune System, and How Does It Function?

A healthy immune system protects the body from infectious diseases, helps heal wounds, and guards against the development of cancers. Made up of cells and tissues throughout the body, the immune system acts as an integrated network to carry out surveillance against invaders and destroy them before they can cause significant tissue damage. Although immune cells communicate with one another extensively, each cell has a specialized protective function in either non-specific or specific immunity.

Non-specific Immune Function Protects Against All Potential Invaders

Non-specific immune function is the body's primary defence against microbes, airborne particles, venom, and ingested toxins. Non-specific immunity is active even if you are encountering the invader for the first time. Because even infants have all of the cells and tissues required for it to operate effectively, it is also called *innate immunity*.

non-specific immune function
Generalized body defence mechanisms that protect against the entry of foreign agents such as microorganisms and allergens; also called innate immunity.

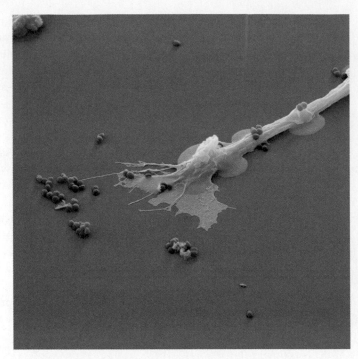

A macrophage is a type of non-specific immune cell. The one shown here is about to engulf an invading microbe.

specific immune function The strongest defence against pathogens. Requires adaptation of lymphocytes that recognize antigens and that multiply to protect against the pathogens carrying those antigens. Also called *adaptive immunity* or *acquired immunity*.

antigens Parts of a molecule, usually proteins, from bacteria, viruses, worms, or toxins that are recognized by specific receptors on lymphocytes and induce formation of antibodies or killing of an organism displaying the antigen.

memory cells Lymphocytes that differentiate from B cells and T cells, recognize a particular antigen for an infectious disease, and remain in the body after the disease is resolved to be ready to respond if the disease is encountered again later. The purpose of vaccination is to create memory lymphocytes.

Non-specific defences include intact skin and healthy mucous membranes, which block invaders from entering the blood, lungs, and other deeper tissues. Coughing, sneezing, vomiting, and diarrhea all serve to expel harmful agents before they can take hold. Food-borne microbes can also be destroyed by stomach acid.

In addition, a variety of immune cells, including macrophages, neutrophils, and natural killer (NK) cells, work together to kill a wide variety of harmful microorganisms, even if they never have been encountered before.

Finally, our non-specific defences include the release of inflammatory chemicals that cause discomfort, loss of appetite, fatigue, and fever: most disease-causing microbes thrive at normal body temperature, whereas a high temperature inhibits their growth. Fever also facilitates the actions of cells and chemicals involved in repair.

Together, our non-specific defences can inhibit the penetration and reproduction of invaders until the slower-acting, but more effective, specific immune system is activated.

Specific Immune Function Protects Against Identified Antigens

Specific immune function is directed against recognized **antigens**—that is, portions of microorganisms, allergens, or other foes that the immune system has encountered before and recognizes as foreign, or *non-self*. But how does this recognition occur?

The first time the immune system encounters a substance with an antigen that is detected as non-self, it produces a primary immune response. This response takes several days to peak, but eventually, in most cases, it destroys the invader. A key process within that primary immune response is the production of **memory cells** dedicated to the task of seeking out and destroying any substance bearing that particular antigen. Memory cells remain in circulation (in some cases for life) so that any subsequent encounter with the same antigen causes a faster and stronger response. Often, the response is so fast that the person does not even feel sick.

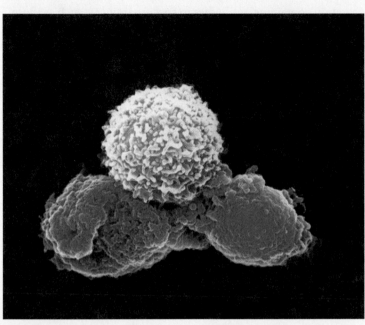

Natural killer (NK) cells are part of our non-specific defences. Here, an NK cell attacks two cancer cells.

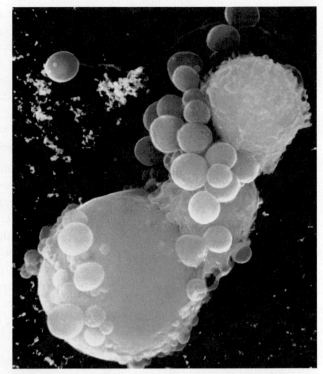

Two cytotoxic T cells (orange) killing another cell (mauve).

Two Main Types of Cells Provide Specific Immunity

In specific immune responses, two primary types of immune cells are activated:

- **B cells** are a type of white blood cell. During a primary immune response, B cells differentiate into two types: the memory cells just described and **plasma cells**. The job of plasma cells is to produce thousands of antibodies, proteins that attach to recognized antigens on invaders and flag them for destruction.

- **T cells** are also white blood cells. They differentiate into several types, the most important of which are cytotoxic T cells and helper T cells. As their name suggests, **cytotoxic T cells** are toxic to body cells harbouring microbes or any other non-self substances. For instance, by killing body cells that have been infected by a flu virus, they keep the virus from multiplying and spreading. **Helper T cells** don't kill directly. Rather, they manufacture chemicals that activate B cells and cytotoxic T cells.

Specific Immunity Can Be Acquired in a Variety of Ways

There are four primary ways in which humans acquire immunity to specific invaders:

- One natural way is to have a disease once. For example, if you had mumps as a child, you will never get it again because memory cells against mumps are continuously circulating throughout your body.

- **Vaccinations** (also called *immunizations*) are another way to develop immunity. When you are vaccinated, a small amount of antigen from a particular microbe is injected into your body. Your plasma cells produce antibodies against the antigen, and memory cells begin to circulate. If you encounter the microbe later, your immune response will protect you from getting sick.

- When a woman is pregnant, antibodies from her blood pass into the bloodstream of her fetus. These maternal antibodies protect a newborn during the first few months of life while the specific immune system is maturing. In addition, breast milk contains antibodies that protect the infant for as long as he or she nurses.

B cells Lymphocytes that can become either antibody-producing plasma cells or memory cells.

plasma cells Lymphocytes that have differentiated from activated B cells and produce millions of antibodies to attach to an antigen during an infection.

T cells Lymphocytes that mature in the thymus gland and are of several varieties, including helper T cells.

cytotoxic T cells Activated T cells that kill infected body cells.

helper T cells Activated T cells that secrete chemicals needed to activate other immune cells.

vaccination Administering a small amount of antigen to elicit an immune response for the purpose of developing memory cells that will protect against the disease at a later time.

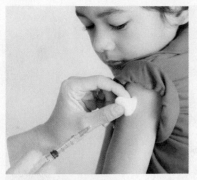

Vaccinations provide active immunity.

- The injection of **antiserum** can provide immediate protection from a specific foe—for instance, to snake venom in the bloodstream of a victim of a snakebite. Antiserum is a pharmacologic preparation containing antibodies to specific antigens, such as those in snake venom. Injection of this antibody-rich serum provides immediate protection. Without it, the snake venom would be fatal before the victim's immune system could produce antibodies.

Immune System Malfunction Can Cause Chronic Inflammation and Infection

A malfunctioning immune system can damage body tissues or prevent resolution of infection. For example, during allergic reactions, harmless proteins in the environment or in food are mistaken for pathogens, producing a hypersensitivity immune response (see Chapter 3). Autoimmune responses occur when the body's own proteins are mistaken for pathogens. This occurs, for example, in rheumatoid arthritis and lupus and results in a chronic inflammatory state.

In some people, infections cannot be resolved and become chronic. Chronic infection is commonly seen in malnourished individuals, as well as in people with immune deficiency diseases. Cancer patients and transplant recipients also are more susceptible to infection when they are taking immunosuppressive drugs.

ReCaP

The main function of the immune system is to protect the body against foreign agents. Non-specific defences include skin, mucous membranes, enzymes, inflammatory chemicals, and certain defensive cells. Specific immunity is provided by B cells and T cells. B cells include plasma cells, which produce antibodies, and memory cells, which circulate throughout the body seeking antigens to which they are sensitized. Cytotoxic T cells kill infected body cells, and helper T cells help B cells and cytotoxic T cells to proliferate. We gain immunity through previous infection, vaccination, maternal antibodies, or the administration of antiserum. Immune system malfunction can result in chronic inflammation or chronic infection.

How Does Nutrition Affect the Immune System?

A nourishing diet provides all the nutrients the immune system needs to carry out its defence of the body. Single-nutrient deficiencies or subclinical deficiencies can cause subtle, but important, abnormalities in immune function, even in apparently healthy people. This type of malnutrition is common in hospitalized individuals and older adults.[37] Recent studies have demonstrated that viruses multiplying in malnourished hosts actually become more infective and destructive than viruses multiplying in well-nourished hosts.[38] Moreover, protein/energy malnutrition and severe deficiencies of several micronutrients reduce immune function. This problem is a leading cause of death in children in developing countries.[39]

Protein/Energy Malnutrition Impairs Immune Function

Malnutrition and infection participate in a vicious cycle: malnutrition increases the risk for infection; infection depresses appetite and often causes vomiting and diarrhea; decreased appetite, vomiting, and/or diarrhea cause malnutrition, which increases vulnerability to infection. Specifically, protein/energy malnutrition (see Chapter 6) is known to severely diminish the ability of the immune system to respond to antigens. Malnourished children show reduced production of antibodies and diminished capacity of their immune cells to kill bacteria.[40] In addition, a healthy immune response requires energy and amino acids, two

antiserum A pharmacologic preparation that contains antibodies to specific antigens.

things that are in short supply in a malnourished individual. The synergistic effect of protein/energy malnutrition and infection in diminishing both the capacity of the immune response and nutritional status is now widely recognized. Because even moderate nutrient deficiencies impair immune function, it has been suggested that decreased **immunocompetence** is a sensitive indicator of reduced nutritional status.

Obesity Increases Incidence and Severity of Infections

Obesity has become a public health issue much more recently than the problem of protein/energy malnutrition. Therefore, fewer studies have been done on the effects of obesity on immune function. However, obesity has been associated with increased incidence of infection, delayed wound healing, and poor antibody response to vaccination.[41]

The mechanisms underlying lower immune function in obese individuals are unclear. Most, but not all, studies show a lower ability of B and T cells from obese individuals to multiply in response to stimulation. This inhibition is resolved after weight loss.[42] Short-term fasting by obese individuals appears to improve the killing capacity of macrophages and increase serum concentrations of antibodies.[41] More consistent are the data documenting chronically elevated levels of macrophages, inflammatory chemicals, and immune proteins in obese individuals, suggesting the existence of a low-grade inflammatory state.[43] This inflammatory state is currently thought to increase the likelihood that obese individuals will develop asthma, hypertension, cardiovascular diseases, and type 2 diabetes.[43]

Obesity has been linked to disorders involving chronic inflammation, such as asthma, hypertension, heart disease, and type 2 diabetes.

Essential Fatty Acids Make Signalling Molecules for the Immune System

As noted in Chapter 5, the essential fatty acids are precursors for important signalling molecules called **eicosanoids**. The immune system requires certain eicosanoids to respond appropriately to threatening agents. Experimental dietary deficiency of essential fatty acids impairs aspects of the immune response. On the other hand, excess amounts given by supplementation can also diminish immune function.[44]

This may be due in part to the importance of the *ratio* of omega-6 and omega-3 fatty acids in modulating the immune response. For example, omega-6 fatty acids are thought to promote the inflammatory response, which helps contain infection. In contrast, clinical trials have shown that omega-3 fatty acids diminish inflammation, including within blood vessels, and thus provide protection against heart disease. Indeed, the potential health benefits of omega-3 fatty acids in fish oils were first observed in Greenland Eskimos who had low levels of heart disease. However, their high incidence of tuberculosis raised the question of whether omega-3 fatty acids might diminish immune response to infections.

For these reasons, caution against both deficient and excessive intake of omega-3 fatty acids is prudent for maintaining appropriate immune response.[45] Both the absolute amount of omega-6 and omega-3 fatty acids and their ratio are considered important for health. The dietary reference intakes for adults over age 19 are 17 g omega-6 (linoleic acid) and 1.6 g omega-3 (linolenic acid) for men and 12 g omega-6 (linoleic acid) and 1.1 g omega-3 (linolenic acid) for women.[46]

Certain Vitamins and Minerals Are Critical to a Strong Immune Response

Although all essential nutrients are likely needed in some measure for effective immune function, certain micronutrient deficiencies and excesses have been recognized as particularly important. These include the following:

- *Vitamin A.* As early as the 1920s, vitamin A was called "the anti-infective vitamin" because it is needed to maintain the mucosal surfaces of the respiratory, gastrointestinal, and genitourinary tracts and for differentiation of immune system cells. More than

immunocompetence Adequate ability to produce an effective immune response to an antigen.

eicosanoids Physiologically active signalling molecules, including prostaglandins, thromboxanes, and leukotrienes, derived from the 20-carbon fatty acids arachidonic acid and eicosapentaenoic acid.

Vitamins E and C can be found in fruits and vegetables, and can contribute to immune system health.

100 clinical trials have shown that vitamin A supplementation in populations with low vitamin A status reduces incidence and fatality of infections of measles, malaria, and diarrheal diseases.[47] However, animal studies suggest that excessive vitamin A can actually suppress immune response and increase susceptibility to pathogens.[48] Thus, screening for vitamin A status before administering supplements has been recommended as part of public health efforts to combat deficiency.[49]

- *Vitamins C and E.* The immune activities of defensive cells such as macrophages require oxygen and generate a highly reactive molecule, called a *reactive oxygen species*, that can damage the cell membrane if there is insufficient antioxidant protection. Both vitamin C and vitamin E provide this protection.

- *Zinc.* The importance of zinc to immune function was suggested by the observation that zinc-deficient dwarves in the Middle East died of infections by their early twenties.[50] Zinc is now known to be necessary for gene expression and enzyme activation for B and T cell proliferation. Even marginal zinc deficiency impairs immune response. However, excessive zinc supplementation depresses immunity, possibly by causing copper deficiency.

- *Copper.* Even a marginal copper deficiency reduces a growth factor needed for immune cells to multiply.[51] Lack of circulating neutrophils is a classic sign of copper deficiency in humans. Lack of copper also impairs the ability of both the neutrophils and macrophages to kill pathogens.

- *Iron.* Iron has a complicated relationship with immune function. It is now clear that a mild iron deficiency impairs immune function, perhaps because activated T cells produce a receptor on their surface that can take up the iron they need for multiplication.[48] Severe deficiency also impairs the function of T and B cells, as well as neutrophils. However, macrophages take up and store iron during an infection and seem unaffected by deficiency. This storage is thought to be beneficial because it keeps iron away from invading microbes, which require iron to multiply. This may explain why some studies show that iron supplementation given to children during infection is detrimental, and why iron toxicity increases the rate of infections.[52] In addition, excessive iron is a potent oxidant that can damage immune-cell membranes.

- *Selenium.* In trace amounts, selenium is necessary for the synthesis of 35 body proteins, many of which are important enzymes.[53] Selenium has two roles in immune function. It is a required coenzyme for glutathione peroxidase, an important antioxidant enzyme in neutrophils and other immune cells. It also promotes proper B and T cell proliferation and antibody production. Selenium deficiency in an infected host also permits viruses to multiply over a longer time period and to mutate into more pathogenic strains.[38] However, selenium excess also impairs immune cell activity.[54] Thus, as with iron and vitamin A, both excess and deficiency of selenium compromise the ability to resolve infection.

RECaP

A nourishing diet is important in optimizing immune response. Protein/energy malnutrition increases the frequency and severity of infection. Obesity compromises immune response, exacerbating infection and inflammation. Balanced consumption of omega-6 and omega-3 essential fatty acids is needed for production of signalling molecules important in immune function. Vitamin A is critically important for maintenance of the skin and mucosal barrier to infection as well as for development of immune cells. Both vitamins C and E function as antioxidants to protect cell membranes from destruction during an immune response. The minerals zinc, copper, iron, and selenium are all necessary for appropriate immune function. In general, adequate micronutrients are critical for immune function, but excessive amounts impair immune response.

SEE FOR YOURSELF

Assessing Supplements

Adequate intake of micronutrients is important for healthy blood and for healthy immune function, but excessive intakes of vitamin A, zinc, copper, iron, and selenium may impair immune response and be toxic. In addition, too much folic acid can mask low vitamin B_{12} deficiency.

It is very easy to buy supplements online. Check out a few supplements websites, and see how variable the amounts of vitamins and minerals are in numerous products. Would it be likely that someone might easily oversupplement one or more of these micronutrients? Did you find any supplements with more than the RDA for folic acid? Did these same supplements also include vitamin B_{12}?

Chapter Review

13

Test Yourself | Answers

1. **T** This deficiency is particularly common in infants, children, and women of childbearing age.

2. **F** To reduce their risk of having a baby with serious central nervous system defects, all women capable of becoming pregnant should take folic acid supplements. Beginning folic acid supplementation after recognizing a pregnancy, typically following the first missed menstrual period, may be too late to prevent a neural tube defect.

3. **T** People who consume a vegan diet need to pay particularly close attention to consuming enough vitamin B_{12}, iron, and zinc. In some cases, these individuals may need to take supplements to consume adequate amounts of these nutrients.

4. **F** The term *anemia* means "without blood" and can refer to any condition in which hemoglobin levels are low. Iron-deficiency anemia is just one type.

5. **T** Fever increases the body temperature, making the internal environment inhospitable to microbes and increasing the rate of protective immune reactions. Vomiting and diarrhea serve to expel microbes and toxins from the GI tract before they can cause widespread tissue damage.

Summary

- Blood is the only fluid tissue in the body. It has four components: erythrocytes, or red blood cells; leukocytes, or white blood cells; platelets; and plasma, or the fluid portion of blood.

- Blood is critical for transporting oxygen and nutrients to cells and for removing waste products from cells so these products can be properly excreted.

- Iron is a trace mineral. Almost two-thirds of the iron in the body is found in hemoglobin, the oxygen-carrying protein in blood. One of the primary functions of iron is to assist with the transportation of oxygen in blood. Iron is a cofactor for many of the enzymes involved in the metabolism of carbohydrates, fats, and protein. It is also a part of the antioxidant enzyme system that fights free radicals.

- Zinc is a trace mineral that acts as a cofactor in the production of hemoglobin; in the superoxide dismutase antioxidant enzyme system; in the metabolism of carbohydrates, fats, and proteins; and in activating vitamin A in the retina. Zinc is also critical for cell reproduction and growth and for proper development and functioning of the immune system.

- Copper is a trace mineral that functions as a cofactor in the metabolic pathways that produce energy, in the production of collagen and elastin, and as part of the superoxide dismutase antioxidant enzyme system. Copper is also a component of ceruloplasmin, a protein needed for the proper transport of iron.

- Vitamin K is a fat-soluble vitamin that acts as a coenzyme assisting in the coagulation of blood. Vitamin K is also a coenzyme in the synthesis of proteins that assist in maintaining bone density.

- The B-vitamins primarily involved in blood health are folate and vitamin B_{12}.

- Neural tube defects, which can result from inadequate folate intake during the first four weeks of pregnancy, are the most common malformations of the fetal central nervous system. Some neural tube defects are minor and can be treated with surgery; other neural tube defects are fatal.

- Inadequate intakes of folate and vitamin B_{12} are associated with elevated homocysteine levels. Elevated homocysteine levels are associated with a greater risk of cardiovascular, cerebrovascular, and peripheral vascular disease. These diseases significantly increase one's risk for a heart attack or stroke.

- *Anemia* is a term that means "without blood." Severe iron deficiency results in microcytic anemia, in which the production of normal, healthy red blood cells decreases and hemoglobin levels are inadequate. Deficiency of vitamin B_6 can also cause microcytic anemia.

- Macrocytic anemia results from folate or vitamin B_{12} deficiency and causes the formation of excessively large red blood cells that have reduced hemoglobin. Symptoms are similar to those of microcytic anemia. One form of macrocytic anemia, called pernicious anemia, is caused by a deficit of intrinsic factor, which in turn results in vitamin B_{12} deficiency.

- A healthy immune system is a network of cells and tissues that protects us from harmful agents.

- Non-specific defences include the skin and mucosal membranes, as well as protective molecules such as mucus, stomach acid, and enzymes, and immune cells such as macrophages, neutrophils, and NK cells that destroy invaders.

- Specific immune function is directed against specific antigens. An initial encounter with a foreign agent triggers development of immune cells that recognize that agent. On subsequent encounters with the same agent, these cells mount a faster, stronger immune response.

- The two primary types of cells involved in specific immunity are B cells and T cells.

- Plasma cells are B cells that produce antibodies that mark antigens for destruction. Memory cells are another type of B cell that, after becoming sensitized to a specific antigen, circulate in the body, seeking that antigen.

- Cytotoxic T cells destroy body cells harbouring foreign agents, and helper T cells signal other immune cells to respond.

- Human beings can acquire immunity by experiencing an infection, being vaccinated, receiving maternal antibodies, or receiving an injection of antiserum.

- Malfunctions of the immune system include allergies, autoimmune diseases, chronic inflammation, and immunodeficiencies.

- Both protein/energy malnutrition and obesity impair immune responses.

- A balanced intake of omega-6 and omega-3 essential fatty acids is important for regulating immune function.

- Critically important to immune function are vitamins A, C, and E and the minerals zinc, copper, iron, and selenium. In general, both deficiency and excess of these micronutrients can impair immune response.

Review Questions

1. The micronutrient most closely associated with blood clotting is
   a. iron.
   b. vitamin K.
   c. zinc.
   d. vitamin B_{12}.

2. Which of the following statements about iron is true?
   a. Iron is stored primarily in the liver, the blood vessel walls, and the heart muscle.
   b. Iron is a component of hemoglobin, myoglobin, and certain enzymes.
   c. Iron is a component of red blood cells, platelets, and plasma.
   d. Excess iron is stored primarily in the form of ferritin, cytochromes, and intrinsic factor.

3. Homocysteine is a
   a. by-product of glycolysis.
   b. trace mineral.
   c. by-product of incomplete methionine metabolism.
   d. B-vitamin.

4. Which of the following cells produce antibodies?
   a. plasma cells
   b. antigens
   c. macrophages
   d. helper T cells

5. Breastfeeding promotes infant health because breast milk contains
   a. antiserum.
   b. ceruloplasmin.

c. intrinsic factor.

d. antibodies.

6. Hannah is a busy university student. She works part time, is president of the Student Union, and is taking a full load of courses. Since the start of the semester, she has had three colds and the stomach flu. It is almost final exam time and she is thinking about taking a vitamin and mineral supplement to boost her immune system. Which micronutrients are particularly important for effective immune function? What non-nutritional factors might be contributing to her illnesses? Are there any potential concerns that Hannah should be aware of before she decides to take a supplement?

7. Kevin has iron-deficiency anemia. His physician has told him to take an iron supplement but Kevin doesn't like taking pills and has decided to try to treat his anemia by eating steak three times a week. Explain to Kevin why it is important to take the supplement. What type of supplement would you recommend?

8. In the chapter-opening story, Mr. Katz was given an injection of vitamin B_{12}. Why didn't his physician simply give him the vitamin in pill form?

9. Jessica is 11 years old and has just begun menstruating. She and her family members are vegans (that is, they consume only plant-based foods). Explain why Jessica's parents should be careful that their daughter consumes not only adequate iron and zinc but also adequate vitamin C.

10. Robert is a lacto-ovo-vegetarian. His typical daily diet includes milk, yogourt, cheese, eggs, nuts, seeds, legumes, whole grains, and a wide variety of fruits and vegetables. He does not take any supplements. What, if any, micronutrients are likely to be inadequate in his diet?

11. Janine is 23 years old and engaged to be married. She is 18 kg overweight, has hypertension, and her mother suffered a mild stroke recently, at age 45. For all these reasons, Janine is highly motivated to lose weight and has put herself on a strict low-carbohydrate diet recommended by a friend. She now scrupulously avoids breads, cereals, pastries, pasta, rice, and "starchy" fruits and vegetables. Identify two reasons why Janine should begin taking a folic acid supplement.

12. What health risk do people who are emaciated and people who are obese have in common? Why?

Web Links

www.publichealth.gc.ca

Public Health Agency of Canada

Search this site for "neural tube defects" and find information on the prevalence and prevention of these conditions.

www.hc-sc.gc.ca

Health Canada

Find information on this site about natural health products, including vitamin and mineral supplements, and how they are regulated in Canada.

www.unicef.org/nutrition/index.html

UNICEF—Nutrition

This site provides information about micronutrient deficiencies in developing countries and the efforts to combat them.

www.aboutkidshealth.ca/En/Pages/default.aspx

About Kids Health

This site provides information related to childrens' health issues. Search for "neural tube defects" for more information on this condition.

www.kidshealth.org/parent

KidsHealth

Search for "immune system" to find a good overview of the immune system.

www.dietitians.ca

Dietitians of Canada

Search this site for fact sheets on vitamins and minerals.

www.anemia.com

Anemia.com

Visit this site to learn about anemia and its various treatments.

www.cspinet.org/canada/

Centre for Science in the Public Interest Canada

This site provides information on vitamins and minerals and food sources.

MasteringNutrition®

www.masteringnutrition.pearson.com

Assignments

Animations: Vitamin B_{12} Absorption

Study Area

Video: Using the Functional Approach to Understand Blood Health & Immunity • Practice Tests • Diet Analysis • eText

References

1. Bernstein, L. 2000. Dementia without a cause: lack of vitamin B$_{12}$ can cause dementia. *Discover*. Available at www.discover.com/issues/feb-00/departments/featdementia.

2. World Health Organization. 2003. Nutrition. Micronutrient deficiencies. Battling iron deficiency anemia. Available at www.who.int/nut/ida.htm.

3. Crichton, R. R. 2006. Iron. In: M. H. Stipanuk, ed. *Biochemical, Physiological, and Molecular Aspects of Human Nutrition*. Philadelphia: W. B. Saunders, pp. 1001–1042.

4. Institute of Medicine, Food and Nutrition Board. 2001. *Dietary Reference Intakes for Vitamin A, Vitamin K, Arsenic, Boron, Chromium, Copper, Iodine, Iron, Manganese, Molybdenum, Nickel, Silicon, Vanadium, and Zinc*. Washington, DC: National Academy Press.

5. Hurrell, R. F., M. B. Reddy, M. Juillerate, and J. D. Cook. 2006. Meat protein fractions enhance nonheme iron absorption in humans. *J. Nutr.* 136:2808–2812.

6. Donovan, A., C. A. Lima, J. L. Pinkus, G. S. Pinkus, L. I. Zon, S. Robine, and N. C. Andrews. 2005. The iron exporter ferroportin/Sic40a1 is essential for iron homeostasis. *Cell Metab.* 1:191–200.

7. Sinclair, L. M., and P. S. Hinton. 2005. Prevalence of iron deficiency with and without anemia in recreationally active men and women. *J. Am. Diet. Assoc.* 105:975–978.

8. U.S. Food and Drug Administration. 1997. Preventing iron poisoning in children. FDA backgrounder. Available at www.fda.gov/opacom/backgrounders/ironbg.html.

9. Craig, W. J., and A. Mangels. 2009. Position of the Academy of Nutrition and Dietetics: vegetarian diets. *J. Am. Diet. Assoc.* 109:1266–1282.

10. Public Health Agency of Canada. 1998. *For the Safety of Canadian Children and Youth—Public Health Agency of Canada*. Available at www.phac-aspc.gc.ca/publicat/fsccy-psjc/ch9-eng.php (accessed February 17, 2011).

11. Bacon, B. R., J. K. Olynyk, E. M. Brunt, R. S. Britton, and R. K. Wolff. 1999. HFE genotype in patients with hemochromatosis and other liver diseases. *Ann. Intern. Med.* 130:953–962.

12. Health Canada. 2009. *Do Canadian Adults Meet Their Nutrient Requirements Through Food Intake Alone?* Available at www.hc-sc.gc.ca/fn-an/surveill/nutrition/commun/art-nutr-adult-eng.php (accessed February 17, 2011).

13. Health Canada. 2009. *Do Canadian Children Meet Their Nutrient Requirements Through Food Intake Alone?* Available at www.hc-sc.gc.ca/fn-an/surveill/nutrition/commun/art-nutr-child-enf-eng.php (accessed February 17, 2011).

14. Baltussen, R., C. Knai, and M. Sharan. 2004. Iron fortification and iron supplementation are cost-effective interventions to reduce iron deficiency in four subregions of the world. *J. Nut.* 134:2678–2684.

15. Grantham-McGregor, S., and C. Ani. 2001. A review of studies on the effect of iron deficiency on cognitive development in children. *J. Nutr.* 131:649S–668S.

16. Gibson, S. R. 2005. *Principles of Nutritional Assessment*, 2nd ed. New York: Oxford University Press.

17. Hinton, P. S., C. Giordano, T. Brownlie, and J. D. Hass. 2000. Iron supplementation improves endurance after training in iron-depleted, nonanemic women. *J. Appl. Physiol.* 88:1103–1111.

18. National Institutes of Health. Office of Dietary Supplements. 2007. *Dietary Supplement Fact Sheet: Iron*. Available at http://ods.od.nih.gov/factsheets/iron/ (accessed June 7, 2011).

19. Centers for Disease Control and Prevention. 1998. CDC recommendations to prevent and control iron deficiency in the United States. *MMWR Recomm. Rep.* 47:1–29.

20. Zlotkin, S., P. Arthur, K. Y. Antwi, and G. Yeung. 2001. Treatment of anemia with microencapsulated ferrous fumarate plus ascorbic acid supplied as sprinkles to complementary (weaning) foods. *Am. J. Clin. Nutr.* 6:791–795.

21. Grider, A. 2006. Zinc, copper, and manganese. In: M. H. Stipanuk, ed. *Biochemical, Physiological, and Molecular Aspects of Human Nutrition*. Philadelphia: W. B. Saunders, pp. 1043–1067.

22. Wallin, R., and S. M Huston . 2006. Vitamin K. In: M. H. Stipanuk, ed. *Biochemical, Physiological and MolecularAspects of Human Nutrition*. Philadelphia: W. B. Saunders, pp. 797–818.

23. Booth, S. L., and J. W. Suttie. 1998. Dietary intake and adequacy of vitamin K. *J. Nutr.* 128:785–788.

24. Presse, N., H. Payette, B. Shatenstein, C. Greenwood, M.-J. Kergoat, and G. Ferland. 2010. A minimum of six days of diet recording is needed to assess usual vitamin K intake among older adults. *J. Nutr.* Epub DOI:10.3945/jn.110.132530.

25. Johnson, M. A. 2005. Influence of vitamin K on anticoagulant therapy depends on vitamin K status and the source and chemical forms of vitamin K. *Nutr. Rev.* 63:91–100.

26. Feskanich, D., S. A. Korrick, S. L. Greenspan, H. N. Rosen, and G. A. Colditz. 1999. Moderate alcohol consumption and bone density among post-menopausal women. *J. Women's Health* 8:65–73.

27. Shane, B. 2006. Folic acid, vitamin B$_{12}$, and vitamin B$_6$. In: M. H. Stipanuk, ed. *Biochemical, Physiological, and Molecular Aspects of Human Nutrition*. Philadelphia: W. B. Saunders, pp. 693–732.

28. Institute of Medicine, Food and Nutrition Board. 1998. *Dietary Reference Intakes for Thiamin, Riboflavin, Niacin, Vitamin B$_6$, Folate, Vitamin B$_{12}$, Pantothenic Acid, Biotin, and Choline*. Washington, DC: National Academy Press.

29. Herbert, V. 1999. Folic acid. In: M. E. Shils, J. A. Olsen, M. Shike, and A. C. Ross, eds. *Modern Nutrition in Health and Disease*, 9th ed. Philadelphia: Lippincott Williams & Wilkins, pp. 433–446.

30. Lane, L. A., and C. Rojas-Fernandez. 2002. Treatment of vitamin B$_{12}$-deficiency anemia: oral versus parenteral therapy. *Ann. Pharmacother.* 36:1268–1272.

31. Public Health Agency of Canada. 1999. *Measuring up—A Health Surveillance Update on Canadian Children and Youth. Neural Tube Defects*. Available at www.phac-aspc.gc.ca/publicat/meas-haut/mu_e-eng.php (accessed February 18, 2011).

32. De Wals, P., F. Tairou, M. Van Allen, S.-H. Uh, R. B. Lowry, B. Sibbald, J. A. Evans, M. C. Van den Hof, P. Zimmer, M. Crowley, B. Fernandez, N. S. Lee, and T. Niyonsenga. 2007. Reduction in neural-tube defects after folic acid fortification in Canada. *New Eng. J. Med.* 357:135–142.

33. Beresford, S. A., and C. J. Boushey. 1997. Homocysteine, folic acid, and cardiovascular disease risk. In: A. Bendich and R. J. Deckelbaum, eds. *Preventive Nutrition: The Comprehensive Guide for Health Professionals*. Totowa, NJ: Humana Press.

34. Mayer, E. L., D. W. Jacobsen, and K. Robinson. 1996. Homocysteine and coronary atherosclerosis. *J. Am. Coll. Cardiol.* 27:517–527.

35. Marti-Carvajal, A. J., I. Sola, D. Lathyris, and G. Salanti. 2009. Homocysteine lowering interventions for preventing cardiovascular events. *Cochraine Database Syst. Rev.* (4):CD006612.

36. Abraham, J. M., and L. Cho. 2010. The homocysteine hypothesis: still relevant to the prevention and treatment of cardiovascular disease? *Cleveland Clinic J. Med.* 77:911–918.

37. Keusch, G. T. 2003. The history of nutrition: malnutrition, infection and immunity. *J. Nutr.* 133:336S–340S.

38. Beck, M. A., J. Handy, and O. A. Levander. 2004. Host nutritional status: the neglected virulence factor. *Trends Microbiol.* 12:417–423.

39. Brundtland, G. H. 2000. Nutrition and infection: malnutrition and mortality in public health. *Nutr. Rev.* 58:S1–4.

40. Scrimshaw, N. S. 2003. Historical concepts of interactions, synergism and antagonism between nutrition and infection. *J. Nutr.* 133:316S–321S.

41. Marti, A., A. Marcos, and J. A. Martinez. 2001. Obesity and immune function relationships. *Obesity Rev.* 2:131–140.

42. Lamas, O., A. Marti, and J. A. Martinez. 2002. Obesity and immunocompetence. *Eur. J. Cin. Nutr.* 56(suppl):S42–45.

43. Fantuzzi, G. 2005. Adipose tissue, adipokines, and inflammation. *J. Allergy Clin. Immunol.* 115:911–919.

44. Calder, P. C., and C. J. Field. 2002. Fatty acids, inflammation and immunity. In: P. C. Calder, C. J. Field, and H. S. Gill, eds. *Nutrition and Immune Function.* New York: CABI Publishing, pp. 57–92.

45. Wu, D. 2004. Modulation of immune and inflammatory responses by dietary lipids. *Curr. Opin. Lipidol.* 15:43–47.

46. Institute of Medicine, Food and Nutrition Board. 2005. *Dietary Reference Intakes for Energy, Carbohydrate, Fiber, Fat, Fatty Acids, Cholesterol, Protein, and Amino Acids (Macronutrients).* Washington, DC: National Academy Press.

47. Semba, R. D. 2002. Vitamin A, infection and immune function. In: P. C. Calder, C. J. Field, and H. S. Gill, eds. *Nutrition and Immune Function.* New York: CABI Publishing, pp. 151–169.

48. Field, C. J., I. R. Johnson, and P. D. Schley. 2002. Nutrients and their role in host resistance to infection. *J. Leukoc. Biol.* 71:16–32.

49. Griffiths, J. K. 2000. The vitamin A paradox. *J. Pediatr.* 137:604–607.

50. Prasad, A. Zinc, infection and immune function. In: P. C. Calder, C. J. Field, and H. S. Gill, eds. *Nutrition and Immune Function.* New York: CABI Publishing, pp. 193–207.

51. Bonham, M., J. M. O'Connor, B. M. Hannigan, and J. J. Strain. 2002. The immune system as a physiological indicator of marginal copper status? *Br. J. Nutr.* 87:393–403.

52. Kuvibidila, S., and B. S. Baliga. 2002. Role of iron in immunity and infection. In: P. C. Calder, C. J. Field, and H. S. Gill, eds. *Nutrition and Immune Function.* New York: CABI Publishing, pp. 209–228.

53. McKenzie, R. C., J. R. Arthur, S. M. Miller, T. S. Rafferty, and G. J. Beckett. 2002. Selenium and the immune system. In: P. C. Calder, C. J. Field, and H. S. Gill, eds. *Nutrition and Immune Function.* New York: CABI Publishing, pp. 229–250.

54. Nair, M. P., and S. A. Schwartz. 1990. Immunoregulation of natural and lymphokine-activated killer cells by selenium. *Immunopharmacology* 19:177–183.

55. Public Health Agency of Canada. 2011. *Understanding Influenza.* Available at www.phac-aspc.gc.ca/influenza/faf2-eng.php (accessed March 5, 2011).

56. Prasad, A. 1996. Zinc: the biology and therapeutics of an ion. *Ann. Intern. Med.* 125:142–143.

57. Jackson, J. L., E. Lesho, and C. Peterson. 2000. Zinc and the common cold: a meta-analysis revisited. *J. Nutr.* 130:1512S–1515S.

58. Caruso, T. J., C. G. Prober, and J. M Gwaltney. 2007. Treatment of naturally acquired common colds with zinc: a structured review. *Clin. Infect Dis.* 45(5):569–574.

59. Chandra, R. K. 1984. Excessive intake of zinc impairs immune responses. *JAMA* 252:1443–1446.

Do Zinc Lozenges Help Fight the Common Cold?

The common cold has plagued human beings since the beginning of time. A cold is a mild infection of the nose and throat caused by a variety of viruses. Characteristic symptoms include a runny nose, sneezing, cough, and sore throat.[55] Children usually have more colds each year than adults. Although colds are typically benign, they result in significant absenteeism from work and cause discomfort and stress. Finding a cure for the common cold has been at the forefront of modern medicine for many years.

It is estimated that more than 200 different viruses can cause a cold. The most frequent causes of adult colds are a group of viruses called coronaviruses; rhinoviruses are another group that causes about one-third of all adult colds. Because of this variety, finding treatments or potential cures for a cold is extremely challenging.

The role of zinc in the overall health of our immune system is well known, but zinc has also been shown to inhibit the replication of rhinoviruses and other viruses that cause the common cold. These specific findings have led to speculation that taking zinc supplements may reduce the length and severity of colds.[56, 57] Consequently, zinc lozenges were formulated as a means of providing potential relief from cold symptoms. These lozenges are readily found in a variety of formulations and dosages in most drugstores.

Does taking zinc in lozenge form actually reduce the length and severity of a cold? During the past 20 years, numerous research studies have been conducted to try to answer this question. Unfortunately, the results of these studies are inconclusive: about half have found that zinc lozenges do reduce the length and severity of a cold, whereas about half have found that zinc lozenges have no effect on cold symptoms or duration.[58] Some reasons that researchers have proposed to explain the different findings of these various studies include the following:

Zinc lozenges come in different formulations and dosages.

- Inability to truly "blind" participants to the treatment: Because zinc lozenges have a unique taste, it may be difficult to keep the research participants uninformed about whether they are getting zinc lozenges or a placebo. Knowing which lozenge they are taking could lead participants to report biased results.

- Self-reported symptoms are subject to inaccuracy: Many studies had the research participants self-report changes in symptoms. Such self-reports may be inaccurate and influenced by mood and other emotional factors.

- Wide variety of viruses that cause a cold: We noted that more than 200 different viruses can cause a cold, and it is highly unlikely that zinc can combat all of these. It is possible that people who do not respond favourably to zinc lozenges are suffering from a cold virus that cannot be treated with zinc.

- Differences in zinc formulations and dosages: The type of zinc formulation, the dosages of zinc consumed, and the timing of consumption differed across studies. For example, it is estimated that for zinc to be effective, at least 80 mg of zinc should be consumed each day and that people should begin using zinc lozenges within 48 hours of onset of cold symptoms. Yet studies followed a variety of dosing and timing protocols. These differences most likely contributed to the wide variety of responses. Also, sweeteners and flavourings found in many zinc lozenges, such as citric acid, sorbitol, and mannitol, may bind the zinc and inhibit its ability to be absorbed into the body, limiting its effectiveness.

- Supplements may provide excessive zinc and actually impair immune function: The level of zinc noted

The congestion, fatigue, and other symptoms of the common cold cause absenteeism from work or school as well as personal discomfort.

earlier as the effective dose—80 mg—is nearly 10 times the RDA and can decrease the absorption of copper and iron if continued for long periods of time. In addition, one experimental study showed that 300 mg/day of supplemental zinc reduced immune cell response and decreased destruction of bacteria by neutrophils.[59] This amount is about six tablets of a zinc gluconate pill that has 50 mg of elemental zinc.

- Measurement of subject compliance: Typically participants need to take the zinc lozenges every two to three hours while they are awake (5–8 lozenges/day) for the duration of the study, which can last 6 to 10 days. Unless the participants are monitored by research staff, researchers have to rely on the participants to self-report their compliance to the study protocol. Of course, different compliance rates could alter the outcomes of different studies.

Because there is no conclusive evidence supporting or refuting the effectiveness of zinc lozenges on the common cold, the debate on whether people should take them to treat their colds will most likely continue for many years.

Using the Evidence

1. Based on what you have learned here, do you think taking zinc lozenges can be an effective means of fighting the common cold?

2. Based on what you know about zinc, do you think that there is any harm in taking a zinc supplement?

3. Even if you have only about a 50% chance of reducing the length and severity of your cold by taking zinc lozenges, do you think they're worth a try?

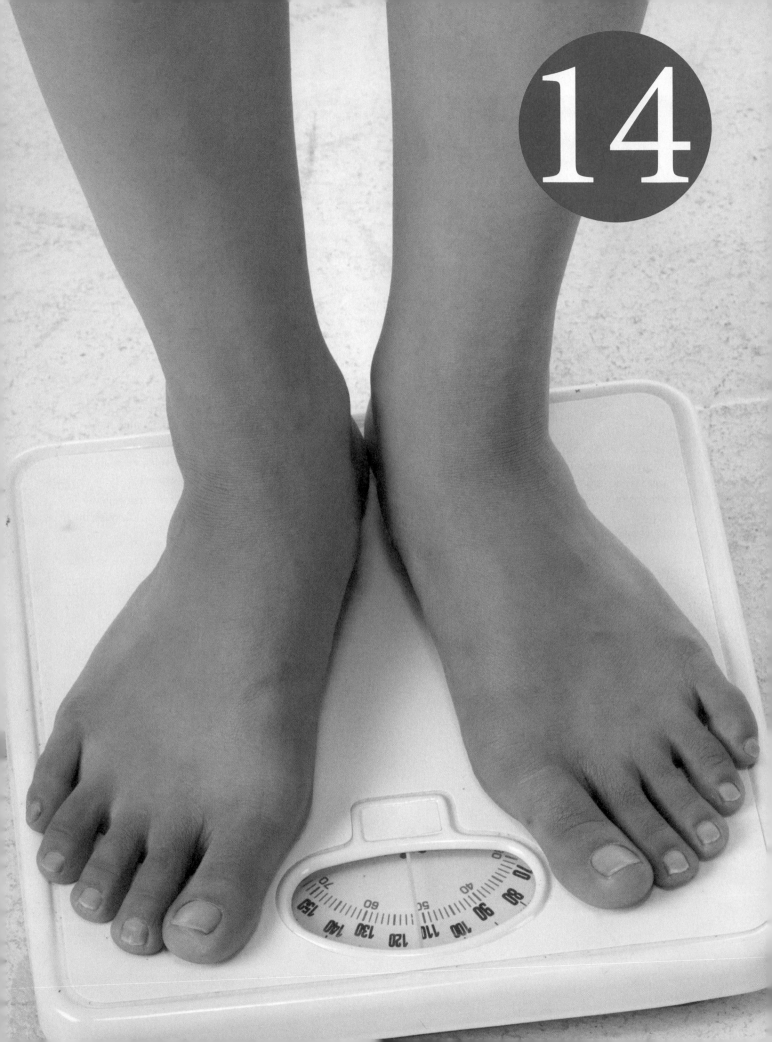

Achieving and Maintaining a Healthy Body Weight

Chapter Objectives | *After reading this chapter, you will be able to:*

1. Define what is meant by a healthy weight, *p. 486.*
2. Define the terms *underweight, overweight, obesity,* and *morbid obesity* and discuss the potential health risks of each of these weight classifications, *pp. 486–487, 521–523.*
3. List three methods that can be used to assess your body composition or risk for obesity, *pp. 489–491.*
4. Define *direct calorimetry, indirect calorimetry,* and *doubly labelled water* and list one strength and one limitation of each of these methods, *p. 494.*
5. Identify and discuss the three components of energy expenditure, *pp. 493–497.*
6. Discuss three factors that can increase BMR and three factors that can decrease BMR, *p. 495.*
7. List and describe at least two theories that link genetic influences to control of body weight, *p. 498.*
8. Discuss at least two societal factors that influence body weight, *pp. 501–505.*
9. Develop an action plan for healthy weight loss, *pp. 506–513.*
10. List and describe three treatment options for obesity, *pp. 513–514, 515–516.*

A healthy body weight varies from person to person. Fashion model Emme's body weight is healthy for her.

As a teenager, she won a full athletic scholarship to Syracuse University, where she was honoured for her "significant contribution to women's athletics and to the sport of rowing." After graduating, she became a television reporter and news anchor in Flagstaff, Arizona. Then she went into modelling, and soon her face smiled out from the covers of fashion magazines, cosmetics ads, even a billboard in Times Square. Now considered a "supermodel," she has her own website, her own clothing line, and even a collection of dolls. *People* magazine has twice selected her as one of the "50 Most Beautiful People," and *Glamour* magazine named her "Woman of the Year." So who is she? Her name is Emme Aronson . . . and by the way, at 1.8 m tall, her average weight is 86 kg.

Emme describes herself as "very well-proportioned." She focuses not on maintaining a certain weight but instead on keeping healthy and fit. A cancer survivor, she follows a nutritious diet and works out regularly. Observing that "We live in a society that is based on the attainment of unrealistic beauty," Emme works hard to get out the message that self-esteem should not be contingent on size. On news programs and talk shows, at high schools, and on college campuses, she speaks out against weight-based discrimination and promotes acceptance of body diversity. Citing reports that 80% of women and many men are unhappy with their bodies, she encourages people of all sizes to celebrate their individuality.[1, 2]

Are you happy with your weight, shape, body composition, and fitness? If not, what needs to change—your diet, your level of physical activity, or maybe just your attitude? What role do diet and physical activity play in maintaining a healthy body weight? How much of your body size and shape is due to genetics? What influence does society—including food advertising—have on your weight? And if you decide that you do need to lose weight, what's the best way to do it? In this chapter, we will explore these questions and provide some answers.

What Is a Healthy Body Weight?

As you begin to think about achieving and maintaining a healthy weight, it's important to understand what a healthy body weight actually means. A healthy weight can be defined as all of the following:[3]

- A weight that is appropriate for your age and physical development
- A weight that you can achieve and sustain without severely curtailing your food intake or constantly dieting
- A weight that is based on your genetic background and family history of body shape and weight
- A weight that is compatible with normal blood pressure, lipid levels, and glucose tolerance
- A weight that promotes good eating habits and allows you to participate in regular physical activity
- A weight that is acceptable to you

As you can see, a healthy weight is not necessarily identified by thinness or extreme muscularity. In truth, there is no one particular body type that can be defined as healthy. Thus, achieving a healthy body weight should not be dictated by the latest fad or current societal expectations of what is acceptable.

Now that we know what a healthy body weight is, let's look at some terms applying to underweight and overweight. Physicians, nutritionists, and other scientists define **underweight** as having too little body fat to maintain health; having too little body fat causes a person to have a weight that is below an acceptably defined standard for a given height. **Overweight** is defined as having a moderate amount of excess body fat; this moderate amount of excess fat results in a person having a weight that is greater than some accepted standard for a given height but is not considered obese. **Obesity** is defined as having an excess amount of body fat that adversely affects health, resulting in a person having a weight that is substantially greater than some

underweight Having too little body fat to maintain health, causing a person to have a weight that is below an acceptable defined standard for a given height.

overweight Having a moderate amount of excess body fat, resulting in a person having a weight that is greater than some accepted standard for a given height but is not considered obese.

obesity Having an excess amount of body fat that adversely affects health, resulting in a person having a weight that is substantially greater than some accepted standard for a given height.

accepted standard for a given height. People can also suffer from **morbid obesity**; in this case, their body weights exceed 100% of normal, putting them at very high risk for serious health consequences. In the next section, we discuss how these terms are defined using certain indicators of body weight and body composition.

How Can You Evaluate Your Body Weight?

Various methods are available to help you determine whether or not you are currently maintaining a healthy body weight. Let's review a few of these methods.

Determine Your Body Mass Index (BMI)

Body mass index (BMI, or *Quetelet's index*) is a commonly used index representing the ratio of a person's body weight to the square of his or her height. A person's BMI can be calculated using the following equation:

$$\text{BMI (kg/m}^2) = \text{weight (kg)/height (m)}^2$$

For those less familiar with the metric system, there is an equation to calculate BMI using weight in pounds and height in inches:

$$\text{BMI (kg/m}^2) = [\text{weight (lb)/height (inches)}^2] \times 703$$

A less exact but often useful method is to use the graph in **Figure 14.1**, which shows approximate BMIs for a person's height and weight. A BMI between 18.5 and 24.9 is considered to be a normal weight, which is associated with the least risk of developing health problems.[4]

morbid obesity A condition in which a person's body weight exceeds 100% of normal, putting him or her at very high risk for serious health consequences.

body mass index (BMI) A measurement representing the ratio of a person's body weight to his or her height.

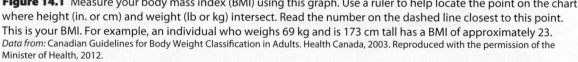

Figure 14.1 Measure your body mass index (BMI) using this graph. Use a ruler to help locate the point on the chart where height (in. or cm) and weight (lb or kg) intersect. Read the number on the dashed line closest to this point. This is your BMI. For example, an individual who weighs 69 kg and is 173 cm tall has a BMI of approximately 23. *Data from:* Canadian Guidelines for Body Weight Classification in Adults. Health Canada, 2003. Reproduced with the permission of the Minister of Health, 2012.

Table 14.1 Risk of Developing Health Problems Based on BMI Category

Classification	BMI Category	Risk of Developing Health Problems
Underweight	< 18.5	Increased
Normal Weight	18.5–24.9	Least
Overweight	25.0–29.9	Increased
Obese		
Class I	30.0–34.9	High
Class II	35.0–39.9	Very High
Class III	≥ 40.0	Extremely High

Note: For persons 65 years and older the "normal" range may begin slightly above BMI 18.5 and extend into the "overweight" range.
Data from: Canadian Guidelines for Body Weight Classification in Adults. Health Canada, 2003. Reproduced with the permission of the Minister of Health, 2012.

Why Is BMI Important?

BMI provides an important clue to a person's overall health. Research studies show that a person's risk for type 2 diabetes, high blood pressure, heart disease, and other diseases largely increases when BMI is above a value of 30. On the other hand, having a very low BMI, defined as a value below 18.5, is also associated with increased risk of health problems and death.

Table 14.1 shows how the risk of developing health problems increases significantly with a BMI value below 18.5 kg/m^2 or above a BMI value of 30 kg/m^2. Having a BMI value within the normal range means that there is a low risk of developing health problems. If a person's BMI value falls outside of this range, either higher or lower, the risk becomes greater than the average risk (see the calculations in the You Do the Math box on the next page).

Limitations of BMI

While calculating your BMI can be very helpful in estimating your health risk, this method has a number of limitations that should be taken into consideration. BMI cannot tell us how much of a person's body mass is composed of fat, nor can it give us an indication of where on the body excess fat is stored. As we'll discuss shortly, fat stores in the abdominal area increase the risk of chronic disease more than fat stores in other areas of the body. A person's age affects his or her BMI; BMI does not give a fair indication of overweight or obesity in people over the age of 65 years, as the BMI standards are based on data from younger people, and BMI does not accurately reflect the differential rates of bone and muscle loss in older people. BMI also cannot reflect differences in bone and muscle growth in children. Recent research indicates that BMI is more strongly associated with height in young people; thus, taller children are more likely to be identified as overweight or obese, even though they may not have higher levels of body fat.[5]

BMI also does not take into account physical and metabolic differences between people of different ethnic backgrounds. That is, at the same BMI people from different ethnic backgrounds will have different levels of body fat. Dr. Scott Lear and colleagues from Simon Fraser University in British Columbia compared the relation between abdominal adipose tissue and total body fat in Canadians of Aboriginal, Chinese, and South Asian origin with people of European descent. Results showed that men and women of Chinese and South Asian origin have a higher amount of abdominal fat at a similar BMI; South Asians also had a greater percentage of total body fat.[6] There is also evidence that, even at the same BMI level, Asian, Hispanic, and African American women have a higher risk for

YOU DO THE MATH

Calculating Your Body Mass Index

Calculate your personal BMI value based on your height and weight. Let's use Theo's values as an example:

$$BMI = weight~(kg)/height(m)^2$$

1. Theo's weight is 200 lb. To convert his weight to kilograms, divide his weight in pounds by 2.2 lb per kg:

    $$200~lb/2.2~lb~per~kg = 90.91~kg$$

2. Theo's height is 6 feet 8 inches, or 80 inches. To convert his height to metres, multiply his height in inches by 0.0254 metres/inch:

    $$80~in. \times 0.0254~m/in. = 2.03~m$$

3. Find the square of his height in metres:

    $$2.03~m \times 2.03~m = 4.13~m^2$$

4. Then, divide his weight in kilograms by his height in squared metres to get his BMI value:

    $$90.91~kg/4.13m^2 = 22.01~kg/m^2$$

    Is Theo underweight according to this BMI value? As you can see in Figure 14.1, this value shows that he is maintaining a normal, healthy weight!

---

diabetes than white women.[7] The same study also found that when Asian and Hispanic women gained weight, their risk of developing diabetes over a 20-year period was approximately twice as high as it was for white and African American women who gained the same amount of weight.

Finally, BMI is limited when used with people who have a disproportionately higher muscle mass for a given height, such as certain types of athletes, and with pregnant and lactating women. For example Randy, a 23-year-old weight lifter, is 1.7 m and weighs 95.5 kg. According to our BMI calculations, Randy's BMI is 33, placing him in the obese Class I and high-risk category for many diseases. Is Randy really obese? In cases such as his, an assessment of body composition is necessary.

Measuring Your Body Composition

There are many methods available to assess your **body composition**, or the amount of **body fat** (or *adipose tissue*) and **lean body mass** (or *lean tissue*) you have. **Figure 14.2** lists and describes some of the more common methods. It is important to remember that tools for measuring body composition can provide only an *estimate* of your body fat and lean body mass; they cannot determine your exact level of these tissues. Because the range of error of these methods can be from 3% to more than 20%, body composition results should not be used as the only indicator of health status.

Let's return to Randy, whose BMI of 33 kg/m² places him in the obese Class I category. But is he obese? Randy trains with weights four days per week, rides the exercise bike for about 30 minutes per session three times per week, and does not take drugs, smoke cigarettes, or drink alcohol. Through his local gym, Randy contacted a trained technician who assesses body composition. The results of his skinfold measurements show that his body fat is 11%. The average percent body fat standard is 15% for men and 23% for women. Minimum healthy fat levels are estimated to be 5% for men and 8% to 12% for women.[8] Randy is an example of a person whose BMI appears very high but who is not actually obese.

Assess Your Fat Distribution Patterns

To evaluate the health of your current body weight, it is also helpful to consider the way fat is distributed throughout your body. This is because your fat distribution pattern is known

BMI is not an accurate indicator of overweight for certain populations, including heavily muscled people.

body composition The ratio of a person's body fat to lean body mass. Also, the amount of bone, fat, and muscle tissue in the body.

body fat mass The amount of body fat, or adipose tissue, a person has.

lean body mass The amount of fat-free tissue, or bone, muscle, and internal organs, a person has.

Method		Limitations
Underwater weighing: Considered the most accurate method. Estimates body fat within a 2%–3% margin of error. This means that if your underwater weighing test shows you have 20% body fat, this value could be no lower than 17% and no higher than 23%. Used primarily for research purposes.		• Must be comfortable in water. • Requires trained technician and specialized equipment. • Does not work well with obese people. • Must abstain from food for at least 8 hours and from exercise for at least 12 hours prior to testing.
Skinfolds: Involves "pinching" a person's fold of skin (with its underlying layer of fat) at various locations on the body. The fold is measured using a specially designed caliper. When performed by a skilled technician, it can estimate body fat with an error of 3%–4%. This means that if your skinfold test shows you have 20% body fat, your actual value could be as low as 16% or as high as 24%.		• Less accurate unless technician is well trained. • Proper prediction equation must be used to improve accuracy. • Person being measured may not want to be touched or may not want to expose their skin. • Cannot be used to measure obese people, as their skinfolds are too large for the caliper.
Bioelectrical impedance analysis (BIA): Involves sending a very low level of electrical current through a person's body. As water is a good conductor of electricity and lean body mass is made up of mostly water, the rate at which the electricity is conducted gives an indication of a person's lean body mass and body fat. This method can be done while lying down, with electrodes attached to the feet, hands, and the BIA machine. Hand-held and standing models (that look like bathroom scales) are now available. Under the best of circumstances, BIA can estimate body fat with an error of 3%–4%.		• Less accurate. • Body fluid levels must be normal. • Proper prediction equation must be used to improve accuracy. • Should not eat for 4 hours and should not exercise for 12 hours prior to the test. • No alcohol should be consumed for 48 hours prior to the test. • Females should not be measured if they are retaining water because of menstrual cycle changes.
Dual-energy X-ray absorptiometry (DXA): The technology is based on using very low level X-ray to differentiate between bone tissue, soft (or lean) tissue, and fat (or adipose) tissue. It involves lying for about 30 minutes on a specialized bed fully clothed, with all metal objects removed. The margin of error for predicting body fat ranges from 2%–4%.	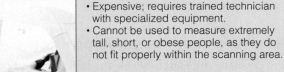	• Expensive; requires trained technician with specialized equipment. • Cannot be used to measure extremely tall, short, or obese people, as they do not fit properly within the scanning area.
Bod Pod: A machine that uses air displacement to measure body compostition. This machine is a large, egg-shaped chamber made from fibreglass. The person being measured sits in the machine wearing a swimsuit. The door is closed and the machine measures how much air is displaced. This value is used to calculate body composition. It appears promising as an easier and equally accurate alternative to underwater weighing in many populations.	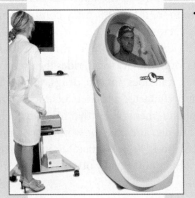	• Expensive.

Figure 14.2 Overview of various body composition assessment methods.

to affect your risk for various diseases. **Figure 14.3** shows two types of fat patterning. *Apple-shaped fat patterning*, or abdominal obesity, is known to significantly increase a person's risk for many chronic diseases, such as type 2 diabetes, heart disease, and high blood pressure. It is thought that the apple-shaped patterning causes problems with the metabolism of fat and carbohydrate, leading to unhealthy changes in blood cholesterol, insulin, glucose, and blood pressure. In contrast, *pear-shaped fat patterning*, or lower-body obesity, does not seem to significantly increase your risk for chronic diseases. Women tend to store fat in their lower body, and men in their abdominal region. In 2004, a study involving more than 10 000 people found that 64% of women are pear-shaped and 38% of men are apple-shaped.[9]

The measurement of waist circumference is often used in combination with BMI to assess health risk (see Table 14.3); however, it can also be used as an indicator of fat distribution and an independent indicator of health risk for those individuals with a BMI in the 19.5 to 34.9 range.[10] You can use the following method to determine your waist circumference:

1. Ask a friend to measure your waist between the bottom of your lower rib and the top of your pelvic bone (see **Figure 14.4** below). You should be standing and your friend should stand beside you, fitting the tape so that it fits snugly against your skin. The circumference should be measured to the nearest 0.5 cm.
2. Now compare this measurement with the recommended waist circumference cut-off points shown in Table 14.2:

Table 14.2 Ethnic-Specific Values for Waist Circumference

Country or Ethnic Group	Waist Circumference (cm/in.)	
	Men	Women
North American	≥ 102/40	≥ 88/35
Europid	≥ 94/37	≥ 80/31.5
South Asian, Chinese	≥ 90/35.4	≥ 80/31.5
Japanese	≥ 85/33.5	≥ 90/35.4
South and Central American	Use South Asian cut-offs	
Sub-Saharan African	Use South Asian cut-offs	
Eastern Mediterranean and Middle East (Arab)	Use South Asian cut-offs	

Waist circumference measurements greater than these cut-off points have been shown to be associated with greatly increased risk of chronic diseases.[10]
Data from: 2006 Canadian clinical practice guidelines on the management and prevention of obesity in adults and children [summary]. © CMAJ (2007). This work is protected by copyright and the making of this copy was with the permission of Access Copyright. Any alteration of its content or further copying in any form whatsoever is strictly prohibited unless otherwise permitted by law.

Once you figure out your BMI and waist circumference (WC), how do you interpret it? Table 14.3 shows the BMI cut-off points above which there are associated health risks. The level of risk refers to relative risk or the risk of developing health problems (such as type 2 diabetes or cardiovascular diseases) in those with abnormal levels and distribution of body fat as measured by BMI and WC. It is important to remember that there are other factors that contribute to your health risk that must be considered in addition to BMI and WC.[10]

Recap

Body mass index, body composition, and waist circumference are tools that can help assess the risk of disease associated with a person's current body weight. None of these methods is completely accurate, but most may be used appropriately as general health indicators.

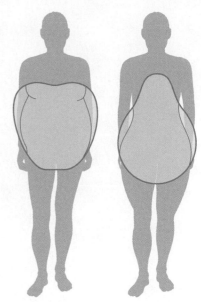

(a) Apple-shaped fat patterning   (b) Pear-shaped fat patterning

Figure 14.3 Fat distribution patterns. (a) An apple-shaped fat-distribution pattern increases an individual's risk for many chronic diseases. (b) A pear-shaped fat-distribution pattern does not seem to be associated with an increased risk for chronic disease.
Data from: Pearson Science

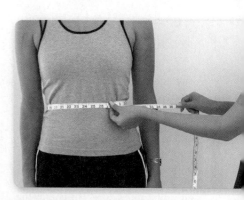

Figure 14.4 Waist circumference measurement.

Table 14.3 Health Risk Classification Using Both BMI and Waist Circumference

		Body Mass Index		
		Normal	**Overweight**	**Obese Class I**
Waist Circumference	< 102 cm/40 in. (Males) < 88 cm/35 in. (Females)	Least Risk	Increased Risk	High Risk
	≥ 102 cm/40 in. (Males) ≥ 88 cm/35 in. (Females)	Increased Risk	High Risk	Very High Risk

Data from: Canadian Guidelines for Body Weight Classification in Adults. Health Canada, 2003. Reproduced with the permission of the Minister of Health, 2012.

What Makes Us Gain and Lose Weight?

Have you ever wondered why some people are thin and others are overweight, even though they seem to eat about the same diet? If so, you're not alone. For hundreds of years, researchers have puzzled over what makes us gain and lose weight. In this section, we explore some information and current theories that may shed light on this complex question.

We Gain or Lose Weight When Energy Intake and Expenditure Are Out of Balance

Fluctuations in body weight are a result of changes in **energy intake** (the food and beverages consumed) and **energy expenditure** (the amount of energy expended at rest and during physical activity). This relationship between what we eat and what we do is defined by the energy balance equation:

Energy balance occurs when energy intake = energy expenditure

This means that energy is balanced when we consume the same amount of energy that we expend each day. **Figure 14.5** shows how our weight changes when we change either side of this equation. From this figure, you can see that to lose body weight, we must expend more energy than we consume. In contrast, to gain weight, we must consume more energy than we expend. Finding the proper balance between energy intake and expenditure allows someone to maintain a healthy body weight.

Energy Intake Is the Food We Eat Each Day

Energy intake is equal to the amount of energy in the food we eat each day. This value includes all foods and beverages. Daily energy intake is expressed as *kilocalories per day* (*kcal/day*, or *kcal/d*). Energy intake can be estimated manually by using food composition tables or computerized dietary analysis programs. (The Canadian Nutrient File can be accessed at http://webprod3.hc-sc.gc.ca/cnf-fce/index-eng.jsp.) The energy content of each food is a function of the amount of carbohydrate, fat, protein, and alcohol that each food contains; vitamins and minerals have no energy value, so they contribute zero kilocalories to our energy intake.

Remember that the energy value of carbohydrate and protein is 4 kcal/g and the energy value of fat is 9 kcal/g. The energy value of alcohol is 7 kcal/g. By multiplying the energy value (in kcal/g) by the amount of the nutrient (in grams), you can calculate how much energy is in a particular food. For instance, 250 mL of quick oatmeal has an energy value of 142 kcal. How is this energy value derived? 250 mL of oatmeal contains 6 g of protein, 25 g of carbohydrate, and 2 g of fat. Using the energy values for each nutrient, you can calculate the total energy content of oatmeal:

6 g protein × 4 kcal/g = 24 kcal from protein
25 g carbohydrate × 4 kcal/g = 100 kcal from carbohydrate
2 g fat × 9 kcal/g = 18 kcal from fat
Total kcal for 250 mL oatmeal = 24 kcal + 100 kcal + 18 kcal = 142 kcal

The energy provided by a bowl of oatmeal is derived from its protein, carbohydrate, and fat content.

energy intake The amount of energy a person consumes; in other words, it is the number of kilocalories consumed from food and beverages.

energy expenditure The energy the body expends to maintain its basic functions and to perform all levels of movement and activity.

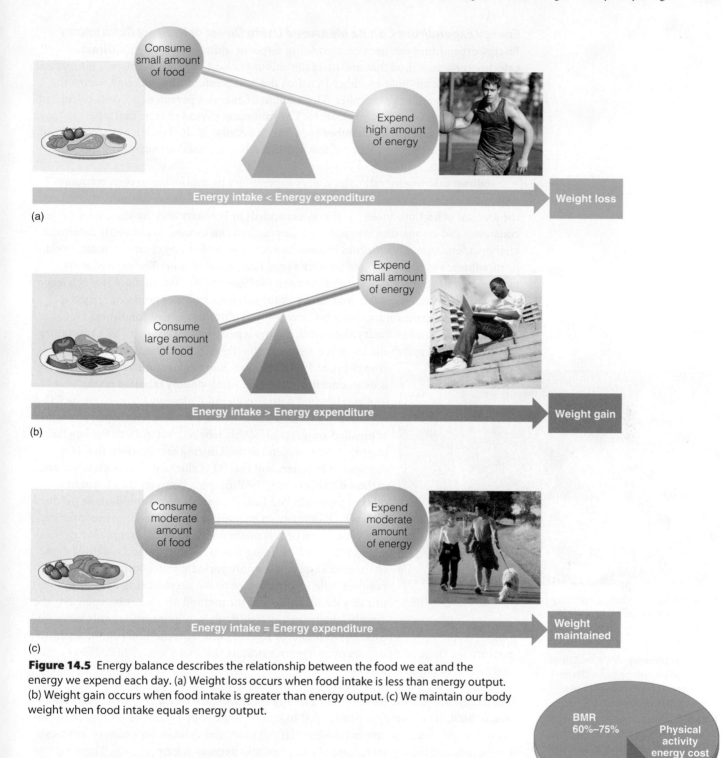

Figure 14.5 Energy balance describes the relationship between the food we eat and the energy we expend each day. (a) Weight loss occurs when food intake is less than energy output. (b) Weight gain occurs when food intake is greater than energy output. (c) We maintain our body weight when food intake equals energy output.

When someone's total daily energy intake exceeds the amount of energy that person expends, then weight gain results. An excess intake of approximately 3500 kcal will result in a gain of 0.45 kg. Without exercise, this gain will likely be fat.

Energy Expenditure Includes More Than Just Physical Activity

Energy expenditure (also known as energy output) is the energy the body expends to maintain its basic functions and to perform all levels of movement and activity. Total 24-hour energy expenditure is calculated by estimating the energy used during rest and as a result of physical activity. There are three components of energy expenditure: basal metabolic rate (BMR), thermic effect of food (TEF), and energy cost of physical activity (**Figure 14.6**). We discuss these components in detail shortly.

Components of energy expenditure

Figure 14.6 The components of energy expenditure include basal metabolic rate (BMR), the thermic effect of food (TEF), and the energy cost of physical activity. BMR accounts for 60% to 75% of our total energy output, whereas TEF and physical activity together account for 25% to 40%.

Energy Expenditure Can Be Measured Using Direct or Indirect Calorimetry

Energy expenditure can be measured using direct or indirect calorimetry. **Direct calorimetry** is a method that measures the amount of heat the body releases. This method is done using an air-tight chamber in which the heat produced by the body warms the water that surrounds the chamber. The amount of energy a person expends is calculated from the changes in water temperature. The minimum period of time that a person must stay in a direct calorimetry chamber is 24 hours; because of the burden to the individual, the high cost, and the complexity of this method, it is rarely used to measure energy expenditure in humans.

Indirect calorimetry estimates energy expenditure by measuring oxygen consumption and carbon dioxide production. Because there is a predictable relationship between the amount of heat produced (or energy expended) by the body and the amount of oxygen consumed and carbon dioxide produced, this method can be used to indirectly determine energy expenditure. This method involves the use of a whole-body chamber, mask, hood, or mouthpiece to collect expired air over a specified period of time. The expired air is analyzed for oxygen and carbon dioxide content (**Figure 14.7**). This method is much less expensive and more accessible than direct calorimetry, so it is most commonly used to measure energy expenditure under both resting and physically active conditions.

Both direct and indirect calorimetry require a person to be confined to a laboratory setting or special metabolic chamber, which limits the ability to determine a person's energy expenditure in a free-living environment. This limitation is overcome in a technique using **doubly labelled water**, that is, water labelled with isotopes of hydrogen (deuterium, or ^{2}H) and oxygen (^{18}O). In this method, the research subject consumes controlled amounts of doubly labelled water. Both the labelled hydrogen and oxygen are used during metabolism; the ^{2}H is eliminated in water, and the ^{18}O is eliminated in both water and carbon dioxide. Thus, the difference between the elimination rates of these labelled isotopes measures carbon dioxide production, which in turn can be used to estimate energy expenditure. The advantages of this method are that it measures energy expenditure in free-living situations over periods of three days to three weeks, requires only periodic collection of urine, and requires little inconvenience to the person being measured. The primary disadvantages of the method are that it is expensive, the doubly labelled water is difficult to acquire, and it only measures total 24-hour energy expenditure. This method cannot separately measure the three components of energy expenditure discussed next: BMR, TEF, or the energy cost of physical activity.

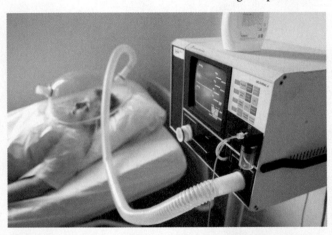

Figure 14.7 Indirect calorimetry can be used to measure the components of energy expenditure.

direct calorimetry A method used to determine energy expenditure by measuring the amount of heat released by the body.

indirect calorimetry A method used to estimate energy expenditure by measuring oxygen consumption and carbon dioxide production.

doubly labelled water A form of indirect calorimetry that measures total daily energy expenditure through the rate of carbon dioxide production. It requires the consumption of water that is labelled with non-radioactive isotopes of hydrogen (deuterium, or ^{2}H) and oxygen (^{18}O).

basal metabolic rate (BMR) The energy the body expends to maintain its fundamental physiologic functions.

Our Basal Metabolic Rate Is Our Energy Expenditure at Rest

Basal metabolic rate, or **BMR**, is the energy expended just to maintain the body's *basal*, or *resting*, functions. These functions include respiration, circulation, maintaining body temperature, synthesis of new cells and tissues, secretion of hormones, and nervous system activity. The majority of our energy output each day (about 60% to 75%) is a result of our BMR. This means that 60% to 75% of our energy output goes to fuel the basic activities of staying alive, aside from any physical activity.

BMR varies widely among people. The primary determinant of our BMR is the amount of lean body mass we have. People with a higher lean body mass have a higher BMR, as lean body mass is more metabolically active than body fat. Thus, it takes more energy to support this active tissue. One common assumption is that obese people have a depressed BMR. This is usually not the case. Most studies of obese people show that the amount of energy they expend for every kilogram of lean body mass is similar to that of a non-obese person. In general, people who weigh more also have more lean body mass and

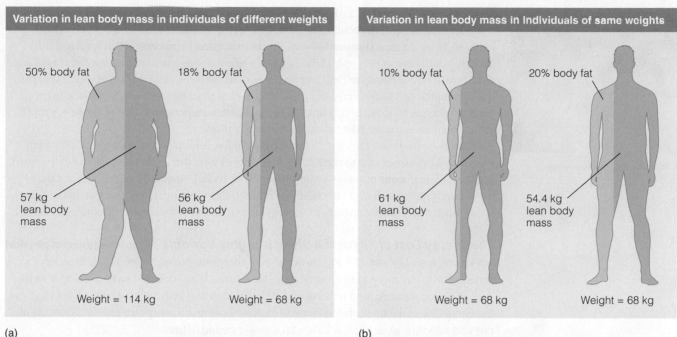

Figure 14.8 Lean body mass varies in people with different body weights and body fat levels. (a) The person on the left has a higher body weight, body fat, and lean body mass than the person on the right. (b) The two people are the same weight but the person on the right has more body fat and less lean body mass than the person on the left.

consequently have a *higher* BMR. See **Figure 14.8** for an example of how lean body mass can vary for people with different body weights and body fat levels.

BMR decreases with age, approximately 3% to 5% per decade after age 30. This age-related decrease results partly from hormonal changes, but much of this change is due to the loss of lean body mass resulting from physical inactivity. Thus, a large proportion of this decrease may be prevented with regular physical activity. There are other factors that can affect a person's BMR, and some of these are listed in Table 14.4.

How can you estimate the amount of energy you expend for your BMR? Of the many methods that can be used, one of the simplest is to multiply your body weight in kilograms by 1.0 kcal per kilogram of body weight per hour for men or by 0.9 kcal per kilogram of body weight per hour for women. A little later in this chapter, you will have an opportunity to calculate your BMR and determine your total daily energy needs.

The Thermic Effect of Food Is the Energy Expended to Process Food   The **thermic effect of food (TEF)** is the energy we expend as a result of processing the food we eat. A certain

Table 14.4 Factors Affecting Basal Metabolic Rate (BMR)

Factors That Increase BMR	Factors That Decrease BMR
Higher lean body mass	Lower lean body mass
Greater height (more surface area)	Lower height
Younger age	Older age
Elevated levels of thyroid hormone	Depressed levels of thyroid hormone
Stress, fever, illness	Starvation or fasting
Male gender	Female gender
Pregnancy and lactation	
Certain drugs such as stimulants, caffeine, and tobacco	

thermic effect of food (TEF) The energy expended as a result of processing food consumed.

Brisk walking expends energy.

amount of energy is needed to digest, absorb, transport, metabolize, and store the nutrients we need. The TEF is equal to about 5% to 10% of the energy content of a meal, a relatively small amount. Thus, if a meal contains 500 kcal, the thermic effect of processing that meal is about 25 to 50 kcal. These values apply to eating what is referred to as a mixed diet, or a diet containing a mixture of carbohydrate, fat, and protein. Most of us eat some combination of these nutrients throughout the day. Individually, the processing of each nutrient takes a different amount of energy. Whereas fat requires very little energy to digest, transport, and store in our cells, protein and carbohydrate require relatively more energy to process.

At one time, it was thought that obese people had a blunted (or reduced) TEF, which was thought to contribute to their obesity. We now know that errors associated with measuring the TEF make our previous assumptions about its link to obesity questionable. One of the most important contributors to obesity in industrialized countries is having an inactive lifestyle, which significantly reduces the energy output due to physical activity, our next topic.

The Energy Cost of Physical Activity Is Highly Variable   The **energy cost of physical activity** represents about 15% to 35% of our total energy output each day. This is the energy we expend due to any movement or work above basal levels. This includes lower-intensity activities such as sitting, standing, and walking, and higher-intensity activities such as running, skiing, and bicycling. One of the most obvious ways to increase how much energy we expend as a result of physical activity is to do more activities for a longer period of time.

Table 14.5 lists the energy costs for certain activities. As you can see, activities such as running, swimming and bicycling that involve moving our larger muscle groups (or more parts of the body) require more energy. The amount of energy we expend during activities is also affected by our body size, the intensity of the activity, and how long we perform the activity. This is why the values in Table 14.5 are expressed as kilocalories of energy per kilogram of body weight per minute.

Using the energy value of 0.175 kcal/kg body weight/minute for running at 9.7 km per hour (or a 6.2 minute-per-kilometre running pace) for 30 minutes, let's calculate how much energy Theo, from the "You Do the Math" box, would expend doing this activity:

- Theo's body weight (in kg) = 90.91 kg
- Energy cost of running at 9.7 kph = 0.175 kcal/kg body weight/min × 90.91 kg = 15.91 kcal/min

Table 14.5 Energy Costs of Various Physical Activities

Moderate Physical Activity	Approximate Kilocalories/Hour for a 70-kg Person	Vigorous Physical Activity	Approximate Kilocalories/Hour for a 70-kg Person
Hiking	370	Running/jogging (8 kph)	590
Light gardening/yard work	330	Bicycling (>16 kph)	590
Dancing	330	Swimming (slow freestyle laps)	510
Golf (walking and carrying clubs)	330	Aerobics	480
Bicycling (<16 kph)	290	Walking (7.2 kph)	460
Walking (5.5 kph)	280	Heavy yard work (chopping wood)	440
Weight lifting (general light workout)	220	Weight lifting (vigorous effort)	440
Stretching	180	Basketball (vigorous)	440

Data from: BLAKE, JOAN SALGE; MUNOZ, KATHY D.; VOLPE, STELLA, NUTRITION: FROM SCIENCE TO YOU, 1st Ed., © 2010. Reprinted and Electronically reproduced by permission of Pearson Education, Inc., Upper Saddle River, New Jersey.

energy cost of physical activity The energy that is expended on body movement and muscular work above basal levels.

- If Theo runs at this pace for 30 minutes, his total energy output = 15.91 kcal/min × 30 min = 477 kcal

Given everything we've discussed so far, you're probably asking yourself, "How many kilocalories do I need each day to maintain my current weight?" This question is not always easy to answer, as our energy needs fluctuate from day to day according to our activity level, environmental conditions, and other factors such as the amount and type of food we eat and our intake of caffeine, which temporarily increases our BMR. However, you can get a general estimate of how much energy your body needs to maintain your present weight. The You Do the Math box describes how you can estimate your total daily energy needs.

RECaP

The energy balance equation relates food intake to energy expenditure. Eating more energy than you expend causes weight gain, while eating less energy than you expend causes weight loss. Energy expenditure can be measured using direct calorimetry, indirect calorimetry, and doubly labelled water. The three components of energy expenditure are basal metabolic rate, the thermic effect of food, and the energy cost of physical activity.

YOU DO THE MATH

Calculating Your Estimated Energy Requirements (EER)

One potential way to estimate how much energy you need each day is to record your total food and beverage intake for a defined period of time, such as three or seven days. You can then use a food composition table or computer dietary assessment program to estimate the amount of energy you eat each day. Assuming that your body weight is stable over this period of time, your average daily energy intake should represent how much energy you need to maintain your present weight.

Unfortunately, many studies of energy intake in humans have shown that dietary records estimating energy needs are not very accurate. Most studies show that humans underestimate the amount of energy they eat by 10% to 30%. Overweight people tend to underestimate by an even higher margin, at the same time overestimating the amount of activity they do. This means that someone who really eats about 2000 kcal/day may record eating only 1400 to 1800 kcal/day. So one reason many people are confused about their ability to lose weight is that they are eating more than they realize.

A more accurate way to estimate your total daily energy needs is to calculate your Estimated Energy Requirement (EER). Refer to the example below to learn how to do this. As the energy cost for the thermic effect of food is very small, you don't need to include it in your calculations.

1. To calculate your EER you need to know your age, weight, height, and physical activity (PA) level.

If you are a male, 19 years of age or older, you would use the following equation:

$$\text{EER} = 662 - [9.53 \times \text{age(years)}] + \text{PA} \times [15.91 \times \text{weight (kg)} + 539.6 \times \text{height (m)}]$$

If you are a female, 19 years of age or older, you would use the following equation:

$$\text{EER} = 354 - [6.91 \times \text{age (years)}] + \text{PA} \times [9.36 \times \text{weight (kg)} + 726 \times \text{height (m)}]$$

2. Estimate your activity level (PA) by selecting the description that most closely fits your general lifestyle from Table 1.4 on page 18.

3. Let's assume you are a male, aged 23 years. You weigh 80 kg and are 1.8 m tall. You lead an active lifestyle and so you choose a PA factor of 1.25. What is your EER?

$$\text{EER} = 662 - [9.53 \times 23] + 1.25 \times [(15.91 \times 80) + (539.6 \times 1.8)]$$

$$= 662 - [219.2] + 1.25 \times [1272.8 + 971.3]$$

$$= 662 - 219.2 + 1.25 \times 2244.1$$

$$= 662 - 219.2 + 2805.1$$

$$= 3247.9 \text{ or approximately 3248 kcal/day}$$

Assuming that you are maintaining your present weight, you require approximately 3248 kcal/day to stay in energy balance.

Percentage (%) contribution to body fat

Figure 14.9 Research indicates that about 25% of body fat is accounted for by genetic heritage. However, non-genetic factors such as diet and exercise play a much larger role.

Genetic Factors Affect Body Weight

Our genetic background influences our height, weight, body shape, and metabolic rate. A classic study shows that the body weights of adults who were adopted as children are similar to the weights of their biological parents, not their adoptive parents.[11] **Figure 14.9** shows that about 25% of our body fat is accounted for by genetic influences. Two theories linking genetics with our body weight are the thrifty gene theory and the set-point theory.

The Thrifty Gene Theory

The **thrifty gene theory** suggests that some people possess a gene (or genes) that causes them to be energetically thrifty. This means that at rest and even during active times, these individuals expend less energy than people who do not possess this gene. The proposed purpose of this gene is to protect a person from starving to death during times of extreme food shortages. This theory has been applied to some Aboriginal groups, as these societies were exposed to centuries of feast and famine. Those with a thrifty metabolism survived when little food was available, and this trait was passed on to future generations. Although an actual thrifty gene (or genes) has not yet been identified, researchers continue to study this explanation as a potential cause of obesity.

If this theory is true, think about how people who possess this thrifty gene might respond to today's environment. Low levels of physical activity, inexpensive food sources that are high in fat and energy, and excessively large serving sizes are the norm in our society. People with a thrifty metabolism would experience a great amount of weight gain, and their bodies would be more resistant to weight loss. Theoretically, having thrifty genes would be advantageous during times of minimal food resources; however, this state could lead to very high levels of obesity in times of plenty.

The Set-Point Theory

The **set-point theory** suggests that our bodies are designed to maintain our weight within a narrow range, or at a "set point." In many cases, the body appears to respond in such a way as to maintain a person's current weight. When we dramatically reduce energy intake (such as with fasting or strict diets), the body responds with physiologic changes that cause BMR to drop. This causes a significant slowing of our energy output. In addition, being physically active while fasting or starving is difficult because a person just doesn't have the energy for it. These two mechanisms of energy conservation may contribute to some of the rebound weight gain many dieters experience after they quit dieting.

Conversely, overeating in some people may cause an increase in BMR and is thought to be associated with an increased thermic effect of food as well as an increase in spontaneous movements, or fidgeting. This in turn increases energy output and prevents weight gain. These changes may explain how some people fail to gain all of the weight expected from eating excess food. We don't eat the exact same amount of food each day; some days we overeat, other days we eat less. When you think about how much our daily energy intake fluctuates (about 20% above and below our average monthly intake), our ability to maintain a certain weight over long periods of time suggests that there is some evidence to support the set-point theory.

Can we change our weight set point? It appears that when we maintain changes in our diet and activity level over a long period of time, weight change does occur. This is obvious in the case of obesity, since many people become obese during middle adulthood, and they are not able to maintain the lower body weight they had as a younger adult. Also, many people do successfully lose weight and maintain that weight loss over long periods of time. Thus, the set-point theory cannot entirely account for the body's resistance to weight loss. An interesting study on weight gain in twins demonstrates how genetics may affect our tendency to maintain a set point; this study is reviewed in the accompanying Did You Know? box.

thrifty gene theory A theory that suggests that some people possess a gene (or genes) that causes them to be energetically thrifty, resulting in them expending less energy at rest and during physical activity.

set-point theory A theory suggesting that the body raises or lowers energy expenditure in response to increased and decreased food intake and physical activity. This action serves to maintain an individual's body weight within a narrow range.

Did You Know?

A classic study done by researchers at Laval University in Quebec shows how genetics may play a role in our responses to overeating.[12] Twelve pairs of male identical twins volunteered to stay in a dormitory where they were supervised 24 hours a day for 120 consecutive days. Researchers measured how much energy each man needed to maintain his body weight at the beginning of the study. For 100 days, the subjects were fed 1000 kcal more per day than they needed to maintain body weight. Daily physical activity was limited, but each person was allowed to walk outdoors for 30 minutes each day, read, watch television and videos, and play cards and video games. The research staff stayed with these men to ensure that they did not stray from the study protocol.

The average weight gain experienced by this group of men was almost 8 kg. Although they were all overfed enough energy to gain about 12 kg, the average weight gain was 3.6 kg less than expected. These men gained mostly fat but also gained about 2.7 kg of lean body mass. Interestingly, there was a very wide range of weight gained. One man gained only about 4.3 kg, whereas another man gained more than 13 kg! Keep in mind that the food these men ate and the activities they performed were tightly controlled.

Identical twins tend to maintain a similar weight throughout life.

This study shows that when people overeat by the same amount of food, they can gain very different amounts of weight and body fat. Whereas each twin gained a similar amount of weight to his twin pair, there was a lot of difference in how each set of twins responded. It is suggested that those more resistant to weight gain when they overeat have the ability to increase BMR, store more excess energy as lean body mass instead of fat, and increase spontaneous movements such as fidgeting. Thus, genetic differences may explain why some people have a better ability to maintain a certain weight set point than others.

Composition of the Diet Affects Fat Storage

As previously discussed, when we eat more energy than we expend, we gain weight. Most people eat what is referred to as a "mixed" diet, meaning it contains a mix of carbohydrate, fat, and protein. Scientists used to think that people would gain the same amount of weight if they ate too much food of any type, but now there is evidence to support the theory that when we overeat dietary fat, we store it more easily as adipose tissue than we do either carbohydrate or protein.[13] This may be due to the fact that eating fat doesn't cause much of an increase in metabolic rate, and the body stores fat in the form of adipose tissue quite easily.

A balanced diet contains protein, carbohydrate, and fat.

In contrast, when we overeat protein or carbohydrate, our body's initial response is to use this extra food for energy, storage, or the building of tissues, with a smaller amount of the excess stored as fat. This does not mean, however, that you can eat as many low-fat foods as you want and not gain weight! It is the overall kilocalories consumed that has the greatest influence on body weight, not the diet composition. Consistently overeating protein or carbohydrate will also lead to weight gain. Instead, maintain a balanced diet combining fat, carbohydrate, and protein, and reduce dietary fat to less than 35% of total energy. This strategy may help reduce the storage of fat energy as adipose tissue.

Physiologic Factors Influence Body Weight

Numerous physiologic factors affect body weight, including hunger, specific proteins, hormones, and blood glucose levels. These various factors contribute to the complexities of weight regulation.

Hunger and Satiety

As introduced in Chapter 3, *hunger* is the innate, physiological drive or need to eat. Physical signals such as a growling stomach and lightheadedness indicate when one is hungry. This drive for food is triggered by physiologic changes such as low blood glucose that affect chemicals in the brain. The hypothalamus plays an important role in hunger regulation. Special hypothalamic cells referred to as *feeding cells* respond to conditions of low blood glucose, causing hunger and driving a person to eat. Once one has eaten and the body has responded accordingly, other centres in the hypothalamus are triggered, and the desire to eat is reduced. The state reached in which there is no longer a desire to eat is referred to as *satiety*. It may be that some people have an insufficient satiety mechanism, which prevents them from feeling full after a meal, allowing them to overeat.

Proteins

Leptin is a protein that is produced by adipose cells and functions as a hormone. First discovered in mice, leptin acts to reduce food intake and cause a decrease in body weight and body fat. A gene called the *ob* gene (obesity gene) codes for the production of leptin. Obese mice were found to have a genetic mutation in the *ob* gene. This mutation reduces the ability of adipose cells to synthesize leptin in sufficient amounts; therefore, food intake increases dramatically, energy output is reduced, and weight gain occurs.[14-16]

When these findings were first published, a great deal of excitement was generated about how leptin might decrease obesity in humans. Unfortunately, studies have shown that although obese mice respond positively to leptin injections, obese humans do not, except in the very rare cases of genetic disorders where leptin or its receptor are affected. Instead, they tend to have very high amounts of leptin in their bodies and are insensitive to leptin's effects. In truth, we have just begun to learn about leptin and its role in the human body. Researchers are currently studying its role in starvation and overeating, and it appears it might play a role in cardiovascular and kidney complications that result from obesity and related diseases.

In addition to leptin, numerous proteins affect the regulation of appetite and storage of body fat. Primary among these is **ghrelin**, a protein synthesized in the stomach. It acts as a hormone and plays an important role in appetite regulation through its actions in the hypothalamus. Ghrelin stimulates appetite and increases the amount of food one eats. Ghrelin levels increase before a meal and fall within about one hour after a meal. This action indicates that ghrelin may be a primary contributor to both hunger and satiety. Ghrelin levels appear to increase after weight loss, and researchers speculate that this factor could help to explain why people who have lost weight have difficulty keeping it off.[17] Researchers have shown that ghrelin levels do not drop in response to food intake in obese adolescents, which results in a blunted satiety response.[18] It has been suggested that this blunting could contribute to weight gain.

leptin A hormone that is produced by body fat that acts to reduce food intake and to decrease body weight and body fat.

ghrelin A protein synthesized in the stomach that acts as a hormone and plays an important role in appetite regulation by stimulating appetite.

Peptide YY, or **PYY**, is a protein produced in the gastrointestinal tract. It is released after a meal, in amounts proportional to the energy content of the meal. In contrast with ghrelin, PYY decreases appetite and inhibits food intake in animals and humans.[19] Interestingly, obese individuals have lower levels of PYY when they are fasting and also show less of an increase in PYY after a meal as compared with non-obese individuals, which suggests that PYY may be important in the manifestation and maintenance of obesity.[20]

Recall that mitochondria are organelles found abundantly within cells that generate ATP, including skeletal muscle cells and adipose cells. Some research suggests that *uncoupling proteins* present in the inner mitochondrial membrane may influence body weight. These proteins uncouple the oxidation of fat from ATP formation; when this occurs, the oxidation of fat produces heat instead of ATP. This production of heat increases energy expenditure and results in less storage of excess energy. Thus, a person with more uncoupling proteins or a higher activity of these proteins would be more resistant to weight gain and obesity.

Three forms of uncoupling proteins have been identified: UCP1 is found exclusively in **brown adipose tissue**, a type of adipose tissue that has more mitochondria than white adipose tissue. It is found in significant amounts in animals and newborn humans. It was traditionally thought that adult humans have very little brown adipose tissue. However, recent evidence suggests that humans may have substantially more brown adipose tissue than previously assumed,[21] and that people with higher BMI values have lower amounts of brown adipose tissue.[22] These findings suggest a possible role of brown adipose tissue in obesity. Two other uncoupling proteins, UCP2 and UCP3, are known to be important to energy expenditure and resistance to weight gain. These proteins are found in various tissues, including white adipose tissue and skeletal muscle. The roles of brown adipose tissue and uncoupling proteins in human obesity are currently being researched.

Other Physiologic Factors

Various other physiologic factors known to increase satiety (or decrease food intake) include:

- Hormones such as serotonin and cholecystokinin (CCK). Serotonin is made from the amino acid tryptophan; and CCK is produced by the intestinal cells and stimulates the gallbladder to secrete bile.
- An increase in blood glucose levels, such as that normally seen after the consumption of a meal.
- Stomach expansion.
- Nutrient absorption from the small intestine.
- GLP-1 (glucagon-like-peptide-1), another hormone currently under study as a potential obesity treatment, has been shown to inhibit appetite and food intake in animals and humans.[23] Studies have also shown that injections of GLP-1 significantly enhance satiety and reduce food intake in both normal weight and obese subjects.[24] GLP-1 analogues have been developed for the treatment of obesity and result in a moderate average weight loss. As with PYY, GLP-1 levels and responses to meals are lower in obesity, possibly contributing to the disease.

Other physiologic factors that can decrease satiety (or increase food intake) include:

- Hormones such as beta-endorphins. Beta-endorphins increase a sense of pleasure while eating, which can increase food intake.
- Neuropeptide Y, an amino-acid-containing compound produced in the hypothalamus, stimulates appetite.
- Decreased blood glucose levels, such as the decrease that occurs after an overnight fast.

Cultural and Economic Factors Affect Food Choices and Body Weight

Both cultural and economic factors can contribute to obesity. As discussed in detail in Chapter 3, cultural factors (including religious beliefs and learned food preferences) affect

peptide YY (PYY) A protein produced in the gastrointestinal tract that is released after a meal in amounts proportional to the energy content of the meal; it decreases appetite and inhibits food intake.

brown adipose tissue A type of adipose tissue that has more mitochondria than white adipose tissue and can increase energy expenditure by uncoupling oxidation from ATP production. It is found in significant amounts in animals and newborn humans.

our food choices and eating patterns. In addition, the customs of many cultures put food at the centre of celebrations of festivals and holidays, and overeating is tacitly encouraged. In addition, as both parents now work outside the home in most Canadian families, more people are embracing the "fast food culture," preferring and almost exclusively choosing highly processed and highly caloric fast foods from restaurants and grocery stores to lower-kilocalorie, home-cooked meals.

Coinciding with these cultural influences on food intake are cultural factors that promote an inactive life. Research with sedentary ethnic minority women in the United States indicates that other common barriers to increasing physical activity include lack of personal motivation, no physically active role models to emulate, acceptance of larger body size, exercise being considered culturally unacceptable, and fear for personal safety in both rural and urban settings.[25, 26] In short, cultural factors influence both food consumption and levels of physical activity, and can contribute to weight gain.

Economic status is known to be related to health status, with individuals of lower socio-economic status tending to have poorer health. This phenomenon is generally referred to as the social gradient of health.[27] Interestingly, however, the social gradient in health does not seem to apply as consistently to overweight and obesity. Although low-income Aboriginal people are more likely than non-Aboriginal Canadians to be obese,[28] analyses of the 2007/08 CCHS data indicated that the relationship between income and obesity varies by gender.[29] For females, as income increases, the prevalence of obesity decreases. However, for men, the opposite was true. As household income increased, the prevalence of obesity also increased. Results also showed that lower income people were less likely to consume vegetables and fruit but higher income households were more likely to eat outside of the home, thus perhaps consuming more kilocalories. These researchers concluded that additional research is needed to explain why income does not seem to be consistently related to obesity in Canada.

It is a common belief that healthy foods are expensive and that only wealthy people can afford to buy them. It is true that some foods considered more healthy, such as imported vegetables and fruit or leaner cuts of some meats, can be costly, particularly in the winter. But does healthy eating always have to be expensive? Refer to the Nutrition Myth or Fact? box on page 504 to learn more about whether a healthy diet can also be an affordable diet. Keep in mind, though, that some Canadians do not have enough money left for food after they pay for their essential living expenses. Even learning how to budget their money will not allow them to meet their nutritional needs.[30] Chapter 19 will discuss some of the programs and supports that are needed to ensure that all Canadians have adequate access to a safe supply of nutritious foods.

Psychologic and Social Factors Influence Behaviour and Body Weight

We explored in Chapter 3 the concept that *appetite* can be experienced in the absence of hunger. Appetite may therefore be considered a psychological drive to eat, being stimulated by learned preferences for food and particular situations that promote eating. For instance, some people learn as children to love or hate certain foods. This may explain why foods such as frogs' legs, cactus, and cultured yeast extract (Marmite) appeal to people in certain cultures who were raised on them but are almost never adopted into the diet as new foods by an adult. Others may follow learned behaviours related to timing and size of meals. In addition, the sight and fragrance of certain foods stimulate the pleasure centres of the brain, whether or not we happen to be hungry at the time. Mood can also affect appetite, as some people will eat more or less if they feel depressed or happy. As you can imagine, appetite leads many people to overeat.

Some Social Factors Promote Overeating

Social factors can encourage people to overeat or choose high-energy foods. For example, pressure from family and friends to eat the way they do and easy access to large servings

Food preferences often depend on culture. Some cultures enjoy foods such as frogs' legs, whereas others do not.

of inexpensive and high-fat foods contribute to overeating. Think about how you might eat differently when you attend a birthday celebration with family or friends. Perhaps you are offered hot dogs, pizza, birthday cake, ice cream, or other dishes that are relatively high in fat and energy. The pressure to overeat on holidays is also high, as family members or friends offer extra servings of favourite holiday foods and follow a very large meal with a rich dessert.

Canadians also have numerous opportunities to overeat because of easy access throughout the day to foods high in fat and energy. Vending machines selling high-fat, low-nutrient-dense foods are everywhere: on campus, in business offices, and even at fitness centres. Shopping malls are filled with fast-food restaurants, where inexpensive, large serving sizes are the norm. Food manufacturers are producing products in ever-larger serving sizes: for instance, in 2005, the Mars candy company introduced a supersize version of M&M's candy, with each piece about 55% larger than the standard-sized M&M's. Other supersize examples include the Grandma™ Prime Rib Burger-Double from A&W, the Double Down from KFC, and the Enormous Omelette Sandwich from Burger King.[31] Serving sizes have become so large that many Canadians are suffering from "portion distortion." To test your understanding of a serving size, take the "Portion Distortion" interactive quiz from the National Institutes of Health at http://hin.nhlbi.nih.gov/portion/. Even foods traditionally considered healthy, such as some brands of peanut butter, yogourt, chicken soup, and milk, are often filled with added sugars and other ingredients that are high in energy. This easy access to large servings of high-energy meals and snacks leads many people to consume excess energy.

Easy-access foods and fast foods may be inexpensive and filling but are often high in fat and sugar.

Some Social Factors Promote Inactivity

Social factors can also cause people to be less physically active. For instance, we don't even have to spend time or energy preparing food anymore, as everything is either ready-to-serve or requires just a few minutes to cook in a microwave oven. Other social factors restricting physical activity include living in an unsafe community; coping with family, community, and work responsibilities that do not involve physical activity; and living in an area with harsh weather conditions. Many overweight people identify such factors as major barriers to maintaining a healthy body weight, and research seems to confirm their influence.

Certainly, social factors are contributing to decreased physical activity among children. There was a time when children played outdoors regularly and when physical education was offered daily in school. In today's society, many children do not play outdoors on account of safety concerns and lack of recreational facilities, and few schools have the resources to regularly offer physical education to children.

Another social factor promoting inactivity in both children and adults is our increasingly technological lifestyle. Watching television, surfing the internet, and playing with video games and other hand-held devices is occupying more and more of our time, both as children and adults. By reducing energy expenditure, these behaviours contribute to weight gain. For instance, a study of 11- to 13-year-old schoolchildren found that children who watched more than two hours of television per night were more likely to be overweight or obese than children who watched less than two hours of television per night. Similarly, adults who reported an increase in television watching of 20 hours per week (approximately three hours per day) over a nine-year period had a significant increase in waist circumference, indicating significant weight gain.[32] Alarmingly, a survey of Canadian children in grades 6 to 12 found that over 50% spend more than two hours per day in screen-based, entertainment activities.

Social Pressures Can Promote Underweight

On the other hand, social pressures to maintain a lean body are great enough to encourage many people to undereat or to avoid foods that are perceived as "bad," especially fats. Our society ridicules and often ostracizes overweight people, many of whom face discrimination in many areas of their lives, including employment. Media images of waiflike fashion models and men in tight jeans with muscular chests and abdomens encourage many

Behaviours learned as a child can affect adult weight and physical activity patterns.

Does It Cost More to Eat Right?

The shelves of Canadian super-markets are filled with an abundance of healthy food options: organic meats and produce, exotic fish, out-of-season fresh fruits and vegetables that are flown in from warmer climates, whole-grain breads and cereals, and low-fat and low-sodium options of traditional foods. With all of this choice, it would seem easy for anyone to consume healthy foods throughout the year. But a closer look at the prices of these foods suggests that, for many, they simply are not affordable. This raises the question: Does eating a healthy diet have to be expensive?

Although specialty foods (such as organic or imported products) can be expensive, lower-cost alternatives can be just as nutritious.

■ Buy frozen vegetables on sale and stock up—these are just as healthy as fresh vegetables, require less preparation, and are often cheaper.

■ If lower-sodium options of canned vegetables are too expensive, buy the less expensive regular option and drain the juice from the vegetables before cooking.

■ Consume smaller amounts of leaner meats—by eating less you'll not only save money but reduce your total intake of energy and fat while still providing the nutrients that support good health.

It is a fact that organic foods are more expensive than non-organic options. However, there is little evidence indicating that organic foods are actually more healthy choices than non-organic foods. In addition, some of the lowest-cost foods currently available in stores are also some of the most nutritious: these include beans, lentils, and other legumes, seasonal fruits, root vegetables such as potatoes and winter squashes, frozen fruits and vegetables, and cooking oils high in mono- and polyunsaturated fats. In fact, frozen as well as canned fruits and vegetables are generally just as nutritious as fresh options, and may be more so depending on how long the fresh produce has been transported and stored and how long it has been sitting on the supermarket shelves. Thus, with some knowledge, skills, and focused attention, people can still eat healthily on a tight budget.

Here are some more tips to help you save money when shopping for healthy foods:

■ Buy whole grains such as cereals, brown rice, and pastas in bulk—they store well for longer periods and provide a good base for meals and snacks.

■ Choose frozen fish or canned salmon or tuna packed in water as an alternative to fresh fish.

■ Avoid frozen or dehydrated prepared meals. These are usually expensive; high in sodium, saturated fats, and energy; and low in fibre and other important nutrients.

■ Buy generic or store brands of foods—be careful to check the labels to ensure the foods are similar in nutrient value as the higher-priced options.

■ Cut coupons from local newspapers and magazines, and watch the sale flyers so that you can stock up on healthy foods you can store.

■ Consider cooking more meals at home; you'll have more control over what goes into your meals and will also be able to cook larger amounts and freeze leftovers for future meals.

As you can see, healthy eating does not have to be expensive. However, it helps to become a savvy consumer by reading food labels, comparing prices, and gaining the skills and confidence to cook at home. The information shared throughout this text should help you acquire these skills so that you can eat healthily, even on a limited budget!

people—especially adolescents and young adults—to skip meals, resort to crash diets, and exercise obsessively. Even some people of normal body weight push themselves to achieve an unrealistic and unattainable weight goal, in the process threatening their health and even their lives. See the accompanying Highlight box for information on disordered eating.

It should be clear that how a person gains, loses, and maintains body weight is a complex matter. Most people who are overweight have tried several weight-loss programs but have been unsuccessful in maintaining long-term weight loss. A significant number of these people have consequently given up all weight-loss attempts. Some even suffer from severe depression related to their body weight. Should we condemn these people as failures and continue to pressure them to lose weight? Should people who are overweight but otherwise healthy (for example, with low blood pressure, cholesterol, triglycerides, and glucose levels) be advised to lose weight? As we continue to search for ways to help people achieve and maintain a healthy body weight, our society must take measures to reduce the social pressures facing people who are overweight or obese.

ReCap

Many factors affect our ability to gain and lose weight. Our genetic background influences our height, weight, body shape, and metabolic rate. The thrifty gene theory suggests that some people possess a gene or set of genes that causes them to expend less energy. The set-point theory suggests that the body is designed to maintain weight within a narrow range. The macronutrient composition of the diet influences the storage of body fat, and physiologic factors such as hunger, leptin, ghrelin, peptide YY, uncoupling proteins, and various other hormones impact body weight by their effects on satiety, appetite, and energy expenditure. A person's diet and activity patterns as a child influence his or her body weight as an adult. Cultural and economic factors can significantly influence the amounts and types of foods we eat. Psychological and social factors influencing weight include ready availability of large portions of high-energy foods and lack of physical activity. Social pressures facing those who are overweight can drive people to use harmful methods to achieve an unrealistic body weight.

disordered eating A general term used to describe a variety of abnormal or atypical eating behaviours that are considered unhealthy but are not severe enough to make the person seriously ill.

eating disorder A psychiatric disorder characterized by severe disturbances in body image and eating behaviours. Anorexia nervosa and bulimia nervosa are two examples of eating disorders for which specific diagnostic criteria must be present for diagnosis.

anorexia nervosa A serious, potentially life-threatening eating disorder that is characterized by self-starvation, which eventually leads to a deficiency in energy and essential nutrients that are required by the body to function normally.

bulimia nervosa A serious eating disorder characterized by recurrent episodes of binge eating and recurrent inappropriate compensatory behaviours to prevent weight gain, such as self-induced vomiting, fasting, excessive exercise, or misuse of laxatives, diuretics, enemas, or other medications.

HIGHLIGHT

Eating Behaviours Occur on a Continuum

Disordered eating is a general term used to describe a variety of atypical eating behaviours that are unhealthy and potentially harmful. These behaviours may be as simple as going on and off diets or as extreme as refusing to eat any fat. Such behaviours don't usually continue for long enough to make the person seriously ill, nor do they significantly disrupt the person's normal routine.

In contrast, some people restrict their eating so much or for so long that they become dangerously underweight or overeat to the point of extreme weight gain. These people have an **eating disorder**, a psychiatric condition that involves extreme body dissatisfaction and long-term eating patterns that negatively affect body functioning. Two recognized eating disorders are anorexia nervosa and bulimia nervosa. **Anorexia nervosa** is a potentially life-threatening eating disorder that is characterized by self-starvation, which eventually leads to a severe nutrient deficiency. In contrast, **bulimia nervosa** is characterized by recurrent episodes of extreme overeating and compensatory behaviours to prevent weight gain, such as self-induced vomiting, misuse of laxatives, fasting, or excessive exercise. Both disorders will be discussed later in the chapter.

When does normal dieting cross the line into disordered eating? Eating behaviours occur on a *continuum*, a spectrum that can't be divided neatly into parts. An example is a rainbow—where exactly does the red end and the orange begin? Thinking about eating behaviours as a continuum makes it easier to understand how a person could progress from relatively normal eating behaviours to a pattern that is disordered. For instance, let's say that for several years you've skipped breakfast in favour of a mid-morning snack, but now you find yourself avoiding the cafeteria until early afternoon. Is this normal? To answer that question, you'd need to consider your feelings about food and your **body image**—the way you perceive your body.

Take a moment to study the Eating Issues and Body Image Continuum (**Figure 14.10**). Which of the five columns best describes your feelings about food and your body? If you find yourself identifying with the statements on the left side of the continuum, you probably have few issues with food or body image. Most likely you accept your body size and view food as a normal part of maintaining your health and fueling your daily physical activity. As you progress to the right side of the continuum, food and body image become bigger issues, with food restriction becoming the norm. If you identify with the statements on the far right, you are probably afraid of eating and dislike your body. If so, what can you do to begin to move toward the left side of the continuum? How can you begin to develop a healthier approach to food selection and to view your body in a more positive light? Before you can begin to find solutions, you need to understand the many complex factors that contribute to eating disorders and disordered eating and the differences between these terms.

FOOD IS NOT AN ISSUE	HEALTHY BUT CONCERNED	FOOD PREOCCUPIED/ OBSESSED	DISRUPTIVE EATING PATTERNS	DISORDERED EATING
• I am not concerned about what others think regarding what and how much I eat. • When I am upset or depressed I eat whatever I am hungry for without any guilt or shame. • I feel no guilt or shame no matter how much I eat or what I eat. • Food is an important part of my life but only occupies a small part of my time. • I trust my body to tell me what and how much to eat.	• I pay attention to what I eat to maintain a healthy body. • I may weigh more than what I like, but I enjoy eating and balance my pleasure with eating with my concern for a healthy body. • I am moderate and flexible in goals for eating well. • I try to follow dietary guidelines for healthy eating.	• I think about food a lot. • I feel I don't eat well most of the time. • It's hard for me to enjoy eating with others. • I feel ashamed when I eat more than others or more than what I feel I should be eating. • I am afraid of getting fat. • I wish I could change how much I want to eat and what I am hungry for.	• I have tried diet pills, laxatives, vomiting, or extra time exercising to lose or maintain my weight. • I have fasted or avoided eating for long periods of time to lose or maintain my weight. • I feel strong when I can restrict how much I eat. • Eating more than I wanted to makes me feel out of control.	• I regularly stuff myself and then exercise, vomit, or use diet pills or laxatives to get rid of the food or calories. • My friends/family tell me I am too thin. • I am terrified of eating fat. • When I let myself eat, I have a hard time controlling the amount of food I eat. • I am afraid to eat in front of others.
BODY OWNERSHIP	**BODY ACCEPTANCE**	**BODY PREOCCUPIED/ OBSESSED**	**DISTORTED BODY IMAGE**	**BODY HATE/ DISASSOCIATION**
• Body image is not an issue for me. • My body is beautiful to me. • My feelings about my body are not influenced by society's concept of an ideal body shape. • I know that the significant others in my life will always find me attractive. • I trust my body to find the weight it needs to be at so I can move and feel confident of my physical body.	• I base my body image equally on social norms and my own self-concept. • I pay attention to my body and my appearance because it is important to me, but it only occupies a small part of my day. • I nourish my body so it has the strength and energy to achieve my physical goals. • I am able to assert myself and maintain a healthy body without losing my self-esteem.	• I spend a significant time viewing my body in the mirror. • I spend a significant time comparing my body to others. • I have days when I feel fat. • I am preoccupied with my body. • I accept society's ideal body shape and size as the best body shape and size. • I'd be more attractive if I was thinner, more muscular, etc....	• I spend a significant amount of time exercising and dieting to change my body. • My body shape and size keep me from dating or finding someone who will treat me the way I want to be treated. • I have considered changing or have changed my body shape and size through surgical means so I can accept myself. • I wish I could change the way I look in the mirror.	• I often feel separated and distant from my body—as if it belongs to someone else. • I hate my body and I often isolate myself from others. • I don't see anything positive or even neutral about my body shape and size. • I don't believe others when they tell me I look OK. • I hate the way I look in the mirror.

Figure 14.10 The Eating Issues and Body Image Continuum. The progression from normal eating (far left) to disordered eating (far right) occurs on a continuum.
Data from: Smiley, L., L. King, and H. Avery. University of Arizona Campus Health Service. Original Continuum, C. Shlaalak. Preventive Medicine and Public Health. Copyright © 1997 Arizona Board of Regents. Used with permission.

How Can You Achieve and Maintain a Healthy Body Weight?

Achieving and maintaining a healthy body weight involves three primary strategies:

- Reduction in energy intake by 500 to 1000 kcal/day
- Incorporation of regular and appropriate physical activity
- Application of cognitive-behavioural modification techniques

body image A person's perception of his or her body's appearance and functioning.

Figure 14.11 summarizes the assessment and stepwise management of the overweight or obese adult as recommended in the 2006 Canadian clinical practice guidelines (available at www.cmaj.ca/content/176/8/S1.full).

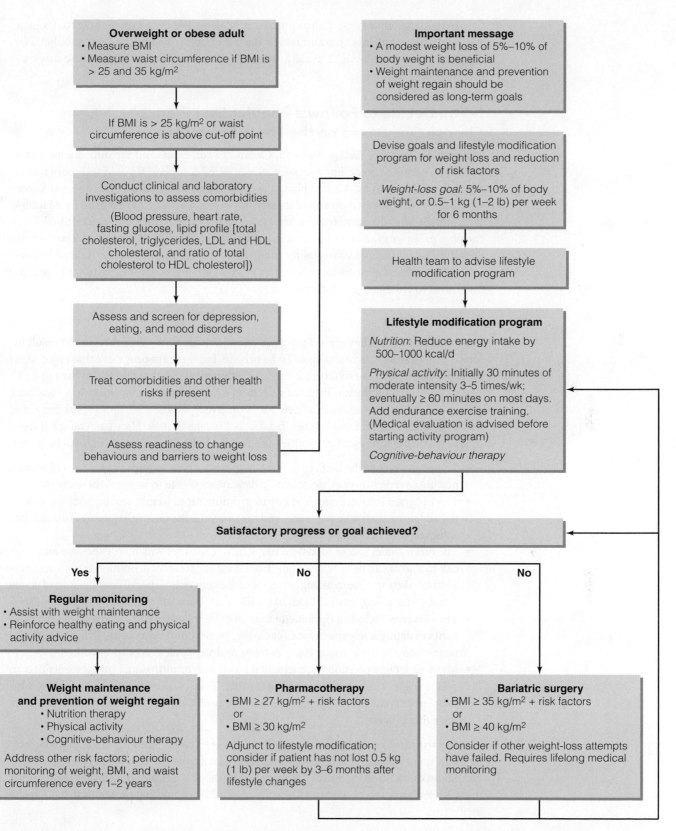

Figure 14.11 Algorithm for the assessment and stepwise management of the overweight or obese adult.
Data from: 2006 Canadian clinical practice guidelines on the management and prevention of obesity in adults and children. Vol. 176. © CMAJ (2007). This work is protected by copyright and the making of this copy was with the permission of Access Copyright. Any alteration of its content or further copying in any form whatsoever is strictly prohibited unless otherwise permitted by law.

In this section, we first discuss popular diet plans. We then explain how to design a personalized weight-loss plan and review the use of prescribed medication and dietary supplements in losing weight. Finally, we briefly discuss the option of bariatric surgery as a treatment for obesity.

If You Decide to Follow a Popular Diet Plan, Choose One Based on the Three Strategies

With the assistance of *Eating Well with Canada's Food Guide* and the information in this book, you are ready to design your own personalized diet plan. If you'd feel more comfortable following an established plan, however, many are available. How can you know whether or not it is based on sound dietary principles, and whether its promise of long-term weight loss will prove true for *you*? Look to the three strategies just identified: Does the plan promote gradual reductions in energy intake? Does it advocate increased physical activity? Does it include strategies for modifying your eating and activity-related behaviours? Reputable diet plans incorporate all of these strategies. Unfortunately, many dieters are drawn to fad diets, which do not.

Avoid Fad Diets

Beware of fad diets! They are simply what their name implies—fads that do not result in long-term, healthy weight changes. To be precise, fad diets are programs that enjoy short-term popularity and are sold based on a marketing gimmick that appeals to the public's desires and fears. Of the hundreds of such diets on the market today, most will "die" within a year, only to be born again as a "new" or "improved" fad diet. The goal of the person or company designing and marketing a fad diet is to make money. How can you tell if the program you are interested in qualifies as a fad diet? Here are some pointers to help you:

- The promoters of the diet claim that the program is new, improved, or based on some new discovery; however, no scientific data are available to support these claims.
- The program is touted for its ability to promote rapid weight loss or body fat loss, usually more than 1 kg per week, and may include the claim that weight loss can be achieved with little or no physical exercise.
- The diet includes special foods and supplements, many of which are expensive and/or difficult to find or can be purchased only from the diet promoter. Common recommendations for these diets include avoiding certain foods, eating only a special combination of certain foods, or including "magic" foods in the diet that "burn fat" and "speed up metabolism."
- The diet may include a rigid menu that must be followed daily or may limit participants to eating a few select foods each day. Variety and balance are discouraged, and restriction of certain foods (such as fruits and vegetables) is encouraged.
- Many programs promote supplemental foods and/or nutritional supplements that are described as critical to the success of the diet. They usually include claims that these supplements can cure or prevent a variety of health ailments or that the diet can stop the aging process.

In a world where many of us feel we have to meet a certain physical standard to be attractive and "good enough," fad diets flourish: it is estimated that we currently spend more than $33 billion on fad diets each year.[33] Unfortunately, the only people who usually benefit from them are their marketers, who can become very wealthy promoting programs that are highly ineffectual.

Diets Focusing on Macronutrient Composition May or May Not Work for You

A comprehensive review of the currently available evidence shows that achieving a negative energy balance is the major factor in successful weight loss.[34] The macronutrient composition of a diet does not appear to affect the amount of weight lost. However, the three main types of weight-loss diets that have been most seriously and comprehensively researched all encourage increased consumption of certain macronutrients and restrict the consumption of others. Provided here is a brief review of these three main types and their general effects on weight loss and health parameters.[34]

Moderate-Fat, High-Carbohydrate, Moderate-Protein Diets

Moderate-fat, high-carbohydrate, moderate-protein diets that are balanced in nutrients typically contain 20% to 30% of total energy intake as fat, 55% to 60% of total energy intake as carbohydrate, and 15% to 20% of energy intake as protein. These diets include Weight Watchers, Jenny Craig, and others that follow the general guidelines of the DASH diet and *Eating Well with Canada's Food Guide*. All of these diet plans emphasize that weight loss occurs when energy intake is lower than energy expenditure. The goal is gradual weight loss, or about 0.5–1.0 kg of body weight per week. Typical energy deficits are between 500 and 1000 kcal/day. It is recommended that women eat no less than 1000 to 1200 kcal/day and that men consume no less than 1200 to 1400 kcal/day. Regular physical activity is encouraged.

To date, these types of low-energy diets have been researched more than any others. A substantial amount of high-quality scientific evidence (from randomized controlled trials) indicates that they are effective in decreasing body weight. In addition, the people who lose weight on these diets also decrease their LDL-cholesterol, reduce their blood triglyceride levels, and decrease their blood pressure. The diets are nutritionally adequate if the individual's food choices follow *Eating Well with Canada's Food Guide*. If the individual's food choices are not varied and balanced, the diets may be low in nutrients such as fibre, zinc, calcium, iron, and vitamin B_{12}. Under these circumstances, supplementation is needed.

High-Fat, Low-Carbohydrate, High-Protein Diets

High-fat, low-carbohydrate, high-protein diets cycle in and out of popularity on a regular basis. By definition, these types of diets generally contain about 55% to 65% of total energy intake as fat and less than 100 g of carbohydrate per day, with the balance of daily energy intake as protein. Examples of these types of diets include Dr. Atkins' Diet Revolution, the Carbohydrate Addict's Diet, Life Without Bread, Sugar Busters, and Protein Power. These diets minimize the role of restricting total energy intake on weight loss. They instead advise participants to restrict carbohydrate intake, proposing that carbohydrates are addictive and that they cause significant overeating, insulin surges leading to excessive fat storage, and an overall metabolic imbalance that leads to obesity. The goal is to reduce carbohydrates enough to cause ketosis, which will decrease blood glucose and insulin levels and can reduce appetite.

Countless people claim to have lost substantial weight on high-fat, low-carbohydrate, high-protein diets; however, reputable scientific studies of their effectiveness are only just beginning to be conducted. The current limited evidence suggests that individuals in both free-living and experimental conditions do lose weight by following these types of diets. In addition, it appears that those people who lose weight may also experience positive metabolic changes such as decreased blood lipid levels, decreased blood pressure, and decreased blood glucose and insulin. However, the amount of weight loss and the improvements in metabolic health measured with these diets are no greater than those seen with higher-carbohydrate diets. Our current limited evidence of the effectiveness, along with concerns about long-term compliance, potential health risks, and side effects, has made these diets controversial. Refer to the Evidence-informed Decision Making section at the end of this chapter to learn more about high-fat, low-carbohydrate, high-protein diets.

"Low-carb" diets may lead to weight loss but are nutritionally inadequate and can cause negative side effects.

Low-Fat and Very-Low-Fat Diets

Low-fat diets contain 11% to 19% of total energy as fat, whereas very-low-fat diets contain less than 10% of total energy as fat. Both of these types of diets are high in carbohydrate and moderate in protein. Examples include Dr. Dean Ornish's Program for Reversing Heart Disease and the New Pritikin Program. These diets do not focus on total energy intake but emphasize eating foods higher in complex carbohydrates

Low-fat and very-low-fat diets emphasize eating foods higher in complex carbohydrates and fibre.

and fibre. Consumption of sugar and white flour is very limited. The Ornish diet is vegetarian, whereas the Pritikin diet allows approximately 100 g of lean meat per day. Regular physical activity is a key component.

These programs were not originally designed for weight loss but rather were developed to decrease or reverse heart disease. Also, these diets are not popular with consumers, who view them as too restrictive and difficult to follow. Thus, there are limited data on their effects. However, high-quality evidence suggests that people following these diets do lose weight, and some data suggest that these diets may also decrease LDL-cholesterol, blood triglyceride levels, glucose, insulin levels, and blood pressure. Few side effects have been reported on these diets; the most common is flatus that typically decreases over time. Low-fat diets are low in vitamin B_{12}, and very-low-fat diets are low in essential fatty acids, vitamins B_{12} and E, and zinc. Thus, supplementation is needed. These types of diets are not considered safe for people with diabetes who are insulin dependent (either type 1 or type 2) or for people with carbohydrate-malabsorption illnesses.

If You Decide to Design Your Own Diet Plan, Include the Three Strategies

As we noted earlier, a healthy and effective weight-loss plan involves a modest reduction in energy intake, incorporating physical activity into each day, and practising changes in behaviour that can assist you in reducing your energy intake and increasing your energy expenditure. Following are some guidelines for designing your own personalized diet plan that incorporates these strategies.

Set Realistic Goals

The first key to safe and effective weight loss is setting realistic goals related to how much weight to lose and how quickly (or slowly) to lose it. Although making gradual changes in body weight is frustrating for most people, this slower change is much more effective in maintaining weight loss over the long term. Ask yourself the question, "How long did it take me to gain this extra weight?" If you are like most people, your answer is that it took one or more years, not just a few months. A fair expectation for weight loss is similarly gradual: experts recommend a pace of about 0.5–1 kg per week. Your weight-loss goals should also take into consideration any health-related concerns you may have. After checking with your physician, you may decide initially to set a goal of simply maintaining your current weight and preventing additional weight gain. After your weight has remained stable for several weeks, you might then write down realistic goals for weight loss.

Goals that are more likely to be realistic and achievable share the following characteristics:

- *They are specific.* Telling yourself "I will eat less this week" is not helpful because the goal is not specific. An example of a specific goal is "I will eat only half of my restaurant entrée tonight and take the rest home and eat it tomorrow for lunch."
- *They are reasonable.* If you are not presently physically active, it would be unreasonable to set a of goal of exercising for 30 minutes every day. A more reasonable goal would be to exercise for 15 minutes per day, three days per week. Once you've achieved that goal, you can increase the frequency, intensity, and time of exercise according to the improvements in fitness that you have experienced.
- *They are measurable.* Effective goals are ones you can measure. An example is "I will lose at least one pound by May 1st," or "I will substitute drinking water for my regular soft drink at lunch each day this week." Recording your specific, measurable goals will help you to better determine whether you are achieving them.

By monitoring your progress regularly you can determine whether you are meeting your goals or whether you need to revise them based on accomplishments or challenges that arise.

Eat Smaller Portions of Lower-Fat Foods

The portion sizes of foods offered and sold in restaurants and grocery stores have expanded considerably over the past 40 years. One of the most challenging issues related to food is understanding what a healthy portion size is and how to reduce the portion sizes of foods that we eat.

Recent studies indicate that when children and adults are presented with large portion sizes of foods and beverages, they eat more energy overall and do not respond to cues of fullness.[35, 36] Thus, it has been suggested that effective weight-loss strategies include reducing both the portion size and energy density of foods consumed, and replacing energy-dense beverages with low-calorie or non-calorie beverages.[36]

What specific changes can you make to reduce your energy intake and stay healthy? Here are some helpful suggestions:

1. Follow the serving sizes recommended in *Eating Well with Canada's Food Guide* (page 58). Making this change involves understanding what constitutes a serving size and measuring foods to determine whether they meet or exceed the recommended serving size.

2. Reduce your consumption of foods that are high in fat and energy. People trying to lose weight should aim to reduce their energy intake by 500 to 1000 kcal/day.[37] This goal can be achieved by eliminating extra fats such as butter, margarine, and mayonnaise and snack foods such as ice cream, donuts, and cakes. Save these foods as occasional special treats. Select lower-fat versions of the foods listed in *Eating Well with Canada's Food Guide*. This means selecting leaner cuts of meat (such as the white meat of poultry and extra-lean ground beef) and reduced-fat or skim dairy products, and selecting lower-fat preparation methods (such as baking and broiling instead of frying). It also means switching from a sugar-filled beverage to a low-calorie or non-caloric beverage during and between meals.

3. Consume foods that are relatively low in energy density. This includes foods such as salads (with low- or non-fat dressings), fruits, vegetables, and soups (broth-based). These foods are low in energy and high in fibre, water, and nutrients. Because they contain relatively more water and fibre than more energy-dense foods, they allow a person to feel satisfied without having to consume large amounts of energy.

Figure 14.12 illustrates two sets of meals, one higher in energy and one lower in energy. You can see from this figure that simple changes to a meal, such as choosing lower-fat dairy products, smaller portion sizes, and foods that are relatively less dense in energy, can reduce energy intake without sacrificing taste, pleasure, or nutritional quality!

Participate in Regular Physical Activity

The Canadian Physical Activity Guideline recommends that adults accumulate 150 minutes of moderate- to vigorous-intensity aerobic activity per week.[38] Why is being physically active so important for achieving changes in body weight and for maintaining a healthy body weight? Of course, we expend extra energy during physical activity, but there's more to it than that because exercise alone (without a reduction of energy intake) does not result in dramatic decreases in body weight. Instead, one of the most important reasons for being regularly active is that it helps us maintain or increase our lean body mass and our BMR. In contrast, energy restriction alone causes us to lose lean body mass. As you've learned, the more lean body mass we have, the more energy we expend over the long term.

The National Weight Control Registry is an ongoing project in the United States that documents the habits of people who have lost at least 13.6 kg and kept their weight off for at least one year. Of the 784 people studied thus far, the average weight loss was 30 kg, and the group maintained the minimum weight-loss criteria of 13.6 kg for more than 5 years.[39] Almost all of the people (89%) reported changing both physical activity and dietary intake to lose weight and maintain weight loss. No one form of exercise seems to be most effective,

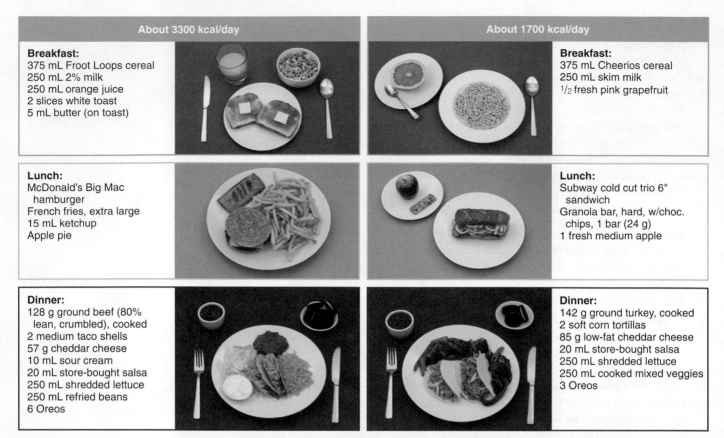

About 3300 kcal/day	About 1700 kcal/day
Breakfast: 375 mL Froot Loops cereal 250 mL 2% milk 250 mL orange juice 2 slices white toast 5 mL butter (on toast)	**Breakfast:** 375 mL Cheerios cereal 250 mL skim milk 1/2 fresh pink grapefruit

Lunch:
McDonald's Big Mac
  hamburger
French fries, extra large
15 mL ketchup
Apple pie
	Lunch:
	Subway cold cut trio 6"
	  sandwich
	Granola bar, hard, w/choc.
	  chips, 1 bar (24 g)
	1 fresh medium apple

Dinner: 128 g ground beef (80% lean, crumbled), cooked 2 medium taco shells 57 g cheddar cheese 10 mL sour cream 20 mL store-bought salsa 250 mL shredded lettuce 250 mL refried beans 6 Oreos	**Dinner:** 142 g ground turkey, cooked 2 soft corn tortillas 85 g low-fat cheddar cheese 20 mL store-bought salsa 250 mL shredded lettuce 250 mL cooked mixed veggies 3 Oreos

Figure 14.12 The energy density of two sets of meals. The set on the left is higher in energy density, while the set on the right is lower in energy density and the preferred choice for a person trying to lose weight.

but many people report doing some form of aerobic exercise (such as bicycling, walking, running, aerobic dance, step aerobics, or hiking) and weight lifting at least 45 minutes most days of the week. In fact, on average, this group expended more than 2800 kcal each week through physical activity! While very few weight-loss studies have documented long-term maintenance of weight loss, those that have find that only people who are regularly active are able to maintain most of their weight loss.

In addition to expending energy and maintaining lean body mass and BMR, regular physical activity improves our mood, results in a higher quality of sleep, increases self-esteem, and gives us a sense of accomplishment (see Chapter 15 for more benefits of regular physical activity). All of these changes enhance our ability to engage in long-term healthy lifestyle behaviours.

Incorporate Appropriate Behaviour Modifications into Daily Life

Successful weight loss and long-term maintenance of a healthy weight require people to modify their behaviours. Some of the behaviour modifications related to food and physical activity have been discussed in the previous sections. Here are a few more tips on modifying behaviour that will assist you in losing weight and maintaining a healthy weight:

- Eat only at set times in one location. Avoid mindless eating by not eating while studying, working, driving, watching television, and so forth.
- Keep a log of what you eat, when, and why. Try to identify social or emotional cues that cause you to overeat, such as getting a poor grade on an exam or feeling lonely. Then strategize about non-food-related ways to cope, such as phoning a sympathetic friend.
- Save high-fat, high-kilocalorie snack foods such as ice cream, donuts, and cakes for occasional special treats.

- Avoid buying problem foods—that is, foods that you may have difficulty eating in moderate amounts.
- Avoid purchasing high-fat, high-sugar foods from vending machines and convenience stores.
- Serve your food portions on smaller dishes so they appear larger.
- Avoid feelings of deprivation by eating small, regular meals throughout the day.
- Whether at home or dining out, share food with others.
- Prepare healthy snacks to take along with you so that you won't be tempted by foods from vending machines, fast food restaurants, and so forth.
- Chew food slowly, taking at least 20 minutes to eat a full meal, and stopping at once if you begin to feel full.
- Always use appropriate utensils.
- Leave food on your plate or store it for the next meal.

Weight Loss Can Be Enhanced with Prescribed Medications

The biggest complaint about the recommendations for healthy weight loss is that they are difficult to maintain. Many people are looking for a "magic bullet" that will allow them to lose weight quickly and easily, requiring little sustained effort on their part to achieve their weight goals. Other people have tried to follow healthy weight-loss suggestions for years and have not been successful. In response to these challenges, prescription drugs have been developed to assist people with weight loss. These drugs typically act as appetite suppressants and may also increase satiety.

Weight-loss medications should be used only with proper supervision from a physician. One reason physician involvement is so critical is that many drugs developed for weight loss have side effects. Some have even proven deadly. Fenfluramine (brand name Pondimin), dexfenfluramine (brand name Redux), and a combination of phentermine and fenfluramine (called "phen-fen") are appetite-suppressing drugs that were banned from the market in 1996. These drugs, while resulting in more weight loss than diet alone, were found to cause two life-threatening conditions: primary pulmonary hypertension and valvular heart disease. Although these drugs were banned many years ago, they still serve as examples illustrating that the treatment of obesity through pharmacological means is neither simple nor risk-free.

One Prescribed Medication Is Available Only one prescription weight-loss drug is currently available in Canada: orlistat. Sibutramine (brand name Meridia), an appetite suppressant, was previously available but was voluntarily removed from the market in October 2010. This decision was made when data became available that found an increased risk of serious cardiovascular events associated with sibutramine use in patients with heart problems.

Orlistat (brand name Xenical) is a drug that acts to inhibit the absorption of dietary fat from the intestinal tract by inhibiting the enzyme lipase, which can result in weight loss in some people. Recent research shows that orlistat results in significant weight loss in obese adolescents, and adults experience significant weight loss and improved blood lipid profiles when orlistat is combined with an energy-restricted diet.[40, 41] The side effects of orlistat include abdominal pain, fatty and loose stools, leaky stools, flatulence, and decreased absorption of fat-soluble nutrients such as vitamins E and D.

For Whom Are Prescription Weight-Loss Medications Prescribed? Although the use of prescribed weight-loss medications is associated with side effects and a certain level of risk, they are justified for people who are obese. That's because the health risks of obesity override the risks of the medications. Specifically, prescription weight-loss medications are advised for people who have:

- a BMI greater than or equal to 30 kg/m^2
- a BMI greater than or equal to 27 kg/m^2 who also have other significant health risk factors such as heart disease, high blood pressure, and type 2 diabetes

These medications should be used only while under a physician's supervision so that progress and health risks can be closely monitored. They are most effective when combined with a program that supports energy restriction, regular exercise, and increasing physical activity throughout the day.

Using Dietary Supplements to Lose Weight Is Controversial

Over-the-counter medications and dietary supplements are also marketed for weight loss. It is important to remember that products needing a prescription are regulated by Health Canada under the Food and Drug Regulations and must undergo rigorous testing for safety and effectiveness before they can be released on the market. Vitamins and minerals, herbal remedies, homeopathic medicines, traditional medicines (e.g., traditional Chinese medicines), probiotics, and other products such as amino acids are considered natural health products. Health Canada regulates these products under the Natural Health Products Regulations. They must be safe to use as over-the-counter products and do not need a prescription to be sold. The NHPRs require manufacturers of these products to report any adverse reactions to Health Canada. Consumers are also encouraged to report any side effects to their healthcare provider or to Health Canada directly. This is important because it enables Health Canada to remove any unsafe products from the market. However, products do slip through the cracks and it is important for consumers to make sure that they check to see that the products they are buying have been approved by looking for an eight-digit Natural Product Number or Homeopathic Medicine Number on the label. This means that the product has been authorized for sale in Canada and is considered safe and effective when used as indicated on the label.[42] Recently, two reviews of various supplements and alternative treatments for weight loss were published.[43, 44] Both concluded that there is insufficient evidence to support the use of the following products widely marketed to enhance weight loss: chromium, spirulina (or blue-green algae), ginseng, chitosan (derived from the exoskeleton of crustaceans), green tea, and psyllium (a source of fibre). Yet these products continue their brisk sales to people desperate to lose weight.

Many products marketed for weight loss do indeed increase metabolic rate and decrease appetite; however, they prompt these effects because they contain *stimulants*, substances that speed up physiologic processes. Stimulants commonly found in weight-loss supplements include caffeine, phenylpropanolamine (PPA), and ephedra. Use of these substances is controversial and may be dangerous, as abnormal increases in heart rate and blood pressure can occur.

Caffeine   In addition to being a stimulant, caffeine is addictive; nevertheless, it is legal and unregulated in most countries and is considered safe when consumed in moderate amounts (up to the equivalent of three to four cups of coffee). The extent to which it affects people is influenced by their tolerance for caffeine, the amount consumed, and their body weight. In most adults, a moderate amount of caffeine causes positive mood changes and increased alertness. Its effects on the body may include increased heart rate, blood pressure, and urine output. Adverse effects of high doses of caffeine include nervousness, irritability, anxiety, muscle twitching and tremors, headaches, elevated blood pressure, and irregular or rapid heartbeat. Long-term overuse of high doses of caffeine can lead to sleep and anxiety disorders that require clinical attention. Caffeine overdose can be fatal; however, the lethal dose of caffeine is estimated to be about 150 to 200 mg/kg body weight, which is about equivalent to the amount of caffeine contained in 80 to 100 cups of coffee. As this volume of coffee is very difficult to consume, deaths due to caffeine have occurred primarily as a result of taking caffeine tablets.

Phenylpropanolamine (PPA)   In the year 2000, Health Canada banned over-the-counter medications containing phenylpropanolamine (PPA), an ingredient that had been used in many cough and cold medications as well as in weight-loss formulas. Health Canada acted in response to the deaths of several women who experienced brain hemorrhage after taking prescribed doses of such medications. Consumers were instructed to throw away any medications in their homes that contained PPA.

Ephedra   The use of ephedra has been associated with dangerous elevations in heart rate, blood pressure, and death. Ephedra has been banned by the International Olympic Committee for many years, and Health Canada has restricted the manufacture and sale of ephedra because of its potentially fatal side effects. Although it is illegal to sell ephedra-containing supplements in Canada, some herbal supplement producers still include *ma huang,* the so-called herbal ephedra, in their weight-loss products; however, *ma huang* is simply the Chinese name for ephedra. Some herbal weight-loss supplements contain a combination of *ma huang,* caffeine, and Aspirin. In 2008, Health Canada reminded consumers not to use products containing ephedra or ephedrine, particularly in combination with caffeine and other stimulants due to the serious, possibly fatal, adverse effects.[45] However, ephedra is still available in some stores in Canada and can be purchased on the internet.

Obesity Treatment Is Challenging

The first line of defence in treating obesity in adults is a low-energy diet and regular physical activity. Overweight and obese individuals should work with a healthcare practitioner to design and maintain a low-fat diet (less than 30% of total energy from fat) that has a deficit of 500 to 1000 kcal/day.[46] Physical activity should be increased gradually so that the person can build a program in which he or she is exercising at least 30 minutes per day, five times per week. The Institute of Medicine[47] concurs that 30 minutes a day, five times a week is the minimum amount of physical activity needed, but up to 60 minutes per day may be necessary for many people to lose weight and to sustain a body weight in the healthy range over the long term.

As discussed earlier in this chapter, changing entrenched dietary and activity patterns is challenging, and prescription medications are sometimes used to treat resistant cases of obesity in adults and children. Again, these medications should only be used while under a physician's supervision, and they appear to be most effective when combined with energy restriction and regular physical activity.

For people who are morbidly obese, surgery may be recommended. Generally, surgery is advised in people with a BMI greater than or equal to 40 kg/m^2 or in people with a BMI greater than or equal to 35 kg/m^2 who have other life-threatening conditions such as diabetes, hypertension, or elevated cholesterol levels.[48] The three most common types of weight-loss surgery performed are gastroplasty, gastric bypass, and gastric banding (**Figure 14.13**).

- *Vertical banded gastroplasty* involves partitioning or "stapling" a small section of the stomach to reduce total food intake.

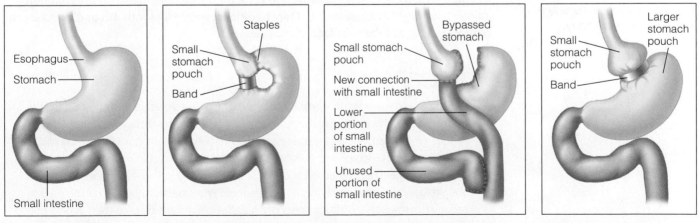

(a) Normal anatomy

(b) Vertical banded gastroplasty

(c) Roux-en-Y Gastric bypass

(d) Gastric banding

Figure 14.13 Three forms of surgery alter the (a) normal anatomy of the gastrointestinal tract to result in weight loss in morbid obesity: (b) vertical banded gastroplasty (c) Roux-en-Y gastric bypass, and (d) gastric banding.

- *Gastric bypass surgery* involves attaching the lower part of the small intestine to the stomach, so that food bypasses most of the stomach and the duodenum of the small intestine. This results in significantly less absorption of food in the intestine.
- *Gastric banding* is a relatively new procedure in which stomach size is reduced using a constricting band, thus restricting food intake.

Surgery is considered a last resort for morbidly obese people who have not been able to lose weight with energy restriction and exercise. This is because despite the improvements in the surgical procedure, there is still a risk for complications. Complications include infections, formation of blood clots, and adverse reactions to anesthesia. After the surgery, many recipients face a lifetime of problems with chronic diarrhea, vomiting, intolerance to dairy products and other foods, dehydration, and nutritional deficiencies resulting from alterations in nutrient digestion and absorption. Thus, the potential benefits of the procedure must outweigh the risks. It is critical that each surgery candidate be carefully screened by a trained physician. If the immediate threat of serious disease and death is more dangerous than the risks associated with surgery, then the procedure is justified.

Are these surgical procedures successful in reducing obesity? A 2009 systematic review concluded that bariatric surgery is clinically effective for moderate to severely obese people.[48] However, weight regain may occur, usually beginning after 18 to 24 months postsurgery.[49] The reasons that some people do not experience long-term success include:

- inability to eat less over time, even with a smaller stomach
- loosening of staples and gastric bands and enlargement of stomach pouch
- failure to survive the surgery or the postoperative recovery period

Although these surgical procedures may seem extremely risky, many of those who survive the surgery lose weight, maintain much of this weight loss over time, reduce their risk for type 2 diabetes and cardiovascular disease, and may even improve their ability to stay physically active over a prolonged period of time.[50]

Liposuction is a cosmetic surgical procedure that removes fat cells from localized areas in the body. It is not recommended or typically used to treat obesity or morbid obesity as it does not help people restrict food intake. Instead, it is often used by normal or mildly overweight people to "spot reduce" fat from various areas of the body. This procedure is not without risks; blood clots, skin and nerve damage, adverse drug reactions, and perforation injuries can and do occur as a result of liposuction. It can also result in deformations in the area where the fat is removed. This procedure is not the solution to long-term weight loss, as the millions of fat cells that remain in the body after liposuction enlarge if the person continues to overeat. In addition, although liposuction may reduce the fat content of a localized area, it does not reduce a person's risk for the diseases that are more common among overweight or obese people. Only traditional weight loss with diet and exercise can reduce body fat and the risks for chronic diseases.

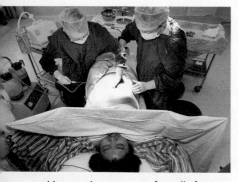

Liposuction removes fat cells from specific areas of the body.

RECaP

Achieving and maintaining a healthy body weight involves gradual reductions in energy intake, such as by eating smaller portion sizes and limiting dietary fat, incorporating regular physical activity, and applying appropriate behavioural modification techniques. Fad diets do not incorporate these strategies and do not result in long-term, healthy weight change. Diets based on macronutrient composition may promote long-term weight loss, but some have unhealthy side effects. When necessary, drugs can be used to reduce obesity with a doctor's prescription and supervision; however, there is only one drug currently approved in Canada. Using dietary supplements to lose weight is controversial and can be dangerous in some instances. Treatments for overweight, obesity, and morbid obesity include low-calorie, low-fat diets in combination with regular physical activity, weight-loss prescription medications, and/or surgery.

CASE STUDY

Energy Balance and Weight Management

Virginia is a charted accountant with a full-time job. She is 45 years old, 165 cm tall, and currently weighs 80 kg. Her waist circumference is 91 cm. She has been trying to lose weight for the past year and has lost 15 kg. Virginia has increased her physical activity to include walking at a slow pace for 30 minutes daily, but no matter what she does she cannot seem to lose any more weight. Virginia goes to see her physician to ask for a prescription for a weight-loss drug. The physician tells Virginia to make an appointment with the dietitian first. The dietitian conducts a dietary assessment and finds out that Virginia has been following a low-carbohydrate weight-loss diet. A typical day's intake would include:

Breakfast:	2 fried eggs
	1 cup coffee with 30 mL cream
Snack:	250 mL almonds
Lunch:	1 large (200 g) baked skinless, boneless chicken breast
	750 mL salad with 30 mL ranch dressing
Snack:	100 g cheese
	¼ pita bread
Dinner:	250 g steak, fried
	250 mL lettuce with 30 mL ranch dressing
Snack	4 boiled eggs

Thinking Critically

1. **Calculate and interpret Virginia's BMI. How much weight does she have to lose to get her BMI into the normal weight range?**
2. **Assess Virginia's health risk using her BMI and waist circumference values.**
3. **Calculate how much energy Virginia expends by walking 30 minutes per day at a slow pace.**
4. **Compare Virginia's diet to the recommendations of *Eating Well with Canada's Food Guide*. What key nutrients are likely to be missing in her diet?**
5. **Why might Virginia be having difficulty losing additional weight?**
6. **Is Virginia a good candidate for a weight-loss medication? Why or why not?**
7. **What suggestions could you give to Virginia to help her to lose the additional weight she needs to lose to reduce her health risks?**

What Disorders Are Related to Energy Intake?

At the beginning of this chapter, we provided some definitions of underweight, overweight, obesity, and morbid obesity. Let's take a closer look at these disorders.

Underweight

As defined earlier in this chapter, underweight occurs when a person has too little body fat to maintain health. People with a BMI of less than 18.5 kg/m^2 are typically considered underweight. Being underweight can be just as unhealthy as being obese, because it increases the risk for infections and illness and impairs the body's ability to recover. Some people are healthy but underweight because of their genetics and/or because they are very physically active and consume adequate energy to maintain their underweight status, but not enough to gain weight. In others, underweight is due to heavy smoking, an underlying disease such as cancer or HIV infection, or an eating disorder such as anorexia nervosa (see the accompanying Highlight on anorexia nervosa and bulimia nervosa).

amenorrhea Lack of menstruation in the absence of pregnancy. Primary amenorrhea is the absence of menstruation by the age of 16 years in a girl who has secondary sex characteristics, whereas secondary amenorrhea is the absence of the menstrual period for three or more months after the onset of menstruation.

HIGHLIGHT

Anorexia Nervosa and Bulimia Nervosa

Anorexia Nervosa Is a Potentially Deadly Eating Disorder

According to the American Psychiatric Association, 90% to 95% of individuals with anorexia nervosa are young girls or women.[51] Approximately 0.5% to 1% of American females develops anorexia, and between 5% and 20% of these will die from complications of the disorder within 10 years of initial diagnosis.[52] These statistics make anorexia nervosa the most common and deadly psychiatric disorder diagnosed in women and the leading cause of death in females between the ages of 15 and 24 years.[52] As the statistics indicate, anorexia nervosa also occurs in males, but the prevalence is much lower than in females.[53]

Signs and Symptoms of Anorexia Nervosa

The classic sign of anorexia nervosa is an extremely restrictive eating pattern that leads to self-starvation. These individuals may fast completely, restrict energy intake to only a few kilocalories per day, or eliminate all but one or two food groups from their diet. They also have an intense fear of weight gain, and even small amounts (for example, 0.5–1 kg) trigger high stress and anxiety.

In females, **amenorrhea** (no menstrual periods for at least three months) is a common feature of anorexia nervosa. It occurs when a young woman consumes insufficient energy to maintain normal body functions.

The American Psychiatric Association identifies the following conditions of anorexia nervosa (reprinted with permission from the *Diagnostic and Statistical Manual of Mental Disorders, Text Revision,* © 2000 American Psychiatric Association):

- Refusal to maintain body weight at or above a minimally normal weight for age and height
- Intense fear of gaining weight or becoming fat, even though considered underweight by all medical criteria
- Disturbance in the way in which one's body weight or shape is experienced, undue influence of body weight or shape on self-evaluation, or denial of the seriousness of the current low body weight
- Amenorrhea in females who are past puberty. Amenorrhea is defined as the absence of at least three consecutive menstrual cycles. A woman is considered to have amenorrhea if her periods occur only when given hormones, such as estrogen or oral contraceptives.

The signs of an eating disorder such as anorexia nervosa may be somewhat different in males. Females with eating disorders say they feel fat even when they are not, while males are more likely to have actually been overweight or even obese prior to developing an eating disorder.[53, 54] In addition, males with disordered eating are less concerned with actual body weight (that is, scale measurement) than females but are more concerned with body composition (that is, percentage of muscle mass compared to fat mass). The methods that men and women use to achieve weight loss also appear to differ. Males are more likely to use excessive exercise as a means of weight control, whereas females tend to use severe energy restriction, vomiting, and laxative abuse.

Health Risks of Anorexia Nervosa

Left untreated, anorexia nervosa eventually leads to a deficiency in energy and other nutrients that are required by the body to function normally. The body will then use stored fat and lean tissue (for example, organ and muscle tissue) as an energy source to maintain brain tissue and vital body functions. The body will also shut down or reduce non-vital body functions to conserve energy. Electrolyte imbalances can lead to heart failure and death. **Figure 14.14** highlights many of the health problems that occur in people with anorexia nervosa.

Because the best chances for recovery occur when an individual receives intensive treatment early, it is important to recognize the signs of anorexia nervosa. Use these signs as a guide to help identify those at risk and to encourage them to seek help.

A Variety of Nutritional Therapies Are Important in Treating Anorexia Nervosa

The goals of nutritional therapies are to restore the individual to a healthy body weight and resolve the nutrition-related eating issues. For hospitalized patients, the expected weight gain per week ranges from 0.5 to 1.5 kilograms. For outpatient settings, the expected weight gain is much lower (0.25 to 0.5 kg/week). During the weight-gain phase of a treatment program, energy intake goals may be set at 1000 to 1600 kcal/day, depending on body size, severity of the disease, and achievable levels of intake.

Patients frequently try a variety of methods to avoid consuming the food presented to them. They may discard the food, vomit, exercise excessively, or engage in a high level of non-exercise motor activity to eliminate the kilocalories they just consumed. For this reason, patients are carefully watched by hospital staff or parents to make sure they swallow all of their food. In addition to increasing amounts of food, patients may be given vitamin and mineral supplements to ensure that adequate micronutrients are consumed.

Nutrition counselling is an important aspect of the treatment to deal with the body image issues that occur as weight is regained. Once the patient reaches an acceptable body weight, nutrition counselling will address issues such as acceptability of certain foods, dealing with food situations such as family gatherings and eating out, and

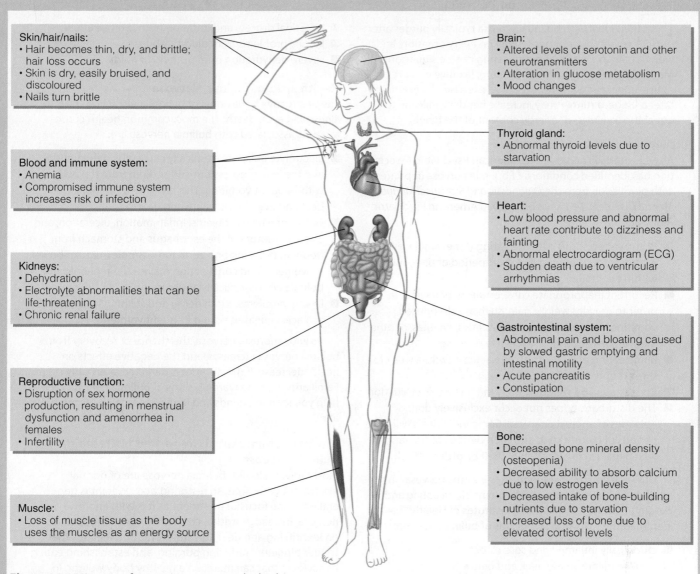

Skin/hair/nails:
- Hair becomes thin, dry, and brittle; hair loss occurs
- Skin is dry, easily bruised, and discoloured
- Nails turn brittle

Blood and immune system:
- Anemia
- Compromised immune system increases risk of infection

Kidneys:
- Dehydration
- Electrolyte abnormalities that can be life-threatening
- Chronic renal failure

Reproductive function:
- Disruption of sex hormone production, resulting in menstrual dysfunction and amenorrhea in females
- Infertility

Muscle:
- Loss of muscle tissue as the body uses the muscles as an energy source

Brain:
- Altered levels of serotonin and other neurotransmitters
- Alteration in glucose metabolism
- Mood changes

Thyroid gland:
- Abnormal thyroid levels due to starvation

Heart:
- Low blood pressure and abnormal heart rate contribute to dizziness and fainting
- Abnormal electrocardiogram (ECG)
- Sudden death due to ventricular arrhythmias

Gastrointestinal system:
- Abdominal pain and bloating caused by slowed gastric emptying and intestinal motility
- Acute pancreatitis
- Constipation

Bone:
- Decreased bone mineral density (osteopenia)
- Decreased ability to absorb calcium due to low estrogen levels
- Decreased intake of bone-building nutrients due to starvation
- Increased loss of bone due to elevated cortisol levels

Figure 14.14 Impact of anorexia nervosa on the body.

learning to put together a healthy food plan for weight maintenance.

Bulimia Nervosa Is Characterized by Bingeing and Purging

Bulimia nervosa is an eating disorder characterized by repeated episodes of **binge eating** followed by some form of **purging**. While binge eating, the person feels a loss of self-control, including an inability to end the binge once it has started. At the same time, the person feels a sense of euphoria not unlike a drug-induced high. A "binge" is usually defined as a quantity of food that is large for the person and for the amount of time in which it is eaten. For example, a person may eat a dozen brownies with two litres of ice cream in 30 minutes.

The prevalence of bulimia nervosa is higher than anorexia nervosa and is estimated to affect 1% to 4% of women. Like anorexia nervosa, bulimia nervosa is found predominately in women: six to ten females are diagnosed for every one male. The mortality rate is lower than for anorexia nervosa, with 1% of patients dying within 10 years of diagnosis.[52]

Although the prevalence of bulimia nervosa is much higher in women, rates for men are significant in some predominately "thin-build" sports in which participants are encouraged to maintain a low body weight (for example, horse racing, wrestling, crew, and gymnastics). Individuals in these sports typically do not have all the characteristics of bulimia nervosa, however, and the purging behaviours they practise typically stop once the sport is discontinued.

An individual with bulimia nervosa typically purges after most episodes, but not necessarily on every occasion, and weight gain as a result of binge eating can be significant. Methods of purging include vomiting, laxative or diuretic abuse, enemas, fasting, or excessive exercise. For example, after a binge, a runner may increase her daily mileage to equal the "calculated" energy content of the binge.

Symptoms of Bulimia Nervosa
As with anorexia nervosa, the American Psychiatric Association has identified conditions of bulimia nervosa (reprinted with permission from the *Diagnostic and Statistical Manual of Mental Disorders, Text Revision,* © 2000 American Psychiatric Association):

- Recurrent episodes of binge eating (for example, eating a large amount of food in a short period of time, such as within two hours)
- Recurrent inappropriate compensatory behaviour in order to prevent weight gain, such as self-induced vomiting, misuse of laxatives, diuretics, enemas, or other medications, fasting, or excessive exercise
- Binge eating occurs on average at least twice a week for three months
- Body shape and weight unduly influence self-evaluation
- The disturbance does not occur exclusively during episodes of anorexia nervosa. Some individuals will have periods of binge eating and then periods of starvation, which makes classification of their disorder difficult.

How can you tell if someone has bulimia nervosa? In addition to the recurrent and frequent binge eating and purging episodes, the National Institutes of Health[55] have identified the following symptoms of bulimia nervosa:

- chronically inflamed and sore throat
- swollen glands in the neck and below the jaw
- worn tooth enamel and increasingly sensitive and decaying teeth as a result of exposure to stomach acids
- gastroesophageal reflux disorder

- intestinal distress and irritation from laxative abuse
- kidney problems from diuretic abuse
- severe dehydration from purging of fluids

Health Risks of Bulimia Nervosa
The destructive behaviours of bulimia nervosa can lead to illness and even death. The most common health consequences associated with bulimia nervosa are:

- Electrolyte imbalance typically caused by dehydration and the loss of potassium and sodium from the body with frequent vomiting. This can lead to irregular heartbeat and even heart failure and death.
- Gastrointestinal problems: inflammation, ulceration, and possible rupture of the esophagus and stomach from frequent bingeing and vomiting. Chronic irregular bowel movements and constipation may result in people with bulimia who chronically abuse laxatives.
- Dental problems: tooth decay and staining from stomach acids released during frequent vomiting.

As with anorexia nervosa, the chance of recovery from bulimia nervosa increases, and the negative effects on health decrease, if the disorder is detected at an early stage. Familiarity with the warning signs of bulimia nervosa can help you identify friends and family members who might be at risk.

Nutrition Counselling Is Important in Treating Bulimia Nervosa
Most individuals with bulimia nervosa are of normal weight or overweight, so restoring body weight is generally not the focus of treatment as it is with anorexia nervosa. Instead, nutrition counselling generally focuses on identifying and dealing with events and feelings that trigger bingeing, reducing purging, and establishing eating behaviours that can maintain a healthy body weight. In addition, nutrition counselling will address negative feelings about foods and the fear associated with uncontrolled binge eating of foods.

binge eating Consumption of a large amount of food in a short period of time, usually accompanied by a feeling of loss of self-control.

purging An attempt to rid the body of unwanted food by vomiting or other compensatory means, such as excessive exercise, fasting, or laxative abuse.

Safe and Effective Weight Gain

With so much emphasis in Canada on obesity and weight loss, some find it surprising that many people are trying to gain weight. People looking to gain weight include those who are underweight to the extent that it is compromising their health and many athletes who are attempting to increase strength and power for competition.[56]

To gain weight, people must eat more energy than they expend. While overeating large amounts of foods high in saturated fats (such as bacon, sausage, and cheese) can cause weight gain, doing this without exercising is not considered healthy because most of the weight gained is fat, and high-fat diets increase our risks for cardiovascular and other diseases. Unless there are medical reasons to eat a high-fat diet, it is recommended that people trying to gain weight eat a diet that is relatively low in dietary fat (less than 30% of total calories) and relatively high in complex carbohydrates (55% of total calories). Recommendations for weight gain include:

- Eat a diet that includes about 500 to 1000 kcal/day more than is needed to maintain present body weight. Although we don't know exactly how much extra energy is needed to gain 0.5 kg, estimates range from 3000 to 3500 kcal. Thus, eating 500 to 1000 kcal/day in excess should result in a gain of 0.5–1 kg of weight each week.
- Eat frequently, including meals and numerous snacks throughout the day. Many underweight people do not take the time to eat often enough.
- Avoid the use of tobacco products, as they depress appetite and increase metabolic rate, and both of these effects oppose weight gain. Tobacco use also causes lung, mouth, and esophageal cancers.
- Exercise regularly and incorporate weight lifting or some other form of resistance training into your exercise routine. This form of exercise is most effective in increasing muscle mass. Performing aerobic exercise (such as walking, running, bicycling, or swimming) at least 30 minutes for three days per week will help maintain a healthy cardiovascular system.

Eating frequent nutrient-dense snacks can help promote healthy weight gain.

The key to gaining weight is to eat frequent meals throughout the day and to select energy-dense foods. When selecting foods that are higher in fat, make sure you select foods higher in polyunsaturated and monounsaturated fats (such as peanut butter, olive and canola oils, and avocados). For instance, smoothies and milkshakes made with milk or yogourt are a great way to take in a lot of energy. Eating peanut butter with fruit or celery and including salad dressings on your salad are other ways to increase the energy density of foods. The biggest challenge to weight gain is setting aside time to eat; by packing a lot of foods to take with you throughout the day, you can enhance your opportunities to eat more.

RecaP

Underweight occurs when a person has too little body fat to maintain health. A person can be underweight and healthy, but it may be a sign of underlying disease. Weight gain can be achieved by eating more and performing weight-lifting and aerobic exercise.

Overweight

Overweight is defined as having a moderate amount of excess body fat, resulting in a person having a weight for a given height that is greater than some accepted standard but is not considered obese. People with a BMI between 25 and 29.9 kg/m^2 are considered overweight. Being overweight does not appear to be as detrimental to our health as being obese, but some of the health risks of overweight include an increased risk for high blood pressure, heart disease, type 2 diabetes, sleep disorders, osteoarthritis, gallstones, and gynecological abnormalities.[46] It is also more likely that overweight people will become obese, and obesity confers an even higher risk for these diseases and for premature death. Because of these concerns, health professionals recommend that overweight individuals adopt a lifestyle that incorporates healthy eating and regular physical activity in an attempt to prevent additional weight gain, to reduce body weight to a normal level, and/or to support long-term health even if body weight is not significantly reduced.

Obesity and Morbid Obesity

Obesity is defined as having an excess body fat that adversely affects health, resulting in a person having a weight for a given height that is substantially greater than some accepted standard. People with a BMI between 30 and 39.9 kg/m^2 are considered obese. Morbid obesity occurs when a person's body weight exceeds 100% of normal; people who are morbidly obese have a BMI greater than or equal to 40 kg/m^2.

Health Effects of Obesity

Both overweight and obesity are now considered an epidemic in Canada. According to measured height and weight data from 2007 to 2009, the prevalence of obesity in Canada was 24.1%, over 10% lower than in the United States (34.4%).[57] This was a doubling in obesity rates across all age groups since the early 1980s. Data from the Canadian Health Measures survey also showed that there is considerable variation in the prevalence of obesity across the country, from a low of 5.3% in Richmond, British Columbia, to a high of 35.9% in northern Saskatchewan.[58] The prevalence of obesity is particularly high among Aboriginal adults. Over one-third (36%) of on-reserve First Nations adults are estimated to be obese according to self-reported data in the First Nations Regional Longitudinal Health Survey (RHS). This figure is likely higher since self-estimates are typically lower than measured data.[58] Measured data from the 2004 Canadian Community Health Survey estimated that 37.8% of Aboriginal adults living off reserve were obese.[59] This alarming rise in obesity is a major health concern because it is linked to many chronic diseases and adverse health conditions. These include:

- hypertension
- dyslipidemia, including elevated total cholesterol, triglycerides, and LDL-cholesterol and decreased HDL-cholesterol
- type 2 diabetes
- heart disease
- stroke
- gallbladder disease
- osteoarthritis
- sleep apnea
- certain cancers such as colon, breast, endometrial, and gallbladder
- menstrual irregularities and infertility
- gestational diabetes, premature fetal deaths, neural tube defects, and complications during labour and delivery
- depression

Both overweight and obesity can also contribute to a condition referred to as the **metabolic syndrome**. The metabolic syndrome is a clustering of risk factors that increase one's risk for heart disease, type 2 diabetes, and stroke. These risk factors include:

- abdominal obesity (defined as a waist circumference greater than or equal to 102 cm for men and 88 cm for women)
- higher-than-normal triglyceride levels (greater than or equal to 150 mg/dL)
- lower-than-normal HDL-cholesterol levels (less than 40 mg/dL in men and 50 mg/dL in women)
- higher-than-normal blood pressure (greater than or equal to 130/85 mm Hg)
- fasting blood glucose levels greater than or equal to 100 mg/dL, including people with diabetes[60]

People with the metabolic syndrome are twice as likely to develop heart disease and five times as likely to develop type 2 diabetes than people without the metabolic syndrome. It is estimated that about 25% of adults in Canada have the metabolic syndrome; it is particularly prevalent among people of South Asian and Aboriginal origin.[61]

Obesity is also associated with an increased risk of premature death: mortality rates for people with a BMI of 30 kg/m^2 or higher are 50% to 100% above the rates for those with a BMI between 20 and 25 kg/m^2. As discussed in Chapter 1, several of the leading causes of death in Canada are associated with obesity (see page 7).

Ironically, the prevalence of dieting is high, especially among adolescent and adult females.[62] How can obesity rates be so high when there are so many people dieting? Certainly, some people who are dieting are actually at a normal or even below-normal

metabolic syndrome A clustering of risk factors that increase one's risk for heart disease, type 2 diabetes, and stroke, including abdominal obesity, higher-than-normal triglyceride levels, lower-than-normal HDL-cholesterol levels, higher-than-normal blood pressure (greater than or equal to 130/85 mm Hg), and elevated fasting blood glucose levels.

weight, and these people account for a small percentage of this total. However, a telephone survey of American adults with a history of obesity found that approximately 20% had been successful in achieving and maintaining at least a 10% weight loss for a minimum of one year.[63] These results suggest that while some obese individuals are able to lose weight and maintain weight loss, about 80% of obese people who are dieting are somehow failing to lose weight or to maintain long-term weight loss. Why?

Obesity Is a Multifactorial Disease

Obesity is known as a **multifactorial disease**, meaning that there are many factors that cause it. This makes it extremely difficult to treat. Although it is certainly true that obesity, like overweight, is caused by eating more energy than is expended, it is also true that some people are more susceptible to becoming obese than others. In addition, as we saw with the twin study, some people are more resistant than others to losing weight and keeping it off. Research on the causes and best treatments of obesity is ongoing, but let's explore some current theories.

Genetic and Physiologic Factors Because a person's genetic background influences his or her height, weight, body shape, and metabolic rate, it can also affect a person's risk for obesity. Some obesity experts point out that, if proved, the existence of a thrifty gene or genes (discussed earlier) would show that obese people have a genetic tendency to expend less energy both at rest and during physical activity. Other researchers are working to determine whether the set-point theory can partially explain why many obese people are very resistant to weight loss. As we learn more about genetics, we will gain a greater understanding of the role it plays in the development and treatment of obesity.

We also discussed earlier several physiologic factors that may influence an individual's experience of hunger and satiation. These include the proteins leptin, ghrelin, PYY, and uncoupling proteins. Other physiologic factors such as beta-endorphins, neuropeptide Y, and decreased blood glucose can reduce satiety or increase hunger, theoretically promoting overeating and weight gain.

Childhood Obesity Is Linked to Adult Obesity The prevalence of overweight in children and adolescents is increasing at an alarming rate in Canada. As shown in **Figure 14.15**, in 2004 the combined overweight/obesity rate for boys and girls was about

Adequate physical activity is instrumental in preventing childhood obesity.

multifactorial disease Any disease that may be attributable to more than one of a variety of causes.

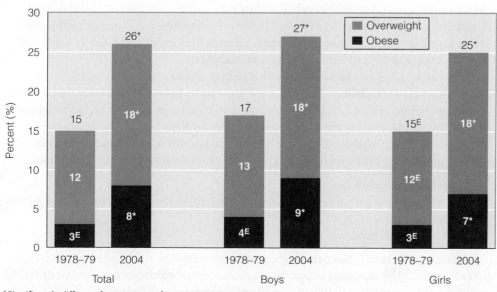

Figure 14.15 Percent (%) of children and adolescents (aged 2 to 17) who were overweight or obese, by sex, in Canada excluding territories, 1978–79 and 2004.
Data from: Shields, M. 2006. Overweight and obesity among children and youth. *Health Reports* 17:3. Reproduced and distributed on an "as is" basis with the permission of Statistics Canada.

* Significantly different from estimate for 1978/79 (p < 0.05)
E Coefficient of variation 16.6% to 33.3% (interpret with caution)

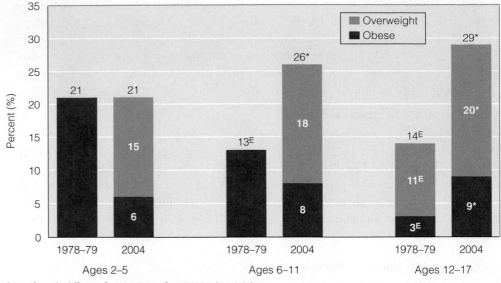

Figure 14.16 Percent (%) of children and adolescents (aged 2 to 17) who were overweight or obese, by sex, in Canada excluding territories, 1978–79 and 2004.
Data from: Shields, M. 2006. Overweight and obesity among children and youth. *Health Reports* 17:3. Reproduced and distributed on an "as is" basis with the permission of Statistics Canada.

* Significantly different from estimate for 1978/79 (p < 0.05)
E Coefficient of variation 16.6% to 33.3% (interpret with caution)

70% higher than it had been in 1978–79, and the obesity rate was about 2.5 times higher. However, these trends were different for the various age groups. As shown in **Figure 14.16**, the percentage of children aged two to five who were overweight or obese was essentially the same. However, the overweight/obesity rate for adolescents aged 12 to 17 more than doubled from 14% to 29%, and their obesity rate tripled from 3% to 9%. There was a time when having extra "baby fat" was considered good for the child. We assumed that childhood overweight and obesity were temporary and that the child would grow out of it. While it is important for children to have a certain minimum level of body fat to maintain health and to grow properly, researchers are now concerned that overweight and obesity are harming children's health and increasing their risk of overweight and obesity in adulthood.

Health data demonstrate that obese children are already showing signs of chronic disease while they are young, including elevated blood pressure, high cholesterol levels, and changes in insulin and glucose metabolism that may increase the risk for type 2 diabetes (formerly known as *adult-onset diabetes*). In some communities, children as young as five years of age have been diagnosed with type 2 diabetes. Unfortunately, many of these children will maintain these disease risk factors into adulthood.

Does being an obese child guarantee that obesity will be maintained during adulthood? Although some children who are obese grow up to have a normal body weight, it has been estimated that about 70% of children who are obese maintain their higher weight as adults.[64] Obviously, this has important consequences for their health.

It has been suggested that there are three critical periods in childhood during which substantial weight gain can increase the risk of obesity and related diseases in adulthood:

- Gestation and early infancy
- The period of weight gain (called *adiposity rebound*) that occurs between 5 and 7 years of age
- Adolescence (or puberty)

Having either one or two overweight parents increases the risk of obesity two to four times.[65] This may be explained in part by genetics or by unhealthy eating patterns or lack of physical activity within the family or a combination of these risk factors.

Binge-Eating Disorder Can Cause Significant Weight Gain

When was the last time a friend or relative confessed to you about "going on an eating binge"? Most likely, they explained that the behaviour followed some sort of stressful event, such as a problem at work, the breakup of a relationship, or a poor grade on an exam. Many people have one or two binge episodes every year or so, in response to stress. But in people with **binge-eating disorder**, the behaviour occurs an average of twice a week or more and is not usually followed by purging. This lack of compensation for the binge distinguishes binge-eating disorder from bulimia nervosa and explains why the person tends to gain a lot of weight.

The prevalence of binge-eating disorder is estimated to be 2% to 3% of the adult population and 8% of the obese population. In contrast to anorexia and bulimia, binge-eating disorder is also common in men. Our current food environment, which offers an abundance of good-tasting, cheap food any time of the day, makes it difficult for people with binge-eating disorder to avoid food triggers.

As you would expect, the increased energy intake associated with binge eating significantly increases a person's risk of being overweight or obese. In addition, the types of foods individuals typically consume during a binge episode are high in fat and sugar, which can increase blood lipids. Finally, the stress associated with binge eating can have psychological consequences, such as low self-esteem, avoidance of social contact, depression, and negative thoughts related to body size.

Night-Eating Syndrome Can Lead to Obesity

Night-eating syndrome was first described in a group of patients who were not hungry in the morning, but spent the evening and night eating and also reported insomnia. Like binge-eating disorder, it is associated with obesity because although night eaters don't binge, they do consume significant energy in their frequent snacks, and they don't compensate for the excess energy intake.

Symptoms of Night-Eating Syndrome The distinguishing characteristic of night-eating syndrome is the time during which most of the day's energy intake occurs. Night eaters eat relatively little during the day, consuming the majority of their energy between 8:00 p.m. and 6:00 a.m. They even get up in the night to eat. Night eating is also characterized by a depressed mood and by insomnia. In short, night eaters appear to have a unique combination of three disorders: an eating disorder, a sleep disorder, and a mood disorder.[66]

Health Risks of Night-Eating Syndrome Night-eating syndrome is important clinically because of its association with obesity, which increases the risk for several chronic diseases, including heart disease, high blood pressure, stroke, type 2 diabetes, and arthritis. Obesity also increases the risk for sleep apnea, which can further disrupt the night eater's already abnormal sleeping pattern.

Someone with night-eating syndrome consumes most of his or her daily energy between 8 p.m. and 6 a.m.

Obesity is a multifactorial disease, and genetics, physiology, and lifestyle choices are all thought to contribute. In addition, childhood obesity is strongly associated with adult obesity. Binge-eating disorder and night-eating syndrome can cause significant weight gain and lead to obesity.

binge-eating disorder A disorder characterized by binge eating an average of twice a week or more, typically without compensatory purging.

night-eating syndrome A disorder characterized by intake of the majority of the day's energy between 8:00 p.m. and 6:00 a.m. Individuals with this disorder also experience mood and sleep disorders.

SEE FOR YOURSELF

Rate the Latest Weight-Loss Craze

Quick: Name the latest weight-loss craze on your campus! Is it sound, or just another fad? To find out, go to your local library or bookstore, or search the internet to find a description of its components. Evaluate the plan by using the recommendations on pp. 506–513. For example, is the total fat intake 15% to 25% of total energy? Does the plan recommend regular daily physical activity? Does the plan include behaviour modification strategies, and if so, do they seem effective? After completing your evaluation, rate the plan on a 1-to-10 scale, with 1 indicating that the plan fails to meet any of the recommendations and 10 indicating that the plan meets all of the recommendations. If you rated the plan lower than 5, check it out against the bulleted points on page 508. Does it meet the criteria for a fad diet? If so, consider submitting your evaluation to your campus newspaper or website. Publishing your results could help other students avoid wasting their time and money—and possibly harming their health.

Chapter Review

14

Test Yourself   Answers

1. **T** Being underweight increases our risk for illness and premature death and in many cases can be just as unhealthy as being obese.

2. **F** Obesity is a multifactorial disease with many contributing factors. Although eating too much food and not getting enough exercise can lead to being overweight and obese, obesity is a complex disease and is not simply caused by overeating.

3. **F** Body composition assessments can help give us a general idea of body fat levels, but most methods are not extremely accurate.

4. **F** According to 2004 CCHS data, approximately one in four (23%) of Candian adults were considered obese.

5. **T** Health can be defined in many ways. An individual who is overweight, but who exercises regularly and has no additional risk factors for various disease such as heart disease and type 2 diabetes is considered a healthy person.

Summary

- Definitions of a healthy body weight include one that is appropriate for someone's age and level of development, promotes healthy blood lipids and glucose, can be achieved and sustained without constant dieting, promotes good eating habits, and allows for regular physical activity.

- Body mass index (BMI) is an index of weight per height squared. It is useful to indicate health risks associated with overweight and obesity in groups of people.

- Underweight is defined as having too little body fat to maintain health, causing a person to have a weight for a given height that is below an acceptably defined standard. A BMI below 18.5 is considered underweight.

- Overweight is defined as having a moderate amount of excess body fat, resulting in a person having a weight for a given height that is greater than some accepted standard but is not considered obese. A BMI of 25 to 29.9 is considered overweight.

- Obesity is defined as having excess body fat that adversely affects health, resulting in a person having a weight for a given height that is substantially greater than some accepted standard. A BMI of 30 to 39.9 is considered obese. Morbid obesity occurs when a person's body weight exceeds 100% of normal, which puts him or her at very high risk for serious health consequences. A BMI of 40 or above is considered morbidly obese.

- Waist circumference is used to determine disease risk and patterns of fat storage. People with large waists have an apple-shaped fat pattern. People with large hips (as compared to the waist) have a pear-shaped fat pattern. Having an apple-shaped pattern increases your risk for heart disease, type 2 diabetes, and other chronic diseases.

- We lose or gain weight based on changes in our energy intake, the food we eat, and our energy expenditure (both at rest and when physically active).

- Basal metabolic rate (BMR) is the energy needed to maintain the body's resting functions. BMR accounts for 60% to 75% of our total daily energy needs.

- The thermic effect of food is the energy we expend to process the food we eat. It accounts for 5% to 10% of the energy content of a meal and is higher for processing proteins and carbohydrates than for fats.

- The energy cost of physical activity represents energy that we expend for physical movement or work we do above basal levels. It accounts for 15% to 35% of our total daily energy output.

- Our genetic heritage interacts with our environment to influence the risk for obesity. It has been hypothesized that possessing a thrifty gene (or genes) or maintaining a weight set point may affect a person's risk for obesity.

- Eating a diet proportionally higher in fat may increase the risk for obesity, as dietary fat is stored more easily as adipose tissue than is dietary carbohydrate or protein.

- Physiologic factors that contribute to obesity include alterations in various proteins and hormones that influence hunger and satiety, including leptin, ghrelin, peptide YY, uncoupling proteins, beta-endorphins, serotonin, GLP-1, and cholecystokinin.

- Cultural and social factors, such as easy access to large portions of inexpensive and high-fat foods and excessive screen time for entertainment, also contribute to obesity. Mood and emotional state also affect appetite.

- Fad diets are weight-loss programs that enjoy short-term popularity and are sold based on a marketing gimmick that appeals to the public's desires and fears. They typically promise rapid weight loss, often without increased physical activity or long-term behavioural modification, and rarely result in long-term maintenance of weight loss.

- Diet plans that restrict intake of certain macronutrients can help many people lose weight, but some have unhealthy side effects.

- A sound weight-loss plan involves gradual reduction in energy intake, incorporating physical activity into each day, and practising changes in behaviour that can assist in meeting realistic weight-change goals.

- Prescription drugs can be used to assist with weight loss when the risks of obesity override the risks associated with the medications.

- Various dietary supplements are marketed as weight-loss products. Many of these products cause dangerous changes in heart rate and blood pressure. Unlike prescription drugs, these products are not strictly regulated by Health Canada.

- Being underweight can be detrimental to one's health. Most of the products marketed for weight gain have been shown to be ineffective. Healthy weight gain involves consuming more energy than expended by selecting ample servings of nutritious, high-energy foods and exercising regularly by including resistance training and aerobic exercise.

- Overweight is not as detrimental to health as obesity, but it is associated with an increased risk for high blood pressure, heart disease, type 2 diabetes, sleep disorders, osteoarthritis, gallstones, and gynecological abnormalities.

- Obesity and morbid obesity are associated with significantly increased risks for many diseases and for premature death. Obesity can be treated with low-energy diets and regular physical activity, prescription medications, and surgery when necessary.

Review Questions

1. The ratio of a person's body weight to height is represented as his or her
   a. body composition.
   b. basal metabolic rate.
   c. bioelectrical impedance.
   d. body mass index.

2. The body's total daily energy expenditure includes
   a. basal metabolic rate, thermal effect of food, and effect of physical activity.
   b. basal metabolic rate, movement, standing, and sleeping.
   c. effect of physical activity, standing, and sleeping.
   d. body mass index, thermal effect of food, and effect of physical activity.

3. All people gain weight when they
   a. eat a high-fat diet (>35% fat).
   b. take in more energy than they expend.
   c. fail to exercise.
   d. take in less energy than they expend.

4. The set-point theory proposes that
   a. obese people have a gene not found in slender people that regulates their weight so that it always hovers near a given set point.
   b. obese people have a gene that causes them to be energetically thrifty.
   c. all people have a genetic set point for their body weight.
   d. all people have a hormone that regulates their weight so that it always hovers near a given set point.

5. A body protein that increases appetite is
   a. leptin.
   b. ghrelin.
   c. PYY.
   d. orlistat.

6. A granola bar has 3.3 grams of protein, 6 grams of fat, and 33 grams of carbohydrate. Calculate the total energy content of this granola bar.

7. When might bariatric surgery be advised for the treatment of obesity?

8. Identify at least four characteristics of a healthy weight.

9. Describe a sound weight-loss program, including recommendations for diet, physical activity, and behavioural modifications.

10. Can you increase your basal metabolic rate? Is it wise to try? Defend your answer.

11. Identify at least four societal factors that may have influenced the rise in obesity rates in Canada since 1978.

12. Your friend Misty joins you for lunch and confesses that she is discouraged about her weight. She says that she has been trying "really hard" for three months to lose weight but that no matter what she does, she cannot drop below 67 kg. Based on her height, you know Misty is not overweight, and she exercises regularly. What questions would you suggest she think about? How would you advise her?

Web Links

www.dietitians.ca
Dietitians of Canada
Go to this site to learn more about fad diets and guidelines for choosing a weight-loss program.

www.heartandstroke.ca
Heart and Stroke Foundation of Canada
Go to this site for information on designing a healthy weight action plan.

www.hc-sc.gc.ca/ahc-asc/media/advisories-avis/index-eng.php
Health Canada Advisories and Warnings
Go to this site to find out information on advisories and warnings related to weight-loss products.

www.hc-sc.gc.ca/fn-an/nutrition/weights-poids/index-eng.php
Health Canada Healthy Weights
Go to this site to calculate your BMI and find additional information on the Canadian Guidelines for Body Weight Classification in Adults.

www.obesitynetwork.ca
Canadian Obesity Network/Obesity Canada
This site has tools for calculating BMI and daily calorie needs, using a pedometer, and learning how to use a food diary.

www.nedic.ca
National Eating Disorder Information Centre

This site has information on eating disorders and weight preoccupation including facts about treatment, prevention, and health promotion.

http://hp2010.nhlbihin.net/portion/
National Institutes of Health Portion Distortion site
Visit this site and take the interactive "Portion Distortion" quiz to challenge your understanding of portion sizes. For instance, how does a standard restaurant cup of coffee compare with a coffee mocha from a national chain coffeehouse? Find out, and then guess how long you'd have to walk to burn off that mocha!

www.niddk.nih.gov/health/nutrit/nutrit.htm
National Institute of Diabetes and Digestive and Kidney Diseases
Find out more about healthy weight loss and how it pertains to diabetes and digestive and kidney diseases.

www.sne.org
Society for Nutrition Education
Click on "Nutrition Resources" and then "Weight Realities Division Resource List" for additional resources related to positive attitudes about body image and healthy alternatives to dieting.

www.oa.org
Overeaters Anonymous
Visit this site to learn about ways to reduce compulsive overeating.

MasteringNutrition®

www.masteringnutrition.pearson.com

Assignments
Animations: Reading Labels
Activities: NutriTools

Study Area
Practice Tests • Diet Analysis • eText

References

1. Emme. 2009. Bio profile. Available at www.emmestyle.com/about.

2. Stoynoff, N. 2008. Emme's cancer battle. *People,* January 21, pp. 99–101.

3. Manore, M. M., N. L. Meyer, and J. L. Thompson. 2009. *Sport Nutrition for Health and Performance,* 2nd ed. Champaign, IL: Human Kinetics.

4. Health Canada. 2003. *Canadian Guidelines for Body Weight Classification in Adults. Quick Reference Tool for Professionals.* Available at www.hc-sc.gc.ca/fn-an/alt_formats/hpfb-dgpsa/pdf/nutrition/cg_quick_ref-ldc_rapide_ref-eng.pdf (accessed March 5, 2011).

5. Wang, Y. 2004. Epidemiology of childhood obesity—methodological aspects and guidelines: What is new? *Int. J. Obes.* 23:S21–S28.

6. Lear, S. A., K. H. Humphries, S. Kohli, A. Chockalingam, J. J. Frohlich, C. L. Birmingham. 2007. Visceral adipose tissue accumulation differs according to ethnic background: results of the Multicultural Community Health Assessment Trial (M-CHAT). *Am. J. Clin. Nutr.* 86:353–359.

7. Shai, I., R. Jiang, J. E. Manson, M. J. Stampfer, W. C. Willett, G. A. Colditz, and F. B. Hu. 2006. Ethnicity, obesity, and risk of type 2 diabetes in women. *Diab. Care* 29:1585–1590.

8. Health Canada. 2003. *Canadian Guidelines for Body Weight Classification in Adults.* Available at www.hc-sc.gc.ca/fn-an/nutrition/weights-poids/guide-ld-adult/weight_book_tclivres_des_poids_tm-e (accessed March 5, 2011).

9. Zernike, K. 2004. U.S. body survey, head to toe, finds signs of expansion. *New York Times,* March 1, pp. 1, 12.

10. Heyward, V. H., L. M. Stolarczyk. 1996. *Applied body composition assessment.* Windsor, ON: Human Kinetics.

11. Stunkard, A. J., T. I. A. Sørensen, C. Hanis, T. W. Teasdale, R. Chakraborty, W. J. Schull, and F. Schulsinger. 1986. An adoption study of human obesity. *N. Engl. J. Med.* 314:193–198.

12. Bouchard, C., A. Tremblay, J. P. Després, A. Nadeau, P. J. Lupien, G. Thériault, J. Dussault, S. Moorjani, S. Pinault, and G. Fournier. 1990. The response to long-term overfeeding in identical twins. *N. Engl. J. Med.* 322:1477–1482.

13. Hellerstein, M. 2001. No common energy currency: de novo lipogenesis as the road less traveled. *Am. J. Clin. Nutr.* 74:707–708.

14. Zhang, Y., et al. 1994. Positional cloning of the mouse obese gene and its human homologue. *Nature* 372:425–432.

15. Masuzaki, H., et al. 1997. Nonadipose tissue production of leptin: leptin as a novel placenta-derived hormone in humans. *Nature Med.* 3:1029–1033.

16. Moon, B. C., and J. M. Friedman. 1997. The molecular basis of the obese mutation in ob[2J] mice. *Genomics* 42:152–156.

17. Cummings, D. E., D. S. Weigle, R. S. Frayo, P. A. Breen, M. K. Ma, E. P. Dellinger, and J. Q. Purnell. 2002. Plasma ghrelin levels after diet-induced weight loss or gastric bypass surgery. *N. Engl. J. Med.* 346:1623–1630.

18. Mittelman, S. D., K. Klier, S. Braun, C. Azen, M. E. Geffner, T. A. Buchanan. 2010. Obese adolescents show impaired meal responses of the appetite-regulating hormones ghrelin and PPY. *Obesity (Silver Spring)* 18:918–925. DOI:10.1038/oby.2009.499.

19. Batterham, R. L., M. A. Cowley, C. J. Small, H. Herzog, M. A. Cohen, C. L. Dakin, A. M. Wren, A. E. Brynes, M. J. Low, M. A. Ghatel, R. D. Cone, and S. R. Bloom. 2002. Gut hormone PYY[3-36] physiologically inhibits food intake. *Nature* 418:650–664.

20. Batterham, R. L., M. A. Cohen, S. M. Ellis, C. W. Le Roux, D. J. Withers, G. S. Frost, M. A. Ghatei, and S. R. Bloom. 2003. Inhibition of food intake in obese subjects by peptide YY[3-36]. *N. Engl. J. Med.* 349:941–948.

21. Virtanen, K. A., M. E. Lidell, J. Orava, M. Heglind, R. Westergren, T. Niemi, M. Taittonen, J. Laine, N-J. Savito, S. Enerbäck, and P. Nuutila. 2009. Functional brown adipose tissue in healthy adults. *N. Engl. J. Med.* 360(15):1518–1525.

22. Cypess, A. M., S. Lehman, G. Williams, I. Tal, D. Rodman, A. B. Goldfine, F. C. Kuo, E. L. Palmer, Y-H. Tseng, A. Doria, G. M. Kolodny, and C. R. Kahn. 2009. Identification and importance of brown adipose tissue in adult humans. *N. Engl. J. Med.* 360(15):1509–1517.

23. Naslund, E., B. Barkeling, N. King, M. Gutniak, J. E. Blundell, J. J. Holst, S. Rossner, P. M. Hellstrom. 1999. Energy intake and appetite are suppressed by glucagon-like peptide-1 (GLP-1) in obese men. *International Journal of Obesity and Related Metabolic Disorders* 23:304–311.

24. Torekov, S.S., S. Madsbad, J. J. Holst. 2011, March 15. Obesity—an indication for GLP-1 treatment? Obesity pathophysiology and GLP-1 treatment potential. *Obesity Reviews* DOI:10.1111/j.1467-789X.2011.00860x.

25. Eyler, A. E., D. Matson-Koffman, D. Rohm-Young, S. Wilcox, J. Wilbur, J. L. Thompson, B. Sanderson, and K. R. Evenson. 2003. Quantitative study of correlates of physical activity in women

from diverse racial/ethnic groups: the Women's Cardiovascular Health Network Project. *Am. J. Prev. Med.* 25(3Si):93–103.

26. Eyler, A. E., D. Matson-Koffman, J. R. Vest, K. R. Evenson, B. Sanderson, J. L. Thompson, J. Wilbur, S. Wilcox, and D. Rohm-Young. 2002. Environmental, policy, and cultural factors related to physical activity in a diverse sample of women: the Women's Cardiovascular Health Network Project—Summary and Discussion. *Women and Health* 36:123–134.

27. Sobal, J., and A. J. Stunkard. 1989. Socioeconomic status and obesity: a review of the literature. *Psych. Bulletin* 105:260–275.

28. Garriguet, D. 2008. Obesity and the eating habits of the Aboriginal population. *Health Reports* 19(1).

29. Kuhle, S., and P. Veugelers. 2008. Why does the social gradient in health not apply to overweight? *Health Reports* 19(4).

30. Williams, P. L., C. P. Johnson, M. L. V. Kratzmann, C. S. Jacob Johnson, B. J. Anderson, C. Chenhall. 2006. Can households earning minimum wage in Nova Scotia afford a nutritious diet? *Can. J. Pub. Health* 97:430–434.

31. Elliott, S. 2005. Calories? Hah! Munch Some Mega M&M's. *New York Times,* August 5. p. C5.

32. Koh-Banerjee, P., N. F. Chu, D. Spiegelman, B. Rosner, G. Colditz, W. Willett, and E. Rimm. 2003. Prospective study of the association of changes in dietary intake, physical activity, alcohol consumption, and smoking with 9-y gain in waist circumference among 16,587 U.S. men. *Am. J. Clin. Nutr.* 78:719–727.

33. Academy of Nutrition and Dietetics. 2002. Position of the Academy of Nutrition and Dietetics: food and nutrition misinformation. *J. Am. Diet. Assoc.* 102(2):260–266.

34. Freedman, M. R., J. King, and E. Kennedy. 2001. Popular diets: a scientific review. *Obes. Res.* 9(suppl. 1):1S–40S.

35. Ello-Martin, J. A., J. H. Ledikwe, and B. J. Rolls. 2005. The influence of food portion size and energy density on energy intake: implications for weight management. *Am. J. Clin. Nutr.* 82(suppl.):236S–241S.

36. Flood, J. E., L. S. Roe, and B. J. Rolls. 2006. The effect of increased beverage portion size on energy intake at a meal. *J. Am. Diet. Assoc.* 106:1984–1990.

37. Obesity Canada Clinical Guidelines Expert Panel. 2007. 2006 Canadian clinical practice guidelines on the management and prevention of obesity in adults and children. *Canadian Medical Association Journal* 176(8). Available at www.cmaj.ca/cgi/data/176/8/S1/DC1/1 (accessed March 12, 2011).

38. Canadian Society for Exercise Physiology. 2011. *Canadian Physical Activity Guidelines for Adults—18 to 64 years.* Available at www.csep.ca/guidelines (accessed March 5, 2011).

39. Klem, M. L., R. R. Wing, M. T. McGuire, H. M. Seagle, and J. O. Hill. 1997. A descriptive study of individuals successful at long-term maintenance of substantial weight loss. *Am. J. Clin. Nutr.* 66:239–246.

40. Chanoine, J.-P., S. Hampl, C. Jensen, M. Boldrin, and J. Hauptman. 2005. Effect of orlistat on weight and body composition in obese adolescents. A randomized controlled trial. *JAMA* 293(23):2873–2883.

41. Hutton, B., and D. Fergusson. 2004. Changes in body weight and serum lipid profile in obese patients treated with orlistat in addition to a hypocaloric diet: a systemic review of randomized clinical trials. *Am. J. Clin. Nutr.* 80:1461–1468.

42. Health Canada. *About Natural Health Products.* Available at www.hc-sc.gc.ca/dhp-mps/prodnatur/about-apropos/cons-eng.php (accessed March 5, 2011).

43. Saper, R. B., D. M. Eisenberg, and R. S. Phillips. 2004. Common dietary supplements for weight loss. *Am. Fam. Phys.* 70(9): 1731–1738.

44. Allison, D. B., K. R. Fontaine, S. Heshka, J. L. Mentore, and S. B. Heymsfield. 2001. Alternative treatments for weight loss: a critical review. *Crit. Rev. Food Sci. Nutr.* 41(1):1–28.

45. Health Canada. *Advisories and Warnings. Health Canada Reminds Canadians Not to Use Ephedra/Ephedrine Products.* Available at www.hc-sc.gc.ca/ahc-asc/media/advisories-avis/_2008/2008_41-eng.php (accessed March 5, 2011).

46. National Institutes of Health. National Heart, Lung, and Blood Institute. 1998. Clinical guidelines on the identification, evaluation, and treatment of overweight and obesity in adults. The Evidence Report. Available at www.nhlbi.nih.gov/guidelines/obesity/ob_gdlns.htm.

47. Institute of Medicine. Food and Nutrition Board. 2002. *Dietary Reference Intakes for Energy, Carbohydrate, Fiber, Fat, Fatty Acids, Cholesterol, Protein, and Amino Acids (Macronutrients).* Washington, DC: The National Academies Press.

48. Picot, J., J. Jones, J. L. Colquitt, E. Gospodarevskaya, E. Loveman, L. Baxter, et al. 2009. The clinical effectiveness and cost-effectiveness of bariatric (weight loss) surgery for obesity: a systematic review and economic evaluation. *Health Technol. Assess.* 13:1–190. Abstract available from www.ncbi.nlm.nih.gov/pubmed/19726018.

49. Zalesin, K. C., B. A. Franklin, W. M. Miller, J. Nori, S. Veri, J. Odom, et al. 2010. Preventing weight regain after bariatric surgery: an overview of lifestyle and psychosocial modulators. *Amer. J. Lifestyle Med.* 4:113–120.

50. Sjöström, L., A-K. Lindroos, M. Peltonen, J. Torgerson, C. Bouchard, B. Carlsson, S. Dahlgren, B. Larsson, K. Narbro, C. D. Sjöström, M. Sullivan, and H. Wedel. 2004. Lifestyle, diabetes, and cardiovascular risk factors 10 years after bariatric surgery. *N. Engl. J. Med.* 351(26):2683–2693.

51. American Psychiatric Association. 1994. *Diagnostic and Statistical Manual of Mental Disorders (DSM-IV),* 4th ed. Washington, DC: Author.

52. Patrick, L. 2002. Eating disorders: a review of the literature with emphasis on medical complication and clinical nutrition. *Altern. Med. Rev.* 7(3):184–202.

53. Robb, A. S., and M. J. Dadson. 2002. Eating disorders in males. *Child Adolesc. Psychiatric. Clin. N. Am.* 11:399–418.

54. Beals, K. A. 2004. *Disordered Eating in Athletes: A Comprehensive Guide for Health Professionals.* Champaign, IL: Human Kinetics Publishers.

55. Garfinkel, P. E. 2002. Classification and diagnosis of eating disorders. In: Fairburn, D. G., and K. D. Brownell, eds. *Eating Disorders and Obesity: A Comprehensive Handbook,* 2nd ed. New York: Guilford Press, pp. 155–161.

56. American College of Sports Medicine, Academy of Nutrition and Dietetics, and Dietitians of Canada. 2009. Nutrition and athletic performance. Joint position statement. *Med. Sci. Sports Exerc.* 41:709–731.

57. Statistics Canada. Adult obesity prevalence in Canada and the United States. Available at www.statcan.gc.ca/pub/82-625-x/2011001/article/11411-eng.htm (accessed October 2, 2011).

58. Public Health Agency of Canada. 2011. *Obesity in Canada.* Available at www.phac-aspc.gc.ca/hp-ps/hl-mvs/oic-oac/assets/pdf/oic-oac-eng.pdf (accessed October 2, 2011).

59. Katzmarzyk, P. T. 2008. Obesity and physical activity among Aboriginal Canadians. *Obesity* 16:184–190.

60. Grundy, S. M., B. Hansen, S. C. Smith, J. I. Cleeman, and R. A. Kahn. 2004. Clinical management of metabolic syndrome: report of the American Heart Association/National Heart, Lung, and Blood Institute/American Diabetes Association Conference on scientific issues related to management. *Circulation* 109:551–556.

61. Anand, S. S., S. Yusef, C. V. Vuskan, et al. 2000. Differences in risk factors, atherosclerosis, and cardiovascular disease between ethnic groups in Canada: The Study of Health Assessment and Risk in Ethnic Groups (SHARE). *Lancet* 356(9226):279–284.

62. Field, A., J. Haines, B. Rosner, and W. C. Willett. 2010. Weight control behaviours and subsequent weight change among adolescents and young adult females. *Am. J. Clinical Nutrition* 91:147–153.

63. McGuire, M. T., R. R. Wing, and J. O. Hill. 1999. The prevalence of weight loss maintenance among American adults. *Int. J. Obes.* 23:1314–1319.

64. Torgan, C. 2002. Childhood obesity on the rise. The NIH Word on Health. Available at www.nih.gov/news/WordonHealth/jun2002/childhoodobesity.htm.

65. Dietz, W. H. 1994. Critical periods in childhood for the development of obesity. *Am. J. Clin. Nutr.* 59:955–959.

66. Stunkard, A. J. 2002. Night eating syndrome. In: D. G. Fairburn, and K. D. Brownell, eds. *Eating Disorders and Obesity: A Comprehensive Handbook,* 2nd ed. New York: Guilford Press, pp. 183–187.

67. Taubes, G. 2002. What if fat doesn't make you fat? *New York Times Magazine,* July 7, section 6.

68. Liebman, B. 2002. Big fat lies: the truth about the Atkins Diet. *Center Sci. Public Interest Nutr. Action Health Letter* 29(9):1–7.

69. Bravata, D. M., L. Sanders, J. Huang, H. M. Krumholz, I. Olkin, and D. M. Bravata. 2003. Efficacy and safety of low-carbohydrate diets: a systematic review. *Journal of the American Medical Association* 289:1837–1850.

70. Brehm, B. J., R. J. Seeley, S. R. Daniels, et al. 2003. A randomized trial comparing a very low carbohydrate diet and a calorie-restricted low fat diet on body weight and cardiovascular risk factors in healthy women. *J. Clin. Endocrinology and Metabolism* 88:1617–1623.

71. Stern, L., N. Iqbal, P. Seshadri, K. L. Chicano, D. A. Daily, J. McGrory, M. Williams, E. J. Gracely, and F. F. Samaha. 2004. The effects of low-carbohydrate versus conventional weight loss diets in severely obese adults: one-year follow-up of a randomized trial. *Ann. Intern. Med.* 140:778–785.

72. Samaha, F. F., N. Iqbal, P. Seshadri, K. L. Chicano, D. A. Daily, J. McGrory, T. Williams, M. Williams, E. J. Gracely, and L. Stern. 2003. A low-carbohydrate as compared with a low-fat diet in severe obesity. *N. Engl. J. Med.* 348:2074–2081.

73. Foster, G. D., H. R. Wyatt, J. O. Hill, et al. 2003. A randomized trial of a low-carbohydrate diet for obesity. *New England Journal of Medicine* 348:2082–2090.

74. Samaha, F. F., N. Iqbal, P. Seshardi, et al. 2003. A low-carbohydrate diet as compared with a low-fat diet in severe obesity. *New England Journal of Medicine* 348:2074–2081.

75. Boden, G., K. Sargrad, C. Homko, M. Mozzoli, and T. P. Stein. 2005. Effect of a low-carbohydrate diet on appetite, blood glucose levels, and insulin resistance in obese patients with type 2 diabetes. *Ann. Intern. Med.* 142:403–411.

76. Bravata, D. M., L. Sanders, J. Huang, H. M. Krumholz, I. Olkin, C. D. Gardner, and D. M. Bravata. 2003. Efficacy and safety of low-carbohydrate diets. A systematic review. *JAMA* 289:1837–1850.

77. Dansinger, M. L., J. A. Gleason, J. L. Griffith, H. P. Selker, E. J. Schaefer. 2005. Comparison of the Atkins, Ornish, Weight Watchers, and Zone diets for weight loss and heart disease: a randomized trial. *Journal of the American Medical Association* 293:43–53.

High-Protein Diets—Are They the Key to Weight Loss?

High-protein diets have been popular over the last 40 years. Very-low-energy, high-protein programs (200 to 400 kcal per day, 1.5 g of protein per kg body weight) were very popular in the 1970s. Many of these diets consisted of low-quality protein, however, and at least 58 people died from heart problems while following them. As a result of these deaths, we now know that these extreme diets are only appropriate for severely obese people under medical supervision, and must include high-quality protein sources.

Proponents of high-protein diets claim that you can eat all your favourite foods and still lose weight. Is this possible? This chapter provided a detailed explanation of weight loss, and you can now see that the key to weight loss is eating less energy than you expend. If you eat more energy than you expend, you can gain weight. Thus, any type of diet, even high-protein diets, must contain fewer kilocalories than a person expends to result in weight loss.

It is important to recognize that high-protein diets are synonymous with low-carbohydrate diets, because high-protein foods typically replace those high in carbohydrates. In addition, many high-protein diets are also high in fat. It is well established that reducing carbohydrate intake causes the body to break down its stored carbohydrate (or glycogen) in the liver and muscle; this is necessary to maintain blood glucose levels and provide energy to the brain. As water is stored along with glycogen, using stored carbohydrate for energy results in the loss of water from the body, which registers on the scale as rapid weight loss.

Among high-protein diets, probably the Atkins Diet is the best known. This diet plan advocates consumption of a diet very low in starches (including potatoes, white bread, pasta, and refined sugars) and very high in protein. A highly controversial article in support of the Atkins Diet was published in 2002 in the *New York Times Magazine*.[67] In this article, supporters of the diet emphasize that eating a high-carbohydrate diet has caused obesity in the United States. They contended that the Atkins Diet results in substantial weight loss, but does not cause unhealthy changes in blood cholesterol despite its high saturated-fat content.

After the publication of the article in the *New York Times Magazine*, the Center for Science in the Public Interest (CSPI) published a response that claimed irresponsible and inaccurate reporting.[68] The CSPI interviewed many of the experts quoted in the article as supporting the Atkins Diet. These experts stated that they were either misquoted or quoted out of context and that the information they shared that was contrary to supporting the Atkins Diet was ignored.

According to many nutrition and obesity experts[69] there are numerous potential health risks associated with eating a low-carbohydrate (and high-fat) diet, including the following:

- Elevated ketones in the blood, which may result in abnormal insulin metabolism and impaired renal function and liver damage. Some high-protein diets are so low in carbohydrate that the body does not receive enough glucose to maintain brain function. As you know, when this happens, the body produces ketones from body fat, as ketones are an alternative energy source for the central nervous system. High ketone levels in the blood can be toxic, as they increase blood acidity. This state is called ketoacidosis and it can be dangerous if maintained over a prolonged period of time. Left untreated, increased blood acidity causes disorientation, eventual loss of consciousness, coma, and even death.
- Increased risk of heart disease caused by excessive consumption of animal proteins and fats which may lead to hyperlipidemia. It is well established that eating a diet high in saturated fat increases a person's LDL-cholesterol, which in turn increases the risk for heart disease.
- Renal function may be impaired by eating high-protein diets, particularly for people with pre-existing kidney disease or those with diabetes. As you know, eating more protein increases protein metabolism and urea production. Additional fluid is required to flush this extra urea from the kidneys.
- Increased risk of some forms of cancer due to eating a diet high in red meat and unhealthy fats and low in fibre. Low-carbohydrate diets may limit foods, such as fruits, that contain antioxidants. These substances have been shown to be protective against some cancers.

The cause of obesity is thought to be complex and multifactorial; however, experts agree that the increased prevalence of obesity in Canada is a result of environmental and cultural influences which have resulted in excess energy intake and decreased energy output.[37] Whether or not the source of that excess energy is a contributing factor has been the subject of many research studies. Unfortunately, the designs of these studies are very heterogeneous and therefore it is sometimes difficult to interpret them. They tend to vary in the definition of low carbohydrate, the type and length of dietary intervention used, and whether or not physical activity is recommended to participants. One early study suggested that a diet containing 30 grams of carbohydrate a day resulted in increased weight loss and improved serum triglyceride and HDL-cholesterol levels when compared to a low-fat diet (25% of energy intake).[70] However, the short duration of this study (six months) was considered a limitation. Stern and colleagues placed participants on either the Atkins Diet or a low-fat diet plan recommended by the American Heart Association.[71] Participants consuming the Atkins Diet lost significantly more weight than those on the low-fat diet during the first six months, but weight loss between the two groups was no longer significant after one year.[72] However, people consuming the low-carbohydrate diets had lower triglyceride levels and less of a decrease in HDL-cholesterol as compared with people eating the low-fat diet. Two others studies conducted over a one-year period have shown similar results.[73, 74] The authors of these studies concluded that the reason why weight loss slowed in those participants following the low-carbohydrate diet was because of reduced adherence to the diet.

Few of these trials have included participants with type 2 diabetes, which is a group that could benefit from both weight loss and a decreased intake of refined carbohydrate foods. Boden and colleagues studied how 10 people with type 2 diabetes responded after following the Atkins Diet for two weeks.[75] Unlike the relatively larger randomized controlled trials done previously, the researchers in this study controlled food intake by having the participants select approved foods through a modified hospital diet. All foods consumed were weighed and recorded daily. Participants were found to lose an average of 1.65 kg of body weight during the study period. Surprisingly, this rapid loss of body weight was not exclusively due to the loss of body water. In fact, six participants lost body water, three participants gained body water, and one had no change in body water. Positive changes in the health of these indi-

Low blood glucose levels often result in feelings of low energy and confusion, and may lead to more serious negative effects.

viduals included normalization of blood glucose levels, an increase in insulin sensitivity, and significant decreases in blood triglyceride and cholesterol levels. The participants were able to lose weight because they spontaneously reduced their energy intake by 1000 kcal per day.

Bravata and colleagues, in a systematic review of the literature on the efficacy and safety of low-carbohydrate diets, concluded that there are not enough data to currently make recommendations for or against their use.[76] The authors of this review state that the weight loss that occurs with low-carbohydrate diets appears to be associated with a decreased energy intake and longer diet duration and is not necessarily due to the reduced carbohydrate content of the diet per se. Further, they concluded that low-carbohydrate diets have no adverse effect on serum lipid, fasting serum glucose, fasting serum insulin levels, or blood pressure. More recently, Dansinger and colleagues conducted a randomized trial to assess adherence rates and the effectiveness of four diets (Atkins, Zone, Weight Watchers, and Ornish) for weight loss and cardiac risk factor reduction.[77] They concluded that "sustained adherence to a diet, rather than diet type was the key predictor of weight loss and cardiac risk factors reduction." (p. 52)

Thus, at this time, it is not possible to state with any certainty that a low-carbohydrate diet is better than other diet plans. The long-term health implications of this type of diet are also unknown at this time, and more research must be conducted in this area.

Using the Evidence

1. Are low-carbohydrate diets more effective for weight loss in adults compared with higher-carbohydrate diets?

2. What impact do low-carbohydrate diets have on cardiovascular risk factors?

3. Would you recommend a low-carbohydrate diet to an individual with diabetes? Why or why not?

4. What diet do you think would work best to help you maintain a healthy weight and muscle mass and provide enough energy and nutrients to maintain your lifestyle and your long-term health?

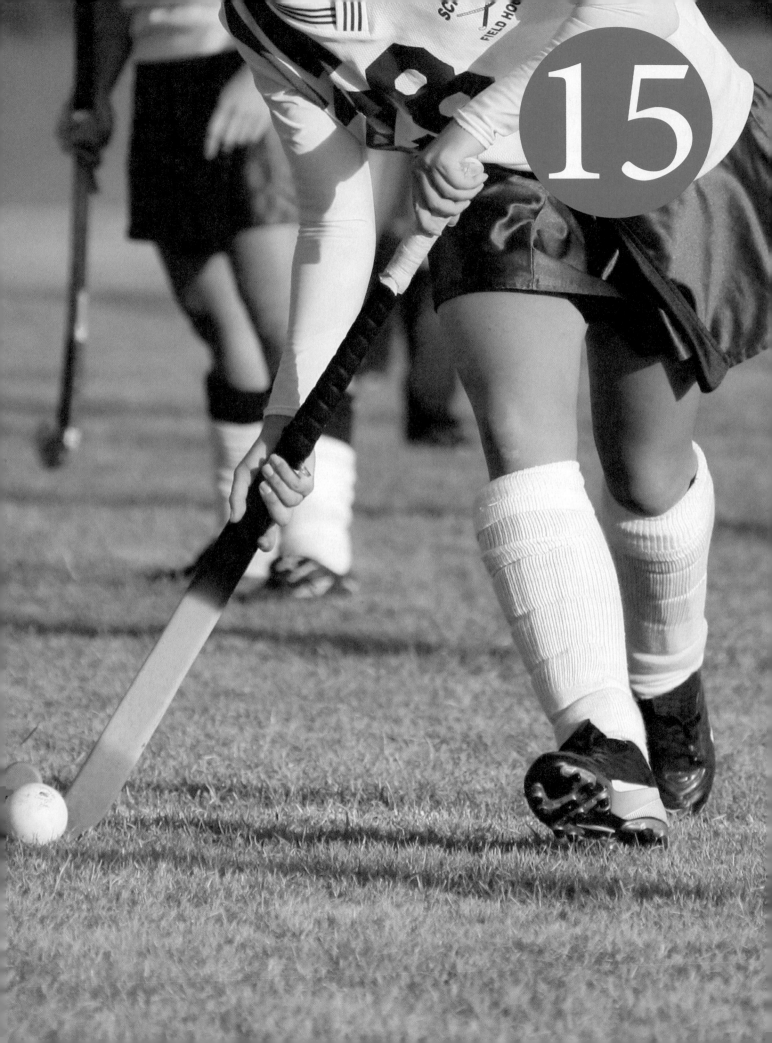

Nutrition and Physical Activity: Keys to Good Health

Chapter Objectives | *After reading this chapter, you will be able to:*

1. Compare and contrast the concepts of physical activity, leisure-time physical activity, exercise, and physical fitness, *p. 536*.

2. Define the four components of fitness, *p. 536*.

3. List at least four health benefits of being physically active on a regular basis, *pp. 536–537*.

4. Describe the FIT principle and calculate your maximal and training heart rate range, *pp. 539–547*.

5. List and describe at least three processes we use to break down fuels to support physical activity, *pp. 548–553*.

6. Explain why lactic acid is not simply a waste product of exercise metabolism, *p. 550*.

7. Discuss at least three changes in nutrient needs that can occur in response to an increase in physical activity or vigorous exercise training, *pp. 553–563*.

8. Describe the concept of carbohydrate loading, and discuss situations in which this practice may be beneficial to athletic performance, *p. 558*.

9. Define the heat illnesses, including heat syncope, heat cramps, heat exhaustion, and heat-stroke, *pp. 560–561*.

10. Define the term *ergogenic aids,* and discuss the potential benefits and risks of at least four ergogenic aids that are currently on the market, *pp. 565–569*.

I n 2003, Ed Whitlock from Milton, Ontario, ran a marathon in less than three hours with a time of 2:54:48; he was 73 years of age! This time is equivalent to a 20-year-old running a marathon in 2:03:57, which would be the fastest marathon ever run. Ed currently holds 13 world records in long-distance running and plans to continue competing until he is 90.

There's no doubt about it: regular physical activity dramatically improves a person's strength, stamina, health, and longevity. But what qualifies as "regular physical activity"? In other words, how much does a person need to do to reap the benefits? And if people do become more active, does their diet have to change, too?

A healthy diet and regular physical activity are like two sides of the same coin, interacting in a variety of ways to improve strength and stamina and to increase resistance to many chronic diseases and acute illnesses. In fact, the nutrition and physical activity recommendations for reducing the risks for heart disease also reduce the risks for high blood pressure, type 2 diabetes, obesity, and some forms of cancer! In this chapter, we define physical activity, identify its many benefits, and discuss the nutrients needed to maintain an active life.

Why Engage in Physical Activity?

A lot of people are looking for a "magic pill" that would help them maintain weight loss, reduce their risk of diseases, make them feel better, and improve their quality of sleep. Although many people are not aware of it, regular physical activity is this magic pill. **Physical activity** describes any movement produced by muscles that increases energy expenditure. Different categories of physical activity include occupational, household, leisure-time, and transportation.[1] **Leisure-time physical activity** is any activity not related to a person's occupation and includes competitive sports, planned exercise training, and recreational activities such as hiking, walking, and bicycling. **Exercise** is therefore considered a subcategory of leisure-time physical activity and refers to activity that is purposeful, planned, and structured.[2]

One of the most important benefits of regular physical activity is that it increases our physical fitness. **Physical fitness** is a state of being that arises largely from the interaction between nutrition and physical activity. It is defined as the ability to carry out daily tasks with vigour and alertness, without undue fatigue, and with ample energy to enjoy leisure-time pursuits and meet unforeseen emergencies.[1] Physical fitness has many components (Table 15.1).[3] These include the following:

- **Cardiorespiratory fitness** is defined as the ability of the heart, lungs, and circulatory system to efficiently supply oxygen and nutrients to working muscles.
- **Musculoskeletal fitness** involves fitness of both the muscles and bones. It includes *muscular strength*, the maximal force or tension level that can be produced by a muscle group, and *muscular endurance*, the ability of a muscle to maintain submaximal force levels for extended periods of time.
- **Flexibility** is the ability to move a joint fluidly through the complete range of motion.
- **Body composition** is the amount of bone, muscle, and fat tissue in the body.

Although many people are interested in improving their physical fitness, some are more interested in maintaining general fitness, while others are interested in achieving higher levels of fitness to optimize their athletic performance.

Other benefits of regular physical activity include the following:

- *Reduces our risks for, and complications of, heart disease, stroke, and high blood pressure:* Regular physical activity increases high-density lipoprotein cholesterol (HDL, the "good" cholesterol) and lowers triglycerides in the blood, improves the strength of the heart, helps maintain healthy blood pressure, and limits the progression of atherosclerosis (or hardening of the arteries).
- *Reduces our risk for obesity:* Regular physical activity maintains lean body mass and promotes more healthy levels of body fat, may help in appetite control, and increases energy expenditure and the use of fat as an energy source.

Hiking is a leisure-time physical activity that can contribute to your physical fitness.

physical activity Any movement produced by muscles that increases energy expenditure; includes occupational, household, leisure-time, and transportation activities.

leisure-time physical activity Any activity not related to a person's occupation; includes competitive sports, recreational activities, and planned exercise training.

exercise A subcategory of leisure-time physical activity; any activity that is purposeful, planned, and structured.

physical fitness The ability to carry out daily tasks with vigour and alertness, without undue fatigue, and with ample energy to enjoy leisure-time pursuits and meet unforeseen emergencies.

cardiorespiratory fitness Fitness of the heart and lungs; achieved through regular participation in aerobic-type activities.

musculoskeletal fitness Fitness of the muscles and bones.

flexibility The ability to move a joint through its full range of motion.

Table 15.1 The Components of Fitness

Fitness Component	Examples of Activities for Achieving Fitness in Each Compnent
Cardiorespiratory	Aerobic-type activities such as walking, running, swimming, cross-country skiing
Musculoskeletal fitness:	Resistance training, weight lifting, calisthenics, sit-ups, push-ups
Muscular strength	Weight lifting or related activities using heavier weights with fewer repetitions
Muscular endurance	Weight lifting or related activities using lighter weights with greater number of repetitions
Flexibility	Stretching exercises, yoga
Body composition	Aerobic exercise and resistance training

- *Reduces our risk for type 2 diabetes:* Regular physical activity enhances the action of insulin, which improves the cells' uptake of glucose from the blood and can improve blood glucose control in people with diabetes, which in turn reduces the risk for, or delays the onset of, diabetes-related complications.
- *Potential reduction in our risk for colon cancer:* Although the exact role that physical activity may play in reducing colon cancer risk is still unknown, we do know that regular physical activity enhances gastric motility, which reduces transit time of potential cancer-causing agents through the gut.
- *Reduces our risk for osteoporosis:* Regular physical activity strengthens bones and enhances muscular strength and flexibility, thereby reducing the likelihood of falls and the incidence of fractures and other injuries when falls occur.

Regular physical activity is also known to improve our sleep patterns, reduce our risk for upper respiratory infections by improving immune function, and reduce anxiety and mental stress. It also can be effective in treating mild and moderate depression.

Despite the plethora of benefits derived from regular physical activity, most people find that this magic pill is not easy to swallow. In fact, most people in Canada are physically inactive. Results from the Canadian Health Measures Survey reveal that only 15.4% of Canadian adults age 20–79 years accumulate 150 minutes or more of moderate-to-vigorous activity in 10 minute bouts per week. Only a further 4.8% do so at least 30 minutes on at least five days.[4] These statistics mirror the reported increases in obesity, heart disease, and type 2 diabetes in industrialized countries.

This trend toward inadequate physical activity levels is also occurring in young people. Additional data from 6–19-year-old children showed that boys and girls are sedentary about 8.5 hours a day. Only 9% of boys and 4% of girls accumulate at least 60 minutes of moderate-to-vigorous physical activity at least six days a week (**Figure 15.1**). On average, boys engage in an hour and girls three-quarters of an hour of moderate-to-vigorous physical activity daily.[5] Since our habits related to eating and physical activity are formed early in life, it is imperative that we provide opportunities for children and adolescents to engage in regular, enjoyable physical activity. An active lifestyle during childhood increases the likelihood of a healthier life as an adult.[6]

RECaP

Physical activity is any movement produced by muscles that increases energy expenditure. Physical fitness is the ability to carry out daily tasks with vigour and alertness, without undue fatigue, and with ample energy to enjoy leisure-time pursuits and meet unforeseen emergencies. Physical activity provides a multitude of health benefits, including reducing our risk for obesity and other chronic diseases and relieving anxiety and stress. Most people in Canada, including many children, are insufficiently active.

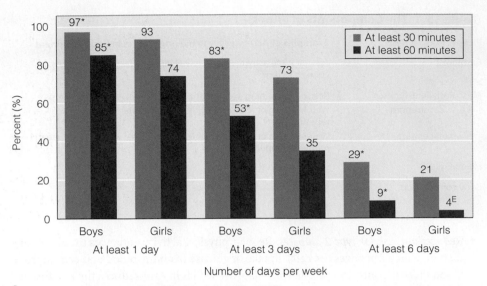

E Use with caution (data with a coefficient of variation from 16.6% to 33.3%)
* Significantly different from estimate for girls (p < 0.05)

Figure 15.1 Percentage of children and youth attaining selected physical activity criteria.
Data from: Trembly, M. S., M. Shields, M. Laviolette, C. L. Craig, I. Janssen, and S. Connor Gorber. 2010. Fitness of Canadian children and youth: results from the 2007–2009 Canadian Health Measures Survey. *Health Reports* (Statistics Canada, Catalogue 82-003-X) 21:1–15. Reproduced and distributed on an "as is" basis with the permission of Statistics Canada.

What Is a Sound Fitness Program?

There are several widely recognized qualities of a sound fitness program, as well as guidelines to help people design one that is right for them. These are explored here. Keep in mind that people with heart disease, high blood pressure, diabetes, osteoporosis, or arthritis should get approval to exercise from their healthcare practitioner prior to starting a fitness program. In addition, a medical evaluation should be conducted before starting an exercise program for an apparently healthy but currently inactive man 40 years or older or woman 50 years or older.

A Sound Fitness Program Meets Your Personal Goals

A fitness program that may be ideal for you is not necessarily right for everyone. Before designing or evaluating any program, it is important that each person define his or her personal fitness goals. Is the goal to prevent osteoporosis, diabetes, or another chronic disease that runs in the family? Is the goal simply to increase energy and stamina? Or is the intent to compete in athletic events? Each of these scenarios would require a very different fitness program.

For example, if a person wants to train for athletic competition, a traditional approach that includes planned exercise sessions under the guidance of a trainer or coach would probably be most beneficial. If the goal is to achieve cardiorespiratory fitness, participating in an aerobics class at least three times per week may be recommended.

In contrast, if the goal is to maintain overall health, one might do better to follow the Canadian Physical Activity Guidelines.[6] They emphasize that significant health benefits, including reducing the risk for chronic diseases, can be achieved by participating in a moderate-to-vigorous physical activity (such as 45 minutes of gardening, 20 minutes of brisk walking, or 30 minutes of basketball) for at least 150 minutes per week. These health benefits occur even when the time spent performing the physical activities is cumulative (for example, brisk walking for 10 minutes three times per day). Although these guidelines

Moderate physical activity, such as gardening, helps maintain overall health.

are appropriate for achieving health benefits, they are not necessarily of sufficient intensity and duration to improve physical fitness.

A Sound Fitness Program Is Varied, Consistent . . . and Fun!

One of the most important goals for everyone is fun; unless you enjoy being active, you will find it very difficult to maintain your physical fitness. What activities do you consider fun? If you enjoy the outdoors, then hiking, camping, fishing, and rock climbing are potential activities for you. If you would rather exercise with friends on your lunch break, then walking, climbing stairs, and bicycle riding may be more appropriate. Or you may find it more enjoyable to stay indoors and use the programs and equipment at your local fitness club or purchase your own treadmill and free weights.

Variety is critical to maintaining your fitness. While some people enjoy doing similar activities day after day, most of us get bored with the same fitness routine. Variety can be achieved by combining indoor and outdoor activities throughout the week, taking a different route when you walk each day, watching a movie or reading a book while you ride a stationary bicycle or walk on a treadmill, or participating in different activities each week such as walking, bicycling, and gardening. This smorgasbord of activities can increase your activity level without leading to monotony and boredom.

A useful tool has been developed to help you increase the variety of your physical activity choices (**Figure 15.2**). The **Canadian Physical Activity Guidelines** makes recommendations for the type and amount of activity that should be done weekly to achieve health benefits. The Canadian Physical Activity Guidelines are evidence-based guidance developed by the Canadian Society for Exercise Physiology and are harmonized with international guidelines. The guidelines are targeted to five age groups: adults 65 years and older, adults 18–64 years, youth 12–17 years, children 5–11 years of age and infants and toddlers 0–4 years of age. It is suggested that adults accumulate 150 minutes of moderate-to-vigorous physical activity per week, in bouts of 10 minutes or more. Children and youth should accumulate 60 minutes of moderate-to-vigorous exercise daily.[6, 7]

It is important to understand that you cannot do just one activity to achieve overall fitness because every activity is specific to a certain fitness component. Refer back to Table 15.1, and notice the different activities listed as examples for the various components. For instance, participating in aerobic-type activities will improve our cardiorespiratory fitness but will do little to improve muscular strength. To achieve that goal, we must participate in some form of **resistance training**, or exercises in which our muscles work against resistance. Flexibility is achieved by participating in stretching activities. By following the recommendations put forth in the Canadian Physical Activity Guidelines, you can achieve physical fitness in all components.

A Sound Fitness Program Appropriately Overloads the Body

To improve fitness, an extra physical demand must be placed on the body. This is referred to as the **overload principle**. A word of caution is in order here: *the overload principle does not advocate subjecting the body to inappropriately high stress,* because this can lead to exhaustion and injuries. In contrast, an appropriate overload on various body systems will result in healthy improvements in fitness. For example, a gain in muscle strength and size that results from repeated work that overloads the muscle is referred to as **hypertrophy**. When muscles are not worked adequately, they **atrophy**, or decrease in size and strength.

To achieve an appropriate overload, three factors should be considered, collectively known as the **FIT principle**: *f*requency, *i*ntensity, and *t*ime of activity. The FIT principle can

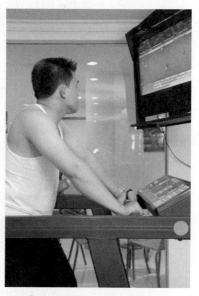

Watching television or reading can provide variety while walking on a treadmill.

Canadian Physical Activity Guidelines Recommendations for the type and amount of activity that should be done weekly to achieve health benefits.

resistance training Exercises in which our muscles work against resistance.

overload principle Placing extra physical demands on your body to improve your fitness level.

hypertrophy The increase in strength and size that results from repeated work to a specific muscle or muscle group.

atrophy A decrease in the size and strength of muscles that occurs when they are not worked adequately.

FIT principle The principle used to achieve an appropriate overload for physical training. Stands for frequency, intensity, and time of activity.

Canadian Physical Activity Guidelines

FOR THE EARLY YEARS - 0 – 4 YEARS

Guidelines:

For healthy growth and development:

 Infants (aged less than 1 year) should be physically active several times daily – particularly through interactive floor-based play.

Toddlers (aged 1–2 years) and preschoolers (aged 3–4 years) should accumulate at least 180 minutes of physical activity at any intensity spread throughout the day, including:

- A variety of activities in different environments;
- Activities that develop movement skills;
- Progression toward at least 60 minutes of energetic play by 5 years of age.

More daily physical activity provides greater benefits.

Being active as an infant means:

- Tummy time
- Reaching for or grasping balls or other toys
- Playing or rolling on the floor
- Crawling around the home

Being active as a toddler or preschooler means:

- Any activity that gets kids moving
- Climbing stairs and moving around the home
- Playing outside and exploring their environment
- Crawling, brisk walking, running or dancing

The older children get, the more energetic play they need, such as hopping, jumping, skipping and bike riding.

Being active can help young kids:

- Maintain a healthy body weight
- Improve movement skills
- Increase fitness
- Build healthy hearts
- Have fun and feel happy
- Develop self-confidence
- Improve learning and attention

All activity counts. Try these tips to get young kids moving:

- ☑ Create safe spaces for play.
- ☑ Play music and learn action songs together.
- ☑ Dress for the weather and explore the outdoors.
- ☑ Make time for play with other kids.
- ☑ Get where you're going by walking or biking.

Any way, every day.
Get active together!

PARTICIPACTION
www.participACTION.com

CSEP | SCPE
THE GOLD STANDARD IN EXERCISE
SCIENCE AND PERSONAL TRAINING
www.csep.ca/guidelines

Figure 15.2a You can use the Canadian Physical Activity Guidelines to achieve health benefits.
Source: Canadian Physical Activity Guidelines, © 2011. Used with permission from the Canadian Society for Exercise Physiology, www.csep.ca/guidelines

Canadian Physical Activity Guidelines

FOR CHILDREN - 5 – 11 YEARS

Guidelines

 For health benefits, children aged 5-11 years should accumulate at least 60 minutes of moderate- to vigorous-intensity physical activity daily. This should include:

 Vigorous-intensity activities at least 3 days per week.

 Activities that strengthen muscle and bone at least 3 days per week.

 More daily physical activity provides greater health benefits.

Let's Talk Intensity!

Moderate-intensity physical activities will cause children to sweat a little and to breathe harder. Activities like:

- Bike riding
- Playground activities

Vigorous-intensity physical activities will cause children to sweat and be 'out of breath'. Activities like:

- Running
- Swimming

Being active for at least **60 minutes** daily can help children:

- Improve their health
- Do better in school
- Improve their fitness
- Grow stronger
- Have fun playing with friends
- Feel happier
- Maintain a healthy body weight
- Improve their self-confidence
- Learn new skills

Parents and caregivers can help to plan their child's daily activity. Kids can:

- ☑ Play tag – or freeze-tag!
- ☑ Go to the playground after school.
- ☑ Walk, bike, rollerblade or skateboard to school.

- ☑ Play an active game at recess.
- ☑ Go sledding in the park on the weekend.
- ☑ Go "puddle hopping" on a rainy day.

60 minutes a day. You can help your child get there!

Figure 15.2b *(Continued)*

Canadian Physical Activity Guidelines

FOR YOUTH - 12 – 17 YEARS

Guidelines

 For health benefits, youth aged 12-17 years should accumulate at least 60 minutes of moderate- to vigorous-intensity physical activity daily. This should include:

 Vigorous-intensity activities at least 3 days per week.

 Activities that strengthen muscle and bone at least 3 days per week.

More daily physical activity provides greater health benefits.

Let's Talk Intensity!

Moderate-intensity physical activities will cause teens to sweat a little and to breathe harder. Activities like:

- Skating
- Bike riding

Vigorous-intensity physical activities will cause teens to sweat and be 'out of breath'. Activities like:

- Running
- Rollerblading

Being active for at least **60 minutes** daily can help teens:

- Improve their health
- Do better in school
- Improve their fitness
- Grow stronger
- Have fun playing with friends
- Feel happier
- Maintain a healthy body weight
- Improve their self-confidence
- Learn new skills

Parents and caregivers can help to plan their teen's daily activity. Teens can:

- ☑ Walk, bike, rollerblade or skateboard to school.
- ☑ Go to a gym on the weekend.
- ☑ Do a fitness class after school.

- ☑ Get the neighbours together for a game of pick-up basketball, or hockey after dinner.
- ☑ Play a sport such as basketball, hockey, soccer, martial arts, swimming, tennis, golf, skiing, snowboarding…

Now is the time. 60 minutes a day can make a difference.

Figure 15.2c *(Continued)*

Canadian Physical Activity Guidelines

FOR ADULTS - 18 – 64 YEARS

Guidelines

 To achieve health benefits, adults aged 18-64 years should accumulate at least 150 minutes of moderate- to vigorous-intensity aerobic physical activity per week, in bouts of 10 minutes or more.

 It is also beneficial to add muscle and bone strengthening activities using major muscle groups, at least 2 days per week.

 More physical activity provides greater health benefits.

Let's Talk Intensity!

Moderate-intensity physical activities will cause adults to sweat a little and to breathe harder. Activities like:

- Brisk walking
- Bike riding

Vigorous-intensity physical activities will cause adults to sweat and be 'out of breath'. Activities like:

- Jogging
- Cross-country skiing

Being active for at least **150 minutes** per week can help reduce the risk of:

- Premature death
- Heart disease
- Stroke
- High blood pressure
- Certain types of cancer
- Type 2 diabetes
- Osteoporosis
- Overweight and obesity

And can lead to improved:
- Fitness
- Strength
- Mental health (morale and self–esteem)

Pick a time. Pick a place. Make a plan and move more!

- ☑ Join a weekday community running or walking group.
- ☑ Go for a brisk walk around the block after dinner.
- ☑ Take a dance class after work.
- ☑ Bike or walk to work every day.

- ☑ Rake the lawn, and then offer to do the same for a neighbour.
- ☑ Train for and participate in a run or walk for charity!
- ☑ Take up a favourite sport again or try a new sport.
- ☑ Be active with the family on the weekend!

Now is the time. Walk, run, or wheel, and embrace life.

CSEP | SCPE
THE GOLD STANDARD IN EXERCISE
SCIENCE AND PERSONAL TRAINING

www.csep.ca/guidelines

Figure 15.2d *(Continued)*

Canadian Physical Activity Guidelines

FOR OLDER ADULTS - 65 YEARS & OLDER

Guidelines

 To achieve health benefits, and improve functional abilities, adults aged 65 years and older should accumulate at least 150 minutes of moderate- to vigorous-intensity aerobic physical activity per week, in bouts of 10 minutes or more.

 It is also beneficial to add muscle and bone strengthening activities using major muscle groups, at least 2 days per week.

 Those with poor mobility should perform physical activities to enhance balance and prevent falls.

 More physical activity provides greater health benefits.

Let's Talk Intensity!

Moderate-intensity physical activities will cause older adults to sweat a little and to breathe harder. Activities like:

- Brisk walking
- Bicycling

Vigorous-intensity physical activities will cause older adults to sweat and be 'out of breath'. Activities like:

- Cross-country skiing
- Swimming

Being active for at least **150 minutes** per week can help reduce the risk of:

- Chronic disease (such as high blood pressure and heart disease) and,
- Premature death

And also help to:
- Maintain functional independence
- Maintain mobility
- Improve fitness
- Improve or maintain body weight
- Maintain bone health and,
- Maintain mental health and feel better

Pick a time. Pick a place. Make a plan and move more!

☑ Join a community urban poling or mall walking group.
☑ Go for a brisk walk around the block after lunch.
☑ Take a dance class in the afternoon.
☑ Train for and participate in a run or walk for charity!

☑ Take up a favourite sport again.
☑ Be active with the family! Plan to have "active reunions".
☑ Go for a nature hike on the weekend.
☑ Take the dog for a walk after dinner.

Now is the time. Walk, run, or wheel, and embrace life.

www.csep.ca/guidelines

Figure 15.2e *(Continued)*

	Frequency	Intensity	Time
Cardiorespiratory fitness	3–5 days per week	64%–90% maximal heart rate	At least 20 consecutive minutes
Muscular fitness	2–3 days per week	70%–85% maximal weight you can lift	1–3 sets of 8–12 lifts* for each set *A minimum of 8–10 exercises involving the major muscle groups such as arms, shoulders, chest, abdomen, back, hips, and legs is recommended.
Flexibility	2–4 days per week	Stretching through full range of motion	2–4 repetitions per stretch* *Hold each stretch for 15–30 seconds.

Figure 15.3 Using the FIT principle to achieve cardiorespiratory and musculoskeletal fitness and flexibility.

be used to design either a general physical fitness program or a performance-based exercise program. **Figure 15.3** shows how the FIT principle can be applied to a cardiorespiratory and muscular fitness program.

Let's consider each of the FIT principle's three factors in more detail.

Frequency

Frequency refers to the number of activity sessions per week. Depending upon the goals for fitness, the frequency of activities will vary. To achieve cardiorespiratory fitness, training should be more than two days per week. On the other hand, training more than five days per week does not cause significant gains in fitness but can substantially increase the risks for injury. Training three to five days per week appears optimal to achieve and maintain cardiorespiratory fitness. In contrast, only two to three days are needed to achieve muscular fitness.

Intensity

Intensity refers to the amount of effort expended or to how difficult the activity is to perform. In general, **low-intensity activities** are those that cause very mild increases in breathing, sweating, and heart rate, whereas **moderate-intensity activities** cause moderate increases in these responses. **Vigorous-intensity activities** produce significant increases in breathing, sweating, and heart rate, so that talking is difficult when exercising at a vigorous intensity.

Traditionally, heart rate has been used to indicate level of intensity during aerobic activities. **Figure 15.4** shows an example of a heart rate training chart. You can calculate the range of exercise intensity that is appropriate for you by estimating your **maximal heart rate**,

frequency Refers to the number of activity sessions per week you perform.

intensity Refers to the amount of effort expended during the activity, or how difficult the activity is to perform.

low-intensity activities Activities that cause very mild increases in breathing, sweating, and heart rate.

moderate-intensity activities Activities that cause moderate increases in breathing, sweating, and heart rate.

vigorous-intensity activities Activities that produce significant increases in breathing, sweating, and heart rate; talking is difficult when exercising at a vigorous intensity.

maximal heart rate The rate at which your heart beats during maximal-intensity exercise.

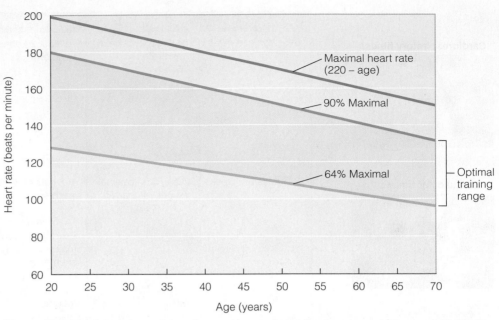

Figure 15.4 This heart rate training chart can be used to estimate your aerobic exercise intensity. The top line indicates the predicted maximal heart rate value for a person's age (220 − age). The shaded area represents the heart rate values that fall between 64% and 90% of maximal heart rate, which is the range generally recommended to achieve aerobic fitness.

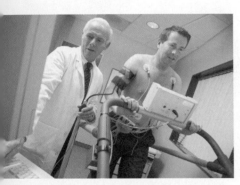

Testing in a fitness lab is the most accurate way to determine maximal heart rate.

which is the rate at which your heart beats during maximal-intensity exercise (see You Do the Math box, page 547). Maximal heart rate is estimated by subtracting your age from 220 and is described in more detail shortly. For achieving and maintaining physical fitness, the intensity range typically recommended is 64% to 90% of a person's estimated maximal heart rate. People who are older or who have been inactive for a long time may want to exercise at the lower end of the range. Those who are more physically fit or are striving for a more rapid improvement in fitness may want to exercise at the higher end of the range. Competitive athletes generally train at a higher intensity, around 80% to 95% of their maximal heart rate.

Time of Activity

Time of activity refers to how long each session lasts. To achieve general health, a person can do multiple short bouts of activity that add up to 30 minutes each day. However, to achieve higher levels of fitness, it is important that the activities be done for at least 20 to 30 consecutive minutes.

For example, let's say you want to compete in triathlons. To be successful during the running segment of the triathlon, you will need to be able to run quickly for at least five kilometres. Thus, it is appropriate for you to train so that you can complete five kilometres during one session, keeping in mind that the run comes after the swim and bike portions, and so will require extra energy. You will need to consistently train at a distance of five kilometres; you will also benefit from running longer distances.

Stretching should be included in the warm-up and the cool-down for exercise.

time of activity How long each exercise session lasts.

warm-up Also called *preliminary exercise*; includes activities that prepare you for an exercise bout, including stretching, calisthenics, and movements specific to the exercise bout.

A Sound Fitness Plan Includes a Warm-Up and a Cool-Down Period

To properly prepare for and recover from an exercise session, warm-up and cool-down activities should be performed. **Warm-up** properly prepares muscles for exertion by increasing blood flow and temperature, and includes general activities (such as stretching and calisthenics) and specific activities that prepare a person for the actual activity (such as jogging or swinging a golf club). The warm-up should be brief (5 to 10 minutes), gradual, and sufficient to increase muscle and body temperature, but should not cause fatigue or deplete energy stores.

YOU DO THE MATH

Calculating Your Maximal and Training Heart Rate Range

Judy was recently diagnosed with type 2 diabetes, and her healthcare provider has recommended she begin an exercise program. She is considered obese according to her body mass index, and she has not been regularly active since she was a teenager. Judy's goals are to improve her cardiorespiratory fitness and achieve and maintain a more healthy weight. Fortunately, Valley Hospital, where she works as a nurse's aide, recently opened a small fitness centre for its employees. Judy plans to begin by either walking on the treadmill or riding the stationary bicycle at the fitness centre during her lunch break.

Judy needs to exercise at an intensity that will help her improve her cardiorespiratory fitness and lose weight. She is 38 years of age, is obese, has type 2 diabetes, and has been approved to do moderate-intensity activity by her healthcare provider. Even though she does a lot of walking and lifting in her work as a nurse's aide, her doctor has recommended that she set her exercise intensity range to begin at a heart rate that is slightly lower than the currently recommended minimal intensity of 64%. Based on this information, Judy should set her training heart rate range between 50% and 75% of her maximal heart rate.

Let's calculate Judy's maximal heart rate values:

- Maximal heart rate: 220 − age = 220 − 38 = 182 beats per minute (bpm)
- Lower end of intensity range: 50% of 182 bpm = 0.50 × 182 bpm = 91 bpm

- Higher end of intensity range: 75% of 182 bpm = 0.75 × 182 bpm = 137 bpm

Because Judy is a trained nurse's aide, she is skilled at measuring a heart rate, or pulse. To measure your own pulse:

- Place your second (index) and third (middle) finger on the inside of your wrist, just below the wrist crease and near the thumb. Press lightly to feel your pulse. Don't press too hard, or you will occlude the artery and be unable to feel its pulsation.
- If you can't feel your pulse at your wrist, try the carotid artery at the neck. This is located below your ear, on the side of your neck directly below your jaw. Press lightly against your neck under the jaw bone to find your pulse.
- Begin counting your pulse with the count of "zero," and then count each beat for 15 seconds.
- Multiply that value by 4 to estimate heart rate over one minute.
- Do not take your pulse with your thumb, as it has its own pulse, which would prevent you from getting an accurate estimate of your heart rate.

As you can see from these calculations, when Judy walks on the treadmill or rides the bicycle, her heart rate should be between 91 and 137 bpm; this will put her in her aerobic training zone and allow her to achieve cardiorespiratory fitness. It will also assist in weight loss.

Cool-down activities are done after the exercise session is completed. The cool-down should be gradual, allowing the body to slowly recover, and should include ample stretching as well as a lower-intensity version of some of the same activities that were performed during the exercise session. Cooling down after exercise assists in the prevention of injury and may help reduce muscle soreness.

RECAP

A sound fitness program must meet your personal fitness goals. It should be fun and include variety and consistency to help you maintain interest and achieve fitness in all components. It must also place an extra physical demand, or an overload, on your body. To achieve appropriate overload, follow the FIT principle: Frequency refers to the number of activity sessions per week. Intensity refers to how difficult the activity is to perform. Time refers to how long each activity session lasts. Warm-up exercises prepare the muscles for exertion by increasing blood flow and temperature. Cool-down activities assist in the prevention of injury and may help reduce muscle soreness.

cool-down Activities done after an exercise session is completed; it should be gradual and allow your body to slowly recover from exercise.

What Fuels Our Activities?

To perform exercise, or muscular work, we must be able to generate energy. **Figure 15.5** provides an overview of all of the metabolic pathways that result in the generation of energy to support exercise. As this figure shows, the body can use carbohydrates, fats, and even relatively small amounts of proteins to fuel physical activity.

As you learned in Chapter 7, the common currency of energy for virtually all cells in the body is ATP, or adenosine triphosphate (refer to Figure 7.2, page 240). Remember that when one of the three phosphates in ATP is cleaved, energy is released. The products

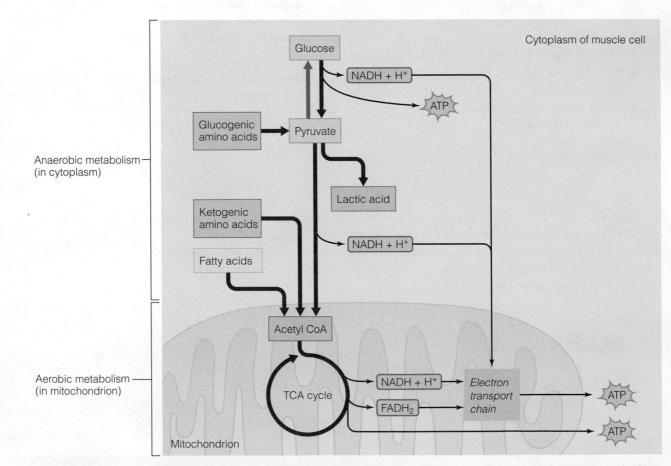

Figure 15.5 An overview of the metabolic pathways that result in ATP production during exercise. Carbohydrate, in the form of glucose, and proteins, in the form of amino acids, can be metabolized via anaerobic and aerobic pathways, whereas fatty acids are predominantly metabolized via aerobic pathways.

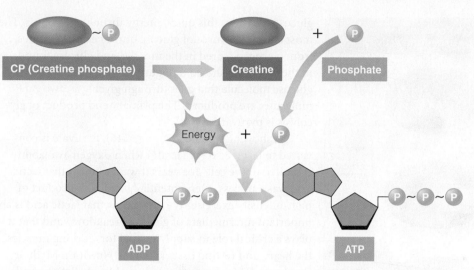

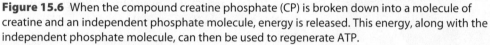

Figure 15.6 When the compound creatine phosphate (CP) is broken down into a molecule of creatine and an independent phosphate molecule, energy is released. This energy, along with the independent phosphate molecule, can then be used to regenerate ATP.

remaining after this reaction are adenosine diphosphate (ADP) and an independent inorganic phosphate group (Pi). In a mirror image of this reaction, the body regenerates ATP by adding a phosphate group back to ADP. In this way, energy is continually provided to the cells both at rest and during exercise.

The amount of ATP stored in a muscle cell is very limited; it can keep the muscle active for only about one to three seconds. Thus, we need to generate ATP from other sources to fuel activities for longer periods of time. Fortunately, we are able to generate ATP from the breakdown of carbohydrate, fat, and protein, providing the cells with a variety of sources from which to receive energy. The primary energy systems that provide energy for physical activities are the adenosine triphosphate–creatine phosphate (ATP-CP) energy system and the anaerobic and aerobic breakdown of carbohydrates. Our bodies also generate energy from the breakdown of fats. As you will see, the type, intensity, and duration of the activities performed determine the amount of ATP needed and therefore the energy system that is used.

The ATP-CP Energy System Uses Creatine Phosphate to Regenerate ATP

As previously mentioned, muscle cells store only enough ATP to maintain activity for one to three seconds. When more energy is needed, a high-energy compound called **creatine phosphate (CP)** (also called *phosphocreatine,* or *PCr*) can be broken down to support the regeneration of ATP (**Figure 15.6**). Because this reaction can occur in the absence of oxygen, it is referred to as an anaerobic reaction (meaning "without oxygen").

Muscle tissue contains about four to six times as much CP as ATP, but there is still not enough CP available to fuel long-term activity. CP is used the most during very intense, short bouts of activity such as lifting, jumping, and sprinting (**Figure 15.7**). Together, the stores of ATP and CP can only support a *maximal* physical effort for about 3 to 15 seconds. The body must rely on other energy sources, such as carbohydrate and fat, to support activities of longer duration.

The Breakdown of Carbohydrates Provides Energy for Both Brief and Long-Term Exercise

During activities lasting about 30 seconds to 3 minutes, the body needs an energy source that can be used quickly to produce ATP. The breakdown of carbohydrates, specifically

creatine phosphate (CP) A high-energy compound that can be broken down for energy and used to regenerate ATP.

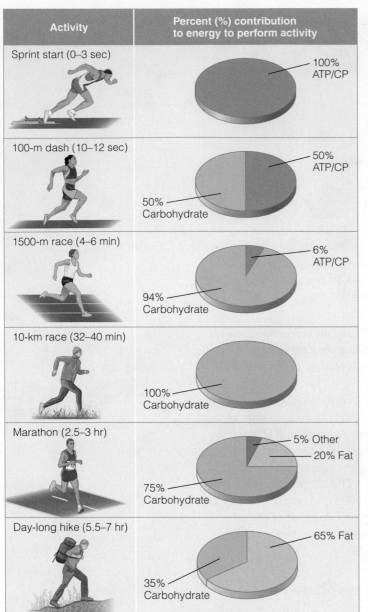

Activity	Percent (%) contribution to energy to perform activity
Sprint start (0–3 sec)	100% ATP/CP
100-m dash (10–12 sec)	50% ATP/CP / 50% Carbohydrate
1500-m race (4–6 min)	6% ATP/CP / 94% Carbohydrate
10-km race (32–40 min)	100% Carbohydrate
Marathon (2.5–3 hr)	5% Other / 20% Fat / 75% Carbohydrate
Day-long hike (5.5–7 hr)	65% Fat / 35% Carbohydrate

Figure 15.7 The relative contributions of ATP-CP, carbohydrate, and fat to activities of various durations and intensities.

glucose, provides this quick energy through glycolysis. The most common source of glucose during exercise comes from glycogen stored in the muscles and glucose found in the blood. As shown in Figure 7.7 (page 245), for every glucose molecule that goes through glycolysis, two ATP molecules are produced. The primary end product of glycolysis is pyruvate.

As shown in Figure 7.8 (page 246), pyruvate is converted to lactic acid (or lactate) when oxygen availability is limited in the cell. For years it was assumed that lactic acid was a useless, even potentially toxic, by-product of high-intensity exercise. We now know that lactic acid is an important intermediate of glucose breakdown and that it plays a critical role in supplying fuel for working muscles, the heart, and resting tissues (see the Nutrition Myth or Fact? box, "Does Lactic Acid Cause Muscle Fatigue and Soreness?"). Any excess lactic acid that is not used by the muscles is transported in the blood back to the liver, where it is converted back into glucose via the Cori cycle (**Figure 15.8**). The glucose produced in the liver via the Cori cycle can recirculate to the muscles and provide energy as needed.

The major advantage of glycolysis is that it is the fastest way to generate ATP for exercise, other than the ATP-CP system. However, this high rate of ATP production can be sustained only for a brief period of time, generally less than three minutes. To perform exercise that lasts longer than three minutes, the body relies on the aerobic energy system.

In the aerobic energy system, pyruvate goes through the additional metabolic pathways of the TCA cycle and the electron transport chain in the presence of oxygen (see Figure 7.12, page 248). Although this process is slower than glycolysis occurring under anaerobic conditions, the breakdown of one glucose molecule going through aerobic metabolism yields 36 to 38 ATP molecules for energy, whereas the anaerobic process yields only two ATP molecules. Thus, this aerobic process supplies 18 times more energy! Another advantage of the aerobic process is that it does not result in the significant production of acids and other compounds that contribute to muscle fatigue, which

Figure 15.8 The Cori cycle is the metabolic pathway by which excess lactic acid can be converted into glucose in the liver.

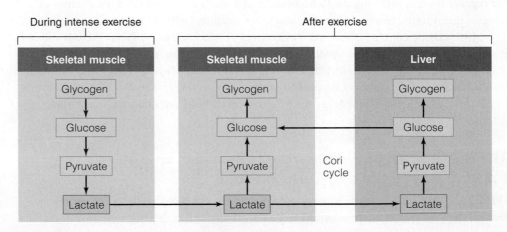

NUTRITION MYTH OR FACT?

Does Lactic Acid Cause Muscle Fatigue and Soreness?

Jamal and his teammates won their basketball game last night, but just barely. With two of the players sick, Jamal got more court time than usual, and when he got back to the dorm, he could hardly get his legs to carry him up the stairs. This morning, Jamal's muscles ache all over, and he wonders if a buildup of lactic acid is to blame.

Lactic acid is a by-product of glycolysis. For many years, both scientists and athletes believed that lactic acid causes muscle fatigue and soreness. Does recent scientific evidence support this belief?

The exact causes of muscle fatigue are not known, and there appear to be many contributing factors. Recent evidence suggests that fatigue may be due not only to the accumulation of many acids and other metabolic by-products but also to the depletion of creatine phosphate and changes in calcium in the cells that affect muscle contraction. Depletion of muscle glycogen, liver glycogen, and blood glucose, as well as psychological factors, can all contribute to fatigue.[9] Thus, it appears that lactic acid only contributes to fatigue and does not cause fatigue independently.

So what factors cause muscle soreness? As with fatigue, there are probably many contributors. It is hypothesized that soreness usually results from microscopic tears in the muscle fibres as a result of strenuous exercise. This damage triggers an inflammatory reaction that causes an influx of fluid and various chemicals to the damaged area. These substances work to remove damaged tissue and initiate tissue repair, but they may also stimulate pain.[9] However, it appears highly unlikely that lactic acid is an independent cause of muscle soreness.

Recent studies indicate that lactic acid is produced even under aerobic conditions! This means it is produced at rest as well as during any intensity of exercise. The reasons for this constant production of lactic acid are still being studied. What we do know is that lactic acid is an important fuel for resting tissues and for working cardiac and skeletal muscles. That's right—skeletal muscles not only *produce* lactic acid, but they also *use* it for energy, both directly and after it is converted into glucose and glycogen in the liver.[9, 10] We also know that endurance training improves the muscle's ability to use lactic acid for energy. Thus, contrary to being a waste product of glucose metabolism, lactic acid is actually an important energy source for muscle cells during rest and exercise.

means that a low-intensity activity can be performed for hours. Aerobic metabolism of glucose is the primary source of fuel for our muscles during activities lasting from three minutes to four hours (see Figure 15.7).

As you learned in Chapter 4, the body can store only a limited amount of glycogen. An average, well-nourished man who weighs about 70 kg can store about 200 to 500 g of muscle glycogen, which is equal to 800 to 2000 kcal of energy. Although trained athletes can store more muscle glycogen than the average person, even their bodies do not have enough stored glycogen to provide an unlimited energy supply for long-term activities. Thus, we also need a fuel source that is abundant and can be broken down under aerobic conditions so that it can support activities of lower intensity and longer duration. This fuel source is fat.

Aerobic Breakdown of Fats Supports Exercise of Low Intensity and Long Duration

When we refer to fat as a fuel source, we mean stored triglycerides. Their fatty acid chains provide much of the energy needed to support long-term activity. The longer the fatty acid, the more ATP that can be generated from its breakdown. For instance, palmitic acid is a fatty acid with 16 carbons. If palmitic acid is broken down completely, it yields 129 ATP molecules! Obviously, far more energy is produced from this one fatty acid molecule than from the aerobic breakdown of a glucose molecule.

There are two major advantages of using fat as a fuel. First, fat is an abundant energy source, even in lean people. For example, a man who weighs 70 kg who has a body fat level of 10% has approximately 7 kg of body fat, which is equivalent to more than 50 000 kcal of energy! This is significantly more energy than can be provided by his stored muscle glycogen (800 to 2000 kcal). Second, fat provides 9 kcal of energy per gram, more than twice as much energy per gram as carbohydrate. The primary disadvantage of using fat as a fuel is that the breakdown process is relatively slow; thus, fat is used predominantly as a fuel source during activities of lower intensity and longer duration. Fat is also our primary energy source during rest, sitting, and standing in place.

What specific activities are fueled by fat? Walking long distances uses fat stores, as does hiking, long-distance cycling, and other low- to moderate-intensity forms of exercise. Fat is also an important fuel source during endurance events such as marathons (42.2 kilometres) and ultra-marathon races (up to 100 kilometres). Endurance exercise training improves our ability to use fat for energy, which may be one reason that people who exercise regularly tend to have lower body fat levels than people who do not exercise.

It is important to remember that we are almost always using some combination of carbohydrate and fat for energy. At rest, very little carbohydrate is used, and the body relies mostly on fat. During maximal exercise (at 100% effort), the body uses mostly carbohydrate and very little fat. However, most activities done each day involve some use of both fuels (**Figure 15.9**).

When it comes to eating properly to support regular physical activity or exercise training, the nutrient to focus on is carbohydrate. This is because most people store more than enough fat to support exercise, whereas our storage of carbohydrate is limited. It is especially important that adequate stores of glycogen are maintained for moderate to intense exercise. Dietary recommendations for fat, carbohydrate, and protein are reviewed later in this chapter (pages 553–559).

Amino Acids Are Not Major Sources of Fuel During Exercise

Proteins, or more specifically, amino acids—are not major energy sources during exercise. As discussed in Chapters 6 and 7, amino acids can be used directly for energy if necessary, but they are more often used to make glucose to maintain blood glucose levels during exercise. The carbon skeletons of amino acids can be converted into pyruvate or acetyl CoA, or they can feed directly into the TCA cycle to provide energy during exercise if necessary (see Figure 7.19, page 253). Amino acids also help build and repair tissues after exercise.

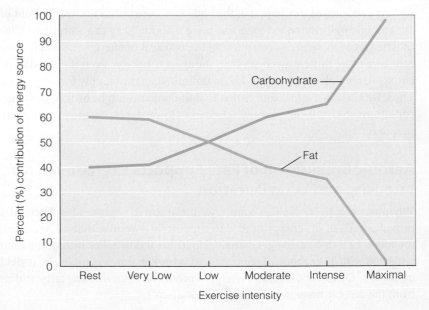

Figure 15.9 For most daily activities, including exercise, we use a mixture of carbohydrate and fat for energy. At lower exercise intensities, we rely more on fat as a fuel source. As exercise intensity increases, we rely more on carbohydrate for energy.
Data adapted from: Brooks, G. A., and J. Mercier. 1994. Balance of carbohydrate and lipid utilization during exercise: the "crossover" concept. *J. Appl. Physiol.* 76[6]: 2253–2261.

Depending upon the intensity and duration of the activity, amino acids may contribute about 3% to 6% of the energy needed.[11]

Given this, why is it that so many people are concerned about their protein intakes? As you learned in Chapter 6, muscles are not stimulated to grow by consuming extra dietary protein. Only appropriate physical training can stimulate muscles to grow and strengthen. Thus, while adequate dietary protein is needed to support activity and recovery, consuming very high amounts does not provide an added benefit. The protein needs of athletes are only slightly higher than the needs of non-athletes, and most people eat more than enough protein to support even the highest requirements for competitive athletes! Thus, there is generally no need for recreationally active people or even competitive athletes to consume protein or amino acid supplements.

RECAP

The amount of ATP stored in a muscle cell is limited and can only keep a muscle active for about one to three seconds. For intense activities lasting about 3 to 15 seconds, creatine phosphate can be broken down to provide energy and support the regeneration of ATP. To support activities that last from 30 seconds to 2 minutes, energy is produced from glycolysis. Fatty acids can be broken down aerobically to support activities of low intensity and longer duration. The two major advantages of using fat as a fuel are that it is an abundant energy source and it provides more than twice the energy per gram as compared with carbohydrate. Amino acids may contribute from 3% to 6% of the energy needed during exercise, depending upon the intensity and duration of the activity. Amino acids help build and repair tissues after exercise.

What Kind of Diet Supports Physical Activity?

Lots of people wonder, "Do my nutrient needs change if I become more physically active?" The answer to this question depends upon the type, intensity, and duration of the chosen activities. It is not necessarily true that our requirement for every nutrient is greater if we are physically active.

People who are performing moderate-intensity daily activities for health can follow the general guidelines put forth in *Eating Well with Canada's Food Guide*. For smaller or less active people, the lower end of the range of recommendations for each food group may be appropriate. For larger or more active people, the higher end of the range is suggested. Modifications may be necessary for people who exercise vigorously every day, and particularly for athletes training for competition. Table 15.2 provides an overview of the nutrients that can be affected by regular, vigorous exercise training.[12] Each of these nutrients is described in more detail in the following sections.

Vigorous Exercise Increases Energy Needs

Athletes generally have higher energy needs than moderately active or sedentary people. The amount of extra energy needed to support regular training is determined by the type, intensity, and duration of the activity. In addition, the energy needs of male athletes are higher than those of female athletes because male athletes weigh more, have more muscle mass, and will expend more energy during activity than female athletes. This is relative, of course: a large woman who trains three to five hours each day will probably need more energy than a small man who trains one hour each day. The energy needs of athletes can range from only 1500 to 1800 kcal per day for a small female gymnast to more than 7500 kcal per day for a male cyclist competing in the Tour de France cross-country cycling race!

Table 15.2 Suggested Intakes of Nutrients to Support Vigorous Exercise[12]

Nutrient	Functions	Suggested Intake
Energy	Supports exercise, activities of daily living, and basic body functions	Depends upon body size and the type, intensity, and duration of activity. For many female athletes: 1800 to 3500 kcal/day For many male athletes: 2500 to 7500 kcal/day
Carbohydrate	Provides energy, maintains adequate muscle glycogen and blood glucose; high complex carbohydrate foods provide vitamins and minerals	45%–65% of total energy intake Depending upon sport and gender, should consume 6–10 g of carbohydrate per kg body weight per day
Fat	Provides energy, fat-soluble vitamins, and essential fatty acids; supports production of hormones and transport of nutrients	20%–35% of total energy intake
Protein	Helps build and maintain muscle; provides building material for glucose; energy source during endurance exercise; aids recovery from exercise	10%–35% of total energy intake Endurance athletes: 1.2–1.4 g per kg body weight Strength athletes: 1.2–1.7 g per kg body weight
Water	Maintains temperature regulation (adequate cooling); maintains blood volume and blood pressure; supports all cell functions	Consume fluid before, during, and after exercise Consume enough to maintain body weight Consume at least 2 L of water daily to maintain regular health and activity Athletes may need up to 10 L every day; more is required if exercising in a hot environment
B-vitamins	Critical for energy production from carbohydrate, fat, and protein	May need slightly more (1–2 times the RDA) for thiamine, riboflavin, and vitamin B_6

Calcium	Builds and maintains bone mass; assists with nervous system function, muscle contraction, hormone function, and transport of nutrients across cell membrane	Meet the current RDA:
		Males:
		    14–18 yr: 1300 mg/day
		    19–70 yr: 1000 mg/day
		    71 and older: 1200 mg/day
		Females:
		    14–18 yr: 1300 mg/day
		    19–50 yr: 1000 mg/day
		    51 and older: 1200 mg/day

Iron	Primarily responsible for the transport of oxygen in blood to cells; assists with energy production	Consume at least the RDA:
		Males:
		    14–18 yr: 11 mg/day
		    19 and older: 8 mg/day
		Females:
		    14–18 yr: 15 mg/day
		    19–50 yr: 18 mg/day
		    51 and older: 8 mg/day

Small snacks can be helpful to meet daily energy demands.

grazing Consistently eating small meals throughout the day; done by many athletes to meet their high energy demands.

Figure 15.10 on page 555 shows a sample of meals that total 1800 kcal per day and 4000 kcal per day, with the carbohydrate content of these meals meeting more than 60% of total energy intake. As you can see, athletes who need more than 4000 kcal per day need to consume very large quantities of food. However, the heavy demands of daily physical training, work, school, and family responsibilities often leave these athletes with little time to eat adequately. Thus, many athletes meet their energy demands by planning regular meals and snacks and **grazing** (eating small meals throughout the day) consistently. They may also take advantage of the energy-dense snack foods and meal replacements specifically designed for athletes participating in vigorous training. These steps help athletes to maintain their blood glucose and energy stores.

If an athlete is losing body weight, then his or her energy intake is inadequate. Conversely, weight gain may indicate that energy intake is too high. Weight maintenance is generally recommended to maximize performance. If weight loss is warranted, food intake should be lowered no more than 200 to 500 kcal per day, and athletes should try to lose weight prior to the competitive season if at all possible. Weight gain may be necessary for some athletes and can usually be accomplished by consuming 500 to 700 kcal per day more than needed for weight maintenance. The extra energy should come from a healthy balance of carbohydrate (45% to 65% of total energy intake), fat (20% to 35% of total energy intake), and protein (10% to 35% of total energy intake).

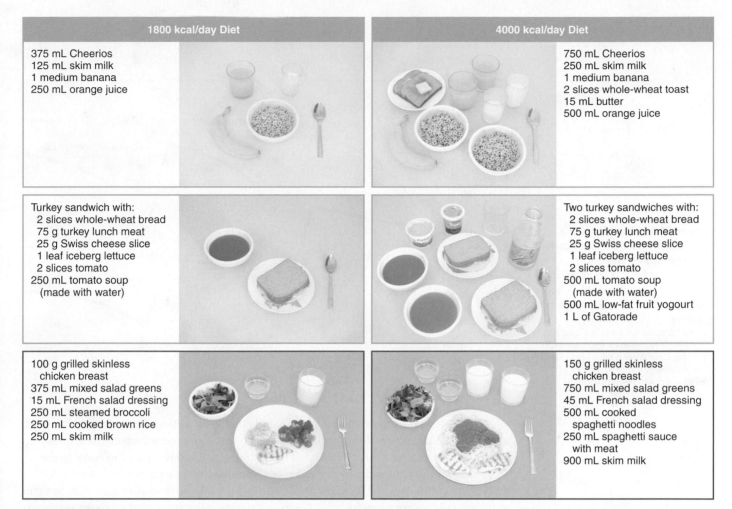

1800 kcal/day Diet	4000 kcal/day Diet
375 mL Cheerios 125 mL skim milk 1 medium banana 250 mL orange juice	750 mL Cheerios 250 mL skim milk 1 medium banana 2 slices whole-wheat toast 15 mL butter 500 mL orange juice
Turkey sandwich with: 　2 slices whole-wheat bread 　75 g turkey lunch meat 　25 g Swiss cheese slice 　1 leaf iceberg lettuce 　2 slices tomato 250 mL tomato soup 　(made with water)	Two turkey sandwiches with: 　2 slices whole-wheat bread 　75 g turkey lunch meat 　25 g Swiss cheese slice 　1 leaf iceberg lettuce 　2 slices tomato 500 mL tomato soup 　(made with water) 500 mL low-fat fruit yogourt 1 L of Gatorade
100 g grilled skinless 　chicken breast 375 mL mixed salad greens 15 mL French salad dressing 250 mL steamed broccoli 250 mL cooked brown rice 250 mL skim milk	150 g grilled skinless 　chicken breast 750 mL mixed salad greens 45 mL French salad dressing 500 mL cooked 　spaghetti noodles 250 mL spaghetti sauce 　with meat 900 mL skim milk

Figure 15.10 High-carbohydrate (approximately 60% of total energy) meals that contain approximately 1800 kcal per day (on left) and 4000 kcal per day (on right). Athletes must plan their meals carefully to meet energy demands, particularly those with very high energy needs.

Many athletes are concerned about their weight. Jockeys, boxers, wrestlers, judo athletes, and others are required to "make weight," or meet a predefined weight category. Others, such as distance runners, gymnasts, figure skaters, and dancers, are required to maintain a very lean figure for performance and aesthetic reasons. These athletes tend to eat less energy than they need to support vigorous training, which puts them at risk for inadequate intakes of all nutrients. They are also at a higher risk of suffering from health consequences resulting from poor energy and nutrient intake, including eating disorders, osteoporosis, menstrual disturbances, dehydration, heat illnesses, physical injuries, and even death.

Carbohydrate Needs Increase for Many Active People

As you know, carbohydrate (in the form of glucose) is one of the primary sources of energy needed to support exercise. Both endurance athletes and strength athletes require adequate carbohydrate to maintain their glycogen stores and provide quick energy.

How Much of an Athlete's Diet Should Be Composed of Carbohydrate?

You may recall from Chapter 4 that the AMDR for carbohydrate is 45% to 65% of total energy intake. Athletes should consume carbohydrate intakes within this same recommended range. Although high-carbohydrate diets (greater than 60% of total energy intake) have been recommended in the past, this percentage value may not be appropriate for all athletes.

Some athletes may diet to meet a predefined weight category.

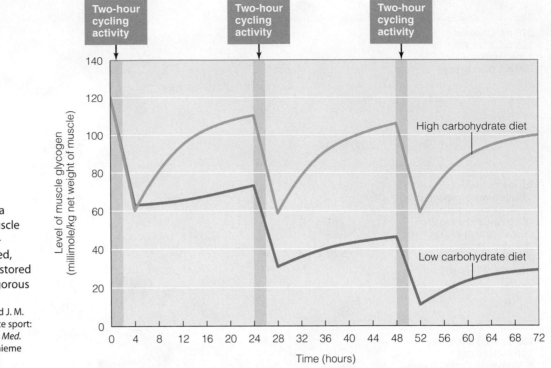

Figure 15.11 The effects of a low-carbohydrate diet on muscle glycogen stores. When a low-carbohydrate diet is consumed, glycogen stores cannot be restored during a period of regular vigorous training.
Data adapted from: Costill, D. L., and J. M. Miller. 1980. Nutrition for endurance sport: CHO and fluid balance. *Int. J. Sports Med.* 1:2–14. Copyright © 1980 Georg Thieme Verlag. Used with permission.

To illustrate the importance of carbohydrate intake for athletes, let's see what happens to Theo when he participates in a study designed to determine how carbohydrate intake affects glycogen stores during a period of heavy training. Theo was asked to come to the exercise laboratory at the university and ride a stationary bicycle for two hours a day for three consecutive days at 75% of his maximal heart rate. Before and after each ride, samples of muscle tissue were taken from his thighs to determine the amount of glycogen stored in the working muscles. Theo performed this series of rides twice, in different weeks—during one week he had been eating a high-carbohydrate diet (80% of total energy intake) and during another he had eaten a moderate-carbohydrate diet (40% of total energy intake). As you can see in **Figure 15.11**, Theo's muscle glycogen levels decreased dramatically after each training session. More important, his muscle glycogen levels did not recover to baseline levels over the three days when Theo ate the lower-carbohydrate diet. He was able to maintain his muscle glycogen levels only when he was eating the higher-carbohydrate diet. Theo also told the researchers that completing the two-hour rides was much more difficult when he had eaten the moderate-carbohydrate diet as compared to when he was eating the diet that was higher in carbohydrate. In fact, athletes use the term "hitting the wall" or "bonking" to refer to the physical and mental fatigue they experience once glycogen stores are depleted; their ability to work typically drops below 50% of their maximum capacity.

When Should Carbohydrates Be Consumed?

It is important for athletes not only to consume enough carbohydrate to maintain glycogen stores but also to time their intake optimally. The body stores glycogen very rapidly during the first 24 hours of recovery from exercise, with the highest storage rates occurring during the first few hours.[13] Higher carbohydrate intakes during the first 24 hours of recovery from exercise are associated with higher amounts of glucose being stored as muscle glycogen. Experts recommend a daily carbohydrate intake of approximately 6 to 10 g of carbohydrate per kg body weight to optimize muscle glycogen stores in athletes. Endurance a athletes who are training heavily daily, should be on the high end of this range as they have less time to recover and require more carbohydrate to support both training and storage needs.

If an athlete has to perform or participate in training bouts that are scheduled less than eight hours apart, then he or she should try to consume enough carbohydrate in the few hours after training to allow for ample glycogen storage. However, with a longer recovery time (generally 24 hours or more), the athlete can eat when he or she chooses, and glycogen levels should be restored as long as the total carbohydrate eaten is sufficient.

Interestingly, studies have shown that muscle glycogen can be restored to adequate levels in the muscle whether the food is eaten in small, multiple snacks or in larger meals,[13, 14] although some studies show enhanced muscle glycogen storage during the first four to six hours of recovery when athletes are fed large amounts of carbohydrate every 15 to 30 minutes.[15, 16]

What Food Sources of Carbohydrates Are Good for Athletes?

What are good carbohydrate sources to support vigorous training? In general, complex, less-processed carbohydrate foods such as whole grains and cereals, fruits, vegetables, and juices are excellent sources that also supply fibre, vitamins, and minerals. The guidelines for intake of simple sugars is less than 10% of total energy intake, but some athletes who need very large energy intakes to support training may need to consume more. In addition, there is evidence that consuming high-glycemic-index foods during the immediate post-recovery period results in higher glycogen storage than is achieved as a result of eating low-glycemic-index foods. This may be due to a greater malabsorption of the carbohydrate in low-glycemic-index foods, as these foods contain more indigestible forms of carbohydrate.[13] Another factor is that the increased insulin sensitivity that occurs after exercise can be utilized to maximize glycogen replenishment. Thus, there are advantages to consuming a wide variety of carbohydrate sources.

Fruit and vegetable juice can be a good source of carbohydrates.

As a result of time constraints, many athletes have difficulties consuming enough food to meet carbohydrate demands. Many beverages and snack bars have therefore been designed to assist athletes with increasing carbohydrate intake. Some of these are listed in Table 15.3, along with other simple, inexpensive foods that contain 50 to 100 g of carbohydrate.

Table 15.3 Nutrient Composition of Various Foods and Sport Bars

Food	Amount	Carbohydrate (grams)	Energy from Carbohydrate (%)	Total Energy (kcal)
Sweetened applesauce	250 mL	50	97	207
Large apple and	1 each	50	82	248
Saltine crackers	8 each			
Whole-wheat bread and	1 slice	50	71	282
Jelly and	20 mL			
Skim milk	375 mL			
Spaghetti noodles (cooked) and	250 mL	50	75	268
Tomato sauce	60 mL			
Brown rice (cooked) and	250 mL	100	88	450
Mixed vegetables and	125 mL			
Apple juice	375 mL			
Grape Nuts cereal and	125 mL	100	84	473
Raisins and	175 mL			
Skim milk	250 mL			
Promax (double fudge brownie)	75 g	38	56	270
Lean Body Gold (caramel peanut)	82 g	32	39	330
Supreme Protein (cookies 'n cream)	88 g	30	32	370
Fullbar (peanut butter crunch)	45 g	27	64	170

Data adapted from: Data on various foods, not including sports bars, is adapted, with permission, from M. M. Manore, N. L. Meyer, and J. Thompson, 2009, *Sport Nutrition for Health and Performance,* 2nd ed. (Champaign, IL: Human Kinetics), 56.

Table 15.4 Recommended Carbohydrate Loading Guidelines

Step 1
Calculate your carbohydrate needs by multiplying your body weight in kg (kg = lbs ÷ 2.2) by 7–12. This will give you a range of carbohydrate intake that you should strive for when carbohydrate loading.

Step 2
Strive to consume the targeted quantity of carbs for the 1–4 days leading up to the race/competition by using high carbohydrate foods.

Step 3
Lower-fibre and quick digesting carbs like fruit juices and breads may be easier to consume than heavier whole-grains at this time.

Step 4
Avoid foods high in fat such as fried foods, and limit high-protein food such as meat, because they will fill you up and make it difficult to consume enough carbohydrates.

Data adapted from: Carbohydrate loading—is it for you? *Sport Nutrition Tip of the Month.* 2011. Coaching Association of Canada. www.coach.ca.

When Does Carbohydrate Loading Make Sense?

As you know, carbohydrate is a critical energy source to support exercise, particularly endurance-type activities. Because of the importance of carbohydrates as an exercise fuel and our limited capacity to store them, discovering ways to maximize the body's storage of carbohydrates has been at the forefront of sports nutrition research for many years. The practice of **carbohydrate loading**, also called *glycogen loading,* involves altering both exercise duration and carbohydrate intake such that it maximizes the amount of muscle glycogen. Table 15.4 reviews a schedule for carbohydrate loading for an endurance athlete. Athletes who may benefit from maximizing muscle glycogen stores are those competing in endurance events lasting at least a couple of hours, including marathons, ultra-marathons, long-distance swimming, cross-country skiing, and triathlons. Athletes who compete in baseball, American football, 10-kilometre runs, walking, hiking, weight lifting, and most swimming events will not gain any performance benefits from this practice, nor will people who regularly participate in moderately intense physical activities to maintain fitness.

It is important to emphasize that carbohydrate loading does not always improve performance. There are many adverse side effects of this practice, including extreme gastro-intestinal distress, particularly diarrhea. We store water along with the extra glycogen in the muscles, which leaves many athletes feeling heavy, bloated, and sluggish. Athletes who want to try carbohydrate loading should experiment prior to competition to determine if it is an acceptable and beneficial approach for them.

Moderate Fat Consumption Is Enough to Support Most Activities

As you have learned, fat is an important energy source for both moderate physical activity and vigorous endurance training. When athletes reach a physically trained state, they are able to use more fat for energy; in other words, they become better "fat burners." This can also occur in people who are not athletes but who regularly participate in aerobic-type fitness activities. This training effect occurs for a number of reasons, including an increase in the number and activity of various enzymes involved in fat metabolism, improved ability of the muscles to store fat, and improved ability to extract fat from the blood for use during exercise. By using fat as a fuel, athletes can spare carbohydrate so they can use it during prolonged, intense training or competition.

Many athletes concerned with body weight and physical appearance believe they should eat less than 15% of their total energy intake as fat, but this is inadequate for vigorous activity and good health. Instead, a fat intake of 20% to 35% of total energy intake is generally recommended for athletes, with less than 10% of total energy intake as

Carbohydrate loading may benefit endurance athletes, such as cross-country skiers.

carbohydrate loading Also known as glycogen loading. A process that involves altering training and carbohydrate intake so that muscle glycogen storage is maximized.

Table 15.5 Estimated Protein Requirements for Athletes[12]

Group	Protein Requirements (grams per kg body weight)
Recreational endurance athletes	0.8
Recreational strength athletes	0.8
Endurance athletes	1.2–1.4
Strength athletes	1.2–1.7

saturated fat. These same recommendations are put forth for non-athletes. Recall from Chapter 5 that fat provides not only energy but also fat-soluble vitamins and essential fatty acids that are critical to maintaining general health. If fat consumption is too low, inadequate levels of these can eventually prove detrimental to training and performance. Athletes who have chronic disease risk factors such as high blood lipids, high blood pressure, or unhealthy blood glucose levels should work with a physician to adjust their intake of fat and carbohydrate according to their health risks.

Many Athletes Have Increased Protein Needs

The protein intakes suggested for competitive athletes and moderately active people are given in Table 15.5. Let's pause a moment to explain the terminology used in the table:

- Endurance athletes are those individuals who train five to seven days per week for more than an hour each day; many of these individuals may train for three to six hours per day. These athletes need significantly more protein than the current RDA of 0.8 g of protein per kg body weight.
- Strength athletes focus on building and maintaining muscle mass and strength. Those who are already trained need less protein than those who are initiating training. Studies do not support the claim that consuming more than 2 g of protein per kilogram body weight improves protein synthesis, muscle strength, or performance.[12]
- Recreational endurance athletes are people exercising four to five times per week for 45 to 60 minutes each time; these individuals may compete in community races and other activities. Their protein needs are equal to or only modestly increased above the RDA.
- Recreational strength athletes are people who are working on building and maintaining muscle mass and strength and exercise four or five times per week for 30 to 60 minutes. These individuals have a protein need that is equal to or only slightly higher than the RDA.

Strength and endurance athletes require significantly more protein than the recommended 0.8 mg/kg BW daily.

As we mentioned earlier, most inactive people and many athletes in Canada consume more than enough protein to support their needs.[17] However, some athletes do not consume enough protein; these typically include individuals with very low energy intakes, vegetarians or vegans who do not consume high-protein food sources, and young athletes who are growing and are not aware of their higher protein needs.

As described in Chapter 6, high-quality protein sources include lean meats, poultry, fish, eggs and egg whites, low-fat dairy products, legumes, and soy products. By following Canada's Food Guide and meeting energy needs, people of all fitness levels can consume more than enough protein without the use of supplements or specially formulated foods.

RECaP

The type, intensity, and duration of activities a person participates in determine his or her nutrient needs. Carbohydrate needs may increase for some active people. In general, athletes should consume 45% to 65% of their total energy as carbohydrate. Carbohydrate loading involves altering physical training and the diet such that the storage of muscle glycogen is maximized. Active people use more fat than carbohydrates for energy because they experience an increase in the number and activity of the enzymes involved in fat metabolism, and they have an improved ability to store fat and extract it from the blood for use during exercise. A dietary fat intake of 20% to 35% is recommended for athletes, with less than 10% of total energy intake as saturated fat. Although protein needs can be higher for athletes, most people in Canada already consume more than twice their daily needs for protein.

Regular Exercise Increases Our Need for Fluids

A detailed discussion of fluid and electrolyte balance is provided in Chapter 10. In this chapter, we will briefly review some of the basic functions of water and its role during exercise.

Functions of Water

Water serves many important functions in the body. It is:

- a lubricant that bathes the tissues and cells
- a transport medium for nutrients, hormones, and waste products
- an important component of many chemical reactions, particularly those related to energy production
- a structural part of body tissues such as proteins and glycogen
- a vital component in temperature regulation; without adequate water, the body cannot cool properly through sweating, which can result in severe heat illness and even death.

Water is essential for maintaining fluid balance and preventing dehydration.

Cooling Mechanisms

Heat production can increase 15 to 20 times during heavy exercise! The primary way in which heat is dissipated is through sweating, which is also called **evaporative cooling**. When body temperature rises, more blood (which contains water) flows to the surface of the skin. Heat is carried in this way from the core of the body to the surface of the skin. By sweating, the water (and body heat) leaves our bodies and the air around us picks up the evaporating water from our skin, cooling our bodies.

Dehydration and Heat-Related Illnesses

Heat illnesses occur because when we exercise in the heat, our muscles and skin constantly compete for blood flow. When there is no longer enough blood flow to simultaneously provide adequate blood to our muscles and our skin, muscle blood flow takes priority and evaporative cooling is inhibited. Exercising in heat plus humidity is especially dangerous because whereas the heat dramatically raises body temperature, the high humidity inhibits evaporative cooling; that is, the environmental air is already so saturated with water that it is unable to absorb the water in sweat. Body temperature becomes dangerously high, and heat illness is likely. Exercise in environmental temperatures at or above 32°C is commonly associated with heat illnesses; heatstroke, a potentially fatal form of heat illness, is highly likely in environmental temperatures at or above 54°C.[18]

It is important to remember that dehydration significantly increases our risk for heat illnesses. The signs and symptoms of dehydration were introduced in Table 3.3 (page 106). In **Figure 15.12**, specific signs of dehydration during heavy exercise are listed.

Heat illnesses include heat syncope, heat cramps, heat exhaustion, and heatstroke. **Heat syncope** is dizziness that occurs when people stand for too long in the heat, and the

evaporative cooling Another term for sweating, which is the primary way in which we dissipate heat.

heat syncope Dizziness that occurs when people stand for too long in the heat or when they stop suddenly after a race or stand suddenly from a lying position; results from blood pooling in the lower extremities.

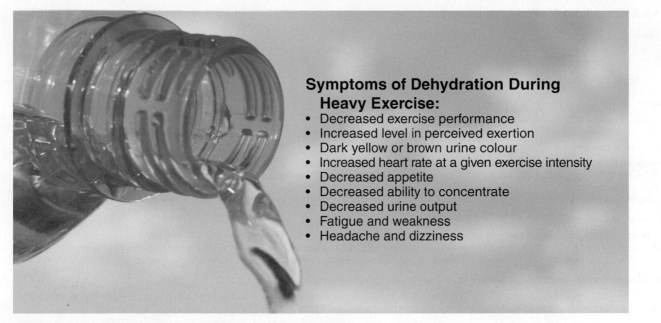

Symptoms of Dehydration During Heavy Exercise:
- Decreased exercise performance
- Increased level in perceived exertion
- Dark yellow or brown urine colour
- Increased heart rate at a given exercise intensity
- Decreased appetite
- Decreased ability to concentrate
- Decreased urine output
- Fatigue and weakness
- Headache and dizziness

Figure 15.12 Symptoms of dehydration during heavy exercise.

blood pools in their lower extremities rather than fully supplying their brains. It can also occur when people stop suddenly after a race or stand suddenly from a lying position. **Heat cramps** are muscle spasms that occur during exercise or even several hours after strenuous exercise. They occur during times when sweat losses and fluid intakes are high, sodium intake is inadequate to replace these losses, and urine volume is low. These cramps generally are felt in the legs, arms, or abdomen after a person cools down from exercise. **Heat exhaustion** and heatstroke occur on a continuum, with unchecked heat exhaustion leading to heatstroke. Early signs of heat exhaustion include excessive sweating, weakness, nausea, dizziness, headache, and difficulty concentrating. As this condition progresses, the sweat response fails entirely. Thus, a cardinal sign that a person is progressing to heatstroke is hot, dry skin. Other signs include a rapid heart rate, vomiting, diarrhea, and a body temperature greater than or equal to 40°C. As consciousness becomes impaired, hallucinations and coma occur. It is critical that the person get proper medical care, or death can result.

Guidelines for Proper Fluid Replacement

How can we prevent dehydration and heat illnesses? Obviously, adequate fluid intake is critical before, during, and after exercise. Unfortunately, our thirst mechanism cannot be relied upon to signal when we need to drink. If we rely on our feelings of thirst, we will not consume enough fluid to support exercise.

General fluid replacement recommendations are based on maintaining body weight. As discussed in Chapter 10, athletes who are training and competing in hot environments should weigh themselves before and after the training session or event and should regain the weight lost over the subsequent 24-hour period. They should avoid losing more than 2% to 3% of body weight during exercise, as performance can be impaired with fluid losses as small as 1% of body weight.

Table 15.6 reviews guidelines for proper fluid replacement. For activities lasting less than one hour, plain water is generally adequate to replace fluid losses. However, for training and competition lasting longer than one hour in any weather, sports beverages containing carbohydrates and electrolytes are recommended. These beverages are also recommended for people who will not drink enough water because they don't like the taste. If drinking these beverages will guarantee adequate hydration, they are appropriate to use.

Drinking sports beverages during training and competition lasting more than one hour replaces fluid, carbohydrates, and electrolytes.

heat cramps Muscle spasms that occur several hours after strenuous exercise; most often occur when sweat losses and fluid intakes are high, urine volume is low, and sodium intake is inadequate.

heat exhaustion A heat illness that is characterized by excessive sweating, weakness, nausea, dizziness, headache, and difficulty concentrating. Unchecked heat exhaustion can lead to heatstroke.

Table 15.6 Guidelines for Fluid Replacement[12]

Activity Level	Environment	Fluid Requirements (litres per day)
Sedentary	Cool	2–3
Active	Cool	3–6
Sedentary	Warm	3–5
Active	Warm	5–10

Before Exercise or Competition:
- Drink adequate fluids during the 24 hours before event; should be able to maintain body weight
- Slowly drink about 5–7 mL per kg body weight of water or a sports drink at least four hours prior to exercise or event to allow time for excretion of excess fluid prior to event
- Consuming beverages with sodium and/or small amounts of salted snacks at a meal will help stimulate thirst and retain fluids consumed

During Exercise or Competition:
- Drink early and regularly throughout event to sufficiently replace all water lost through sweating
- Amount and rate of fluid replacement depend on individual sweating rate, exercise duration, weather conditions, and opportunities to drink
- Fluids should be cooler than the environmental temperature and flavoured to enhance taste and promote fluid replacement

During Exercise or Competition That Lasts More Than One Hour:
- Fluid replacement beverage should contain 6%–8% carbohydrate to maintain blood glucose levels; sodium and other electrolytes should be included in the beverage in amounts of 0.5–0.7 g of sodium and 0.8–2.0 g of potassium per litre of water to replace the sodium lost by sweating

Following Exercise or Competition:
- Consume about 450–675 mL of fluid for each 0.5 kg of body weight lost
- Fluids after exercise should contain water to restore hydration status, carbohydrates to replenish glycogen stores, and electrolytes (for example, sodium and potassium) to speed rehydration
- Consume enough fluid to permit regular urination and to ensure the urine colour is very light or light yellow in colour

In General:
- Products that contain fructose should be limited, as these may cause gastrointestinal distress
- Caffeine and alcohol should be avoided, as these products increase urine output and reduce fluid retention
- Carbonated beverages should be avoided, as they reduce the desire for fluid intake on account of stomach fullness

Inadequate Intakes of Some Vitamins and Minerals Can Diminish Health and Performance

When individuals train vigorously for athletic events, their requirements for certain vitamins and minerals may be altered. Many highly active people do not eat enough food or a variety of foods that allows them to consume enough of these nutrients, yet it is imperative that active people do their very best to eat an adequate, varied, and balanced diet to try to meet the increased needs associated with vigorous training.

B-Vitamins

The B-complex vitamins are directly involved in energy metabolism (see pages 303–315). There is reliable evidence that the requirements of active people for thiamine, riboflavin, and vitamin B_6 may be slightly higher than the current RDA.[12, 17] However, these increased needs are easily met when athletes consume the increased food required to meet their increased energy needs, provided they focus on complex carbohydrates, fruits, and vegetables. Athletes and physically active people at risk for poor B-complex vitamin status are those who consume inadequate energy or who consume mostly refined carbohydrate foods such as soft drinks and sugary snacks. Vegan athletes and active individuals may be at risk for inadequate intake of vitamin B_{12}; food sources enriched with this nutrient include soy and soy products.

Calcium and the Female Athlete Triad

Calcium supports proper muscle contraction and ensures bone health (see pages 412–414). Calcium intakes are inadequate for most women in Canada, including both sedentary and active women. This is most likely due to the failure to consume foods that are high in calcium, particularly dairy products. Although vigorous training does not appear to directly increase our need for calcium, we need to consume enough calcium to support bone health. If we do not, stress fractures and severe loss of bone can result.

Some female athletes suffer from what is referred to as the female athlete triad (see the Highlight on page 564 for more details). In this triad, nutritional inadequacies from insufficient energy intake and/or disordered eating cause irregularities in the menstrual cycle; these in turn cause hormonal disturbances that lead to a significant loss of bone mass. Thus, for female athletes, consuming the recommended amounts of calcium is critical. For female athletes who are physically small and consume lower energy intakes, calcium supplementation may be needed to meet current recommendations.

Iron

Iron is a part of the hemoglobin molecule and is critical for the transport of oxygen in the blood to the cells and working muscles. Iron also is involved in energy production. Research has shown that active individuals lose more iron in their sweat, feces, and urine than do inactive individuals, and that endurance runners lose iron when their red blood cells break down in their feet in response to the impact of running.[19] Female athletes and non-athletes lose more iron than male athletes because of menstrual blood losses, and females in general tend to eat less iron in their diet. Vegetarian athletes may also consume less iron. Thus, many athletes and active people are at higher risk of iron deficiency. Depending upon its severity, poor iron status can impair athletic performance and the ability to maintain regular physical activity.

Not all athletes suffer from iron deficiency. A phenomenon known as *sports anemia* was identified in the 1960s. Sports anemia is not true anemia, but a transient decrease in iron stores that occurs in some people at the start of an exercise program. It is also seen in some athletes who increase their training intensity. Exercise training increases the amount of water in the blood (called *plasma volume*); however, the amount of hemoglobin does not increase until later into the training period. Thus, the iron content in the blood appears to be low, but it is falsely depressed because of increases in plasma volume. Sports anemia, since it is not true anemia, does not affect performance.

The stages of iron deficiency are described on pages 454–455. In general, it appears that physically active females are at relatively high risk of suffering from the first stage of iron depletion, in which iron stores are low.[21, 22] Because of this, it is suggested that blood tests of iron stores and monitoring of dietary iron intakes be part of routine healthcare for active females.[17] In some cases, iron needs cannot be met through the diet, and supplementation is necessary. Iron supplementation should be done with a physician's approval and proper medical supervision.

RECaP

Regular exercise increases fluid needs. Fluid is critical to cool internal body temperature and prevent heat illnesses. Dehydration is a serious threat during exercise in extreme heat and high humidity. Heat illnesses include heat syncope, heat cramps, heat exhaustion, and heatstroke. Active people may need more thiamine, riboflavin, and vitamin B_6 than inactive people. Exercise itself does not increase calcium needs, but most women, including active women, do not consume enough calcium. Some female athletes suffer from the female athlete triad, a condition that involves the interaction of low energy availability, osteoporosis, and amenorrhea. Many active individuals require more iron, particularly female athletes and vegetarian athletes.

HIGHLIGHT

The Female Athlete Triad Consists of Three Disorders

The **female athlete triad** is a term used to describe a serious syndrome that consists of three clinical conditions in some physically active females: low energy availability (with or without eating disorders), amenorrhea, and osteoporosis (**Figure 15.13**).[23] Sports that emphasize leanness or a thin body build may place a young girl or a woman at risk for the female athlete triad. These include figure skating, gymnastics, diving, and others. Classical ballet dancers are also at increased risk for the disorder.

Components of the Female Athlete Triad

Active women experience the general social and cultural demands placed on women to be thin, as well as pressure from their coach, teammates, judges, and/or spectators to meet weight standards or body-size expectations for their sport. Failure to meet these standards can result in severe consequences, such as being cut from the team, losing an athletic scholarship, or decreased participation with the team.

As the pressure to be thin mounts, active women may restrict their energy intake, typically by engaging in disordered eating behaviours. Energy restriction combined with high levels of physical activity can disrupt the menstrual cycle and result in amenorrhea. Menstrual dysfunction can also occur in active women who are not dieting and don't have an eating disorder. These women are just not eating enough to cover the energy costs of their exercise training and all the other energy demands of the body and daily living. Female athletes with menstrual dysfunction, regardless of the cause, typically have reduced levels of the reproductive hormones estrogen and progesterone. When estrogen levels in the body are low, it is difficult for bone to retain calcium, and gradual loss of bone mass occurs. Thus, many female athletes develop premature bone loss (osteoporosis) and are at increased risk for fractures.

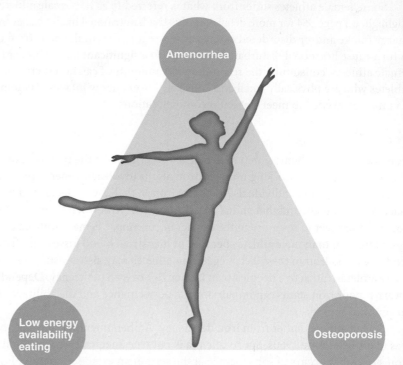

Figure 15.13 The female athlete triad is a syndrome composed of three coexisting disorders: low energy availability (with or without eating disorders), menstrual dysfunction such as amenorrhea, and osteoporosis. Energy availability is defined as dietary energy intake minus exercise energy expenditure.

Former gymnast Christy Henrich and her fiancé, a year before she died.

Recognizing and Treating the Female Athlete Triad

Recognition of an athlete with one or more of the components of the female athlete triad can be difficult, especially if the athlete is reluctant to be honest when questioned about the symptoms. For this reason, familiarity with the early warning signs is critical. These include excessive dieting and/or weight loss, excessive exercise, stress fractures, and self-esteem that appears to be dictated by body weight and shape. You may not know whether a female

Sports that emphasize leanness or require the athlete to wear body-contouring clothing increase the risk for female athlete triad.

friend or teammate is experiencing irregular periods, but you might overhear her commenting negatively on her body or see her head off to the gym after eating only a lettuce salad for lunch.

Treating an athlete requires a multidisciplinary approach. This means that the sports medicine team, sports dietitian, exercise physiologist, psychologist, coach, trainer, parents, friends of the athlete, and the athlete all must work together. As with any health problem, prevention is the best treatment. Thus, recognition of the risk factors by the sports medicine team and education of athletes, coaches, and parents are imperative, as all causes of menstrual dysfunction need to be examined. If the athlete is having trouble with weight and body shape issues, care should be taken to deal with these issues before they develop into something more serious.

Are Ergogenic Aids Necessary for Active People?

Many competitive athletes and even some recreationally active people continually search for that something extra that will enhance their performance. **Ergogenic aids** are substances used to improve exercise and athletic performance. For example, nutrition supplements can be classified as ergogenic aids, as can anabolic steroids and other pharmaceuticals. Interestingly, people report using ergogenic aids not only to enhance athletic performance but also to improve their physical appearance, prevent or treat injuries, treat diseases, and help them cope with stress. Some people even report using them because of peer pressure!

As you have learned in this chapter, adequate nutrition is critical to athletic performance and to regular physical activity, and products such as sports bars and beverages can assist athletes with maintaining their competitive edge. However, as we will explore shortly, many ergogenic aids are not effective, some are dangerous, and most are very expensive. For the average consumer, it is virtually impossible to track the latest research findings for these products. In addition, many have not been adequately studied, and unsubstantiated false claims surrounding them are rampant. How can you become a more educated consumer about ergogenic aids? See the Highlight box (page 566) for questions you should ask before you take any supplement.

You should also know that, in many cases, research done on a product is conducted by an inexperienced investigator. It is important that experienced, independent laboratories conduct some of the research, as they are more likely to be unbiased.[24]

New ergogenic aids are available virtually every month, and keeping track of these substances is a daunting task. It is therefore not possible to discuss every available product in this chapter. However, a brief review of a number of currently popular ergogenic aids is provided.

Anabolic Products Are Touted as Muscle and Strength Enhancers

Many ergogenic aids are said to be **anabolic**, meaning that they build muscle and increase strength. Most anabolic substances promise to increase testosterone, which is the hormone

female athlete triad Refers to the interrelationship between three conditions seen in female athletes: inadequate energy intake, menstrual dysfunction (for example, amenorrhea), and reduced bone strength (for example, stress fractures, osteopenia, osteoporosis).

ergogenic aids Substances used to improve exercise and athletic performance.

anabolic Refers to a substance that builds muscle and increases strength.

HIGHLIGHT

Should You Use Supplements?

The following questions should be considered prior to use of any supplements:

- Are you informed about all the ingredients in the product? (If you are unsure of what you are consuming, you should not take that particular product.)
- Do you know if the product is safe (from a short- and long-term health perspective)? A product that is promoted as "natural" is not guaranteed to be safe.
- Does the product contain any banned or restricted substances from the World Anti-Doping Agency (WADA) list? (If you are unsure of what you are consuming, you should not take that particular product.) To find out check out the WADA website at www.wada-ama.org/en/World-Anti-Doping-Program/Sports-and-Anti-Doping-Organizations/International-Standards/Prohibited-List/

- Have you sought professional advice from medical, physiological, and/or nutritional experts?
- Is your training plan optimal (in terms of nutrition, recovery, and mental and physical preparation)?

Data adapted from: Carbohydrate loading—is it for you? *Sport Nutrition Tip of the Month.* 2011. Coaching Association of Canada. www.coach.ca.

associated with male sex characteristics and that increases muscle size and strength. Although some anabolic substances are effective, they are generally associated with harmful side effects.

Anabolic Steroids

Anabolic steroids are testosterone-based drugs that have been used extensively by strength and power athletes. Anabolic steroids are known to be effective in increasing muscle size, strength, power, and speed. However, these products are illegal in Canada without a prescription, and their use is banned by all major collegiate and professional sports organizations, in addition to both the Canadian and the International Olympic Committees. Proven long-term and irreversible effects of steroid use include infertility; early closure of the plates of the long bones, resulting in permanent shortened stature; shrivelled testicles, enlarged breast tissue (that can only be surgically removed), and other signs of "feminization" in men; enlarged clitoris, facial hair growth, and other signs of "masculinization" in women; increased risk of certain forms of cancer; liver damage; unhealthy changes in blood lipids; hypertension; severe acne; hair thinning or baldness; and depression, delusions, sleep disturbances, and extreme anger (so-called "roid rage").

Androstenedione and Dehydroepiandrosterone

Anabolic substances are often marketed to people wishing to increase muscle size, but many cause harmful side effects.

Androstenedione ("andro") and dehydroepiandrosterone (DHEA) are precursors of testosterone. Manufacturers of these products claim that taking them will increase testosterone levels and muscle strength. Androstenedione became very popular after baseball player Mark McGwire claimed he used it during the time he was breaking home run records. A U.S. survey found that, in 2002, about one of every forty high school seniors had used "andro" in the past year.[25] Contrary to popular claims, recent studies have found that neither androstenedione nor DHEA increases testosterone levels, and androstenedione has been shown to increase the risk of heart disease in men aged 35 to 65 years.[26]

There are no studies that support the products' claims of improving strength or increasing muscle mass.

Gamma-Hydroxybutyric Acid

Gamma-hydroxybutyric acid, or GHB, has been promoted as an alternative to anabolic steroids for building muscle. The production and sale of GHB have never been approved in Canada; however, it was illegally produced and sold on the black market. For many users, GHB caused only dizziness, tremors, or vomiting, but others experienced severe side effects, including seizures. Many people were hospitalized and some died.

After GHB was banned in the US, a similar product (gamma-butyrolactone, or GBL) was marketed in its place. This product was also found to be dangerous and was removed from the market. Recently, another replacement product called BD, or 1,4-butanediol, was banned because it has caused at least 71 deaths, with 40 more under investigation. BD is an industrial solvent and is listed on ingredient labels as tetramethylene glycol, butylene glycol, or sucol-B. Side effects include wild, aggressive behaviour, nausea, incontinence, and sudden loss of consciousness.

Creatine

Creatine is a supplement that has become wildly popular with strength and power athletes. Creatine, or creatine phosphate, is found naturally in foods such as meat and fish and stored in our muscles. As described earlier in this chapter, we use creatine phosphate (or CP) to regenerate ATP. By taking creatine supplements, it is hypothesized that more CP is available to replenish ATP, which will prolong a person's ability to train and perform in short-term, explosive activities such as weight lifting and sprinting. Between 1994 and 2009, more than 1700 research articles related to creatine and exercise in humans were published. Studies have shown that creatine does not enhance performance in aerobic-type events, but does enhance sprint performance in swimming, running, and cycling.[27–31] Other studies have shown that creatine increases the work performed and the amount of strength gained during resistance exercise.[28, 30, 32] Currently, creatine is not banned by any sports governing bodies, and many sports programs readily provide creatine supplements for their athletes.

In January 2001, the *New York Times* reported that the French government claimed that creatine use could lead to cancer.[33] The news spread quickly across national and international news organizations and over the internet. These claims were found to be false, as there are absolutely no studies in humans that suggest an increased risk of cancer with creatine use. In fact, there are numerous studies that show an anticancer effect of creatine.[34, 35] Although side effects such as dehydration, muscle cramps, and gastrointestinal disturbances have been reported with creatine use, we have very little information on how long-term use of creatine impacts health. A recent study by Schilling and colleagues found that the incidence of muscle cramps, injuries, or other side effects was similar for athletes who had never used creatine as compared with those using creatine for up to four years.[36] Long-term creatine supplementation appears to be safe at intakes of up to 5 g per day.[37] Further research is needed to determine the effectiveness and safety of creatine use over prolonged periods of time.

Some Products Are Said to Optimize Fuel Use During Exercise

Certain ergogenic aids are touted as increasing energy levels and improving athletic performance by optimizing the use of fat, carbohydrate, and protein. The products reviewed here include caffeine, ephedrine, carnitine, chromium, and ribose.

Caffeine

Caffeine is a stimulant that makes us feel more alert and energetic, decreasing feelings of fatigue during exercise. Caffeine has been shown to increase the use of fat as a fuel during

HIGHLIGHT

Muscle Dysmorphia: The Male Eating Disorder?

Is there an eating disorder unique to men? Recently, some eating disorder experts who work with men have suggested that there is. Observing men who are distressed by the idea that they are not sufficiently lean and muscular, who spend long hours lifting weights, and who follow an extremely restrictive diet, they have defined a disorder called *muscle dysmorphia*. (The disorder is also called *reverse anorexia nervosa*.) Men with muscle dysmorphia perceive themselves as small and frail even though they may actually be quite large and muscular. Thus, like men with anorexia nervosa, they suffer from a body image distortion, but it is reversed. No matter how "buff" or "chiselled" they become, their biology cannot match their idealized body size and shape.[38]

A common behaviour of men with muscle dysmorphia is abuse of performance-enhancing drugs. Additionally, whereas people with anorexia eat little of anything, men with muscle dysmorphia tend to consume excessive high-protein foods and dietary supplements like protein powders.

On the other hand, men with muscle dysmorphia share some characteristics with men and women with other eating disorders. For instance, they too report "feeling fat" and engage in the same behaviours indicating an obsession with appearance (such as looking in the mirror). They also express significant discomfort with the idea of having to expose their bodies to others (for example, take off their clothes in the locker room) and have increased rates of mental illness.[39]

There are some outward indications that someone may be struggling with muscle dysmorphia. Not all of them apply to all men with the disorder. If you notice any of these behaviours in a friend or relative, talk about it with him and let him know that help is available.

■ Rigid and excessive schedule of weight training
■ Strict adherence to a high-protein, muscle-enhancing diet
■ Use of anabolic steroids, protein powders, or other muscle-enhancing drugs or supplements
■ Poor attendance at work, school, or sports activities because of interference with rigid weight-training schedule
■ Avoidance of social engagements in which the person will not be able to follow his strict diet
■ Avoidance of situations in which the person would have to expose his body to others
■ Frequent and critical self-evaluation of body composition

Whereas muscle dysmorphia isn't typically life-threatening, it can cause distress and despair. Therapy—especially participation in an all-male support group—can help.

---

endurance exercise, which spares muscle glycogen and improves performance.[40, 41] Energy drinks that contain high amounts of caffeine, such as Red Bull, have become popular with athletes and many university students. These drinks should be avoided during exercise, as severe dehydration can result due to the combination of fluid loss from exercise and caffeine consumption. It should be recognized that in some instances caffeine is a controlled or restricted drug in the athletic world, although usually at high levels. Side effects of caffeine use include increased blood pressure, increased heart rate, dizziness, insomnia, headache, and gastrointestinal distress.

Ephedrine

Ephedrine, also known as ephedra, Chinese ephedra, or *ma huang,* is a strong stimulant marketed as a weight-loss supplement and energy enhancer. In reality, many products sold as Chinese ephedra (or herbal ephedra) contain ephedrine synthesized in a laboratory and other stimulants such as caffeine. The use of ephedra supplements does not appear to enhance performance, but supplements containing both caffeine and ephedra have been shown to prolong the amount of exercise that can be done until exhaustion is reached.[42] Ephedra is known to reduce body weight and body fat in sedentary women, but its impact on weight loss and body fat levels in athletes is unknown. Side effects of ephedra use include headaches, nausea, nervousness, anxiety, irregular heart rate, and high blood pressure; and at least 17 deaths have been attributed to its use.[43] As discussed in Chapter 14, it is currently illegal to sell ephedra-containing supplements in Canada.

Ephedrine is made from the herb *Ephedra sinica* (Chinese ephedra).

Carnitine

Carnitine is a compound made from amino acids and is found in the membranes of mitochondria in our cells. Carnitine helps shuttle fatty acids into the mitochondria so they can be used for energy. In theory, it has been proposed that exercise training depletes our cells of carnitine and that supplementation should increase the amount of carnitine in our mitochondrial membranes. By increasing cellular levels of carnitine, we should be able to improve the use of fat as a fuel source. Thus, carnitine is marketed not only as a performance-enhancing substance but also as a "fat burner." Research studies of carnitine supplementation do not support these claims,[44, 45] as neither the transport of fatty acids nor their oxidation appear to be enhanced with supplementation. Use of carnitine supplements has not been associated with significant side effects.

Chromium

Chromium is a trace mineral that enhances insulin's action of increasing the transport of amino acids into the cell (see Chapter 9). It is found in whole-grain foods, cheese, nuts, mushrooms, and asparagus. It is theorized that many people are chromium deficient and that supplementation will enhance the uptake of amino acids into muscle cells, which will increase muscle growth and strength. Like carnitine, chromium is marketed as a fat burner, as it is speculated that its effect on insulin stimulates the brain to decrease food intake.[43] Chromium supplements are available as chromium picolinate and chromium nicotinate. Early studies of chromium supplementation showed promise, but more recent, better-designed studies do not support any benefit of chromium supplementation on muscle mass, muscle strength, body fat, or exercise performance.[46]

Ribose

Ribose is a five-carbon sugar that is critical to the production of ATP. Ribose supplementation is claimed to improve athletic performance by increasing work output and by promoting a faster recovery time from vigorous training. While ribose has been shown to improve exercise tolerance in patients with heart disease, several studies have reported that ribose supplementation has no impact on athletic performance.[47–50]

From this review of ergogenic aids, you can see that most of these products are not effective in enhancing athletic performance or in optimizing muscle strength or body composition. It is important to be a savvy consumer when examining these products to make sure you are not wasting your money or putting your health at risk by using them.

RECaP

Ergogenic aids are substances used to improve exercise and athletic performance. Anabolic steroids are effective in increasing muscle size, power, and strength, but they are illegal and can cause serious health problems. Androstenedione and dehydroepiandrosterone are precursors of testosterone; neither of these products has been shown to effectively increase testosterone levels or to increase strength or muscle mass. Creatine supplements are popular and can enhance sprint performance in swimming, running, and cycling. Caffeine is a stimulant that increases the use of fat during exercise and may improve physical performance; however, it has several negative side effects. Ephedrine is a stimulant that has potentially fatal side effects. Carnitine, chromium, and ribose are marketed as ergogenic aids but studies do not support their effectiveness.

SEE FOR YOURSELF

Tips for Increasing Your Physical Activity

There are 1440 minutes in every day. Spend just 30 of those minutes in physical activity, and you'll be taking an important step toward improving your health. Here are some tips for working activity into your daily life:

- Walk as often and as much as possible: park your car farther away from your dorm, lecture hall, or shops; walk to school or work; go for a brisk walk between classes; get on or off the bus one stop away from your destination.
- Take the stairs instead of the elevator.
- Exercise while watching television, for example, by doing sit-ups, stretching, or using a treadmill or stationary bike.
- Put on a CD and dance!
- Get an exercise partner: join a friend for walks, hikes, cycling, skating, tennis, or a fitness class.
- Take up a group sport.

- Register for a class from the physical education department in an activity you've never tried before, maybe yoga or fencing.
- Register for a dance class, such as jazz, tap, or ballroom.
- Join a health club, gym, or YMCA and use the swimming pool, weights, rock-climbing wall, and other facilities.
- Join an activity-based club such as a skating or hiking club.

If you have been inactive for a while, use a sensible approach by starting out slowly. Gradually build up the time you spend doing the activity by adding a few minutes every few days until you reach 30 minutes a day. As this 30-minute minimum becomes easier, gradually increase either the length of time you spend in activity or the intensity of the activities you choose, or both.

CASE STUDY   Improving Athletic Performance

Shane is on the university soccer team. He is very busy with practice, weight training, and school work. Lately, he has been feeling wiped out, especially after games. The team has won four out of the last five games, and Shane has been giving it his all. He has been watching his carbohydrates and consumes about 400 g daily. Shane wonders if all the focus on carbohydrates means that he is neglecting his protein intake. In total he is eating about 180 g of protein each day, but thinks he should try one of the protein powders that are sold at the gym. Shane's weight is about 80 kg.

Shane's teammate, Theo, thinks that Shane should consider taking a creatine supplement to help with his lack of energy. Theo said that creatine will provide quick energy and speed recovery after exercise, and that there are no harmful side effects.

Thinking Critically

1. Calculate Shane's protein requirement.
2. Would you recommend that Shane try the protein supplement? Why or why not?
3. Is there a scientific basis for Theo's creatine claim?
4. Should Shane take a creatine supplement?
5. What other dietary strategies might be helpful for Shane to consider?

Chapter Review

Test Yourself | Answers

1. **T** About 15% of Canadians accumulate 150 minutes of moderate-to-vigorous activity weekly.

2. **F** Each person has to design a fitness program based on his or her own interests and needs. Depending upon a person's fitness goals, being active 20 to 30 minutes each day could be enough for a given individual.

3. **F** Carbohydrate loading may help improve performance for endurance events such as marathons and triathlons, but does not improve performance in non-endurance types of athletic events such as a 1500-metre run.

4. **F** Our muscles are not stimulated to grow when we eat extra protein, whether as food or supplements. Weight-bearing exercise appropriately stresses the body and produces increased muscle mass and strength.

5. **T** Most ergogenic aids are ineffective or do not produce the results that are advertised. Many ergogenic aids, such as anabolic steroids and ephedrine, can actually cause serious health consequences and can even cause death in some instances.

Summary

- Physical activity is any movement produced by muscles that increases energy expenditure.

- Leisure-time physical activity is any activity not related to a person's occupation and includes competitive sports and recreational activities. Exercise is a subcategory of leisure-time physical activity and is purposeful, planned, and structured.

- Physical fitness has many components and is defined as the ability to carry out daily tasks with vigour and alertness, without undue fatigue, and with ample energy to enjoy leisure-time pursuits and meet unforeseen emergencies.

- Physical activity provides a multitude of health benefits, including reducing our risks for heart disease, stroke, high blood pressure, obesity, type 2 diabetes, and osteoporosis. Despite these benefits, most Canadians are inactive.

- The components of fitness include cardiorespiratory fitness, musculoskeletal fitness (which includes muscular strength and muscular endurance), flexibility, and body composition. Physical fitness is specific to each one of these components.

- To achieve the appropriate overload for fitness, the FIT principle should be followed. Frequency refers to the number of activity sessions per week. Intensity refers to how difficult the activity is to perform. Time refers to how long each activity session lasts.

- Warm-up exercises prepare the muscles for exertion by increasing blood flow and temperature. Cool-down activities assist in the prevention of injury and may help reduce muscle soreness.

- The amount of ATP stored in a muscle cell is limited and can only keep a muscle active for about one to three seconds.

- For activities lasting about 3 to 15 seconds, creatine phosphate can be broken down in an anaerobic reaction to provide energy and support the regeneration of ATP.

- To support activities that last from 30 seconds to 2 minutes, energy is produced from glycolysis. Glycolysis produces two ATP molecules for every glucose molecule broken down. Pyruvate is the final end product of glycolysis.

- The further metabolism of pyruvate in the presence of adequate oxygen provides energy for activities that last from three minutes to four hours. During this aerobic process, each molecule of glucose can yield 36 to 38 ATP molecules.

- Fat can be broken down aerobically to support activities of low intensity and long duration.

- Amino acids can be used to make glucose to maintain our blood glucose levels during exercise and can contribute from 3% to 6% of the energy needed during exercise. Amino acids also help build and repair tissues after exercise.

- Vigorous-intensity exercise requires extra energy, and male athletes typically need more energy than female athletes because of their higher muscle mass and larger body weight. Athletes who are concerned with making a competitive weight or with the aesthetic demands of their sport may be at risk for insufficient energy and nutrient intakes.

- It is generally recommended that athletes should consume 45% to 65% of their total energy as carbohydrate.

- Carbohydrate loading involves altering physical training and the diet such that the storage of muscle glycogen is maximized in an attempt to enhance endurance performance.

- A dietary fat intake of 20% to 35% is generally recommended for athletes, with less than 10% of total energy intake as saturated fat.

- Protein needs can be higher for athletes and regularly active people, but most people in Canada already consume more than twice their daily needs for protein.

- Regular exercise increases our fluid needs to help cool our internal body temperature and prevent heat illnesses. Heat illnesses include heat syncope, heat cramps, heat exhaustion, and heatstroke. Adequate fluid intake before, during, and after exercise will help prevent heat illnesses.

- Active people may need more thiamine, riboflavin, and vitamin B_6 than inactive people. Most women, including active women, do not consume enough calcium. Many active individuals also require more iron, particularly female athletes and vegetarian athletes.

- Ergogenic aids are substances used to improve exercise and athletic performance, to improve physical appearance, prevent or treat injuries, treat diseases, or to cope with stress. Many ergogenic aids are not effective, some are dangerous, and most are expensive.

Review Questions

1. For achieving and maintaining cardiorespiratory fitness, the intensity range typically recommended is
   a. 25% to 50% of your estimated maximal heart rate.
   b. 35% to 75% of your estimated maximal heart rate.
   c. 64% to 90% of your estimated maximal heart rate.
   d. 75% to 95% of your estimated maximal heart rate.

2. The amount of ATP stored in a muscle cell can keep a muscle active for about
   a. 1 to 3 seconds.
   b. 10 to 30 seconds.
   c. 1 to 3 minutes.
   d. 1 to 3 hours.

3. To support a long afternoon of gardening, the body predominantly uses which nutrient for energy?
   a. carbohydrate
   b. fat
   c. amino acids
   d. lactic acid

4. Creatine
   a. enhances performance in aerobic-type events.
   b. increases an individual's risk for bladder cancer.
   c. can increase strength gained in resistance exercise.
   d. is stored in the liver.

5. I read in a magazine that I should take protein supplements to increase my muscle mass. Should I take them? Why or why not?

6. Megan is a competitive boxer. Her coach recommended that she lose four pounds before her match this weekend. Megan decides the easiest way to do this is to restrict her water intake. What do you think of her approach to weight loss?

7. Write a plan for a weekly activity/exercise routine that does the following:
   - meets your personal fitness goals
   - is fun for you to do
   - includes variety and consistency
   - uses all components of the FIT principle
   - includes a warm-up and cool-down period

8. Determine how many grams of carbohydrate, protein, and fat you need to consume daily to support the activity/exercise routine you described in the previous question.

9. You decide to start training for your school's annual marathon. After studying this chapter, which of the following preparation strategies would you pursue, and why?
   - use of B-vitamin supplements
   - use of creatine supplements
   - use of sports beverages
   - carbohydrate loading

10. Gustavo is a 56-year-old accountant who last participated in a regular exercise program when he was in his late 20s. Would you advise him to begin a planned exercise program of low-to-moderate intensity? Why or why not? If so, what steps should he take before starting an exercise program?

11. Marisa and Conrad are students at the same university. Marisa walks to and from school each morning from her home seven blocks away. Conrad lives in a suburb 20 km away and drives to school. Marisa, an early childhood education major, covers the lunch shift, two hours a day, at the university's day care centre, cleaning up the lunchroom and supervising the children on the playground. Conrad, an accounting major, works in his department office two hours a day, entering data into computer spreadsheets. On weekends, Marisa and her sister walk downtown and go shopping. Conrad goes to the movies with his friends. Neither Marisa nor Conrad participates in sports or scheduled exercise sessions. Marisa has maintained a normal, healthy weight throughout the school year, but in the same period of time, Conrad has gained several kilograms. Identify at least two factors that might play a role in Marisa's and Conrad's current weights.

Web Links

www.hc-sc.gc.ca/hl-vs/physactiv/index-eng.php
Health Canada
This site has resources to help Canadians incorporate physical activity into their daily lives.

www.casm-acms.org
Canadian Academy of Sport and Exercise Medicine
Visit this site for position statements on a range of sport medicine topics.

www.phac-aspc.gc.ca/hp-ps/hl-mvs/pa-ap/index-eng.php
Public Health Agency of Canada
Find the latest physical activity guidelines for Canadians and tips for becoming more active.

www.participaction.com/en-us/Home.aspx
ParticipACTION
ParticipACTION is the national voice of physical activity and sport participation in Canada.

www.csep.ca/english/view.asp?x=804
Canadian Society for Exercise Physiology
Visit this site to download PAR-Q forms and to access research related to physical activity, fitness, health, nutrition, epidemiology, and human performance.

www.activehealthykids.ca
Active Healthy Kids Canada
Go to this site for ideas to increase physical activity among children and youth.

www.heartandstroke.com/site/c.ikIQLcMWJtE/b.2796497/k.BF8B/Home.htm
Heart and Stroke Foundation
Click on "Healthy Living" under the "Health Information" section for ways to incorporate more physical activity into your daily life.

www.coach.ca
Coaching Association of Canada
Visit this site for sports nutrition resources for athletes, parents, and coaches.

www.cces.ca
Canadian Centre for Ethics in Sport
The Canadian Centre for Ethics in Sport advocates on issues regarding ethics in Canadian sport.

MasteringNutrition®

www.masteringnutrition.pearson.com

Assignments
Activities: NutriTools

Study Area
Practice Tests • Diet Analysis • eText

References

1. U.S. Department of Health and Human Services. 1996. *Physical Activity and Health: A Report of the Surgeon General.* Atlanta, GA: U.S. Department of Health and Human Services, Centers for Disease Control and Prevention, National Centers for Chronic Disease Prevention and Health Promotion.
2. Caspersen, C. J., K. E. Powell, and G. M. Christensen. 1985. Physical activity, exercise, and physical fitness: definitions and distinctions for health-related research. *Public Health Rep.* 100:126–131.
3. Heyward, V. H. 2006. *Advanced Fitness Assessment and Exercise Prescription,* 5th ed. Champaign, IL: Human Kinetics.
4. Colley, R. C., D. Garriguet, I. Janssen, C. L. Craig, J. Clarke, and M. S. Tremblay. 2011. Physical activity of Canadian adults: accelerometer results from the 2007 to 2009 Canadian Health Measures Survey. *Health Reports* (Statistics Canada, Catalogue 82-003-XPE) 22:1–8.
5. Trembly, M. S., M. Shields, M. Laviolette, C. L. Craig, I. Janssen, and S. Connor Gorber. 2010. Fitness of Canadian children and youth: results from the 2007–2009 Canadian Health Measures Survey. *Health Reports* (Statistics Canada, Catalogue 82-003-X) 21:1–15.
6. Warburton, D. E. R., S. Charlesworth, A. Ivey, L. Nettlefold, and S. S. D. Bredin. 2010. Systematic review of the evidence for Canada's Physical Activity Guidelines for Adults. *Int. J. Behav. Nutr. Phys. Act.* 11:7–39.
7. Janssen, I., and A. G. LeBlanc. 2010. Systematic review of the health benefits of physical activity and fitness in school aged children and youth. *Int. J. Behav. Nutr. Phys. Act.* 11:7–40.
8. Findlay, L. C. 2011. Physical activity among First Nations people off reserve, Métis and Inuit. Available at www.statcan.gc.ca/pub/82-003-x/2011001/article/11403-eng.htm (accessed March 16, 2011).
9. Brooks, G. A. 2000. Intra- and extra-cellular lactate shuttles. *Med. Sci. Sports Exerc.* 32:790–799.
10. Gladden, L. B. 2000. Muscle as a consumer of lactate. *Med. Sci. Sports Exerc.* 32:764–771.
11. Tarnopolsky, M. 2006. Protein and amino acid needs for training and bulking up. In: Burke, L., and V. Deakin, eds. *Clinical Sports Nutrition,* 3rd ed. Sydney, Australia: McGraw-Hill, pp. 73–98.
12. American College of Sports Medicine, American Dietetic Association, and Dietitians of Canada. 2009. Nutrition and athletic performance. Joint position statement. *Med. Sci. Sports Exerc.* 41:709–731.

13. Burke, L. 2006. Nutrition for recovery after competition and training. In: Burke, L., and V. Deakin, eds. *Clinical Sports Nutrition*, 3rd ed. Sydney, Australia: McGraw-Hill, pp. 415–440.

14. Costill, D. L., W. M. Sherman, W. J. Fink, C. Maresh, M. Witten, and J. M. Miller. 1981. The role of dietary carbohydrates in muscle glycogen resynthesis after strenuous running. *Am. J. Clin. Nutr.* 34:1831–1836.

15. van Hall, G., S. M. Shirreffs, and J. A. L. Calbert. 2000. Muscle glycogen resynthesis during recovery from cycle exercise: no effect of additional protein ingestion. *J. Appl. Physiol.* 88:1631–1636.

16. Jentjens, R. L., L. J. C. van Loon, C. H. Mann, A. J. M. Wagenmakers, and A. E. Jeukendrup. 2001. Addition of protein and amino acids to carbohydrates does not enhance postexercise muscle glycogen synthesis. *J. Appl. Physiol.* 91:839–846.

17. Manore, M. M, N. L. Meyer, and J. L. Thompson. 2009. *Sports Nutrition for Health and Performance*, 2nd ed. Champaign, IL: Human Kinetics.

18. National Weather Service Forecast Office. 2006. Heat index. Available at www.crh.noaa.gov/pub/heat.php.

19. Weaver, C. M., and S. Rajaram. 1992. Exercise and iron status. *J. Nutr.* 122:782–787.

20. Haymes, E. M. 1998. Trace minerals and exercise. In: Wolinsky, I., ed. *Nutrition and Exercise and Sport.* Boca Raton, FL: CRC Press, pp. 1997–2218.

21. Haymes, E. M., and P. M. Clarkson. 1998. Minerals and trace minerals. In: Berning, J. R., and S. N. Steen, eds. *Nutrition and Sport and Exercise.* Gaithersburg, MD: Aspen Publishers, pp. 77–107.

22. Haymes, E.M. 1998. Trace minerals and exercise. In: Wolinsky, L., ed. *Nutrition and Exercise and Sport.* Boca Raton, FL: CRC Press, pp. 1997–2218.

23. Nattiv A., A. B. Loucks, M. M. Manore, C. F. Sanborn, J. Sundgot-Borgen, and M. P. Warren. 2007. The female athlete triad. *Medicine and Science in Sport and Exercise.* 39(10):1867–1882.

24. Lightsey, D. M., and J. R. Attaway. 1992. Deceptive tactics used in marketing purported ergogenic aids. *Natl. Strength Cond. Assoc. J.* 14:26–31.

25. U.S. Department of Health and Human Services (HHS). 2004. News release. HHS launches crackdown on products containing andro. Available at www.hhs.gov/news/press/2004pres/20040311.html.

26. Broeder, C. E., J. Quindry, K. Brittingham, L. Panton, J. Thomson, S. Appakondu, K. Breuel, R. Byrd, J. Douglas, C. Earnest, C. Mitchell, M. Olson, T. Roy, and C. Yarlagadda. 2000. The Andro Project: physiological and hormonal influences of androstenedione supplementation in men 35 to 65 years old participating in a high-intensity resistance training program. *Arch. Intern. Med.* 160:3093–3104.

27. Balsom, P. D., K. Söderlund, B. Sjödin, and B. Ekblom. 1995. Skeletal muscle metabolism during short duration high-intensity exercise: influence of creatine supplementation. *Acta. Physiol. Scand.* 1154:303–310.

28. Grindstaff, P. D., R. Kreider, R. Bishop, M. Wilson, L. Wood, C. Alexander, and A. Almada. 1997. Effects of creatine supplementation on repetitive sprint performance and body composition in competitive swimmers. *Int. J. Sport Nutr.* 7:330–346.

29. Kreider, R. B., M. Ferreira, M. Wilson, P. Grindstaff, S. Plisk, J. Reinardy, E. Cantler, and A. L. Almada. 1998. Effects of creatine supplementation on body composition, strength, and sprint performance. *Med. Sci. Sports Exerc.* 30:73–82.

30. Tarnopolsky, M. A., and D. P. MacLennan. 2000. Creatine monohydrate supplementation enhances high-intensity exercise performance in males and females. *Int. J. Sport Nutr. Exerc. Metab.* 10:452–463.

31. Kreider R., M. Ferreira, M. Wilson, and A. L. Almada. 1999. Effects of calcium beta-hydroxy-beta methylbutyrate (HMB) supplementation during resistance-training on markers of catabolism, body composition and strength. *Int. J. Sports Med.* 20(8):503–509.

32. Volek, J. S., N. D. Duncan, S. A. Mazzetti, R. S. Staron, M. Putukian, A. L. Gomez, D. R. Pearson, W. J. Fink, and W. J. Kraemer. 1999. Performance and muscle fiber adaptations to creatine supplementation and heavy resistance training. *Med. Sci. Sports Exerc.* 31:1147–1156.

33. Reuters. 2001. Creatine use could lead to cancer, French government reports. *New York Times,* January 25, www.nytimes.com.

34. Jeong, K. S., S. J. Park, C. S. Lee, T. W. Kim, S. H. Kim, S. Y. Ryu, B. H. Williams, R. L. Veech, and Y. S. Lee. 2000. Effects of cyclocreatine in rat hepatocarcinogenesis model. *Anticancer Res.* 20(3A):1627–1633.

35. Ara, G., L. M. Gravelin, R. Kaddurah-Daouk, and B. A. Teicher. 1998. Antitumor activity of creatine analogs produced by alterations in pancreatic hormones and glucose metabolism. *In Vivo* 12:223–231.

36. Schilling, B. K., M. H. Stone, A. Utter, J. T. Kearney, M. Johnson, R. Coglianese, L. Smith, H. S. O'Bryant, A. C. Fry, M. Starks, R. Keith, and M. E. Stone. 2001. Creatine supplementation and health variable: a retrospective study. *Med. Sci. Sports Exerc.* 33:183–188.

37. Shao, A., and J. N. Hathcock. 2006. Risk assessment for creatine monhydrate. *Regul. Toxicol. Pharmacol.* 45:242–225.

38. Andersen, A. E. 2001. Eating disorders in males: gender divergence management. *Currents* 2(2). University of Iowa Health Care. Available at www.uihealthcare.com/news/currents/vol2issue2/eatingdisordersinmen.html.

39. Pope H. G., K. A. Phillips, and R. Olivardia. 2000. *The Adonis Complex: The Secret Crisis of Male Body Obsession.* New York: The Free Press.

40. Anderson, M. E., C. R. Bruce, S. F. Fraser, N. K. Stepto, R. Klein, W. G. Hopkins, and J. A. Hawley. 2000. Improved 2000-meter rowing performance in competitive oarswomen after caffeine ingestion. *Int. J. Sport Nutr. Exerc. Metab.* 10:464–475.

41. Spriet, L. L., and R. A. Howlett. 2000. Caffeine. In: Maughan, R. J., ed. *Nutrition in Sport.* Oxford: Blackwell Science, pp. 379–392.

42. Bucci, L. 2000. Selected herbals and human exercise performance. *Am. J. Clin. Nutr.* 72:624S–636S.

43. Williams, M. H. 1998. *The Ergogenics Edge.* Champaign, IL: Human Kinetics.

44. Hawley, J. A. 2002. Effect of increased fat availability on metabolism and exercise capacity. *Med. Sci. Sports Exerc.* 34(9):1485–1491.

45. Heinonen, O. J. 1996. Carnitine and physical exercise. *Sports Med.* 22:109–132.

46. Vincent, J. B. 2003. The potential value and toxicity of chromium picolinate as a nutritional supplement, weight loss agent and muscle development agent. *Sports Med.* 33(3):213–230.

47. Pliml, W., T. von Arnim, A. Stablein, H. Hofmann, H. G. Zimmer, and E. Erdmann. 1992. Effects of ribose on exercise-induced ischaemia in stable coronary artery disease. *Lancet* 340(8818):507–510.

48. Earnest, C. P., G. M. Morss, F. Wyatt, A. N. Jordan, S. Colson, T. S. Church, Y. Fitzgerald, L. Autrey, R. Jurca, and A. Lucia. 2004. Effects of a commercial herbal-based formula on exercise performance in cyclists. *Med. Sci. Sports Exerc.* 36(3):504–509.

49. Hellsten, Y., L. Skadhauge, and J. Bangsbo. 2004. Effect of ribose supplementation on resynthesis of adenine nucleotides after intense intermittent training in humans. *Am. J. Physiol. Regul. Integr. Comp. Physiol.* 286:R182–R188.

50. Kreider, R. B., C. Melton, M. Greenwood, C. Rasmussen, J. Lundberg, C. Earnest, and A. Almada. 2003. Effects of oral D-ribose supplementation on anaerobic capacity and selected metabolic markers in healthy males. *Int. J. Sport Nutr. Exerc. Metab.* 13(1):76–86.

51. World Health Organization. 2010. Global Recommendations on Physical Activity for Health. Available at http://whqlibdoc.who.int/publications/2010/9789241599979_eng.pdf (accessed May 26, 2011).

How Much Physical Activity Is Enough?

Your aerobics instructor tells you to work out at your target heart rate for 20 minutes a day, whereas your doctor tells you to walk for half an hour three or four times a week. A magazine article encourages you to work out to the point of exhaustion, while a new weight-loss book claims that you can be perfectly healthy without ever breaking a sweat.

So how much activity is really enough?

To try to answer this question, let's take a closer look at how the Canadian Physical Activity Guidelines, released in 2011, were established. The guidelines were developed based on evidence examined from systematic reviews of relevant literature.[6, 7] The authors critically appraised the strength of the relationship between physical activity and seven specific health outcomes—cardiovascular disease, stroke, hypertension, colon cancer, breast cancer, type 2 diabetes, and osteoporosis—from over 400 research articles.

They found a clear dose-response relationship between increased levels of physical activity and decreased risk for disease. Further, they established that physical activity should include a combination of moderate and vigorous intensity activities and incorporate resistance activities that tax the musculoskeletal system. What was less clear was whether this activity needs to be done daily, or even every other day for maximum effect. Previous Canadian guidelines recommended 60 minutes of physical

Older and less fit individuals can improve their health and physical fitness with moderate daily activity.

activity every day to stay healthy and improve health. The updated guidelines recommend a weekly reference amount that better reflects the evidence, and allows more flexibility to meet the recommendation.

These guidelines are relevant to all apparently healthy children, youth, and adults, irrespective of gender, race, ethnicity, or socio-economic status. Canadians are encouraged to participate in a variety of physical activities that are enjoyable and safe. Changes were also made to harmonize guidelines with other countries and organizations to minimize the confusion. A comparison of the newest Canadian Physical Activity Guidelines with previous Canadian and World Health Organization Guidelines can be found below.

Children (5–17 Years Old)

New Canadian Guidelines

For health benefits, children (5–11) and youth (12–17) should accumulate at least 60 minutes of moderate-to-vigorous-intensity physical activity daily. This should include vigorous-intensity activities at least three days per week and activities that strengthen muscles and bone at least three days per week.

Previous Canadian Guidelines

Children who are sedentary are encouraged to start being active for 30 minutes a day and gradually increase to 90 minutes a day. Moderate activities such as skating, bike riding, and outdoor play should be combined with vigorous activities like running and soccer. There should be a mix of endurance activities like jumping and swimming, flexibility activities like gymnastics and dancing, and strength activities like climbing.

World Health Organization Guidelines[51]

Children and young people should take part in moderate-to-vigorous physical activity for at least 60 minutes each day. Most physical activity should be aerobic, which means activities like walking, biking, skating, and running that move the body's large muscles for a sustained period of time. Activities that strengthen muscle and bone should be performed at least three times per week.

Adults (18–64 Years Old)

New Canadian Guidelines

To achieve health benefits, adults aged 18–64 years should accumulate at least 150 minutes of moderate-to-vigorous-intensity aerobic physical activity per week, in bouts of 10 minutes or more. It is also beneficial to add muscle and bone strengthening activities using major muscle groups, at least two days per week.

Previous Canadian Guidelines

Adults are encouraged to perform a cumulative 60 minutes daily of light activities like walking, volleyball, gardening, and easy stretching in increments of at least 10 minutes each. Or they can do moderate activities like brisk walking, biking, swimming, and dancing for 30 minutes, four days a week. Endurance activities like lawn-mowing, bike riding, and walking should be done four to seven days a week.

There is no single exercise recommendation for everyone. The amount of daily physical activity you should participate in will be determined by your personal fitness goals.

World Health Organization Guidelines[51]

Do at least 150 minutes of moderate physical activity, or at least 75 minutes of vigorous physical activity, or a combination of the two, throughout the week. Aerobic activity should be performed in bouts of at least 10 minutes each. Muscle-strengthening activities should be done involving major muscle groups on two or more days a week.

Older Adults (65 Years and Older)

New Canadian Guidelines

To achieve health benefits, and improve functional abilities, adults aged 65 years and older should accumulate at least 150 minutes of moderate-to-vigorous-intensity aerobic physical activity per week, in bouts of 10 minutes or more. It is also beneficial to add muscle and bone strengthening activities using major muscle groups at least two days per week. Those with poor mobility should perform physical activities to enhance balance and prevent falls.

Previous Canadian Guidelines

Moderate physical activity should be performed for a cumulative 30 to 60 minutes most days in increments of at least 10 minutes each. Increase endurance activities like walking, swimming, and line dancing to four to six days a week. Do flexibility activities like stretching, bowling, or tai chi daily. Do strength and balance activities like stair climbing and weight lifting two to four days a week.

World Health Organization Guidelines[51]

At least 150 minutes of moderate physical activity or at least 75 minutes of vigorous aerobic physical activity, or a combination of the two, should be performed throughout the week in bouts of at least 10 minutes duration. Adults of this age group with poor mobility should perform physical activity to enhance balance and prevent falls on three or more days per week. Muscle-strengthening activities should be done on two or more days a week.

So, are these recommendations really that different? Probably not. Results of ongoing research will help to resolve some of the apparently conflicting recommendations. In the meantime, we need to remember that nutrition experts, exercise physiologists, and other healthcare professionals all recognize that weight loss and healthy weight maintenance are easier to achieve in people who do more physical activity each day, not less.

Using the Evidence

1. Are the "new" Canadian guidelines a dramatic change from previous recommendations?

2. Do you think that more Canadians can be persuaded to become physically active now that the recommendations have been lowered?

3. Are population-based recommendations useful for Canadians?

4. Do you consider any physical activity better than no physical activity?

16

Nutrition Through the Life Cycle: Pregnancy and the First Year of Life

Test Yourself | True or False?

1. A pregnant woman needs to consume twice as many calories as she did prior to the pregnancy. T or F

2. Despite popular belief, very few pregnant women actually experience morning sickness, food cravings, or food aversions. T or F

3. Breastfed infants tend to have fewer infections and allergies than formula-fed infants. T or F

4. When a breastfeeding woman drinks caffeinated beverages such as coffee, the caffeine enters the breast milk. T or F

5. Most infants begin to require solid foods by about three months (12 weeks) of age. T or F

Test Yourself answers are located in the Chapter Review.

Chapter Objectives | *After reading this chapter, you will be able to:*

1. List four reasons why maintaining a nutritious diet is important for a woman of childbearing age even prior to conception, *pp. 580–581*.

2. Explore the relationship between fetal development, physiologic changes in the pregnant woman, and increasing nutrient requirements during the course of a pregnancy, *pp. 581–584*.

3. Identify the ranges of optimal weight gain for pregnant women, including adolescent and adult pregnancies, singleton and multiple pregnancies, and normal, underweight, and overweight/obese women, *pp. 585–586*.

4. Describe the physiologic basis of lactation, *pp. 598–599*.

5. Compare and contrast the nutrient requirements of pregnant and lactating women, *pp. 587–592, 599–601*.

6. Identify the primary advantages and most common challenges of breastfeeding, *pp. 601–606*.

7. Relate the growth and activity patterns of infants to their nutrient needs, *pp. 606–612*.

8. Discuss the timing and sequencing of introducing solid foods to infants, *pp. 613–615*.

9. Identify those factors that increase the risk of food allergies in infants, *p. 616*.

When she was a baby, Theresa showed poor coordination, was slow to walk and start talking, and was what her grandmother called "a real handful." Now an energetic 12-year-old, she still struggles every day to learn new information and keep up with her classmates physically and academically. Even though she tries hard, Theresa has a poor attention span and is often in trouble for misbehaving in class. Unfortunately, Theresa's physical, mental, and behavioural problems are likely to persist, and new ones may develop. That's because Theresa was born with fetal alcohol spectrum disorder (FASD). During her pregnancy, Theresa's mother consumed beer and hard alcohol several times a week, causing lifelong health problems for her daughter.

What role does prenatal diet play in determining the future health and well-being of the child? What is the link between alcohol and birth defects? Why is inadequate iron or folate intake especially dangerous to a pregnant woman and her fetus? What roles do protein, zinc, calcium, and other nutrients play in maternal and fetal health? In this chapter, we discuss how adequate nutrition supports fetal development, maintains the pregnant woman's health, and contributes to lactation. We then explore the nutrient needs of breast-feeding and formula-feeding infants.

Starting Out Right: Healthy Nutrition in Pregnancy

At no stage of life is nutrition more crucial than during fetal development and infancy. From conception through the end of the first year of life, adequate nutrition is essential for tissue formation, neurologic development, and bone growth, modelling, and remodelling. The ability to reach peak physical and intellectual potential in adult life is in part determined by the nutrition received during fetal development and the first year of life.

Is Nutrition Important Before Conception?

Several factors make adequate nutrition important even before **conception**, the point at which a woman's ovum (egg) is fertilized with a man's sperm. First, some problems related to nutrient deficiency develop extremely early in the pregnancy, typically before the mother even realizes she is pregnant. An adequate and varied preconception diet reduces the risk of such problems, providing "insurance" during those first few weeks of pregnancy.

For example, failure of the spinal cord to close results in *neural tube defects;* these defects are closely related to inadequate folate status during the first few weeks after conception. For this reason, all women capable of becoming pregnant are encouraged to take 400 μg of folic acid daily, in addition to natural sources of folate from a varied, healthy diet. This recommendation should be followed by all women of childbearing age whether or not they plan to become pregnant.

Second, adopting a healthy diet and lifestyle prior to conception requires women to avoid alcohol, illicit drugs, and other known **teratogens** (substances that cause birth defects). Women should also consult their healthcare provider about their consumption of caffeine, medications, herbs, and supplements; and if they smoke, they should attempt to quit.

Third, a healthy diet and appropriate levels of physical activity can help women achieve and maintain an optimal body weight prior to pregnancy. Women with a prepregnancy body mass index (BMI) between 19.8 and 26.0 have the best chance of an uncomplicated pregnancy and delivery, with low risk of negative outcomes such as prolonged labour and Cesarean section.[1] As we will discuss in greater detail shortly, women with a BMI below or above this range prior to conception are at greater risk for pregnancy-related complications.

Finally, maintaining a balanced and nourishing diet before conception reduces a woman's risk of developing a nutrition-related disorder during her pregnancy. These disorders,

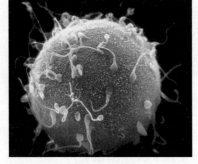

During conception, a sperm fertilizes an egg, creating a zygote.

conception (also called *fertilization*) The uniting of an ovum (egg) and sperm to create a fertilized egg, or zygote.

teratogen Any substance that can cause a birth defect.

which we discuss later in the chapter, include gestational diabetes mellitus and hyperten sive disorders. Although genetic and metabolic abnormalities are beyond the woman's control, following a healthy diet prior to conception is something a woman can do to help her fetus develop into a healthy baby.

The man's nutrition prior to pregnancy is important as well, because malnutrition contributes to abnormalities in sperm.[2] Both sperm number and motility (ability to move) are reduced by alcohol consumption, as well as the use of certain prescription and illicit drugs. Finally, infections accompanied by a high fever can destroy sperm; so, to the extent that adequate nutrition keeps the immune system strong, it also promotes a man's fertility.

Why Is Nutrition Important During Pregnancy?

A balanced, nourishing diet throughout pregnancy provides the nutrients needed to support fetal growth and development without depriving the mother of nutrients she needs to maintain her own health. It also minimizes the risks of excess energy intake. A full-term pregnancy, also called the period of **gestation**, lasts 38 to 42 weeks and is divided into three **trimesters**, with each trimester lasting about 13 to 14 weeks.

The First Trimester

About once each month, a non-pregnant woman of childbearing age experiences *ovulation*, the release of an ovum (egg cell) from an ovary. The ovum is then drawn into the uterine (fallopian) tube. The first trimester (approximately weeks 1 through 13) begins when the ovum and sperm unite to form a single, fertilized cell called a **zygote**. As the zygote travels through the uterine tube, it further divides into a ball of 12 to 16 cells that, at about day 4, arrives in the uterus (**Figure 16.1**). By day 10, the inner portion of the zygote, called the *blastocyst,* implants into the uterine lining. The outer portion becomes part of the placenta, which is discussed shortly.

gestation The period of intrauterine development from conception to birth.

trimester Any one of three stages of pregnancy, each lasting 13 to 14 weeks.

zygote A fertilized egg (ovum) consisting of a single cell.

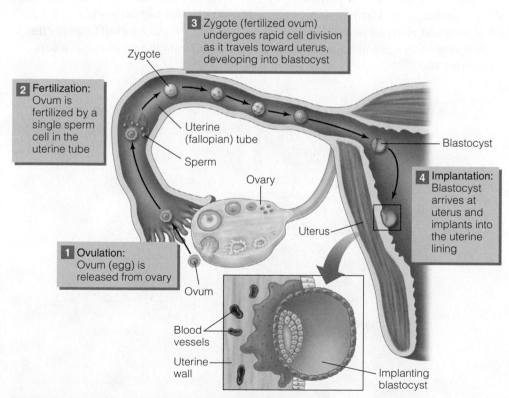

Figure 16.1 Ovulation, conception, and implantation.
Data from: Germann, W. and Stanfield, C. Principles of Human Physiology, 2/e, Fig. 22.20a, Copyright © 2004 Benjamin Cummings. Reprinted by permission of Pearson Education, Inc.

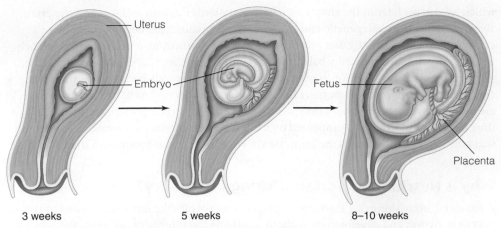

3 weeks   5 weeks   8–10 weeks

Figure 16.2 Human embryonic development during the first 10 weeks. Organ systems are most vulnerable to teratogens during this time, when cells are dividing and differentiating.
Data from: Germann, W. and Stanfield, C. Principles of Human Physiology, 2/e, Fig. 22.21, Copyright © 2004 Benjamin Cummings. Reprinted by permission of Pearson Education, Inc.

embryo Human growth and developmental stage lasting from the third week to the end of the eighth week after fertilization.

spontaneous abortion (also called *miscarriage*) Natural termination of a pregnancy and expulsion of pregnancy tissues because of a genetic, developmental, or physiologic abnormality that is so severe that the pregnancy cannot be maintained.

placenta A pregnancy-specific organ formed from both maternal and embryonic tissues. It is responsible for oxygen, nutrient, and waste exchange between mother and fetus.

Further cell growth, multiplication, and differentiation occurs, resulting in the formation of an **embryo**. Over the next six weeks, embryonic tissues fold into a primitive tubelike structure with limb buds, organs, and facial features recognizable as human (**Figure 16.2**). It isn't surprising, then, that the embryo is most vulnerable to teratogens during this time. Not only alcohol and illicit drugs but also prescription and over-the-counter medications, megadoses of supplements such as vitamin A, certain herbs, viruses, cigarette smoking, and radiation can interfere with embryonic development and cause birth defects.[2] In some cases, the damage is so severe that the pregnancy is naturally terminated in a **spontaneous abortion** (*miscarriage*), which occurs most often in the first trimester.

During the first weeks of pregnancy, the embryo obtains its nutrients from cells lining the uterus. But by the fourth week, a primitive **placenta** has formed in the uterus from both embryonic and maternal tissue. Within a few more weeks, the placenta will be a fully functioning organ through which the mother will provide nutrients and remove fetal wastes (see **Figure 16.3**).

Figure 16.3 Placental development. The placenta is formed from both embryonic and maternal tissues. When the placenta is fully functional, fetal blood vessels and maternal blood vessels are intimately intertwined, allowing the exchange of nutrients and wastes between the two. The mother transfers nutrients and oxygen to the fetus, and the fetus transfers wastes to the mother for disposal.
Data from: Germann, W. and Stanfield, C. Principles of Human Physiology, 2/e, Fig. 22.22, Copyright © 2004 Benjamin Cummings. Reprinted by permission of Pearson Education, Inc.

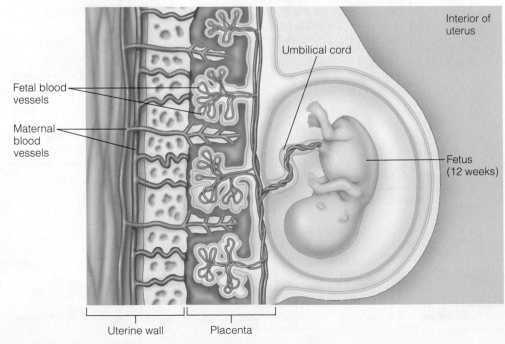

By the end of the embryonic stage, about eight weeks postconception, the embryo's tissues and organs have differentiated dramatically. A primitive skeleton, including fingers and toes, has formed. Muscles have begun to develop in the trunk and limbs, and some movement is now possible. A primitive heart has also formed and begun to beat, and the digestive system is differentiating into distinct organs (stomach, liver, and so forth). The brain and cranial nerves have differentiated, and the head has a mouth, eyespots with eyelids, and primitive ears.[2]

The third month of pregnancy marks the transition from embryo to **fetus**. The fetus requires abundant nutrients from the mother's body to support its dramatic growth during this period. The placenta is now a mature organ that can provide these nutrients. It is connected to the fetal circulatory system via the **umbilical cord**, an extension of fetal blood vessels emerging from the fetus's navel (called the *umbilicus*). Blood rich in oxygen and nutrients flows through the placenta and into the umbilical vein (Figure 16.3). Once inside the fetus's body, the blood travels to the fetal liver and heart. Wastes are excreted in blood returning from the fetus to the placenta via the umbilical arteries. Although many people think there is a mixing of blood from the fetus and the mother, the two blood supplies remain separate; the placenta is the "go-between" that allows the transfer of nutrients and wastes.

Because the formation of body limbs, eyes and ears, and organs occurs during the first trimester, nutrient deficiencies during this time can lead to irreversible structural or functional damage. At the same time, nutrient toxicities as well as exposure to drugs, alcohol, certain medications, or microbes during this trimester can also result in fetal malformation. The consequences of specific nutrient deficiencies and toxicities are discussed shortly.

The Second Trimester

During the second trimester (approximately weeks 14 to 27 of pregnancy), the fetus continues to grow and mature (**Figure 16.4**). The fetus can suck its thumb, its ears begin to hear, and its eyes can open and close and react to light. The placenta is now fully functional. At the beginning of the second trimester, the fetus is about 8 cm long and weighs about 680 g. By the end of the second trimester, the fetus is generally more than 30 cm long and weighs more than 1000 g. Some babies born prematurely in the last weeks of the second trimester survive with intensive **neonatal** care.

The Third Trimester

The third trimester (approximately weeks 28 to birth) is a time of remarkable growth for the fetus. During three short months, the fetus gains nearly half its body length and three-quarters of its body weight! At the time of birth, an average baby will be approximately 46 to 56 cm long and about 3400 g in weight (see Figure 16.4). Brain growth (which continues to be rapid for the first two years of life) is also quite remarkable, and the lungs become fully mature. Because of the intense growth and maturation of the fetus during the third trimester, it continues to be critical that the mother eat an adequate and balanced diet.

Impact of Nutrition on Newborn Maturity and Birth Weight

An adequate, nourishing diet is one of the most important modifiable variables increasing the chances for birth of a mature newborn. Proper nutrition also increases the likelihood that the newborn's weight will be appropriate for his or her gestational age. Generally, a birth weight of at least 2500 g is considered a marker of a successful pregnancy.

An undernourished mother is likely to give birth to a **low-birth-weight** infant.[3] Any infant weighing less than 2500 g at birth is considered to be of low birth weight and is at increased risk of infection, learning disabilities, impaired physical development, and death in the first year of life (**Figure 16.5** on page 585). Many low-birth-weight infants are born **preterm**—that is, before 38 weeks of gestation. Others are born at term but weigh less than would be expected for their gestational age; this condition is called **small for gestational age (SGA)**. Although nutrition is not the only factor contributing to maturity and birth weight, its role cannot be overstated.

fetus Human growth and developmental stage lasting from the beginning of the ninth week after conception to birth.

umbilical cord The cord containing arteries and veins that connects the baby (from the navel) to the mother via the placenta.

neonatal Referring to a newborn.

low birth weight A weight of less than 2500 g at birth.

preterm Birth of a baby prior to 38 weeks of gestation.

small for gestational age (SGA) Infants whose birth weight for gestational age falls below the 10th percentile.

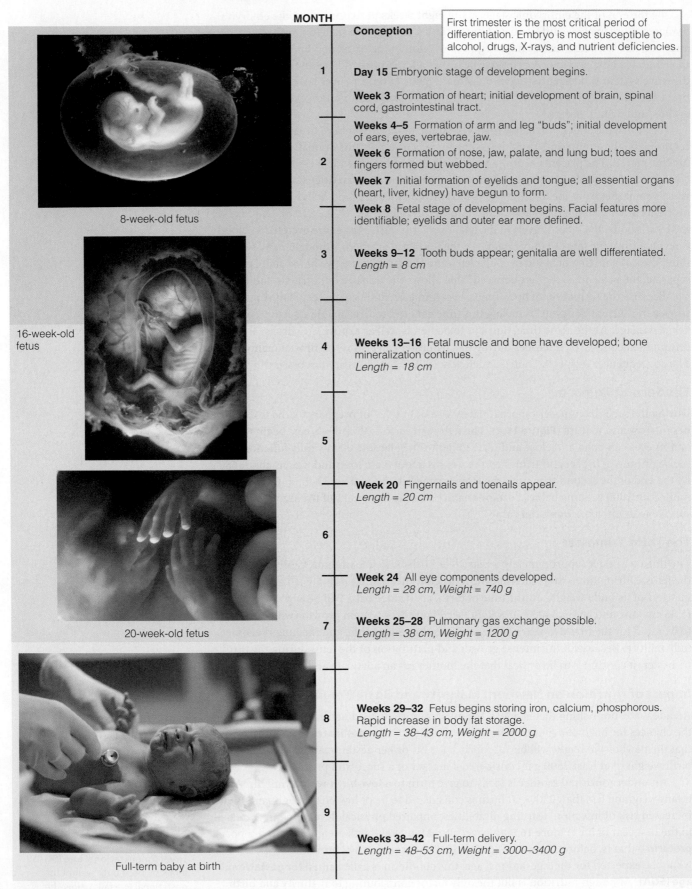

MONTH

Conception

> First trimester is the most critical period of differentiation. Embryo is most susceptible to alcohol, drugs, X-rays, and nutrient deficiencies.

1

Day 15 Embryonic stage of development begins.

Week 3 Formation of heart; initial development of brain, spinal cord, gastrointestinal tract.

Weeks 4–5 Formation of arm and leg "buds"; initial development of ears, eyes, vertebrae, jaw.

2

Week 6 Formation of nose, jaw, palate, and lung bud; toes and fingers formed but webbed.

Week 7 Initial formation of eyelids and tongue; all essential organs (heart, liver, kidney) have begun to form.

Week 8 Fetal stage of development begins. Facial features more identifiable; eyelids and outer ear more defined.

3

Weeks 9–12 Tooth buds appear; genitalia are well differentiated. *Length = 8 cm*

8-week-old fetus

4

Weeks 13–16 Fetal muscle and bone have developed; bone mineralization continues. *Length = 18 cm*

16-week-old fetus

5

Week 20 Fingernails and toenails appear. *Length = 20 cm*

6

Week 24 All eye components developed. *Length = 28 cm, Weight = 740 g*

7

Weeks 25–28 Pulmonary gas exchange possible. *Length = 38 cm, Weight = 1200 g*

20-week-old fetus

8

Weeks 29–32 Fetus begins storing iron, calcium, phosphorous. Rapid increase in body fat storage. *Length = 38–43 cm, Weight = 2000 g*

9

Weeks 38–42 Full-term delivery. *Length = 48–53 cm, Weight = 3000–3400 g*

Full-term baby at birth

Figure 16.4 A timeline of embryonic and fetal development.

RecaP

A full-term pregnancy lasts from 38 to 42 weeks and is traditionally divided into trimesters lasting 13 to 14 weeks. During the first trimester, cells differentiate and divide rapidly to form the various tissues of the human body. The fetus is especially susceptible to nutrient deficiencies, toxicities, and teratogens during this time. The second and third trimesters are characterized by continued growth and maturation. Nutrition is important before and throughout pregnancy to support fetal development without depleting the mother's reserves. An adequate, nourishing diet increases the chance that a baby will be born after 37 weeks and will weigh at least 2500 g.

How Much Weight Should a Pregnant Woman Gain?

Recommendations for weight gain vary according to a woman's weight *before* she became pregnant (Table 16.1) and whether the pregnancy is singleton (one fetus) or multiple (two or more fetuses). Health Canada has adopted the 2009 U.S. Institute of Medicine (IOM) recommendations for gestational weight gain for singleton pregnancies.[4] As you can see in Table 16.1, the average recommended weight gain for women of normal prepregnancy weight is 11.5 to 16 kg; underweight women should gain a little more than this amount, and overweight and obese women should gain somewhat less.[5] Adolescents should follow the same recommendations as those for adults. Women of normal prepregnancy weight who are pregnant with twins are advised to gain 17 to 25 kg.[5]

Women who have a low prepregnancy BMI (<18.5) or gain too little weight during their pregnancy increase their risk of having a preterm or low-birth-weight baby and of dangerously depleting their own nutrient reserves. Gaining *too much* weight during pregnancy or being overweight (BMI ≥25) or obese (BMI ≥30) prior to conception is also risky. Excessive prepregnancy weight or prenatal gain increases the risk that the fetus will be large for his or her gestational age, and large babies have an increased risk of trauma during vaginal delivery and of Cesarean birth. Also, children born to overweight or obese mothers have higher rates of childhood obesity[6] and childhood metabolic syndrome.[7] A high birth weight has also been linked to increased risk of adolescent obesity. In addition, the more weight gained during pregnancy, the more difficult it is for the mother to return to her prepregnancy weight and the more likely it is that her weight gain will be permanent. This weight retention can become especially problematic if the woman has two or more children; the extra weight also increases her long-term risk for type 2 diabetes and high blood pressure.

In addition to the amount of weight, the *pattern* of weight gain is important. During the first trimester, a woman of normal weight should gain between 0.5 and 2 kg in the first trimester. During the second and third trimester, an average of about 0.4 kg a week is considered healthy for normal-weight women. For overweight women, a gain of 0.3 kg/week is appropriate, and obese women should gain 0.2 kg/week.[5] If weight gain is excessive in a single week, month, or trimester, the woman should not attempt to lose weight. Dieting during pregnancy can harm the health of both mother and fetus by depriving them of critical nutrients. Instead, the woman should merely attempt to slow the rate of weight gain. On the other hand, if a woman has not gained sufficient weight in the early months of her

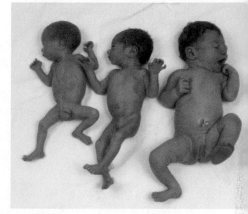

Figure 16.5 A healthy two-day-old infant (right) compared with two low-birth-weight infants.

Table 16.1 Recommended Weight Gain for Women During Pregnancy[5]

Prepregnancy Weight Status	Body Mass Index (kg/m2)	Recommended Total Weight Gain (kg)
Normal	18.5–24.9	11.5–16
Underweight	<18.5	12.5–18
Overweight	25.0–29.9	7–11.5
Obese	≥30	5–9

Following a physician-approved exercise program helps pregnant women maintain a positive body image and prevents excess weight gain.

pregnancy, she should gradually increase her energy and nutrient intake. The newborns of women who lose weight during the first trimester, due to severe nausea and vomiting, for example, are likely to be of lower birth weight than newborns of women with appropriate weight gain.[8] If inappropriately low maternal weight gain occurs, the woman should not attempt to "catch up" all at once; rather, she should gradually increase her rate of weight gain. In short, weight gain throughout pregnancy should be slow and steady.

In a society obsessed with thinness, it is easy for pregnant women to worry about weight gain. Focusing on the quality of food consumed, rather than the quantity, can help women feel more in control. In addition, following a physician-approved exercise program helps women maintain a positive body image and prevent excessive weight gain.

A pregnant woman may also feel less anxious about her weight gain if she understands how that weight is distributed. Of the total weight gained in pregnancy, 4.5 to 5.5 kg are accounted for by the fetus itself, the amniotic fluid, and the placenta (**Figure 16.6**). Another 1.5 to 2 kg represents an increase of 40% to 50% in maternal blood volume. A woman can expect to be about 4.5 to 5.5 kg lighter immediately after the birth and, within about two weeks, another 2.5 to 3.5 kg lighter because of fluid loss (from plasma and interstitial fluid).

After the first two weeks, losing the remainder of pregnancy weight requires that more energy be expended than is taken in. Appropriate physical activity can help women lose those extra pounds. Also, because production of breast milk requires significant energy, breastfeeding helps many new mothers lose the remaining weight. Moderate weight reduction is safe while breastfeeding and will not compromise the weight gain of the nursing infant.[9] We discuss breastfeeding on pages 598–606.

RecaP

Sufficient calories should be consumed so that a pregnant woman gains an appropriate amount of weight, typically 11.5 to 16 kg, to ensure adequate growth of the fetus. The calories consumed during pregnancy should be nutrient-dense so that both the mother and the fetus obtain the nutrients they need from food.

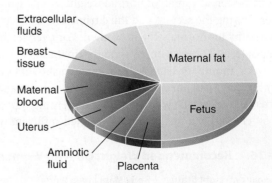

Figure 16.6 The weight gained during pregnancy is distributed between the mother's own tissues and the pregnancy-specific tissues.

What Are a Pregnant Woman's Nutrient Needs?

The requirements for nearly all nutrients increase during pregnancy to accommodate the growth and development of the fetus without depriving the mother of the nutrients she needs to maintain her own health. With the exception of iron, most women can meet these increased needs by carefully selecting foods high in nutrient density. *Eating Well with Canada's Food Guide* is a useful tool that reinforces the concepts of adequacy, balance, and variety in food choices; it also suggests food patterns across the three trimesters of pregnancy.

Macronutrient Needs of Pregnant Women

In pregnancy, macronutrients provide necessary energy for building tissue. They are also the very building blocks for the fetus, as well as for the mother's pregnancy-associated tissues.

Energy   Given what you've just learned about pregnancy weight gain, you've probably figured out that energy requirements increase only modestly during pregnancy. In fact, during the first trimester, a woman should consume approximately the same number of kilocalories daily as during her non-pregnant days. Instead of eating more, she should attempt to maximize the nutrient density of what she eats. For example, drinking low-fat milk or calcium-fortified soy milk is preferable to drinking soft drinks. Low-fat milk and fortified soy milk provide valuable protein, vitamins, and minerals to feed the fetus's rapidly dividing cells, whereas soft drinks provide nutritionally empty calories.

During the last two trimesters of pregnancy, energy needs increase by about 350 to 450 kcal/day. For a woman normally consuming 2000 kcal/day, an extra 400 kcal represents only a 20% increase in energy intake, a goal that can be met more easily than many pregnant women realize. For example, 175 mL of low-fat yogourt and a bran muffin is about 400 kcal. At the same time, some vitamin and mineral needs increase by as much as 50%—so again, the key for getting adequate micronutrients while not consuming too many extra calories is choosing nutrient-dense foods.

If a woman maintains a safe and physician-approved program of regular moderate physical activity, she will be able to consume more kilocalories without worrying about excessive weight gain. Walking, swimming, yoga, bicycling, and other low-stress aerobic activities are all healthy for pregnant women. As further discussed on page 597, experts recommend pregnant women engage in 30 to 40 minutes of moderate physical activity on most, if not all, days. Pregnant women should avoid exercising in hot and humid weather or if any type of discomfort occurs. During exercise, pregnant women need to drink plenty of water and other fluids because they are at high risk for dehydration and overheating. If a woman has led a sedentary lifestyle prior to her pregnancy, she should not begin a program of vigorous physical activity while pregnant but should consult her physician or nurse practitioner for an appropriate exercise program and plan for a more challenging program after the birth.

Protein   During pregnancy, protein needs increase to about 1.1 grams per day per kilogram of body weight over the entire nine-month period.[10] This is an increase of 25 g of protein per day. One half of a turkey (50 g) and cheese (25 g) sandwich would provide the extra 25 g of protein. For a pregnant woman weighing approximately 64.5 kg, the total recommended intake would average 71 g per day. Keep in mind that many women already eat this much protein each day. Dairy products, meats, fish, poultry, eggs, and soy products are all rich sources of protein, as are legumes, nuts, and seeds.

Carbohydrate   Pregnant women are advised to aim for a carbohydrate intake of at least 175 g per day.[10] All pregnant women should be counselled on the potential hazards of very-low-carbohydrate diets. Glucose is the primary metabolic fuel of the developing fetus; thus, pregnant women need to consume healthy sources of carbohydrate throughout the day. The recommended intake will also prevent ketosis (discussed on page 252) and help maintain normal blood glucose levels. Additional carbohydrate may be needed to support daily physical activity.

Meats provide complete protein, which is essential for building and maintaining maternal and fetal tissues.

The recommendation of 175 g is easily met by consuming a balanced diet. The majority of carbohydrate intake should come from whole foods, such as whole-grain breads and cereals, brown rice, fruits, vegetables, and legumes. Not only are these carbohydrate-rich foods good sources of micronutrients such as the B-vitamins, but they also contain a lot of fibre, which can help prevent constipation. Fibre-rich foods contribute to one's sense of fullness and can be a boon to women who need to be careful not to gain too much weight.

Fat   The guideline for the percentage of daily calories that comes from fat does not change during pregnancy.[10] Pregnant women should be aware that because new tissues and cells are being built, adequate consumption of dietary fat is even more important than in the non-pregnant state. In addition, during the third trimester, the fetus stores most of its own body fat, which is a critical source of fuel in the newborn period. Without adequate fat stores, newborns cannot effectively regulate their body temperature.

Consumption of the right kinds of fats is important. Like anyone else, pregnant women should limit their intakes of saturated and *trans* fats because of their negative impact on cardiovascular health (as discussed in Chapter 5). Poly- and monounsaturated fats should be chosen whenever possible. The omega-3 polyunsaturated fatty acid *docosahexaenoic acid (DHA)* has been found to be uniquely critical for both neurologic and eye development. Because the fetal brain grows dramatically during the third trimester, DHA is especially important in the maternal diet. Good sources of DHA are oily fish such as anchovies, mackerel, salmon, and sardines. It is also found in lesser amounts in tuna, chicken, and eggs (some eggs are DHA-enhanced by feeding hens a DHA-rich diet). *Eating Well with Canada's Food Guide* recommends that Canadians consume at least 150 g of cooked fish each week as part of a healthy eating pattern (as discussed in Chapter 2), and that women continue this practice during pregnancy.

Pregnant women who eat fish should be aware of the potential for mercury contamination, as even a limited intake of mercury during pregnancy can impair a fetus's developing nervous system. To minimize mercury exposure from fish, Health Canada has issued specific advice for women who are or may become pregnant to limit their intake of tuna (fresh and frozen), shark, swordfish, marlin, orange roughy, and escolar to no more than 150 grams per month. Further, women are encouraged to limit their intake of canned (white) albacore tuna to no more than 300 grams per week. This advice does not apply to canned light tuna as it contains other species of tuna such as skipjack, yellowfin, and tongol, which are low in mercury.[11]

Micronutrient Needs of Pregnant Women

The need for micronutrients increases during pregnancy because of the expansion of the mother's blood supply and growth of the uterus, placenta, breasts, body fat, and the fetus itself. In addition, the increased need for energy during pregnancy correlates with an increased need for micronutrients involved in the metabolism of macronutrients and ATP production. Discussions about the micronutrients most critical during pregnancy follow. Refer to Table 16.2 for an overview of the changes in micronutrient needs with pregnancy.

Folate   Because folate is necessary for cell division, it follows that during a time when both maternal and fetal cells are dividing rapidly, the requirement for this vitamin would be increased. Adequate folate is especially critical during the first 28 days after conception, when it is required for the formation and closure of the **neural tube**, an embryonic structure that eventually becomes the brain and spinal cord. Folate deficiency is associated with neural tube defects such as **spina bifida** (**Figure 16.7**) and **anencephaly**, a fatal defect in which there is partial absence of brain tissue.[12] Adequate folate intake does not guarantee normal neural tube development, as the precise cause of neural tube defects is unknown, and, in some cases, there is a genetic component. It is estimated, however, that up to 70% of all neural tube defects could be prevented by simply improving maternal intake of folic acid or folate.[13]

neural tube Embryonic tissue that forms a tube, which eventually becomes the brain and spinal cord.

spina bifida Embryonic neural tube defect that occurs when the spinal vertebrae fail to completely enclose the spinal cord, allowing it to protrude.

anencephaly A fatal neural tube defect in which there is partial absence of brain tissue most likely caused by failure of the neural tube to close.

Table 16.2 Changes in Nutrient Recommendations with Pregnancy for Adult Women

Micronutrient	Pre-pregnancy	Pregnancy	% Increase
Folate	400 µg/day	600 µg/day	50
Vitamin B$_{12}$	2.4 µg/day	2.6 µg/day	8
Vitamin C	75 mg/day	85 mg/day	13
Vitamin A	700 µg/day	770 µg/day	10
Vitamin D	15 µg/day	15 µg/day	0
Calcium	1000 mg/day	1000 mg/day	0
Iron	18 mg/day	27 mg/day	50
Zinc	8 mg/day	11 mg/day	38
Sodium	1500 mg/day	1500 mg/day	0
Iodine	150 µg/day	220 µg/day	47

To reduce the risk of a neural tube defect, all women capable of becoming pregnant are encouraged to consume 400 µg of folic acid per day from supplements, fortified foods, or both in addition to a variety of foods naturally high in folates. The emphasis on obtaining folic acid from supplements and fortified foods is due to the higher bioavailability of these sources. Of course, folate remains very important even after the neural tube has closed. The RDA for folate for pregnant women is therefore 600 µg/day, a full 50% increase over the RDA for a non-pregnant female.[12] A deficiency of folate during pregnancy can result in macrocytic anemia (a condition in which blood cells do not mature properly) and has been associated with low birth weight, preterm delivery, and failure of the fetus to grow properly. Sources of food folate are discussed on page 464 and include orange juice, green leafy vegetables such as spinach and broccoli, and lentils. For more than a decade, Health Canada has mandated that all enriched grain products such as cereals, breads, and pastas be fortified with folic acid; thus, including these foods, ideally as whole grains, in the daily diet can further increase folate intake. Since the introduction of mandatory fortification, there has been a reported 50% reduction in neural tube defects in Canada.[14]

Spinach is an excellent source of folate.

Vitamin B$_{12}$ Vitamin B$_{12}$ (cobalamin) is vital during pregnancy because it regenerates the active form of folate. Not surprisingly, deficiencies of vitamin B$_{12}$ can also result in

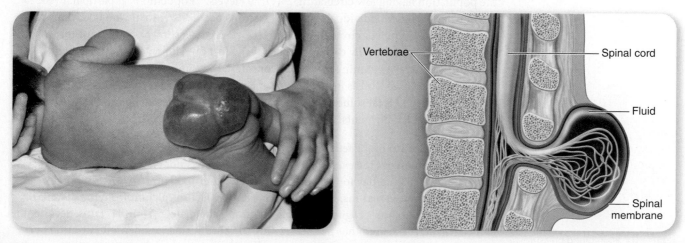

(a) (b)

Figure 16.7 Spina bifida, a common neural tube defect. (a) An external view of an infant with spina bifida. (b) An internal view of the protruding spinal membrane and fluid-filled sac.

macrocytic anemia. Yet the RDA for vitamin B_{12} for pregnant women is only 2.6 μg/day, a mere 8% increase over the RDA of 2.4 μg/day for non-pregnant women.[12] How can this be? One reason is that during pregnancy, absorption of vitamin B_{12} is more efficient. The required amount of vitamin B_{12} can easily be obtained from animal food sources such as meats, dairy products, and eggs. However, deficiencies have been observed in women who have followed a vegan diet for several years; these deficiencies have also been observed in the infants of some mothers who follow a vegan diet. Fortified foods or supplementation provides these women with the needed amounts of vitamin B_{12}.

Vitamin C   Because blood plasma volume increases during pregnancy, and because vitamin C is being transferred to the fetus, the concentration of vitamin C in maternal blood decreases. Vitamin C deficiency during pregnancy has been associated with an increased risk of premature birth and other complications. The RDA for vitamin C during pregnancy is increased by a little more than 10% over the RDA for non-pregnant women (from 75 mg to 85 mg per day for adult pregnant women; 65 mg to 80 mg per day for pregnant adolescents). Women who smoke during pregnancy should consume even higher levels of vitamin C, because smoking lowers both serum and amniotic fluid levels. As described on page 374, many foods are rich sources of vitamin C, such as citrus fruits and juices, peppers, and numerous other fruits and vegetables.

Vitamin A   Vitamin A needs increase during pregnancy by about 10%, to 770 μg per day for adult pregnant women and 750 μg per day for pregnant adolescents. Vitamin A deficiency during pregnancy has been linked to an increased risk of low birth weight, growth problems, and preterm delivery. However, excess preformed vitamin A exerts teratogenic effects. Consumption of excessive preformed vitamin A, particularly during the first trimester, increases the risk for birth of an infant with craniofacial malformations, including cleft lip or palate, heart defects, and abnormalities of the central nervous system.[15] A well-balanced diet supplies sufficient vitamin A, so supplementation during pregnancy is not recommended. Note that provitamin A, in the form of beta-carotene (which is converted to vitamin A in the body), has not been associated with birth defects.

Vitamin D   Despite the role of vitamin D in calcium absorption, the RDA for this nutrient does not increase during pregnancy. According to the Institute of Medicine, the amount of vitamin D transferred from the mother to the fetus is relatively small and does not appear to affect overall vitamin D status.[16] However, pregnant women with poor vitamin D status do have an increased risk of **pre-eclampsia**, impaired fetal growth, and fetal bone defects.[17] There is strong evidence of widespread vitamin D deficiency in Canada, with over 70% of the population having low circulating 25(OH)D levels.[18] Populations at particular risk include dark skinned individuals and First Nations peoples. Women who take vitamin D supplements have higher circulating 25(OH)D levels, suggesting an important role for supplementation, especially during pregnancy.[19] Most prenatal vitamin supplements contain 10 μg/day of vitamin D, which is considered safe and acceptable, although some researchers view that level as inadequate for maintaining normal serum levels of vitamin D.[16] Because vitamin D is fat soluble, pregnant women should avoid consuming excessive vitamin D from supplements, as toxicity can cause developmental disability in the newborn.

Calcium   Growth of the fetal skeleton requires as much as 30 g of calcium, most during the last trimester. However, the RDA for calcium does not change during pregnancy; it remains at 1300 mg/day for pregnant adolescents and 1000 mg/day for adult pregnant women for two reasons. First, pregnant women absorb calcium from the diet more efficiently than do non-pregnant women, assuming adequate vitamin D status. Second, the extra demand for calcium has not been found to cause permanent demineralization of the mother's bones or to increase fracture risk; thus, there is no justification for recommending higher intakes.[16] Sources of calcium are discussed on pages 415–416. Pregnant women who are lactose intolerant can meet their calcium requirements by consuming calcium-fortified

pre-eclampsia High blood pressure that is pregnancy-specific and accompanied by protein in the urine, edema, and unexpected weight gain.

soy milk, rice milk, juices, cereals, reduced-lactose milk, and low-lactose dairy foods such as yogourt and aged cheeses.

Iron Recall from Chapter 13 the importance of iron in the formation of red blood cells, which transport oxygen throughout the body so that cells can produce ATP. During pregnancy, the demand for red blood cells increases to accommodate the needs of the expanded maternal blood volume, growing uterus, placenta, and the fetus itself. Thus, more iron is needed. Fetal demand for iron increases even further during the last trimester, when the fetus stores iron in the liver for use during the first few months of life. This iron storage is protective because breast milk is low in iron. Women of childbearing age who may become pregnant are encouraged to eat foods high in heme iron, such as meat, fish, and poultry, and/or consume iron-rich plant foods, such as legumes, or iron-fortified foods with vitamin C–rich foods.[9]

Severely inadequate iron intake certainly has the potential to harm the fetus, resulting in an increased rate of low birth weight, preterm birth, stillbirth, and death of the newborn in the first weeks after birth. However, in most cases, the iron-deprived fetus builds adequate stores by "robbing" maternal iron, resulting in iron-deficiency anemia in the mother. During pregnancy, maternal iron deficiency causes extreme paleness and exhaustion, but at birth it endangers the mother's life: anemic women are more likely to die during or shortly after childbirth because they are less able to tolerate blood loss and fight infection.

The RDA for iron during pregnancy is 27 mg per day, compared with 18 mg per day for non-pregnant women and 15 mg per day for non-pregnant adolescents.[15] This represents a 50% to 80% increase, despite the fact that iron loss is minimized during pregnancy because menstruation ceases. Typically, women of childbearing age have poor iron stores, and the demands of pregnancy are likely to produce deficiency. To ensure adequate iron stores during pregnancy, an iron supplement (as part of, or separate from, a total prenatal supplement) is routinely prescribed during the last two trimesters. Vitamin C enhances iron absorption, as do dietary sources of heme iron, whereas substances in coffee, tea, milk, bran, and oxalate-rich foods decrease absorption. Therefore, many healthcare providers recommend taking iron supplements with foods high in vitamin C and/or heme iron. Sources of iron are discussed on page 452.

Zinc The RDA for zinc for adult pregnant women increases by about 38% over the RDA for non-pregnant adult women, from 8 mg per day to 11 mg per day, and the RDA increases from 9 mg per day to 12 mg per day for pregnant adolescents.[15] Because zinc has critical roles in DNA, RNA, and protein synthesis, it is extremely important that adequate zinc status be maintained during pregnancy to ensure proper growth and development of both maternal and fetal tissues. Inadequate zinc can lead to fetal malformations, premature birth, decreased birth size, and extended labour. It should be noted that the absorption of zinc from supplements is inhibited by high intakes of non-heme iron, such as those found in iron supplements, when these two minerals are taken with water.[20] However, when food sources of iron and zinc are consumed together in a meal, absorption of zinc is not affected, largely because the amount of iron in the meal is not high enough to block zinc uptake. Good dietary sources of zinc include red meats, shellfish, and fortified cereals; other sources of zinc are discussed on page 458.

Sodium and Iodine During pregnancy, the AI for sodium is the same for a non-pregnant adult woman, or 1500 mg (1.5 g) per day.[21] Although too much sodium is associated with fluid retention and bloating, as well as high blood pressure, increased body fluids are a normal and necessary part of pregnancy, so some sodium is necessary to maintain fluid balance.

Iodine needs increase significantly during pregnancy, but the RDA of 220 μg per day is easy to achieve by using a modest amount of iodized salt (sodium chloride) during cooking.[15] Sprinkling salt onto food at the table is unnecessary; a balanced, healthy diet will provide all the iodine needed during pregnancy.

It is important that pregnant women drink about 2.3 L of fluid a day.

Do Pregnant Women Need Supplements?

Prenatal multivitamin and mineral supplements are not strictly necessary during pregnancy, but most healthcare providers recommend them. Meeting all the nutrient needs would otherwise take careful and somewhat complex dietary planning. Prenatal supplements are especially good insurance for vegans, adolescents, and others whose diets might normally be low in one or more micronutrients. It is important that pregnant women understand, however, that supplements are to be taken *in addition to,* not as a substitute for, a nutrient-rich diet.

Fluid Needs of Pregnant Women

Fluid plays many vital roles during pregnancy. It allows for the necessary increase in the mother's blood volume, acts as a lubricant, aids in regulating body temperature, and is necessary for many metabolic reactions. Fluid that the mother consumes also helps maintain the **amniotic fluid** that surrounds, cushions, and protects the fetus in the uterus. The AI for total fluid intake, which includes drinking water, beverages, and food, is 3 litres per day. This recommendation includes approximately 2.3 litres of fluid as total beverages, including drinking water.[21]

Drinking adequate fluid helps combat two common discomforts of pregnancy: fluid retention and, possibly, constipation. Drinking lots of fluids (and going to the bathroom as soon as the need is felt) will also help prevent **urinary tract infections**, which are common in pregnancy. Fluids also combat dehydration, which can develop if a woman with morning sickness has frequent bouts of vomiting. For these women, fluids such as soups, juices, and sports beverages are usually well tolerated and can help prevent dehydration.

Recap

Protein, carbohydrates, and fats provide the building blocks for fetal growth. Folate deficiency has been associated with neural tube defects. Most healthcare providers recommend prenatal supplements for pregnant women to ensure that sufficient micronutrients such as iron are consumed. Fluid provides for increased maternal blood volume and amniotic fluid.

Nutrition-Related Concerns for Pregnant Women

Pregnancy-related conditions involving a particular nutrient, such as iron-deficiency anemia, have already been discussed. The following sections describe some of the most common discomforts and disorders of pregnant women that are related to their general nutrition.

Morning Sickness

Morning sickness, or *nausea and vomiting of pregnancy* (NVP), is gaining recognition as a potentially serious medical condition.[22] It can vary from occasional mild queasiness to constant nausea with bouts of vomiting. In truth, "morning sickness" is not an appropriate name because the nausea and vomiting can begin at any time of the day and may last all day. NVP usually resolves by week 12 to 16 and the mother and fetus do not suffer lasting harm. However, some women experience such frequent vomiting that they require hospitalization or in-home intravenous (IV) therapy. There is no cure for morning sickness. However, here are some practical tips for reducing the severity:

- Eat small, frequent meals and snacks throughout the day. An empty stomach can trigger nausea.
- Consume most of the day's fluids between meals. Frozen ice pops, watermelon, gelatin desserts, and mild broths are often well-tolerated sources of fluid.
- Keep snacks such as crackers at the bedside to ease nighttime queasiness or to eat before rising.
- Prenatal supplements should be taken at a time of day when vomiting is least likely.

amniotic fluid The watery fluid contained within the innermost membrane of the sac containing the fetus. It cushions and protects the growing fetus.

urinary tract infection A bacterial infection of the urethra, the tube leading from the bladder to the body exterior.

morning sickness Varying degrees of nausea and vomiting associated with pregnancy, most commonly in the first trimester.

- Avoid sights, sounds, smells, and tastes that bring on or worsen queasiness. Cold or room-temperature foods are often better tolerated than hot foods.
- For some women, alternative therapies such as acupuncture, acupressure wrist bands, biofeedback, meditation, and hypnosis help. Women should always check with their healthcare provider to ensure that the therapy they are using is safe and does not interact with other medications or supplements.

Cravings and Aversions

It seems as if nothing is more stereotypical about pregnancy than the image of a frazzled husband getting up in the middle of the night to run to the convenience store to get his pregnant wife some pickles and ice cream. This image, although humorous, is far from reality. Although some women have specific cravings, most crave a particular type of food (such as "something sweet" or "something salty") rather than a particular food.

Why do pregnant women crave certain tastes? Does a desire for salty foods mean that the woman is experiencing a sodium deficit? Although there may be some truth to the assertion that we crave what we need, scientific evidence for this claim is lacking.

Most cravings are, of course, for edible substances. But a surprising number of pregnant women crave non-foods like laundry starch, chalk, and clay. This craving, called **pica**, may result in nutritional or health problems for the mother and fetus.

Food aversions are also common during pregnancy and may originate from social, cultural, or religious beliefs. In some cultures, for example, women would traditionally avoid shellfish ("it causes allergies") or duck ("child will be born with webbed feet"). Such aversions and taboos are often strongly woven into the family's belief system.[23]

Deep-fried foods are often unappealing to pregnant women.

Heartburn

Heartburn, along with indigestion, is common during pregnancy. Pregnancy-related hormones relax lower esophageal smooth muscle, increasing the incidence of heartburn. During the last two trimesters, the enlarging uterus pushes up on the stomach, compounding the problem. Practical tips for minimizing heartburn during pregnancy include the following:

- Avoid excessive weight gain.
- Eat small, frequent meals and chew food slowly.
- Don't wear tight clothing.
- Wait for at least one hour after eating before lying down.
- Sleep with your head elevated.
- Ask your healthcare provider to recommend an antacid that is safe for use during pregnancy.

Constipation

Hormone production during pregnancy causes the smooth muscles to relax, including the muscles of the large intestine, slowing colonic movement of food residue. In addition, pressure exerted by the growing uterus on the colon can slow movement even further, making elimination difficult. Practical hints that may help a woman avoid constipation include the following:

Consuming foods high in fibre, such as dried fruits, may reduce the chances of constipation.

- Include 25 to 35 g of fibre in the daily diet, concentrating on fresh fruits and vegetables, dried fruits, legumes, and whole grains.
- Keep fluid intake high as fibre intake increases. Drink plenty of water and eat water-rich fruits and vegetables such as melons, citrus, and lettuce.
- Keep physically active, as exercise is one of many factors that help increase motility of the large intestine.

Pregnant women should use over-the-counter fibre supplements only as a last resort and should not use any laxative product without first discussing it with their healthcare provider.

pica An abnormal craving to eat something not fit for food, such as clay, paint, and so forth.

Gestational Diabetes Mellitus

In Canada, the incidence of **gestational diabetes mellitus (GDM)** is higher than previously thought, varying from 3.7% in non-Aboriginal women to 8%–18% in Aboriginal women.[24] GDM is usually a temporary condition in which a pregnant woman is unable to produce sufficient insulin or becomes insulin resistant, and thus develops elevated levels of blood glucose. Fortunately, GDM has no ill effects on either the mother or the fetus if blood glucose levels are strictly controlled through diet, physical activity, and/or medication. Screening for GDM is routine for almost all healthcare practitioners and is necessary because several of the symptoms, which include frequent urination, fatigue, and an increase in thirst and appetite, can be indistinguishable from normal pregnancy symptoms. If uncontrolled, GDM can result in a baby who is too large as a result of receiving too much glucose across the placenta during fetal life. Infants who are overly large are at risk for early birth and trauma during vaginal birth, and may need to be born by Cesarean section. There is also evidence that exposing a fetus to maternal diabetes significantly increases the risk for type 2 diabetes and overweight later in life.[25, 26]

Women who are obese, women who are age 35 years or older, women who have a family history of diabetes, and women who are of Aboriginal, African, or Hispanic origin have a greater risk of developing GDM, as do women who previously delivered a large-for-gestational-age infant. Any woman who develops GDM has a 35% to 60% risk of developing type 2 diabetes within the next 10 to 20 years—particularly if she is obese to begin with or fails to maintain normal body weight after pregnancy.[27] As with any type of diabetes, attention to diet, weight control, and physical activity reduces the risk of GDM.

Hypertensive Disorders in Pregnancy

About 6% of Canadian pregnancies are complicated by some form of hypertension, or high blood pressure.[28] The term *hypertensive disorders in pregnancy* encompasses several different conditions.[29] A woman who develops high blood pressure, with no other symptoms, during the pregnancy is said to have *gestational hypertension*. Pre-eclampsia is characterized by a sudden increase in maternal blood pressure during pregnancy with the presence of swelling, excessive and rapid weight gain unrelated to food intake, and protein in the urine. If left untreated, it can progress to eclampsia, a condition characterized by seizures and kidney failure and, if untreated, fetal and/or maternal death.

No one knows exactly what causes the various hypertensive disorders in pregnancy, but women who are pregnant for the first time, adolescents, over the age of 35 to 40 years, African, diabetic, or from a low-income background, as well as those who have a family history of eclampsia, are at greater risk.[30] Deficiencies in dietary protein, vitamin C, vitamin E, calcium, and magnesium also seem to increase the risk. Management of pre-eclampsia focuses mainly on blood pressure control. Typical treatment includes bed rest and medical oversight. Ultimately, the only thing that will cure the condition is childbirth. Today, with good prenatal care, gestational hypertension is nearly always detected early and can be appropriately managed, and prospects for both mother and fetus are usually very good. In nearly all women without prior chronic high blood pressure, blood pressure returns to normal within about a day or so after the birth.

Adolescent Pregnancy

Throughout the adolescent years, a girl's body is still changing and growing. Peak bone mass has not yet been reached. Full physical stature may not have been attained, and teens are more likely to be underweight than are young adult women. Thus, pregnant adolescents have higher nutrient needs for calories and bone-related nutrients such as calcium, phosphorous, and magnesium. In addition, many adolescents have not established healthy dietary patterns. Inadequate maternal weight gain, poor prenatal care, and higher rates of prenatal alcohol and drug use contribute to higher rates of preterm births, low-birthweight babies, and other complications.[31]

Pregnant women have their blood pressure measured to screen for pregnancy-related hypertension.

gestational diabetes mellitus (GDM) Insufficient insulin production or insulin resistance that results in consistently high blood glucose levels, specifically during pregnancy; condition typically resolves after birth occurs.

With adequate and thorough prenatal care and close attention to proper nutrition and other healthy behaviours, the likelihood of a positive outcome for both the adolescent mother and infant is greatly increased.

Vegetarianism

With the possible exception of iron and zinc, vegetarian women who consume dairy products and eggs (lacto-ovo-vegetarians) have no nutritional concerns beyond those encountered by every pregnant woman. In contrast, women who are vegan (consume no animal products) need to be more vigilant than usual about their intake of nutrients that are derived primarily or wholly from animal products. These include vitamin D (unless regularly exposed to sunlight throughout the pregnancy), vitamin B_6, vitamin B_{12}, calcium, iron, and zinc. Supplements containing these nutrients are usually necessary.[32, 33] A regular prenatal supplement will fully meet the vitamin, iron, and zinc needs of a vegan woman but does not fulfill calcium needs, so a separate calcium supplement, or consumption of calcium-fortified soy milk or orange juice, is usually required.

Consumption of Caffeine

Caffeine, a stimulant found in coffee, tea, soft drinks, and some foods, crosses the placenta and thus reaches the fetus. Current thinking holds that women who consume less than about 200 mg of caffeine per day (the equivalent of 250–300 mL of coffee) are very likely doing no harm to the fetus. Evidence suggests that consuming higher daily doses of caffeine (the higher the dose, the more compelling the evidence) may slightly increase the risk of miscarriage and impair fetal growth.[34–36] It is sensible, then, for pregnant women to limit daily caffeine intake to no more than the equivalent of 500 mL of coffee.

Another reason for avoiding coffee and soft drinks during pregnancy is that they can make one feel full and provide considerable calories (if sweetened). If a pregnant woman retains a very strong desire for coffee, she might try a low- or non-fat decaf café latte, which offers a healthier nutrient profile than coffee alone.

Consumption of Alcohol

Alcohol is a known teratogen that readily crosses the placenta and accumulates in the fetal bloodstream. The immature fetal liver cannot readily metabolize alcohol, and its presence in fetal blood and tissues is associated with a variety of birth defects. These effects are dose-dependent: the more the mother drinks, the greater the potential harm to the fetus.

Heavy drinking (greater than three to four drinks per day) throughout pregnancy can result in the birth of a baby with fetal alcohol spectrum disorder (FASD). These infants have a high mortality rate, and, as we saw with Theresa in our opening vignette, those who survive typically face lifelong emotional, behavioural, social, and learning problems. Another consequence is fetal alcohol effects (FAE), a milder set of alcohol-related abnormalities. These include developmental and behavioural problems (for example, hyperactivity, attention deficit disorder, and impaired cognition) and possibly physical abnormalities.[37] See highlight on next page for additional information on FASD.

In addition to FASD and FAE, frequent drinking (more than seven drinks per week) or occasional binge drinking (more than four to five drinks on one occasion) during pregnancy increases the risk for spontaneous abortion, complications during delivery, low birth weight, and sudden infant death syndrome.

Although some pregnant women do have the occasional alcoholic drink with no apparent ill effects, there is no amount of alcohol that is known to be safe. The best advice regarding alcohol during pregnancy is to abstain, if not from before conception, then as soon as pregnancy is suspected.[37, 38, 39]

Smoking

Despite the well-known consequences of cigarette smoking and the growing social stigma associated with smoking during pregnancy, more than 10% of pregnant women smoke, and the rate is even higher among adolescents.[40]

Maternal smoking is extremely harmful to the fetus.

HIGHLIGHT

Fetal Alcohol Spectrum Disorder

Health Canada estimates that almost 3000 babies are born each year with some type of alcohol-related defect.[39] Alcohol is a known teratogen (a substance that causes fetal harm) that readily crosses the placenta into the fetal bloodstream. Because the immature fetal liver cannot effectively break down the alcohol, it accumulates in the fetal blood and tissues, increasing the risk for various birth defects. The effects of maternal alcohol intake are dose related: the more the mother drinks, the greater the potential harm to the fetus. In addition to the amount of alcohol consumed during pregnancy, the timing of the mother's alcohol intake influences the risk of fetal complications. Binge or frequent drinking during the first trimester of pregnancy is more likely to result in birth defects and other permanent abnormalities, whereas alcohol consumption in the third trimester typically results in low birth weight and growth retardation.

Fetal alcohol spectrum disorder (FASD) is a condition characterized by malformations of the face, limbs, heart, and nervous system. The characteristic facial features persist throughout the child's life. Exposure to alcohol while in the womb impairs fetal growth; FASD babies are often underweight at birth and rarely normalize their growth after birth. Newborn and infant death rates are abnormally high, and those who do survive suffer from emotional, behavioural, social, learning, and developmental

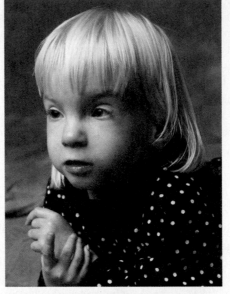

A child with fetal alcohol spectrum disorder (FASD). The facial features typical of children with FASD include a short nose with a low, wide bridge; drooping eyes with an extra skinfold; and a flat, thin upper lip. These external traits are typically accompanied by behavioural problems and learning disorders. The effects of FASD are irreversible.

problems throughout life. FASD is one of the most common causes of mental retardation in Canada and the only one that is completely preventable.

Fetal alcohol effects (FAE) are a more subtle set of consequences related to maternal alcohol intake. While usually not identified at birth, this condition often becomes evident when the child enters preschool or kindergarten. The child may exhibit attention deficit/hyperactivity disorder, or impaired learning abilities. It is estimated that the incidence of FAE is 10 times greater than that of FASD.

Can a pregnant woman safely consume any amount of alcohol? Although some pregnant women do have an occasional alcoholic drink with no apparent ill effects, there is no amount of alcohol known to be safe. In one recent study, researchers identified a number of subtle but long-term negative consequences of light to moderate alcohol consumption during pregnancy: children of women who had as little as one alcoholic drink a week during their pregnancy were more aggressive and more likely to engage in delinquent behaviours compared to children who had no fetal exposure to alcohol. The best advice regarding alcohol intake during pregnancy is to abstain if there is any chance of becoming pregnant, as well as throughout the pregnancy.

---

fetal alcohol spectrum disorder (FASD) A set of serious, irreversible alcohol-related birth defects characterized by certain physical and mental abnormalities.

fetal alcohol effects (FAE) A milder set of alcohol-related birth defects characterized by behavioural problems such as hyperactivity, attention deficit disorder, poor judgment, sleep disorders, and delayed learning.

Maternal smoking exposes the fetus to toxins such as lead, cadmium, cyanide, nicotine, and carbon monoxide. Fetal blood flow is reduced, which limits the delivery of oxygen and nutrients, resulting in impaired fetal growth and development. Maternal smoking greatly increases risk of miscarriage, stillbirth, placental abnormalities, intrauterine growth retardation, preterm delivery, and low birth weight. Rates of sudden infant death syndrome, overall neonatal mortality (within the first 28 days of life), respiratory illnesses, and allergies are higher in the infants and children of smokers compared with non-smokers.

Illicit Drugs

Despite the fact that illicit drug use during pregnancy is a concern in Canada, prevalence data is scarce.[41] Most drugs pass through the placenta into the fetal blood, where they accumulate in fetal tissues and organs, including the liver and brain.

Drugs such as marijuana, cocaine, heroin, ecstasy, and amphetamines all pose similar risks: impaired placental blood flow (thus, reduced transfer of oxygen and nutrients to the fetus) and higher rates of low birth weight, premature delivery, placental defects, and miscarriage. Newborns suffer signs of withdrawal including tremors, excessive crying, sleeplessness, and poor feeding. Even after several years, children born to women who used illicit drugs during pregnancy are at greater risk for developmental delays, impaired learning, and behavioural problems.[41]

All women are strongly advised to stop taking drugs before becoming pregnant. There is no safe level of use for illicit drugs during pregnancy.

Food Safety

Health Canada recommends that pregnant women avoid raw or partially cooked eggs, raw or undercooked meat/fish/poultry, raw sprouts, and unpasteurized juices and milk.[42] Soft cheeses such as Brie, feta, Camembert, and Roquefort, should be avoided unless the label specifically states the product is made with pasteurized milk. Unpasteurized milk and cheeses may be contaminated with the bacterium *Listeria monocytogenes*, which triggers miscarriage, premature birth, or fetal infection.

Processed meats may also pose a risk to pregnant women; Health Canada recommends that deli meats should be heated until steaming (74°C) prior to consumption.

Exercise

Physical activity during pregnancy is recommended for women experiencing normal pregnancies.[43] Exercise can help keep a woman physically fit during pregnancy, enhance mood, and help women feel more in control of their changing bodies. Moderate exercise during pregnancy will reduce the risk of gestational diabetes, help keep blood pressure down, and reduce the risks for pre-eclampsia.[44, 45] Regular exercise can also lessen lower back pain[46] and shorten the duration of active labour.

If a woman was not active prior to pregnancy, she should begin an exercise program slowly and progress gradually under the guidance of her healthcare provider. If a woman was physically active before pregnancy, she can continue to be physically active during pregnancy, within comfort and reason. Walking, the most common activity among pregnant women, is an excellent low-impact exercise.[47] Hiking, swimming, and water aerobics are also excellent choices. Women who have been avid runners before pregnancy can often continue to run, as long as they feel comfortable. However, they should probably limit the distance and intensity of their runs as the pregnancy progresses.

During pregnancy, women should adjust their physical activity to comfortable low-impact exercises.

RECAP

About half of all pregnant women experience morning sickness, and many crave or feel aversions to specific types of foods. Heartburn and constipation in pregnancy are related to hormonal relaxation of smooth muscle. Gestational diabetes mellitus and hypertensive disorders can seriously affect maternal and fetal well-being. The nutrient needs of pregnant adolescents are so high that adequate nourishment becomes difficult. Women who follow a vegan diet usually need to consume multivitamin and mineral supplements, plus supplemental calcium, during pregnancy. Caffeine intake should be limited; and use of alcohol, cigarettes, and illicit drugs should be completely avoided during pregnancy. Safe food-handling practices are especially important during pregnancy. Exercise (provided the mother has no contraindications) can enhance the health of a pregnant woman.

CASE STUDY ▶ Eating During Pregnancy

Marie-Eve just discovered that she is pregnant. Starting a family is very important to her and her partner, Francois, and they are thrilled with the news. Marie-Eve weighs 55 kg and is 160 cm tall. She has always been active, walking to and from work most days, and biking and swimming on weekends. She loves to cook, and tries to eat healthily by following Canada's Food Guide. She drinks occasionally, a glass of wine with Francois when they go out to dinner two or three times a month.

Marie-Eve wants to have the best possible outcome for this pregnancy.

Thinking Critically

1. **How much weight should Marie-Eve gain throughout her pregnancy? How should she adjust her diet to accommodate this gain?**
2. **Should Marie-Eve give up eating fish while she is pregnant? Why or why not?**
3. **Marie-Eve's doctor prescribed a prenatal supplement. Explain which nutrients the supplement should contain and in what amounts.**
4. **Marie-Eve heard that many pregnant women suffer from heartburn and constipation. What advice would you give her to avoid these problems?**

Lactation: Nutrition for Breastfeeding Mothers

Throughout most of human history, infants have thrived on only one food: breast milk. During the first half of the 20th century, commercially prepared infant formulas slowly began to replace breast milk as the mother's preferred feeding method. Aggressive marketing campaigns promoting formula as more nutritious than breast milk convinced many families, even in developing nations, to switch. Soon formula-feeding had become a status symbol, proof of the family's wealth and modern thinking.

In the 1970s, this trend began to reverse with a renewed appreciation for the natural simplicity of breastfeeding. At the same time, several international organizations, including the World Health Organization, UNICEF, and La Leche League, began to promote the nutritional, immunologic, financial, and emotional advantages of breastfeeding and developed programs to encourage and support breastfeeding worldwide.

These efforts have paid off. In 2006, 90% of new mothers in Canada initiated breastfeeding in the hospital, an all-time high, and almost 54% of mothers were still breastfeeding their babies at six months of age.[48] Worldwide, slightly more than half of all women breastfeed *exclusively* for at least six months; however, this value is significantly lower in Canada, where only 15% of children are breastfed exclusively at six months of age. Breastfeeding initiation rates in Canada vary across provinces with the highest rates, over 96%, in British Columbia and the Yukon Territory and the lowest rates, 72% and 76% in Prince Edward Island and Newfoundland and Labrador, respectively.[48]

How Does Lactation Occur?

Lactation, the production of breast milk, is a process that is set in motion during pregnancy in response to several hormones. Once established, lactation can be sustained as long as the mammary glands continue to receive the proper stimuli.

The Body Prepares During Pregnancy

Throughout pregnancy, the placenta produces estrogen and progesterone. In addition to performing various functions to maintain the pregnancy, these hormones physically prepare the breasts for lactation. The breasts increase in size, and milk-producing glands

lactation The production of breast milk.

(alveoli) and milk ducts are formed (**Figure 16.8**). Toward the end of pregnancy, the hormone **prolactin** increases. Prolactin is released by the anterior pituitary gland and is responsible for milk synthesis. However, estrogen and progesterone suppress the effects of prolactin during pregnancy.

What Happens After Childbirth?

By the time a pregnancy has come to full term, the level of prolactin is about 10 times higher than it was at the beginning of pregnancy. At birth, the suppressive effect of estrogen and progesterone ends, and prolactin is free to stimulate milk production. The first substance to be released from the breasts for intake by the newborn is **colostrum**, sometimes called premilk or first milk. It is thick, yellowish in colour, rich in protein, and includes antibodies that help protect the newborn from infection. It is also relatively high in vitamins and minerals. Colostrum also contains a factor that fosters the growth of "friendly" bacteria in the infant's GI tract. These bacteria in turn prevent the growth of other bacteria that could potentially be harmful. Finally, colostrum has a laxative effect in infants, helping the infant to expel *meconium,* the sticky "first stool."

Within two to four days, colostrum is fully replaced by mature milk. Mature breast milk contains protein, fat, and carbohydrate (as the sugar lactose).

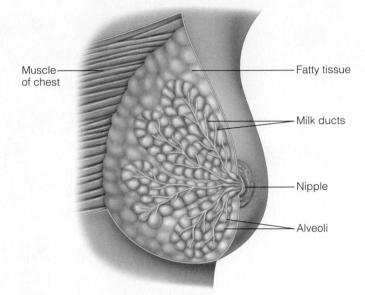

Figure 16.8 Anatomy of the breast. During pregnancy, estrogen and progesterone secreted by the placenta foster the preparation of breast tissue for lactation. This process includes breast enlargement and development of the milk-producing glands, or alveoli. *Data from:* Germann, W. and Stanfield, C. Principles of Human Physiology, 2/e, Fig. 22.26a, Copyright © 2004 Benjamin Cummings. Reprinted by permission of Pearson Education, Inc.

Mother–Infant Interaction Maintains Milk Production

Continued, sustained breast milk production depends entirely on infant suckling (or a similar stimulus like a mechanical pump). Infant suckling stimulates the continued production of prolactin, which in turn stimulates more milk production. The longer and more vigorous the feeding, the more milk will be produced. Thus, even twins and triplets can be successfully breastfed.

Prolactin allows for milk to be produced, but that milk has to move through the milk ducts to the nipple to reach the baby's mouth. The hormone responsible for this "let-down" of milk is **oxytocin**. Like prolactin, oxytocin is produced by the pituitary gland and its production is dependent on the suckling stimulus at the beginning of a feeding (**Figure 16.9**). This response usually occurs within 10 to 30 seconds but can be inhibited by stress. Finding a relaxed environment in which to breastfeed is therefore important. Many women experience let-down in response to other cues, such as hearing a baby cry, or even thinking about their infant.

What Are a Breastfeeding Woman's Nutrient Needs?

You might be surprised to learn that breastfeeding requires even more energy and nutrients than pregnancy! This is because breast milk has to supply an adequate amount of all of the nutrients an infant needs to grow and develop.

Energy and Macronutrient Recommendations for Breastfeeding Women

It is estimated that milk production requires about 700 to 800 kcal/day. It is generally recommended that lactating women aged 19 years and above consume 330 kcal/day above their prepregnancy energy needs during the first six months of breastfeeding and 400 additional kcal/day during the second six months.[10] This additional energy is sufficient to support adequate milk production. At the same time, the remaining energy deficit will assist in the gradual loss of excess body weight gained during pregnancy. It is critical that

prolactin A hormone responsible for milk synthesis.

colostrum The first fluid made and secreted by the breasts from late in pregnancy to about a week after birth. It is rich in immune factors and protein.

oxytocin A hormone responsible for the "let-down" of milk.

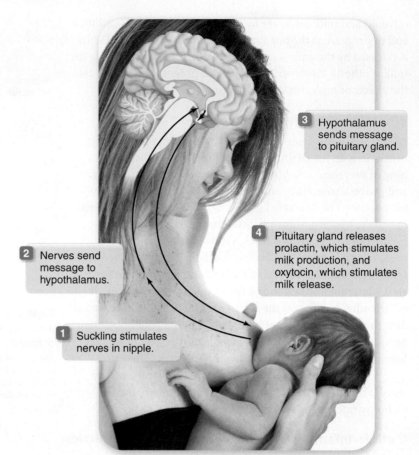

3 Hypothalamus sends message to pituitary gland.

4 Pituitary gland releases prolactin, which stimulates milk production, and oxytocin, which stimulates milk release.

2 Nerves send message to hypothalamus.

1 Suckling stimulates nerves in nipple.

Figure 16.9 Sustained milk production depends on the mother–child interaction during breastfeeding, specifically the suckling of the infant. Suckling stimulates the continued production of prolactin, which is responsible for milk production, and also oxytocin, which is responsible for the let-down response.

lactating women avoid severe energy restriction, as this practice can result in decreased milk production.

The weight loss that occurs during breastfeeding should be gradual, approximately 0.5 to 2 kg per month. Participating in regular physical activity can assist with weight loss; neither occasional nor regular exercise negatively affect a woman's ability to successfully breastfeed.[9] There are, however, some active women who may lose too much weight during breastfeeding and must either increase their energy intake or reduce their activity level to maintain health and milk production.

A lactating woman's needs for carbohydrate and protein increase over pregnancy requirements. Increases of 25 g of protein per day and 80 g of carbohydrate per day above prepregnancy requirements are recommended.[10] Women who breastfeed also need good dietary sources of DHA to support the rapid brain growth that occurs during the first three months of life. The DHA in the mother's diet is incorporated into the breast milk, to the benefit of the infant.

Micronutrient Recommendations for Breastfeeding Women

Micronutrient requirements for several vitamins and minerals increase over the requirements of pregnancy. These include vitamins A, C, E, riboflavin, vitamin B_{12}, biotin, and choline, and the minerals copper, chromium, manganese, iodine, selenium, and zinc. The requirement for folate during lactation is 500 μg/day, which is decreased from the 600 μg/day required during pregnancy but is higher than prepregnancy needs (400 μg/day).[12]

Requirements for iron decrease significantly during lactation, to a mere 9 mg/day. This is because iron is not a significant component of breast milk and breastfeeding usually suppresses menstruation for at least a few months, minimizing iron losses.[15]

Calcium is a significant component of breast milk; however, as in pregnancy, calcium absorption is enhanced during lactation and urinary loss of calcium is decreased. In addition, some calcium appears to come from the demineralization of the mother's bones, and increased dietary calcium does not prevent this. Thus, the recommended intake for calcium for a lactating woman is unchanged from pregnancy and non-pregnant guidelines: 1000 mg/day. Because of their own continuing growth, however, teen mothers who are breastfeeding should continue to consume 1300 mg/day.[16] Typically, if calcium intake is adequate, a woman's bone density returns to normal shortly after lactation ends.

Do Breastfeeding Women Need Supplements?

If a breastfeeding woman appropriately increases her energy intake, and does so with nutrient-dense foods, her nutrient needs can usually be met without supplements. *Eating Well with Canada's Food Guide* provides recommendations for food choices for women who are exclusively or partially breastfeeding their infants. However, there is nothing wrong with taking a basic multivitamin, as long as it is not considered a substitute for proper nutrition. Lactating women should consume omega-3 fatty acids either in fish or supplements to increase breast-milk levels of DHA. Women who do not consume dairy products should monitor their calcium intake carefully and may need supplements.

Fluid Recommendations for Breastfeeding Women

Because extra fluid is expended with every feeding, lactating women need to consume about an extra 1 litre of fluid per day. The AI for total water is 3.8 litres per day for breastfeeding women, including about 3 litres of beverages.[21] This extra fluid enhances milk production and reduces the risk of dehydration. Many women report that within a minute or two of beginning to nurse their baby, they become intensely thirsty. To prevent this thirst and achieve the recommended fluid intake, women are encouraged to drink a nutritious beverage (water, juice, milk, and so forth) each time they nurse their baby. However, it is not good practice to drink hot beverages while nursing because accidental spills could burn the infant.

RECaP

Lactation is the result of the coordinated effort of several hormones. Breasts are prepared for lactation during pregnancy, and infant suckling provides the stimulus that sustains the production of prolactin and oxytocin needed to maintain the milk supply. It is recommended that lactating women consume extra energy above prepregnancy guidelines, including increased protein, certain vitamins and minerals, and fluids. The requirements for folate and iron decrease from pregnancy levels, while the requirement for calcium remains the same. If nutrient intake is inadequate, milk production will decline and the woman will produce a smaller volume of breast milk.

Getting Real About Breastfeeding: Advantages and Challenges

Breastfeeding is recognized as the preferred method of infant feeding because of the nutritional value and health benefits of human milk.[49] However, the technique does require patience and practice, and teaching from an experienced mother or certified lactation consultant is important. La Leche League International is an advocacy group for breastfeeding: its Canadian website (www.lllc.ca), publications, and local meetings are all valuable resources for breastfeeding mothers and their families. Many Public Health Units offer lactation classes for their members, and some hospitals, designated as "Baby Friendly," have adopted policies that enhance lactation success.[50] See highlight on next page for additional information on supports for breastfeeding mothers.

Breastfeeding has benefits for the mother and infant.

HIGHLIGHT

Finding Support for Breastfeeding Moms

Although a natural process, the art of breastfeeding for many women takes a fair amount of education, support, and practice. Fortunately, women today have more opportunities to learn "the art of breastfeeding" than ever before.

Prenatal classes—that is, classes held before the birth—are one such opportunity. Typically taught by certified nurse practitioners, midwives, or other childbirth specialists, these classes provide essential information—including information about breastfeeding—to parents-to-be. In many communities, special breastfeeding classes are offered by certified lactation consultants or other maternity healthcare providers to help women who plan to breastfeed for the first time or who want to improve upon a previous breastfeeding experience.

Many hospitals and birthing centres also now provide breastfeeding support. Hospitals can seek the designation "Baby Friendly" based on the World Health Organization/UNICEF Baby-Friendly Hospital Initiative, meaning their facilities have shown that they have adopted certain practices to support successful breastfeeding. Some of those practices include:[51]

- Having a written breastfeeding policy communicated to all healthcare staff
- Informing all pregnant women about the benefits and management of breastfeeding
- Helping mothers initiate breastfeeding within a half-hour of birth and helping them to maintain lactation
- Giving newborn infants no food or drink other than breast milk, unless medically indicated
- Practising rooming-in to encourage breastfeeding on demand
- Fostering the establishment of breastfeeding support groups and referring mothers to them on discharge from the hospital or clinic

Unfortunately, as of 2011, there were fewer than 40 Baby Friendly hospitals and clinics in Canada, a discouragingly low number.[50] A current list can be found at www.breastfeedingcanada.ca. Even without this credential, however, many hospitals and clinics are much more proactive in supporting breastfeeding than in years past.

La Leche League International (see the end-of-chapter Web Links) is a worldwide organization dedicated to supporting breastfeeding mothers. La Leche League offers local meetings and conferences, as well as books, CDs, podcasts, online forums, and other materials to help pregnant women and new moms succeed in breastfeeding. However, its most significant contribution may be the free in-home visits offered by experienced members to help women establish or maintain breastfeeding and troubleshoot problems. La Leche League also offers resources for moms of multiples (twins, triplets, and so on), premature infants, or special-healthcare-need babies, as well as materials for working mothers and those who want to provide their infants with breast milk even though they themselves can't nurse. Resources are now available in dozens of different languages, providing education and support to millions of women in Canada and across the globe. Other grassroots organizations provide additional assistance to breastfeeding women and their babies.

To help families identify qualified lactation consultants, groups such as IBLCE, the International Board of Lactation Consultant Examiners, develop and administer certification examinations. When searching for a qualified lactation consultant, parents-to-be can thus confirm a candidate's professional qualifications.

In some communities, local mothers serve as *doulas*, knowledgeable, experienced lay companions who stay with the new mom and family through labour, birth, and beyond, often supporting the breastfeeding process. While these women may not have academic or professional credentials, they are typically well known and respected within the local community.

Advantages of Breastfeeding

As adept as formula manufacturers have been at simulating components of breast milk, an exact replica has never been produced. In addition, there are other benefits that mother and baby can access only through breastfeeding.

Nutritional Superiority of Breast Milk The amount and types of proteins in breast milk are ideally suited to the human infant. The main protein in breast milk, lactalbumin, is easily digested in infants' immature GI tracts, reducing the risk of gastric distress. Other proteins in breast milk bind iron and prevent the growth of harmful bacteria that require iron. Antibodies from the mother are additional proteins that help prevent infection while the infant's immune system is still immature. Certain proteins in human milk improve the absorption of iron; this is important because breast milk is low in iron. Cow's milk contains too much protein for infants, and the types of protein in cow's milk are harder for the infant to digest.

The primary carbohydrate in breast milk is lactose; its galactose component is important in nervous system development. Lactose provides energy and prevents ketosis in the infant, promotes the growth of beneficial bacteria, and increases the absorption of calcium. Breast milk has more lactose than cow's milk.

The amounts and types of fat in breast milk are ideally suited to the human infant. DHA and arachidonic acid (ARA) have been shown to be essential for the growth and development of the infant's nervous system and for development of the retina of the eyes. Until 2003, these fatty acids were omitted from commercial infant formulas in Canada, although they have been available in formulas in other parts of the world for the better part of a decade. Interestingly, the concentration of DHA in breast milk varies considerably, is sensitive to maternal diet, and is highest in women who consume large quantities of fish.[52, 53]

The fat content of breast milk, which is higher than that of whole cow's milk, changes according to the gestational age of the infant and during the course of every feeding: the milk that is initially released (called *foremilk*) is watery and low in fat, somewhat like skim milk. This milk is thought to satisfy the infant's initial thirst. As the feeding progresses, the milk acquires more fat and becomes more like whole milk. Finally, the very last 5% or so of the milk produced during a feeding (called the *hindmilk*) is very high in fat, similar to cream. This milk is thought to satiate the infant. It is important to let infants suckle for at least 20 minutes at each feeding so that they get this hindmilk. Breast milk is also relatively high in cholesterol, which supports the rapid growth and development of the brain and nervous system.

Another important aspect of breastfeeding (or any type of feeding) is the fluid it provides the infant. Because of their small size, infants are at risk of dehydration, which is one reason why feedings must be consistent and frequent. This topic will be discussed at greater length in the section on infant nutrition.

In terms of micronutrients, breast milk is a good source of readily absorbed calcium and magnesium. It is low in iron, but the iron it does contain is easily absorbed. Because healthy full-term infants store iron in preparation for the first few months of life, most experts agree that their iron needs can be met by breast milk alone for the first six months, after which iron-rich foods are needed. Although breast milk has some vitamin D, the Canadian Paediatric Society recommends that all breastfed infants be provided with a vitamin D supplement.[54]

Some breastfed babies refuse to take a bottle.

Breast milk composition continues to change as the infant grows and develops. Because of this ability to change as the baby changes, breast milk alone is entirely sufficient to sustain infant growth for the first six months of life. Throughout the next six months of infancy, as solid foods are gradually introduced, breast milk remains the baby's primary source of superior-quality nutrition. The Canadian Paediatric Society encourages exclusive breastfeeding (no food or other source of sustenance) for the first six months of life, continuing breastfeeding for at least the first year of life and, if acceptable within the family unit, into the second year of life.[55]

Protection from Infections and Allergies   Immune factors from the mother, including antibodies and immune cells, are passed directly from the mother to the newborn through breast milk. These factors provide important disease protection for the infant while its immune system is still immature. It has been shown that breastfed infants have a lower incidence of respiratory tract, gastrointestinal tract, and ear infections than formula-fed infants.[56] Even a few weeks of breastfeeding is beneficial, but the longer a child is breastfed, the greater the level of passive immunity from the mother. In Canada, breastfeeding has the potential to lower healthcare costs in part because of a reduction in infant mortality rates in breastfed infants.[49, 57]

In addition, breast milk is non-allergenic, and breastfeeding is associated with a reduced risk of allergies during childhood and adulthood. Breastfed babies also die less frequently from **sudden infant death syndrome (SIDS)** and have a decreased chance of developing diabetes, overweight and obesity, hypercholesterolemia, and chronic digestive disorders.[49]

Physiologic Benefits for Mother   Breastfeeding causes uterine contractions that quicken the return of the uterus to prepregnancy size and reduce bleeding. Many women also find that breastfeeding helps them lose the weight they gained during pregnancy, particularly if it continues for more than six months. In addition, breastfeeding appears to be associated with a decreased risk for breast cancer.[56, 58] The relationship between breastfeeding and osteoporosis is still unclear and more research on this topic is needed.[56, 59, 60]

Breastfeeding also suppresses ovulation, lengthening the time between pregnancies and giving a mother's body the chance to recover before she conceives again. This benefit can be life-saving for malnourished women living in countries that discourage or outlaw the use of contraceptives. Ovulation may not cease completely, however, so it is still possible to become pregnant while breastfeeding. Healthcare providers typically recommend use of additional birth control methods while breastfeeding to avoid another conception occurring too soon to allow a mother's body to recover from the earlier pregnancy.

Mother–Infant Bonding   Breastfeeding is among the most intimate of human interactions. Ideally, it is a quiet time away from distractions when mother and baby begin to develop an enduring bond of affection known as *attachment*. Breastfeeding enhances attachment by providing the opportunity for frequent, direct skin-to-skin contact, which stimulates the baby's sense of touch and is a primary means of communication.[2] The cuddling and intense watching that occur during breastfeeding begin to teach the mother and baby about the other's behavioural cues. Breastfeeding also reassures the mother that she is providing the best possible nutrition for her baby. Healthcare providers now recommend that hospitals permit continuous rooming-in of breastfed infants throughout the day and night to enhance the initiation and continuation of breastfeeding.[49, 61]

Undoubtedly, bottle-feeding does not preclude parent–infant attachment! As long as attention is paid to closeness, cuddling, and skin contact, bottle-feeding can foster bonding as well.

Convenience and Cost   Breast milk is always ready, clean, at the right temperature, and available on demand, whenever and wherever it's needed. In the middle of the night, when the baby wakes up hungry, a breastfeeding mother can respond almost instantaneously, and both are soon back to sleep. In contrast, formula-feeding is a time-consuming process: parents have to continually wash and sterilize bottles, and each batch of formula must be mixed and heated to the proper temperature.

In addition, breastfeeding costs nothing other than the price of a modest amount of additional food for the mother. In contrast, formula can be relatively expensive, and there are the additional costs of bottles and other supplies, as well as the cost of energy used for washing and sterilization. A hidden cost of formula-feeding is its effect on the environment: the energy used and waste produced during formula manufacturing, marketing, shipping and distribution, preparation, and disposal of used packaging. In contrast, breastfeeding is environmentally responsible, using no external energy and producing no external wastes.

Challenges Associated with Breastfeeding

For some women and infants, breastfeeding is easy from the very first day. Others experience some initial difficulty, but with support from an experienced nurse, lactation consultant, or volunteer mother from La Leche League, the experience becomes successful and

sudden infant death syndrome (SIDS) The sudden death of a previously healthy infant; the most common cause of death in infants older than one month of age.

pleasurable. Some families, however, encounter difficulties that make formula-feeding their best choice. This section discusses some challenges that may impede the success of breastfeeding.

Effects of Drugs and Other Substances on Breast Milk

Many substances, including illicit, prescription, and over-the-counter drugs, pass into breast milk. Breastfeeding mothers should inform their physicians that they are breastfeeding. If a safe and effective form of the necessary medication cannot be found, the mother will have to avoid breastfeeding while she is taking the drug. During this time, she can pump and discard her breast milk so that her milk supply will be adequate when she resumes breastfeeding.

Caffeine and alcohol also enter breast milk. Caffeine can make the baby agitated and fussy, whereas alcohol can make the baby sleepy, depress the central nervous system, and slow motor development, in addition to inhibiting the mother's milk supply. Breastfeeding women should abstain from alcohol in the early stages of lactation since it easily passes into the breast milk at levels equal to blood alcohol concentrations. Nicotine also passes into breast milk; therefore, it is best for the woman to quit smoking altogether.

Environmental contaminants, including pesticides, industrial solvents, and heavy metals such as lead and mercury, can pass into breast milk when breastfeeding mothers are exposed to these chemicals.[62] Mothers can limit their infants' exposure to these harmful substances by controlling their environment. Fresh fruits and vegetables should be thoroughly washed and peeled to minimize exposure to pesticides and fertilizer residues. Exposure to solvents, paints, gasoline fumes, furniture strippers, and similar products should also be limited. Even with some exposure to these environmental contaminants, Canadian and international health agencies all agree that the benefits of breastfeeding almost always outweigh potential concerns.[63, 64]

Food components that pass into the breast milk may seem innocuous; however, some substances, such as those found in garlic, onions, peppers, broccoli, and cabbage, are distasteful enough to the infant to prevent proper feeding. Some babies have allergic reactions to foods the mother ate, such as wheat, cow's milk, eggs, or citrus, and suffer gastrointestinal upset, diaper rash, or another reaction. The offending foods must then be identified and avoided.

Maternal HIV Infection and Other Diseases

HIV, which causes AIDS, can be transmitted from mother to baby through breast milk. Thus, HIV-positive women in the United States and Canada are encouraged to feed their infants formula.[65] This recommendation does not apply to all women worldwide, however, because the low cost and sanitary nature of breast milk, as compared to the high cost and potential for waterborne diseases with formula-feeding, often make exclusive breastfeeding the best choice for women in developing countries.[65]

Conflict Between Breastfeeding and the Mother's Employment

Breast milk is absorbed more readily than formula, making more frequent feedings necessary. Newborns commonly require breastfeedings every one to three hours versus every two to four hours for formula-feedings. Mothers who are exclusively breastfeeding and return to work within the first six months after the baby's birth must leave several bottles of pumped breast milk for others to feed the baby in their absence each day. This means that working women have to pump their breasts to express the breast milk during the work day. This can be a challenge in companies that do not provide the time, space, and privacy required.

Work-related travel is also a concern: if the mother needs to be away from home for longer than 24 to 48 hours, she can typically pump and freeze enough breast milk for others to give the baby in her absence. When longer business trips are required, some mothers bring the baby with them and arrange for childcare at their destination.

Working moms can be discouraged from breastfeeding in various ways.

Others resort to pumping, freezing, and shipping breast milk home via overnight mail. Understandably, many women cite returning to work as the reason they switch to formula-feeding.[66]

Some working women successfully combine breastfeeding with commercial formula. For example, a woman might breastfeed in the morning before she leaves for work, as soon as she returns home, and once again before retiring at night. The remainder of the feedings are formula given by the infant's father or a childcare provider. Women who choose supplemental formula feedings usually find that their bodies adapt quickly to the change and produce ample milk for the remaining breastfeedings.

Social Concerns In North America, women have occasionally been insulted or otherwise harassed for breastfeeding in public. In the past decade, however, both social customs and provincial laws have become more accommodating for nursing mothers. For example, separate nursing rooms can often be found in public buildings such as shopping malls. Some provinces (Ontario and British Columbia) have passed legislation preserving a woman's right to breastfeed in public. When women feel free to breastfeed in public, the baby's feeding schedule becomes much less confining.

What About Bonding for Fathers and Siblings?

With all the attention given to attachment between a breastfeeding mother and infant, it is easy for fathers and siblings to feel left out. One option that allows other family members to participate in infant feeding is to supplement breastfeedings with bottle-feedings of stored breast milk or formula. If a family decides to share infant feeding in this manner, bottle-feedings can begin as soon as breastfeeding has become well established. That way, the mother's milk supply will be established, and the infant will not become confused by the artificial nipple. Fathers and other family members can also bond with the infant when bathing and/or dressing the infant as well as through everyday cuddling and play.

Fathers and siblings can bond with infants through bottle-feeding.

Breastfeeding provides many benefits to both mother and newborn, including superior nutrition, heightened immunity, mother–infant bonding, convenience, and cost. However, breastfeeding may not be the best option for every family. The mother may need to use a medication that enters the breast milk and makes it unsafe for consumption. A mother's job may interfere with the baby's requirement for frequent feedings. The infant's father and siblings can participate in feedings using a bottle filled with either pumped breast milk or formula.

Infant Nutrition: From Birth to One Year

Most first-time parents are amazed at how rapidly their infant grows and develops. Optimal nutrition is extremely important during the first year, as the baby's organs and nervous system continue to develop and mature and as the baby grows physically and acquires new skills. In fact, physicians use length and weight measurements as the main tools for assessing an infant's nutritional status. These measurements are plotted on growth charts (there are separate charts for boys and girls), which track an infant's growth over time (**Figure 16.10**).

During the first year of life, breast milk remains the food of choice; however, iron-fortified formula is an acceptable substitute for those families who have decided that breastfeeding is not an option. After approximately six months, most infants are ready for *complementary* foods, which provide key nutrients and introduce the infant to new tastes

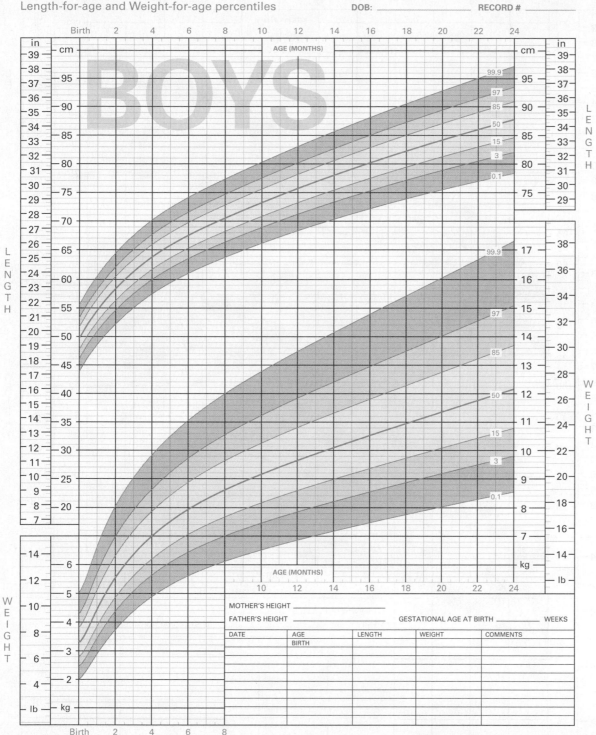

WHO GROWTH CHARTS FOR CANADA

BOYS

BIRTH TO 24 MONTHS: BOYS
Length-for-age and Weight-for-age percentiles

NAME: _____

DOB: _____ RECORD # _____

Figure 16.10a These weight-for-age growth charts are used by healthcare practitioners to monitor and assess the growth of an infant/toddler from birth to 24 months.
Data from: World Health Organization (WHO) Child Growth Standards (2006) and WHO Reference (2007) adapted for Canada by Dietitians of Canada, Canadian Paediatric Society, the College of Family Physicians of Canada, and Community Health Nurses of Canada ©2010. Dietitians of Canada. All rights reserved.

BIRTH TO 24 MONTHS: GIRLS
Length-for-age and Weight-for-age percentiles

NAME: _____

DOB: _____ RECORD # _____

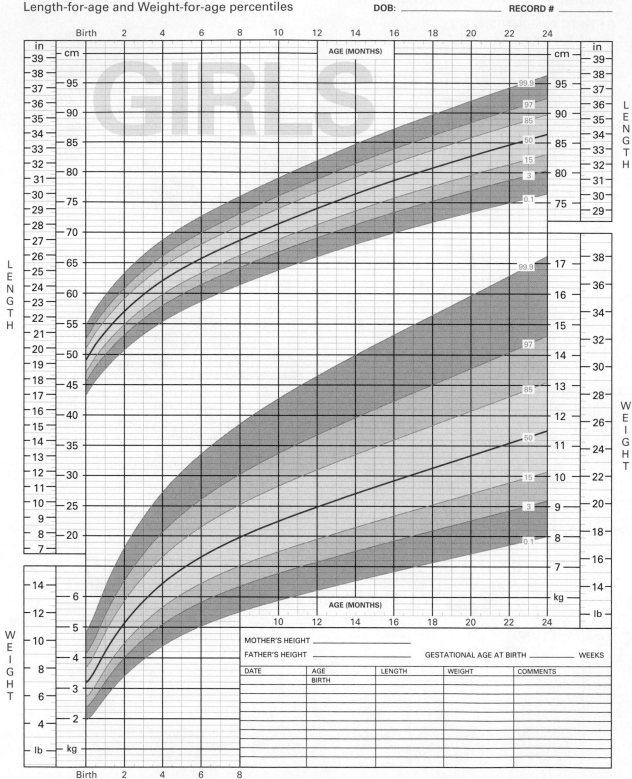

SOURCE: Based on the World Health Organization (WHO) Child Growth Standards (2006) and adapted for Canada by Dietitians of Canada, Canadian Paediatric Society, the College of Family Physicians of Canada and Community Health Nurses of Canada.

Figure 16.10b *(Continued)*
Data from: World Health Organization (WHO) Child Growth Standards (2006) and WHO Reference (2007) adapted for Canada by Dietitians of Canada, Canadian Paediatric Society, the College of Family Physicians of Canada, and Community Health Nurses of Canada ©2010. Dietitians of Canada. All rights reserved.

and textures. An infant who is lovingly and consistently fed when hungry will feel secure and well cared for. A relaxed, consistent feeding relationship between parent and child fosters a positive and healthy outlook toward food. In many ways, an infant's diet during his or her first year of life "sets the stage" for future health and development.

Typical Infant Growth and Activity Patterns

In the first year of life, an infant generally grows about 25 cm in length and triples in weight—a growth rate more rapid than will ever occur again. To support this phenomenal growth, energy needs per unit of body weight are also the highest they will ever be, approximately triple that of adults. Energy needs are also very high because the basal metabolic rates of babies are high (**Figure 16.11**). This is in part because the body surface area of a baby is large compared with its body size, increasing its loss of body heat. Still, the limited physical activity of a baby keeps total energy expenditure relatively low.

For the first few months of life, an infant's activities consist mainly of eating and sleeping. As the first year progresses, the range of activities gradually expands to include rolling over, sitting up, crawling, standing, and finally taking the first few wobbly steps. As shown in Figure 16.11, the relative need for energy to support growth slows during the second six months of life, just as activity begins to increase.

Growth charts, one set for girls and one set for boys, are routinely used by healthcare providers and parents to track growth. They are available from Dietitians of Canada free of charge. Charts for children from birth to 24 months assess length-for-age, weight-for-age, and weight-for-length, all expressed as percentiles. If an infant is in the 90th percentile for length, he or she is longer than 89% of infants of that age and gender and thus is considered very long. If an infant is in the 10th percentile for weight, only 10% of infants of the same age and gender weigh less than he or she does, so that baby can be viewed as relatively underweight compared with other infants. Although every infant is unique, in general, healthcare providers look for a close correlation between length and weight rankings. In other words, an infant who is in the 60th percentile for length is usually in about the 50th to 70th percentile for weight. A child in the 50th percentile for length but the 5th percentile for weight may be malnourished. Consistency over time is also a consideration: for example, an infant who suddenly drops well below her established profile for weight might be underfed or ill. BMI-for-age charts for children over 24 months of age have also been developed.

Although growth charts are effective tools for assessing an infant's nutrition status, there are some limitations. For example, it is important to consider the physical stature of the baby's parents. If both parents are tall, you would expect the infant to remain close to the upper percentiles for length. Exclusively breastfed infants often track at a lower weight-for-age compared with formula-fed infants, although no differences in length-for-age or head circumference are noted.[1] This is why Dietitians of Canada, the Canadian Paediatric Society, the College of Family Physicians of Canada, and Community Health Nurses of Canada have adapted the World Health Organization (WHO) Child Growth Standards (2006) and WHO Reference (2007) for Canada. The WHO standards are based on growth patterns for breastfed infants. See Appendix D for additional information on interpreting growth charts.

The growth of the brain is more rapid during the first year than at any other time, and infants' heads are typically large in proportion to the rest of their bodies, approximately one-fourth of their total length. Pediatricians use head circumference as an additional tool for the assessment of growth and nutritional status; growth charts for head-circumference-for-age are available for infants and toddlers birth to 24 months of age. After around 18 months of age, the rate of brain growth slows, and gradually the body "catches up" to head size, resulting in body proportions that are closer to those of a child.

As infants grow and develop, their proportion of muscle, fat, and bone evolve. Body fat, as a percentage of total body weight, increases after birth and peaks around nine months of age. Muscle tissue increases slowly but steadily, and body calcium, a marker for

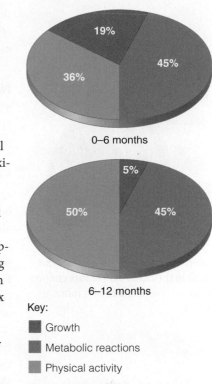

0–6 months

6–12 months

Key:

■ Growth

■ Metabolic reactions

■ Physical activity

Figure 16.11 Energy expenditure during infancy. During the first six months of life, infants expend more energy to support growth and less energy on physical activity than in the second six months of life.

The proportions of muscle, fat, and bone in the bodies of infants change as they grow and become more active.

skeletal growth, more than doubles during the first year of life.[16] Body water, as a percentage of total body weight, is highest in newborns and gradually decreases through and beyond early childhood.[21]

Nutrient Needs for Infants

Three characteristics of infants combine to make their nutritional needs unique. These are (1) their high energy needs per unit of body weight to support rapid growth; (2) their immature digestive tracts and kidneys; and (3) their small size.

Macronutrient Needs of Infants

An infant needs to consume about 90 to 110 kcal/kg of body weight per day, with newborns at the higher end of the range, and infants 6 to 12 months old at the lower end. This amounts to about 600 (girls) to 650 (boys) kcal/day at around six months of age.[10] Given the immature digestive tracts and kidneys of infants, as well as their high fluid needs, providing this much energy may seem difficult. Fortunately, breast milk and commercial formulas are energy-dense, providing about 650 kcal/L of fluid.[10] When complementary (solid) foods are introduced, they provide even more energy in addition to the breast milk or formula.

Infants are not small versions of adults; they are growing rapidly compared with the typically stable adult phase of life. The proportions of macronutrients they require differ from adult proportions, as do the types of food they can tolerate. It is generally agreed that about 40% to 50% of an infant's diet should come from fat during the first year of life (30–31 g/day) and that fat intakes below this level can be harmful before the age of two years. Given the high energy needs of infants, it makes sense to take advantage of the energy density of fat (9 kcal/g). Breast milk and commercial formulas are both high in fat (about 50% of total energy).

Specific fatty acids are essential for the rapid brain growth, maturation of the retina of the eye, and nervous system development that happens in the first one to two years of life. The Adequate Intake (AI) fatty acid guidelines for infants are based on the composition of breast milk, which is always the standard for infant nutrient guidelines. For infants 7 to 12 months of age, the contributions of complementary foods are considered. The infant AI for omega-6 fatty acids is 4.4 to 4.6 g/day, about 6% to 8% of total calories, whereas the infant AI for omega-3 fatty acids is 0.5 g/day, approximately 1% of total calories.[10] Breast milk is an excellent source of the fatty acids arachidonic acid (ARA) and docosahexaenoic acid (DHA), although levels of DHA vary widely with the mother's diet. Both of these fats have been associated with short-term improvements in visual function and, possibly, cognitive development.[1] Many formula manufacturers are now adding ARA and DHA to their products.

The recommended carbohydrate intake for infants zero to six months of age is based on the lactose content of human milk.[10] The AI for infants zero to six months of age is 60 g/day of carbohydrate. The carbohydrate AI for older infants 7 to 12 months of age reflects the intake of human milk and complementary foods and is set at 95 g/day.

The recommended intake of protein for infants zero to six months of age is 9.1 g/day or about 1.5 g/kg of body weight per day.[10] Again, this value is based on the protein content of human milk. Formula-fed infants typically consume higher amounts of protein compared with breastfed infants; however, the proteins in commercial formulas are less efficiently digested and absorbed. The protein guideline for infants 7 to 12 months of age is 13.5 g/day or 1.5 g/kg of body weight per day.[10] Recall that the adult RDA for protein is 0.8 g/kg body weight/day. The relatively higher intake for infants is to accommodate their rapid growth. However, no more than 20% of an infant's daily energy requirement should come from protein. Immature infant kidneys are not able to process and excrete the excess amine groups from higher-protein diets. Breast milk and commercial formulas both provide adequate total protein and appropriate essential amino acids to support growth and development.

Micronutrient Needs of Infants

An infant's micronutrient needs are also high to accommodate rapid growth and development. Micronutrients of particular note include iron, vitamin D, zinc, fluoride, and, for infants of breastfeeding vegans, vitamin B_{12}. Fortunately, breast milk and commercial formulas provide most of the micronutrients needed for infant growth and development, with some special considerations discussed later in this chapter.

In addition, all infants are routinely given an injection of vitamin K shortly after birth. This provides vitamin K until the infant's intestine can develop its own healthy bacteria, which provide vitamin K thereafter.

Do Infants Need Supplements?

Breast milk and commercial formulas provide most of the vitamins and minerals infants need. However, breast milk is low in vitamin D, and deficiencies of this nutrient have been detected in breastfed infants with dark skin and in those with limited sunlight exposure.[1] Breastfed infants are commonly prescribed a supplement containing vitamin D.[49]

Breastfed infants also require additional iron beginning no later than six months of age because the infant's iron stores become depleted and breast milk is a poor source of iron. Iron is extremely important for cognitive development and prevention of iron-deficiency anemia. Infant rice cereal fortified with iron can serve as an additional iron source and is an excellent first solid food.

Fluoride is important for strong tooth development, but fluoride supplementation is not recommended during the first six months of life. Depending on the fluoride content of the household water supply, breastfed infants over the age of six months may need a fluoride supplement. Most brands of bottled water have low levels of fluoride and many home water treatment systems remove fluoride as well. On the other hand, fluoride toxicity may be a risk for infants simultaneously exposed to fluoridated toothpaste and rinses, fluoridated water, and fluoride supplements.

There are special conditions in which additional supplements may be needed for breastfed infants. For example, if a woman is a vegan, her breast milk may be low in vitamin B_{12}, and a supplement of this vitamin should be given to the baby.

For formula-fed infants, the need for supplementation depends on the formula composition and other factors. Most formulas are already fortified with iron, for example; thus, no additional iron supplement is necessary. If the baby is getting adequate vitamin D through either the ingestion of at least 500 mL of vitamin D–fortified formula or via regular sun exposure, then an extra supplement may not be necessary.

If a supplement is given, careful consideration should be given to dose. The supplement should be formulated specifically for infants, and the recommended daily dose should not be exceeded. High doses of micronutrients can be dangerous. For example, too much iron can be fatal, and too much fluoride can cause mottling, pitting, and staining of the teeth. Excessive vitamin D can cause abnormally high levels of serum calcium and calcification of soft tissues such as the kidney.

Fluid Recommendations for Infants

Fluid is critical for everyone, but for infants the balance is more delicate for two reasons. First, they proportionally lose more water through evaporation from the skin surface area than adults. Second, their kidneys are immature and unable to concentrate urine. Hence, they are at even greater risk of dehydration. An infant needs about 50 mL of fluid per kilogram of body weight, and either breast milk or formula is almost always adequate in providing this amount. The AI for total water for infants is 0.7L/d for 0 to 6 months and 0.8L/d for 7–12 months. Experts recently confirmed that "infants exclusively fed human milk do not require supplemental water."[21] This is true for infants living in hot and humid climates as well as more moderate environments. Parents can be reassured that their infant's fluid intake is appropriate if the infant produces six to eight wet diapers per day.

Certain conditions, such as diarrhea, vomiting, fever, or extreme hot weather, can accelerate fluid loss. In these instances, supplemental fluid, ideally as water, may be needed.

Infants are at high risk for dehydration and should be offered water and other nutritious beverages on a regular basis.

Because too much fluid can be dangerous for an infant, supplemental fluids (whether water or an infant electrolyte formula) should be given only under the advice of a physician. Generally, it is advised that supplemental fluids not exceed 125 mL per day. Parents should avoid giving breastfed or formula-fed infants sugar water, fruit juices, or sweetened beverages in a bottle, especially at bedtime, as the practice can cause decay of developing teeth.

RecaP

Infancy is characterized by the most rapid rate of growth a human being will ever experience, and an infant's energy needs are correspondingly high. Assessment of the infant's growth pattern can provide important clues to his or her nutritional state.

Breast milk is the ideal infant food for the first six months of life; iron-fortified formula also provides the necessary nutrients for young infants. Vitamin D supplements are recommended for exclusively breastfed infants; iron and fluoride supplements may be prescribed for infants older than six months of age.

What Types of Formula Are Available?

We discussed the advantages of breastfeeding earlier in this chapter, and indeed both national and international healthcare organizations consider breastfeeding the best choice for infant nutrition, when possible. However, if breastfeeding is not feasible, several types of commercial formulas provide nutritious alternatives. In Canada, as many as 80% to 85% of infants are fed commercial formula by the age of one year. Formula manufacturers must comply with the Food and Drugs Act, which establishes minimum and maximum levels for nutrients. Although most formula manufacturers try to mimic the nutritional value of breast milk, these formulas still cannot completely duplicate the immune factors, enzymes, and other unique components of human milk.

Most formulas are based on cow's milk that is modified to make it more appropriate for human infants. The amount of total protein is reduced and levels of milk proteins are altered to mirror the types of proteins in breast milk. In addition, the product is heated to denature the proteins and make them more digestible. The naturally occurring lactose may be supplemented with sucrose to provide adequate carbohydrate. Vegetable oils and/or microbiologically produced fatty acids replace the naturally occurring butterfat. A range of vitamins and minerals such as iron is added to meet national standards. Recently, some manufacturers have added compounds such as taurine, carnitine, and the fatty acids ARA and DHA to more closely mimic the nutrient profile of breast milk. This chapter's Nutrition Label Activity on page 614 gives you the opportunity to review some of these ingredients.

Soy-based formulas are effective alternatives for infants who are lactose intolerant (although this is rare in infants) or cannot tolerate the proteins in cow's milk–based formulas. Soy formulas may also satisfy the requirements of families who are strict vegans. However, soy-based formulas are not without controversy.[67] Because soy contains isoflavones, or plant forms of estrogens, there is some concern over the effects these compounds have on growing infants. Babies can also have allergic reactions to soy-based formulas.[68] Currently, it is believed that soy formulas are safe, but they should only be used when breast milk or cow's milk–based formulas are contraindicated. Soy-based formulas are not the same as soy milk, which is not suitable for infant feeding.

Finally, there are specialized formulas for specific medical conditions. Some contain proteins that have been predigested, for example, or have nutrient compositions designed to accommodate certain genetic abnormalities. Others have been developed to meet the unique nutritional needs of preterm infants. Many of these specialized or medical formulas are available only through a physician.

Commercial formulas provide infants with a nutritious alternative to breast milk. Cow's milk, including fresh, evaporated, condensed, and dried milks, should not be introduced to infants until after one year of age. Cow's milk is too high in protein, the protein is difficult to digest, and the poor digestibility may contribute to gastrointestinal bleeding. In addition, cow's milk has too much sodium, too little iron, and a poor balance of other vitamins and minerals. Goat's milk is also inappropriate for infants and should not be used as a substitute for breast milk or formula.

When Do Infants Begin to Need Solid Foods?

As a result of declining nutrient stores, particularly iron, and continued growth, infants begin to need complementary, or solid, foods at around six months of age (Table 16.3). As previously noted, the Canadian Paediatric Society recommends exclusive breastfeeding for the first six months of life, but also recognizes that there is no evidence of significant harm if complementary foods are offered no earlier than four months of age.[55]

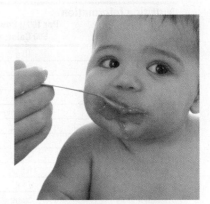

One factor limiting an infant's ability to take solid foods is the *extrusion reflex*. During infant feeding, the suckling response depends on a particular movement of the tongue that draws liquid out of the breast or bottle. But when solid foods are introduced with a spoon, this tongue movement (the extrusion reflex), causes the baby to push most of the food back out of the mouth. The extrusion reflex begins to lessen around four to five months of age.

The extrusion reflex will push solid food out of an infant's mouth.

Another factor is muscle development. To minimize the risk of choking, the infant must have gained muscular control of the head and neck and must be able to sit up (with or without support).

Still another part of being ready for solid foods is sufficient maturity of the digestive and kidney systems. Infants can digest and absorb lactose from birth; however, the ability to digest starch does not fully develop until the age of three to four months. If an infant is fed cereal, for example, before he can digest the starch, diarrhea and discomfort may develop. In addition, early introduction of solid foods can lead to improper absorption of intact, undigested proteins, setting the stage for allergies. Finally, the kidneys must have matured so that they are better able to process nitrogen wastes from proteins and concentrate urine.

The need for solid foods is also related to nutrient needs. At about six months of age, infant iron stores become depleted; thus, iron-fortified infant cereals are often the first foods introduced. Rice cereal rarely provokes an allergic response and is easy to digest. If all goes well with the rice cereal, another single-grain cereal (other than wheat, which is highly allergenic) can be introduced, or the family may choose to gradually introduce different single-item foods such as strained vegetables, meats, or fruits. Some nutritionists recommend meat as a good source of iron and zinc, and others encourage the introduction of vitamin C–rich fruits and vegetables.

Table 16.3 Guidelines for the Introduction of Solid Foods to Infants

Guideline	Explanation
Introduce single-item foods, one at a time, at three- to five-day intervals. Avoid multigrain cereals and mixed dishes.	Makes it easier to identify possible food allergies.
Start with foods that provide key nutrients such as iron-fortified infant cereals and pureed meats.	Iron and zinc are the most common nutrient deficiencies in infants. Meat provides both.
Do not introduce fruit juices until the infant is at least six months of age. When introduced, limit to 125–175 mL/day and vary the types of juice offered.	High juice intake displaces calcium- and protein-rich breast milk and formula. Many popular juices, such as apple juice, offer limited nutritional value.
Do not introduce cow's milk until the infant is at least nine months old. When introduced, provide whole milk, not reduced-fat milk.	The nutrient profile of cow's milk is not optimal to meet the needs of the growing infant. Healthy babies need the energy provided by whole milk.
Introduce a variety of foods by the age of one year.	Variety and diversity in foods improve nutrient intake, stimulate the senses of taste, odour, and touch, and positively influence future eating habits.

NUTRITION LABEL ACTIVITY

Reading Infant Food Labels

Baby Best
Contains a blend of DHA and ARA
(0+ months baby)
Our closest formula to breast milk

Nutrition Information

Energy	Per 100 g Powder 500 Calories	Per 100 mL diluted 70 Calories
Protein	10 g	1.5 g
Fat	28 g	3.7 g
Linoleic acid	4 g	0.5 g
Linolenic acid	0.4 g	0.05g
Arachidonic acid	100 mg	15 mg
Docosahexaenoic acid	50 mg	7 mg
Carbohydrate	56 g	7.5 g
Vitamin A	430 RE	60 RE
Vitamin D	6.5 µg	0.85 µg
Vitamin E	21 IU	3 IU
Vitamin K	50 µg	6.5 µg
Vitamin C	75 mg	10 mg
Thiamine	0.4 mg	0.05 mg
Riboflavin	0.7 mg	0.1 mg
Niacin	5.5 mg	0.75 mg
Vitamin B_6	0.4 mg	0.05 mg
Vitamin B_{12}	0.0015 mg	0.0002 mg
Folacin	0.08 mg	0.01 mg
Pantothenic acid	2.2 mg	0.3 mg
Biotin	0.015 mg	0.002 mg
Choline	100 mg	14 mg
Taurine	35 mg	4.5 mg
L-carnitine	6.5 mg	0.85 mg
Calcium	400 mg	50 mg
Phosphorous	200 mg	25 mg
Potassium	550 mg	75 mg
Magnesium	40 mg	5 mg
Chloride	330 mg	45 mg
Sodium	140 mg	20 mg
Iron	9 mg	1.2 mg
Zinc	4 mg	0.5 mg
Manganese	0.1 mg	0.01 mg
Selenium	0.12 mg	0.002 mg
Copper	0.4 mg	0.05 mg
Iodine	0.05 mg	0.008 mg

INGREDIENTS: REDUCED MINERALS WHEY, SKIM MILK, SOYBEAN OIL, LACTOSE, COCONUT OIL, MINERALS (POTASSIUM CITRATE, CALCIUM CARBONATE, POTASSIUM HYDROXIDE, MAGNESIUM CHLORIDE, SODIUM CHLORIDE, CALCIUM CHLORIDE, FERROUS SULPHATE, ZINC SULPHATE, CUPRIC SULPHATE, MANGANESE SULPHATE, SODIUM SELENATE), M. ALPINA OIL*, C. COHNII OIL**, VITAMINS (ASCORBIC ACID, INOSITOL, CHOLINE BITARTRATE, ALPHA-TOCOPHERYL ACETATE, NIACINAMIDE, CALCIUM D-PANTOTHENATE, VITAMIN A PALMITATE, THIAMINE HYDROCHLORIDE, PYRIDOXINE RIBOFLAVIN, FOLIC ACID, POTASSIUM IODIDE, PHYLLOQUINONE, BIOTIN, VITAMIN D3, COBALAMIN), L-CARNITINE, SOY LECITHIN, TAURINE.
*A source of ARA (arachidonic acid)
**A source of DHA (docosahexaenoic acid)

Figure 16.12 An infant formula label. Notice that there is a long list of ingredients and no % Daily Value.

Imagine that you are a new parent shopping for infant formula. **Figure 16.12** shows the label from a typical can of formula. As you can see, the ingredients list is long and has many technical terms. Even well-informed parents would probably be stumped by many of them. Fortunately, with the information you learned in previous chapters, you can probably answer the following questions.

■ The first ingredient listed is a modified form of *whey protein*. Why is the whey protein modified?
■ The fourth ingredient listed is *lactose*. Is lactose a form of protein, fat, or carbohydrate? Why is lactose important for infants?
■ The label states the formula has *DHA* (docosahexaenoic acid) and *ARA* (arachidonic acid). Are DHA and ARA forms of protein, fat, or carbohydrate? Why are these two nutrients thought to be important for infants?

The label also claims that this formula is *"Our Closest Formula to Breast Milk."* Can you think of some differences between breast milk and this formula that still exist? Look at the list of nutrients on the label. You'll notice that there is no "% Daily Value" column that you see on most food labels. Next time you are at the grocery store, look at other baby food items, such as baby cereal or pureed fruits. Do their labels simply list the nutrient content or is the "% Daily Value" column used? Why do you think infant formula has a different label format?

Let's say you are feeding a six-month-old infant who needs about 500 kcal/day. Using the information from the nutrition section of the label, you can calculate the number of mL of formula the baby needs (this assumes that no cereal or other foods are eaten):

There are 70 kcal (calories) per 100 mL

500 kcal ÷ 70 kcal = 7.2 (100 mL) portions of 720 mL of formula per day to meet this baby's energy needs

A six-month-old infant needs about 210 mg calcium per day. Based on an intake of 720 mL of formula per day, as just calculated, you can use the label nutrition information to calculate the amount of calcium that is provided:

There are 50 mg calcium per 100 mL serving of formula:

50 mg × 7.2 (100 mL) portions or 720 mL
= 360 mg calcium per day

You can see that the infant's need for calcium is easily met by the formula alone.

Commercial baby foods are convenient and are typically made without added salt; some are made only with organic ingredients. Dessert items and dinner-type foods are not recommended because they contain added sugars and starches. Parents can use an inexpensive food grinder to prepare home-made baby foods that cost little and reflect the cultural diversity of the family.

Throughout the first year, solid foods should only be a supplement to, not a substitute for, breast milk or iron-fortified formula. Infants still need the nutrient density and energy that breast milk and formula provide.

Did You Know?

The first fortified baby food, Pablum, was invented by Drs. Alan Brown, Fred Tisdal, and Theo Drake in 1930 at the Hospital for Sick Children in Toronto, Ontario. Pablum became commercially available in 1931, and by the early 1960s, all North American commercial infant cereal products were fortified with iron. Currently, the major source of iron in the diets of Canadian children is commercial infant cereal or fortified formula.

What *Not* to Feed an Infant

The following foods should never be offered to an infant:

- *Foods that could cause choking.* Foods such as grapes, hot dogs, nuts, popcorn, raw carrots, raisins, and hard candies cannot be chewed adequately by infants and can cause choking.
- *Corn syrup and honey.* These may contain spores of the bacterium *Clostridium botulinum.* These spores can germinate and grow into viable bacteria in the immature digestive tracts of infants, where they produce a potent toxin that can be fatal. Children older than one year can safely consume these substances because their digestive tracts are mature enough to kill any *C. botulinum* bacteria.
- *Goat's milk.* Goat's milk is notoriously low in many nutrients that infants need, such as folate, vitamin C, vitamin D, and iron.
- *Cow's milk.* For children under one year, cow's milk is too concentrated in minerals and protein and contains too few carbohydrates to meet infant energy needs. Infants can begin to consume whole cow's milk after the age of one year. Infants and toddlers should not be given reduced-fat cow's milk before the age of two years, as it does not contain enough fat and is too high in mineral content for the kidneys to handle effectively. Infants should not be given evaporated milk or sweetened condensed milk.
- *Large quantities of fruit juices.* Fruit juices are poorly absorbed in the infant digestive tract, causing diarrhea if consumed in excess. Large quantities of fruit juice can make

an infant feel full and reject breast milk or formula at feeding time, thus causing him or her to miss out on essential nutrients. Plain water will also effectively quench an infant's thirst.

- *Too much salt and sugar.* Infant foods should not be seasoned with salt or other seasonings, or sweetened. Cookies, cakes, and other excessively sweet, processed foods also should be avoided.
- *Too much breast milk or formula.* As nutritious as breast milk and formula are, once infants reach the age of six months, solid foods should be introduced gradually. Six months of age is a critical time, as that is when a baby's iron stores begin to be depleted. In addition, infants are physically and psychologically ready to incorporate solid foods at this time, and solid foods can help appease their increasing appetites. Between six months and the time of weaning (from breast or bottle), solid foods should gradually make up an increasing proportion of the infant's diet. Overreliance on breast milk or formula, to the exclusion or displacement of iron-rich foods, can result in a condition known as *milk anemia.*

Recap

In the absence of breastfeeding, iron-fortified formulas provide adequate nutrition for infants. Solid foods can gradually be introduced into an infant's diet at four to six months of age beginning with rice cereal, other non-wheat cereals, and then moving to single-item vegetables and fruits. Parents should carefully select and prepare the foods to be given to their infants, avoiding those that represent a choking hazard and limiting high-sugar foods and beverages. Solid foods expand the infant's exposure to tastes and textures and represent an important developmental milestone.

Nutrition-Related Concerns for Infants

Nutrition is one of the biggest concerns of new parents. Infants cannot speak, and their cries are sometimes indecipherable. Feeding time can be very frustrating for parents, especially if the child is not eating, not growing appropriately, or has problems like diarrhea, vomiting, or persistent skin rashes. Following are some nutrition-related concerns for infants.

Allergies

Early introduction of solid foods may play a role in the development of food allergies, especially if infants are introduced to highly allergenic foods early on.

Many foods have the potential to stimulate an allergic reaction. Breastfeeding reduces the risk of allergy development, as does delaying the introduction of solid foods until the age of six months. One of the most common allergies in infants is to the proteins in cow's milk–based formulas. Egg whites, peanuts, and wheat are other common triggers to allergic reactions. Every food should be introduced in isolation, so that any allergic reaction can be identified and the particular food avoided.

Symptoms of an allergic reaction vary but may include gastrointestinal distress such as diarrhea or vomiting, rashes or hives, runny nose or sneezing, or even difficulty breathing. Peanut allergy is the leading cause of fatal food reactions in Canada. (See Chapter 3 page 103 for information on food allergies.) While about 85% of infants who are allergic to cow's milk and eggs develop a tolerance for them by the age of five years, only about 20% of infants allergic to peanuts are able to safely tolerate them by age five years.

Colic

colic Unconsolable infant crying of unknown origin that lasts for hours at a time.

Perhaps nothing is more frustrating to new parents than the relentless crying spells of some infants, typically referred to as **colic**. In this condition, newborns and young infants who appear happy, healthy, and well nourished suddenly begin to cry or even shriek and continue no matter what their caregiver does to console them. The spells tend to occur at the same time of day, typically late in the afternoon or early in the evening, and often occur daily for a period of several weeks. Crying lasts for hours at a time. Overstimulation of the nervous system, feeding too rapidly, swallowing of air, and intestinal gas pain are considered possible culprits, but the precise cause is unknown.

As with allergies, if a colicky infant is breastfed, breastfeeding should be continued, but the mother should try to determine whether eating certain foods seems to prompt crying and, if so, eliminate the offending food(s) from her diet. Avoidance of spicy or other strongly flavoured foods may also help. Formula-fed infants may benefit from a change in type of formula. In the worst cases of colic, a physician may prescribe medication. Fortunately, most cases disappear spontaneously, possibly because of maturity of the GI tract, around three months of age.

Gastroesophageal Reflux

The regurgitation, or reflux, of stomach contents into the esophagus often results in the all too familiar "spitting up" of young infants. Particularly common in preterm infants, gastroesophageal reflux occurs in about 3% of newborns. Typically, as the gastrointestinal tract matures within the first 12 months of life, this condition resolves. Caretakers should avoid overfeeding the infant, keep the infant upright after each feeding, and watch for choking or gagging.

Failure to Thrive

At times, seemingly healthy infants reach an inappropriate plateau or decline in their growth. Pediatric healthcare providers describe **failure to thrive (FTT)** as a condition in which, in the absence of disease or physical abnormalities, the infant's weight or weight-for-height is below the third percentile, or the infant has fallen more than two percentile lines on the growth charts after a previously stable pattern of growth.[1] Acute malnutrition often results in *wasting*, or low weight-for-height, and chronic malnutrition typically produces growth *stunting*, in which the child has low height-for-age.

Psychosocial factors that increase the risk for FTT include poverty, inadequate knowledge, extreme nutritional beliefs, social isolation, domestic violence, and/or substance abuse. If not corrected in a timely manner, FTT may result in developmental, motor, and cognitive delays typically associated with infants in developing nations.

Anemia

As stated earlier, full-term infants are born with sufficient iron stores to last for approximately the first six months of life. In older infants and toddlers, however, iron is the mineral most likely to be deficient. Iron-deficiency anemia causes pallor, lethargy, and impaired growth. Iron-fortified formula is a good source for formula-fed infants. Some pediatricians prescribe a supplement containing iron especially formulated for infants. Iron for older infants is typically supplied by iron-fortified rice cereal or pureed meats. Overconsumption of cow's milk remains a common cause of anemia among North American infants and children.

Dehydration

Whether the cause is diarrhea, vomiting, prolonged fever, or inadequate fluid intake, dehydration is extremely dangerous to infants, and if left untreated can quickly result in death. The factors behind infants' increased risk of dehydration were discussed on page 611. Treatment includes providing fluids, a task that is difficult if vomiting is occurring. In some cases, the physician may recommend that a pediatric electrolyte solution, readily available at most grocery and drug stores, be administered on a temporary basis. In more severe cases, hospitalization may be necessary. If possible, breastfeeding should continue throughout an illness. A physician or other healthcare provider should be consulted on decisions related to the use of formula and solid foods.

Nursing Bottle Syndrome

Infants should never be left alone with a bottle, whether lying down or sitting up. As infants manipulate the nipple of the bottle, the high-carbohydrate fluid (whether breast

Colicky babies will begin crying for no apparent reason even if they otherwise appear well nourished and happy.

failure to thrive (FTT) An unexplained condition in which the infant's weight gain and growth are far below usual levels for age and previous pattern of growth.

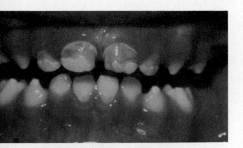

Figure 16.13 Leaving a baby alone with a bottle can result in the tooth decay of nursing bottle syndrome.

milk, formula, or fruit juice) drips out, coming into prolonged contact with the developing teeth. This high-carbohydrate fluid provides an optimal food source for bacteria that are the underlying cause of dental caries (cavities). Severe tooth decay can result (**Figure 16.13**). Encouraging the use of a cup around the age of eight months helps prevent nursing bottle syndrome, as does weaning the baby from a bottle entirely by the age of 15 to 18 months.

Lead Poisoning

Lead is especially toxic to infants and children because their brains and central nervous systems are still developing. Lead poisoning can result in decreased mental capacity, behavioural problems, anemia, impaired growth, impaired hearing, and other problems. Unfortunately, lead in old pipes and lead paint can still be found in older homes and buildings. Measures to reduce lead exposure include:

- Allowing tap water to run for a minute or so before use, to clear the pipes of any lead-contaminated water
- Using only cold tap water for drinking, cooking, and infant formula preparation, as hot tap water is more likely to leach lead
- Professionally removing lead-based paint or painting over it with latex paint

ReCaP

Risk for food allergies can be reduced by delaying the introduction of solid foods until the infant is at least six months of age. Infants with colic or gastroesophageal reflux present special challenges, but both conditions generally improve over time. Infants who present with failure to thrive require close monitoring by healthcare providers, as do infants experiencing severe dehydration. Anemia is easily prevented through the use of iron-fortified formulas and cereals. Nursing bottle syndrome is characterized by dental caries in infants left lying down or sitting up with a bottle. Lead poisoning can result in cognitive, behavioural, and other problems.

SEE FOR YOURSELF

Planning a Nutrient-Packed Snack

We said earlier in this chapter that, during the last two trimesters of pregnancy, energy needs increase by about 350 to 450 kcal/day. At the same time, a pregnant woman's need for protein increases by 25 g per day. To help you appreciate how important it is for pregnant women to choose nutrient-dense foods, here's a two-part challenge:

Part 1. Design a healthy mid-morning snack that provides a woman with 350 to 450 kcal and also fulfills at least half of her increased protein needs (that is, 12.5 g). List each food item, the amount, the kcals, and the g protein provided.

Part 2. Let's "flip" the assignment: write out your own favourite mid-morning snack that totals about 350 to 450 kcal, identifying the amount of protein just as you did for the snack in part 1. How much protein does your favourite snack provide? Would you recommend it to a pregnant woman? Is it a healthy snack for *you*?

Chapter Review

16

Summary

- Nutrition is important before conception because critical stages of cell division, tissue differentiation, and organ development occur in the early weeks of pregnancy, often before a woman even knows she is pregnant.

- A plentiful, nourishing diet is important throughout pregnancy to provide the nutrients needed to support fetal development without depriving the mother of nutrients she needs to maintain her own health.

- A normal pregnancy progresses over the course of 38 to 42 weeks. This time is divided into three trimesters of 13 to 14 weeks. Each trimester is associated with particular developmental phases of the embryo/fetus.

- Pregnant women of normal weight should consume adequate energy to gain 11.5 to 16 kg during pregnancy. Women who are underweight should gain slightly more, and women who are overweight or obese should gain less.

- Pregnant women need to be especially careful to consume adequate amounts of folate, vitamin B_{12}, vitamin C, vitamin D, calcium, iron, and zinc. A supplement is often prescribed to ensure adequate intake of these nutrients.

- Many pregnant women experience nausea and/or vomiting during pregnancy, and many crave or feel aversions to specific types of foods and non-food substances.

- Heartburn and constipation in pregnancy are related to the relaxation of smooth muscle caused by certain pregnancy-related hormones.

- Gestational diabetes mellitus and pre-eclampsia are nutrition-related disorders that can seriously affect maternal and fetal health.

- The bodies of adolescents are still growing and developing; thus, their nutrient needs during pregnancy are higher than those of older pregnant women.

- Dieting during pregnancy can lead to inadequate nutrition for mother and fetus.

- Alcohol is a teratogen and should not be consumed in any amount during pregnancy.

- Cigarette smoking reduces placental transfer of oxygen and nutrients, limiting fetal growth and development.

- Successful breastfeeding requires the coordination of several hormones, including estrogen, progesterone, prolactin, and oxytocin. These hormones govern the preparation of the breasts, as well as actual milk production and the let-down response.

- Breastfeeding women require more energy than is needed during pregnancy. Protein needs increase, and an overall nutritious diet with plentiful fluids is important in maintaining milk quality and quantity, as well as preserving the mother's health.

- The advantages of breastfeeding include nutritional superiority of breast milk, protection from infections and allergies, promotion of attachment, convenience, and lower cost.

- Breastfeeding exclusively for the first six months of a baby's life is recommended by North American and international healthcare organizations.

- Challenges that might be encountered with breastfeeding include the effect of medications on breast milk, concerns related to transmission of HIV to a breastfeeding infant, scheduling conflicts for mothers who return to work, and social concerns.

- Infants are characterized by their extremely rapid growth and brain development.

- Physicians use length and weight measurements as the main tools for assessing an infant's nutritional status.

- Because infant stores of iron become depleted after about six months, an iron supplement is sometimes prescribed for breastfeeding infants.

- Breast milk or formula is entirely sufficient for the first six months of life. After that, solid foods can be introduced (for example, rice cereal fortified with iron) and expanded gradually, with breast milk or formula remaining very important throughout the first year.

- Infants need to be monitored carefully for appropriate growth and appropriate number of wet diapers every day to assess adequate nutrient intake and hydration.

- Nutrition-related concerns for infants include the potential for allergies, colic, gastroesophageal reflux, dehydration, failure to thrive, anemia, nursing bottle syndrome, and ingestion of lead.

Review Questions

1. Folate deficiency in the first weeks after conception has been linked with which of the following problems in the newborn?
   a. anemia
   b. neural tube defects
   c. low birth weight
   d. preterm delivery

2. Which of the following hormones is responsible for the let-down response?
   a. progesterone
   b. estrogen
   c. oxytocin
   d. prolactin

3. Which of the following nutrients should be added to the diet of breastfed infants when they are around six months of age?
   a. protein
   b. fat
   c. iron
   d. vitamin A

4. A pregnancy weight gain of 12.5 to 18 kg is recommended for
   a. all women.
   b. women who begin their pregnancy underweight.
   c. women who begin their pregnancy overweight.
   d. women who begin their pregnancy at a normal weight.

5. One of the best solid foods to introduce first to infants is
   a. Cream of Wheat cereal.
   b. applesauce.
   c. teething biscuits.
   d. iron-fortified rice cereal.

6. Plan a one-day menu for Ashtyn, an active eight-month-old baby girl.

7. Research the *World Health Organization International Code of Marketing of Breast-milk Substitutes*. What is the purpose of this document?

8. Identify five advantages and five disadvantages of breastfeeding. Can you think of others?

9. You are a registered dietitian in a public health clinic. A pregnant 15-year-old is referred to you for nutrition-related counselling and services. Identify at least three topics that you would discuss with this client.

10. Your cousin, who is pregnant with her first child, tells you that her physician prescribed supplemental iron tablets for her but that she decided not to take them. "You know me," she says, "I'm a natural food nut! I'm absolutely certain that my careful diet is providing all the nutrients my baby needs!" Is it possible that your cousin is partly right and partly wrong? Explain.

11. You visit your neighbours one afternoon to congratulate them on the birth of their new daughter, Katie. While you are there, two-week-old Katie suddenly starts crying as if she is in terrible pain. "Oh, no," Katie's dad says to his wife. "Here we go again!" He turns to you and explains, "She's been like this every afternoon for the past week, and it goes on until sunset. I just wish we could figure out what we're doing wrong." What would you say?

12. You are on a picnic with your sister at a park, who drapes a shawl over her shoulders and breastfeeds her 11-month-old son. A woman walking by stops and says, "Isn't that child getting too old for that?" What information could you share with the woman in response to her question?

Web Links

www.hc-sc.gc.ca/fn-an/nutrition/prenatal/index-eng.php

Health Canada—Prenatal Nutrition

Find nutrition resources and guidelines for pregnant women.

www.lllc.ca

La Leche League—Canada

Information that encourages and promotes breastfeeding and provides mother-to-mother breastfeeding support and educational opportunities.

www.motherisk.org/women/index.jsp

Motherisk

Here you will find up-to-date resources for pregnancy and breastfeeding.

www.hc-sc.gc.ca/fn-an/pubs/infant-nourrisson/ nut_infant_nourrisson_term-eng.php

Health Canada

The latest guidelines for nutrition for healthy term infants.

www.phac-aspc.gc.ca/hp-gs/index-eng.php

Public Health Agency of Canada

Outlines the national guidelines for a healthy pregnancy.

www.breastfeedingcanada.ca

Breastfeeding Committee for Canada

The Breastfeeding Committee for Canada is the national authority for the WHO/UNICEF Baby Friendly Hospital Initiative (BFHI) in Canada.

www.cps.ca

Canadian Paediatric Society

The Canadian Paediatric Society is the national association for pediatricians. It is committed to working to advance the health of children and youth by nurturing excellence in health care, advocacy, education, research, and support of its membership.

www.beststart.org/resources

Beststart Resource Centre

Go to this site to find up-to-date resources on pregnancy and infant feeding.

MasteringNutrition®

www.masteringnutrition.pearson.com

Study Area

Practice Tests • Diet Analysis • eText

References

1. Kleinman, R.E., ed. American Academy of Pediatrics, Committee on Nutrition. 2009. *Pediatric Nutrition Handbook.* 6th ed. Elk Grove Village, IL: American Academy of Pediatrics.

2. Davidson, M. R., M. L. London, and P. W. Ladewig. 2008. *Olds' Maternal-Newborn Nursing and Women's Health Across the Lifespan,* 8th ed. Upper Saddle River, NJ: Prentice Hall Health.

3. UNICEF (United Nations Children's Fund). 2004. Maternal nutrition and low birth weight. Available at www.unicef.org/ nutrition/index_lowbirthweight.html.

4. Health Canada. *Canadian gestational weight gain recommendations.* Available at www.hc-sc.gc.ca/fn-an/nutrition/prenatal/ qa-gest-gros-qr-eng.php (accessed June 22, 2011).

5. Rasmussen, K. M., and A. L. Yaktine, eds. 2009. *Weight Gain During Pregnancy: Reexamining the Guidelines.* Institute of Medicine; National Research Council. Washington, DC: National Academy Press.

6. Wrotniak, B. H., J. Shults, S. Butts, and N. Stettler. 2008. Gestational weight gain and risk of overweight in the offspring at age 7 y in a multicenter, multiethnic cohort study. *Am. J. Clin. Nutr.* 87:1818–1824.

7. Boney, C. M., A. Verma, R. Tucker, and B. R. Vohr. 2005. Metabolic syndrome in childhood: association with birth weight, maternal obesity, and gestational diabetes mellitus. *Pediatrics* 115:e290–e296.

8. Brown, J. E., M. A. Murtaugh, D. R. Jacobs, and H. C. Margellos. 2002. Variation in newborn size according to pregnancy weight change by trimester. *Am. J. Clin. Nutr.* 76:205–209.

9. U.S. Department of Health and Human Services and U.S. Department of Agriculture. 2005. *Dietary Guidelines for Americans 2005,* 6th ed. Washington, DC: U.S. Government Printing Office. Available at www.healthierus.gov/dietaryguidelines.

10. Institute of Medicine, Food and Nutrition Board. 2002. *Dietary Reference Intakes for Energy, Carbohydrate, Fiber, Fat, Fatty Acids, Cholesterol, Protein, and Amino Acids.* Washington, DC: National Academy Press.

11. Health Canada (2009). *Prenatal Nutrition Guidelines for Health Professionals: Fish and Omega-3 Fatty Acids.* Available at www. hc-sc.gc.ca/fn-an/alt_formats/hpfb-dgpsa/pdf/pubs/omega3-eng. pdf (accessed September 20, 2011).

12. Institute of Medicine, Food and Nutrition Board. 1998. *Dietary Reference Intakes for Thiamin, Riboflavin, Niacin, Vitamin B_6, Folate, Vitamin B_{12}, Pantothenic Acid, Biotin, and Choline*. Washington, DC: National Academy Press.

13. Centers for Disease Control and Prevention (CDC). 2009. Facts about folic acid: folic acid home page. Available at www.cdc.gov/ncbddd/folicacid/about.html (accessed May 2009).

14. Lindzon, G., and D. L. O'Connor. 2007. Folate during reproduction: the Canadian experience with folic acid fortification. *Nutr. Res. Pract.* 1:163–174.

15. Institute of Medicine, Food and Nutrition Board. 2001. *Dietary Reference Intakes for Vitamin A, Vitamin K, Arsenic, Boron, Chromium, Copper, Iodine, Iron, Manganese, Molybdenum, Nickel, Silicon, Vanadium, and Zinc*. Washington, DC: National Academy Press.

16. Institute of Medicine, Food and Nutrition Board. 2011. *Dietary Reference Intakes for Calcium, and Vitamin D,* Washington, DC: National Academy Press.

17. Bodnar, L. M., J. M. Catov, H. N. Simhan, M. F. Holick, R. W. Powers, and J. M. Roberts. 2007. Maternal vitamin D deficiency increases the risk of preeclampsia. *J. Clin. Endocrinology & Metab.* 92:3517–3522.

18. Schwalfenberg, G. K., S. J. Genius, and M. N. Hiltz. 2010. Addressing vitamin D deficiency in Canada: a public health innovation whose time has come. *Public Health* 124:350–359.

19. Whiting, S. J., K. A. Langlois, H. Vatanparast, and L. S. Greene-Finestone. 2011. The vitamin D status of Canadians relative to the 2011 dietary reference intakes: an examination in children and adults with and without supplement use. *Am. J. Clin. Nutr.* 94:128–135.

20. Office of Dietary Supplements. 2007. Dietary supplement fact sheet: iron. National Institutes of Health. Available at http://dietary-supplements.info.nih.gov/factsheets/Iron_pf.asp (accessed May 2009).

21. Institute of Medicine, Food and Nutrition Board. 2004. *Dietary Reference Intakes for Water, Potassium, Sodium, Chloride, and Sulfate*. Washington, DC: National Academy Press.

22. Gordon, M. C. 2007. Maternal physiology. In: Gabbe, S. G., J. R. Niebyl, and J. L. Simpson, eds. *Obstetrics: Normal and Problem Pregnancies,* 5th ed. Philadelphia: Elsevier Churchill Livingstone.

23. Kittler, P. G., and K. P. Sucher. 2001. *Food and Culture.* Belmont, CA: Wadsworth Thomson Learning.

24. Canadian Diabetes Association. *Gestational diabetes: preventing complications in pregnancy.* Available at www.diabetes.ca/diabetes-and-you/what/gestational/ (accessed June 22, 2011).

25. Keely, E. J., J. C. Malcolm, S. Hadjiyannakis, I. Gaboury, G. Lough, and M. L. Lawson. 2008. Prevalence of metabolic markers of insulin resistance in offspring of gestational diabetes pregnancies. *Pediatr. Diabetes* 9:53–59.

26. Vääräsmäki, M. A., P. Pouta, P. Elliot, U. Tapanainen, A. Sovio, A. L. Ruokonen, M. Hartikainen, M. McCarthy, and M. R. Järvelin. 2009. Adolescent manifestations of metabolic syndrome among children born to women with gestational diabetes in a general-population birth cohort. *Am. J. Epidemiol.* 169:1209–1215.

27. Damm, P. 2009. Future risk of diabetes in mother and child after gestational diabetes mellitus. *International J. Gynec. Obstetrics* 104:S25–S26; National Institute of Diabetes and Digestive and Kidney Diseases (NIDDK). June 2008. National diabetes statistics, 2007. Available at http://diabetes.niddk.nih.gov/dm/pubs/statistics/DM_Statistics.pdf.

28. Roberts, C. L., J. B. Ford, C. S. Algert, et al. 2011. Population-based trends in pregnancy hypertension and pre-eclampsia: an international comparative study. *BMJ Open* doi:10.1136/bmjopen-2011-000101.

29. Leeman, L., and P. Fontaine. 2008. Hypertensive disorders of pregnancy. *Am. Fam. Physician.* 78:93–100.

30. Solomon, C. G., and E. W. Seely. 2006. Hypertension in pregnancy. *Endocrin. Metab. Clinics. N. Amer.* 35:157–171.

31. Markovitz, B. P., R. Cook, L. H. Flick, and T. L. Leet. 2005. Socioeconomic factors and adolescent pregnancy outcomes: distinctions between neonatal and post-neonatal deaths? *BMC Public Health* 5:79–85.

32. Koebnick, C., I. Hoffmann, P. C. Dagnelie, U. A. Heins, S. N. Wickramasinghe, I. D. Ratnayaka, S. Gruendel, J. Landemans, and C. Leitzmann. 2004. Long-term ovo-lacto vegetarian diet impairs vitamin B_{12} status in pregnant women. *J. Nutr.* 134:3319–3326.

33. Weiss, R., Y. Fogelman, and M. Bennett. 2004. Severe vitamin B_{12} deficiency in an infant associated with a maternal deficiency and a strict vegetarian diet. *J. Pediatr. Hematol. Oncol.* 26:270–271.

34. Weng, X., R. Odouli, and D. Li. 2008. Maternal caffeine consumption during pregnancy and the risk of miscarriage: a prospective cohort study. *Am. J. Obstet. Gynecol.* 198:279.e1–279.e8.

35. Vik, T., L. S. Bakketeig, K. U. Trygg, K. Lund-Larsen, and G. Jacobsen. 2003. High caffeine consumption in the third trimester of pregnancy: gender-specific effects on fetal growth. *Pediatric and Perinatal Epidemiology* 17:324–331.

36. CARE Study Group. 2008. Maternal caffeine intake during pregnancy and risk of fetal growth restriction: a large prospective observational study. *British Medical Journal* 337:a2332.

37. March of Dimes. 2008. Drinking alcohol during pregnancy. Available at www.marchofdimes.com/professionals/14332_1170.asp (accessed June 23, 2011).

38. Atrash, H. K., K. Johnson, M. Adams, J. F. Cordero, and J. Howse. 2006. Preconception care for improving perinatal outcomes: the time to act. *Matern. Child. Health. J.* 10:S3–S11.

39. Health Canada. *Fetal alcohol syndrome/Fetal alcohol effects.* Available at www.hc-sc.gc.ca/fniah-spnia/famil/preg-gros/intro-eng.php (accessed June 23, 2011).

40. Al-Sahab, B., M. Saqib, H. Gabriel, and H. Tamim. 2010. Prevalence of smoking during pregnancy and associated risk factors among Canadian women: a national survey. *BMC Pregnancy and Childbirth* 10:24.

41. Hutson, J. 2006. A prenatal perspective on the cost of substance abuse in Canada. *JFAS Int.* 4:e9.

42. Health Canada. *Safe food handling for pregnant women.* Available at www.hc-sc.gc.ca/fn-an/securit/kitchen-cuisine/pregnant-women-femmes-enceintes-eng.php (accessed June 23, 2011).

43. Wolfe, L. A., and G. A. L. Davies. 2003. Canadian guidelines for exercise in pregnancy. *Clin. Obs. Gyn.* 46:488–495.

44. Lewis, B., M. Avery, E. Jennings, N. Sherwood, B. Martinson, and A. L. Crain. 2008. The effect of exercise during pregnancy on maternal outcomes: practical implications for practice. *Am. J. Lifestyle Med.* 2:441–455.

45. Dempsey, J. C., T. K. Sorensen, M. A. Williams, I. M. Lee, R. S. Miller, E. E. Dashow, and D. A. Luthy. 2004. Prospective study of gestational diabetes mellitus risk in relation to maternal recreational physical activity before and during pregnancy. *Am. J. Epidemiol.* 159:663–670.

46. Garshasbi, A., and S. F. Zadeh. 2004. The effect of exercise on the intensity of low back pain in pregnant women. *Intern. J. Gynec. Obstetr.* 88:271–275.

47. Petersen, A. M., T. L. Leet, and R. C. Brownson. 2005. Correlates of physical activity among pregnant women in the United States. *Med. Sci. Sports Exerc.* 37:1748–1753.

48. Chalmers, B., C. Levitt, M. Heaman, et al. 2009. Breastfeeding rates and hospital breastfeeding practices in Canada: a national survey of women. *Birth* 36:2.

49. American Academy of Pediatrics, Section on Breastfeeding. 2005. Breastfeeding and the use of human milk policy statement. *Pediatrics* 115:496–506.

50. Breastfeeding Committee for Canada. *Canadian Facilities Designated as Baby Friendly.* Available at www.breastfeedingcanada.ca (accessed July 4, 2011).

51. UNICEF/WHO. 2006. Baby Friendly Hospital Initiative, revised, updated and expanded for integrated care. Available at www.who.int/nutrition/topics/bfhi/en/index.html (accessed May 2009).

52. Brenna, J. T., B. Varamini, R. G. Jensen, D. A. Diersen-Schade, J. A. Boettcher, and L. M. Arterburn. 2007. Docosahexaenoic and arachidonic acid concentrations in human breast milk worldwide. *Am. J. Clin. Nutr.* 85:1457–1464.

53. Health Canada. Novel Food Information - DHASCO® and ARASCO® as Sources of Docosahexaenoic Acid and Arachidonic Acid in Infant Formulas. Available at www.hc-sc.gc.ca/fn-an/gmf-agm/appro/dhasco_arasco-eng.php (accessed June 24, 2010).

54. Canadian Paediatric Society. Reaffirmed 2010. *Vitamin D supplementation: recommendations for Canadian mothers and infants.* Available at www.cps.ca/english/statements/ii/fnim07-01.htm (accessed July 4, 2011).

55. Canadian Paediatric Society. Reaffirmed 2009. *Exclusive breastfeeding should continue to six months.* Available at www.cps.ca/english/statements/N/BreastfeedingMar05.htm (accessed July 4, 2011).

56. Agency for Healthcare Research and Quality. 2007. *Breastfeeding and Maternal and Infant Health Outcomes in Developed Countries.* U.S. Department of Health and Human Services. Rockville, MD. AHRQ Publication No. 07-E007.

57. UNICEF (United Nations Children's Fund). 2003. Protecting, promoting and supporting breastfeeding. Available at www.unicef.org/nutrition/index_breastfeeding.html (accessed May 2009).

58. Collaborative Group on Hormonal Factors in Breast Cancer. 2003. Breast cancer and breastfeeding: collaborative reanalysis of individual data from 47 epidemiological studies in 30 countries, including 50,302 women with breast cancer and 96,973 women without the disease. *Lancet* 360:187–195.

59. Grimes, J. P., and S. J. Wimalawansa. 2003. Breastfeeding and postmenopausal osteoporosis. *Curr. Women's Health Rep.* 3(3):193–198.

60. Paton, L. M., J. L. Alexander, C. A. Nowson, C. Margerison, M. G. Frame, B. Kaymakci, and J. D. Wark. 2003. Pregnancy and lactation have no long-term deleterious effect on measures of bone mineral in healthy women: a twin study. *Am. J. Clin. Nutr.* 77:707–714.

61. Merewood, A., S. D. Mehta, L. B. Chamberlain, B. L. Philipp, and H. Bauchner. 2005. Breastfeeding rates in US baby-friendly hospitals: results of a national survey. *Ped.* 116:628–634.

62. Nickerson, K. 2006. Environmental contaminants in breast milk. *J. Midwifery Women's Health* 51:26–34.

63. Berlin, C. M., J. S. LaKind, B. R. Sonawane, S. Kacew, C. J. Borgert, M. N. Bates, N. Birnbach, R. Campbell, A. Dermer, K. G. Dewey, S. M. Ellerbee, P. Furst, G. P. Giacoia, L. Gartner, M. Groer, S. G. Haynes, S. S. Humerick, R. A. Lawrence, M. Lorber, C. Lovelady, A. Mason, L. L. Needham, M. F. Picciano, J. Plautz, J. J. Ryan, S. G. Selevan, C. V. Sumaya, M. R. Tully, K. Uhl, E. Vesell, and J. T Wilson. 2002. Conclusions, research needs, and recommendations of the expert panel: technical workshop on human milk surveillance and research for environmental chemicals in the United States. *Journal of Toxicology and Environmental Health, Part A* 65(22):1929–1935.

64. Bauchner, E. 2004. Environmental contaminants and human milk. *LEAVEN* 39:123–125.

65. Coovadia, H. M., N. C. Rollins, R. M. Bland, K. Little, A. Coutsoudis, M. L. Bennish, and M. L. Newell. 2007. Mother-to-child transmission of HIV-1 infection during exclusive breastfeeding in the first 6 months of life: an intervention cohort study. *Lancet* 369:1107–1116.

66. Adams, C., R. Berger, P. Conning, L. Cruikshank, and K. Dore. 2001. Breastfeeding trends at a community breastfeeding center: an evaluative survey. *J. Obstet. Gynecol. Neonatal Nurs.* 30(4):392–400.

67. Merritt, R. J., and B. H. Jenks. 2004. Safety of soy-based infant formulas containing isoflavones: the clinical evidence. *J. Nutr.* 134:1220S–1224S.

68. ESPGHAN Committee on Nutrition: C. Agostoni, I. Axelsson, O. Goulet, B. Koletzko, K. F. Michaelsen, J. Puntis, D. Rieu, J. Rigo, R. Shamir, H. Szajewska, and D. Turck. 2006. Soy protein infant formulae and follow-on formulae: a commentary by the ESPGHAN committee on nutrition. *J. Ped. Gastroenterol. Nutr.* 42:352–361.

69. Grummer-Strawn, L. M., and M. Zuguo. 2004. Does breastfeeding protect against pediatric overweight? Analysis of longitudinal data from the Centers for Disease Control and Prevention Pediatric Nutrition Surveillance System. *Pediatrics* 113:e81–e86.

70. Weyermann, M., D. Rothenbacher, and H. Brenner. 2006. Duration of breastfeeding and risk of overweight in childhood: a prospective birth cohort study from Germany. *Int. J. Obesity. (London)* 30:1281–1287.

71. Koletzko, B., R. von Kries, R. Closa Monasterolo, J. Excribano Subias, S. Scaglioni, M. Giovannini, J. Beyer, et al., for the European Childhood Obesity Trial Study Group. 2009. Can infant feeding choices modulate later obesity risk? *Am. J. Clin. Nutr.* 89(suppl):1502S–1508S.

72. Gillman, M. W., S. L. Rifas-Shiman, C. A. Camargo Jr., C. S. Berkey, A. L. Frazier, H. R. Rockett, A. E. Field, and G. A. Colditz. 2001. Risk of overweight among adolescents who were breastfed as infants. *JAMA* 285:2461–1467.

73. Owen, C. G., R. M. Martin, P. H. Whincup, D. Smith, and D. G. Cook. 2005. Effect of infant feeding on the risk of obesity across the life course: a quantitative review of published evidence. *Pediatrics* 115:1367–1377.

74. O'Tierney, P. F., D. J. P. Barker, C. Osmond, E. Kajantie, and J. G. Eriksson. 2009. Duration of breast-feeding and adiposity in adult life. *J. Nutr.* 139:422S–425S.

75. Public Health Agency of Canada & Canadian Institute for Health Information. 2011. *Obesity in Canada.* Available at www.phac-aspc.gc.ca/hp-ps/hl-mvs/oic-oac/assets/pdf/oic-oac-eng.pdf (accessed July 15, 2011).

EVIDENCE-INFORMED DECISION MAKING

Should Breastfeeding Be Mandatory?

The year is 2021. In Canada, obesity rates have continued to skyrocket—especially among children. Type 2 diabetes is increasingly being diagnosed in elementary school children, and schools have begun screening third graders for high blood glucose levels, high blood pressure, unhealthy blood lipids, and other indicators of metabolic syndrome. In this climate, Marcy goes shopping for infant formula. She has been breastfeeding her daughter Sidney exclusively, but next week she returns to work full-time and wants to switch four-month-old Sidney to formula. Marcy picks up a large can of powdered formula and takes it to the check-out. When the clerk at the register announces the price, she gasps. "There must be some mistake! This is only enough formula to feed my daughter for a week!"

"It's not our fault," the clerk replies. "Only half that cost is for the formula. The rest is the new federal tax to discourage you from buying it! Took effect last month—didn't you hear about it?" Marcy shakes her head as she digs back into her wallet for the extra cash. The clerk offers a sympathetic smile. "I guess it's just one more reason why breast is best!"

If this scenario sounds like bad fiction, you might be interested to learn that some healthcare providers are actually proposing that governments implement a system of rewards for breastfeeding and penalties for formula-feeding—and a tax like the one just described is among the various proposals. Why? What's behind these recommendations, and could they ever really become law? Let's have a look.

As rates of pediatric and adult obesity have continued to climb, more and more researchers have been asking the question: "Do breastfed infants have lower rates of obesity as children, adolescents, and adults compared to people who were formula-fed as infants?"[69–74] These researchers

point to the theory of *metabolic programming,* which states that nutritional and other factors in early postnatal life greatly influence one's physiology and subsequent risk of adult-onset, chronic diseases. Specifically, researchers have been investigating the hypothesis that infant feeding practices (breast- vs. formula-feeding) modify patterns of infant growth and development, which then influence the individual's future health, including risk of obesity. Supporting this theory is the established fact that breastfed infants grow in length and weight at a slower rate than formula-fed infants. But does this lower weight persist into childhood and adulthood?

While some studies show no protective effect, most have concluded that breastfeeding for longer than three to six months does, in fact, lower rates of child and adult overweight and obesity.[69–72] One researcher estimated that early breastfeeding reduced risk of childhood (school age) obesity by 15% to 25%.[73] Others concluded exclusive breastfeeding provides greater protection than partial breastfeeding, and that the longer breastfeeding persists, the greater the protection against obesity.[69, 73] At least one study reported that the most benefit was seen among Caucasian infants, with less of a protective effect in Hispanic and African-American breastfed infants.[69]

While researchers continue to investigate possible mechanisms, it has been suggested that the obesity risk reduction associated with breastfeeding may stem from the lower protein and energy intakes of breastfed infants, alterations in their regulation of insulin secretion, and/or differences in adipocyte metabolism.[73] Rapid weight gain during infancy, which is more common among formula-fed infants, is associated with a higher risk of obesity later in life.[69] Some scientists have suggested the differences in feeding patterns between breast- and formula-fed infants impacts risk of obesity: formula-fed infants suck at a faster and more powerful rate, have fewer "meals" per day, consume a larger volume at each meal, and have longer intervals between feedings compared to breastfed infants.[71] It is possible that these feeding differences translate into different eating habits as the infant transitions to child and adult diets.

In light of the convincing data from these studies, a new question arises: Does this difference in weight gain suggest that our society should do more to encourage or even require prolonged breastfeeding? Before you answer, consider the costs of obesity and its related chronic diseases: as you have learned in previous chapters of this book, obesity is a well-established risk factor for heart disease, stroke, type 2 diabetes, and some forms of cancer.

Formula-feeding has been associated with an increased risk of obesity in childhood and adulthood.

One proposed disincentive for formula-feeding is a tax on purchases of formula similar to the taxes on alcohol and tobacco products.

As such, it is one of the primary underlying causes of preventable death in Canada. What's more, obesity-related costs account for an estimated $4.6 billion annually, with additional costs for those who are overweight, but not obese.[75] Estimates rise to approximately $7.1 billion when based on the costs associated with 18 chronic diseases linked to obesity.

Given this staggering financial burden of obesity, and the fact that much of it is borne by the public in the form of higher healthcare costs, not to mention reduced tax revenues (from lost productivity) and increased disability payments, does the government have a right to legislate actions that could possibly reduce obesity rates? Let's look at some precedents: by law, most municipal water supplies are fluoridated to reduce incidence of tooth decay. By law, all grain products are fortified with folic acid to reduce incidence of neural tube defects. By law, sales of alcohol and tobacco are restricted to adults, and carry heavy taxes, to reduce the incidence of alcohol abuse, smoking, and substance-related diseases. All of these laws were enacted not only to improve the public health, but also to reduce the financial burden of disease on the Canadian public. Although some would argue that such regulations take away our "personal freedoms," others point out that they primarily protect children and adolescents, either from the poor choices of their parents, or from the harmful consequences of their own choices, which they are too young to fully understand.

Using the Evidence

1. If breastfeeding were shown to significantly lower the rates of child, adolescent, and adult obesity, do you think it should be highly encouraged? If so, how?

2. Would it be fair to impose a tax on all infant formula sales?

3. Or, do you think the decision to breast- or formula-feed an infant should rest with the family?

17

Nutrition Through the Life Cycle: Childhood and Adolescence

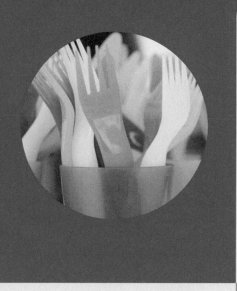

Test Yourself True *or* False?

1. After their first birthday, all children should be fed non-fat milk products to reduce their risk for obesity. T *or* F

2. The nutrient needs of boys do not differ from those of girls for the first eight or nine years of life. T *or* F

3. Images in the media are the primary cause of disordered eating. T *or* F

4. Adolescents experience an average 10% to 15% increase in height during the pubertal years. T *or* F

5. It is now believed that diet has virtually no role in the development of acne. T *or* F

Test Yourself answers are located in the Chapter Review.

Chapter Objectives | *After reading this chapter, you will be able to:*

1. Compare and contrast the growth and activity patterns of toddlers and children, *pp. 628–635, 635–641.*

2. List at least three nutrients of concern when feeding a vegan diet to young children, *pp. 634, 636.*

3. Describe how micronutrient needs change as a child matures to adolescence, *p. 638.*

4. Describe the consequences of iron-deficiency anemia in young children, *p. 640.*

5. Define puberty and describe how it influences changes in body composition, *pp. 642–643.*

6. Identify the most common nutrient deficiencies and excesses of the typical adolescent diet, *pp. 643–648.*

7. List at least two factors that increase risk of obesity during childhood and adolescence, *pp. 649–652.*

The Williams children are growing up in a typical time-pressed Canadian household. Breakfast often means grabbing a donut or granola bar, lunch is supplied by their school or preschool, and dinners are usually eaten in the car on the way to a music lesson, sports practice, Scouts meeting, or community event. Six-year-old Kimberly is often rewarded by her piano instructor with a piece of candy for a job well done. Eight-year-old Chris typically ends soccer practice with a soda and a fistful of chips, and 11-year-old Sam looks forward to Scout meetings mainly for the cupcakes and cookies that are served. Even when the family finds time for a "home-cooked dinner," parents Bill and Emily often serve frozen fried chicken or fish sticks to avoid arguments over carrot sticks or green vegetables. Neither parent will go to the grocery store with the children: the constant food advertising on children's TV programs has led to relentless nagging by the kids for one high-sugar/high-fat food after another.

What are the consequences of this type of haphazard approach to family eating? Are families like the Williams able to meet the changing nutrient needs of their children as they grow and develop? How does the current "epidemic" of childhood obesity relate to the haphazard eating practices of many Canadian families? This chapter will help you answer these and related questions. Although most topics are discussed within specific age groupings (toddlers, children, and adolescents), the chapter closes with a review of pediatric obesity, a critically important issue that affects children of all ages.

Many families typically grab quick meals "on the go."

Nutrition for Toddlers

When babies celebrate their first birthday, they transition out of infancy and into the active world of toddlers. Personality and behavioural changes introduce potential conflict into mealtimes, and parents who have been accustomed to making all decisions about their child's diet must now begin to consider the child's preferences. In addition, toddlers attending day care may be exposed to foods that may be more or less nutritious than the foods served at home. These and other circumstances add new challenges to the feeding process.

Toddler Growth and Activity Patterns

Toddlers expend significant amounts of energy actively exploring their world.

The rapid growth rate of infancy begins to slow during toddlerhood, the second and third years of life. A toddler will grow a total of about 14 to 19 cm and gain an average of 4 to 5 kg. Toddlers expend more energy to fuel increasing levels of activity as they explore their ever-expanding world and develop new skills. They progress from taking a few wobbly steps to running, jumping, and climbing with confidence, and they begin to dress, feed, and toilet themselves. Thus, their diet should provide an appropriate quantity and quality of nutrients to fuel their growth and activity.

What Are a Toddler's Nutrient Needs?

Nutrient needs increase as a child progresses from infancy to toddlerhood. Although their rate of growth has slowed, toddlers' increased nutrient needs are based on their larger body size. Refer to Table 17.1 for a review of specific nutrient recommendations.

Energy and Macronutrient Recommendations for Toddlers

Although the energy requirement per kilogram of body weight for toddlers is just slightly less than for infants, *total* energy requirements are higher because toddlers are larger and much more active than infants. The estimated energy requirement (EER), or the total energy needed per day, varies according to the toddler's age, body weight, and level of activity.

Although there is currently insufficient evidence available to set a DRI for fat for toddlers, healthy toddlers of appropriate body weight need to consume 30% to 40% of their total daily energy intake as fat.[1] That's because fat provides a concentrated source of energy in a relatively small amount of food, and this is important for toddlers, especially those who

Table 17.1 Nutrient Recommendations for Children and Adolescents[1, 4–6]

Nutrient	Children Age 1–3 Years	Children Age 4–8 Years	Children Age 9–13 Years	Adolescents (14–18 Years)
Fat	No DRI	No DRI	No DRI	No DRI
Protein	1.10 g/kg body weight per day	0.95 g/kg body weight per day	0.95 g/kg body weight per day	0.85 g/kg body weight per day
Carbohydrate	130 g/day	130 g/day	130 g/day	130 g/day
Vitamin A	300 µg/day	400 µg/day	600 µg/day	Boys = 900 µg/day Girls = 700 µg/day
Vitamin C	15 mg/day	25 mg/day	45 mg/day	Boys = 75 mg/day Girls = 65 mg/day
Vitamin D	15 µg/day	15 µg/day	15 µg/day	15 µg/day
Vitamin E	6 mg/day	7 mg/day	11 mg/day	15 mg/day
Calcium	700 mg/day	1000 mg/day	1300 mg/day	1300 mg/day
Iron	7 mg/day	10 mg/day	8 mg/day	Boys = 11 mg/day Girls = 15 mg/day
Zinc	3 mg/day	5 mg/day	8 mg/day	Boys = 11 mg/day Girls = 9 mg/day
Fluid	1.3 L/day	1.7 L/day	Boys = 2.4 L/day Girls = 2.1 L/day	Boys = 3.3 L/day Girls = 2.3 L/day

are fussy eaters or have little appetite. Fat is also necessary during the toddler years to support the continuously developing nervous system.

Toddlers' protein needs increase modestly because they weigh more than infants and are still growing rapidly. The RDA for protein for toddlers is 1.1 g/kg body weight per day, or approximately 13 g of protein daily.[1] Recall that 500 mL of milk alone provides 16 g of protein; thus, most toddlers have little trouble meeting their protein needs.

The RDA for carbohydrate for toddlers is 130 g/day, and carbohydrate intake should be about 45% to 65% of total energy intake.[1] As is the case for older children and adults, most of the carbohydrates eaten should be complex, and refined carbohydrates from high-fat/high-energy foods such as cookies and candy should be kept to a minimum. Fruits and many fruit juices are nutritious sources of simple carbohydrates that can also be included. Keep in mind, however, that too much fruit juice can displace other foods and nutrients and can cause diarrhea. If consumed at bedtime or between meals, the sugars in fruit juice may also contribute to tooth decay. The Canadian Paediatric Society recommends that the intake of fruit juice be limited to 120 to 160 mL per day for children one to six years of age.[2]

Adequate fibre is important for toddlers to maintain regularity. The AI is 14 g of fibre per 1000 kcal of energy, or, based on the average energy intake of this age group, 19 g/day.[1] In one study, 98% of young children (one to four years) failed to meet this AI for fibre.[3] Whole-grain cereals, fresh fruits and vegetables, and whole-grain breads are healthy choices for toddlers' meals and snacks. Too much fibre, however, can inhibit the absorption of several nutrients such as iron and zinc, harm toddlers' small digestive tracts, and cause them to feel too full to consume adequate nutrients.

Determining the macronutrient requirements of toddlers can be challenging. See the upcoming box, You Do the Math, for analysis of the macronutrient levels in one toddler's daily diet.

Micronutrient Recommendations for Toddlers

As toddlers grow, their micronutrient needs increase. Of particular concern with toddlers are adequate intakes of the micronutrients associated with fruits and vegetables. In addition, calcium and iron have been identified as "priority nutrients" for children aged two to four years.[3]

Calcium is necessary for children to promote optimal bone mass, which continues to accumulate until early adulthood. For toddlers, the RDA for calcium is 700 mg/day.[4] Dairy products are excellent sources of calcium. When a child reaches the age of one year, whole cow's milk can be given; however, reduced-fat milk (2% or less) should *not* be given until age two. If dairy products are not feasible, calcium-fortified orange juice, soy milk, or rice milk can supply calcium, or children's calcium supplements can be given. Toddlers generally cannot consume enough food to depend on alternative calcium sources such as dark-green vegetables.

Iron-deficiency anemia is the most common nutrient deficiency in young children in Canada and around the world. Iron-deficiency anemia can affect a child's energy level, attention span, and ability to learn. The RDA for iron for toddlers is 7 mg/day.[5] Good sources of well-absorbed heme iron include lean meats, fish, and poultry; non-heme iron is provided by eggs, legumes, greens, and fortified foods such as breakfast cereals. When toddlers consume non-heme sources of iron, such as beans or greens, a source of vitamin C at the same meal will enhance the absorption of iron from these sources.

Fluid Recommendations for Toddlers

Toddlers lose less fluid from evaporation than infants, and their more mature kidneys are able to concentrate urine, conserving the body's fluid. However, as toddlers become active, they start to lose significant fluid through sweat, especially in hot weather. Parents need to make sure an active toddler is drinking adequately. The recommended fluid intake for toddlers is listed in Table 17.1 and includes about 1 L as beverages, including water.[6] Suggested beverages include plain water, milk, calcium-fortified soy milk or rice milk, and foods high in water content, such as vegetables and fruits.

Do Toddlers Need Nutritional Supplements?

Toddlers can be well nourished by consuming a balanced, varied diet. But given their typically erratic eating habits, the child's physician may recommend a multivitamin and mineral supplement as a precaution against deficiencies. The toddler's physician or dentist may also prescribe a fluoride supplement, if the community water supply is not fluoridated. Supplements should also be considered for children in vegan families, children from families who cannot afford adequate amounts of nourishing foods, children with certain medical conditions or dietary restrictions, or very picky or erratic eaters.

As always, if a supplement is given, it should be formulated especially for toddlers and the recommended dose should not be exceeded. A supplement should not contain more than 100% of the Daily Value of any nutrient per dose.

Many parents choose special cereals, snack foods, and packaged dinners for their young children. How do the nutrient values of these foods compare to those of similar versions for adults? See the Nutrition Label Activity, on page 632, to find out.

Encouraging Nutritious Food Choices with Toddlers

Parents and pediatricians have long known that toddlers tend to be choosy about what they eat. Some avoid entire foods groups, such as all meats or vegetables. Others refuse all but one or two favourite foods (such as peanut butter on crackers) for several days or longer. Still others eat in extremely small amounts, seemingly satisfied by a single slice of apple or two bites of toast. These behaviours frustrate and worry many parents, but in fact, as long as a variety of healthy food is available, most normal-weight toddlers are able to match their food intake with their needs. A toddler will most likely make up for one day's nutrient or energy deficiency later in the week. Parents who offer only nutritious foods can feel confident that their children are being well fed, even if a child's choices seem odd or erratic on any particular day. Food should never be "forced" on a child, as doing so sets the stage for eating and control issues later in life.

YOU DO THE MATH

Is This Menu Good for a Toddler?

A dedicated mother and father want to provide the best nutrition for their young son, Ethan, who is now 1½ years old and has just been completely weaned from breast milk. Ethan weighs 11.8 kg. Following is a typical day's menu for Ethan. Grams of protein, fat, and carbohydrate are given for each food. The day's total energy intake is 1168 kcal. Calculate the percentage of Ethan's kilocalories that come from protein, fat, and carbohydrate (numbers may not add up to exactly 100% because of rounding). Where are Ethan's parents doing well, and where could they use some advice for improvement?

Meal	Foods	Protein (g)	Fat (g)	Carbo-hydrate (g)
Breakfast	Oatmeal (125 mL, cooked)	2.5	1.5	13.5
	Brown sugar (5 mL)	0	0	4
	Milk (1%, 125 mL)	4	1.25	5.5
	Grape juice (125 mL)	0	0	20
Mid-morning Snack	Banana slices (1 small banana)	0	0	16
	Yogourt (non-fat fruit flavoured, 90 mL)	5.5	0	15.5
	Orange juice (125 mL)	1	0	13
Lunch	Whole-wheat bread (1 slice)	1.5	0.5	10
	Peanut butter (15 mL)	4	8	3.5
	Strawberry jam (15 mL)	0	0	13
	Carrots (cooked, 30 mL)	0	0	2
	Applesauce (sweetened, 60 mL)	0	0	12
	Milk (1%, 125 mL)	4	1.25	5.5
Afternoon Snack	Bagel (1/2)	3	1	20
	Processed cheese (1 slice)	3	5	1
	Water	0	0	0
Dinner	Scrambled egg (1)	11	5	1
	Baby food spinach (90 mL)	2	0.5	5.5
	Whole-wheat toast (1 slice)	1.5	0.5	10
	Mandarin orange slices (60 mL)	0.5	0	10
	Milk (1%, 125 mL)	4	1.25	5.5

Note: This activity focuses on the macronutrients. It does not ask you to consider Ethan's intake of micronutrients or fluids.

Calculations:
There is a total of 47.5 g protein in Ethan's menu.

$$47.5 \text{ g} \times 4 \text{ kcal/g} = 190 \text{ kcal}$$
190 kcal protein/1168 total kcal × 100 = 16% protein

There is a total of 25.75 g fat in Ethan's menu.

$$25.75 \text{ g} \times 9 \text{ kcal/g} = 232 \text{ kcal}$$
232 kcal fat/1168 total kcal × 100 = 20% fat

There is a total of 186.5 g carbohydrate in Ethan's menu.

$$186.5 \text{ g} \times 4 \text{ cal/g} = 746 \text{ kcal}$$
746 kcal carbohydrate/1168 total kcal × 100
= 64% carbohydrate

Analysis: Ethan's parents are doing very well at offering a wide variety of foods from various food groups; they are especially doing well with fruits and vegetables. Also, according to his EER, Ethan requires about 970 kcal/day, and he is consuming 1168 kcal/day, thus meeting his energy needs.

Ethan's total carbohydrate intake for the day is 186.5 g, which is higher than the RDA of 130 g per day; however, this value falls within the recommended 45% to 65% of total energy intake that should come from carbohydrates. Thus, his carbohydrate intake is adequate to meet his energy needs.

However, Ethan is being offered far more than enough protein. The DRI for protein for toddlers is about 13 g per day, and Ethan is being offered more than three times that much!

It is also readily apparent that Ethan is being offered too little fat for his age. Toddlers need at least 30% to 40% of their total energy intake from fat, and Ethan is only consuming about 20% of his calories from fat. He should be drinking whole milk, not 1% milk. He should occasionally be offered higher-fat foods like cheese for his snacks or macaroni and cheese for a meal. Yogourt is fine, but it shouldn't be non-fat at Ethan's age.

In conclusion, Ethan's parents should be commended for offering a variety of nutritious foods but should be counselled that a little more fat is critical for toddlers' growth and development. Some of the energy currently being consumed as protein and carbohydrate should be shifted to fat.

Toddlers' stomachs are still very small, and they cannot consume all of the energy they need in three meals. They need small meals, interspersed with nutritious snacks, every two to three hours. A successful technique is to create a snack tray filled with small portions of nutritious food choices, such as one-third of a banana, two pieces of cheese, and two whole-grain crackers, and leave it within reach of the child's play area. The child can then

NUTRITION LABEL ACTIVITY

Comparing Foods for Children and Adults

Parents who purchase foods such as "junior dinners" for their toddlers often check the Nutrition Facts table for information on the ingredients and nutrient values of the products. Many of these parents may not realize that Health Canada has specific label requirements for products aimed at children less than two years old.

Food products designed for children under two years of age cannot list:

- the % Daily Value for fat, cholesterol, sodium, potassium, carbohydrate, fibre, and the sum of saturated and trans fatty acids
- the energy value from fat and the sum of saturated and trans fatty acids
- any of the footnotes to the subheading "% Daily Value"

The amount of saturated fatty acids, trans fatty acids, and cholesterol may be omitted from the Nutrition Facts table for foods for children under two. However, when cholesterol is declared, the amount of saturated fatty acids and trans fatty acids must also be declared.[7]

Compare the labels of the "Junior Vegetable Chicken Noodle" dinner (**Figure 17.1a**) and the adult "Chicken and Vegetables with Pasta" (Figure 17.1b). What other differences in the Nutrition Facts table do you see? Compare the ingredient list for the two products.

What is the most prevalent ingredient in the toddler food? Does the toddler food contain all or any of the food additives listed in the adult product? Why do you believe there is a difference?

Chicken & Vegetables with Pasta
Nutrition Facts
Per 1 package (280 g)

Amount	% Daily Value
Calories 245	
Fat 6 g	9 %
Saturated 2.5 g	
+ Trans 0.1 g	13 %
Cholesterol 30 mg	
Sodium 570 mg	24 %
Carbohydrate 30 g	10 %
Fibre 3 g	
Sugars 4 g	
Protein 18 g	
Vitamin A	20 %
Vitamin C	20 %
Calcium	10 %
Iron	8 %

INGREDIENTS: ENRICHED PASTA (WATER, DURUM WHEAT, SEMOLINA), WHITE CHICKEN MEAT, CARROTS, BROCCOLI, BELL PEPPER, CELERY, ONION, SALT, MALTODEXTRIN, SUGAR, GARLIC, SPICES, GUAR GUM, PARTIALLY HYDRO-GENATED SOYBEAN OIL, CORN SYRUP SOLIDS, SODIUM PHOSPHATE, YEAST EXTRACT, COLOUR.

Junior Vegetable Chicken Noodle
(8+ months baby)
Nutrition Facts
Per ½ jar (100 mL)

Amount	% Daily Value
Calories 70	
Fat 1 g	
Sodium 80 mg	
Carbohydrate 10 g	
Fibre 2 g	
Sugars 2 g	
Protein 3 g	
Vitamin A	50 %
Vitamin C	4 %
Calcium	2 %
Iron	4 %

INGREDIENTS: WATER, PEAS, CARROTS, CHICKEN, PASTA (ENRICHED DURUM WHEAT), SWEET POTATOES, GREEN SPLIT PEAS, ONION POWDER, SPICES.

(a)   (b)

Figure 17.1 Label guidelines for foods targeting infants and children under the age of two years differ from the labelling regulations for other foods. (a) Label from junior vegetable chicken noodle dinner. (b) Label from an adult chicken and vegetables with pasta dinner.

Foods for children under two years of age cannot be labelled with some nutrient claims ("low-fat") or health claims that often appear on food labels. Only the following five nutrient content claims can be used for foods intended solely for children under two:

- "source of protein"
- "excellent source of protein"
- "more protein"
- "no added sodium" (or salt)
- "no added sugars"

Vitamin and mineral nutrient content claims are permitted provided the foods meet the daily intake criteria for the age group. Claims regarding the amount of starch in a food are also permitted. However, diet-related health claims are not allowed on foods that are intended solely for children under two.[7]

The small size of children two years and under means they have lower nutrient needs than adults. Nutrition Facts information for products marketed to young children is therefore based on smaller serving sizes and age-appropriate Daily Values. Because there are no Daily Values (DVs) for total and saturated fat, cholesterol, sodium, or fibre for children under the age of two years, there are also no percentage daily value figures for those nutrients on the labels of foods aimed at these children.

"graze" on these healthy foods while he or she plays. A snack tray, plus a spill-proof cup of milk or water, is particularly useful on car trips.

Foods prepared for toddlers should be developmentally appropriate. Nuts, carrots, grapes, raisins, and cherry tomatoes are difficult for a toddler to chew and pose a choking hazard. Foods should be soft and sliced into strips or wedges that are easy for children to grasp. As the child develops more teeth and becomes more coordinated, the foods offered can become more varied. Though certainly not necessary, several food companies now market "toddler foods" geared specifically to their developmental stage. The Nutrition Label Activity provides the opportunity to compare labelling practices for toddler and adult foods.

Most toddlers are delighted by food prepared in a "fun" way.

Foods prepared for toddlers should also be fun. Parents can use cookie cutters to turn a peanut-butter sandwich into a pumpkin face or arrange cooked peas or carrot slices to look like a smiling face on top of mashed potatoes. Juice and yogourt can be frozen into "popsicles" or blended into "milkshakes."

A positive environment helps toddlers develop good mealtime habits as well. Parents should consistently seat the toddler in the same place at the table and make sure that the child is served first. Television and other distractions should be turned off, and pleasant conversation should include the toddler, even if the toddler hasn't begun to speak. Toddlers should not be forced to sit still until they finish every bite, as they still have short attention spans.

Even at mealtime, portion sizes should be small. Fifteen mL of a food for each year of age constitutes a serving throughout the toddler and preschool years (**Figure 17.2**). Realistic portion sizes can give toddlers a sense of accomplishment when they "eat it all up" and reduce parents' fears that their child is not eating enough.

New foods should be introduced gradually. Most toddlers are leery of new foods, spicy foods, hot (temperature) foods, mixed foods such as casseroles, and foods with strange textures. A helpful rule is to encourage the child to eat at least one bite of a new food: if the child does not want the rest, nothing negative should be said, and the child should be praised just for the willingness to try. The same food should be reintroduced a few weeks later. Eventually, after several tries, the child might accept the food. Some foods, however, won't be accepted until well into adulthood as tastes expand and develop. Parents should never bribe with food—for example, promising dessert if the child finishes her squash. Bribing teaches children that food can be used to reward and manipulate. Instead, parents should try to positively reinforce good behaviours; for

Figure 17.2 Portion sizes for toddlers and preschoolers are much smaller than for older children. Use the following guideline: 15 mL of the food for each year of age equals 1 serving.

example, "Wow! You ate every bite of your squash! That's going to help you grow big and strong!"

Role modelling is important because toddlers mimic older children and adults: if they see their parents eating a variety of healthy foods, toddlers will be likely to do so as well. Limiting the alternatives can also help toddlers to make nutritious food choices. For example, parents might say, "It's snack time! Would you like apples and cheese, or bananas and yogourt?" Finally, toddlers are more likely to eat food they help prepare: encourage them to assist in the preparation of simple foods, such as helping pour a bowl of cereal or helping to arrange the raw vegetables on a plate.

Nutrition-Related Concerns for Toddlers

Just as toddlers have their own specific nutrient needs, they also have toddler-specific nutrition concerns.

Continued Allergy Watch

As during infancy, wheat, peanuts, cow's milk, soy, citrus, egg whites, and seafood remain common food allergens. New foods should be presented one at a time, and the toddler should be monitored for allergic reactions for a week before additional new foods are introduced. To prevent the development of food allergies, even foods that are established in the diet should be rotated rather than served every day.

Vegetarian Families

For toddlers, an ovo-lacto-vegetarian diet in which eggs and dairy foods are included can be as wholesome as a diet including meats and fish.[8] However, because meat, fish, and poultry are excellent sources of zinc and heme iron, the most bioavailable form of iron, vegetarian families must be careful to include enough zinc and iron from other sources in their child's diet.

In contrast, a vegan diet, in which no foods of animal origin are consumed, poses several potential nutritional risks for toddlers:

Foods that may cause allergies, such as peanuts and citrus fruits, should be introduced to toddlers one at a time.

- Protein: Vegan diets can be too low in protein for toddlers, who need protein for growth and increasing activity. Few toddlers can consume enough legumes and whole grains to provide sufficient protein. The high-fibre content of these foods quickly produces a sense of fullness for the toddler, decreasing total food intake.
- Calcium, iron, and zinc: Calcium is a concern because of the avoidance of milk, yogourt, and cheese. As with protein, few toddlers can consume enough calcium from plant sources to meet their daily requirement, and supplementation is advised. Iron and zinc are also commonly low in vegan diets because of the absence of meat, fish, and poultry. They need to be provided by fortified cereals, legumes, and possibly supplements.
- Vitamins D and B_{12}: Both vitamins are typically lower in strict vegan diets. Soy milks are now fortified with vitamin D; however, some toddlers may still need a vitamin D–containing supplement. Vitamin B_{12} is not available naturally in any amount from plant foods and must be supplemented.
- Fibre: Vegan diets often contain a higher amount of fibre than is recommended for toddlers, resulting in lowered absorption of iron and zinc as well as a premature sense of fullness or satiety at mealtimes.

The practice of feeding a vegan diet to infants and young children is highly controversial. See the Nutrition Myth or Fact? box, on the next page, for more information about this controversy.

Soy milk can be a part of a healthy vegan diet for toddlers.

Nutrition for Preschool and School-Age Children

Children develop increased language fluency, improved decision-making skills, and greater physical coordination and dexterity as they progress through the preschool and school-age years. The nutrient requirements and nutrition issues of importance to children are discussed in this section.

Childhood Growth and Activity Patterns

Growth rate slows and activity ideally increases. Children experience a slow and steady rate of growth, averaging 5 to 10 cm per year, until the rapid growth of adolescence begins. Activity levels among children vary dramatically—some love sports and physical activity, whereas others prefer quieter activities like reading and drawing. Television, computer-based activity, and electronic games often tempt children into a sedentary lifestyle. All children can be encouraged to enjoy walking, to appreciate nature and exploration, and to have fun using their minds and their muscles in various ways that suit their interests. Activity-based interactive DVD games are ideal for children who must remain indoors for extended periods of time. The Canadian Society for Exercise Physiology has developed guidelines for physical activity for children 5–11 years of age (see page 541).

What Are a Child's Nutrient Needs?

Three-year-olds have the same set of nutrient recommendations that apply to toddlers (see Table 17.1). From age four through eight, the values for most nutrients increase. Until age nine, the nutrient needs of young boys do not differ significantly from those of girls; because of this, the DRI values for macronutrients, fibre, and micronutrients are grouped together for boys and girls aged four to eight years. The onset of sexual maturation, however, has a dramatic effect on the nutrient needs of children. Boys' and girls' bodies develop differently in response to gender-specific hormones. Because the process of sexual maturation begins subtly between the ages of eight and nine, the DRI values are separately defined for boys and girls beginning at age nine.[1, 4–6] (See Table 17.1.)

Energy and Macronutrient Recommendations for Children

Total energy requirements continue to increase throughout childhood because of increasing body size and, for some children, higher levels of physical activity. The EER varies according to the child's age, body weight, and level of activity. Parents should provide diets

NUTRITION MYTH OR FACT?

Are Vegan Diets Appropriate for Young Children?

Among Canadian adolescents, approximately 1.0%–2.4% of males and 3.3%–8.8% of females are vegetarians.[9] Whereas the adoption of a vegan diet among older children and teens is rarely viewed with concern, it only takes an online search in the archives of any major news outlet to realize that feeding a vegan diet to very young children is a controversial practice. Proponents of the vegan diet assert that feeding animal products to children is forcing them into a life of obesity, clogged arteries, and chronic diet-related diseases. In addition, many people who consume a vegan diet feel that consumption of animal products wastes natural resources and contributes to environmental damage and is therefore morally wrong. In contrast, opponents emphasize that feeding a vegan diet to young children deprives them of essential nutrients that can only be found in animal products. Some people even suggest that veganism for young children is, in essence, a form of child abuse.

As with many controversies, there are truths on both sides. For example, there have been documented cases of children failing to thrive, and even dying, on extreme vegan diets.[10, 11] Some research studies document deficiencies of vitamin B_{12}, vitamin D, iron, calcium, and protein in vegan children and infants.[12, 13] These nutrients are found primarily in animal products and are often better utilized from animal vs. plant sources. Deficiencies of these nutrients can have serious and lifelong consequences. For example, not all of the neurologic impairments caused by vitamin B_{12} deficiency can be reversed by timely B_{12} supplement intervention. In addition, inadequate zinc, calcium, and vitamin D can result in impaired bone growth and strength, failure to reach peak bone mass, and retarded growth in general.

However, close inspection of published reports of nutrition-related illness in children, including protein-energy malnutrition, that cite veganism as the culprit reveals that lack of education, fanaticism, and/or extremism is usually at the root of the problem. Informed parents following responsible vegan diets are rarely involved.[14] On the other hand, such cases do point out that veganism is not a lifestyle one can safely undertake without thorough education regarding the necessity of supplementation of those nutrients not available in plant products. Parents also need to understand that typical vegan diets are high in fibre and low in fat, a combination that can be dangerous for very young children.[14] Moreover, certain staples of the vegan diet, such as wheat, soy, and nuts, commonly provoke allergic reactions in children; when this happens, finding a plant-based substitute that contains adequate nutrients can be challenging.

Most nutrition experts recommend a more moderate diet—one that includes fish, dairy products, and eggs—rather than a vegan diet for young children. This snack of peanut-butter sandwiches and milk is a healthy choice.

Both the Academy of Nutrition and Dietetics, in conjunction with Dietitians of Canada,[15] and the American Academy of Pediatrics[16] have stated that a balanced vegan diet can promote normal childhood growth and development—*provided* that adequate supplements and/or fortified foods are consumed to account for the nutrients that are normally obtained from animal products. However, most healthcare organizations stop short of outright endorsement of a vegan diet for young children. Instead, many advocate a more moderate approach during the early childhood years. Reasons for this level of caution include acknowledgment of several factors:

- Some vegan parents are not adequately educated on the planning of meals, the balancing of foods, and the inclusion of supplements to ensure adequate levels of all nutrients.
- Most young children are picky eaters and are hesitant to eat certain food groups, particularly vegetables, a staple in the vegan diet.
- The high fibre content of vegan diets may not be appropriate for very young children.
- Young children have small stomachs, and they are not able to consume enough plant-based foods to ensure adequate intakes of all nutrients and energy.

Because of these concerns, most nutrition experts advise parents to take a more moderate dietary approach, one that emphasizes plant foods but also includes some animal-based foods, such as fish, dairy, and/or eggs.

Once children reach school age, the low fat, abundant fibre, antioxidants, and many micronutrients in a vegan diet will promote their health as they progress into adulthood. However, those who consume animal products can also live a healthy life and reduce their risk for chronic diseases by choosing low-fat, nutrient-dense foods such as lean meats, non-fat dairy products, whole grains, and fruits and vegetables. Because animal products are consumed, there are fewer worries about consuming adequate amounts of micronutrients such as vitamin B_{12}, calcium, vitamin D, iron, and zinc.

In summary, the appropriateness of a vegan diet varies according to several factors. Although the potential for malnutrition is ever present, well-educated parents of school-age children can ensure a healthy vegan diet with careful meal planning, including appropriate use of fortified foods and beverages, and supplements.

School-aged children grow an average of 5 to 7.5 cm per year.

that support normal growth and appropriate physical activity while minimizing risk of excess weight gain.

Fat Although dietary fat remains a key macronutrient in the preschool years, as the child ages, total fat should gradually be reduced to a level closer to that of an adult, around 25% to 35% of total energy.[1] One easy way to start reducing dietary fat is to slowly introduce lower-fat dairy products such as 2% or 1% milk, low-fat yogourt, and low-fat mozzarella cheese sticks while minimizing the intake of fried foods. A diet providing fewer than 25% of calories from fat is not recommended for children, as they are still growing, developing, and maturing. In fact, unless the child is overweight or has specific health concerns, parents should avoid putting too much emphasis on fat restriction during this age span. Impressionable and peer-influenced children may be prone to categorizing foods as "good" or "bad." This may lead to skewed views of food and inappropriate dietary restrictions.

Carbohydrate The RDA for carbohydrate for children is 130 g/day, which is about 45% to 65% of total daily energy intake.[1] Complex carbohydrates from whole grains, fruits, vegetables, and legumes should be emphasized. Simple sugars should come from fruits and fruit juices, with foods high in refined sugars, such as cakes, cookies, and candies, saved for occasional indulgences. The AI for fibre for children is 14 g/1000 kcal, which can be met by the consumption of fresh fruits, vegetables, legumes, and whole grains.[1] As was the case with toddlers, too much fibre can be detrimental because it can make a child feel full and interfere with adequate food intake and lower the absorption of certain nutrients such as iron and zinc.

Protein Total need for protein (shown in Table 17.1) increases for children because of their larger size, even though their growth rate has slowed. The RDA for protein is 0.95 g/kg of body weight per day.[1] This protein requirement is easily met by portions such as one chicken drumstick and two glasses of milk or 125 mL pinto beans, 25 g of cheese, and half a peanut-butter sandwich. Lean meats, fish, poultry, lower-fat dairy products, soy-based foods, and legumes are nutritious sources of protein that can be provided to children of all ages. Children who follow a vegetarian diet can meet their protein needs by following dietary guidelines such as those in *Eating Well with Canada's Food Guide.*[17]

Micronutrient Recommendations for Children

The need for most micronutrients increases slightly for children up to age eight because of their increasing size. A sharper increase occurs during the transition years approaching adolescence; this increase is due to the impending adolescent growth spurt and the early phases of sexual maturation. Children who fail to consume the recommended amount of fruits and vegetables each day may become deficient in vitamins A, C, and E. Offering fruits and fresh vegetables as snacks as well as during mealtimes can increase intakes of these vitamins as well as fibre and potassium, two priority nutrients found lacking in the diets of low-income children.[3]

Minerals of concern continue to be calcium, iron, and zinc, which come primarily from animal-based foods. The RDA for calcium is 1000 mg/day for children aged 4 to 8 years and 1300 mg/day for children aged 9 to 13 years.[4] As you learned in Chapter 12, peak bone mass is achieved in the late teens or early 20s, and childhood and adolescence are critical times to ensure adequate deposition of bone tissue. Inadequate calcium intake during childhood and adolescence leads to poor bone health and potential osteoporosis in later years.

Low-fat milk, yogourt, cheese, and fortified fruit juices are child-friendly and convenient sources of calcium. The problem of "milk displacement," when children stop drinking milk in favour of soda, punch, energy drinks, and juice, is a recognized factor in low calcium intake.[18] Diets that are low in calcium also tend to be low in other nutrients, so attention to calcium intake can help ensure a healthier overall diet for children.

The RDAs for children aged four to eight years for iron and zinc increase slightly to 10 mg/day and 5 mg/day, respectively.[5] The RDA for iron drops to 8 mg/day for boys and girls aged 9 to 13 years. These recommendations are based on the assumption that most girls do not begin menstruation until after age 13.[5] Mild-flavoured, tender cuts of meat and poultry are readily accepted by most children, and legumes offer a fibre-rich, fat-free alternative that will also add iron and zinc to the diet. Refer again to Table 17.1 for a review of the micronutrient needs of children.

Figure 17.3 outlines the amount of food recommended for a child aged 4–8 years. If there is any concern that a child's nutrient needs are not being met for any reason, such as missed meals or inadequate family resources, vitamin and mineral supplements may help correct any deficit. If used, the supplement should be age-specific and the recommended dose (not more than 100% DV) should not be exceeded.

Fluid Recommendations for Children

The fluid recommendations for children are summarized in Table 17.1 and average about 1.3 to 2 L of beverages per day, including water.[6] The exact amount of fluid needed varies according to the child's level of physical activity and weather conditions. At this point in their lives, children are mostly in control of their own fluid intake. However, as they become more active during school, in sports, and while playing, young children in particular may need reminders to drink to stay properly hydrated, especially if the weather is hot. Most, if not all, of the beverages offered should be caffeine free.

Encouraging Nutritious Food Choices in Children

Peer pressure can be extremely difficult for both parents and their children to deal with during this stage of life. Most children want to feel that they "belong" and will mirror the actions of children they view as popular. Some children have their own spending money, and most are very susceptible to TV and other messages encouraging unhealthy food choices. Children also spend more time visiting friends and eating more meals and snacks

Children's multivitamins often appear in shapes or bright colours.

Although reminders to drink help keep school-aged children hydrated, they mostly control their own fluid intake.

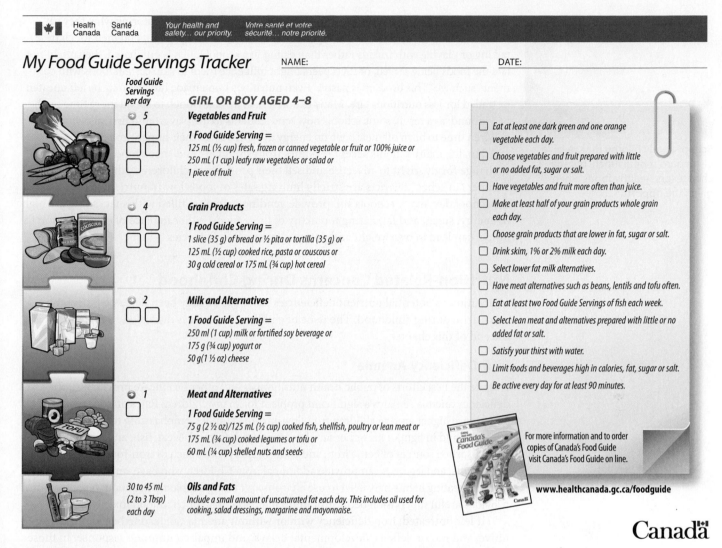

Figure 17.3 Health Canada has developed age-specific guidelines for preschool and school-age children.
Data from: My Food Guide Servings Tracker. Health Canada, 2011. Reproduced with the permission of the Minister of Health, 2012.

without their parents' supervision. The impact of this increasing autonomy on the health of children can be profound, yet parents remain important role models.

Parents and children can work together to find compromises by planning and talking about healthy foods. Families who plan, prepare, and eat meals together are more successful at promoting good food choices. Parents should continue to demonstrate healthy eating and physical activity patterns to maintain a consistent message to their children.

What Is the Effect of School Attendance on Nutrition?

School attendance can affect a child's nutrition in several ways. First, hectic schedules and long bus rides cause many children to minimize or skip breakfast completely. School-aged children who don't eat breakfast may not get a chance to eat until lunch. If the entire morning is spent in a state of hunger, children are more likely to do poorly on schoolwork, have decreased attention spans, and have more behavioural problems than their peers who do eat breakfast.[19] For this reason, many schools now offer breakfast programs. These breakfasts help children to optimize their nutrient intake and avoid the behavioural and learning problems associated with hunger in the classroom.

School-aged children may receive a standard school lunch, but many choose less healthy foods when given the opportunity.

Another consequence of attending school is that with no one monitoring what they eat, children do not always consume adequate amounts of food. They may spend their lunch time talking or playing with friends rather than eating. If a school lunch is purchased, they might not like the foods being served, or their peers might influence them to skip certain foods with comments such as, "This broccoli is nasty!" Even nutritious homemade lunches may be left uneaten or traded for less nutritious fare. Many children rush through lunch to spend more time on the playground; as a result, some schools now send students to the playground first, allowing the children time to burn off their pent-up energy as well as build their hunger and thirst.

Finally, many schools accept revenues from soft drink and snack food companies in exchange for the right to advertise and sell their products to children. Although increasing numbers of school districts are strictly limiting sales of foods low in nutrient value during the school day, many schools still provide vending machines filled with snacks that are high in energy, sugar, and fat. Eating too many of these foods, either in place of or in addition to lunch, can lead to overweight and potential nutrient deficiencies.

Nutrition-Related Concerns During Childhood

In addition to potential nutrient deficiencies that have already been discussed, new concerns arise during childhood. The issue of childhood obesity is discussed in more detail at the end of this chapter.

Iron-Deficiency Anemia

Despite the best efforts of public health nutritionists and other healthcare providers, iron-deficiency anemia remains a significant problem for many children. Rates of iron-deficiency anemia are higher among children from low-income families, emphasizing the need to evaluate each child in light of his or her family's unique risk factors.[3] Meat, fish, and poultry provide well-absorbed sources of heme iron, and child-friendly foods such as iron-fortified cereals, dried fruits, and legumes can provide additional iron. Children who have very poor appetites or erratic eating habits may need to use an iron-containing supplement, although parents must provide careful supervision because of iron's high potential for childhood toxicity.

If left untreated, iron deficiency with or without anemia can lead to behavioural, cognitive, and motor deficits, developmental delays, and impaired immune response. In those children exposed to lead, iron deficiency increases the rate of lead absorption and severity of lead toxicity.[16] Iron-deficiency anemia reduces the child's energy level and contributes to passivity and lethargy. The cognitive and behavioural consequences of iron deficiency in young children can be long-standing, making prevention a critical goal. Early detection through dietary assessments and simple blood tests, followed by effective treatment, ensures all children will enter school healthy and ready to learn.

Dental Caries

As discussed in Chapter 4, *dental caries,* or cavities, occur when bacteria in the mouth feed on carbohydrates deposited on teeth. As a result of metabolizing the carbohydrates, the bacteria secrete acid that begins to erode tooth enamel, leading to tooth decay. The occurrence of dental caries can be minimized by limiting between-meal sweets, especially jelly beans, caramels, and others that stick to teeth, such as fruit leathers. Frequent brushing helps to eliminate the sugars on teeth, as well as the bacteria that feed on them.

Fluoride, either through a municipal water supply or through supplements, will also help deter the development of dental caries. Because "baby teeth" make room for and guide the permanent teeth into position, preschoolers need regular dental care as much as older children. Children should start having regular dental visits at the age of three years.

Body-Image Concerns

As children approach puberty, appearance and body image play increasingly important roles in food choices by both girls and boys. These concerns are not necessarily detrimental to health,

Figure 17.4 Normal, healthy school-aged children come in a variety of shapes and sizes.

particularly if they result in children making more healthy food choices, such as eating more whole grains, fruits, and vegetables. However, it is important for children to understand that being thin does not guarantee health, popularity, or happiness and that a healthy body image includes accepting our own individual body type and recognizing that we can be physically fit and healthy at a variety of weights, shapes, and sizes (**Figure 17.4**). Excessive concern with thinness can lead children to experiment with fad diets, food restriction, and other behaviours that can result in undernutrition and perhaps even trigger a clinical eating disorder.

RECAP

Children have a slower growth rate than toddlers, yet their larger body size and greater level of physical activity increase total energy and nutrient needs. Children need a lower percentage of energy from fat than toddlers but slightly more than adults. Among highly active children, fluid intake should be monitored and encouraged.

Peer pressure has a strong influence on nutritional choices in school-aged children, but parents can encourage healthy eating and act as role models. Calcium needs increase as children mature but intake often declines. Iron deficiency is a common problem and can lead to severe behavioural, learning, and motor deficits. Body-image concerns arise in both boys and girls as they approach the adolescent years.

Did You Know?

Sprinkles are small packets of microencapsulated-iron that can be added to food without changing its taste, colour, or texture (see **Figure 17.5**). This unique product was developed at the Hospital for Sick Children in Toronto, Ontario, as a way to

(*continued*)

prevent and treat micronutrient deficiencies among children. Sprinkles have been used successfully throughout the world to reduce malnutrition in young children, and have been explored as a treatment for anemia in Canadian Aboriginal populations.[20]

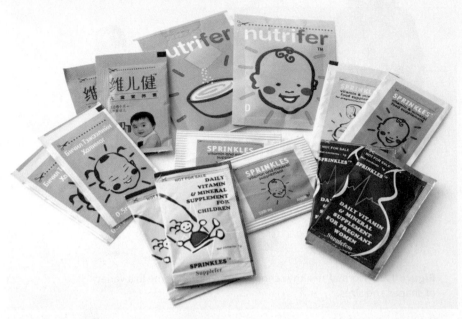

Figure 17.5 Sprinkles can be used to easily fortify foods.
Data from: Sprinkles Global Health Initiative. Available online at www.sghi.org/about_us/index.html.

Nutrition for Adolescents

The adolescent years are typically defined as beginning with the onset of **puberty**, the period in life in which secondary sexual characteristics develop and there is the capacity for reproducing. Adolescence continues through age 18. This is a physically and emotionally tumultuous time.

Adolescent Psychosocial Development

Adolescence is a period when emotions and behaviours often seem unpredictable and confusing. It is characterized by increasing independence as the adolescent establishes a personal sense of identity and works toward greater self-reliance. Adolescents may, for example, decide to follow a vegetarian or vegan diet as a means of setting themselves apart from the family unit. Whereas younger adolescents tend to be self-centred, living for the present, older teens typically focus on defining their role in life. All teens deal with their emerging sexuality and many experiment with lifestyle choices, such as use of drugs, alcohol, or cigarettes, that lie outside their traditional cultural or social boundaries. During this developmental phase, they may be unresponsive to parental guidance and may ignore attempts to improve their diet and/or activity patterns. Most adolescents, however, successfully navigate the challenges of this life stage and mature into emotionally stable, self-reliant, productive adults.

Adolescent Growth and Activity Patterns

Growth during adolescence is primarily driven by hormonal changes, including increased levels of testosterone for boys and estrogen for girls. Both boys and girls experience *growth spurts,* or periods of accelerated growth, during later childhood and adolescence. Growth

puberty The period in life in which secondary sexual characteristics develop and people are biologically capable of reproducing.

spurts for girls tend to begin around 10 to 11 years of age, and growth spurts for boys begin around 12 to 13 years of age. These growth periods last about two years.

Adolescents experience an average 20% to 25% increase in height during the pubertal years. During an average one-year spurt, girls tend to grow 9 cm and boys tend to grow 10 cm.[21] The average girl reaches almost full height by the onset of menstruation (called **menarche**). Boys typically experience continual growth throughout adolescence, and some may even grow slightly taller during early adulthood.

Skeletal growth ceases once closure of the *epiphyseal plates* occurs (**Figure 17.6**). The **epiphyseal plates** are plates of cartilage located toward the end of the long bones (that is, the bones of the arms and legs) that provide for growth in length. In some circumstances, such as malnutrition or use of anabolic steroids, the epiphyseal plates can close early in adolescents and result in a failure to reach full stature.

Weight and body composition also change dramatically during adolescence. Weight gain is extremely variable during this time and reflects the adolescent's energy intake, physical activity level, and genetics. The average weight gained by girls and boys during these years is 16 and 20.5 kg, respectively. The weight gained by girls and boys is dramatically different in terms of its composition. Girls tend to gain significantly more body fat than boys, with this fat accumulating around the buttocks, hips, breasts, thighs, and upper arms. Although many girls are uncomfortable or embarrassed by these changes, they are a natural result of maturation. Boys gain significantly more muscle mass than girls, and they experience an increase in muscle definition. Other changes that occur with sexual maturation include a deepening of the voice in boys and growth of pubic hair in both boys and girls.

The physical activity levels of adolescents are highly variable. Many are physically active in sports, dance, or other organized activities, whereas others become more interested in intellectual or artistic pursuits. This variability in activity levels of adolescents results in highly individual energy needs. Although the rapid growth and sexual maturation that occur during puberty require a significant amount of energy, adolescence is often a time in which overweight begins.

What Are an Adolescent's Nutrient Needs?

The nutrient needs of adolescents are influenced by rapid growth, weight gain, and sexual maturation, in addition to the demands of physical activity.

Energy and Macronutrient Recommendations for Adolescents

Adequate energy intake is necessary to maintain adolescents' health, support their dramatic growth and maturation, and fuel their physical activity. Because of these competing demands, the energy needs of adolescents can be quite high. To calculate the EER for this life stage, you must know the person's age, physical activity level, weight, and height.[1]

As with the younger age groups, there is no DRI for fat for adolescents.[1] However, adolescents are at risk for the same chronic diseases as adults, including type 2 diabetes, obesity, coronary heart disease, and various cancers. Thus, it is prudent for adolescents to consume 25% to 35% of total energy from fat and to consume no more than 10% of total energy from saturated fat sources.

The RDA for carbohydrate for adolescents is 130 g/day.[1] As with adults, this amount of carbohydrate covers what is needed to supply adequate glucose to the brain, but it does not cover the amount of carbohydrate needed to support daily activities. Thus, it is recommended that adolescents consume more than the RDA, or about 45% to 65% of their total energy as carbohydrate, and most carbohydrate should come from complex carbohydrate sources. The AI for fibre for adolescent girls is 26 g/day and for adolescent boys is 38 g/day. These levels are virtually the same as for adult women and men.

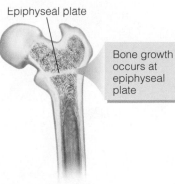

Figure 17.6 Skeletal growth ceases once closure of the epiphyseal plates occurs.
Data from: Germann, W. and Stanfield, C. Principles of Human Physiology, Fig. 7.13, Copyright © 2004. Reprinted by permission of Pearson Education, Inc.

Because of rapid growth and the active lifestyle of many adolescents, their energy needs can be quite high.

menarche The beginning of menstruation, or the menstrual period.
epiphyseal plates Plates of cartilage located toward the end of long bones that provide for growth in the length of long bones.

The RDA for protein for adolescents, at 0.85 g of protein per kilogram of body weight per day, is similar to that of adults, which is 0.80 g per kilogram of body weight.[1] This amount is assumed to be sufficient to support health and to cover the additional needs of growth and development during the adolescent stage. As with adults, most Canadian adolescents consume protein in amounts that far exceed the RDA.

Micronutrient Recommendations for Adolescents

Micronutrients of particular concern for adolescents include calcium, iron, and vitamin A. Adequate calcium intake is critical to achieve peak bone density, and the RDA for calcium for adolescents is 1300 mg/day.[4] This amount of calcium can be difficult for many adolescents to consume because the quality of foods they select is often less than optimal to meet their nutrient needs. To achieve this level of calcium intake, adolescents need to eat at least four servings of dairy foods or calcium-fortified products daily.

The iron needs of adolescents are relatively high; this is because iron is needed to replace the blood lost during menstruation in girls and to support the growth of muscle mass in boys. The RDA for iron for boys is 11 mg/day, and the RDA for girls is 15 mg/day.[5] If energy intake is adequate and adolescents consume heme-iron food sources such as animal products each day, they should be able to meet the RDA for iron. However, some young people adopt a vegetarian lifestyle during this life stage, or they consume foods that have limited nutrient density. Both of these situations can prevent adolescents from meeting the RDA for iron.

Vitamin A is critical to support the rapid growth and development that occurs during adolescence. The RDA for vitamin A is 900 µg per day for boys and 700 µg per day for girls,[5] which can be met by consuming five to nine servings of fruits and vegetables each day. As with iron and calcium, meeting the RDA for vitamin A can be a challenging goal in this age group because of their potential to make less healthy food choices.

If an adolescent is unable or unwilling to eat adequate amounts of nutrient-dense foods, then a multivitamin and mineral supplement that provides no more than 100% of the Daily Value for the micronutrients could be beneficial as a safety net. As with younger children and adults, a supplement should not be considered a substitute for a balanced, healthy diet.

Fluid Recommendations for Adolescents

The fluid needs of adolescents are higher than those for children because of their higher physical activity levels and the extensive growth and development that occur during this phase of life. The recommended daily fluid intakes for adolescents are summarized in Table 17.1 and average about 3.3 L of beverages, including water, for boys and 2.3 L for girls.[6] Boys are generally more active than girls and have more lean tissue; thus, they require a higher fluid intake to maintain fluid balance. Very active adolescents who are exercising in the heat may have higher fluid needs than the AI, and these individuals should be encouraged to drink often to quench their thirst and avoid dehydration.

Fluid needs of adolescents are generally higher than those of children.

Encouraging Nutritious Food Choices with Adolescents

Adolescents make many of their own food choices and buy and prepare a significant amount of the foods they consume. Although parents can still be effective role models, adolescents are generally strongly influenced by their peers, mass media, personal preferences, and their own developing sense of what foods make up a healthy and adequate diet.

Areas of particular concern in the adolescent diet are the lack of vegetables, fruits, and whole grains. Many teens eat on the run, skip meals, and select fast foods and convenience foods because they are inexpensive, accessible, and taste good. Parents, caregivers, and school food-service programs can capitalize on adolescents' preferences for pizza, burgers, spaghetti, and sandwiches by providing more healthy meat and cheese alternatives, whole-grain breads, and plenty of appealing vegetable-based sides or additions to these foods. In addition, keeping healthy snacks such as fruits and vegetables that are already cleaned and prepared in easy-to-eat pieces may encourage adolescents to consume more of these foods as between-meal snacks. Teens should also be encouraged to consume adequate milk and other calcium-enriched beverages.

Many teens move out of their family home when they attend university or college or get their first full-time job. The Highlight box on page 648, "On Your Own: Stocking Your First Kitchen," identifies staples to keep on hand for healthy snacks and meals.

Nutrition-Related Concerns for Adolescents

Nutrition-related concerns for adolescents continue to include bone density and body-image issues as well as the health of their skin and hair. Additional concerns include cigarette smoking and the use of alcohol and illicit drugs.

Bone Density Watch

Early adolescence, 13 to 15 years of age, is a crucial time for ensuring adequate dietary calcium to maximize bone calcium uptake and bone mineral density over the next several years.[4] Achieving and maintaining optimal bone density during adolescence and into young adulthood is critical for delaying or preventing the onset of osteoporosis.

As previously noted, meeting the adolescent DRI for calcium (1300 mg/day) is challenging. One of the most reliable sources of calcium is dairy foods, yet by age 18, average fluid milk consumption has fallen by more than 25% compared to intake at age eight years, whereas soda intake has tripled.[18] Although not the only factor, milk consumption during adolescence is strongly linked to higher bone mineral content and lower risk of adult bone fractures.[22] Dairy farmers and processors across Canada promote milk as part of a healthy diet through education programs targeted to elementary school children (**Figure 17.7**).

ELEMENTARY SCHOOL
MILK PROGRAM

Figure 17.7 Elementary School Milk Programs across Canada encourage milk consumption in children and adolescents.
Data from: Dairy Farmers of Canada. Available online at www.dairyfarmers.ca/what-we-do/programs.

Disordered Eating and Eating Disorders

An initially healthy concern about body image and weight can turn into a dangerous obsession during this emotionally challenging life stage. Clinical eating disorders frequently begin during adolescence and can occur in boys as well as girls. Warning signs include rapid and excessive weight loss, a preoccupation with weight and body image, going to the bathroom regularly after meals, and signs of frequent vomiting or laxative use. Factors that contribute to disordered eating are discussed in the Highlight box below.

HIGHLIGHT

Many Factors Contribute to Disordered Eating Behaviours

The factors that result in the development of disordered eating are very complex, but research indicates that a number of psychological, interpersonal, social, and biological factors may contribute in any particular individual.

Influence of Family

Research suggests that family conditioning, structure, and patterns of interaction can influence the development of an eating disorder. Based on observational studies, compared to families without a member with an eating disorder, families with an anorexic member show more rigidity in their family structure and less clear interpersonal boundaries, and tend to avoid open discussions on topics of disagreement.

Conversely, families with a member diagnosed with bulimia nervosa tend to have a less stable family organization and to be less nurturing, more angry, and more disruptive.[23] In addition, childhood physical or sexual abuse can increase the risk of an eating disorder.[24]

Influence of Media

As media saturation has increased over the last century, so has the incidence of eating disorders among white women.[25] Every day, we are confronted with advertisements in which computer-enhanced images of lean, beautiful women promote everything from beer to cars. Most adult men and women understand that these images are unrealistic, but adolescents, who are still developing a sense of their identity and body image, lack the same ability to distance themselves from what they see.[26] Because body image influences eating behaviours, it is not unlikely that the barrage of media models may be contributing to the increase in eating disorders. However, scientific evidence demonstrating that the media is *causing* increased eating disorders is difficult to obtain.

Influence of Social and Cultural Values

Eating disorders are significantly more common in white females in Western societies than in other women worldwide. This may be due in part to the white Western culture's association of slenderness with health, wealth, and high fashion. In contrast, until recently, the prevailing view in developing societies has been that excess body fat is desirable as a sign of health and material abundance.

The members of society with whom we most often interact—our family members, friends, classmates, and co-workers—also influence the way we see ourselves. Their comments related to our body weight or shape can be particularly hurtful—enough so to cause some people to start down the path of disordered eating. For example, individuals with bulimia nervosa report that they perceived greater pressure from their peers to be thin than controls, while research shows that peer teasing about weight increases body dissatisfaction and eating disturbances.[27] Thus, our comments to others regarding their weight do count.

Influence of Personality

A number of studies suggest that people with anorexia nervosa exhibit increased rates of obsessive-compulsive behaviours and perfectionism. They also tend to be socially inhibited, compliant, and emotionally restrained.[28] Unfortunately, many studies observe these behaviours only in

Photos of celebrities or models are often airbrushed or altered to "enhance" physical appearance. Unfortunately, many people believe that these are accurate portrayals and strive to reach an unrealistic level of physical beauty.

Until recently, the preferred look among runway models required extreme emaciation, often achieved by self-starvation and/or drug abuse.

individuals who are very ill and in a state of starvation, which may affect personality. Thus, it is difficult to determine if personality is the cause or effect of the disorder.

In contrast to people with anorexia nervosa, people with bulimia nervosa tend to be more impulsive, have low self-esteem, and demonstrate an extroverted, erratic personality style that seeks attention and admiration. In these people, negative moods are more likely to cause overeating than food restriction.[28]

Influence of Genetic Factors

Overall, the diagnosis of anorexia nervosa and bulimia nervosa is several times more common in siblings and other blood relatives who also have the diagnosis than in the general population.[29] This observation might imply the existence of an "eating disorder gene"; however, it is difficult to separate the contribution of genetic and environmental factors within families.

Family environment influences when, what, and how much we eat.

Adolescent Acne and Diet

Acne flare-ups plague many adolescents. Acne is an inflammation of the sebaceous (oil) glands associated with hair follicles. These glands produce an oily secretion called *sebum* that normally flows out onto the skin surface, keeping skin soft and moist and repelling microbes. In acne, excessive sebum collects in and plugs up hair follicles. "Blackheads" occur when follicles are exposed to air, and the top layer of sebum oxidizes. They are not caused by dirt! "Whiteheads" are collections of sebum in follicles not exposed to air.

The hormonal changes that occur during puberty are largely responsible for the sudden appearance of acne in many adolescents. Emotional stress, genetic factors, and personal hygiene are most likely secondary contributors. But what about foods? For decades, chocolate, fried foods, fatty foods, sweets, and other foods have been wrongfully linked to acne; it is now believed that diet plays virtually no role in its development. On the other hand, a healthy diet, rich in fruits, vegetables, whole grains, and lean meats, can provide vitamin A, vitamin C, zinc, and other nutrients to optimize skin health and maintain an effective immune system.

Prescription medications, including a vitamin A derivative 13-*cis*-retinoic acid (Accutane), effectively control severe forms of acne. Neither Accutane nor any other prescription vitamin A derivative should be used by women who are pregnant, planning a pregnancy, or may become pregnant. Accutane is a known teratogen, causing severe fetal malformations. The teratogenic effect is so severe that Health Canada now recommends all women of childbearing age who use Accutane register in a risk-management program to ensure that pregnancies do not occur while under treatment. Incidentally, vitamin A taken in supplement form is not effective in acne treatment and, due to its own risk for toxicity, should not be used in amounts that exceed 100% of the Daily Value.

Other Nutrition-Related Concerns

Cigarette smoking and use of alcohol and illicit drugs are additional nutrition-related concerns that face adolescents. Adolescents are naturally curious, and many are open to experimenting with tobacco, illicit drugs, and alcohol.

Cigarette smoking diminishes appetite; indeed, it is frequently used by adolescent girls to maintain a low body weight. Smoking can also interfere with the metabolism of some nutrients, including calcium, vitamins C, E, and B_6, and beta-carotene.[30, 31] Short-term effects of smoking include reduced physical fitness, impaired health, and higher rates of alcohol and drug abuse. Most people who begin smoking during adolescence continue to smoke throughout adulthood, increasing their long-term risks for lung cancer, other cancers, heart disease, osteoporosis, and emphysema. Unfortunately, many adolescents do not accurately perceive smoking-related risks.[32]

Alcohol and drug use can start at early ages, even in school-aged children. Alcohol can interfere with nutrient absorption and metabolism, and it can take the place of foods in an

Cigarette smoking may interfere with nutrient metabolism.

Recap

Adolescents experience rapid increases in height, weight, and lean body mass and fat mass. Adequate energy is needed to support growth, maturation, and physical activity. Fat intake should be 25% to 35% of total energy, and carbohydrate intake should be 45% to 65% of total energy intake. Calcium is needed to optimize bone growth and to achieve peak bone density, and iron needs are increased due to increased muscle mass in boys and to menstruation in girls. Adolescents' food choices are influenced by peer pressure and personal preferences. They may select fast foods and high-fat/high-energy snack foods in place of whole grains, fruits, and vegetables. Adolescents with lower levels of physical activity may therefore experience overweight for the first time during this period. Suboptimal bone density, disordered eating behaviours, acne, cigarette smoking, and use of alcohol and illicit drugs are also concerns for this age group.

adolescent's diet, putting adolescents at risk for nutrient deficiencies. Alcohol and marijuana use is also associated with getting "the munchies," a food craving that usually results in people eating large quantities of high-fat, high-sugar, nutrient-poor foods. This behaviour can result in overweight or obesity and also increases the risk of nutrient deficiencies. Teens who use drugs and alcohol are typically in poor condition, are either underweight or overweight, have poor appetites, and perform poorly in school.

HIGHLIGHT

On Your Own: Stocking Your First Kitchen

Many teens move out of the house around age 18 or 19 and settle into apartments, college or university housing, or shared housing. One question teens often have is how to stock their first kitchen. What basic foods—or staples—do they need to always have on hand, so that they can quickly and easily assemble healthy meals and snacks? The following checklist includes the foods that many Canadians consider staples. It can be modified to include items that are staples in non-Western cultures and to address vegetarian, vegan, low-fat, low-sodium, or other diets. By stocking healthy foods like the ones listed here, you'll be much more likely to make healthy food choices every day!

Keep your refrigerator stocked with:

- Low-fat or skim milk and/or soy milk
- Calcium-enriched orange juice
- Hard cheeses
- Eggs
- Lean deli meats
- Tofu
- Hummus, peanut butter, low-fat cream cheese, and/or other perishable spreads
- Two- to three-day supply of dark-green lettuce and other salad fixings or ready-to-eat salads
- Two- to three-day supply of other vegetables
- Two- to three-day supply of fresh fruits
- Low-fat salad dressings, mustards, salsas, and so forth
- Whole-grain breads, rolls, bagels, pizza crusts
- Tortillas: corn, whole-wheat flour

Stock your freezer with:

- Individual portions of chicken breast, extra lean ground beef, pork loin chops, fish fillets, or soy alternatives

- Lower-fat frozen entrees ("boost" with salad, whole-grain roll, and extra vegetables)
- Frozen vegetables (no sauce)
- Frozen cheese or veggie pizza ("boost" with added mushrooms, green peppers, and so forth)
- Low-fat ice cream, sherbet, or sorbet

Stock your kitchen cupboards with:

- Potatoes, sweet potatoes, onions, garlic, and so forth, as desired
- Canned or vacuum-packed tuna, salmon, crab (in water, not oil)
- Canned vegetables: corn, tomatoes, mushrooms, and so forth
- Canned legumes: black beans, refried beans, pinto/kidney beans, garbanzo beans
- Canned soups that are low in sodium and fat and high in fibre—read the Nutrition Facts tables!
- Dried beans and/or lentils, if desired
- Pasta and rice, preferably whole grain
- Bottled tomato-based pasta sauces
- Canned fruit in juice
- Dried fruits, including golden raisins, dried cranberries, dried apricots
- Nuts, including peanuts, almonds, walnuts, and so forth
- Whole-grain ready-to-eat cereals for breakfast and snacking; whole-grain cooked cereals like oatmeal
- Whole-grain, lower-fat crackers
- Pretzels, low-fat tortilla/corn chips, low/no-fat microwave popcorn
- Salt, pepper, balsamic vinegar, soy sauce, other condiments and spices as desired
- Olive oil, canola oil, and so forth, as desired

Pediatric Obesity Watch: A Concern for Children and Adolescents

During the past 30 years, the rate of obesity has almost tripled for Canadian children.[33] In 1978, only 15% of children were overweight or obese. By 2004, Statistics Canada found that 29% of adolescents had unhealthy weights.[34] Most adolescents do not outgrow this problem and in fact many continue to gain excess weight.

Overweight and obese children are at higher risk of numerous short- and long-term health problems. Even in early childhood, significant overweight can worsen asthma, cause sleep apnea, impair the child's mobility, and lead to intense teasing, low self-esteem, and social isolation. Among children and adolescents who are overweight, rates of type 2 diabetes have increased tenfold over the past 20 years. Fatty liver is diagnosed in one-third of obese children, and increasing numbers of obese children are experiencing high blood lipids, high blood pressure, gallstones, depression, and other medical problems.[35] Obese children are at much higher risk of becoming overweight adults than are normal-weight children, so preventing childhood overweight is important for long-term health and happiness. While there is some evidence that the prevalence rates of childhood obesity and overweight may have levelled off,[36] reversal of the epidemic of pediatric obesity can be accomplished only through an aggressive, comprehensive nationwide health campaign.

The Seeds of Pediatric Obesity

Believe it or not, early signs indicating a tendency toward overweight can occur as early as the toddler years. Toddlers should *not* be denied nutritious food; however, they should not be force-fed nor should they be encouraged to eat when they say or take actions that indicate they are full. In the toddler years, a child who is above the 80th percentile for weight should be monitored. The preschool years are also an important time for parents to be watchful of potential overweight and obesity. Preschoolers should be encouraged and supported in increasing their physical activity, and as for all children, foods with low nutrient density, such as sodas, cookies, and candies, should be limited. Parents should not be offended if the child's pediatrician or other healthcare provider expresses concern over the child's weight status; early intervention is often the most effective measure against lifelong obesity.

Pediatric Obesity: Prevention Through a Healthy Diet

Nutrition and healthcare experts agree that the main contributors to childhood obesity are similar to those involved in adult obesity: eating and drinking too many kilocalories and moving around too little. Parental overweight, low parental concern about the child's weight, and tantrums over food are additional factors contributing to childhood overweight.[37] The introduction and retention of healthy eating habits are key interventions in the fight against pediatric obesity.

The Role of the Family in Healthy Eating

Rather than singling out overweight children and placing them on restrictive diets, experts encourage family-wide improvements in food choices and mealtime habits.[38] Parents should strive to consistently provide nutritious food choices, encourage children to eat a healthy breakfast every morning, and sit down to a shared family meal each evening or as often as possible.[39] The television should be off throughout mealtimes to encourage attentive eating and true enjoyment of the food. Children typically mimic their parents, especially at the younger ages, so parents have many opportunities to improve the dietary patterns of their children.

Parents should retain control over the purchasing and preparation of foods until older children and teens are responsible and knowledgeable enough to make healthy decisions. Parents can keep a selection of fruits, vegetables, whole-grain products, and low-fat dairy foods readily available as healthy alternatives to high-fat, high-sugar snacks. For children "on the run," parents can keep a supply of non-perishable snacks such as granola bars, dried fruits, and nuts, along with kid-friendly fruits such as apples, bananas, and oranges,

Parents should try to have shared family meals with their children whenever possible.

to grab as everyone dashes out the door. Mealtimes, especially dinner, should offer a colourful variety of foods with the emphasis on green, yellow, orange, and red vegetables and deep-brown grains.

Whenever possible, parents should minimize the number of meals eaten in restaurants, especially fast food franchises. Although there is some evidence that children are ordering fewer cheeseburgers, fries, and sodas, many still opt for high-fat, high-sugar foods and larger portion sizes. When families do eat out, large portion sizes can be shared, and grilled, broiled, or baked foods substituted for fried foods.

Many children and adolescents resent parental oversight and involvement in their weight-control program. Parents should not allow the dinner table to turn into a battleground; instead, parents should model healthy eating behaviours, provide a diverse array of healthy foods, and encourage healthy lifestyle choices, including physical activity.[40] Even if the child's weight stabilizes rather than declines, parents should praise the absence of additional weight gain as a positive step.

Pediatric Obesity: Prevention Through an Active Lifestyle

Increased energy expenditure through increased physical activity is essential for successful weight management among children.[41] It is now recommended that children participate in daily physical activity and exercise for at least an hour each day,[42] and bone- and muscle-strengthening activities at least three days each week.[33] Table 17.2 offers suggestions for physical activities that may appeal to children and adolescents.

Table 17.2 Examples of Physical Activities for Children and Adolescents

Type of Physical Activity	Age Group: Children	Age Group: Adolescents
Moderate-intensity aerobic	• Active recreation, such as hiking, skateboarding, rollerblading • Bicycle riding • Brisk walking	• Active recreation, such as canoeing, hiking, skateboarding, rollerblading • Brisk walking • Bicycle riding (stationary or road bike) • Housework and yard work, such as sweeping or pushing a lawn mower • Games that require catching and throwing, such as baseball and softball
Vigorous-intensity aerobic	• Active games involving running and chasing, such as tag • Bicycle riding • Jumping rope • Martial arts, such as karate • Running • Sports such as soccer, ice or field hockey, basketball, swimming, tennis • Cross-country skiing	• Active games involving running and chasing, such as flag football • Bicycle riding • Jumping rope • Martial arts, such as karate • Running • Sports such as soccer, ice or field hockey, basketball, swimming, tennis • Vigorous dancing • Cross-country skiing
Muscle-strengthening	• Games such as tug-of-war • Modified push-ups (with knees on the floor) • Resistance exercises using body weight or resistance bands • Rope or tree climbing • Sit-ups (curl-ups or crunches) • Swinging on playground equipment/bars	• Games such as tug-of-war • Push-ups and pull-ups • Resistance exercises with exercise bands, weight machines, hand-held weights • Climbing wall • Sit-ups (curl-ups or crunches)
Bone-strengthening	• Games such as hopscotch • Hopping, skipping, jumping • Jumping rope • Running • Sports such as gymnastics, basketball, volleyball, tennis	• Hopping, skipping, jumping • Jumping rope • Running • Sports such as gymnastics, basketball, volleyball, tennis

Note: Some activities, such as bicycling, can be moderate or vigorous intensity, depending upon level of effort.
Data from: Janssen, I., and A. G. LeBlanc. 2010. Systematic review of the health benefits of physical activity and fitness in school aged children and youth. *Int. J. Behav. Nutr. Phys. Act.* 7:40.

For younger children, this can be divided into two or three shorter sessions, allowing them to regroup, recoup, and refocus between activity sessions. Older children should be able to be active for an hour without stopping. Overweight children are more likely to engage in physical activities that are noncompetitive, fun, and structured in a way that allows them to proceed at their own pace. Children should be exposed to a variety of activities so that they move different muscles, play at various intensities, avoid boredom, and find out what they like and don't like to do. Canadian Physical Activity Guidelines have been developed for children 0–4 years and 5–11 years, and youth 12–17 years. (See Chapter 15 pages 540–542).

The Role of the Family in Physical Activity

As with healthy eating, parental and adult role models are vitally important in any effort to increase the physical activity level of children and adolescents. When parents and children are active together, healthy activity patterns are established early. To encourage activity throughout the day, parents should encourage shared activities such as ball games, bicycle rides, hikes, skating outings, and so forth. In addition, community organizations such as the YMCA and municipal recreational centres also have supervised youth-oriented weight-training programs, climbing walls, skateboard parks, and other non-traditional activity options that are typically open to the whole family.

Encouraging physical play with friends is a good way to combat childhood obesity.

In the past, children played freely outdoors and even kept active indoors in times of bad weather. In recent years, however, several factors have prompted childhood activities to become increasingly sedentary. One such factor is simply the availability of sedentary entertainment technologies, including television, video games, and computer games. Experts recommend no more than two hours per day of TV viewing for preschoolers; children who watch more than that are at increased risk for overweight.[41, 42] Too much television can also interfere with the acquisition of physical skills and can hinder children's use of their own imaginations, dampening creativity. Moreover, an abundance of television commercials during children's programs advertise less healthy foods, such as sweetened breakfast cereals made with refined grains, candies, pastries, and high-fat snacks. Even parents who limit television watching should sit with their younger children during several commercials and explain to them, in age-appropriate language, that these foods are made to look appealing to kids but are not healthy choices.

Another factor contributing to low levels of physical activity among youth is the high number of households in which no adult is home after school, either because of single-parent families or because both parents have to work to support the family. Safety concerns cause working parents to forbid their children, when they are home alone after school, to venture out of the house. If this is the case, the family may consider investing in some of the new electronic game systems that offer virtual tennis, step aerobics, dancing, and other active simulations.

By increasing their physical activity, many overweight children are able to "catch up" to their weight as they grow taller without restricting their food (and thus nutrient) intake. Increased activity also helps young children acquire motor skills and muscle strength, establish good sleep patterns, and develop self-esteem as they feel themselves becoming faster, stronger, and more skilled. Regular physical activity also optimizes bone mass, strengthens muscles, enhances cardiovascular and respiratory function, and lowers emotional stress in overweight children.

The Role of the School in Physical Activity

As academic standards increase across the country, many schools are reducing or eliminating physical education classes and, in elementary schools, recess periods. Budget cuts have also led to the reduction or elimination of physical activity programs, including high school sports programs. Unfortunately, these decisions are short-sighted because daily physical activity not only helps regulate body weight, but also improves academic performance. Researchers have noted that when children have the opportunity to take part in recess, classroom behaviour improves,[43] children are more attentive to their teachers, and students are more focused on assigned tasks. In addition, children classified as physically fit have higher levels of academic achievement compared to unfit children.[44]

Parents, healthcare providers, and other community members can join forces to work with local school boards to optimize opportunities for physical activity within the schools. Daily physical education in schools, continued funding for team and individual sports, and non-competitive physical activity options outside of schools can help reduce the prevalence of overweight and obesity among children and adolescents, slowly reversing what has been an alarming health issue for the past 30 years.[45]

RECaP

Obesity is an important concern for children of all ages, their families, and their communities. Parents should model healthy eating and activity behaviours. Schools play an important role in providing nutritious breakfasts and lunches and varied opportunities for daily physical activity.

CASE STUDY   Feeding Young Children

Colin is an active four-year-old who is excited about trying new foods. However, he seems to get full in the middle of his meals and it is a constant battle to keep him focused on food. His mother gives him his meals before she feeds the rest of the family, hoping that this will be less distracting. Often Colin twitches in his chair wanting to get down and refuses to eat more than a few bites. Oddly, at snack time he gulps his juice and asks for more.

Colin's typical daily intake is as follows:

8:00 a.m.	250 mL skim milk
	125 mL crisped rice cereal
11:00 a.m.	25 g ground beef
	½ tortilla in small pieces
	60 mL cup carrot
	250 mL apple juice
2:00 p.m.	250 mL of apple juice
4:00 p.m.	60 mL cup green beans
	125 mL rice
	60 mL diced canned pears
	250 mL skim milk
8:00 p.m.	250 mL of apple juice
	2 peanut butter cookies

Thinking Critically

1. **Assess Colin's diet according to the recommendations in Canada's Food Guide.**
2. **Is Colin at risk for nutrient deficiencies? Is so, which ones?**
3. **What advice would you give to Colin's parents to improve his diet?**
4. **Should Colin's mother be concerned about his fat intake? Why or why not?**

SEE FOR YOURSELF

Is Your Local School Committed to Children's Nutrition?

Contact your local elementary school, middle school, or high school and request permission to visit the school's cafeteria. While there, ask for a weekly or monthly breakfast and lunch menu. Also ask how the nutritional value of each meal is determined, including portion sizes, levels of nutrients, and so forth. Ask if there is an RD at the school or district level; if not, ask who is responsible for menu development. In addition to the meals on the menu, what snacks or meal alternatives, if any, are available for purchase? Does the school have vending machines, and if so, what foods and beverages are available? Are vending machine sales restricted during lunch hours or at any other time during the school day? Finally, within the cafeteria setting, what behavioural strategies, if any, are used to promote healthy food choices—for example, serving healthy foods in a fun way, decorating the cafeteria with nutrition-related posters, personnel encouraging children to finish meals, and so forth?

Write up your findings and report them to your classmates. When discussing the school's level of commitment to its students' nutrition, use the following criteria:

- Meals served provide appropriate energy, macronutrients, and micronutrients for population served.
- Available snacks provide appropriate energy, macronutrients, and micronutrients for population served.
- Vending machine choices provide appropriate energy, macronutrients, and micronutrients for population served.
- Cafeteria environment and personnel demonstrate strategies to encourage healthy eating.

Chapter Review

Test Yourself Answers

1. **F** Children under the age of two years have a higher need for fat than do older children or adults, so they should consume foods that are higher in fat, including full-fat milk.

2. **T** The DRI guidelines do not differentiate between girls and boys until the age of nine years.

3. **F** Many factors contribute to disordered eating: family, media, culture, and genetics all play a role.

4. **F** Adolescents experience an average 20% to 25% increase in height during the pubertal years.

5. **T** Hormonal changes, emotional stress, genetic factors, and personal hygiene are the most likely contributors to adolescent acne.

Summary

- Toddlers grow more slowly than infants but are far more active. They require small, frequent, nutritious snacks and meals, and food should be cut in small pieces so it is easy to handle and swallow.

- For toddlers and young children, a serving of food equals 15 mL for each year of age. For example, 60 mL of yogourt is a full serving for a four-year-old child.

- Energy, fat, and protein requirements are higher for toddlers than for infants. Many toddlers will not eat vegetables, so micronutrients of concern include vitamins A, C, and E.

- Until age two, toddlers should drink whole milk rather than reduced-fat milk to meet calcium requirements. Iron deficiency is a concern in the toddler years and can be minimized by the consumption of foods naturally high in iron and iron-fortified foods.

- Feeding vegan diets to toddlers is controversial and poses potential deficiencies for protein, iron, calcium, zinc, vitamin D, and vitamin B_{12}.

- School-aged children are more independent and can make more of their own food choices. Physical activity levels can vary dramatically.

- Sexual maturation begins during the early school-age years. School-aged children should eat 25% to 35% of their total energy as fat and 45% to 65% of their total energy as carbohydrate.

Calcium needs increase as children mature, whereas iron needs decrease slightly.

- Although relatively rare, iron-deficiency anemia occurs in some children. Healthy food choices and, if appropriate, use of an iron supplement can prevent the fatigue, illness, and impaired learning that often accompany childhood iron deficiency. Consuming adequate calcium to support the development of peak bone mass is a primary concern for school-aged children.

- Many school-aged children skip breakfast and do not choose healthy foods during school lunch. Peer pressure and popularity are strong influences on food choices. The foods that children choose to eat at school, both during and outside of the lunch break, can be high in fat, sugar, and energy and low in nutrients.

- Puberty is the period in life in which secondary sexual characteristics develop and the physical capability to reproduce begins. Puberty results in rapid increases in height, weight, and lean body mass and fat mass.

- Energy needs for adolescents are variable and can be quite high, and adequate energy is needed to support growth, maturation, and physical activity. Fat intake should be 25% to 35% of total energy, and carbohydrate intake should be 45% to 65% of total energy intake.

- Many adolescents replace whole grains, fruits, and vegetables with fast foods and high-fat/high-energy snack foods, placing them at risk for deficiencies for calcium, iron, and vitamin A. Calcium is needed to optimize bone growth and to achieve peak bone density, and iron needs are increased because of increased muscle mass in boys and menstruation in girls.

- Disordered eating, due to personal appearance, cigarette smoking, and use of alcohol and illicit drugs are concerns for adolescents.

- Overweight and obesity can begin to develop at any time from toddlerhood through adolescence if energy intake exceeds energy spent in physical activity. Both families and schools can play important roles in encouraging smart food choices and increased physical activity.

Review Questions

1. The RDA for calcium for adolescents is
 a. less than that for young children.
 b. less than that for adults.
 c. less than that for pregnant adults.
 d. greater than that for young children, adults, and pregnant adults.

2. Carbohydrate should make up what percentage of total energy for school-aged children?
 a. 25% to 40%
 b. 35% to 50%
 c. 45% to 65%
 d. 45% to 70%

3. Which of the following is a common nutrition-related concern for school-aged children?
 a. inappropriately low fat intake
 b. skipping breakfast
 c. botulism
 d. protein deficiency

4. Which of the following breakfasts would be most appropriate to serve a 22-month-old child?
 a. 250 mL of iron-fortified cooked oat cereal, 30 mL of mashed pineapple, and 250 mL of skim milk
 b. 30 mL of plain yogourt, 30 mL of applesauce, 30 mL of fortified whole-grain oat cereal, and 125 mL of calcium-fortified orange juice
 c. 125 mL of iron-fortified cooked oat cereal, 125 mL of cubed pineapple, and 250 mL of low-fat milk
 d. 2 small link sausages cut in 1 cm pieces, 2 scrambled eggs, 1 slice of whole-wheat toast, 4 cherry tomatoes, 125 mL of applesauce, and 250 mL of whole milk

5. Which of the following statements about cigarette smoking is true?
 a. Cigarette smoking can interfere with the metabolism of nutrients.
 b. Cigarette smoking commonly causes food cravings such as "getting the munchies."
 c. Cigarette smoking can reduce appetite.
 d. All of the above statements are true.

6. Discuss the potential benefits and disadvantages of snacking for preschoolers.

7. Explain why substituting soft drinks for milk can increase an adolescent's risk for osteoporosis later in life.

8. Identify some advantages and disadvantages of modern technology (such as television and computers) in terms of its impact on lifestyle and nutrition.

9. Explain why a toddler in a vegan family might be at risk for protein deficiency.

10. Imagine that you are taking care of four five-year-old children for an afternoon. Design a menu for the children's lunch that is nutritious and that will be fun for them to eat.

11. Imagine that you plan meals for a high school cafeteria. Design a menu with three lunch choices that are nutritious and that are likely to be popular with teens.

12. Your classmate Lydia is a bit eccentric. An engineering major, she spends an average of six hours a day at her computer, drinking diet colas and eating pretzels. She is unusually slender, even though she admits to getting no regular exercise. Your university is in Vancouver and Lydia is from Ottava. If you were a registered dietitian (RD) and Lydia were your client, what nutrition-related health concern(s) might you discuss with her? Identify *at least* three elements in Lydia's story that are known risk factors for the health problem(s) you identify.

Web Links

www.caringforkids.cps.ca
Caring For Kids
Find information on child and youth health from the Canadian Paediatric Society.

www.sghi.org
Sprinkles Global Health Initiative
Explore this site to discover research on nutritional deficiencies and methods of improving the nutritional health of individuals.

www.dairyfarmers.ca/what-we-do/programs
Dairy Farmers of Canada—School Milk Programs
Find resources for teaching healthy eating to elementary school children.

www.dietitians.ca
Dietitians of Canada
Visit this site to find nutrition labelling and healthy eating resources.

www.childhoodobesityfoundation.ca/home
Childhood Obesity Foundation
Site dedicated to teaching Canadian children, their families and care givers, educators, business, and government about the problem of childhood obesity.

MasteringNutrition®

www.masteringnutrition.pearson.com

Study Area
Practice Tests • Diet Analysis • eText

References

1. Institute of Medicine, Food and Nutrition Board. 2002. *Dietary Reference Intakes for Energy, Carbohydrates, Fiber, Fat, Protein and Amino Acids (Macronutrients).* Washington, DC: The National Academy of Sciences.
2. Canadian Paediatric Society. Revision 2009. *Weaning from the breast.* Available at www.cps.ca/english/statements/CP/cp04-01.htm (accessed July 19, 2011).
3. Institute of Medicine, Committee to Review the WIC Food Packages. 2005. *Proposed Criteria for Selecting the WIC Food Packages.* Washington, DC: National Academy Press.
4. Institute of Medicine, Food and Nutrition Board. 2011. Dietary Reference Intakes for Calcium and Vitamin D. Washington, DC: National Academy Press.
5. Institute of Medicine, Food and Nutrition Board. 2001. *Dietary Reference Intakes for Vitamin A, Vitamin K, Arsenic, Boron, Chromium, Copper, Iodine, Iron, Manganese, Molybdenum, Nickel, Silicon, Vanadium, and Zinc.* Washington, DC: National Academy Press.
6. Institute of Medicine, Food and Nutrition Board. 2004. *Dietary Reference Intakes for Water, Potassium, Sodium, Chloride, and Sulfate.* Washington, DC: National Academy Press.
7. Canadian Food Inspection Agency. 2007. *Guide to Food Labelling and Advertising.* Chapter 7. Available at www.inspection.gc.ca/english/fssa/labeti/guide/toce.shtml (accessed July 19, 2011).
8. Oldways. 2000. *The Vegetarian Diet Pyramid for Children.* Available at http://oldwayspt.org/vegetarian_pyramid.html (accessed June 2009).
9. Greene-Finestonea, L. S., M. K. Campbell, S. E. Evers, and I. A. Gutmanis. 2008. Attitudes and health behaviours of young adolescent omnivores and vegetarians: a school-based study. *Appetite* 51:104–110.
10. Stern, R. 2007. Diet from hell. *Phoenix New Times*, May 10. Available at www.phoenixnewtimes.com/2007-05-10/news/diet-from-hell/.
11. Second Opinions. 2002. Vegan child abuse. Available at www.second-opinions.co.uk/child_abuse.html.
12. Doron, D., K. Hershkop, and E. Granot. 2001. Nutritional deficits resulting from an almond-based infant diet. *Clinical Nutrition* 20:259–261.
13. Giannini, A., N. Mirra, and M. F. Patria. 2006. Health risks for children raised on vegan or vegetarian diets (Letter to the editor). *Pediatr. Crit. Care Med.* 7:188.

14. Messina, V. and A. R. Mangels. 2001. Considerations in planning vegan diets: children. *J. Am. Diet. Assoc.* 101:661–669.

15. Academy of Nutrition and Dietetics and Dietitians of Canada. 2003. Position statement: vegetarian diets. *J. Am. Diet. Assoc.* 103:748–756.

16. Kleinman, R. E., ed. 2009. *Pediatric Nutrition Handbook,* 6th ed. Elk Grove Village, IL: American Academy of Pediatrics.

17. Health Canada. *Eating Well with Canada's Food Guide.* Available at www.hc-sc.gc.ca/fn-an/alt_formats/hpfb-dgpsa/pdf/food-guide-aliment/print_eatwell_bienmang-eng.pdf (accessed July 19, 2011).

18. Striegel-Moore, R. H., D. Thompson, S. G. Affenito, D. L. Franko, E. Obarzanek, B. A. Barton, G. B. Schreiber, S. R. Daniels, M. Schmidt, and P. B. Crawford. 2006. Correlates of beverage intake in adolescent girls: the National Heart, Lung, and Blood Institute growth and health study. *J. Pediatr.* 148:183–187.

19. Rampersaud, G. C., M. A. Pereira, B. L. Girard, J. Adams, and J. D. Metzl. 2005. Breakfast habits, nutritional status, body weight, and academic performance in children and adolescents. *J. Am. Diet. Assoc.* 105:743–760.

20. Christofides A., C. Schauer, W. Sharieff, S. H. Zlotkin. 2005. Acceptability of micronutrient sprinkles: a new food-based approach for delivering iron to First Nations and Inuit children in Northern Canada. *Chronic Dis. Can.* 26:114–120.

21. Steinberg, L. 2007. *Adolescence,* 8th ed. New York: McGraw-Hill.

22. Kalkwarf, H. J., J. C. Khoury, and B. P. Lanphear. 2003. Milk intake during childhood and adolescence, adult bone density, and osteoporotic fractures in US women. *Am. J. Clin. Nutr.* 77:257–265.

23. Vandereycken, W. 2002. Families of patients with eating disorders. In: Fairburn, D. G., and K. D. Brownell, eds. *Eating Disorders and Obesity: A Comprehensive Handbook,* 2nd ed. New York: Guilford Press, pp. 215–220.

24. Patrick, L. 2002. Eating disorders: a review of the literature with emphasis on medical complication and clinical nutrition. *Altern. Med. Rev.* 7(3):184–202.

25. Striegel-Moore, R. H., and L. Smolak. 2002. Gender, ethnicity, and eating disorders. In: Fairburn, D. G., and K. D. Brownell, eds. *Eating Disorders and Obesity: A Comprehensive Handbook,* 2nd ed. New York: Guilford Press, pp. 251–255.

26. Steinberg, L. 2002. *Adolescence,* 6th ed. New York: McGraw-Hill.

27. Stice, E., 2002. Sociocultural influences on body image and eating disturbances. In: Fairburn, D. G., and K. D. Brownell, eds. *Eating Disorders and Obesity: A Comprehensive Handbook,* 2nd ed. New York: Guilford Press, pp. 103–107.

28. Wonderlich, S. A. 2002. Personality and eating disorders. In: Fairburn, D. G., and K. D. Brownell, eds. *Eating Disorders and Obesity: A Comprehensive Handbook,* 2nd ed. New York: Guilford Press, pp. 204–209.

29. American Psychiatric Association. 1994. *Diagnostic and Statistical Manual of Mental Disorders (DSM-IV),* 4th ed. Washington, DC: Author.

30. Bruno, R. S., R. Ramakrishnan, T. J. Montine, T. M. Bray, and M. G. Traber. 2005. α-Tocopherol disappearance is faster in cigarette smokers and is inversely related to their ascorbic acid status. *Am. J. Clin. Nutr.* 81:95–103.

31. Preston, A. M., C. Rodriquez, C. E. Rivera, and H. Sahai. 2003. Influence of environmental tobacco smoke on vitamin C status in children. *Am. J. Clin. Nutr.* 77:167–172.

32. Song, A. V., H. E. R. Morrell, J. L. Cornell, M. E. Ramos, M. Biehl, R. Y. Kropp, and B. L. Halpern-Felsher. 2009. Perceptions of smoking-related risks and benefits as predictors of adolescent smoking initiation. *Am. J. Public Health* 99:487–492.

33. Public Health Agency of Canada. 2009. *Obesity in Canada: Snapshot.* Available at www.phac-aspc.gc.ca/publicat/2009/oc/pdf/oc-eng.pdf (accessed July 19, 2011).

34. Shields M. Overweight and obesity among children and youth. *Health Reports* 17:27. Statistics Canada catalogue 82-003.

35. Ludwig, D. S. 2007. Childhood obesity—the shape of things to come. *New Engl. J. Med.* 357:2325–2327.

36. Ogden, C. L., M. D. Carroll, and K. M. Flegal. 2008. High body mass index for age among US children and adolescents, 2003–2006. *JAMA* 299:2401–2405.

37. Agras, W. S., L. D. Hammer, F. McNicholas, and H. C. Kraemer. 2004. Risk factors for childhood overweight: a prospective study from birth to 9.5 years. *J. Pediatr.* 145:19–24.

38. Zeller, M., and S. Daniels. 2004. The obesity epidemic: family matters. *J. Pediatr.* 145:3–4.

39. Ritchie, L. D., G. Welk, D. Styne, D. E. Gerstein, and P. B. Crawford. 2005. Family environment and pediatric overweight: what is a parent to do? *J. Am. Diet. Assoc.* 105:S70–S79.

40. Canadian Society for Exercise Physiology. 2012. Canadian Physical Activity Guidelines and Canadian Sedentary Behaviour Guidelines. Available at www.csep.ca/english/view.asp?x=804 (accessed July 16, 2012).

41. Mendoza, J. A., F. J. Zimmermann, and D. A. Christakis. 2007. Television viewing, computer use, obesity, and adiposity in US preschool children. *Int. J. Behav. Nutr. Physical Activity* 4:44. Available at www.ijbnpa.org/content/4/1/44 (accessed June 2009).

42. Janssen, I., and A. G. LeBlanc. 2010. Systematic review of the health benefits of physical activity and fitness in school aged children and youth. *Int. J. Behav. Nutr. Phys. Act.* 7:40.

43. Barros, R. M., E. J. Silver, and R. E. K. Stein. 2009. School recess and group classroom behavior. *Pediatrics* 123:431–436.

44. Chomitz, V. R., M. M. Slining, R. J. McGowan, S. E. Mitchell, G. F. Dawson, and K. A. Hacker. 2009. Is there a relationship between physical fitness and academic achievement? Positive results from public school children in the northeastern United States. *J. School Health* 79:30–37.

45. Levi, J., S. Vinter, L. Richardson, R. St. Laurent, and L. M. Segal. 2009. *F as in Fat: How Obesity Policies Are Failing in America, 2009.* Washington, DC: Trust for America's Health.

46. Huh, S. Y., and C. M. Gordon. 2008. Vitamin D deficiency in children and adolescents: epidemiology, impact and treatment. *Rev. Endocr. Metab. Disord.* 9:161–170.

47. Smolders, J., J. Damoiseaux, P. Menheere, and R. Hupperts. 2008. Vitamin D as an immune modulator in multiple sclerosis, a review. *J. Neuroimmunology* 194:7–17.

48. Lee, J. H., J. H. O'Keefe, D. Bell, D. D. Hensrud, and M. F. Holick. 2008. Vitamin D deficiency: an important, common, and easily treatable cardiovascular risk factor? *J. Am. Coll. Cardiol.* 52:1949–1956.

49. Lucas, R. M., and A. L. Ponsonby. 2006. Considering the potential benefits as well as adverse effects of sun exposure: can all the potential benefits be provided by oral vitamin D supplementation? *Prog. Biophys. Molec. Biol.* 92:140–149.

50. Reichrath, J. 2006. The challenge resulting from positive and negative effects of sunlight: how much solar UV exposure is appropriate to balance between risks of vitamin D deficiency and skin cancer? *Prog. Biophys. Molec. Biol.* 92:9–16.

51. Wagner, C. L., F. R. Greer, and the Section on Breastfeeding and Committee on Nutrition. 2008. Prevention of rickets and vitamin D deficiency in infants, children, and adolescents. *Pediatrics* 122:1142–1152.

52. Schwalfenberg, G. K., S. J. Genius., and M. N. Hiltz. 2010. Addressing vitamin D deficiency in Canada: a public health innovation whose time has come. *Public Health* 124:350–359.

53. Wolpowitz, D., and B. A. Gilchrest. 2006. The vitamin D question: how much do you need and how should you get it? *J. Am. Acad. Dermatol.* 54:301–307.

54. Mohr, S. B., C. F. Garland, E. D. Gorham, and F. C. Garland. 2008. The association between ultraviolet B irradiance, vitamin D status and incidence rates of type 1 diabetes in 51 regions worldwide. *Diabetologia* 51:1391–1398.

The Vitamin D Dilemma: Supplements versus Sunshine

Since Lani's birth, her parents have conscientiously followed the healthcare advice they've received. So when Lani's pediatrician phones them shortly after her 18-month check-up to report that she is deficient in vitamin D, they are stunned. Fighting back tears, Lani's mother asks how her daughter could have developed a vitamin deficiency. "I still breastfeed Lani, and she eats a very healthy diet! I take good care of my daughter!"

Lani's pediatrician assures her mother that she is not to blame. He points out that children with darker skin, like Lani, are at increased risk for vitamin D deficiency, then asks how much time Lani spends outdoors in the sun. "Oh, we're very careful!" her mother exclaims. "Before we take her outside, we always put on her sunscreen. She's never been burned—but even if she had been, what does that have to do with her vitamin problem?"

A surprisingly high number of Canadian children are at risk for vitamin D deficiency.[46] As discussed in Chapter 12, vitamin D is essential for normal bone growth and development. It also protects against autoimmune diseases, internal cancers, and cardiovascular disease.[47–50] Recall that vitamin D is referred to as the "sunshine vitamin" because it is synthesized by skin cells exposed to sunlight. Thus, unlike most nutrients, not only can we meet our need for vitamin D by consuming it from foods or supplements, we can also synthesize it following exposure to the sun. Here, we explore another angle in the vitamin D dilemma: should public health authorities advise Canadians, especially children and adolescents, to spend more time in the sun?

Historically, the discovery of vitamin D was sparked by researchers' attempts to combat rickets, a disfiguring and potentially fatal bone disorder due to vitamin D deficiency. Around the turn of the 20th century in North America, several hundred children died each year, especially in northern regions, from rickets. Blacks and Aboriginal people were affected at higher rates than those of European descent. A series of careful studies in the early 20th century led scientists to identify vitamin D as the "anti-rickets" factor present in cod liver oil, a common folk remedy for rickets, and to the recognition of the role of ultraviolet radiation in the body's natural synthesis of vitamin D. Once vitamin D–fortification of milk began in the 1930s, death rates of infants and children from rickets began to drop. Still, rickets continues to be reported among Canadian infants, children, and adolescents, particularly among those, like Lani, with darker skin pigmentation.[51] A recent review of vitamin D deficiency in Canada revealed that between 70% and 97% of Canadians demonstrate vitamin D insufficiency as defined by blood levels of 25(OH)D below 75 nmol/L. Further, 69% of boys and 35% of girls between 2 and 16 years of age have levels below 40 nmol/L.[52]

Why has the rate of pediatric vitamin D deficiency increased, and what can families and healthcare providers do to improve vitamin D status in children and adolescents? Remember, humans have three sources of vitamin D: foods, supplements, and sun exposure. For reasons that will be discussed shortly, a number of researchers are now promoting what was previously shunned: increased sunlight exposure. They claim that a lack of exposure to ultraviolet radiation is increasing vitamin D deficiency, and that increased, but prudent, sun exposure is necessary to improve vitamin D status.[49, 50] Let's take a look at the facts behind these assertions.

Historically, humans have obtained most of their vitamin D from internal synthesis following sunlight exposure.[46] During summer months, adults with light skin pigmentation can easily meet their daily vitamin D needs with as little as 10 to 15 minutes of full-body exposure.[53] People with darker pigmentation require a significantly longer exposure. However, as discussed in Chapter 12, no amount of exposure is sufficient to enable vitamin D synthesis for people of any skin tone in winter months in northern latitudes. And, due in part to recent lifestyle changes, it is not clear that children and adolescents are obtaining even 10 to 15 minutes of full-body sun exposure in the summertime.[53]

In addition to increasingly popular indoor activities for children and adolescents, parents have been heeding warnings from Health Canada and the Canadian Cancer Society, which have aggressively publicized the dangers of excessive sunlight exposure and the risk of skin cancer in youth. Parents are advised to limit children's exposure to full sunlight, to provide hats and sunglasses, and to use high-potency sunscreen, all of which greatly impair the ability of the body to produce adequate vitamin D. Lately, even makers of children's summer clothing advertise its ability to "Block the sun, not the fun" with special UV-protective fabrics. Thus, children's natural ability to synthesize vitamin D through their skin appears to be constrained.

In opposition to these advisories to restrict sun exposure in children and adolescents, a number of researchers are actively *promoting* moderate sun exposure as an inexpensive and effective means of optimizing vitamin D status.[49, 50] They claim that increased sun exposure will help reduce rates of rickets and possibly lower long-term

UV SAFETY

THE GLOBAL SOLAR ULTRAVIOLET INDEX

Be extra careful outdoors!
Lighter skin will burn in minutes without protection.
Avoid exposure from 10:00 to 4:00 and shield skin and eyes.

11+ EXTREME

UV levels are dangerous.
A change in skin color means UV radiation has damaged
your skin. White sand and water increase your UV exposure.

**10
9
8 VERY HIGH**

Sunburn can happen quickly.
Children are especially sensitive to UV exposure.
Cover up, use sunscreen, and play in the shade.

**7
6 HIGH**

It may *seem* safe but...
Up to 80% of solar UV radiation can penetrate light cloud
cover. Use UV-blocking sunglasses and protect your skin.

**5
4
3 MODERATE**

Always protect yourself from the sun.
Even with a low index rating, you can be overexposed. On a sunny
day, snow reflects enough UV radiation to damage eyes and skin.

**2
1 LOW**

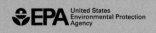

United States
Environmental Protection
Agency

EPA430-H-04-001
May 2004

Canada adopted the Global Solar Ultraviolet Index in 2006.

risk for multiple sclerosis, type 1 diabetes, non-skin cancers, and other chronic diseases. Research strongly supports an inverse relationship between UVB exposure and incidence of type 1 diabetes: regions with intense and prolonged sun exposure had the lowest rates of type 1 diabetes.[54]

As noted, vitamin D status can be maintained through appropriate intake from foods and/or supplements. In fact, the Canadian Dermatology Association recommends that we "Get vitamin D safely through a healthy diet that may include vitamin supplements." Newly revised vitamin D intake guidelines for healthy children and adolescents are triple that of previous recommendations: 15 μg/day.[41] One 250 mL glass of vitamin D–fortified milk provides 200 IU, therefore, children and teens would have to drink 750 mL of milk each day to meet the new recommendation. Milk intake among adolescent girls has decreased by almost 40% over the past three decades, so it is very unlikely that the typical teenager will consume that much milk on a regular basis. Children and teens are also unlikely to eat salmon or mackerel—other rich sources—three times a week, as would be required to meet these newly revised vitamin D guidelines. While fortified cereals and egg yolk can add small amounts to the diet (about 1.25 μg per serving), it would be difficult for most children and adolescents to meet the increased recommendations from these sources either. Thus, dietary sources alone are unlikely to meet the vitamin D requirements of Canadian youth. So, what about supplements?

Many healthcare providers now recommend that most children and adolescents who do not or cannot get adequate sun exposure should take a supplement that provides up to 10 μg of vitamin D per day. Supplementation with vitamin D is efficient, inexpensive, and effective. Used correctly, it is also very safe. Vitamin D toxicity is rare, but is more likely to occur as the result of inappropriate supplementation as compared to excessive consumption of food sources. Thus, parents must monitor their child's intake of vitamin D supplements to ensure a safe as well as adequate intake.

As just noted, supplements are highly effective but do carry some risk of toxicity when used inappropriately. That leads us back to the issue of sun exposure. Responsible, safe exposure to sunlight offers many advantages: it will never lead to vitamin D toxicity, it is easy and virtually

cost-free, and sun exposure may offer benefits beyond that of improved vitamin D status.[49] Most advocates of moderate sun exposure simply want to soften the "sun avoidance" campaigns of recent years; they would like to see "well-balanced" recommendations that promote brief (15 minutes or so) periods of sun exposure, two to three times a week, with avoidance of mid-day sun during summer months.[50]

There is no debate over the need to maintain appropriate vitamin D status, especially in children and adolescents. But the debate over appropriate sun exposure as a means of achieving this status will likely rage on as scientists continue to explore the pros and cons.

Using the Evidence

1. Do you think the benefits of regular sun exposure outweigh the increased risk of skin cancer? Why or why not?

2. As a parent, would you encourage greater sun exposure to enhance your child's vitamin D status and possibly promote long-term health benefits; or would you discourage sun exposure to protect your child against skin cancer and other skin disorders?

18

Nutrition Through the Life Cycle: The Later Years

Test Yourself   True *or* False?

1. Experts agree that within the next 20 to 30 years, the human lifespan will exceed 150 years. **T** *or* **F**

2. Loss of odour perception is more common among older adults than is loss of taste perception. **T** *or* **F**

3. Older adults have a specific need for vitamin B_{12} supplements even if they are consistently eating a healthy diet. **T** *or* **F**

4. The need for iron increases with aging. **T** *or* **F**

5. Approximately 7% of older Canadians experience food insecurity. **T** *or* **F**

Test Yourself answers are located in the Chapter Review.

Chapter Objectives | *After reading this chapter, you will be able to:*

1. Describe the demographic changes related to aging in Canada, *pp. 664–665*.

2. Identify current theories of human aging and how each relates to nutrient intake and/or status of older adults, *pp. 665–666*.

3. Describe the most common changes in sensory perception and organ function that occur as we age, *pp. 666–671*.

4. Explain how lifestyle choices can influence the rate at which we age, *pp. 671–672*.

5. Compare and contrast the nutrient requirements of older adults to those of younger or middle-aged adults, *pp. 672–675*.

6. Explain the various factors that contribute to inappropriate weight loss in older adults, *pp. 677–678*.

7. Describe what role, if any, dietary choices play in the prevention and/or treatment of age-related diseases such as osteoporosis, arthritis, dementia, and macular degeneration, *pp. 678–680*.

8. Identify the social and environmental factors that can contribute to food insecurity and malnutrition in older adults, *pp. 683–684*.

9. Discuss the various health promotion programs available to older adults in Canada, *pp. 684–685*.

10. Evaluate the options for "end-of-life care" that relate to diet and nutritional support, *pp. 684–685*.

Many adults can remain highly active in their later years with the help of a nutritious diet and regular activity.

I t was a sunny day and hundreds of spectators sat in the bleachers cheering on their favourite athletes competing in a variety of swimming, track, and other events. Strong and fit bodies, laughing companionship, and discussions about future competitions filled the stadium. A typical high school or university competition? Guess again: the competitors were world-class Masters Athletes, all over the age of 40 and a surprisingly high proportion over the age of 60. Were these participants always so athletic or did they come to their sport late in life? Was it genetics or lifestyle that allowed them to maintain such high levels of fitness into middle and late adulthood? Specifically, did they follow a rigid diet and supplement plan or choose the same types of foods as others their age?

Decades of research confirms the importance of a nutritious diet and regular physical activity in helping to prevent chronic disease, enhance productivity, and improve quality of life as we age. What are the unique nutritional needs and concerns of older adults? How can diet and lifestyle affect the aging process? These and other questions will be addressed in this chapter.

What Are the Demographics of Aging?

Before we can discuss meaningfully the nutrient needs and concerns of older adults, it's essential that we understand who makes up the older adult population in Canada—both their numbers and their characteristics.

The Canadian Population Is Aging

The Canadian population is getting older each year. In 2001, approximately four million Canadians were 65 years of age or older, two-thirds more than in 1981.[1] The aging of the baby boom generation (born between 1946 and 1965) has begun to sharply increase the number and percentage of older Canadians. It is estimated that by the year 2041, nearly one in four Canadians will be over the age of 65.[1]

The racial and ethnic profile of older Canadian adults is changing as well. In 1996, only 2.5% of Canada's Aboriginal population were over the age of 65; the number of Aboriginal seniors is expected to triple by 2016. One in four Canadian seniors was born outside of Canada; however, only a small percentage of immigrants to Canada each year are over age 65.[1]

Fortunately, the quality of life of older Canadians has improved. The rate of low income has declined, fewer Canadian seniors are living in poverty, and the majority have good housing. Although today's seniors have, on average, lower levels of formal education than younger Canadian adults, seniors in the future will have more education and many continue to learn as they age.[1]

Those 85 years and over, sometimes referred to as the "oldest old," currently represent the fastest-growing Canadian population subgroup, projected to grow to 1.6 million in 2041, or 4% of the overall population.[1] The number of *centenarians*, persons over the age of 100 years, continues to grow as well. By 2031, it has been estimated that 14 000 Canadians will be centenarians.[2]

The racial and ethnic profile of Canadian older adults will change over the next several decades.

life expectancy The expected number of years remaining in one's life; typically stated from the time of birth. Children born in Canada in 2010 could expect to live, on average, 80.7 years.

Lifespan Differs from Life Expectancy

Celebrating one's 60th birthday is common today. Yet when George Washington turned 60 years old in 1792, he had outlived most of his peers by about 15 years. Canadian **life expectancy**, about 47 years in the year 1900, has increased dramatically during the past century due largely to medical advances, better nutrition, and improved sanitation.

In 2010, the average Canadian life expectancy reached 80.7 years. Women live longer on average than men, and racial disparities in life expectancy exist. The Canadian Aboriginal population has a life expectancy that is significantly lower than the Canadian average, with the lowest (64 years for men and 73 years for women) among the Inuit population.[3] Whereas some researchers have argued that the growing rate of obesity and its medical consequences will drive down Canadian life expectancy during the next several decades, others refute this claim, citing the likely impact of future advances in health care.[2, 4]

For most older adults, the goal is not to live as long as possible but to live a life free of disability and disease for as long as possible. This concept of healthy longevity is often referred to as *active life expectancy, successful aging,* or *compression of morbidity.*

Lifespan is the age to which the longest-living member of the species has lived. Madame Jeanne Calment, born in France in 1875, survived to the age of 122 and is generally viewed as achieving the oldest age in the world. There are also dozens of documented cases of people surviving to the ages of 114 to 116 years. Though very difficult to authenticate, one international volunteer organization estimates that there are currently about 75 super-centenarians (those over 110 years of age) living around the world, over 90% of them female.[5] Although some researchers have sought ways of extending human lifespan (see the Evidence-informed Decision Making feature on energy restriction at the end of this chapter), most agree that a lifespan beyond 125 to 130 years is unlikely.

Centenarians represent the future of Canadian older adults.

Why and How Do We Age?

The process of aging is natural and inevitable, influenced by genetic and environmental factors. Researchers have made great progress toward understanding the aging of humans, but much remains unknown.[6] Scientists can't even agree when the aging process begins: some believe it starts at birth, whereas others argue it begins after peak reproductive age. While the debate continues, however, gerontologists agree that humans can positively influence the aging process through specific lifestyle and environmental choices.

Many Mechanisms Are Thought to Contribute to Aging

Aging occurs at the molecular, cellular, and tissue levels. Some signs of aging, such as the greying of hair, do not impair function or health. Other age-related changes, however, contribute to declines in functionality, health, and well-being. Scientists use the term **senescence** to describe those age-related processes that increase risk of disability, disease, and death.

Theories attempting to explain the mechanisms of aging can be categorized into two lines of research (see Table 18.1). First are the **programmed theories of aging**, proposing that aging follows a biologically driven timeline, similar to that of adolescence. In programmed theories of aging, nutrition has little, if any, potential or practical impact on senescence. For example, there is no doubt that genes exert tremendous influence on the aging process. Siblings of centenarians are four times more likely to live into their 90s than others. Researchers have even found a genetic mutation dubbed the "I'm Not Dead Yet" gene, which prolongs the lifespan of certain laboratory animals. Although researchers may never develop a "fountain of youth," they are well on their way to understanding how genetics contributes to cell senescence and human aging.

The second category includes the **error theories of aging**, which argue that senescence occurs as a result of cell and tissue damage caused largely by environmental insults. These mechanisms include the following:

- As cells age, cell membrane function declines, allowing waste products to accumulate within the cell and decreasing normal uptake of nutrients and oxygen.[6]
- Gerontologists have also linked the aging process to a progressive accumulation of free radicals, which are known to damage DNA and various cell proteins.
- Cellular aging has also been linked to a progressive failure in DNA repair.[6] Throughout the life cycle, human DNA is subjected to various insults including free radicals, toxins, and random coding errors. Normally, the cell detects and repairs damaged DNA. With aging, however, the repair process becomes less efficient, leading to abnormal protein synthesis, which then results in cell, tissue, and organ senescence.

lifespan The highest age reached by any member of a species; currently, the human lifespan is 122 years.

senescence The progressive deterioration of bodily functions over time, resulting in increased risk of disability, disease, and death.

programmed theories of aging Aging is biologically determined, following a predictable pattern of physiologic changes, although the timing may vary from one person to another.

error theories of aging Aging is a cumulative process determined largely by exposure to environmental insults; the fewer the environmental insults, the slower the aging process.

Table 18.1 Theories of Aging

Model	Description	Nutrition Interface
Programmed theories of aging	Aging follows a biologically driven timeline, similar to that of adolescence	None evident
Hayflick theory of aging	Cells have a limited reproductive lifespan; in essence, cells can divide only so many times before they are no longer able to proliferate	None evident
Theory of programmed longevity	Aging occurs when certain genes are turned on or off; the activation or suppression of these genes then triggers age-related loss of function	Indirectly, a diet rich in antioxidants such as vitamins C and E could lower free-radical damage to DNA
Endocrine theory of aging	Senescence is due to hormonal changes such as declines in growth hormone, DHEA, estrogen, and/or testosterone	None directly evident
Immunologic theory of aging	Aging is linked to loss of immune system activity and/or an increase in autoimmune diseases	Adequate protein, zinc, iron, and vitamins A, C, and E help preserve remaining immune function
Error theories of aging	Senescence occurs as the result of cell and tissue damage caused largely by environmental insults	Several theoretical benefits of nutrient adequacy or supplementation
Wear-and-tear theory	Over time, cells simply wear out and eventually die. The greater the exposure to toxins and stressors, the more rapid the rate of decline	Protein, zinc, and vitamins A and C could theoretically delay the aging process by improving cellular repair and recovery
Cross-linkage theory	Abnormal cross-linkages of proteins such as collagen damage cells and tissues, impairing the function of organs	Glycosylation, the abnormal attachment of glucose to proteins, can be limited by controlling blood glucose levels. Adequate intakes of vitamin C, selenium, and copper may reduce other types of protein cross-linkages
Free-radical theory	Senescence is due to the cumulative damage caused by various free radicals	Diets and/or supplements rich in vitamins C and E, selenium, and antioxidant phytochemicals may limit the cellular accumulation of free radicals
Rate-of-living theory	In general, the higher the species' average basal metabolic rate (BMR), the shorter its lifespan	Theoretically, energy restriction would lower BMR and prolong life (see the Evidence-informed Decision Making feature on pages 690–691)

- Tissue and organ senescence has been linked to the process of **glycosylation**. This abnormal attachment of glucose to proteins results in loss of protein structure and function. As a result, lung tissue, blood vessels, and tendons become rigid and inflexible.

Changes identified by the error theories of aging are directly or indirectly linked to nutrient or energy status. Thus, consumption of adequate levels of antioxidant nutrients could theoretically delay some of these changes.

In truth, the programmed and error theories of aging are not mutually exclusive: it is likely that aging stems from a complex interplay of the factors identified in Table 18.1.

Characteristic Physiologic Changes Accompany Aging

Older adulthood is a time in which growth is complete and body systems begin to slow and degenerate. If the following discussion of this degeneration seems disturbing or depressing, remember that the changes described are at least partly within an individual's control. For instance, some of the decrease seen in muscle mass, bone mass, and muscle strength is due to low physical activity levels. Older adults who regularly participate in strengthening exercises and aerobic-type activities reduce their risks for low bone mass and muscle atrophy and weakness, which in turn reduces their risk for falls.

Age-Related Changes in Sensory Perception

For most individuals, eating is a social and pleasurable process; the sights, sounds, odours, and textures associated with food are closely linked to appetite. Odour, taste, tactile, and visual perception all decline with age; as they do, an older adult's food intake and nutritional status can decline as well.

glycosylation Addition of glucose to blood and tissue proteins; typically impairs protein structure and function.

More than half of older adults experience significant loss of olfactory (odour) perception, a condition more common than loss of taste perception.[7] The enjoyment of food relies heavily on the sense of smell: think of your own response to the smell of bread baking in the oven or the aroma of grilled meat or poultry. Older adults who cannot adequately appreciate the appealing aromas of food may be unable to fully enjoy the foods offered within the meal. Loss of olfaction also restricts the ability to detect spoiled food, increasing the risk of food poisoning. Although often a simple consequence of aging, loss of odour perception can also be caused by zinc deficiency or occur as a side effect of medication. If this is the case, a zinc supplement or change of medication may be a simple solution. If a zinc supplement is taken, it is important to remember that toxicity can occur if excess amounts are ingested (see page 458 in Chapter 13).

As people age, their ability to smell foods can decrease.

With increasing age, taste perception dims as well, which is one reason why older adults seem to add so much salt to their foods or complain about the blandness of their foods. The ability to perceive sweetness and sourness also declines, but to a lesser extent. Some older adults experience **dysgeusia**, or abnormal taste perception, which can be caused by disease or medication use. For example, an older person might experience the sensation of bitterness from a freshly cooked piece of chicken that others would find perfectly enjoyable.

Loss of visual acuity has unexpected consequences for the nutritional health of the older adult. Many older adults have difficulty reading food labels, including nutrient information. Driving skills decline, limiting the ability of some older Canadians to acquire healthy, affordable foods. Older adults with vision loss may not be able to see the temperature knobs on stoves or the controls on microwave ovens and may therefore choose cold meals, such as sandwiches, rather than meals that require heating. The visual appeal of a colourful, attractively arranged plate of food is also lost to visually impaired older adults, further reducing their desire to eat healthy meals.

Friends and family members can help older adults adjust to these sensory losses by encouraging appropriate food selections and preparation techniques. Flavour enhancers such as herbs and spices, meat concentrates, and sauces can increase the desirability of otherwise bland foods. Visual enhancements such as brightly coloured garnishes and an array of different shapes and textures on the plate can compensate for diminished olfaction. Some older adults experience an increase in appetite from sipping a small glass of wine, which can be healthy if the person has no disease or medication restrictions or history of alcohol abuse.

Age-Related Changes in Gastrointestinal Function

Significant changes in the mouth and gastrointestinal tract occur with aging.[8] Some of these changes have the potential to increase the risk of nutrient deficiency.

With increasing age, salivary production declines. In older adults with **xerostomia**, teeth are more susceptible to decay, chewing and swallowing become more difficult, and taste perception declines. A diet rich in moist foods including fruits and vegetables, sauces or gravies on meats, and high-fluid desserts such as puddings is well tolerated by older adults with xerostomia. In the most severe cases, older adults can use an artificial saliva, which is sprayed into the mouth.

Some older adults, including those with Parkinson's disease, experience **dysphagia** (difficulty swallowing foods). Smooth, thick foods such as cream soups or applesauce are easy to swallow but foods with mixed textures, such as gelatin with fruit pieces, should be avoided. Milkshakes, fruit nectars, and other thick or viscous beverages are better tolerated than thin liquids such as water and coffee. Dysphagia requires professional assessment and treatment, drawing upon the expertise of an occupational therapist, a physician, and a dietitian. If not accurately diagnosed and treated, dysphagia could lead to malnutrition, inappropriate weight loss, aspiration of food or fluid into the lungs, and pneumonia.

Older adults are at risk for a reduced secretion of gastric acid, intrinsic factor, pepsin, and mucus.[9] Atrophic gastritis contributes to bacterial overgrowth and gastric inflammation.

dysgeusia Abnormal taste perception.

xerostomia Dry mouth due to decreased saliva production.

dysphagia Abnormal swallowing.

A variety of gastrointestinal and other physiologic changes can lead to weight loss in older adults.

Achlorhydria, a severe reduction in gastric hydrochloric acid production, limits the absorption of minerals such as calcium, iron, and zinc and food sources of folic acid and vitamin B_{12}. Lack of intrinsic factor, produced by the same cells that secrete gastric hydrochloric acid, reduces the absorption of vitamin B_{12} (see page 466 in Chapter 13). These older adults, therefore, benefit from vitamin B_{12} supplements. Older adults may also experience a delay in gastric emptying, resulting in a prolonged sense of fullness and a reduced appetite. Although this may be viewed as a positive factor in people who are overweight or obese, it can lead to inappropriate weight loss.

Compared with younger adults, healthy older adults demonstrate no significant loss in digestive enzyme activity, the ability to absorb nutrients, or intestinal motility. Therefore, healthy older adults generally digest and absorb protein, fat, and carbohydrate as efficiently as younger adults. The one exception is the digestion of lactose: only about 30% of older adults retain an "adequate" level of lactase enzyme activity. Black, Hispanic, Aboriginal, and Asian older adults are at very high risk for lactose intolerance and may need to restrict their fluid milk intake to 125 mL servings, use lactose-reduced milk or lactase enzyme supplements, or eliminate milk from their diet entirely. Although tolerance for dairy foods may decrease with aging, the need for calcium does not. Older adults may need to turn to calcium-fortified fruit juices and cereals, calcium-enriched tofu, and other sources to ensure an adequate intake. Finally, although gastrointestinal (GI) function remains largely unaffected by aging, nutrient availability may be severely compromised if an older adult has a disease of the liver, pancreas, or GI tract that impairs digestion of food and absorption of nutrients.

Age-Related Changes in Body Composition

With aging, body fat increases and muscle mass declines. It has been estimated that women and men lose 20% to 25% of their lean body mass, respectively, as they age from 35 to 70 years. Decreased production of certain hormones, including testosterone and growth hormone, and chronic diseases contribute to this loss of muscle, as does poor diet and an inactive lifestyle. Older adults with **sarcopenia** are often so weak that they are unable to rise from a seated position, climb stairs, or carry a bag of groceries. Along with adequate dietary intake, according to the 2011 Canadian Physical Activity Guidelines (page 544), older adults can achieve health benefits and improve their functional abilities by accumulating at least 150 minutes of moderate- to vigorous-intensity physical activity per week, in bouts of 10 minutes or more. Strength or resistance training is also recommended to help older adults maintain their muscle mass and strength.[10] Older adults with poor mobility should add exercises (such as yoga) to improve their balance and prevent falls. (Refer to the Highlight, "Seniors on the Move," on page 670 and Chapter 15 for additional information on the recommendations for physical activity for older adults.)

Body fat increases from young adulthood through middle age, peaking at approximately 55 to 65 years of age. Females experience a sharper increase in percentage of body fat compared with males. Percentage of body fat tends to decline in persons over the age of 70 years. With aging, body fat shifts from subcutaneous stores, just below the skin, to internal or visceral fat stores.[11] Older women tend to deposit more fat in their abdominal region compared with younger women; this shift in body fat stores is most dramatic after the onset of menopause and coincides with an increased risk for heart disease, type 2 diabetes, and metabolic syndrome. Older men are also at higher risk for increases in abdominal fat as they age. Maintaining an appropriate energy intake and remaining physically active can help keep body fat to a healthy level.

An increasing number of older adults are at risk for **sarcopenic obesity**, which is strongly associated with frailty, disability, and inability to perform normal activities of daily living.[12] While total body weight and body fat are increased in these persons, their underlying muscle mass is not adequate in amount or strength to support normal mobility and health.

achlorhydria Lack of gastric acid secretion.

sarcopenia Age-related progressive loss of muscle mass, muscle strength, and muscle function.

sarcopenic obesity A condition in which increased body weight and body fat mass coexist with inappropriately low muscle mass and strength.

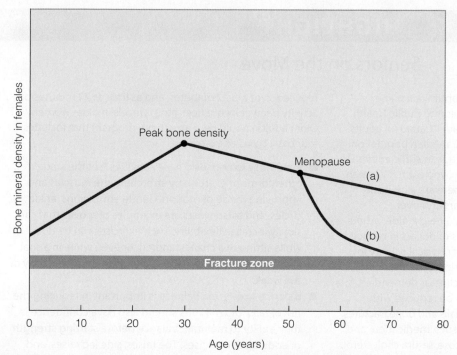

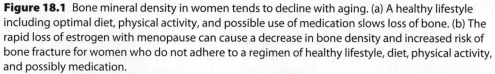

Figure 18.1 Bone mineral density in women tends to decline with aging. (a) A healthy lifestyle including optimal diet, physical activity, and possible use of medication slows loss of bone. (b) The rapid loss of estrogen with menopause can cause a decrease in bone density and increased risk of bone fracture for women who do not adhere to a regimen of healthy lifestyle, diet, physical activity, and possibly medication.

Bone mineral density declines with age and may eventually drop to the critical fracture zone. Among older women, the onset of menopause leads to a sudden and dramatic loss of bone due to the lack of estrogen (**Figure 18.1**). Although less dramatic, older males also experience loss of bone due in part to decreasing levels of testosterone. The nutrients recognized as essential to optimal bone health are identified in Chapter 12. As noted in the Highlight box, "Seniors on the Move," on page 670, bone health can be promoted through regular weight-bearing activity in adults well into their nineties and beyond.

Age-Related Changes in Organ Function

Aged organs are less adaptable to environmental or physiologic stressors. Young adults, for example, readily adapt to varying levels of fluid and sodium intakes because of the ability of the kidneys to maintain fluid balance. With increasing age, however, the kidneys lose their ability to concentrate waste products, leading to an increase in urine output and greater risk of dehydration. The aging liver is less efficient at breaking down drugs or alcohol, and the aging heart lacks the endurance to sustain a sudden increase in physical activity. The pancreas is less precise in regulating blood glucose levels, and bladder control may decline with aging. In most instances, older adults can adapt to these age-related changes through minor lifestyle adjustments such as eating meals and snacks on a regular basis and ensuring an adequate fluid intake.

As a result of abnormal protein cross-linkages, connective tissues and blood vessels become increasingly stiff. Joint pain, elevated blood pressure, and impaired blood flow are typical consequences. The skin of older adults can become thin, dry, and fragile. Bruises and skin tears are very common and are slow to heal. The growth of nails slows and hair loss is common among older males and females. Although some of these consequences are simply cosmetic and represent no disease risk, the skin's tendency to bruise and tear may increase the risk of infection. A diet rich in vitamins C and A, zinc, copper, and protein may reduce the severity of bruising in some older adults.

HIGHLIGHT

Seniors on the Move

Although this chapter began with an optimistic scene from a competition for Masters Athletes, the Public Health Agency of Canada has reported that older Canadian adults are the most inactive segment of the Canadian population. Almost two-thirds of them do not engage in sufficient levels of physical activity to maintain or improve health.[13] Women tend to be less active than men and there are significant declines in activity levels at age 75 years and over.

For a minor investment of time and energy, older adults reap benefits worth literally thousands of dollars in reduced healthcare costs. A regular program of physical activity lowers the risk of heart disease, hypertension, type 2 diabetes, obesity, depression, and cognitive decline or dementia.[14] The complications of arthritis can also be reduced with appropriate exercise, as can the risk of falls and bone fractures. The need for healthcare visits, diagnostics, medication, and other treatments to control blood glucose, serum cholesterol, blood pressure, and other factors in chronic illness can be reduced or eliminated with regular exercise.

Physically active older adults live longer and enjoy better health while they live. Muscular strength and total daily energy expenditure are independently associated with lower risk of death among older adults.[15, 16] The level of activity needed to improve health is not even that great; both moderate- and even light-intensity activity greatly

reduce risk of type 2 diabetes, and as little as 72 minutes of activity per week enhances fitness levels in older women.[17–19] Older adults should plan an activity program that includes four basic types of exercises:

- **Flexibility exercises:** These activities "set the stage" for other forms of exercise by stretching the muscles and improving range of motion. Gentle arm swings, ankle circles, and torso twists are examples of moves that can slowly increase flexibility. Such exercises can be done while sitting in a chair, standing, or even while in a shallow pool. Ideally, older adults should stretch every day of the week.

- **Balance exercises:** Balance is important in reducing the risk of falls. Older adults should also have confidence in their ability to maintain balance before starting strength or endurance exercises. Toe raises, side leg raises, and rear leg swings are examples of balance activities; *Tai Chi* is another popular way to improve balance. Fitness experts advise adults to start balance exercises by holding a table or large chair with both hands; with practice, individuals will progress to using one hand only, then grasping with fingers only, and finally they may feel secure enough to try some balance activities with no hand-holds at all. Older adults should practise balance activities daily.

- **Strength or resistance training:** This type of activity can increase muscle mass and strength as well as enhance bone density, preserving the ability of older adults to maintain an independent lifestyle. Gains in muscle strength also improve balance and provide the foundation for endurance exercise. A growing number of retirement communities and long-term care centres offer "weight rooms" where strength training equipment is available. Community centres, including congregate meal sites, offer strength training using cans of food, bottles of water, and other common items; the exercises are designed for mobile and chair-bound older adults.

Ideally, older adults should engage in resistance training at least two days a week.

- **Endurance or aerobic exercise:** Activities such as brisk walking, bicycle riding, swimming, and dancing increase heart rate and improve cardiorespiratory function. These activities should be low impact (no jump ropes or high-impact aerobics classes!) to minimize risk to aging bones, joints, and muscles. Older adults should aim for an intensity perceived as "fairly light" to "somewhat hard"—a level that is challenging but not exhausting. As with resistance training, older adults should check with their healthcare provider before starting on a program of endurance exercise. Once given approval, they should try to take part in at least 150 minutes of moderate- to vigorous-intensity aerobic activity each week. Examples of moderate-intensity physical activity include walking quickly or bike riding. A vigorous-intensity activity would include swimming or cross-country skiing.[10]

Some older adults may be vulnerable to exercise-related complications such as dehydration, heat stress, fractures, or falls. Exercise rooms should offer appropriate temperature, ventilation, and lighting; participants should wear appropriate clothing and comfortable shoes; and supervised warm-up and cool-down periods should be incorporated into each activity. As always, a thorough medical exam is advised prior to the start of programmed exercise.

The benefits of regular physical activity by older adults almost always far outweigh potential risks—the payoff is better health, more independence, less disability, and a longer, happier life!

The number of neurons in the brain decreases with age, impairing memory, reflexes, coordination, and learning ability. Whereas some believe that dementia is an inevitable part of the aging process, a healthy diet, regular physical activity, and other lifestyle choices can promote cognitive functioning.

What Lifestyle Factors Accelerate Aging?

The way we live greatly influences the way we age. Whereas chronologic age is immovable, **biologic age** can be greatly influenced by personal choices and decisions. It is now possible to predict one's biologic age through a series of scored questions related to smoking habits, alcohol consumption, sun exposure, weight status, level of physical activity, and other factors. A similar approach is used to estimate potential longevity.[20]

In addition to causing a variety of cancers, direct or second-hand exposure to cigarette and cigar smoke accelerates the aging process; inhalation of the thousands of toxins found in smoke impairs lung function, damages the cardiovascular system, increases the risk for osteoporosis, and impairs taste and odour perception. Smoking also causes premature facial wrinkling and impairs dental health. Older adults should be reminded that it is never too late to quit; improvements in taste perception, physical endurance, and lung function can be detected within weeks of smoking cessation.

Excessive consumption of alcohol also speeds up the aging process by interfering with nutrient intake and utilization, injuring the liver, increasing risk for osteoporosis, and contributing to accidental injuries and deaths. These effects are cumulative over the years, so the earlier the alcohol abuse begins, the greater the damage to body systems.

Sunlight exposure is the primary risk factor for age-related discoloration and thinning of the skin as well as skin cancer. Although its use decreases skin production of vitamin D, most healthcare providers recommend lifelong use of sunscreen to limit sun-induced skin damage. See the Evidence-informed Decision Making feature in Chapter 17 for more information.

Maintaining a normal weight is associated with healthy and successful aging. Excess body weight, at any age, speeds up the deterioration of joints, increasing the risk of osteoarthritis and contributing to functional limitations.[21] In addition, successful control of blood glucose—in part through weight management—can delay the glycosylation of blood and tissue proteins. When people with diabetes fail to control their blood glucose levels, they experience chronic hyperglycemia and develop complications that seem to mimic the aging

Sunlight exposure over a lifetime can lead to discoloration and thinning of the skin in old age.

biologic age Physiologic age as determined by health and functional status; often estimated by scored questionnaires.

process. Obesity also accelerates age-related declines in cardiovascular health. For more information, see Chapter 14.

Lack of physical activity accelerates loss of muscle mass and bone density, increases risk of falls, and impairs the ability to perform simple activities of daily living.[14] The Highlight box, "Seniors on the Move," describes the benefits of regular physical activity in older adults.

RecaP

The Canadian population continues to age at an unprecedented rate. The oldest old, 85 years and above, represent the fastest-growing segment of the Canadian population. Scientists are beginning to understand some of the basic cellular changes that contribute to aging and how diet and nutrition might influence the aging process. With aging, sensory perception declines, muscle mass is lost, fat mass increases, bone density decreases, and nutrient metabolism is impaired. Body organs can lose functional capacity and are less tolerant of stressors. These age-related changes influence the nutritional needs of older adults and their ability to consume a healthy diet. Tobacco use, alcohol abuse, excessive sun exposure, overweight, and inactivity accelerate the aging process.

What Are an Older Adult's Nutrient Needs?

As you can see by reviewing the DRI tables (inside covers of book), the requirements for many nutrients are the same for older adults as for young and middle-aged adults. A few nutrient requirements increase, and a few are actually lower. It should be noted that several factors (i.e., nutrient bioavailability and physiological, lifestyle, and health characteristics) have an impact on an individual's nutrient requirements. After age 70, it is known that people of the same age can have differing levels of physiological functioning and physical activity.[22] Thus, it is necessary to consider these factors when planning dietary intakes for older adults. Table 18.2, page 673, identifies nutrient recommendations that change with age, as well as the physiologic reason behind these changes.

Energy Needs of Older Adults

The energy needs of older adults are lower than those of younger adults because loss of muscle mass and lean tissue results in a lower basal metabolic rate, and most older adults have a less physically active lifestyle. It is estimated that total daily energy expenditure decreases approximately 10 kcal each year for men and 7 kcal each year for women ages 19 and older.[23] This means that a woman who needed 2000 kcal at age 20 needs just 1650 kcal at age 70. Some of this decrease in energy expenditure is an inevitable response to aging, but some of the decrease can be delayed or minimized by staying physically active.

Because their total daily energy needs are lower, older adults need to pay particularly close attention to consuming a diet high in nutrient-dense foods but not too high in energy in order to avoid weight gain. My Food Guide is an interactive tool that can be used to personalize the information in *Eating Well with Canada's Food Guide* for older adults.[23]

Macronutrient Recommendations for Older Adults

Because there is no evidence suggesting a minimal amount of dietary fat needed to maintain health, there is no DRI for total fat intake for older adults.[24] However, to reduce the risk for heart disease and other chronic diseases, it is recommended that total fat intake remain within 20% to 35% of total daily energy intake, with no more than 10% of total energy intake coming from saturated fat. Dietary sources of *trans* fatty acids should be kept to a minimum.

The RDA for carbohydrate for older adults is 130 g/day.[24] As with all other age groups, this level of carbohydrate is sufficient to support glucose utilization by the brain. There is no evidence to indicate what percentage of carbohydrate should come from sugars or starches. However, it is recommended that older individuals consume a diet that contains no more than 25% of total energy intake as sugars.[24] The fibre recommendations are slightly lower for older adults than for younger adults because older adults consume less energy. After age 50, 30 g of fibre per day for men and 21 g per day for women is assumed sufficient to reduce the risks for constipation and diverticular disease, maintain healthy blood levels of glucose and lipids, and provide good sources of nutrient-dense, low-energy foods.

A less physically active lifestyle leads to lower total energy requirements in older adults.

The DRI for protein is the same for adults of all ages: 0.8 g of protein per kilogram of body weight per day.[24] Although some researchers have argued for a higher protein allowance for older adults to optimize protein status, a recent study confirmed no apparent difference in the protein requirement between healthy older and younger adults.[25] Protein is critically important in helping reduce the loss of muscle and lean tissue,[26] maintaining immunity, enhancing wound healing and disease recovery, and helping to prevent excessive loss of bone. Protein-rich foods are also important sources of vitamins and minerals that are typically low in the diets of older adults.

Micronutrient Recommendations for Older Adults

The vitamins and minerals of particular concern for older adults are identified in Table 18.2. Preventing or minimizing the consequences of osteoporosis is a top priority for older adults. The requirements for both calcium and vitamin D are higher than for younger adults because of a reduced absorption of calcium from the gut, along with an age-related reduction in the production of vitamin D in the skin. An increasing number of older adults are at risk for vitamin D deficiency because they are institutionalized and are not exposed to adequate amounts of sunlight. Others may limit intake of milk and dairy products because of lactose intolerance or perceived concerns over the fat content of these foods. Older adults living in the community are also at risk for vitamin D deficiency on account of the widespread use of sunscreen; these creams and lotions are important to prevent skin cancer, but they block the sunlight needed for vitamin D synthesis in the skin. A cross-sectional study of healthy community-dwelling older adults living in Quebec found that although the actual prevalence of vitamin D deficiency was low, more than 50% of the participants had suboptimal

Table 18.2 Nutrient Recommendations That Change with Increased Age

Changes in Nutrient Recommendations	Rationale for Changes
Increased need for vitamin D from 15 µg/day for children and adults 9–70 years to 20 µg/day for adults over age 70 years.	• Decreased bone density • Decreased ability to synthesize vitamin D in the skin
Increased need for calcium from 1000 mg/day for young adults to 1200 mg/day for adult women 51 years of age and older. For men, calcium needs increase to 1200 mg/day after age 70.	• Decreased absorption of dietary calcium • Decreased bone density
Decreased need for fibre from 38 g/day for young men to 30 g/day for men 51 years and older. Decreases for women are from 25 g/day for young women to 21 g/day for women 51 years and older.	• Decreased energy intake
Increased need for vitamin B_6. Need for vitamin B_{12} *from fortified foods or supplements*, as opposed to foods of animal origin.	• Lower levels of stomach acid • Decreased absorption of vitamin B_{12} from gastrointestinal tract • Increased need to reduce homocysteine levels and to optimize immune function
Decreased need for iron from 18 mg/day for young women to 8 mg/day for women 51 years and older. No change in iron recommendations for men 51 years and older.	• Cessation of menstruation in women; some loss of muscle and lean tissue in men and women

blood levels of vitamin D.[27] It is critical that older adults consume foods that are high in calcium and vitamin D and, over the age of 50, take a daily vitamin D supplement of 10 μg (400 IU) per day.[23]

Iron needs decrease with aging as a result of reduced muscle mass in both men and women and the cessation of menstruation in women. The decreased need for iron in older men is not significant enough to change the recommendations for iron intake in this group; thus, the RDA for iron is the same for older men as for younger, 8 mg/day. The RDA for iron in older women is also 8 mg/day, but this represents a significant decrease from the 18 mg/day RDA for younger women. Although zinc recommendations are the same for all adults, zinc is especially critical for optimizing immune function and wound healing in older adults. Intakes of both zinc and iron can be inadequate in older adults if they do not regularly eat red meats, poultry, and fish. These foods are relatively expensive, and older adults on a limited income may not be able to afford to eat them regularly. Also, the loss of teeth and/or use of dentures may increase the difficulty of chewing meats.

Although it is speculated that older adults have increased oxidative stress, the recommendations for vitamin C and vitamin E are the same as for younger adults because there is insufficient evidence that consuming amounts higher than the current RDA has any additional health benefits.[28] Researchers continue, however, to investigate the potential benefits of dietary or supplemental antioxidants, including vitamins C and E, and the roles they may play in lowering the risk of cataracts and age-related macular degeneration (see Chapter 11).[29]

Older adults need to pay close attention to consuming adequate amounts of the B-vitamins, specifically vitamin B_{12}, vitamin B_6, and folate. Low levels of these nutrients may be related to cognitive function in the elderly,[30] and several observational studies have suggested a relationship between low vitamin B_6, vitamin B_{12}, and folate status and depression.[31] The RDA for vitamin B_{12} is the same for younger and older adults; however, up to 30% of older adults cannot absorb enough vitamin B_{12} from foods because of atrophic gastritis (see page 467). It is recommended that older adults consume foods that are fortified with vitamin B_{12} or take B_{12} supplements, because the vitamin B_{12} in these products is absorbed more readily. Vitamin B_6 recommendations are slightly higher for older adults, as these higher levels appear necessary to optimize immune function in this population.[32]

Vitamin A requirements are the same for adults of all ages; however, older adults should be careful not to consume more than the RDA, as absorption of vitamin A is actually greater in older adults. Older adults are at greater risk for vitamin A toxicity, which can cause liver damage and neurologic problems. However, consuming foods high in beta-carotene or other carotenoids is safe and does not lead to vitamin A toxicity.

A variety of factors may limit an older adult's ability to eat a healthy diet. Limited financial resources may prevent some older adults from buying nutrient-dense foods on a regular basis; others may experience a reduced appetite, social isolation, inability to prepare foods, or illnesses that limit nutrient absorption and metabolism. Thus, some older adults benefit from taking a multivitamin and multimineral supplement that contains no more than the RDA for each nutrient. *Eating Well with Canada's Food Guide* recommends that all adults over age 50 take a vitamin D supplement of 10 μg (400 IU) daily.[23] Additional supplementation may be necessary for nutrients such as calcium and vitamin B_{12}. However, supplementation with individual nutrients should be done only under the supervision of the individual's primary healthcare provider, as the risk of nutrient toxicity is high in this population. The accompanying Highlight box, "Supplements for Seniors," reviews the advantages and potential disadvantages of selecting a commercial product designed specifically for older adults.

Fluid Recommendations for Older Adults

The AI for fluid is the same for all adults. Men should consume 3.7 L (about 15.5 cups) of total fluid per day, which includes 3.0 L (about 13 cups) as total beverages, including

Older adults need the same amount of fluid as other adults.

drinking water. Women should consume 2.7 L (about 12.7 cups) of total fluid per day, which includes 2.2 L (about 9 cups) as total beverages, including drinking water. In general, older adults do not perceive thirst as effectively as do younger adults. Thus, they are at increased risk for chronic dehydration and hypernatremia (elevated blood sodium levels). Some older adults will intentionally limit their beverage intake because they have urinary incontinence or do not want to be awakened for nighttime urination. This practice can endanger their health, so it is important for these individuals to seek treatment for the incontinence and continue to drink adequate fluids.

Did You Know?

Dr. Heather Keller, at the University of Guelph, received the prestigious New Investigator Award from the Canadian Institutes of Health Research in 2000 for her research with older adults. Community-dwelling older adults are at increased nutritional risk because of the variety of factors that impair their ability to eat a healthy diet. Dr. Keller developed a brief questionnaire to assess nutritional risk among vulnerable seniors—SCREEN™ (Seniors in the Community Risk Evaluation for Eating and Nutrition). This tool has undergone extensive validation and reliability testing and can be self- or interviewer-administered. A SCREEN™ toolkit is also available that includes various versions of SCREEN and additional background material. For more information about SCREEN™ you can go to Dr. Keller's website at www.drheatherkeller.com.

Recap

Older adults have lower energy needs because of their loss of lean tissue and lower physical activity levels. They should consume 20% to 35% of total energy as fat and 45% to 65% as carbohydrate. Protein recommendations are currently the same as for younger adults, although some research suggests the need for slightly higher intakes. Micronutrients of concern for older adults include calcium, vitamin D, the B-vitamins, and the antioxidant vitamins. Older adults are at risk for chronic dehydration and hypernatremia, so sufficient fluid intake should be encouraged.

Are Older Canadian Adults Meeting Their Nutrient Needs?

Most older Canadian adults are meeting their energy and macronutrient needs; however, there are some areas of concern, particularly in the oldest old age group.[33] The average daily energy intake for older men (65 years and older) is 1950 kcalories; older women consume approximately 1550 kcalories daily. Most older Canadians eat the recommended number of servings of meats and alternatives, but 15% of women aged 71 and older do not. Vegetable and fruit consumption also decreases with age. Between the ages of 51 and 70, 41% of males and 48% of females do not meet the minimum recommended number of servings; these figures increase to 52% for males and 60% of females after age 71. Calcium and vitamin D intake is of particular concern as more than 80% of older men and women do not consume the minimum recommended number of servings of milk products daily.

HIGHLIGHT

Supplements for Seniors

Consumers have thousands of different options when shopping for nutritional supplements. Even if looking for a "simple" multivitamin/multimineral (MVMM) supplement, there are many targeted products, including those formulated specifically for seniors. How do these senior (or "silver") products differ from other MVMM products? Are they actually better for seniors or just a marketing ploy? A close look at such products yields some interesting information.

Although every product line has its own unique formulation, a side-by-side comparison of the nutrients in a typical "adult" MVMM supplement with those in a "senior" MVMM product from the same manufacturer reveal very few differences. Of the 33 nutrients in the adult product, two (iron and tin) are omitted from the senior supplement, one (vitamin K) is provided at a lower dosage, three (calcium and vitamins E and B$_6$) are included at slightly higher levels, and one (vitamin B$_{12}$) is four times higher in the senior supplement. Although not all of these product modifications reflect age-specific DRI values (see the inside covers of this book for DRI values), there are good reasons for most of these product adjustments. As you compare the product labels, remember that Health Canada uses "% Daily Value" to describe nutrient levels, not the newer DRI recommendations.

Although the DRI for vitamin E does not change for males or females ages 19 to 70 years or above, there is good evidence that older adults are often in a state of "oxidative stress." Chronic inflammation, as occurs with arthritis and other conditions, is more common among older adults than younger populations and may increase the need for antioxidants such as vitamin E. In addition, as previously discussed, there is preliminary, but inconsistent, research supporting the use of vitamin E in lowering the risk of age-associated eye disorders and dementia. Knowing that vitamin E has a relatively low risk of toxicity, the small increase provided in the senior supplement certainly poses no harm.

As with vitamin E, the DRI for vitamin K does not change with increased age. Why then, does the senior supplement provide a lower dose? Persons on anticoagulant drugs, many of them older, are advised to tightly regulate vitamin K intake. By minimizing the amount of vitamin K in the senior supplement, there would be less risk of a negative drug–nutrient interaction among seniors taking both the MVMM supplement and anticoagulant drugs. Some physicians might consider even 13% of the vitamin K Daily Value to be too much, so it would be important for each senior to check

Many supplements are specifically formulated for older adults.

with his or her doctor before using a MVMM with any vitamin K.

Although the senior supplement provides about 40 mg more calcium than the more general adult product, that amount does not go very far toward satisfying the DRI guideline of an additional 200 mg calcium per day for adult females 51 years and above and for males over the age of 70 years. Calcium is too "bulky" for most MVMM supplements, so all adults, regardless of their stage of life, should choose a specific calcium supplement (possibly one with vitamin D and/or vitamin K) if their food choices do not provide adequate dietary calcium.

The DRI for vitamin B$_6$ for adults 51 years and older is slightly higher than that for younger adults, and the senior supplement reflects that increase by providing 50% more vitamin B$_6$ than the MVMM product targeting the general adult population.

As discussed earlier, adults over the age of 50 years often poorly absorb vitamin B$_{12}$ from food sources. Older adults are advised to consume foods that are fortified with vitamin B$_{12}$ or supplements, because the vitamin B$_{12}$ in these sources is absorbed more readily than food sources of vitamin B$_{12}$. Although the DRI recommends a change in the *source* of vitamin B$_{12}$ not in the *amount,* the higher dosage in the senior supplement poses no harm.

What about the omission of iron from the senior supplement? Certainly, iron is a nutrient essential for good health; why would a manufacturer totally omit it from the product? Recall from Chapter 13 that a woman's need for iron decreases dramatically after menopause; most women can easily meet that need from food alone. In addition, risk of iron overload increases with age, particularly in older men; thus, eliminating iron from senior supplements actually lowers the risk of inappropriate iron loading. If an older adult has a specific need for supplemental iron, for example, following significant blood loss, his or her physician can recommend an iron-only supplement. Tin is the other mineral eliminated from the senior product; because tin has no % Daily Value or DRI, there is no strong justification for including it in the senior supplement.

Each age-specific MVMM product line should be evaluated carefully to determine if the nutrient balance is appropriate for seniors. When consumed with a well-balanced diet, the small but important differences between supplements designed for seniors and supplements designed for middle-aged adults can help seniors obtain the appropriate amounts of all the nutrients that they need.

What Nutritional Concerns Threaten the Health of Older Adults?

In this section, we discuss several common nutrition-related concerns of older adults. As we explore each concern, we will attempt to answer two questions: (1) What, if any, nutrient concerns develop as a result of a specific medical disorder? (2) What, if any, effect does nutrition have on the risk of developing that disorder?

Overweight and Underweight

Not surprisingly, overweight and obesity are of concern to older adults. Data from the 1996–97 Canadian National Population Health Survey indicated that 13% of Canadian older adults were classified as obese.[34] In 2004, this figure rose to 20%.[35] Only those individuals over the age of 75 years had a lower obesity rate at 11%. Using BMI to define obesity in older adults has its limitations however. As previously discussed, lean body mass decreases and fat mass increases as adults age. These age-related changes in body composition tend to underestimate fatness based on BMI.[36] Thus fat distribution may be a more important indicator for health risk for older adults. It has been shown that the prevalence of abdominal obesity increases with age, particularly among women. As discussed in Chapter 14, abdominal obesity is assessed by measuring waist circumference. A waist circumference of 102 cm (40 in.) or higher in men and 88 cm (35 in.) or higher in women is a risk factor for several chronic diseases (including heart disease, hypertension, type 2 diabetes, and cancer) and one of the conditions associated with metabolic syndrome, the prevalence of which is higher in older adults. Data from the Canadian Health Measures survey showed that 17% of Canadian adults aged 18 to 39 had metabolic syndrome; this figure rose to 39% for adults between the ages of 70 and 79.[37] Obesity also increases the severity and consequences of osteoarthritis, limits the mobility of older adults, and is associated with functional declines in daily activities.[21] In contrast, overweight can be protective against osteoporosis and fall-related fractures in older adults.

Although some healthcare providers may question the necessity or value of attempting treatment at the age of 70 or 75 years, even moderate weight loss in obese older adults can improve functional status.[38] The interventions for obese older adults are the same as for younger and middle-aged adults: use of dietary modifications to achieve an energy deficit while retaining adequate nutrient intakes; gradual and medically appropriate initiation of physical activity; and culturally appropriate behaviour modification. The benefit of bariatric (weight-loss) surgery for this population is not clear. Obese older adults experience more complications, remain in the hospital longer, and have a higher rate of in-hospital deaths following bariatric surgery compared to younger adults.[39]

As we noted in Chapter 14, mortality rates are higher in adults who are underweight (BMI below 18.5) compared with people who are overweight (see Table 14.1 on page 488). Significantly underweight older adults have fewer protein reserves to call upon during periods of catabolic stress, such as after surgery or after trauma, and are more susceptible to infection. Inappropriate weight loss suggests inadequate intake of both energy and nutrients. Chronic deficiencies of protein, vitamins, and minerals leave older adults at risk for poor wound healing and a depressed immune response.

Because underweight is so risky for older adults, geriatric weight loss is an important healthcare concern. Gerontologists have identified nine "Ds" that account for most cases of geriatric weight loss (**Figure 18.2**). Several of these factors promote weight loss by reducing energy intake. They include drugs that decrease appetite, and eating impairments caused by dementia, poor dentition, dysgeusia, dysphagia, and dysfunction. Depression, which is common after the death of family members and friends or when adult children move out of the area, also contributes to reduced food intake. Treatment of inappropriate weight loss in the older adult is often a complex and lengthy process, relying on behavioural, medical, and psychological interventions.

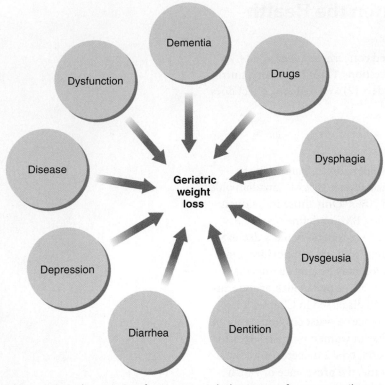

Figure 18.2 The nine Ds of geriatric weight loss: many factors contribute to inappropriate weight loss in older adults.

In summary, any of the nine Ds can promote underweight, nutrient deficiencies, and frailty, significantly increasing the risk of serious illnesses, injuries, and death. A condition known as **geriatric failure-to-thrive**, also called "the dwindles," characterizes the complexity of age-related weight loss.[40]

Osteoporosis

Osteoporosis was discussed in detail in Chapter 12. It is estimated that approximately 1.4 million Canadians suffer from osteoporosis.[41] Among women, it is typically diagnosed within a few years of menopause as estrogen levels sharply decline. Due in part to a higher peak bone density, the onset in males is usually delayed until their 70s or 80s and is linked to declining testosterone levels, steroid therapy, and alcohol abuse.[42] Men with osteoporosis are less likely to be diagnosed or treated for osteoporosis compared to women, although the medical community is now more aware of and responsive to the problem in men.

One of the most serious risks associated with osteoporosis is that of hip fracture; about 30% of all hip fractures now occur in men.[42] Close to 20% of older women and almost 40% of older men will die within one year of their hip fracture; males have a higher mortality rate due to the fact that they are typically much older at the time of fracture.[42]

Many options are available for the treatment of osteoporosis, including a combination of vitamin D and calcium supplementation, strength or resistance training, and medications (see Chapter 12). In addition, it is important to minimize an older adult's risk of a fall-induced fracture by assessing vision and balance, evaluating the need for a cane or walker, surveying the home environment for hazards, and reviewing medications.

Arthritis

Arthritis is one of the most prevalent chronic diseases among older adults, affecting as many as half of all adults over the age of 65. It can affect one or multiple joints, cause pain on a daily or intermittent basis, and limit range of motion of one or more joints. The two most common forms of arthritis among older adults are osteoarthritis and rheumatoid arthritis.

Osteoarthritis has been called a disease of "wear and tear." People with arthritis who are overweight or obese are strongly advised to lose weight and to participate in water exercise or other acceptable forms of physical activity. Pain medications and anti-inflammatory drugs may be prescribed. In extreme cases, hip or knee replacement surgery is required to re-establish normal mobility and function.

Rheumatoid arthritis (RA) typically strikes younger adults and is not associated with obesity or overuse syndromes. It often affects both hands, wrists, or knees. Because many people with RA are underweight, the nutritional goals focus on appropriate weight gain and a healthy, balanced intake of all nutrients. A wide range of medications are used to treat RA, but some of these interfere with nutrient utilization.

Arthritic adults may turn to non-traditional treatments. Glucosamine has shown some promise in relieving the symptoms of osteoarthritis;[43] however, the majority of herbs, oils, and other dietary products touted as cures for arthritis are ineffective and can be very expensive. An appropriate balance of physical activity and rest, a healthy diet, and use of

Rheumatoid arthritis often affects the hands.

geriatric failure-to-thrive
Inappropriate, unexplained loss of body weight and muscle mass; usually results from a combination of environmental and health factors.

physician-monitored medications are the most effective and safest treatments currently available.

Constipation

Although constipation is four to eight times more common in older adults than in younger adults, older adults who are healthy and physically active are not at greater risk.[9] Certain medications, chronic diseases, laxative abuse, and possibly low fibre and fluid intakes contribute to risk of constipation, as does immobility, for instance with wheelchair- or bed-bound older adults. Initial treatment usually revolves around dietary intervention: increased fluid intake and an emphasis on insoluble fibre from foods such as wheat bran. However, medication may be necessary, especially in patients with underlying disease. Use of laxatives by older adults should be monitored by a healthcare provider.

Dental Health Issues

Diet and nutritional status play important roles in the maintenance of dental health in the older adult. A lack of adequate calcium, vitamin D, protein, vitamin C, and the B-vitamins all worsen dental health. As described earlier, saliva production decreases with age, increasing the risk of dental decay. Older adults should be counselled on the importance of a healthy diet in maintaining good oral health.

Despite great advances in dental health over the past several decades, older adults remain at high risk for losing some or all of their teeth, suffering from gum disease, or having poorly fitting dentures, which cause mouth pain and make chewing difficult. Thus, older adults may avoid eating healthy foods such as meats and firm fruits and vegetables. Older adults can select soft protein-rich foods such as eggs, peanut butter, cheese, yogourt, ground meat, fish, and well-cooked legumes. Red meats and poultry can be stewed or cooked in liquid for a long period of time. Oatmeal and other whole-grain cooked cereals can provide needed fibre as will berries, canned corn, bananas, and ripened melons. Shredded and minced raw vegetables can be added to dishes. With planning, older adults with oral health problems can maintain a varied, healthy diet.

Age-Related Eye Diseases

As discussed in Chapter 11, cataracts cause cloudiness in the lens that impairs vision. The condition affects 20% of adults in their 60s and almost 70% of those in their 80s. Another eye disorder, called age-related macular degeneration (AMD), is the most common cause of blindness in Canadian older adults (see Figure 11.22 on page 396). Although these are different conditions, sunlight exposure and smoking are lifestyle practices that increase the risk of each.

Recent research suggests, but does not definitively prove, that dietary choices may slow the progress of these two degenerative eye diseases, saving millions of dollars and preventing or delaying the functional losses associated with impaired vision. Several studies have shown beneficial effects of antioxidants, including vitamins C and E, on cataract formation, whereas others reported no significant benefit.[29] Two phytochemicals, lutein and zeaxanthin, have also been identified as protective by some, but not all, studies.[44] These four antioxidants, as well as zinc, may also provide protection against AMD. Although the research is not yet conclusive, older adults can benefit by consuming foods rich in these nutrients, primarily colourful fruits and vegetables, nuts, and whole grains. Vision-enhancing nutrient supplements remain an unproved therapy.

Older adults can benefit from the antioxidants and phytochemicals available in colourful fruits and vegetables.

Dementia

Between 20% and 40% of very old adults (85 years and older) have Alzheimer's disease, a slow yet progressive form of dementia. An unknown number of the very old are afflicted by other forms of dementia and cognitive impairment. As with other age-related disorders, lifelong dietary choices may influence risk and, once in place, the conditions have a significant effect on food intake and nutrient status.

Some research suggests that long-term intake of antioxidants such as vitamin E and certain unsaturated fatty acids may lower risk of dementia and cognitive decline.[45] Elevated serum homocysteine, linked to deficiencies of folate and vitamin B_{12}, has also been linked to Alzheimer's disease and dementia.[46] However, studies have also shown that supplementation with these nutrients has not consistently been associated with improved cognitive function or in preventing the progression of cognitive impairment in adults with Alzheimer's disease.[47, 48] Mid-life obesity also increases the risk of cognitive decline.[49] These studies emphasize the critical importance of consuming a balanced, healthy diet throughout life.

Dementia is one of the "nine Ds" of geriatric weight loss. Odour and taste perception are often significantly impaired, and many people with dementia refuse to eat. Alzheimer's disease can trigger agitation and pacing, increasing energy expenditure. As the disease progresses, the person loses the ability to manipulate utensils and eventually even to swallow.

Helping people with dementia to eat adequately can be challenging. Finger foods, such as cut-up fruit, cheese or meat cubes, vegetable slices, and small pieces of bread, can be eaten without utensils. Between-meal snacks and liquid nutritional supplements can also improve dietary intake. A multivitamin/multimineral supplement may be necessary.

Interactions Between Medications and Nutrition

Although older adults account for about 14% of the Canadian population, they buy 30% of all prescription medication. The use of multiple medications, a condition termed **polypharmacy**, is a common concern among seniors. In 2005, individuals aged 60 to 79 were prescribed an average of 35 prescriptions per person; this number rose to 74 per person for those 80 years or older. In comparison, the overall Canadian average was 14 prescriptions per person.[50]

Prescription drugs interact not only with each other but also with nutrients (Table 18.3). Some medications affect appetite, either increasing or decreasing food intake, and others alter nutrient digestion and absorption. Several drugs negatively affect the activation or metabolism of nutrients such as vitamin D, folate, and vitamin B_6, and others increase the kidney's excretion of nutrients. For example, older adults taking the blood-thinning

Medications taken by older adults can interact with nutrients.

polypharmacy Concurrent use of five or more medications.

Table 18.3 Examples of Common Drug–Nutrient Interactions

Category of Drug	Common Nutrient/Food Interactions
Antacids	May decrease the absorption of iron, calcium, folate, vitamin B_{12}
Antibiotics	May reduce the absorption of calcium, fat-soluble vitamins; reduce the production of vitamin K by gut bacteria
Anticonvulsants	Interfere with the activation of vitamin D
Anticoagulants ("blood thinners")	Oppose the clotting activity of vitamin K
Antidepressants	May cause weight gain as a result of increased appetite
Antiretroviral agents (treatment of HIV/AIDS)	Reduce the absorption of most nutrients
Aspirin	Decrease blood folate levels; increase loss of iron due to gastric bleeding
Diuretics	Some types may increase urinary loss of potassium, sodium, calcium, magnesium; others cause retention of potassium and other electrolytes
Laxatives	Increase fecal excretion of dietary fat, fat-soluble vitamins, calcium, and other minerals

drug warfarin (Coumadin) should avoid consuming excess vitamin E, as vitamin E magnifies the effects of this drug. Both ibuprofen (Advil or Motrin) and acetaminophen (Tylenol) are commonly prescribed for muscle, joint, and headache pain, but taking these drugs with alcohol increases the risk for liver damage and bleeding, so alcohol should not be consumed with these medications.

Some medications should be taken before or between meals, whereas others are best utilized when taken with meals. Foods as diverse as grapefruit juice, spinach, and aged cheese are known to react negatively with specific drugs. Pharmacists and registered dietitians are able to provide information on such drug–food interactions and can give recommendations on dietary choices and the potential need for nutrient supplements. All older adults should be counselled on the potential for drug–food, drug–nutrient, and drug–supplement interactions.

Use of Supplements

Should older adults use supplements? If so, what types? Are there risks associated with supplement use?

In establishing the DRI for vitamin B_{12} for men and women over the age of 50 years, the Institute of Medicine stated, "It is advisable for most of this amount to be obtained by consuming foods fortified with B_{12} or a B_{12} containing supplement."[32] This is the first time that this agency specifically acknowledged and supported the use of a nutrient supplement as an adjunct to a healthy diet. *Eating Well with Canada's Food Guide* recommends that all adults 50 years of age and older take a vitamin D supplement (10 μg, or 400 IU).[23] Beyond these guidelines, use of nutrient supplements by older adults should be encouraged under the following conditions:

- When the amount and/or variety of food is so restricted that nutrient intake is probably deficient
- If the older adult eats fewer than two meals per day or limits food choices because of dental problems
- Whenever there are lifestyle or functional limitations that prevent adequate food intake
- If the older adult suffers from depression, dementia, social isolation, or extreme poverty
- If the older adult has a disease that impairs nutrient status or could be relieved by nutrient supplementation
- If the older adult has osteoporosis, gastrointestinal diseases, or anemia

While there is little risk associated with a broad-spectrum supplement (see the Highlight box, "Supplements for Seniors"), high-potency nutrient supplements can pose real risks to older adults. Older adults are more vulnerable to high-potency vitamin A supplements than younger adults, especially if they abuse alcohol. Vitamin D is also extremely toxic at high levels of intake, and megadoses of vitamin C can produce diarrhea and cramping. Inappropriate supplementation with iron leads to its accumulation in the liver, pancreas, and other soft tissues, particularly in middle-aged and older men.

Non-traditional supplements such as herbs (e.g., *Ginkgo biloba,* St. John's wort, black cohosh, evening primrose), food derivatives (e.g., flaxseed oil, grapeseed extract, garlic, lecithin), and metabolic compounds (e.g., lipoic acid, coenzyme Q-10, dehydroepiandrosterone [DHEA]) have grown in popularity during the past decade. More than 20% of adults on prescription medication also use non-traditional dietary supplements,[51] and are therefore at risk for potentially harmful drug–supplement interactions.

Up to 70% of older adults do not tell their healthcare providers about their use of non-traditional dietary supplements, even when scheduled for surgery.[51] All healthcare providers should ask their clients about supplement use, discuss possible advantages and potential risks, and refer them to reliable sources of information on supplement use.

CASE STUDY — Nutrition Supplements for Older Adults

Gustavo is a 71-year-old man with a history of high blood pressure who lives at home by himself. He has a very sedentary lifestyle but he has been losing weight since his wife died a year ago. He currently weighs 66 kg. Gustavo has limited cooking skills and often just has a bowl of soup for supper. He does not drink milk and recently started to limit his fluid intake after lunch in an attempt to minimize the number of trips to the bathroom in the evening. His daughter has been nagging him to start taking a multivitamin supplement and his doctor has suggested that he take a calcium and vitamin D supplement. Gustavo is referred to a dietitian who completes a dietary assessment. The results indicate that Gustavo's usual daily protein intake is adequate, but his energy intake is only 1000 kcal and he is not eating the recommended number of servings from the milk and milk products or grain products food groups. His fluid intake is less than 1 litre per day.

Thinking Critically

1. Are there any factors in Gustavo's history that suggest that his ability to eat a healthy diet is limited?
2. Approximately how many kcal should Gustavo be eating? What are the consequences of an inadequate energy intake?
3. How much fluid should Gustavo be consuming? What are the consequences of an inadequate fluid intake?
4. What recommendations would you make to Gustavo to improve his diet?
5. Should Gustavo be encouraged to take a calcium and vitamin D supplement? If so, how much should he take? If not, why not?
6. Would you support or oppose his taking a multivitamin supplement? Why or why not?

RECaP

Osteoporosis, dental problems, arthritis, vision disorders, GI distress, and age-related dementia are examples of "two-way streets" in which nutritional status influences an older adult's risk for the condition, and the condition itself has the potential to influence nutritional status. An older adult's nutritional status and intake can also influence the effectiveness of certain medications, and many of the drugs used by older adults contribute to nutrient deficiencies. Appropriate use of nutrient supplements can enhance the nutritional status of older adults; however, use of herbal and other non-traditional supplements, including high-potency vitamin or mineral supplements, should be discussed with a healthcare provider.

What Social Concerns Affect the Nutrition of Older Adults?

We have explored the physical conditions that affect an older adult's nutritional status and needs, but social factors play a role as well. These include elder abuse and neglect, food insecurity, and social isolation.

Elder Abuse and Neglect

Between 2004 and 2009, the reported incidences of elder abuse rose by 14% in Canada. Of these, approximately one-third were committed by family members (most commonly

Isolation and other social problems can affect an older adult's nutritional status.

a grown child or spouse), one-third were committed by friends or acquaintances, and one-third were committed by a stranger.[52] Elder abuse can be physical, sexual, emotional, financial, neglectful, or unintentional. Denial of healthy food and adequate fluid falls within the scope of elder abuse and neglect. Although it may be difficult to detect, possible signs of such abuse include fear of the caregiver, anxiety, increased depression, and a desire for death. Homebound older adults may demonstrate new health problems, unexplained weight loss, dehydration and malnutrition, poor personal hygiene, and suspicious physical injuries. Older adults without a trusted relative or friend may need to turn to a healthcare provider, court representative, or social service agency for protection. Every province and local municipality has laws against elder abuse and can offer assistance if abuse or neglect is suspected. More information is available from the Government of Canada (Seniors Canada, www.seniors.gc.ca.)

Food Insecurity Among Older Adults

Food insecurity occurs when a family is not able to ensure a consistent, dependable supply of safe and nutritious food.[53] "Very low food security" is a more severe economic state in which the family actually experiences reduced food intake and disruption of normal eating patterns. It is estimated that approximately 7% of older men and women in Canada experience some form of food insecurity at least once during the course of a year.[54]

Older adults cope with food insecurity in several ways. Some make use of social and community services such as Meals-on-Wheels programs. Others may turn to food banks or soup kitchens for short-term assistance; however, the foods available there may not be appropriate for older adults and there is a stigma attached to these services that may limit accessibility.[55] A study by Keller and colleagues found that fee-based services, such as grocery shopping assistance, were rarely used by older adults who had to budget carefully to make the most of their limited incomes. Instead, they shopped only once a month, eating very well in the first two weeks and then hardly anything at all closer to the end of the month.[55]

The most common cause of food insecurity and hunger among older adults is lack of income and poverty. It has been estimated that 6.8% of all Canadian seniors live below the after-tax low income cut off (LICO), Canada's unofficial poverty line.[56] Many Canadian adults rely on the federal government's two public pension programs (Old Age Security and the Canada Pension Plan) as a source of income after age 65. Studies have shown that these programs are the only source of income for more than 25% of seniors and are the main source for more than two-thirds of this population group.[57] These individuals may not be able to afford a nutritious diet, especially if they are single. A study by Green and colleagues with seniors living in Nova Scotia in 2005 showed that single-member households relying solely on a public pension lacked sufficient funds for a nutritious diet.[58] Older adults in poverty often live in areas with few or no supermarkets, may not be able to afford transportation to buy healthy food, and may fear leaving their home to shop for groceries. Their homes may lack working refrigerators and/or stoves, limiting the types of foods that can be bought, stored, and prepared. Healthcare and social service providers should carefully probe for information on the ability of low-income older adults to afford an adequate and healthy food supply.

The Impact of Social Isolation

Older adults may become socially isolated for many reasons. Those who are restricted to beds or wheelchairs, have impaired walking, or are in poor health are prone to isolation even if they live in a household with others. The death of a spouse can precipitate isolation, especially among the very old who have also lost siblings and friends.

Lack of adequate transportation also increases the risk of isolation. Family members or friends may not always be able to offer rides, and even where public transportation is available, older adults may be concerned about cost and personal safety. Even if government-funded vans or buses are available for older adults, transportation may be limited to weekdays and certain hours of the day.

Among minority older adults, particularly recent immigrants with language barriers, isolation can occur after the death of a bilingual spouse or as bilingual children move out of the household. These adults may lack the communication skills to navigate public transportation, shop, and secure social services. Ideally, communities with large immigrant populations can provide translators to help integrate these older adults into the community at large.

Social isolation increases the risk for alcohol and substance abuse, depression, and malnutrition. Personal healthcare habits decline, household maintenance is put off, and behaviour becomes increasingly erratic. Isolated older adults are at high risk for victimization, such as telephone scams, and premature institutionalization. Religious, neighbourhood, and social service agencies offer many programs to ensure that older adults are not forgotten within their homes.

Community Services Can Help Meet the Nutritional Needs of Older Adults

As the Canadian population continues to age, greater demands are placed on social service agencies. This section identifies several programs available for older adults in need.

Community Nutrition Programs for Older Adults

In Canada, the volunteer sector, various levels of government, and public health and education professionals have responded to food insecurity in various ways; none of which have demonstrated long-term success as a solution to the problem.[59] These approaches have included:

For homebound and disabled older adults, community programs such as Meals on Wheels provide nourishing, balanced meals as well as vital social contact.

- Charitable food distribution (food banks, soup kitchens)
- Community-based responses (community kitchens, community gardens)
- School- and community-based feeding programs (breakfast programs)
- Policy initiatives (National Child Benefit, Canada Prenatal Nutrition Program)

Research has identified that the lack of coordination and promotion of the various programs and services available to seniors limits their effectiveness, and policies often limit involvement or eligibility for services.[55]

Participation in community-based food programs has been shown to improve the dietary quality and nutrient intakes of older adults.[60] However, there is limited funding available for food-based services in Canada. As the number of older adults grows, the demand and need for these essential services will continue to increase.

Serving Minority Older Adults

The changing profile of the Canadian older adult population will require adaptations in current medical and social service interventions. For example, members of certain minority groups are at a greater risk for nutrition-related chronic diseases and their complications: Hispanics have higher rates of diabetes; black Canadians experience greater rates of stroke, kidney failure, high blood pressure, colon cancer, and glaucoma; and Aboriginal Canadians are at higher risk for diabetes, obesity, and alcohol abuse. Dietary counselling and other therapies can be used to lower the risk of such chronic diseases and for their treatment. To meet the needs of minority older adults, nutrition professionals must develop an awareness of the cultures they serve, maintain flexibility in foods/meals provided or prescribed, and work toward effective communication with their minority clients.

End-of-Life Care

Advances in medical care can prolong the lives of seriously ill persons, resulting in challenging legal and ethical issues. Healthcare providers must be well informed on end-of-life issues, including the provision of food and fluids, in order to help older clients and families make difficult decisions that honour the client's personal wishes. Ideally, an advance directive such as a living will is available to guide decision making.

The legalities surrounding end-of-life care are in continual flux as courts and legislative bodies enact, then modify, decisions on enteral nutrition (tube feeding), hydration, and other nutritional issues. Religious and cultural considerations often overlay legal issues, contributing to their complexity.

Healthcare providers, with agreement from the patient and/or appropriate legal authority, can provide **palliative care** to terminally ill individuals. With palliative care, no attempt is made to cure or treat the underlying condition; the care provided is designed primarily to minimize patient discomfort, offer social and spiritual support, and extend assistance to family and friends. Individuals who are facing imminent death rarely express hunger and have little or no thirst. If requested, specific foods or fluids are provided, even if they have no nutritional value, to comfort the patient. Hospice organizations are growing in number and availability and can provide palliative care to terminally ill individuals, either in their own home or in a care facility.

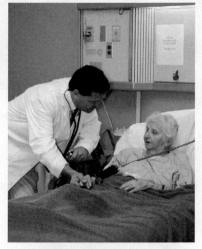

End-of-life care can be provided to older individuals who are terminally ill.

RECaP

Approximately 7% of Canadian older adults experience food insecurity. Disease, disability, death of a spouse, lack of transportation, and language barriers increase the risk for social isolation, which in turn increases the risk for malnutrition. Programs and services are available in Canada to help older Canadians with their nutritional needs, but there is a lack of coordination that limits their effectiveness.

Minority older adults present additional challenges, such as overcoming language barriers and providing culturally appropriate foods. As older adults face end-of-life decisions, healthcare providers must be ready to assist them and their families with difficult decisions related to the provision of food and fluid.

palliative care Reducing an individual's pain and discomfort without any attempts at treatment or cure.

SEE FOR YOURSELF

Are Meal Supplement Drinks Appropriate for Everyone?

You've probably seen the ad on TV: an animated bottle displaying the name of a national brand of a meal supplement beverage struts his stuff among the fruits and veggies inside a fridge. But are his boasts about boosting our health on the level?

For decades, meal supplement drinks have been important in providing adequate energy and nutrients to frail older adults and others who are unable to obtain sufficient nutrition via solid foods. But now, manufacturers of these beverages are marketing them to the general public. Do such drinks provide benefits to average consumers beyond the benefits of traditional foods and drinks costing less? Or are they a waste of money? See for yourself by taking the following steps:

1. Go to your local grocer and check out the Nutrition Facts table of either the Ensure or Boost brands of nutritional drinks. Or check out the nutrition information provided on their websites. Note the kcals, grams of protein, and micronutrients per serving that the drink provides. Focus

on the micronutrients discussed in this chapter as important for older adults, such as calcium, vitamin D, and so on.
2. Now take a look at the ingredients list. Specifically, note the first four ingredients listed. Bear in mind that, as you learned in Chapter 2, ingredients must be listed in order of quantity, with the ingredient of greatest quantity first. Does anything about the composition of the beverage surprise you? If so, what?
3. Next, jot down the cost per serving of the beverage.
4. Finally, list the corresponding nutrient data, and the cost, for the same serving size of skim milk.

Summarize your research findings, addressing the following questions: Are meal supplement beverages cost-effective ways of improving our nutrient intake? Would you feel comfortable recommending that your older relatives consume such beverages regularly instead of a glass of milk or a small snack containing some of their favourite foods? Why or why not?

Chapter Review

Test Yourself | Answers

1. (F) Experts agree that it is unlikely that the human lifespan will increase much beyond 125 to 130 years.

2. (T) Older adults are more likely to lose their sense of smell than their sense of taste; however, loss of smell reduces the sense of taste.

3. (T) Because of an age-related decrease in gastric acid production, older adults are advised to get most of their vitamin B$_{12}$ from supplements or fortified foods.

4. (F) Older men and women need less iron because of their loss of muscle mass, and older women require less iron because of the cessation of menstruation.

5. (T) On average, 7% of older Canadians experience food insecurity at least once each year.

Summary

- The Canadian population is aging at an unprecedented rate, including minority older adults. The very old, 85 and above, are the fastest-growing segment of the Canadian population; the numbers of centenarians and super-centenarians (over age 110) also continue to climb.

- The physiological changes of aging include sensory declines, loss of muscle, increased fat mass, decreased bone density, and impaired ability to absorb and metabolize nutrients. Body organs lose functional capacity. These changes influence the nutritional needs of older adults and their ability to consume a healthy diet.

- Scientists are learning about various genetic and biochemical factors that contribute to senescence. Tobacco use, alcohol abuse, excessive sun exposure, overweight, and inactivity accelerate the aging process.

- Older adults need less energy but the same amount of protein as younger adults.

- Micronutrients of concern for older adults include calcium, vitamin D, the B-vitamins, and the antioxidants. Iron needs decrease.

- Older adults are at risk for chronic dehydration, so ample fluid intake should be encouraged.

- Nutritional status influences an older adult's risk for osteoporosis, dental problems, arthritis, vision problems, GI distress, and dementia; these conditions have the potential to influence nutritional status as well.

- An older adult's nutritional status and intake can alter the effectiveness of medications; many drugs used by older adults contribute to nutrient deficiencies. Appropriate use of supplements can enhance the nutritional status of older adults; however, certain herbal and other non-traditional supplements, including high-dose single supplements, can be dangerous.

- Social issues affecting the nutrition of older adults include elder abuse and neglect, food insecurity, and social isolation.

- Demands on social service agencies increase as the population ages. As older adults face end-of-life decisions, healthcare providers must be ready to assist them and their families with difficult decisions related to the provision of food and fluid.

Review Questions

1. Which of the following nutrients is needed in increased amounts in older adulthood?
- **a.** Fibre
- **b.** Vitamin D
- **c.** Vitamin A
- **d.** Iron

2. Abnormal taste perception is clinically known as
- **a.** dysgeusia.
- **b.** dysphagia.
- **c.** dysphasia.
- **d.** dysphonia.

3. Currently, the human lifespan is
   a. about 74 years.
   b. about 81 years.
   c. 114 years.
   d. 122 years.

4. Which of the following conditions results in defective protein cross-linkages and loss of tissue structure and function?
   a. xerostomia
   b. macular degeneration
   c. glycosylation
   d. achlorhydria

5. Providing cookies and lemonade to a terminally ill patient is an example of
   a. long-term care.
   b. geriatric care.
   c. palliative care.
   d. inappropriate care.

6. The programmed theories of aging suggest that aging follows a biologically driven timeline, similar to that of adolescence. What role does nutrition play in the development of disease, disability, or mortality according to these theories?

7. Why does the percentage of body fat typically increase between young adulthood and age 70? How does this influence energy requirements?

8. Why does the Institute of Medicine recommend that older adults obtain the DRI for vitamin B_{12} by consuming foods fortified with vitamin B_{12} or a B_{12}-containing supplement?

9. Explain why achieving and maintaining a healthy weight is associated with successful aging.

10. Identify four nutrient deficiencies that may arise from atrophic gastritis.

11. State two reasons why a recent older adult immigrant from Southeast Asia may experience nutrient deficiencies after the death of her husband.

12. Identify several factors that increase the risk of dehydration in older adults.

13. Describe the nutritional counselling you would provide to a male client who is 86 years old and
- eats only two meals per day: cold cereal with milk for breakfast and canned soup, crackers, and canned peaches or pears for dinner;
- takes a daily antioxidant supplement containing levels of vitamins A, E, and C and selenium about five times higher than the DRI for these micronutrients;
- drinks three beers every night so he can "sleep better."

14. Marta and her parents live in Toronto. A year ago, her maternal grandmother, who lives in Saskatoon, stayed with them for several weeks after the death of Marta's grandfather. She seemed fit at the time, going for walks and cooking large meals for the family throughout her stay. Last night, Marta's mother received a phone call from a Saskatoon hospital saying that her mother had been admitted after a hip fracture suffered in a fall at home and was battling significant dehydration and some cognitive impairment as well. Identify several factors that might have contributed to Marta's grandmother's condition.

Web Links

www.cdc.gov
Centers for Disease Control and Prevention
Select "Healthy Living" and choose topics such as "Aging" for accurate information on the health of America's seniors.

www.nia.nih.gov
National Institute on Aging
The National Institute on Aging provides information about how older adults can benefit from physical activity and good diet.

www.nihseniorhealth.gov
NIH Senior Health
This website, written in large print, was developed for older adults and offers up-to-date information on popular health topics for older adults.

www.healthyfamiliesbc.ca/home/articles/audience/seniors
Act Now BC
Search this site for information on healthy eating for seniors.

www.carp.ca
CARP
A national advocacy group committed to enhancing the quality of life for all Canadians as they age. The website has links to articles focusing on all aspects of health, finances, housing, and legal issues that are of importance to older adults.

www.seniors.gc.ca/c.4nt.2nt3col@.jsp?cid=161
Seniors Canada
Search this site for information on services for seniors, health and wellness tips, and prevention of elder abuse.

www.phac-aspc.gc.ca/seniors-aines/index-eng.php
Public Health Agency of Canada Division of Aging & Seniors
This website provides information on age-related and chronic diseases, health promotion programs and services, injury prevention tips, and information on healthy aging.

References

1. Health Canada. *Canada's Aging Population*. Available at http:// dsp-psd. pwgsc.gc.ca/Collection/H39-608-2002E.pdf (accessed May 6, 2011).

2. Cravit, C. R. 2007. *Canadians living longer than ever*. CARP Advocacy. Available at www.carp.ca/advocacy/adv-article-display. cfm?documentID=2608 (accessed May 6, 2011).

3. Statistics Canada. 2005. *Projections of the Aboriginal populations, Canada, provinces, and territories. 2001 to 2017*. Available at www. statcan.gc.ca/pub/91-547-x/91-547-x2005001-eng.pdf (accessed May 6, 2011).

4. Public Health Agency of Canada. 2010. *Curbing childhood obesity: A F/P/T framework for action to promote healthy weights*. Available at www.phac-aspc.gc.ca/hp-ps/hl-mvs/framework-cadre/intro-eng. php (accessed May 6, 2011).

5. Young, R. D. 2009. GRG Tables on Supercentenarians. Available at www.grg.org/calment.html (accessed July 2009).

6. Weinert, B. T., and P. S. Timiras. 2003. Physiology of aging: invited review: theories of aging. *J. Appl. Physiol.* 95:1706–1716.

7. Duffy, V. B., and A. K. Chapo. 2006. Smell, taste, and somatosensation in the elderly. In: R. Chernoff, ed., *Geriatric Nutrition: The Health Professional's Handbook* (pp. 115–162), 3rd ed. Sudbury, MA: Jones and Bartlett Publishers.

8. Moskovitz, D. N., J. Saltzman, and Y. I. Kim. 2006. The aging gut. In: R. Chernoff, ed., *Geriatric Nutrition: The Health Professional's Handbook* (pp. 233–272), 3rd ed. Sudbury, MA: Jones and Bartlett Publishers.

9. Dryden, G. W., and S. A. McClave. 2004. Gastrointestinal senescence and digestive diseases of the elderly. In: C. W. Bales and C. S. Ritchie, eds. *Handbook of Clinical Nutrition and Aging* (pp. 569–582). Totowa, NJ: Humana Press.

10. Canadian Society for Exercise Physiology. *Canadian Physical Activity Guidelines for older adults—65 years & older*. Available at www.csep.ca/CMFiles/Guidelines/CSEP-InfoSheets-older%20 adults-ENG.pdf (accessed June 30, 2011).

11. Zamboni, M., G. Mazzali, F. Fantin, A. Rossi, and V. DiFrancesco. 2007. Sarcopenic obesity: a new category of obesity in the elderly. *Nutr., Metab., Cardiovascular Dis.* 18:388–395.

12. Jarosz, P. A., and A. Bellar. 2008. Sarcopenic obesity: an emerging cause of frailty in older adults. *Ger. Nursing* 30:64–70.

13. Public Health Agency of Canada. 2009. *Physical activity and healthy aging*. Available at www.phac-aspc.gc.ca/seniors-aines/ publications/pro/healthy-sante/haging_newvision/vison-rpt/ physical-physique-eng.php (accessed May 6, 2011).

14. Chodzko-Zajko, W. 2009. Successful aging: the role of physical activity. *Am. J. Lifestyle Med.* 3:20–28.

15. Ruiz, J. R., X. Sui, F. Lobelo, J. R. Morrow Jr., A. W. Jackson, M. Sjostrom, and S. N. Blair. 2008. Association between muscular strength and mortality in men: prospective cohort study. *Brit. Med. J.* 337:a439.

16. Manini, T. M., J. E. Everhart, K. V. Patel, D. A. Schoeller, L. H. Colbert, M. Visser, F. Tylavsky, D. C. Bauer, B. H. Goodpaster, and T. B. Harris. 2006. Daily activity energy expenditure and mortality among older adults. *JAMA* 296:171–179.

17. Jeon, C. Y., R. P. Lokken, F. B. Hu, and R. M. van Dam. 2007. Physical activity of moderate intensity and risk of type 2 diabetes: a systematic review. *Diabetes Care* 30:744–752.

18. Healy G. N., D. W. Dunstan, J. Salmon, E. Cerin, J. E. Shaw, P. Z. Zimmet, and N. Owen. 2007. Objectively measured lightintensity physical activity is independently associated with 2-h plasma glucose. *Diabetes Care* 30:1384–1389.

19. Church, T. S., C. P. Earnest, J. S. Skinner, and S. N. Blair. 2007. Effects of different doses of physical activity on cardiorespiratory fitness among sedentary, overweight or obese postmenopausal women with elevated blood pressure: a randomized controlled trial. *JAMA* 297:2081–2091.

20. Life Expectancy Calculator. Available at http://moneycentral.msn. com/investor/calcs/n_expect/main.asp (accessed July 2009).

21. Zoico, E., V. DiFrancesco, J. M. Guralnik, G. Mazzali, A. Bortolani, S. Guariento, G. Sergi, O. Bosello, and M. Zamboni. 2004. Physical disability and muscular strength in relation to obesity and different body composition indexes in a sample of healthy elderly women. *International J. Obesity* 28:234–241.

22. Institute of Medicine of the National Academies. 2006. *Dietary reference intakes: the essential guide to nutrient requirements*. Washington, DC: The National Academies Press.

23. Health Canada. *Eating Well with Canada's Food Guide: A Resource for Educators and Communicators*. 2011. Available at www.hc-sc. gc.ca/fn-an/alt_formats/hpfb-dgpsa/pdf/pubs/res-educat-eng.pdf (accessed September 27, 2011).

24. Institute of Medicine, Food and Nutrition Board. 2002. *Dietary Reference Intakes for Energy, Carbohydrates, Fiber, Fat, Protein and Amino Acids (Macronutrients)*. Washington, DC: The National Academy of Sciences.

25. Campbell, W. W., C. A. Johnson, G. P. McCabe, and N. S. Carnell. 2008. Dietary protein requirements of younger and older adults. *Am. J. Clin. Nutr.* 88:1322–1329.

26. Houston, D. K., B. J. Nicklas, J. Ding, T. B. Harris, F. A. Tylavsky, A. B. Newman, J. Sun Lee, N. R. Sahyoun, M. Visser, and S. B. Kritchevsky for the Health ABC Study. 2008. Dietary protein intake is associated with lean mass change in older, communitydwelling adults: The Health, Aging, and Body Composition (Health ABC) Study. *Am. J. Clin. Nutr.* 87:150–155.

27. Barake, R., Weiler, H., Payette, H., and K. Gray-Donald. 2010. Vitamin D status in healthy free-living elderly men and women living in Quebec Canada. J. Am. Coll. Nutr. 29:25–30.

28. Institute of Medicine, Food and Nutrition Board. 2000. *Dietary Reference Intakes for Vitamin C, Vitamin E, Selenium, and Carotenoids*. Washington, DC: National Academy Press.

29. Chiu, C. J., and A. Taylor. 2007. Nutritional antioxidants and age-related cataract and maculopathy. *Experimental Eye Research* 84:229–245.

30. Robins Wahlin, T. B., A. Wahlin, B. Winblad, and L. Backman. 2001. The influence of serum vitamin B_{12} and folate status

on cognitive functioning in very old age. *Biol. Psychol.* 56(3): 247–265.

31. Gilbody, S., T. Lightfoot, T. Sheldon. 2007. Is low folate a risk factor for depression? A meta-analysis and exploration of heterogeneity. *J. Epidemiol. Community Health* 61(7):631–667.

32. Institute of Medicine, Food and Nutrition Board. 1998. *Dietary Reference Intakes for Thiamin, Riboflavin, Niacin, Vitamin B$_6$, Folate, Vitamin B$_{12}$, Pantothenic Acid, Biotin, and Choline.* Washington, DC: National Academy Press.

33. Garriguet, D. 2007. Canadians' eating habits. *Health Reports* 18(2):17–32.

34. Kaplan, M. S., N. Huguet, J. T. Newsom, B. H. McFarland, J. Lindsay. 2003. Prevalence and correlates of overweight and obesity among older adults: findings from the Canadian National Population Health Survey. *J. Gerontol. A. Biol. Sci. Med. Sci.* 58:1018–1030.

35. Tjepkema, M. 2005. Adult obesity in Canada: measured height and weight. Available at www.statcan.gc.ca/pub/82-620-m/2005001/pdf/4224906-eng.pdf (accessed June 30, 2011).

36. Houston. D. K., B. Niclas, C. A. Zizza. 2009. Weighty concerns: the growing prevalence of obesity among older adults. *J. Am. Diet. Assoc.* 109:1886–1895.

37. Riediger, N. D., I. Clara. 2011. Prevalence of metabolic syndrome in the Canadian adult population. *CMAJ* DOI:10.1503/cmaj.110070.

38. Villareal, D. T., M. Banks, D. R. Sinacore, C. Siener, and S. Klein. 2006. Effect of weight loss and exercise on frailty in obese older adults. *Arch. Intern. Med.* 166:860–866.

39. Varela, J. E., S. E. Wilson, and N. T. Nguyen. 2006. Outcomes of bariatric surgery in the elderly. *Am. Surg.* 72:865–869.

40. University of Toronto Experts. 2003. The dwindles and failure to thrive: when does an elderly patient have failure to thrive and how can it be treated? *Can. J. CME* Available at www.stacommunications.com/journals/pdfs/cme/CMEfebruary2003/yaa.pdf (accessed June 30, 2011).

41. McMaster University. Osteoporosis in Canada fact sheet. Available at http://fhs.mcmaster.ca/main/documents/osteoporosis.pdf (accessed June 30, 2011).

42. Ebeling, P. R. 2008. Osteoporosis in men. *NEJM* 358:1474–1482.

43. Thakral, R., U. K. Debnath, and C. Dent. 2007. Role of glucosamine in osteoarthritis. *Current Orthopaedics* 21:386–389.

44. Bartlett, H. E., and F. Eperjesi. 2008. A randomized controlled trial investigating the effect of lutein and antioxidant dietary supplementation on visual function in healthy eyes. *Clinical Nutr.* 27:218–227.

45. Del Parigi, A., F. Panza, C. Capurso, and V. Solfrizzi. 2006. Nutritional factors, cognitive decline, and dementia. *Brain Res. Bull.* 69:1–19.

46. Clarke, R. 2008. B-vitamins and prevention of dementia. *Proc. Nutr. Soc.* 67:75–81.

47. Ellinson, M., J. Thomas, J. Patterson. 2004. A critical evaluation of the relationship between serum vitamin B, folate and total homocysteine with cognitive impairment in the elderly. *J. Hum. Nutr. Diet.* 17(4):371–383.

48. Aisen, P. S., L. S. Schneider, M. Sano, R. Diaz-Arrastia, C. H. van Dyck, M. F. Weiner, et al. 2008. High-dose B vitamin supplementation and cognitive decline in Alzheimer disease: a randomized controlled trial. *JAMA* 300(15):1774–1783.

49. Whitmer, R. A., E. P. Gunderson, E. Barrett-Connor, C. P. Quesenberry Jr., and K. Yaffe. 2005. Obesity in middle age and future risk of dementia: a 27-year longitudinal population based study. *Brit. Med.* Cited as DOI:10.1136/bmj.38446.466238.EO.

50. Ramage-Morin, P. 2009. Medication use among senior Canadians. *Health Reports* 20:1.

51. Gardiner, P., R. E. Graham, A. T. R. Legedza, D. M. Eisengerg, and R. S. Phillips. 2006. Factors associated with dietary supplement use among prescription medication users. *Arch. Intern. Med.* 166:1968–1974.

52. Statistics Canada. 2010. *Population Projections: Canada, the Provinces and Territories.* Available at www.statcan.gc.ca/daily-quotidien/100526/dq100526b-eng.htm (accessed June 30, 2011).

53. Nord, M., M. Andrews, and S. Carlson. 2008. Household Food Security in the United States, 2007. U.S.D.A. Economic Research Service Report No. (ERR-66). Available at www.ers.usda.gov/publications/err66/ (accessed July 2009).

54. Statistics Canada. 2006. A portrait of seniors in Canada. Available at www.statcan.gc.ca/ads-annonces/89-519-x/index-eng.htm (accessed July 4, 2011).

55. Keller, H. H., J. J. M. Dwyer, V. Edwards, C. Senson. 2007. Food security in older adults: community service provider perceptions of their roles. *Canadian Journal on Aging* 26:317–328.

56. National Advisory Council on Aging. 2005. *Seniors on the margins: aging in poverty in Canada.* Ottawa: Minister of Public Works and Government Services Canada.

57. Human Resources Development Canada. 2002. 1927–2002 public pensions: 75 years of helping Canadians. Hull, QC: Author.

58. Green, R. J., P. L. Williams, C. Shanthi Johnson, I. Blum. 2008. Can Canadian seniors on public pensions afford a nutritious diet? *Can. J. Aging* 27:69–79.

59. Dietitians of Canada. 2005. Individual and household food insecurity in Canada: position of Dietitians of Canada. *Canadian Journal of Dietetic Practice and Research* 66:43–46.

60. Keller, H. 2007. Promoting food intake in older adults living in the community: a review. *Appl. Physiol. Nutr. Metab.* 32:991–1000.

61. Speakman, J. R., and C. Hambly. 2007. Starving for life: what animal studies can and cannot tell us about the use of caloric restriction to prolong human lifespan. *J. Nutr.* 137:1078–1086.

62. Masoro, E. J. 2005. Overview of caloric restriction and aging. *Mechanisms of Ageing and Development* 126:913–922.

63. Wang, C., R. Weindruch, J. R. Fernández, C. S. Coffey, P. Patel, and D. B. Allison. 2004. Caloric restriction and body weight independently affect longevity in Wistar rats. *Int. J. Obesity* 28(3):357–362.

64. Heilbronn, L. K., and E. Ravussin. 2003. Calorie restriction and aging: review of the literature and implications for studies in humans. *Am. J. Clin. Nutr.* 78(3):361–369.

65. Heilbronn, L. K., L. de Jonge, M. I. Frisard, J. P. DeLany, D. E. Larson-Meyer, J. Rood, T. Nguyen, C. K. Martin, J. Volaufova, M. M. Most, F. L. Greenway, S. R. Smith, W. A. Deutsch, D. A. Williamson, and E. Ravussin. 2006. Effect of 6-month calorie restriction on biomarkers of longevity, metabolic adaptation, and oxidative stress in overweight individuals: a randomized controlled trial. *JAMA* 295:1539–1548.

66. Holloszy, J. O., and L. Fontana. 2007. Caloric restriction in humans. *Experimental Gerontology* 42:709–712.

67. Sohal, R. S., M. Ferguson, B. H. Sohal, M. J. Forster. 2009. Life span extension in mice by food restriction depends on an energy imbalance. *Journal of Nutrition* 139:533–539.

68. Willcox, B. J., D. C. Willcox, H. Todoriki, A. Fujiyoshi, K. Yano, Q. He, J. D. Curb, M. Suzuki. 2007. Caloric restriction, the traditional Okinawan diet and healthy aging: the diet of the world's longest-lived people and its potential impact on morbidity and life span. *Ann. N.Y. Acad. Sci.* 1114:434–555.

69. Varady, K. A., and M. K. Hellerstein. 2007. Alternate-day fasting and chronic disease prevention: a review of human and animal trials. *Am. J. Clin. Nutr.* 86:7–13.

Can We Live Longer by Eating a Low-Energy Diet?

How old do you want to live to be—80 years, 100 years, 120 years? If you were to discover that you could live to be 150 years of age by eating a little more than half of your current energy intake and still be healthy as you age, would you do it? Believe it or not, a growing number of people are already severely limiting their energy intake in response to studies indicating that low-kcal diets can significantly increase the lifespan of animals.

Current research shows that consuming low-kcal diets, a practice known as *caloric restriction* (CR), can significantly extend the lifespan of small species; until recently, however, most of this research had been done in rats, mice, fish, flies, and yeast cells.[61–63] Primate studies followed, with similar results. Only in the past few years have studies of CR been conducted in humans. The results of these preliminary studies suggest that CR can also improve metabolic measures of health in humans, and thus may be able to extend the human lifespan.[64, 65]

How might CR prolong lifespan? The answer to this question is not fully understood, but it is speculated that the reduction in metabolic rate that occurs with restricting energy intake results in a much lower production of free radicals, also known as reactive oxygen species (ROS), which in turn significantly reduces oxidative damage and can prolong life. Caloric restriction also causes marked improvements in insulin sensitivity and results in hormonal changes that contribute to a lower incidence of chronic diseases such as heart disease and diabetes. There is also evidence that CR can alter gene expression, which can reduce the effects of aging and prevent diseases such as cancer. Some of the metabolic effects of CR noted in several, but not all, human studies include:[61, 65, 66]

- Decreased fat mass and lean body mass
- Decreased insulin levels and improved insulin sensitivity; decreased fasting serum glucose
- Decreased core body temperature and blood pressure
- Decreased serum LDL and total cholesterol; increased serum HDL cholesterol
- Decreased energy expenditure, beyond that expected for the weight loss that occurred
- Decreased oxidative stress, reduced levels of DNA damage, lower levels of chronic inflammation
- Protective changes in various hormone levels

It is important to emphasize that species that live longer with caloric restriction are fed highly nutritious diets. Unhealthy energy-restriction situations such as starvation, wasting caused by diseases such as cancer, and eating disorders such as anorexia nervosa do not result in prolonged life. In fact, these situations are associated with increased risks for illness and premature death. It is also possible that CR may only be beneficial for people who are obese. Sohal and colleagues compared the lifespan and caloric intake of two genetically different strains of mice (a lean strain and a fat strain) and found that caloric restriction extended only the lives of the obese mice.[66]

Although CR is successful in extending the lives of some animal species, we have at this time only preliminary evidence that this same effect will occur in humans. Studies that can definitively answer this question in humans might never be conducted because of ethical and logistical concerns. Finding enough people to participate in any research study over their entire lifetime would be extremely difficult. In addition, most people find it challenging to follow a caloric-restricted diet for just a few months; compliance with this type of diet for 80 years or more could be almost impossible.[61] Institutional committees that review research studies are hesitant to approve CR research in humans not only because of these logistical problems but also because of the potential risks of malnutrition that could occur. Studying the diet of Okinawan adults—the world's longest-lived people—has provided some epidemiological support for the benefits of CR in humans.[67] Okinawans typically consume 8% fewer

Maintaining a calorically restricted diet that is also highly nutritious requires significant planning and the preparation of most of your own meals.

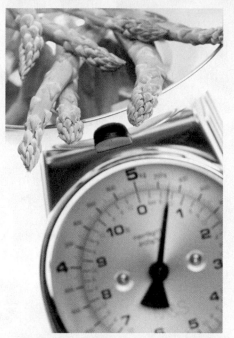

All food must be carefully measured and weighed in a calorie-restricted diet.

A calorie-restricted diet can make family meals challenging.

calories than other Japanese and have the longest life expectancy in Japan. They also tend to have low BMIs, gain very little weight as they age, and have high levels of physical activity. Willcox and colleagues have hypothesized that an adaptive response to early and mid-life energy restriction may be implicated in their exceptionally long lives.[67] The formation of several voluntary CR groups, including a Caloric Restriction Society, has also provided researchers with some data,[65] but there is still very little information on how well and for how long free living adults actually follow the rigid and extensive demands of CR protocols.[60]

You may be wondering how much less energy you would have to consume to meet the caloric-restriction levels studied in animals. Most studies have found a significant extension of lifespan when animals are fed 30% to 40% less energy than control animals. A recent assessment estimated that humans would need to restrict their typical caloric intake by at least 20% for 40 years or more to gain an additional four to five years of healthy living. If you are a woman who normally eats about 2000 kcal/day, a 20% reduction would result in an energy intake of about 1600 kcal per day. Although this amount of energy reduction does not seem excessive, it is very difficult to achieve this reduction every day over a lifetime—particularly if you live to be 130 years of age!

You must also keep in mind that this diet must be of very high nutritional quality, a requirement that presents a huge number of challenges, including meticulous planning of meals, preparation of most, if not all, of your own foods, limited options for eating meals outside of your home, and the challenge of working the demands of your special diet around the eating behaviours of family members and friends. In addition to the practical barriers of following the CR protocol, there is concern that this type of long-term restriction, initiated in early adulthood, would increase the individual's risk of osteoporosis and prompt inappropriate loss of lean body mass, as well as impair a woman's fertility. Interestingly, most of the members of the Caloric Restriction Society are men with an average age of 50 years.[66]

An interesting alternative to caloric restriction is the practice of intermittent fasting (IF), also known as every-other-day-feeding (EODF) or alternate-day fasting (ADF). This approach, which does *not* reduce average caloric intake but simply alters the pattern of food intake, has also been shown, in animals, to prolong lifespan and improve a range of metabolic measures of health.[68] Although not as well studied as caloric restriction, IF has produced beneficial changes in insulin and glucose status, blood lipid levels, and blood pressure in at least some studies.

The debate over the effectiveness of CR in humans will continue as more research is conducted. In the meantime, some people are already consuming diets that are low in energy in the hope that they will live much longer, healthier lives.

Using the Evidence

1. Given the pros and cons noted above, do you think it's advisable to follow a restricted calorie diet? Why or why not?

2. Are you willing to make the sacrifices necessary to try to prolong your life, even though you can't be sure that CR works in humans?

3. If research were to eventually show that CR substantially improves health and prolongs life, would you support recommending it on a large-scale basis? Explain your reasoning.

19

Malnutrition at Home and Around the World

Test Yourself   True *or* False?

1. In Canada, fewer than 1% of the population experiences food insecurity.
    T *or* **F**

2. The major cause of undernutrition in the world is famine.   T *or* **F**

3. Income is the number one determinant of food security in Canada.
    T *or* F

4. Research suggests that inadequate nourishment during fetal life increases the risk of obesity in adulthood.   **T** *or* F

5. Once considered a problem affecting only the affluent, obesity is increasingly prevalent worldwide in the poor.   **T** *or* F

Test Yourself answers are located in the Chapter Review.

Chapter Objectives | *After reading this chapter, you will be able to:*

1. Delineate the acute and long-term health problems caused by the three types of malnutrition, *pp. 694–699*.

2. Identify the major global nutrient deficiencies, *pp. 696–698*.

3. Explain how natural disasters and wars can lead to famine, *pp. 699–700*.

4. Discuss several factors that commonly contribute to chronic food shortages, *pp. 700–702*.

5. Describe the nutritional challenges facing transitioning nations, *pp. 702–703*.

6. Discuss the extent of food insecurity in Canada, and identify the populations most affected, *pp. 704–705*.

7. Describe short-term and long-term solutions to achieve food security at home and globally, *pp. 705–707*.

8. Discuss the achievements of the Green Revolution and the importance of sustainable agriculture in global nutrition, *pp. 707–709*.

9. Discuss the effect of individual actions on the global food supply, *pp. 709–710*.

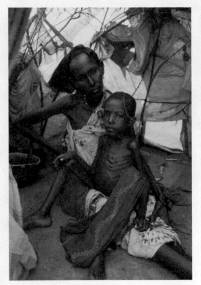

Hunger and malnutrition are still felt by many in the world today.

I n Sierra Leone, West Africa, a child and her father beg for food. He is blind, and she leads him by the hand through the crowded streets with assurance. Though she looks no more than five years old, when asked her age, she says, "I'm eight or nine. Maybe ten." Her father searches with his hand to stroke his daughter's head. He calls her the strong one. "Her two brothers died, then her mother. Now she takes care of me."

Despite abundant natural resources, including diamonds, gold, and iron, Sierra Leone is one of the poorest countries on earth. Now emerging from a decade of civil war, its physical infrastructure is barely developed, corruption is endemic, and income disparity is extreme. Life expectancy hovers around 40 years, and in 2007 a staggering 262 out of every 1000 children died before reaching their fifth birthday.[1] Of those who survive, more than one in three will be abnormally small for their age.[2] Tragically, Sierra Leone is not alone in these sobering statistics: throughout West and Central Africa, undernutrition is the cause of more than half of all deaths of children,[3] and from 20% to more than 40% of the total population is hungry.[4]

Despite advances in food production and preservation, many of the world's people still experience hunger and other forms of malnutrition. Why is this so? What causes malnutrition, and what are some solutions? Is there anything you can do in your day-to-day life to combat malnutrition, not only locally but throughout the world? We explore these questions in this chapter.

Why Is Malnutrition a Global Concern?

Throughout this book, you've learned how a nourishing diet contributes to human health and wellness. Adequate nutrient intake helps children to grow at an optimal rate, young adults to be strong and productive, and older adults to experience less disease and live independently. When adequate and nourishing food either is not available or is not chosen, malnutrition occurs.

Increasingly today, malnutrition is a fiend with two faces. In developing nations, it typically appears in the form of *undernutrition*; that is, people simply don't have enough to eat. In addition, for about the past decade, *overnutrition* has been emerging all over the world, causing rising rates of obesity and threatening its victims with chronic diseases such as heart disease and type 2 diabetes. Overnutrition is now common not only in developed regions like North America and Western Europe, but also in nations transitioning from the very poorest to the middle range of gross national income, including Brazil, India, and China.

In this chapter, we explore these two forms of malnutrition and explain how they're linked. And if what you read and see on the next few pages spurs you to action, we'll give you plenty of suggestions about how you can fight malnutrition, both globally and in your community.

Undernutrition Causes Acute and Long-Term Health Problems

The Food and Agriculture Organization (FAO) of the United Nations estimates that one in five people in the developing world is chronically undernourished.[5] The prevalence of undernutrition is greatest in sub-Saharan Africa and Southeast Asia, in countries ranging from Liberia to Ethiopia and India to Laos (**Figure 19.1**). Closer to home, parts of Central and South America also experience undernutrition at rates ranging from 16% to 25% of the population (see Figure 19.1).

As discussed in Chapter 6, when a person consumes too little protein and energy, the result is protein-energy malnutrition (PEM) (see page 227). The two main forms of PEM are kwashiorkor and marasmus. Kwashiorkor develops when the diet is lacking adequate amounts of protein, while marasmus results from grossly inadequate intakes of protein, energy, and other nutrients. People with these conditions suffer more acute and long-term health problems than those who are adequately nourished. Here we discuss the acute and long-term effects of undernutrition throughout the life cycle (**Figure 19.2**).

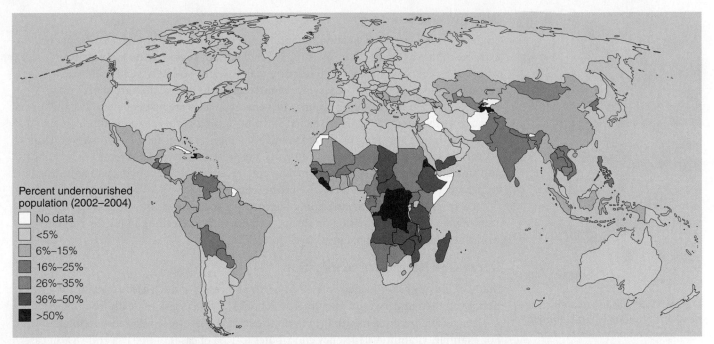

Figure 19.1 Undernutrition occurs throughout the world but is more prevalent in parts of sub-Saharan Africa and Southeast Asia.
Data from: Food and Agriculture Organization of the United Nations. 2011. Prevalence of undernourishment in developing countries 2006–2008. Rome. © FAO, 2011.

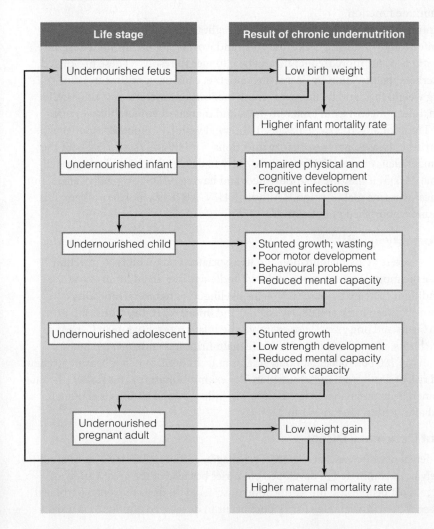

Figure 19.2 Acute and long-term effects of undernutrition throughout the life cycle.

Figure 19.3 Wasting (extreme thinness) and stunting (short stature for age) are commonly seen in undernourished children.

wasting A condition of very-low-body-weight-for-height or extreme thinness.

severe acute malnutrition A state of extreme energy deficit defined as a weight-for-height more than three standard deviations below the mean or the presence of nutrition-related edema, and associated with a risk of death five to twenty times higher than that of well-nourished individuals.

stunted growth A condition of shorter stature than expected for chronological age.

neonatal mortality Death rate of newborns between birth and 28 days.

infant mortality Death rate of infants between birth and one year.

maternal mortality Death rate of women from pregnancy-related causes, including in the immediate postpartum period.

Wasting and Stunting

Undernutrition results in **wasting,** a condition of very-low-body-weight-for-height or extreme thinness (**Figure 19.3**). Wasting is a hallmark of **severe acute malnutrition** (SAM), which causes approximately 1 million preventable deaths annually.[6] Children who are chronically undernourished experience **stunted growth;** that is, they are shorter than expected for their age. Stunting occurs when energy intakes are inadequate to sustain normal linear growth. Recall the child described at the beginning of this chapter: although eight to ten years old, she appeared no more than five. Chances are, her father's growth was stunted, too. In some impoverished communities, the great majority of residents are very short and small; thus, community members may not perceive their stunted growth as unusual or recognize it as a sign of chronic malnourishment.

Early termination of breastfeeding is strongly associated with wasting and growth stunting. For more information on the importance of breastfeeding in the developing world, see the Highlight box, next page.

Decreased Resistance to Infection

Many of the deaths associated with SAM occur as a result of decreased resistance to infection. Even mild underweight is estimated to double a child's risk of death from infection.[7]

Single and multiple micronutrient deficiencies also decrease resistance to infection. For example, vitamin A deficiency contributes to 16% of cases of malaria and 18% of cases of diarrhea worldwide.[7] Vitamin A supplementation in malnourished children has been found to improve immune function and reduce deaths by almost 25%.[8] As you learned in Chapter 13, deficiencies of protein, vitamins C and E, zinc, copper, selenium, and iron also compromise immune function.

Undernutrition and nutrient deficiencies are thought to make individuals more vulnerable to infection by reducing energy reserves and weakening the immune response. Therefore, infections occur more frequently and take longer to resolve. These prolonged infections exacerbate malnutrition by decreasing appetite, causing vomiting and diarrhea, producing weight loss, and further weakening the immune system. A vicious cycle of malnutrition, infection, worsening malnutrition, and increased vulnerability to infection develops.[9] Traditionally, this cycle has been observed with childhood diseases such as measles, diarrheal diseases, and respiratory infections. Today, adults infected with the human immunodeficiency virus (HIV) are more likely to develop acquired immunodeficiency syndrome (AIDS) if they are malnourished, and having AIDS (originally called "thin disease" in Africa) worsens malnutrition.[10] Although HIV/AIDS is a global problem, it is most severe in undernourished populations.

Increased Mortality

We have seen how severe acute malnutrition and its associated vulnerability to infection together increase the mortality rate among children under age five. In addition, these two interrelated conditions increase by close to 50% the likelihood of **neonatal mortality** (the death of newborns between birth and 28 days of life) and **infant mortality** (the death of infants between births and one year).[11] For example, the infant mortality rate in Canada is 4.9 per 1000 live births, whereas in countries where malnutrition is endemic, the infant mortality rate can top 100 per 1000.[12] Not only infants and children, but childbearing women are at increased risk of death from undernutrition. For example, **maternal mortality** (the rate of deaths of women from pregnancy-related causes) in industrialized nations is about 1 in 6000. In sub-Saharan Africa, the rate is 1 in 22.[13]

Micronutrient Deficiency Diseases

Micronutrient deficiency diseases, such as scurvy, pellagra, goiter, rickets, and night blindness, have largely been eliminated in developed countries because of the great variety of foods available to most people and the fortification of selected foods to prevent a particular deficiency disease. When nutrient deficiency does occur in developed nations, it is usually

HIGHLIGHT

Encouraging Breastfeeding in the Developing World

In Canada and other industrialized nations, the benefits of breastfeeding include its precise correspondence with the infant's nutritional needs, protection of the infant from infections and allergies, promotion of mother–infant bonding, low cost, and convenience. In developing countries, however, breastfeeding may also save the newborn's or mother's life. Here are some reasons why.

It is estimated that a quarter of the earth's population may lack sanitary drinking water. Breastfeeding protects newborns from contaminated water supplies. The least expensive form of infant formula is a packaged powder that must be carefully measured and mixed with a precise quantity of sterilized water. If the water is not sterilized and is contaminated with disease-causing organisms, the baby will become ill.

At the same time, a baby who is fed formula instead of breast milk receives none of the mother's beneficial antibodies; this means that when formula-fed infants do contract an infection, whether from contaminated water or any other source, they are not as well-prepared to fight it off as breastfed infants would be. As we discuss in this chapter, reduced resistance to infection is extremely dangerous for infants and children throughout the developing world.

In addition, in an attempt to make their supply of formula last longer, some impoverished parents add more water than the amount specified by the manufacturer. In this case, even when the water is sterilized, the child is at risk of malnutrition because the nutrients in the formula are being diluted.

Breastfeeding is highly recommended for developing countries.

These factors explain why breastfeeding is protective of the infant, but why does it help the mother? First, breastfeeding stimulates the uterus to contract vigorously after childbirth. This reduces the woman's risk of prolonged or excessive postpartum bleeding, a common cause of maternal mortality in developing nations. Second, breastfeeding reduces a woman's risk of developing ovarian and breast cancer. Third, breastfeeding is a natural form of birth control; although not 100% effective as a contraceptive, prolonged, exclusive breastfeeding does delay the onset of ovulation. In regions where access to contraceptives may be lacking, breastfeeding can help a woman to put space between births, giving her body a chance to recover from the physical and metabolic changes of pregnancy, and to nourish her baby adequately without also having to support the development of a growing fetus.

The human immunodeficiency virus (HIV), which causes AIDS, can be transmitted from mother to child via breast milk. For this reason, in areas where sanitary water is available, women with HIV or AIDS may be advised against breastfeeding.*

In summary, international organizations like the World Health Organization and UNICEF encourage all HIV-negative women to breastfeed exclusively until their baby is six months of age and to continue supplemented breastfeeding until at least the age of two.

*World Health Organization. 2007. HIV and infant feeding: update based on the technical consultation held on behalf of the Inter-agency Task Team (IATT) on Prevention of HIV Infection in Pregnant Women, Mothers and Their Infants, Geneva, October 25–27, 2006. Available at http://whqlibdoc.who.int/publications/2007/9789241595964_eng.pdf.

caused by inadequate selection from available foods and supplements, as, for example, when poverty encourages the selection of inexpensive, nutrient-poor, energy-dense foods.

In impoverished nations, deficiencies of five micronutrients are major public health concerns. These are iron, iodine, zinc, and vitamins A and B_{12}.

Iron Iron deficiency is the most common micronutrient deficiency in the world. Although iron deficiency occurs in both males and females of all ages, it is more prevalent in pregnant women and young children because of their high needs for iron during growth. Contributing factors to low iron intake are poor availability of the non-heme iron in staple foods and the high cost of animal products, the source of highly absorbable heme iron. In addition, blood loss from intestinal worms and other parasites in developing countries increases the need for iron.

Meals composed of adequate, nourishing food are important to avoid nutrient deficiency.

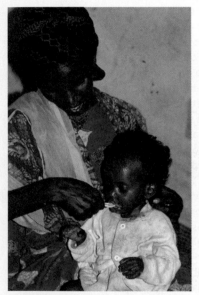

In developing nations, providing vitamin A supplements twice a year to children under age five has significantly reduced mortality.

Iodine As noted in Chapter 16, prenatal iodine intake is particularly important for fetal brain development. Severe deficiency leads to irreversible neurological deficits, physical deformities, and mental retardation, a condition known as cretinism. Mild deficits in school-age children lead to impaired cognitive performance and retarded physical development. In 2004, the World Health Organization (WHO) estimated insufficient iodine intake at just over 35% of the general population worldwide.[14] Iodine deficiency disorders have largely been eliminated in areas of the world with access to iodized salt or oil and areas where iodine is added to irrigation water.

Zinc Mild to severe zinc deficiency is estimated to affect about 2.2 billion people worldwide.[7] As we discussed in Chapter 13, severe zinc deficiency impairs growth and sexual maturation and is associated with reduced resistance to infectious diseases such as respiratory tract infections, malaria, and diarrheal diseases. Deficiency is common in populations with low consumption of zinc-rich meats and seafoods and high consumption of either plant foods containing high levels of phytates and fibres, which inhibit zinc absorption, or refined grains and polished rice, which are poor sources of zinc.

Vitamin A Vitamin A deficiency, which affects more than 40% of children under age five in West and Central Africa, is the leading cause of blindness in children.[15] In addition, because of greater vulnerability to severe infection, these children are at high risk of death. As noted earlier, international initiatives to supplement vitamin A in deficient children can bring about an average of nearly 25% reduction in deaths of children under age five—saving the lives of more than 300 000 children annually.[15]

Vitamin B$_{12}$ We noted in Chapter 13 that deficiency of vitamin B$_{12}$ can result in significant cognitive impairments, including deficits in learning and memory. Unfortunately, the prevalence of vitamin B$_{12}$ deficiency in children breastfed by mothers with lifelong limited access to animal products may be very high. Because meat, fish, and poultry are rich sources of iron, zinc, and vitamin B$_{12}$, it is possible that multiple subclinical deficiencies occur in children with limited access to these foods and impair their development.[16]

Poor Work Capacity of Adults

Undernutrition has long been known to diminish work capacity. The debilitating weakness from undernutrition affects the productivity of adults in developing nations throughout the world today and is especially detrimental when manual labour involved in subsistence farming is the main source of food and income.

Micronutrient deficiency also contributes to poor work capacity; for example, the World Bank estimates that a loss of 5% of the gross domestic product worldwide is attributable specifically to micronutrient deficiencies.[17] Iron-deficiency anemia is particularly debilitating because of iron's role in oxygen transport. Because iron deficiency is a problem among women of childbearing age in both developed and developing countries, it is a global drain on work capacity and productivity.

Susceptibility to Chronic Disease as Undernutrition Is Relieved

A team of scientists in England observed that stunted children, particularly if they were undernourished in the womb and were born at term with low birth weight during war-related famines, were susceptible to obesity and its related chronic diseases as adults. These observations gave rise in the early 1990s to the hypothesis known as "fetal origins of adult disease," which states that adaptations to poor maternal nutrition made by a malnourished fetus as organs are developing help the child during times of food shortages but make the child susceptible to obesity and chronic disease when food is plentiful.[18] For example, when the mother is malnourished during the pregnancy, the baby will tend to have a low birth weight but be relatively fat. This may occur because the fetal body has preserved growth of the brain, which is more than 50% fat, at the expense of muscle tissue. There is now significant evidence supporting this hypothesis.

Overnutrition Causes Overweight, Obesity, and Chronic Disease

As you learned in Chapter 14, overconsumption of energy in excess of energy use increases weight in everyone, to a larger or lesser degree depending on their metabolic efficiency. Chronic overconsumption in any individual leads to obesity, and obesity increases the risk for chronic diseases.

The Prevalence of Obesity and Chronic Disease Is Increasing Worldwide

Throughout the world, the prevalence of obesity and its associated chronic diseases is increasing at an alarming rate. The WHO estimated that more than 1.6 billion adults were overweight in 2005, with 400 million of them clinically obese.[19] As alarming as these statistics are, the predictions for the future are not optimistic as they report in 2010 40 million children under the age of five were overweight. As we have pointed out throughout this text, overweight and obesity increase the risk of cardiovascular disease, type 2 diabetes, and some cancers. Of these, type 2 diabetes is fast becoming an especially significant burden in the developing world. The WHO predicts that by 2020, deaths due to diabetes will increase worldwide by more than 50%.[19] We'll identify the factors contributing to the increase in global obesity later in this chapter.

Increasing Global Economic Burden of Chronic Disease Management

Management of chronic disease is costly. For example, people with diabetes have medical costs that are two to three times higher than those without diabetes and may have direct costs for medication and supplies that range from $1000 to $15 000 per year. In addition, indirect costs include factors such as absenteeism from work, reduced productivity, and lost productive capacity due to early death. It has been estimated that diabetes will cost the Canadian healthcare system $16.9 billion a year by 2020.[20] As diabetes and other chronic diseases increase in countries without the resources of Canada, lack of access to effective health care will increase the indirect economic costs. Families and communities will experience more lost work time, increased disability, and earlier death of adults who would have contributed to the family's resources and local economy.

RECAP

Worldwide, malnutrition is increasingly becoming a problem with two very different manifestations: undernutrition, the most serious manifestation of which is severe acute malnutrition, and overnutrition. Undernutrition causes wasting and stunting, increased susceptibility to infection, high mortality rates, micronutrient deficiency diseases, and poor work capacity. The theory called "fetal origins of adult disease" suggests that undernutrition during fetal and childhood development contributes to obesity and chronic disease in adulthood. Overnutrition causes overweight and obesity and underlies the rising prevalence of chronic diseases throughout the world.

What Causes Undernutrition in the Developing World?

Any situation that results in inadequate food for an individual or community will prompt undernutrition. Natural disasters, wars, overpopulation, poor farming practices, disease, inequities in resource distribution, and other factors can result in a food supply that is inadequate to support the needs of all of the people in a particular place.

An Indian farmer inspects what is left of his crop during a drought.

Famines Are Acute, Widespread Shortages of Food

Famines are severe food shortages affecting a large percentage of the population in a limited geographic area at a particular time. Famines have occurred throughout human history and typically cause significant loss of life. For example, an estimated 30 million people died in the so-called "great famine" in China from 1958–1961 when disastrous governmental land-use policies combined with both floods and droughts to dramatically limit crop yields.

Natural disasters like floods and droughts are often to blame for widespread famine. The drought that occurred in the summer of 2004 in Western Africa brought life-threatening undernutrition to about 20% of the population of Niger and Mali.[21] Other natural disasters that can destroy substantial amounts of local crops in a short time are tsunamis, high winds, hurricanes, frosts, pest infestations, and plant diseases.

Wars can induce famine when they interfere with planting or harvest times or destroy standing crops. Abandonment of farmland in war-torn areas or takeover of farmland by military forces can lead to widespread shortages. In addition, military actions or policies may unintentionally or deliberately disrupt production, distribution, or sale of foods in regions affected by the conflict. Civil wars in Ethiopia led to a severe famine in the 1980s that killed over a million people. Wars can also contribute to famine when they interfere with food relief assistance by other nations.

Both natural disasters and wars often cause migrations of large populations who are forced to flee their homes and means of livelihood. Refugees may live in hastily erected camps with little access to sanitary water, medical care, or adequate food. Food safety is compromised by rodents and lack of refrigeration. Relief assistance by other countries or areas is vital for survival in these emergencies because infection and malnutrition act synergistically in the crowded camps to erode health. Women, children, and older adults in refugee camps are especially vulnerable when food supplies are delayed by damaged roads, poor transportation, political embargoes, or active conflict.

Multiple Factors Contribute to Chronic Food Shortages

Less dramatic than famines, but affecting more people over time, are chronic food shortages that lead to **food insecurity,** a condition in which individuals are unable to obtain enough energy and nutrients to meet their physical needs every day. **Food shortages** occur in areas where food production and import are not sufficient to meet the needs of the population in that area. Direct food aid in these situations must be carefully considered. If wealthy nations send food to a developing country in time of need, it provides more food for hungry people in the short term but can also decrease the price that local farmers receive for their products, with the possible effect of increasing poverty in the area in the long run. Food aid is more detrimental if it floods the market at harvest and less detrimental if it is available only when local foods are absent from the market in very lean years.

Several factors contribute to food shortages and food insecurity in different parts of the world. The most common include overpopulation, poor farming practices, use of agricultural land for cash crops, lack of infrastructure, disease, and unequal distribution of limited food supplies. These are discussed briefly here.

Overpopulation

An area is said to be **overpopulated** when its resources are insufficient to support the number of people living there. In parts of the world with fertile land and adequate rainfall or irrigation systems to support abundant harvests, food shortages rarely happen. However, in more arid climates, especially in areas with high birth rates and poor access to imported foods, seasonal and chronic food shortages are common. Slowing population growth is one way of improving an area's **food/population ratio.**

Likely the most effective method of reducing birth rates is to improve the education of women and girls.[22] Their increased earning potential, access to information about contraception, and better health practices lead to smaller, healthier, more economically stable

Hungry children living in refugee camps are highly susceptible to death from infectious disease. The skeletal limbs and swollen bellies of these toddlers suggest severe acute malnutrition.

famines Widespread, acute food shortages that affect a substantial portion of a population, often associated with starvation and death.

food insecurity Condition in which the individual is unable to regularly obtain enough food to provide sufficient energy and nutrients to meet physical needs.

food shortage Condition in which food production and import in an area are not sufficient to meet the needs of the population in that area.

overpopulated Characteristic used to describe a region that has insufficient resources to support the number of people living there.

food/population ratio The amount of food available for each individual; also food availability per capita.

families. Other methods of improving the food/population ratio are to increase food production and the importation of foods into the area.

The population of the earth was about 6.7 billion in 2008 and reached 7 billion on October 31, 2011. So is the earth itself overpopulated? Or will it soon become so? In other words, will we soon suffer worldwide food insufficiency? Unfortunately, no one can answer these questions precisely because we cannot predict how advances in technology will affect our depletion of the earth's natural resources or our ability to produce more food with fewer resources. We do know that, currently, the greatest population growth is occurring in the areas of the world least able to support increased population. For example, whereas the birthrate in Canada is estimated at 1.7 births per woman, which is below replacement rate (considered to be two births per woman), the birthrate in some impoverished African countries is six births per woman. Although many more of these impoverished children die before their fifth birthday, the net effect is population growth.

Cotton is a cash crop that farmers often grow instead of local food crops.

Agricultural Practices

Some traditional farming practices have the potential to destroy useable land. Deforestation by burning or any other means and overgrazing pastures and croplands destroy the trees and grass roots that preserve soils from wind and water erosion. Growing the same crop year after year on the same plot of ground can deplete the soil of nutrients and reduce crop yield. Some modern agricultural practices, such as avoiding overgrazing and using **crop rotation** to renew the nutrients in a parcel of ground, have benefited small farmers and increased the employment of agricultural workers.

Use of agricultural land for **cash crops** such as cotton, coffee, and tobacco may replace land use for local food crops such as sorghum and corn, also called **subsistence crops.** The end result may be detrimental if less local production of subsistence crops means less food available for local consumption. Another problem with cash crops is that they are likely to be produced by large landholders who pay insufficient wages to their hired labourers. However, if political trade policies result in imports of nutritious foods and effective distribution systems are in place, then the greater variety of available foods will improve nutrition status.

Lack of Infrastructure

Exacerbating the scarcity of food production in some areas is a lack of infrastructure. For example, many developing countries lack roads and transportation into the areas of the country away from ports and major cities. This limits available food to whatever can be produced locally. In addition, lack of electricity and refrigeration can limit storage of perishable foods before they can be used.

Millet is a common subsistence crop.

Water management is a second aspect of infrastructure that influences nutrition. In dry areas, irrigation can improve food production, but it must be managed carefully to prevent increasing the numbers of mosquitoes and other pests, which can spread infectious diseases such as malaria. The provision of safe drinking water and sewage systems is another aspect of water management that help prevent disease.

Other critically important aspects of infrastructure are sanitation services, communication systems, an adequate healthcare delivery system, and adequate public education. In summary, public health depends on public policies that support the development of personnel, physical structures, and technological innovations that promote health and prevent disease.

crop rotation The practice of alternating crops in a particular field to prevent nutrient depletion and erosion of the soil and to help with control of crop-specific pests.

cash crops Crops grown to be sold rather than eaten, such as cotton, tobacco, jute, and sugar cane.

subsistence crops Crops grown to be eaten by a family or community such as rice, millet, and garden vegetables. Surpluses may be sold locally.

Impact of Disease

Disease and lack of healthcare resources to fight disease reduce the work capacity of individuals, and this in turn reduces their ability to ward off poverty and malnutrition.

This economic phenomenon is demonstrated by the AIDS epidemic. There are now 33.3 million people living with HIV, and 1.8 million people died from AIDS in 2009.[23] HIV is most likely to affect young, sexually active adults who are the primary wage earners in their families. Thus, their illness or death can impoverish their children, younger siblings, and/or older parents. In Africa, AIDS is the leading cause of death, and the death of both parents to AIDS has made orphans of millions of children. By creating populations in which children and older adults predominate, the AIDS epidemic has exacerbated the risk of undernutrition in many developing countries.[24]

Unequal Distribution of Food

Overpopulation, poor agricultural practices, lack of infrastructure, and diseases like AIDS all can contribute to chronic food shortages, but the major cause of undernutrition in the world is unequal distribution of food because of poverty. In the developing world, more than three-fourths of malnourished children live in countries with food surpluses.[25] The most at-risk populations are the rural poor. Lacking sufficient land to grow their own foods, the rural poor must work for others to earn money to buy food, but because they live in rural areas, employment opportunities are limited.

Unequal distribution also occurs because of cultural biases. In many countries, limited food is distributed first to men and boys and only secondarily to women and girls.[25] In such situations, pregnant women and growing girls are the most vulnerable because of their increased needs. Food distribution to older adults is sometimes also limited, particularly in developing countries where nutrition services are primarily directed toward pregnant and lactating women, infants, and young children.[26] Access to food also can differ by ethnicity and religion. For example, officials in authority may order that food aid be distributed preferentially to areas where their own ethnic group dominates.

RECaP

Famines are widespread, severe food shortages that can result in starvation and death. They are most commonly caused by natural disasters or wars. Less severe but chronic food shortages can be influenced by regional overpopulation, poor agricultural practices, and the burden of disease; however, unequal distribution of food due to poverty is the major cause of food shortages—and resulting undernutrition—in the world.

What Causes Overnutrition in the Developing World?

Parallel to the ancient, and as yet unsolved, problem of underweight in the developing world is a growing obesity problem that is straining public health resources in a new way. Called the **nutrition paradox,** this new public health problem is characterized by the coexistence of underweight and obesity in the same region and even in the same family. The nutrition paradox is especially common in countries transitioning from the very poorest to the middle range of gross national income, such as Mexico, Brazil, Egypt, India, China, and Thailand.

Changes in Diet and Activity Underlie the Nutrition Paradox

The WHO identifies two key factors behind the nutrition paradox in transitioning nations:[27]

nutrition paradox Coexistence of undernutrition and overnutrition in the same region or in the same family.

- A trend toward decreased physical activity because of the increasingly sedentary nature of many forms of work, changing modes of transportation, and increasing urbanization

HIGHLIGHT

The Poverty–Obesity Link

In developing countries, obesity used to be considered healthy and desirable; it demonstrated that the individual was wealthy enough to afford abundant food. But, as poor people move from rural farms to take low-paying service jobs in cities, where energy-dense, low-cost foods are widely available, obesity is increasingly being linked to poverty. Energy-dense foods with longer shelf lives, such as vegetable oils, sugar, refined flour, snack foods, soft drinks, and canned goods, are less expensive than healthier, more nutrient-dense foods such as meats, fish, milk, and fresh fruits and vegetables.[28] In developed countries such as Canada, low-income families are also struggling to meet their nutrient needs and are resorting to purchasing less healthy food options. In a study of low-income families in Toronto, Dachner and colleagues found that, although their respondents attempted to shop wisely, many were unable to purchase adequate amounts of milk, fruit and vegetables, and meat.[29] Interestingly, as we discussed in Chapter 14, although we

know that low-income Canadians are at a higher risk of developing certain chronic diseases that are associated with obesity, the association between socioeconomic status (SES) and obesity is less clear. The relationship between income and obesity appears to vary by gender.[30] Kuhle and Veugelers found that for females, as income increases, the prevalence of obesity decreases. However, for men the opposite was true; as household income increased, the prevalence of obesity also increased. However, these researchers also identified the limitations of using household income as an indicator of SES and suggested that differences in food consumption and smoking behaviours between SES groups may have contributed to the lack of a clear negative association between household income and overweight in the CCHS (Canadian Community Health Survey). More research is needed to clarify the mechanisms by which obesity and poverty are linked in both developed and developing countries.

- A global shift in diet toward increased intake of energy-dense foods that are high in fat and sugars but low in micronutrients

Transitioning countries are characterized by major migrations from rural to urban areas, less dependence on subsistence farming, more motorized transportation, and better public health measures that increase access to medical care, safe water, and more abundant food. As a transitioning nation's economy improves, employment shifts away from farming, forestry, and fishing toward service occupations. Work becomes more sedentary, motorized transportation becomes more common, and the daily requirement for physical activity declines. At the same time, the types of foods available change from starchy, low-fat, high-fibre subsistence crops to foods of higher nutrient density, including meats, poultry, dairy products, inexpensive vegetable oils, snack foods, and sweets. Over the past 20 years, foreign investment in companies producing highly processed foods has made energy-dense foods available at lower cost to more people in developing countries. While these changes bring greater dietary variety and alleviate some nutrient deficiencies, they also increase a population's risk of obesity. Refer to the Highlight box above for more information on the link between poverty and obesity.

Overnutrition is becoming a problem for impoverished people now that energy-dense foods are more widely available.

RECAP

Overnutrition resulting in obesity is now a public health concern not only in developed nations but also in countries transitioning out of poverty. Lack of physical activity and increased availability of low-cost, energy-rich, nutrient-poor foods have shifted the burden of obesity and chronic diseases toward the poor.

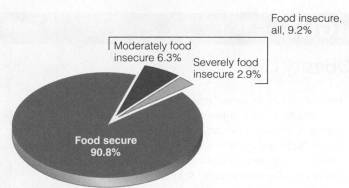

Figure 19.4 Income-related food security status in Canada. *Data from:* Canadian Community Health Survey Cycle 2.2, Nutrition (2004), Figure 3.1: Income-Related Household Food Security in Canada Cat. H164-42/2007E http://www.hc-sc.gc.ca/fn-an/alt_formats/hpfb-dgpsa/pdf/surveill/income_food_sec-sec_alim-eng.pdf, Statistics Canada. Reproduced with the permission of the Minister of Public Works and Government Services, 2012.

Many single mothers face economic burdens that leave them and their children vulnerable to food insecurity.

food security Exists when all people, at all times, have physical and economic access to sufficient, safe, and nutritious food to meet their dietary needs and food preferences for an active and healthy life.

How Many Canadians Go Hungry?

As we discussed in Chapter 14, overnutrition is becoming a national health crisis. Many Canadians are now overweight or obese, and the prevalence of type 2 diabetes and other chronic diseases associated with obesity is increasing. But even in Canada, unequal distribution of abundant food leads to undernutrition among the nation's poorest citizens.

How Many Canadians Are Food Insecure?

As shown in **Figure 19.4**, Health Canada estimates that 9.2% of Canadian households (more than 1.1 million households) experienced food insecurity in 2004. This means that the people living in these homes were unable to obtain enough food to meet their physical needs every day. Of the 9.2%, 6.3% were considered moderately food insecure while 2.9% were severely food insecure. The term "moderate" indicates that the household reported multiple indicators of problems with food access among adults and/or children, but typically reported few, or no, indicators of reduced food intake. Examples of these problems included inadequate amounts of available food or the need to alter the quality of food consumed. Households in the "severe" food insecurity category reported disrupted eating patterns and reduced food intake among adults and/or children in addition to the conditions reported by the moderately food insecure households.[31]

At greatest risk for food insecurity are families consisting of single mothers and their children. In 2004, 24.9% of households led by a female lone parent were food insecure compared to 7.5% of households led by a couple.[31] Also at risk are off-reserve Aboriginal households, older people with pensions/seniors' benefits as their main source of income, the working poor, and the homeless.[32]

What Causes Food Insecurity in Canada?

The Public Health Agency of Canada has identified income/social status as the number one determinant of health, hunger, and **food security**.[33] The role of poverty in food insecurity is undeniable. The prevalence of food insecurity is higher among households with incomes in the lowest (48.3%) and lower middle (29.1%) categories of household income adequacy, compared with those in the middle (13.6%), upper middle (5.2%) and highest (1.3%) categories of household income adequacy.[31]

Physical, psychological, and social factors can contribute to food insecurity among Canadians. Having paid employment does not guarantee food security. In 2007, approximately 535 800 working Canadians (4.7% of all workers) were classified among the working poor. For these Canadians, their family income was lower than the cost of family needs for basic necessities.[34]

People with chronic diseases or disabilities may lose paid hours because of illness, have to accept lower-wage jobs, or have medical expenses that limit money for food. Depression, addiction to alcohol or other substances, and other psychological disorders can similarly limit productivity and reduce income. Divorce frequently leads to financial stressors, especially for women, who may be unable to collect alimony or child-support payments and who may have jobs that do not provide sufficient income.

Having access to nutritious foods is one aspect of food security. Unfortunately, many Canadians cannot afford to purchase a nutritious diet. In Nova Scotia, researchers have found that people working for minimum wage and lone seniors living on a public pension do not have enough income to meet their basic needs, including a nutritious diet.[32, 35]

What Is the Impact of Food Insecurity in Canada?

Several studies have shown that Canadians who are food insecure are more likely to suffer from poor health. Che and Chen, using data from the 1998–99 Canadian National Population Health survey, reported that 17% of those who were food insecure had poor or fair health compared to 7% of those who were food secure.[36] Vozoris and Tarasuk also found that food insecure individuals were more likely to self-report that their health was poor or fair and to state that they had heart disease, diabetes, high blood pressure, and food allergies.[37] More recently, Gucciardi and colleagues, using data from the 2005 CCHS, found that the prevalence of food insecurity is higher among Canadians with diabetes.[38] Food insecurity is also associated with poor mental health. Studies have shown a significant relationship between food insecurity and depression.[39, 40] Further, adolescents in food insecure households are four times more likely to have suicidal tendencies than those in food secure households.[41]

Approximately 9.2% of Canadian households experienced food insecurity in 2004. Food insecurity leads to poor health and is higher among low-income Canadians.

What Solutions Are Needed to Achieve and Maintain Food Security?

The United Nations Millennium Development Goals include the eradication of extreme poverty and hunger.[42] For such a goal to be achieved, both short-term and long-term solutions are needed. Short-term solutions are imperative to prevent famine following natural disasters and in war-torn regions. For example, the U.S. Agency for International Development (USAID) has developed a Famine Early Warning System Network to monitor droughts, floods, and other problems that affect food supplies so that interventions can be provided quickly and efficiently.[43]

Long-term solutions are critical to achieve and maintain global food security. The United Nations identifies the need for the world community to develop a long-term "global partnership for development" involving international, national, community, household, and individual strategies.[42] We discuss some local initiatives and technological strategies to meet these challenges in this section.

Local Initiatives

Local initiatives include programs to encourage breastfeeding, to combat infectious disease, and to promote equitable distribution of available food.

Programs to Encourage Breastfeeding

Among the most important local initiatives for improving the health and nutrition of children worldwide are programs that encourage breastfeeding. As we discussed in Chapter 16, breast milk not only provides optimal nutrition for healthy growth of the newborn but also contains antibodies that protect against infections. Particularly in developing countries, feeding infants with formula is risky: the use of unsanitary water for mixing batches of formula results in diarrheal diseases, and overdilution of formula by families who cannot afford adequate amounts results in inadequate intake. In developing countries, breastfeeding is considered to reduce diarrheal deaths in young children by 50% to 95%.

In 1991, WHO and UNICEF initiated the Baby-Friendly Hospital Initiative to increase breastfeeding rates worldwide. Under this initiative, new mothers are educated about the benefits of breast milk, the dangers of bottle-feeding, and the importance of maternal nutrition during lactation. They are encouraged to breastfeed exclusively for the first six months of the child's life and to continue breastfeeding as part of the child's daily diet until the child is at least two years old.

Programs to Combat Infectious Disease

In 1982, UNICEF began a campaign to eliminate common infections of childhood by four inexpensive local strategies referred to as **GOBI**:

G—growth monitoring to assess childhood well-being
O—oral rehydration therapy to stop death from dehydration during diarrheal diseases using a simple solution containing a balance of fluids and electrolytes
B—breastfeeding
I—immunization against tuberculosis, diphtheria, whooping cough, tetanus, polio, and measles[44]

By 1990, GOBI was estimated to have saved 12 million children. These four successful strategies continue as parts of various local initiatives to reach the United Nations Millennium Development Goals.[42]

In 1998, the Vitamin A Global Initiative was launched by a coalition of international agencies to attempt to increase the intake of vitamin A by fortification of foods and provision of vitamin A–rich fruits and vegetables for home gardens. Because of the critical role of vitamin A in immune defence, these measures also combat infectious disease. In addition, programs for deworming and mosquito control combat not only helminth and malarial infection but their accompanying iron deficiency.

Programs to Promote Equitable Distribution of Food

Addressing the issue of food insecurity in Canada requires several strategies located within a continuum which includes:[45]

Stage 1: Short-term relief strategies: These strategies provide immediate and temporary relief from hunger and food issues (e.g., food banks and soup kitchens) but do little to address the underlying issues that cause food insecurity (i.e., inadequate income).

Stage 2: Individual and community capacity building strategies: These strategies help improve food security and the sustainability of the food system by building skills and mobilizing people to work for change.[46] At the individual level, this may involve programs where people develop the skills needed to grow, produce, and prepare their own food (e.g., community gardens or community kitchens). Community capacity building involves creating partnerships and networks within communities to involve those experiencing food insecurity and help them develop the capacity to improve or control their own situations.

Stage 3: Food systems redesign for sustainability: The core issues of poverty and food system sustainability can be most effectively addressed through supportive, healthy public policy. These strategies require long-term commitment from all levels of government and representatives from the entire food system.[47] Communities must also be involved in the process of developing healthy public policy to make sure that there is a link between the policy and people's experience. Examples of system-change strategies include forming a food policy group and doing participatory food costing. For additional information on influencing public policy and strategies for action, check out the *Thought About Food?* workbook developed by the Nova Scotia Nutrition Council and the Atlantic Health Promotion Research Centre, available at foodthoughtful.ca.[46]

Many international organizations help improve the nutrient status of the poor by enabling them to produce their own foods. For example, both USAID and the Peace Corps have agricultural education programs, the World Bank provides loans to fund small

GOBI UNICEF campaign to eliminate common infections of childhood by four inexpensive strategies: growth monitoring, oral rehydration therapy, breastfeeding, and immunization.

business ventures, and many non-profit and non-governmental organizations (NGOs) support community and family farms.

Did You Know?

Food Banks Canada is a national charitable organization that represents and supports the food banking community across Canada. In 2010, it released a report that indicated that 867 948 Canadians used the services of a food bank during March. This was a 9% increase since 2009 and the highest level of food bank use on record.[48] Who are these Canadians? Thirty-eight percent are children or youth under the age of 18; 51% are families with children; 40% are single-person households, many of whom rely on social assistance as their primary source of income. Food Banks Canada has outlined eight recommendations for reducing hunger and food bank use, which include implementing a federal poverty prevention and reduction strategy, maintaining current levels of federal cash and tax transfers to the provinces and territories, continuing to reform income support programs, creating a federal housing strategy, overhauling the Employment Insurance system to make it more equitable, increasing federal investment in childcare, addressing the high poverty rates among seniors, and increasing investment in the Canada Child Tax Benefit.

CASE STUDY ▶ Food Insecurity

Judith is a single mother with a daughter in first-year university. She works as a cashier in a retail store making minimum wage with no benefits. Judith has type 2 diabetes and has to buy her own medication. By the time she pays rent and the utilities there is only about $50.00 per week left to purchase food. A typical week's worth of groceries consists of five cans of soup or beans, powdered milk, some hamburger meat, a box of store brand cereal, and bread and crackers from the discount bin. Sometimes she is able to buy a bag of apples but rarely can she afford fresh vegetables.

Thinking Critically

1. **What, if any, nutrients do you think might be missing from Judith's weekly food choices?**
2. **Do you think that it is possible for Judith to buy sufficient food to meet her family's nutrient needs on $50.00 per week? Why or why not?**
3. **What options are available to Judith to increase her food security?**

Technological Strategies

Technological strategies for increasing the world's food supply include the Green Revolution, the sustainable agriculture movement, and the application of biotechnology, including the use of genetically modified organisms (GMOs).

The Green Revolution

The **Green Revolution,** one of the major agricultural advances of the past 50 years, has increased the productivity of cultivated land while maintaining environmental quality.[49] As part of the Green Revolution, new **high-yield varieties** of grain were produced by cross-breeding plants and selecting for the most desirable traits. The new semi-dwarf varieties of

Green Revolution The tremendous increase in global productivity between 1944 and 2000 due to selective cross-breeding or hybridization to produce high-yield grains and industrial farming techniques.

high-yield varieties Semi-dwarf varieties of plants that are unlikely to fall over in wind and heavy rains and thus can carry larger amounts of seeds, greatly increasing the yield per acre.

rice, corn, and wheat are less likely to fall over in wind and heavy rains and can carry more seeds. They have been widely adopted in North and South America and Asia and have doubled or tripled the yield per acre while reducing costs. It is likely that 1 billion people were saved from starvation between 1960 and 2000 by these varieties.[50]

Less success was achieved in creating high-yield varieties of staples traditional to sub-Saharan Africa, such as sorghum, millet, and cassava, which are grown in hot, dry conditions. Thus, Africa has shared least in the alleviation of hunger achieved during the Green Revolution.

Although it has achieved higher yields at lower costs, which greatly benefited farmers and consumers, the Green Revolution has prompted new problems. Because it requires the use of chemical fertilizers, pesticides, irrigation, and mechanical harvesters to reduce labour costs, it has mostly benefited larger, wealthier landowners and has not helped small, family farms. Environmental damages associated with the Green Revolution have included loss of topsoil due to erosion from heavy tilling, from extensive planting of row crops such as corn and soybeans, and from run-off due to irrigation.

Sustainable Agriculture

In response to these drawbacks of the Green Revolution, a new movement toward **sustainable agriculture** has evolved. The goal of the sustainable agriculture movement is to develop local, site-specific farming methods that improve soil conservation, crop yields, and food security in a sustainable manner, minimizing adverse environmental impact. For example, soil erosion can be controlled by crop rotation, by terracing sloped land for the cultivation of crops (**Figure 19.5**), by tillage that minimizes disturbance to the topsoil, and by the use of herbicides to remove weeds rather than hoeing. Another practice associated with sustainable agriculture is the use of **transgenic crops,** plant varieties that have had one or more genes altered. Such crops can reduce the need for insecticides or permit the cultivation of marginally fertile land.

Meat production is a particularly controversial issue within the sustainable agriculture movement. Critics emphasize the inefficiency of eating meat from grain-fed cattle instead of eating the grains themselves. They also point out the contribution of livestock production to deforestation, release of greenhouse gases, and global warming. Supporters of meat production emphasize the benefits of using livestock to convert otherwise unusable plants to high-quality food, to improve the nutritional quality of the diet of people in developing countries, and to contribute non-chemical fertilizer to renew the soil.

Figure 19.5 Terracing sloped land to avoid soil erosion is one practice of sustainable agriculture.

Biotechnology

Some agricultural scientists see the application of biotechnology, specifically the production of genetically modified foods, as the next step in the Green Revolution. They contend that genetically modified crops can produce higher yields on limited land, allowing peasant farmers to feed their families with disease-resistant crops that can be farmed without chemicals and using traditional methods. In addition, genetically modified crops with improved nutrient density, when grown in areas already being cultivated by the family, can improve nutrient status with no change in farming practices.[51]

However, there is currently considerable controversy surrounding the long-term safety and environmental impact of genetically modified crops. In addition, patents on the technological tools of biotechnology limit their use. Conferring public right to the necessary technological tools would allow more widespread use of advanced technologies for assisting poor farmers to improve food security.[52]

sustainable agriculture Term referring to techniques of food production that preserve the environment indefinitely.

transgenic crops Plant varieties that have had one or more genes altered by use of genetic technologies; also called genetically modified organisms, or GMOs.

RECAP

Short-term aid prevents death during emergency food shortages. Long-term solutions to global food security include programs to encourage breastfeeding, to combat infectious disease, and to promote equitable distribution of available food, which help maximize local solutions. The Green Revolution, sustainable agriculture practices, and biotechnology are controversial strategies aimed at increasing the world's food supply. In Canada, a three-stage approach is needed to address the issue of food insecurity. Short-term relief strategies, such as food banks, do not address the underlying issues. Community capacity building and developing policies that address food system change are needed.

What Can You Do to Combat Malnutrition at Home and Around the World?

Two general strategies for combating malnutrition are to make personal choices that promote food equity and environmental quality and to volunteer with an organization that works to relieve hunger.

Make Personal Choices That Promote Food Equity and Preserve the Environment

The personal choices that each individual makes can contribute to or combat global malnutrition by influencing local and global markets. Choosing to purchase certain foods makes those foods more likely to be produced in the future. If you choose vegetables, fruits, nuts, whole grains, and beans and other legumes, then you will influence greater production of these healthy foods. If you buy organic foods, you encourage reduction in the use of chemical pesticides and herbicides. If you buy produce from a local farmers' market, you encourage greater local availability of fresh foods. This reduces the costs and resources devoted to distribution, transportation, and storage of foods.

To combat overnutrition, the major type of malnutrition in Canada, avoid or limit energy-dense, nutrient-poor choices and encourage your friends to follow your lead. Read labels: Do you really want high-fructose corn syrup in your peanut butter? When large numbers of people stop purchasing foods high in saturated fats or added sugars, the profitability of these foods declines and they are more likely to disappear from the marketplace. And whatever you eat, avoid overconsumption. You'll be leaving more food for others as well as reducing your risk for obesity and its accompanying chronic diseases. Not convinced? Consider the competing philosophies in the Nutrition Myth or Fact? box, on the next page.

The amount of meat you eat also affects the global food supply. As we noted earlier, the production of plant-based foods requires a lower expenditure of natural resources and releases fewer greenhouse gases than the production of animal-based foods, so making plant foods the main source of your diet preserves land, water, and global energy, and reduces global warming. However, animal-based foods do contribute high-quality nutrients and can be consumed in moderation worldwide without harm to either health or the environment.

Remember that physical activity is important in maintaining health and combating overnutrition, so walk and bike as often as you can in your everyday life. Walking, biking, and taking public transportation also limits your consumption of non-renewable fossil fuels. When it's time to purchase a car, research your options and choose the one with the best fuel economy.

Bicycling is a healthy option that limits your use of fossil fuels.

Volunteer with an Organization That Fights Hunger

You can gather foods for local food banks, volunteer to work in a soup kitchen, help distribute food to homebound older adults, or start a community or school garden. You can also hold fundraisers and donate cash directly. This financial assistance is urgently needed: for example, in 2005, 24% of U.S. emergency food providers surveyed reported that they had turned away requests for food in the past year because of a lack of resources.[53] And food insecurity in Canada has only increased since then. Check out the Web Links at the end of this chapter for the names of national agencies and get involved!

Because obesity is likely to be as much or more of a problem in your community as hunger, you can also volunteer to fight overnutrition. For instance, you could teach children about healthy eating at after-school programs or on Saturday in the local library. You could help provide opportunities for your neighbours to be physically active. Start a walking group or help with community marathons and "fun runs." You might volunteer to coach after-school sports for children or assist with summer camps that teach children about physical fitness.

You can also get involved with one of the many international agencies that assist developing nations in fighting hunger. Research a few of those listed in the Web Links at the end of this chapter. When you find one you like, volunteer time or donate or raise money to help its cause. The See for Yourself feature identifies more steps you can take to help combat malnutrition.

If you still wonder whether or not your acts can make a difference, consider the advice of historian and civil rights activist Howard Zinn. He urges us to "just do something, to join with millions of others who will just do something, because all of those somethings, at certain points in history, come together and make the world better."[54]

NUTRITION MYTH OR FACT?

If You Clean Your Plate, Will It Help the Starving Children in Africa?

It used to be considered polite to finish all the food on your plate and wasteful to throw food away. Children were told, "Clean your plate—it will help the starving children in Africa!" Today, this admonition raises a serious issue that you might want to consider if you are or plan to be a parent or to work with children.

The primary reason for not teaching children that they must clean their plates is that overeating is becoming a worldwide problem, and coaxing children to eat when they are no longer hungry teaches them to ignore their body's hunger/satiation signals. This can set the stage for disordered eating. Instead of overfilling a child's plate, parents and caregivers should serve children a reasonable portion of food (see Chapter 17). If the child eats that and is still hungry, he or she can be given more.

Forcing children to finish meals is not a strategy for fighting global hunger.

In addition, "cleaning your plate" at home does not help children in Africa or anywhere else. If anything, encouraging children at home to eat just the amount of food their bodies need may help children in developing nations by preserving more of the global harvest. Healthy eating behaviours also reduce children's risk of developing obesity and its associated chronic diseases, thereby reducing their use of limited medical resources as they age.

So next time you're tempted to admonish a child to "clean your plate," try something new. Get down on the child's level, and ask the child about it: "I notice you haven't finished your dinner. Check in with your tummy—are you still hungry, or have you had enough?" Your question may not help a starving child in Africa, but it might help the very child you're talking to.

SEE FOR YOURSELF

What Can You Do to Combat Malnutrition?

Have you ever wondered if your actions inadvertently contribute to the problem of malnutrition? Or whether efforts you make locally can help feed people thousands of kilometres away? In this exercise, you'll reflect on your behaviour in three different roles you play every day: consumer, student, and citizen of the world.

In your role as a consumer, ask yourself:

How can I use my food purchases to promote the production of healthier, less-processed foods?
Any grocery store manager will tell you that your purchases influence the types of foods that are manufactured and sold. If people become aware of the benefits of eating whole-grain bread and stop buying soft white bread, stores will stop carrying it and food companies will stop making it. In our global economy, your food choices can even influence the types of foods that are imported.

1. Choose fresh, locally grown, organic foods more often to support local sustainability.
2. Choose whole or less-processed versions of packaged foods. This encourages their increased production and saves energy.
3. Both when you're shopping and when you're eating out, avoid nutrient-poor foods and beverages to discourage their profitability.

How often do I eat vegetarian?
Plant-based sources of protein can be produced with less energy cost than animal-based sources, so reducing your consumption of animal foods saves global energy.

1. Experiment with some recipes in a vegetarian cookbook. Try making at least one new vegetarian meal each week.
2. Introduce friends and family members to your new vegetarian dishes.
3. When eating out, choose restaurants that provide vegetarian menu choices. If the campus cafeteria or a favourite restaurant has no vegetarian choices, request that some be added to the menu.

How much do I eat?
Eating just the kilocalories you need to maintain a healthy weight leaves more of the global harvest for others and will likely reduce your use of medical resources as well.

1. To raise your consciousness about the physical experience of hunger, consider fasting for one day. If health or other reasons prevent you from fasting safely, try keeping silent during each meal throughout one day so that

you can more fully appreciate the food you're eating and reflect on those who are hungry.
2. For one week, keep track of how much food you throw away, and why. Do you put more food on your plate than you can eat? Do you allow foods stored in your refrigerator to spoil? Do you often buy new foods to "try" and then throw them away because you don't like them?
3. On a daily basis, check in with your body before and as you eat: are you really hungry, and if so, how much and what type of food does your body really need right now?

In your role as a student, ask yourself:

How can I use what I have learned about nutrition to combat malnutrition in my neighbourhood?
1. Visit each of your local fast food restaurants and ask for information about the nutritional value of their foods. Analyze the information, and then summarize it in simple language. Offer to submit a series of articles about your findings to your school or local newspaper.
2. Research what local produce is available in each season. Write an article for your school newspaper identifying the foods in season and include two healthy recipes using those foods.
3. Begin or join a food cooperative, community garden, or shared farming program. Donate a portion of your produce each week to a local food pantry.

What careers could I consider to help combat global malnutrition?
No matter what career you choose, use your unique talents to advocate global food security.

1. You could become a member of Cuso International and serve in a developing country.
2. If you're interested in science, you could have a career helping to develop more nutrient-dense or perennial crops, better food-preservation methods, or projects to improve food or water safety.
3. If you plan a career in business, you could enter the food industry and work for the production and marketing of healthy products.
4. If you pursue a career in health care, you could join an international medical corps to combat deficiency diseases.

In your role as a world citizen, ask yourself:

How can I improve the lives of people in my own community?
1. You can volunteer at a local soup kitchen, homeless shelter, food bank, or community garden.

2. You can join a food cooperative, that is, a store or farm in which you work a number of hours each week in exchange for discounts on healthy foods.

3. Because obesity is likely to be a significant problem in your community, you can help increase opportunities for physical activity in your community. Start a walking group, or volunteer to coach children in a favourite sport.

How can I improve the lives of people in developing nations?

1. Donate time or raise money for one of the international agencies that work to relieve global hunger. Check out options for charitable contributions and volunteer efforts at www.charitynavigator.org.

2. Join efforts to influence government foreign policies to support global food security.

3. Research the human rights records of international food companies whose products you buy. If you don't like what you find out, switch brands, and write to the company to tell it why you did.

Chapter Review

19

Test Yourself   Answers

1. **F** Currently, about 9% of the population of Canada are unable to obtain enough energy and nutrients to meet their physical needs every day.

2. **F** The major cause of undernutrition in the world is unequal distribution of adequate food supplies because of poverty.

3. **T** The Public Health Agency of Canada has identified income/social status as the number one determinant of food security. The prevalence of food insecurity is highest in households with the lowest household income adequacy.

4. **T** Significant evidence supports the theory that physiologic adaptations to poor maternal nutrition made as a fetus is developing help the child during times of food shortages but make the child susceptible to obesity and chronic disease when food is plentiful.

5. **T** Currently, the global burden of obesity is shifting to the poor. For example, the prevalence of obesity in both children and adults in many developing nations is increasing at a faster rate than in developed countries.

Summary

- A nourishing diet contributes to health, wellness, and work capacity, improving the prosperity of everyone worldwide.

- Both undernutrition and overnutrition are significant global problems.

- Undernutrition contributes to wasting, growth stunting, reduced resistance to infection, increased mortality, micronutrient deficiency diseases, and diminished work capacity in adults.

- Fetal malnutrition is associated with increased risk of chronic diseases when undernutrition is relieved during childhood and young adulthood.

- Prevalence of obesity is increasing worldwide.

- Chronic diseases such as diabetes, hypertension, and cardiovascular disease are a significant and growing economic burden worldwide.

- Undernutrition results from famines or chronic food shortages due to overpopulation, poor agricultural practices, lack of infrastructure, disease, and unequal distribution of limited food supplies.

- Because the current global food supply is adequate for the current global population, food insecurity is largely a problem of unequal distribution.

- Overconsumption of energy in developed and transitioning countries is exacerbated by sedentary occupations and motorized transportation.

- Poverty exacerbates overnutrition, perhaps because less-expensive foods are energy-dense with a higher satiety value, widely available, and highly promoted.

- The GOBI initiative of UNICEF combats common infections of childhood by encouraging growth monitoring, oral rehydration therapy, breastfeeding, and immunizations.

- The Green Revolution, sustainable agriculture, and biotechnology are controversial programs with a common goal of increasing the world food supply in a sustainable manner.

- The WHO recognized a need for a global strategy to address prevention and control of obesity and chronic diseases by encouraging healthy patterns of diet and activity worldwide.

- Your efforts to combat global malnutrition are urgently needed.

Review Questions

1. The region of the world where undernutrition is most acute is
   a. sub-Saharan Africa.
   b. Southern Africa.
   c. Central America.
   d. Central Asia.

2. Which of the following statements about the Green Revolution is true?
   a. It has most greatly benefited small, family farms.
   b. It has dramatically reduced undernutrition throughout South America, Asia, and Africa.
   c. It has dramatically increased worldwide production of rice, corn, and wheat at lower costs.
   d. It has reduced the traditional farmer's reliance on chemical fertilizers and pesticides.

3. Which of the following results of undernutrition is most directly linked to death in childhood?
   a. decreased work capacity
   b. reduced resistance to infection
   c. growth stunting
   d. impaired cognitive development

4. At greatest risk for food insecurity in Canada are
   a. adults over age 65.
   b. single mothers and their children.
   c. the working poor.
   d. Aboriginal people.

5. Which of the following health problems has been linked to inadequate intake of vitamin A?
   a. diarrhea
   b. malaria

   c. night blindness
   d. all of the above

6. Explain why iron deficiency is the most common micronutrient deficiency in the world.

7. Why are female lone-parent households more likely to be food insecure than households led by a male or a couple?

8. What is the nutrition paradox and why is it a problem in developing countries?

9. Explain why food insecurity exists in countries with food surpluses.

10. Why might programs to improve the education of women also improve a nation's food/population ratio?

11. Explain why breastfeeding is an essential element of UNICEF's GOBI campaign to eliminate common infections of childhood.

12. Jeanette is a healthcare provider in a free clinic in an impoverished area of India. She is 168 cm tall. Explain why she is not surprised to hear the patients who come to the clinic refer to her as a giant.

13. Davie is two years old and lives in rural Saskatchewan. He is the youngest of three children, all of whom live with their mother in an abandoned van. Their mother relies on a local food pantry for food, and the family drinks water from a nearby pond. Neither Davie nor his siblings have been vaccinated, and they have no regular medical care. Pointing to the interrelationship of several factors, explain why Davie's risk of dying before he reaches age five is significant.

14. José grew up in a slum in Mexico City, but his brilliance in school earned him recognition and a patron who funded his education. Now in medical school in Canada, he plans to return to Mexico as a pediatrician and specialize in the treatment of children with type 2 diabetes. Explain why José might be drawn to work with this population.

Web Links

www.actionagainsthunger.org
Action Against Hunger
This site explains the mission of an international organization that helps in emergency situations and also promotes long-term food security and lets you know how to volunteer to help.

www.bread.org
Bread for the World
Visit this site to learn about a faith-based effort to advocate local and global policies that help the poor obtain food.

www.care.org
CARE
This site is the international page that links to CARE organizations in many countries working to improve economic conditions in more than 70 developing nations.

www.feedingminds.org
Feeding Minds Fighting Hunger
Visit this international electronic classroom to explore the problems of hunger, malnutrition, and food insecurity.

www.freefromhunger.org
Freedom from Hunger
Visit this site to learn about an established international development organization, founded in 1946, that works toward sustainable self-help against chronic hunger and poverty.

www.heifer.org
Heifer International
Visit this site to learn how you can give a cow, some rabbits, or a flock of chickens to a community in a developing country so that they are better able to provide food for themselves.

www.hki.org/index.html
Helen Keller International
This site describes sustainable ways of preventing blindness and childhood deaths by fighting poverty and malnutrition.

www.oxfam.ca
Oxfam Canada
Oxfam International is a confederation of organizations in more than 100 countries working together for a more equitable world. This website explains the Canadian initiatives fighting global poverty, hunger, and social injustice.

www.unicef.org/nutrition/index.html
The United Nations Children's Fund
Visit this site to learn about international concerns affecting the world's children, including nutrient deficiencies and hunger.

www.who.int/nutrition/en
The World Health Organization Nutrition Site
Visit this site to learn about global malnutrition, micronutrient deficiencies, and the nutrition transition.

www.ryerson.ca/foodsecurity
Centre for Studies in Food Security
Visit this site to find information on definitions of food security, projects supported by the centre, and courses offered in the Certificate in Food Security program.

www.kahcanada.org
Kids Against Hunger
Visit this site to find out what Canadian youth can do to help feed starving people in Canada and around the world.

www.breakfastforlearning.ca
Breakfast for Learning
This is the leading national non-profit organization dedicated to child nutrition programs in Canada. Go to this website for nutrition program management and nutrition education resources related to child nutrition programs.

www.foodbankscanada.ca
Food Banks Canada
Food Banks Canada is the national charitable organization representing the food bank community. Visit this website to learn more about hunger in Canada.

www.foodstudies.ca
Canadian Association for Food Studies
Visit this website for information on sustainable food systems and food policy.

www.foodsecureCanada.org
Food Secure Canada
Visit this website for information on food sovereignty and the People's Food Policy project. Food sovereignty is a concept related to justice and sustainability in the food system.

www.foodsecurityresearchcentre.ca
Participatory Action Research and Training Centre on Food Security
The purpose of this centre is to support an interdisciplinary research program that brings together students, faculty, community members, practitioners, and decision makers to impact policy related to addressing the problem of food insecurity in Canada. Visit this website for resources on the prevalence of food insecurity and programs and how to influence policy decisions.

MasteringNutrition®

www.masteringnutrition.pearson.com

Study Area
Practice Tests • Diet Analysis • eText

References

1. Central Intelligence Agency. Sierra Leone. 2009, May 14. *The World Factbook.* Available at www.cia.gov/library/publications/the-world-factbook/geos/sl.html; UNICEF. 2009, June. 68 countdown countries with high mortality: selected health and nutrition indicators. Data companion to the Annual Report of the Executive Director (p. 5). Available at www.unicef.org/about/execboard/files/UNICEF_Data_Companion_2009_Eng_light.pdf.

2. World Health Organization. 2008, May. Core health indicators: Sierra Leone. *WHO Statistical Information System* (WHOSIS). Available at http://apps.who.int/whosis/database/core/core_select_process.cfm.

3. Aguayo, V. M., D. Garnier, and S. K. Baker. 2007. *Drops of Life: Vitamin A Supplementation for Child Survival, Progress and Lessons Learned in West and Central Africa.* UNICEF Regional Office for West and Central Africa.

4. International Food Policy Research Institute. 2008, October 14. Global hunger index. Available at www.ifpri.org/PUBS/cp/ghi08.asp.

5. FAO. 2008. The spectrum of malnutrition. Available at www.fao.org.

6. World Health Organization/World Food Programme/United Nations System Standing Committee on Nutrition/The United Nations Children's Fund. 2007, May. *Community-Based Management of Severe Acute Malnutrition* Available at www.who.int/nutrition/topics/Statement_community_based_man_sev_acute_mal_eng.pdf; Collins, S. 2007, May. Treating severe acute malnutrition seriously. *Arch. Dis. Child.* 92(5):453–461.

7. WHO. 2002. *The World Health Report, 2002: Reducing risks, promoting healthy life.* Geneva: World Health Organization.

8. Aguayo, V. M., D. Garnier, and S. K. Baker. 2007. *Drops of Life: Vitamin A Supplementation for Child Survival, Progress and Lessons Learned in West and Central Africa.* UNICEF Regional Office for West and Central Africa.

9. Scrimshaw, N. S. 2003. Historical concepts of interactions, synergism and antagonism between nutrition and infection. *J. Nutr.* 133:316S–321S.

10. Ambrus, J. L. Sr., and J. L. Ambrus Jr. 2004. Nutrition and infectious diseases in developing countries and problems of acquired immunodeficiency syndrome. *Exp. Biol. Med.* 229:464–472.

11. Black, R. E., S. S. Morris, and J. Bryce. 2003. Where and why are 10 million children dying every year? *Lancet* 361:2226–2234.

12. Central Intelligence Agency. 2009, May 14. *The World Factbook.* Available at www.cia.gov/library/publications/the-world-fact-book/geos/sl.html.

13. Population Reference Bureau. 2008. 2008 World Population Data Sheet. Available at www.prb.org/Publications/Datasheets/2008/2008wpds.aspx.

14. World Health Organization. 2004. Proportion of general population with insufficient iodine intake: iodine status worldwide. Available at www.who.int/vmnis/iodine/status/summary/iodine_data_status_summary_t2/en/index.html.

15. Aguayo, V. M., D. Garnier, and S. K. Baker. 2007. *Drops of Life: Vitamin A Supplementation for Child Survival, Progress and Lessons Learned in West and Central Africa.* UNICEF Regional Office for West and Central Africa.

16. Demment, M. W., M. M. Young, and R. L. Sensenig. 2003. Providing micronutrients through food-based solutions: a key to human and national development. Supplement: animal source foods to improve micronutrient nutrition and human function in developing countries. *J. Nutr.* 133:3879S–3885S.

17. Hunt, J. M. 2002. Reversing productivity losses from iron deficiency: the economic case. *J. Nutr.* 132(4 Suppl):794S–801S.

18. Adair, L. S., and A. M. Prentice. 2004. A critical evaluation of the fetal origins hypothesis and its implications for developing countries. *J. Nutr.* 134:191–193.

19. World Health Organization. 2006, September. Obesity and overweight. Available at www.who.int/mediacentre/factsheets/fs311/en/.

20. Canadian Diabetes Association. 2009. *The prevalence and costs of diabetes.* Available at www.diabetes.ca/diabetes-and-you/what/prevalence/ (accessed July 5, 2011).

21. NASA. Earth Observatory: Famine in Niger and Mali. Available at http://earthobservatory.nasa.gov/NaturalHazards/natural_hazards_v2.php3?img_id=13028.

22. Herz, B. 2004. The importance of educating girls. *Science* 305:1910–1911.

23. AVERT. 2009. *Worldwide HIV and AIDS statistics.* Available at www.avert.org/worlstatinfo.htm (accessed July 5, 2011).

24. De Waal, A., and A. Whiteside. 2003. New variant famine: AIDS and food crisis in southern Africa. *Lancet* 362:1234–1237.

25. Struble, M. B., and L. L. Aomari. 2003. Position of the Academy of Nutrition and Dietetics: addressing world hunger, malnutrition and food insecurity. *J. Am. Diet. Assoc.* 103:1046–1057.

26. Charlton, K. E., and D. Rose. 2001. Nutrition among older adults in Africa: the situation at the beginning of the millennium. *J. Nutr.* 131:2424S–2428S.

27. World Health Organization. 2006, September. Obesity and overweight. Available at www.who.int/mediacentre/factsheets/fs311/en/.

28. Drewnowski, A. 2009. Obesity, diets, and social inequalities. *Nutrition Reviews* 67(Suppl.1):S36–S39.

29. Dachner, N., L. Ricciuto, S. I. Kirkpatrick, and V. Tarasuk. 2010. Food purchasing and food insecurity among low-income families in Toronto. *Can. J. Diet. Prac. Res.* 71:e51–e56.

30. Kuhle S., P. Veugelers. 2008. Why does the social gradient in health not apply to overweight? *Health Reports* 19(4):7–15.

31. Health Canada. 2007. Income-related household food security in Canada. Ottawa, ON: Health Canada Publications. Available at www.hc-sc.gc.ca/fn-an/alt_formats/hpfb-dgpsa/pdf/surveill/income_food_sec-sec_alim-eng.pdf (accessed November 1, 2011).

32. Green R. J., P. L. Williams, S. Johnson, and I. Blum. 2008. Can Canadian seniors on public pensions afford a nutritious diet? *Can. J. Aging* 27:69–79.

33. Public Health Agency of Canada. 2008. *The Chief Public Health Officer's Report on the State of Public Health in Canada.* Available at www.phac-aspc.gc.ca/cphorsphc-respcacsp/2008/fr-rc/pdf/CPHO-Report-e.pdf (accessed July 5, 2011).

34. Human Resources and Skills Development Canada. 2007. *Financial security—low income incidence.* Available at www4.hrsdc.gc.ca/.3ndic.1t.4r@-eng.jsp?iid=2 (accessed October 13, 2011).

35. Williams P. L., C. P. Johnson, M. L. V. Kratzmann, C. S. Johnson, B. J. Anderson, and C. Chenhall. 2006. Can households earning minimum wage in Nova Scotia afford a nutritious diet? *Can. J. Pub. Health* 97:430–434.

36. Che, J., and J. Chen. 2001. Food insecurity in Canadian households (1998/99 data). *Health Reports* 12:11–22.

37. Vozoris, N. T., and V. S. Tarasuk. 2003. Household food insufficiency is associated with poorer health. *J. Nutr.* 133:120–126.

38. Gucciardi, E., J. A. Vogt, M. DeMelo, and D. E. Stewart. 2009. Exploration of the relationship between household food insecurity and diabetes in Canada. *Diabetes Care* 32:2218–2224.

39. Hamelin, A.-M., J. Habicht, and M. Beaudry. 1999. Food insecurity: consequences for the household and broader social implications. *J. Nutr.* 129:525S–528S.

40. Siefert, K., C. M. Heflin, M. E. Corcoran, and D. R. Williams. 2011. Food insufficiency and the physical and mental health of low-income women. *Women Health* 59:159–177.

41. Alaimo, K., C. M. Olson, and E. A. Frongillo. 2002. Family food insufficiency, but not low family income, is positively associated with dysthymia and suicide symptoms in adolescents. *J. Nutr.* 312:719–725.

42. United Nations. 2005. The Millennium Development Goals Report. Available at www.un.org/millenniumgoals/.

43. USAID. 2005. Famine early warning system. Available at www.fews.net/.

44. UNICEF. 1996. Fifty years for children. Available at www.unicef.org/sowc96/1980s.htm.

45. Dietitians of Canada. 2007. Community food security: position of Dietitians of Canada. Public Policy Statement 1–13.

46. Nova Scotia Nutrition Council and the Atlantic Health Promotion Research Centre. 2005. *Thought About Food? A Workbook on Food Security and Influencing Policy.* Available at www.foodthoughtful.ca (accessed October 13, 2011).

47. Meal Exchange. 2006. *Hunger and food security in Canada.* Available at www.mealexchange.com/index.php?option=com_content&task=view&id=40&Itemid=74 (accessed July 5, 2011).

48. Food Banks Canada. 2010. *Hunger Count 2010.* Available at www.afbna.ca/media/uploads/resources/HungerCount2010_web.pdf (accessed November 1, 2011).

49. Evenson, R. E., and D. Gollin. 2003. Assessing the impact of the Green Revolution, 1960 to 2000. *Science* 2:758–762.

50. Center for Global Food Issues. 2005. Declaration in support of protecting nature with high-yield farming and forestry, 2002. Available at www.highyieldconservation.org.

51. Sakamoto, T., and M. Matsuoka. 2004. Generating high-yielding varieties by genetic manipulation of plant architecture. *Curr. Opin. Biotechnol.* 15:144–147; Gibson, R. W., V. Aritua, E. Byamukama,

I. Mpembe, and J. Kayongo, 2004. Control strategies for sweet potato virus disease in Africa. *Virus Res.* 100(1):115–22; and Welch, R. M., and R. D. Graham. 2004. Breeding for micronutrients in staple food crops from a human nutrition perspective. *J. Exp. Botany* 55:353–364.

52. Knight, J. 2003. A dying breed. *Nature* 421:568–570.

53. National Student Campaign Against Hunger and Homelessness. 2005, February. Communities in crisis: survey of hunger and homelessness in America. Available at www.studentsagainsthunger.org/hunger.asp?id2=15761.

54. Zinn, H. 2006. *Original Zinn*, p. 167. New York: Harper Perennial.

55. Florence, M. D., M. Asbridge, and P. J. Veugelers. 2008. Diet quality and academic performance. *Journal of School Health* 78:209–215.

56. Edward, G., and S. Evers. 2001. Benefits and barriers associated with participation in food programs in three low-income Ontario communities. *Canadian Journal of Dietetic Practice and Research* 62:76–81.

57. Jacoby, E. R., S. Cueto, and E. Pollitt. 1998. When science and politics listen to each other: good prospects from a new school breakfast program in Peru. *Am. J. Clin. Nutr.* 67:795S–797S.

58. Meyers, A. F., A. E. Sampson, M. Weltzman, B. L. Rogers, and H. Kanye. 1989. School breakfast program and school performance. *American Journal of Diseases of Children* 143:1234–1239.

59. Hyndman, B. 2000. *Feeding the body, feeding the mind: an overview of school-based nutritional programs in Canada.* Toronto: ON, Breakfast for Learning.

60. Papmandjaris, A. 2000. *Breakfast and learning in children: a review of the effects of breakfast on scholastic performance.* Toronto: ON, Breakfast for Learning Canadian Living Foundation.

61. Bhattachya, J., J. Currie, and S. Haider. 2004. *Evaluating the impact of school nutrition programs: final report. USDA Economic Research Service.* Available at www.ers.usda.gov/publications/efan04008 (accessed July 5, 2011).

62. Eagle, T. F., R. Gurm, C. S. Goldberg, J. DuRussel-Weston, E. Kline-Rogers, L. Palma-Davis, S. Aaronson, C. M. Fitzgerald, L. R. Mitchell, B. Riogers, P. Bruenger, E. A. Jackson, and K. A Eagle. 2010. Health status and behavior among middle-school children in a Midwest community: what are the underpinnings of childhood obesity? *Am. Heart J.* 160:1185–1189.

63. Butler-Jones, D. 2008. *The Chief Public Health Officer's Report on the State of Public Health 2008.* Ottawa, ON: Public Health Agency of Canada.

64. Story, M. 2009. The Third School Nutrition Dietary Assessment Study: findings and policy implications for improving the health of US children. *J. Am. Diet. Assoc.* 109:S7–S13.

65. Russell, J., S. Evers, J. M. Dwyer, C. Uetrecht, and L. Macaskill. 2007. Best practices among child nutrition programs in Ontario: evaluation findings. *Journal of Hunger & Environmental Nutrition* 2:111–127.

66. Ernesto, P. 1995. Does breakfast make a difference in school? *J. Am. Diet. Assoc.* 95:1134–1139.

67. McIntyre, L., K. Travers, and J. B. Boyle. 1999. Children's feeding programs in Atlantic Canada: reducing or reproducing inequities? *The Canadian Journal of Public Health* 90:196–200.

68. Alaimo, K., C. M. Olson, and E. A. Fregille Jr. 2005. Food insufficiency and American school-aged children's cognitive, academic, and psychosocial development. *Pediatrics* 108:44–53.

69. Tarasuk, V. 2001. A critical examination of community-based responses to household food insecurity in Canada. *Journal of Health Education and Behaviour* 28:487–499.

Does Canada Need a National School Meal Program?

Although most children in Canada grow up with an abundant and healthy supply of food, more than 700 000 children lived in households that experienced food insecurity at some time in 2004.[31] Food insecurity occurs when a family is not able to ensure a consistent, dependable supply of safe and nutritious food. Approximately 5.2% of households with children can be classified as food insecure. The prevalence of food insecurity is even higher in households led by a lone parent (22.5%), especially a lone female parent (24.9%), compared with households led by a couple (7.6%).[31] These statistics are definitely at odds with Canada's image as a "land of plenty."

The effects of food insecurity and hunger can be very harmful to children. Without an adequate energy and nutrient intake, they will not be able to concentrate or pay attention to their parents, teachers, or other caretakers, leading to poor academic performance.[55] Impaired nutrient status can blunt children's immune responses, making them more susceptible to common childhood illnesses. Studies have shown that the implementation of a school meal program can result in improvements in the classroom learning environment, substantially increasing student attendance rates and lowering tardiness, having fewer classroom disruptions, and experiencing improved classroom behaviour.[56–62]

Options for families facing food insecurity in Canada are limited as Canada is the only westernized nation without a national, federally funded school meal program. Parents are expected to provide their children with breakfast and send a lunch or provide them with money to purchase foods from vending machines, cafeterias (where available), or nearby fast food restaurants if they are unable to return home for a meal. Some schools are fortunate enough to have parent volunteers who come into the school to prepare a hot lunch for the students, but the choices are often limited by the available resources (food, money) and kitchen facilities. Unfortunately, not all parents have the necessary funds to give to their children to allow them to purchase these foods and studies

have shown that 31% of elementary students and 62% of secondary students do not eat a nutritious breakfast before school.[63]

The National School Lunch Program in the United States was created in 1946 to address the problem of childhood food insecurity. It is usually administered by state education agencies that operate the program through agreements with school food authorities. Over the years, this program has expanded to include the School Breakfast program, Snack program, Child and Adult Care Feeding program, and the Summer Food Service program. Currently, 99% of public schools participate in the program, serving over 30 million children.[64] The lunches provided must meet the fat, saturated fat, and sodium standards of the Dietary Guidelines for Americans as well as provide one-third of the 1989 Recommended Dietary Allowances for protein, vitamin A, vitamin C, iron, calcium, and energy and comply with the Healthy Meals for Americans Act. On the surface, it would appear that these federally funded school lunches would be expected to improve children's diets.

However, when delving into this question a little more deeply, we discover that the answer is not that clear. First of all, very few school lunch programs actually meet all of the Dietary Guidelines. Virtually none meet the sodium guideline; and only 30% meet the saturated fat guideline (no more than 10% of total energy).[64] Second, the actual amount of nutrients a student gets depends on what the student actually eats. School lunch programs don't have to meet the federal guidelines every day but only over the course of a week's meals. Thus, the school lunches that students actually eat (not necessarily those planned or served to the student) tend to be higher in fat because students choose to eat the foods they like the best, such as pizza, hamburgers, hot dogs, and other higher-fat entrées. Children typically prefer to eat French fries instead of other vegetables offered, such as green beans or carrots. A 2010 study of 1003 Michigan junior high school students found that the students who ate school meals for lunch were significantly more likely to be obese than those who didn't.[62] Third, keep in mind that children in many schools can still buy high-fat and high-sugar snacks and beverages from vending machines or bring them from home, and some schools actually have fast food restaurants selling their food in competition with the school lunch program!

The effectiveness of school breakfast programs has also been questioned. While researchers agree that increased access to healthy food is important to address

providing meals addresses only the short-term needs of the community and not the root cause of food insecurity—poverty.[69]

the problem of food insecurity, how these programs are administered and who should administer them remains controversial.[65-69] Critics have also pointed out that

Using the Evidence

1. Based on the evidence provided, should the Government of Canada provide funding for a national school meal program for Canadian children?

2. What other actions can we take to address the problem of childhood food insecurity in Canada?

Appendices

Appendix A Metabolism Pathways and Biochemical Structures

When learning about the science of nutrition, it is important to understand basic principles of metabolism and to know the molecular structures of important nutrients and molecules. Chapter 7 of this text provides a detailed discussion of the major metabolic processes that occur within the body. This appendix gives additional information and detail on several metabolism pathways and biochemical structures of importance. As in Chapter 7, red arrows indicate catabolic reactions.

Metabolism Pathways

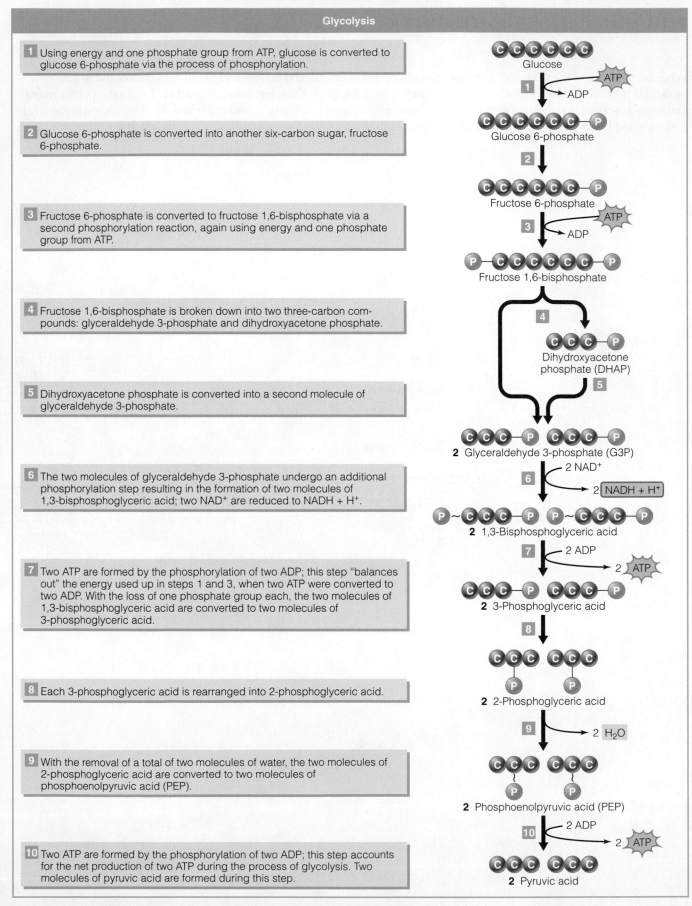

Glycolysis

1. Using energy and one phosphate group from ATP, glucose is converted to glucose 6-phosphate via the process of phosphorylation.

2. Glucose 6-phosphate is converted into another six-carbon sugar, fructose 6-phosphate.

3. Fructose 6-phosphate is converted to fructose 1,6-bisphosphate via a second phosphorylation reaction, again using energy and one phosphate group from ATP.

4. Fructose 1,6-bisphosphate is broken down into two three-carbon compounds: glyceraldehyde 3-phosphate and dihydroxyacetone phosphate.

5. Dihydroxyacetone phosphate is converted into a second molecule of glyceraldehyde 3-phosphate.

6. The two molecules of glyceraldehyde 3-phosphate undergo an additional phosphorylation step resulting in the formation of two molecules of 1,3-bisphosphoglyceric acid; two NAD^+ are reduced to $NADH + H^+$.

7. Two ATP are formed by the phosphorylation of two ADP; this step "balances out" the energy used up in steps 1 and 3, when two ATP were converted to two ADP. With the loss of one phosphate group each, the two molecules of 1,3-bisphosphoglyceric acid are converted to two molecules of 3-phosphoglyceric acid.

8. Each 3-phosphoglyceric acid is rearranged into 2-phosphoglyceric acid.

9. With the removal of a total of two molecules of water, the two molecules of 2-phosphoglyceric acid are converted to two molecules of phosphoenolpyruvic acid (PEP).

10. Two ATP are formed by the phosphorylation of two ADP; this step accounts for the net production of two ATP during the process of glycolysis. Two molecules of pyruvic acid are formed during this step.

Figure A.1 Glycolysis.

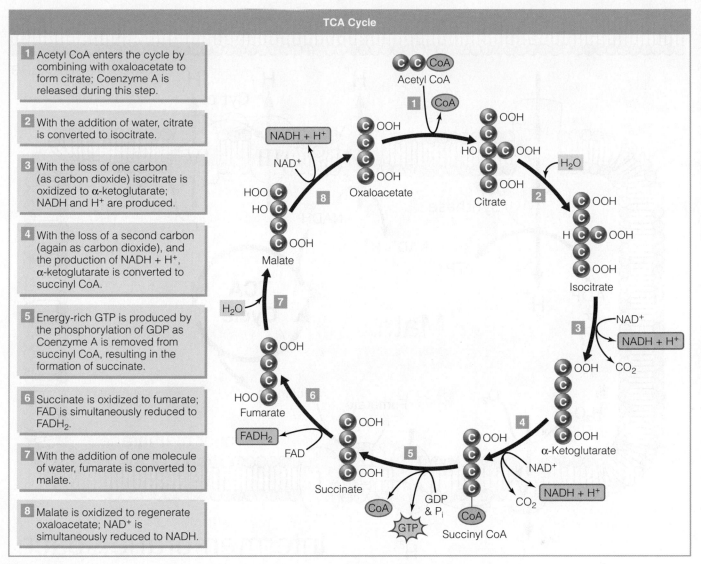

Figure A.2 TCA cycle.

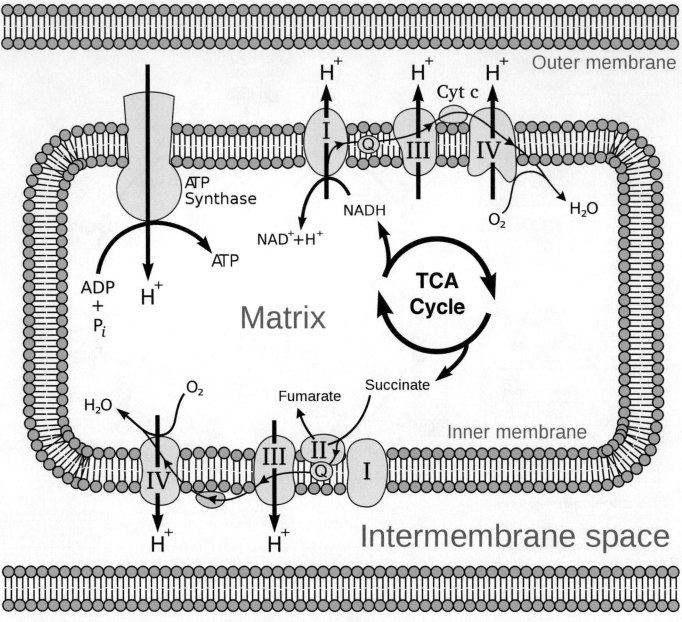

Figure A.3 Electron transport chain. ATP is released at various points in the electron transport chain as electrons are passed from one molecule to another. The process, termed *oxidative phosphorylation*, occurs within the electron transport chain.
Source: TimVickers

Net Energy Production for Glucose Oxidation

	Metabolic reaction	Reaction by-product	Number used	Number produced	Net usage/ production
Glycolysis	Glucose ⟶ Fructose 1,6-bisphosphate	ATP	2		−2 ATP
	Glyceraldehyde 3-phosphate ⟶ 1,3-Bisphosphoglyceric acid	NADH + H⁺		2	2 NADH + H⁺ via electron transport chain
	1,3-Bisphosphoglyceric acid ⟶ Pyruvic acid	ATP		4	4 ATP
Intermediate step	Pyruvic acid ⟶ Acetyl CoA	NADH + H⁺		2	2 NADH + H⁺ via electron transport chain
TCA cycle	Isocitrate ⟶ Succinyl CoA	NADH + H⁺		4	4 NADH + H⁺ via electron transport chain
	Succinyl CoA ⟶ Succinate	GTP		2	2 GTP
	Succinate ⟶ Fumarate	FADH₂		2	2 FADH₂ via electron transport chain
	Malate ⟶ Oxaloacetate	NADH + H⁺		2	2 NADH + H⁺ via electron transport chain

(a) Sources of energy use and production during glucose oxidation

Reaction by-product	Number produced	Number of ATP produced per product	Net usage/ production
ATP	4 − 2 = 2	1	2 x 1 = 2 ATP
NADH + H⁺ (from glycolysis)	2	2 to 3	2 x 2 = 4 or 2 x 3 = 6 ATP
NADH + H⁺ (from TCA cycle)	8	3	8 x 3 = 24 ATP
GTP	2	1	2 x 1 = 2 ATP
FADH₂ (via electron transport chain)	2	2	2 x 2 = 4 ATP

Balance of energy from the oxidation of one unit of glucose

36 to 38 ATP

(b) Energy balance sheet for glucose oxidation

Figure A.4 Net energy production for glucose oxidation.

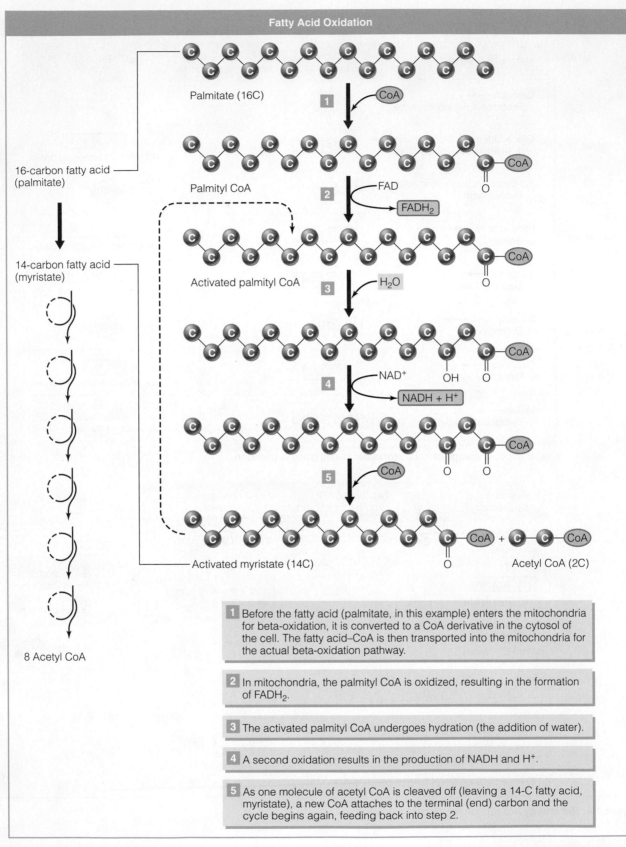

Fatty Acid Oxidation

16-carbon fatty acid (palmitate)

14-carbon fatty acid (myristate)

8 Acetyl CoA

Palmitate (16C)

Palmityl CoA

Activated palmityl CoA

Activated myristate (14C)

Acetyl CoA (2C)

1   Before the fatty acid (palmitate, in this example) enters the mitochondria for beta-oxidation, it is converted to a CoA derivative in the cytosol of the cell. The fatty acid–CoA is then transported into the mitochondria for the actual beta-oxidation pathway.

2   In mitochondria, the palmityl CoA is oxidized, resulting in the formation of $FADH_2$.

3   The activated palmityl CoA undergoes hydration (the addition of water).

4   A second oxidation results in the production of NADH and H^+.

5   As one molecule of acetyl CoA is cleaved off (leaving a 14-C fatty acid, myristate), a new CoA attaches to the terminal (end) carbon and the cycle begins again, feeding back into step 2.

Figure A.5 Fatty acid oxidation.

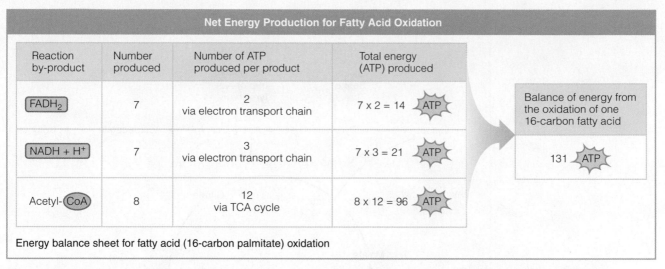

Reaction by-product	Number produced	Number of ATP produced per product	Total energy (ATP) produced	Balance of energy from the oxidation of one 16-carbon fatty acid
FADH₂	7	2 via electron transport chain	7 x 2 = 14 ATP	
NADH + H⁺	7	3 via electron transport chain	7 x 3 = 21 ATP	131 ATP
Acetyl-CoA	8	12 via TCA cycle	8 x 12 = 96 ATP	

Energy balance sheet for fatty acid (16-carbon palmitate) oxidation

Figure A.6 Net energy production for fatty acid oxidation (16-carbon palmitate). With each sequential cleavage of the two-carbon acetyl CoA, one FADH₂ (which yields 2 ATP when oxidized by the electron transport chain) and one NADH (which yields 3 ATP when oxidized by the electron transport chain) are produced. Each molecule of acetyl CoA yields 12 ATP when metabolized through the TCA cycle. The complete oxidation of palmitate yields 7 FADH₂ (14 ATP), 7 NADH (21 ATP), and 8 acetyl CoA (96 ATP), for a grand total of 131 ATP.

Synthesis of Ketone Bodies

1 As acetyl CoA accumulates, it reacts with acetoacetyl CoA to form a short-lived metabolite β-hydroxy-β-methylglutaryl CoA.

2 β-hydroxy-β-methylglutaryl CoA is rapidly cleaved to form acetyl CoA and acetoacetate (a ketone body). During this step, acetyl CoA is released.

3 Acetoacetate can either be reduced to β-hydroxybutyrate (3a) or decarboxylated to form acetone (3b) and carbon dioxide. Both β-hydroxybutyrate and acetone are ketone bodies. All three ketone bodies accumulate during the condition of ketosis.

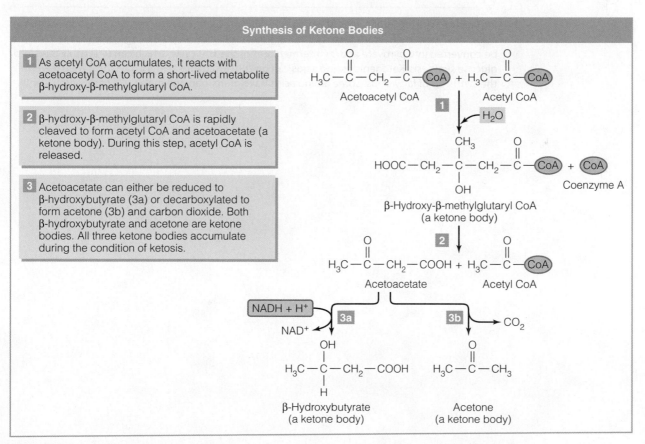

Figure A.7 The synthesis of ketone bodies.

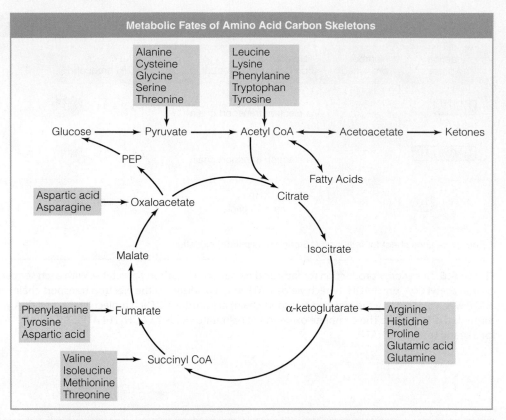

Figure A.8 The metabolic fates of amino acid carbon skeletons. After the deamination of amino acids, their carbon skeletons feed into various metabolic pathways. Glucogenic amino acids can be converted into pyruvate and/or intermediates of the TCA cycle, which can ultimately feed into glucose synthesis. Ketogenic amino acids can be converted into acetyl CoA, which then feeds into the synthesis of fatty acids. Some amino acids have more than one metabolic pathway available.

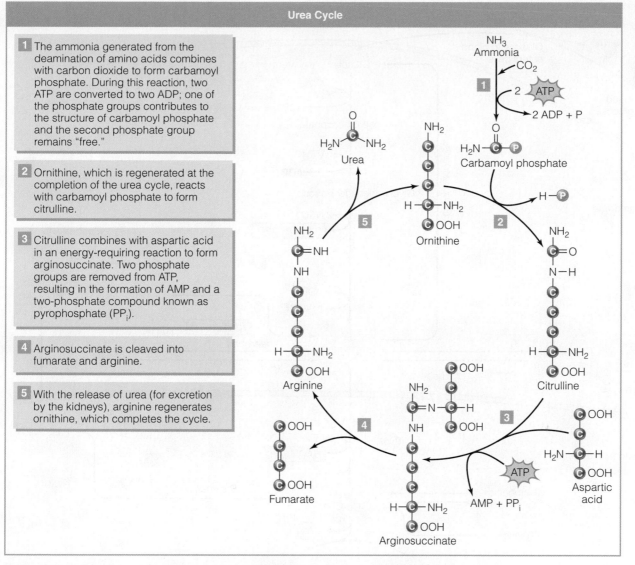

Urea Cycle

1. The ammonia generated from the deamination of amino acids combines with carbon dioxide to form carbamoyl phosphate. During this reaction, two ATP are converted to two ADP; one of the phosphate groups contributes to the structure of carbamoyl phosphate and the second phosphate group remains "free."

2. Ornithine, which is regenerated at the completion of the urea cycle, reacts with carbamoyl phosphate to form citrulline.

3. Citrulline combines with aspartic acid in an energy-requiring reaction to form arginosuccinate. Two phosphate groups are removed from ATP, resulting in the formation of AMP and a two-phosphate compound known as pyrophosphate (PP$_i$).

4. Arginosuccinate is cleaved into fumarate and arginine.

5. With the release of urea (for excretion by the kidneys), arginine regenerates ornithine, which completes the cycle.

Figure A.9 Urea cycle.

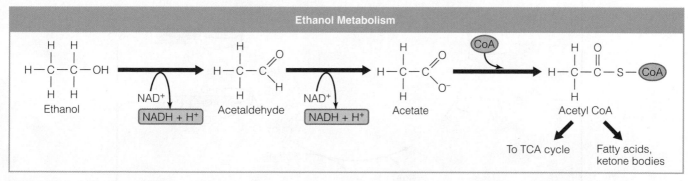

Ethanol Metabolism

Figure A.10 Ethanol metabolism.

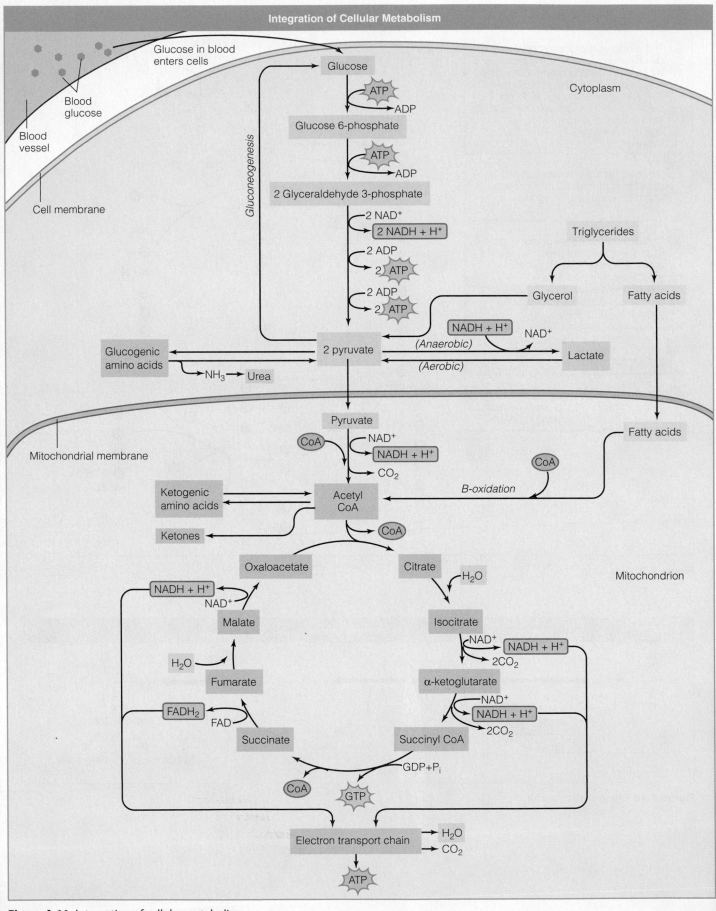

Figure A.11 Integration of cellular metabolism.
Source: Pearson Science

Biochemical Structures

Amino Acid Structures

Amino acids all have the same basic core but differ in their side chains. The following amino acids have been classified according to their specific type of side chain. Amino acids that are essential to humans are noted in bold print.

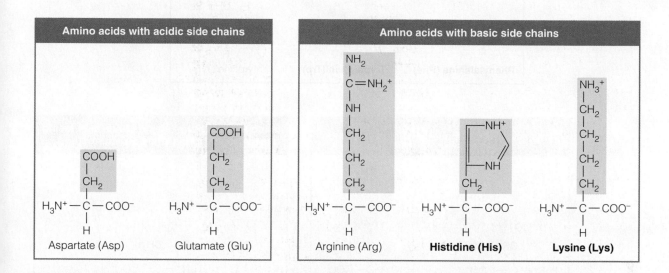

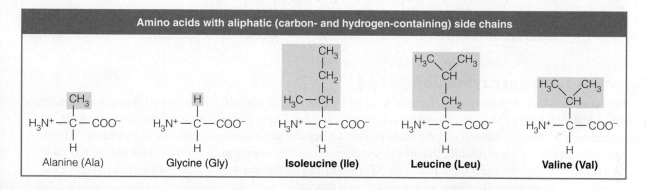

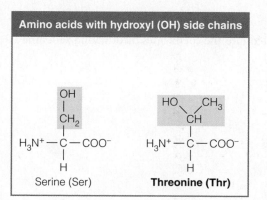

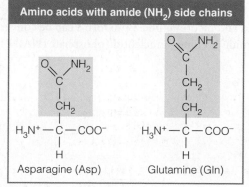

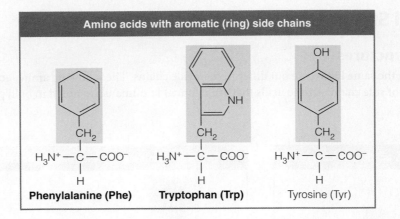

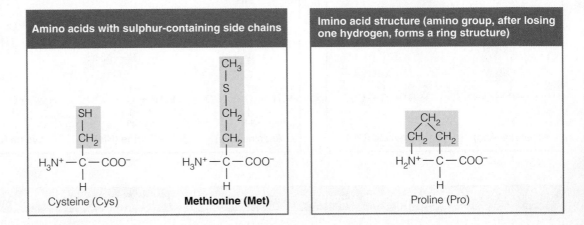

Vitamin Structures and Coenzyme Derivatives

Many vitamins have common names (for example, vitamin C, vitamin E) as well as scientific designations (for example, ascorbic acid, α-tocopherol). Most vitamins are found in more than one chemical form. Many of the vitamins illustrated here have an active coenzyme form; review both the vitamin and the coenzyme structures and see if you can locate the "core vitamin" structure within each of the coenzymes. The vitamins found in foods or supplements are not always in the precise chemical form needed for metabolic activity, and therefore the body often has to modify the vitamin in one way or another. For example, many of the B-vitamins are phosphorylated, meaning they have a phosphate group attached.

Water-Soluble Vitamins

Niacin has two forms: nicotinic acid and nicotinamide. Both forms can be converted into the coenzymes nicotinamide adenine dinucleotide (NAD$^+$) and nicotinamide adenine dinucleotide phosphate (NADP$^+$).

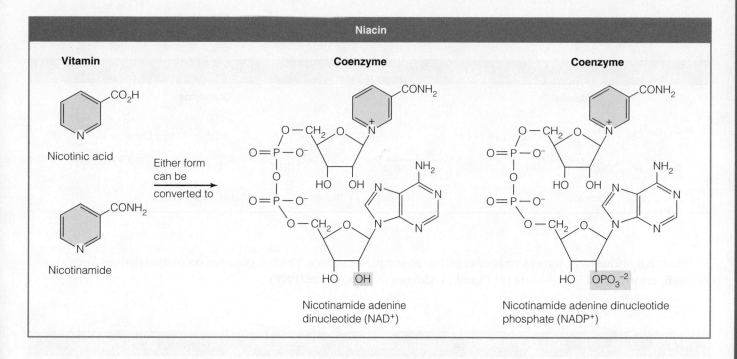

Riboflavin can be converted into the coenzymes flavin adenine dinucleotide (FAD) and flavin mononucleotide (FMN).

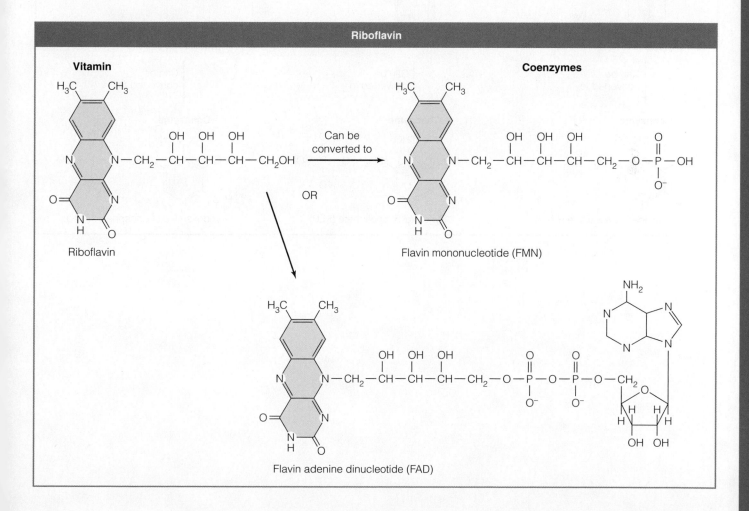

Thiamine can be converted into the coenzyme thiamine pyrophosphate (TPP).

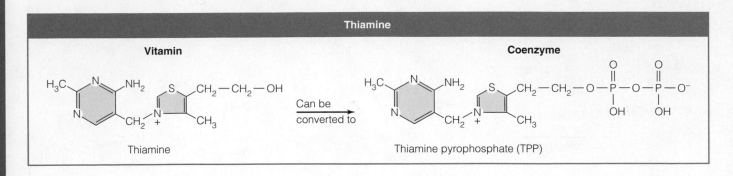

Vitamin B$_6$ includes the forms pyridoxine, pyridoxal, and pyridoxamine. The two common coenzymes derived from vitamin B$_6$ are pyridoxal 5′ phosphate (PLP) and pyridoxamine 5′ phosphate (PNP).

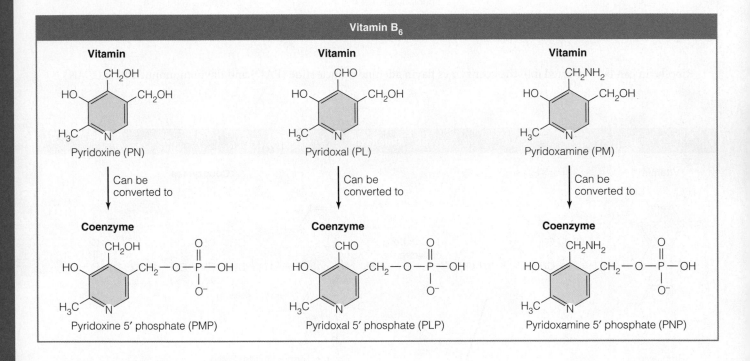

Two forms of vitamin B_{12} are cyanocobalamin and methylcobalamin.

Vitamin B_{12}

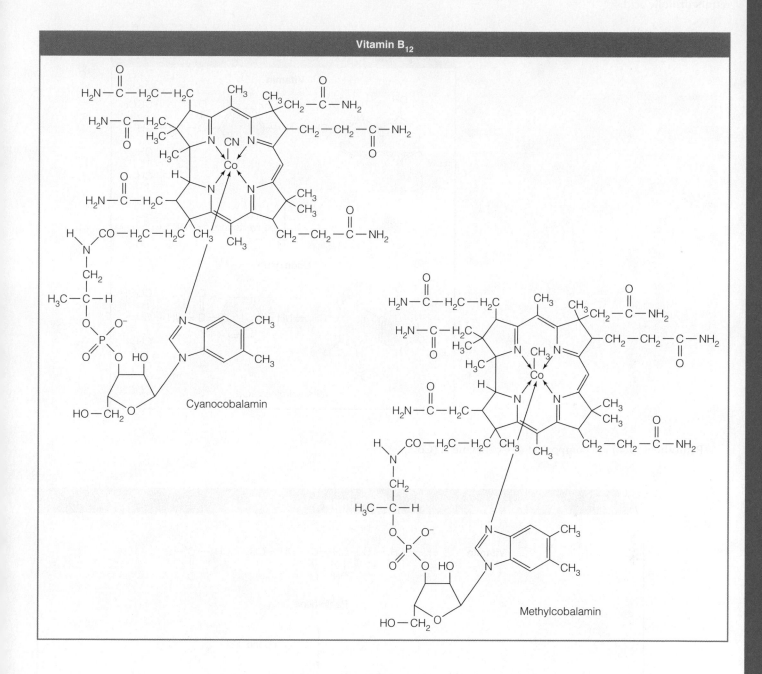

Cyanocobalamin

Methylcobalamin

Folic acid is one specific chemical form of folate. This vitamin can be converted into several coenzymes, including tetrahydrofolic acid.

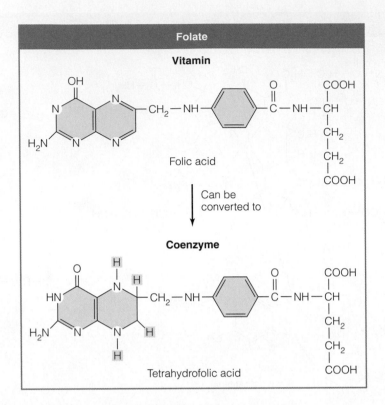

Pantothenic acid is a component of Coenzyme A (CoA).

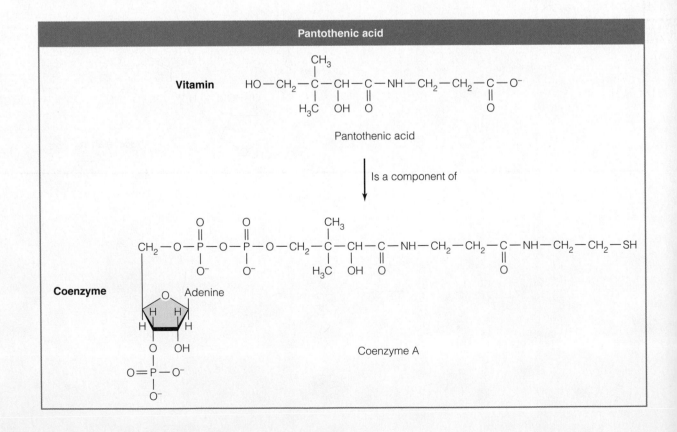

Biotin binds to several different metabolic enzymes. Choline serves as a methyl donor and as a precursor of acetylcholine and phospholipids.

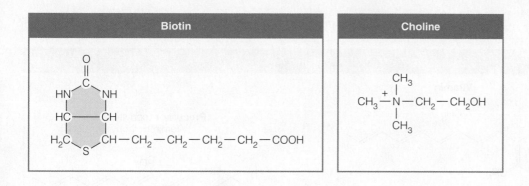

The two forms of vitamin C (ascorbic acid and dehydroascorbic acid) are readily interconverted as two hydrogens are lost through the oxidation of ascorbic acid or gained through the reduction of dehydroascorbic acid.

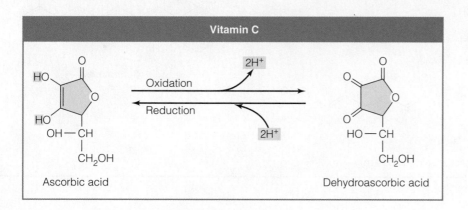

Fat-Soluble Vitamins

Vitamin A exists as an alcohol (retinol), an aldehyde (retinal), and an acid (retinoic acid). Beta-carotene is a common and highly potent precursor that can be converted into vitamin A by the body.

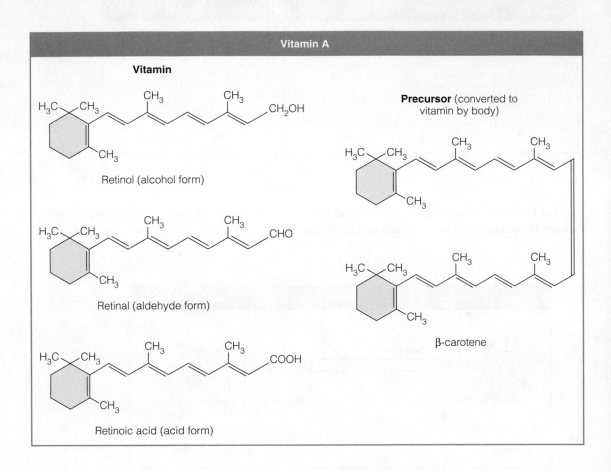

Vitamin A

Vitamin

Retinol (alcohol form)

Retinal (aldehyde form)

Retinoic acid (acid form)

Precursor (converted to vitamin by body)

β-carotene

Vitamin D as cholecalciferol must be activated by two hydroxylation reactions (the addition of one OH group at each step) to form the active form of the vitamin, calcitriol (also called 1,25 (OH)$_2$D).

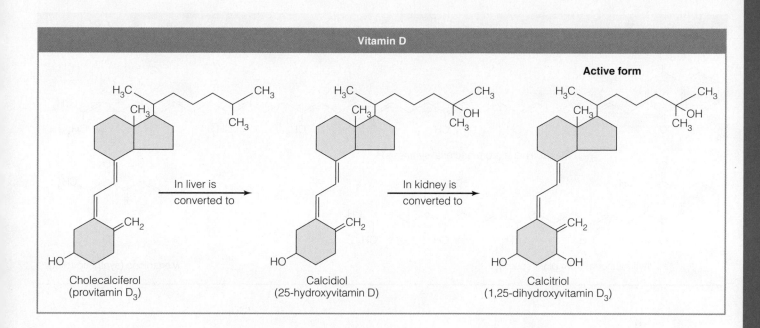

α-tocopherol is the most active form of vitamin E; the number and location of the methyl (CH$_3$) groups attached to the ring structure distinguish the four unique forms of the tocopherols.

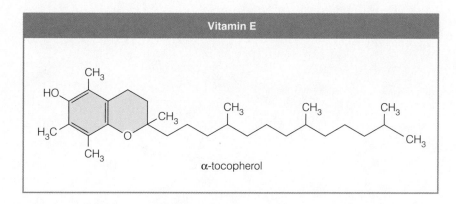

Vitamin K can be derived from plant sources (phylloquinones) and bacterial synthesis (menaquinones). A synthetic form of vitamin K (menadione) is also available.

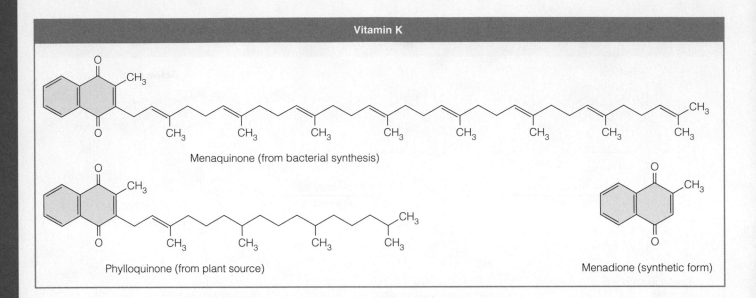

Vitamin K

Menaquinone (from bacterial synthesis)

Phylloquinone (from plant source)

Menadione (synthetic form)

Appendix B Protein Synthesis

The Structure of Genes

A *gene* is a segment of deoxyribonucleic acid (DNA) that serves as a template for the synthesis—or expression—of a particular protein.

The building blocks of DNA are **nucleotides**, molecules composed of a "backbone" made up of a phosphate group and a pentose sugar called deoxyribose, to which is attached one of four nitrogenous bases: adenine (A), guanine (G), cytosine (C), or thymine (T). Within DNA molecules, these nucleotides occur in two long, parallel chains coiled into the shape of a double helix (**Figure B.1**). Because nucleotides vary only in their nitrogenous bases, the astonishing variability of DNA arises from the precise sequencing of nucleotides along these chains.

Chains of nucleotides are held together by hydrogen bonds that link their nitrogenous bases. Each base can bond only to its *complementary base:* A always bonds to T, and G always bonds to C. The complementary nature of bases guides the transfer of genetic instructions from DNA into the resulting protein.

Transcription and Translation

Proteins are actually manufactured by ribosomes in the cell's cytoplasm. But DNA never leaves the nucleus. So for gene expression to occur (**Figure B.2**), a gene's DNA has to replicate itself—that is, it must make an exact copy of itself, which can then be carried out to the cytoplasm. DNA replication ensures that the genetic information in the original gene is identical to the genetic information used to build the protein. Through the process of replication, DNA provides the instructions for building every protein in the body (Figure B.2).

Cells use a special molecule to copy, or transcribe, the information from DNA and carry it to the ribosomes. This molecule is *messenger RNA (messenger ribonucleic acid,* or *mRNA).* In contrast with DNA, RNA is a single strand of nucleotides, and its four nitrogenous bases are A, G, C, and U (stands for uracil, which takes the place of the thymine found in DNA). Also, as its name suggests, it contains the pentose sugar ribose instead of deoxyribose. During **transcription**, mRNA copies to its own base sequence the genetic information from DNA's base sequence. The mRNA then detaches from the DNA and leaves the nucleus, carrying its genetic "message" to the ribosomes in the cytoplasm.

Once the genetic information reaches the ribosomes, **translation** occurs; that is, the language of the mRNA nucleotide sequences is translated into the language of amino acid sequences, or proteins (see Figure B.2). At the ribosomes, mRNA binds with ribosomal RNA (rRNA) and its nucleotide sequences are distributed, somewhat like orders for parts in an assembly plant, to molecules of transfer RNA (tRNA). Now the tRNA molecules roam the cytoplasm until they succeed in binding with the specific amino acid that matches their "order." They then transfer their amino acid to the ribosome, which assembles the amino acids into proteins. Once the amino acids are loaded onto the ribosome, tRNA works to manoeuvre each amino acid into its proper position. When synthesis of the new protein is completed, it is released from the ribosome and can either go through further modification in the cell or can be functional in its current state.

The proper sequencing of amino acids determines both the shape and function of a particular protein. Genetic abnormalities can occur when the DNA contains errors in proper nucleotide sequencing or when mistakes occur in the translation of this sequencing. Two examples of the consequences of these types of genetic abnormalities are sickle cell anemia and cystic fibrosis.

Although the DNA for making every protein in our bodies is contained within each cell nucleus, not all genes are expressed and each cell does not make every type of protein. For example, each cell contains the DNA to manufacture the hormone insulin. However, only the cells of the pancreas *express* the insulin gene to produce insulin. As we explored in

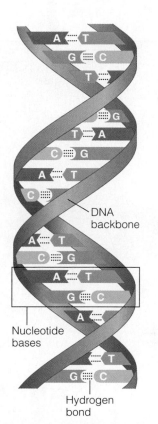

Figure B.1 The double helix of DNA. DNA is a complex compound made up of molecules called nucleotides, each of which consists of a deoxyribose sugar and phosphate backbone and a nitrogenous base. Hydrogen bonding of complementary bases holds the two strands of DNA together.

nucleotide A molecule composed of a phosphate group, a pentose sugar called deoxyribose, and one of four nitrogenous bases: adenine (A), guanine (G), cytosine (C), or thymine (T).

transcription The process through which messenger RNA copies genetic information from DNA in the nucleus.

translation The process that occurs when the genetic information carried by messenger RNA is translated into a chain of amino acids at the ribosome.

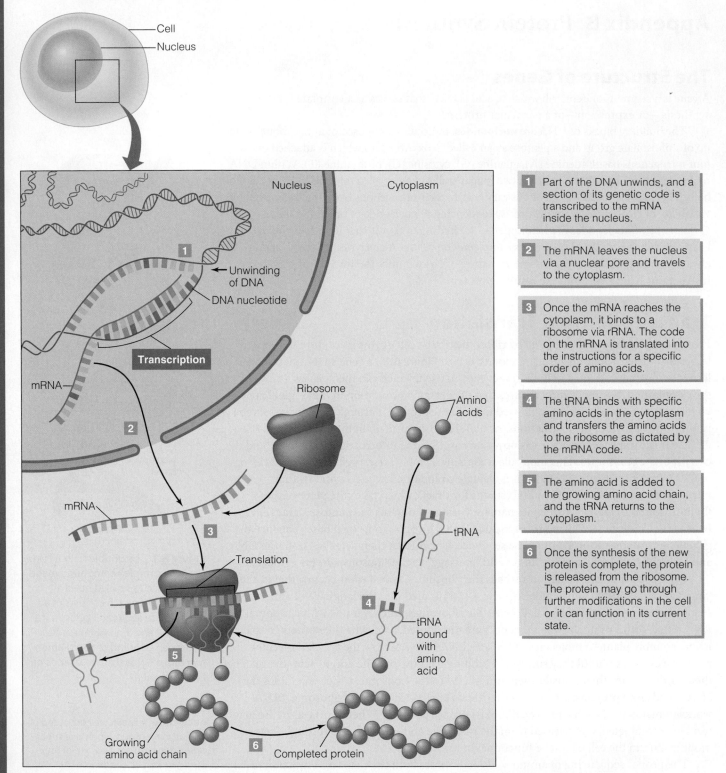

Figure B.2 Gene expression. Messenger RNA (mRNA) transcribes the genetic information from DNA in the nucleus and carries it to ribosomes in the cytoplasm. At the ribosome, this genetic information is translated into a chain of amino acids that eventually makes a protein.

the Evidence-informed Decision Making feature in Chapter 1, our physiologic needs alter gene expression, as do various nutrients. For instance, a cut in the skin that causes bleeding will prompt the production of various proteins that clot the blood. Or if we consume more dietary iron than we need, the gene for ferritin (a protein that stores iron) will be expressed so that we can store this excess iron. Our genetic makeup and how appropriately we express our genes are important factors in our health.

Appendix C Calculations and Conversions

Calculation and Conversion Aids

Commonly Used Metric Units

millimetre (mm): one-thousandth of a metre (0.001)
centimetre (cm): one-hundredth of a metre (0.01)
kilometre (km): one-thousand times a metre (1000)
kilogram (kg): one-thousand times a gram (1000)
milligram (mg): one-thousandth of a gram (0.001)
microgram (µg): one-millionth of a gram (0.000001)
millilitre (ml): one-thousandth of a litre (0.001)

International Units

Some vitamin supplements may report vitamin content as International Units (IU).

- Vitamin D (cholecalciferol): divide the IU value by 40 or multiply by 0.025.
- Vitamin E (alpha-tocopherol): divide the IU value by 1.5 if vitamin E is from natural sources or 2.22 if vitamin E is from synthetic sources.
- Vitamin A: 1 IU = 0.3 µg retinol or 1 IU beta-carotene = 0.5 IU retinol.

Retinol Activity Equivalents

Retinol Activity Equivalents (RAE) are a standardized unit of measure for vitamin A. RAE account for the various differences in bioavailability from sources of vitamin A. Many supplements will report vitamin A content in IU, as just shown, or Retinol Equivalents (RE).

1 RAE = 1 µg retinol
12 µg beta-carotene
24 µg other vitamin A carotenoids

To calculate RAE from the RE value of vitamin carotenoids in foods, divide RE by 2. For vitamin A supplements and foods fortified with vitamin A, 1 RE = 1 RAE.

Folate

Folate is measured as Dietary Folate Equivalents (DFE). DFE account for the different factors affecting bioavailability of folate sources.

1 DFE = 1 µg food folate
0.6 µg folic acid from fortified foods
0.5 µg folic acid supplement taken on an empty stomach
0.6 µg folic acid as a supplement consumed with a meal

To convert micrograms of synthetic folic acid, such as that found in supplements or fortified foods, to DFE:

$$\mu g \text{ synthetic} \times \text{folate } 1.7 = \mu g \text{ DFE}$$

For naturally occurring food folate, such as spinach, each microgram of folate equals 1 microgram DFE:

$$\mu g \text{ folate} = \mu g \text{ DFE}$$

Niacin Equivalents

The EAR and RDA for niacin are expressed in niacin equivalents (NEs), which allows for some conversion of the amino acid tryptophan to niacin.

1 NE = 1 mg of niacin or 60 mg of tryptophan

Conversion Factors

Use the following table to convert between U.S. measurements and metric equivalents:

Original Unit	Multiply by	To Get
ounces avdp	28.3495	grams
pounds	0.4536	kilograms
grams	0.0353	ounces
grams	0.002205	pounds
kilograms	2.2046	pounds
litres	0.9081	quarts (dry)
litres	1.0567	quarts (liquid)
litres	0.2642	gallons (U.S.)
quarts (dry)	1.1012	litres
quarts (liquid)	0.9463	litres
gallons (U.S.)	3.7853	litres
millimetres	0.0394	inches
centimetres	0.3937	inches
centimetres	0.03281	feet
inches	25.4000	millimetres
inches	2.5400	centimetres
inches	0.0254	metres
feet	0.3048	metres
metres	3.2808	feet
metres	1.0936	yards

Length: U.S. and Metric Equivalents

¼ inch = 0.6 centimetres
1 inch = 2.5 centimetres
1 foot = 0.3048 metre
30.48 centimetres
1 yard = 0.91144 metre
1 millimetre = 0.03937 inch
1 centimetre = 0.3937 inch
1 decimetre = 3.937 inches
1 metre = 39.37 inches
1 .094 yards
1 micrometre = 0.00003937 inch

Weights and Measures
Food Measurement Equivalencies from U.S. to Metric
Capacity

⅛ teaspoon = 1 millilitre
¼ teaspoon = 1.25 millilitres
½ teaspoon = 2.5 millilitres
1 teaspoon = 5 millilitres
1 tablespoon = 15 millilitres
1 fluid ounce = 28.4 millilitres
¼ cup = 60 millilitres
⅓ cup = 80 millilitres
½ cup = 120 millilitres
1 cup = 225 millilitres
1 quart (4 cups) = 0.95 litre
1 litre (1.06 quarts) = 1000 millilitres
1 gallon (4 quarts) = 3.84 litres

Weight

0.035 ounce = 1 gram
1 ounce = 28 grams
1 pound (16 ounces) = 454 grams
2.2 pounds (35 ounces) = 1 kilogram

Food Measurement Equivalents

3 teaspoons = 1 tablespoon
2 tablespoons = ⅛ cup
4 tablespoons = ¼ cup
8 tablespoons = ½ cup
16 tablespoons = 1 cup
4 cups = 1 quart
4 quarts = 1 gallon

Energy Units

1 kilocalorie (kcal) = 4.2 kilojoules
1 millijoule (MJ) = 240 kilocalories
1 kilojoule (kJ) = 0.24 kcal
1 gram carbohydrate = 4 kcal
1 gram fat = 9 kcal
1 gram protein = 4 kcal
1 gram alcohol = 7 kcal

Temperature Standards

	°Fahrenheit	°Celsius
Body temperature	98.6°	37°
Comfortable room temperature	65°–75°	18°–24°
Boiling point of water	212°	100°
Freezing point of water	32°	0°

Temperature Scales
To Convert Fahrenheit to Celsius:

$[(°F − 32) 5]/9$

1. Subtract 32 from °F.
2. Multiply (°F − 32) by 5, then divide by 9.

To Convert Celsius to Fahrenheit:

$[(°C × 9)/5] + 32$

1. Multiply °C by 9, then divide by 5.
2. Add 32 to (°C × 9/5).

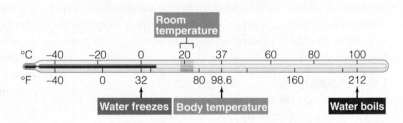

Appendix D WHO Growth Charts

The WHO Growth Charts adapted for Canada are now recommended for monitoring and assessment of growth of Canadian infants and children. Table D.1 identifies the cut-offs recommended for birth to two years of age. Table D.2 identifies the cut-offs recommended for ages 2 to 19 years. These cut-offs are to be used as a guide for further assessment, referral, or intervention but not as diagnostic criterion for classifying children. For additional information on using the new WHO growth charts see the *Collaborative Public Policy Statement on Promoting Optimal Monitoring of Child Growth in Canada: Using the New WHO Growth Charts* from Dietitians of Canada, the Canadian Paediatric Society, the College of Family Physicians of Canada, and the Community Health Nurses of Canada. Available at www.dietitians.ca/Downloadable-Content/Public/tcg-position-paper.aspx.

Table D.1 Cut-Off Points (Birth to 2 Years)

Growth Status	Indicator	Percentile
Underweight	Weight-for-age	< 3rd
Severe underweight		< 0.1st
Stunting	Length-for-age	< 3rd
Severe stunting		< 0.1st
Wasting	Weight-for-length	< 3rd
Severe wasting		< 0.1st
Risk of overweight		>85th
Overweight		>97th
Obesity		>99.9th

Data from: the World Health Organization (WHO) Child Growth Standards (2006) and WHO Reference (2007) adapted for Canada by Dietitians of Canada, Canadian Paedriatric Society, the College of Family Physicians of Canada and Community Health Nurses of Canada. © 2010.Dietitians of Canada. All rights reserved.

Table D.2 Cut-Off Points (2 to 19 Years)

Growth Status	Indicator	Percentile 2–5 years **	Percentile 5–19 years **
Underweight	Weight-for-age *	< 3rd	< 3rd *
Severe underweight		< 0.1st	< 0.1st *
Stunting	Height-for-age	< 3rd	< 3rd
Severe stunting		< 0.1st	< 0.1st
Wasting	BMI-for-age	< 3rd	< 3rd
Severe wasting		< 0.1st	< 0.1st
Risk of overweight		>85th	Not applicable
Overweight		>97th	>85th
Obesity		>99.9th	>97th
Severe obesity		Not applicable	>99.9th

*Weight-for-age not recommended after age 10 years; use BMI-for-age instead
**More conservative cut-off criteria are used for young children because of growth and the lack of data on functional significance of upper cut-offs, and to avoid the risk of putting young children on diets.
Data from: the World Health Organization (WHO) Child Growth Standards (2006) and WHO Reference (2007) adapted for Canada by Dietitians of Canada, Canadian Paediatric Society, the College of Family Physicians of Canada and Community Health Nurses of Canada. © 2010.Dietitians of Canada. All rights reserved.

WHO GROWTH CHARTS FOR CANADA

BOYS

2 TO 19 YEARS: BOYS
Body mass index-for-age percentiles

NAME: _____

DOB: _____ RECORD # _____

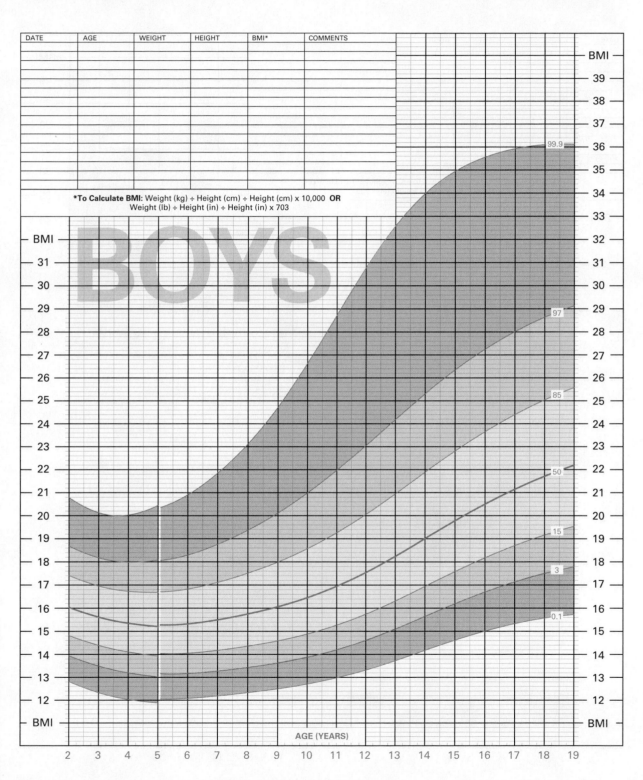

DATE	AGE	WEIGHT	HEIGHT	BMI*	COMMENTS

*To Calculate BMI: Weight (kg) ÷ Height (cm) ÷ Height (cm) x 10,000 **OR**
Weight (lb) ÷ Height (in) ÷ Height (in) x 703

AGE (YEARS)

SOURCE: Based on the World Health Organization (WHO) Child Growth Standards (2006) and WHO Reference (2007) adapted for Canada by Dietitians of Canada, Canadian Paediatric Society, the College of Family Physicians of Canada and Community Health Nurses of Canada.

WHO GROWTH CHARTS FOR CANADA

GIRLS

2 TO 19 YEARS: GIRLS
Body mass index-for-age percentiles

NAME: _____

DOB: _____ RECORD # _____

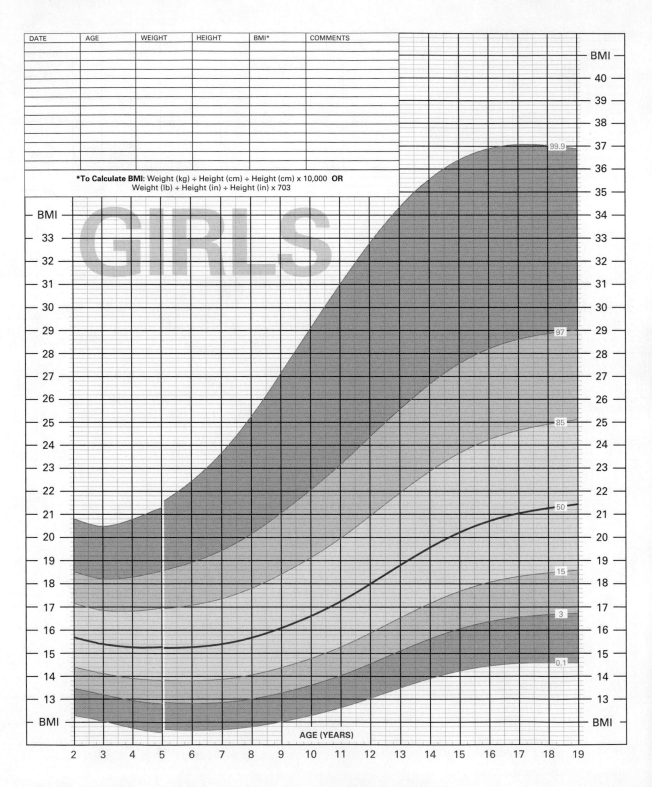

*To Calculate BMI: Weight (kg) ÷ Height (cm) ÷ Height (cm) x 10,000 **OR**
Weight (lb) ÷ Height (in) ÷ Height (in) x 703

AGE (YEARS)

WHO GROWTH CHARTS FOR CANADA

BOYS

BIRTH TO 24 MONTHS: BOYS
Head Circumference and Weight-for-length percentiles

NAME: _____

DOB: _____ RECORD # _____

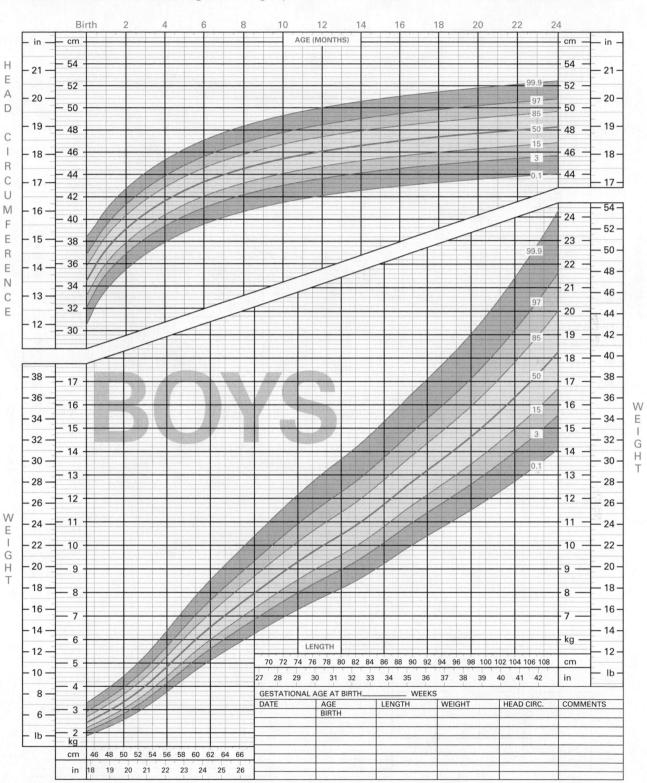

SOURCE: Based on the World Health Organization (WHO) Child Growth Standards (2006) adapted for Canada by Dietitians of Canada, Canadian Paediatric Society, the College of Family Physicians of Canada and Community Health Nurses of Canada.

WHO GROWTH CHARTS FOR CANADA

GIRLS

BIRTH TO 24 MONTHS: GIRLS
Head Circumference and Weight-for-length percentiles

NAME: _____

DOB: _____ RECORD # _____

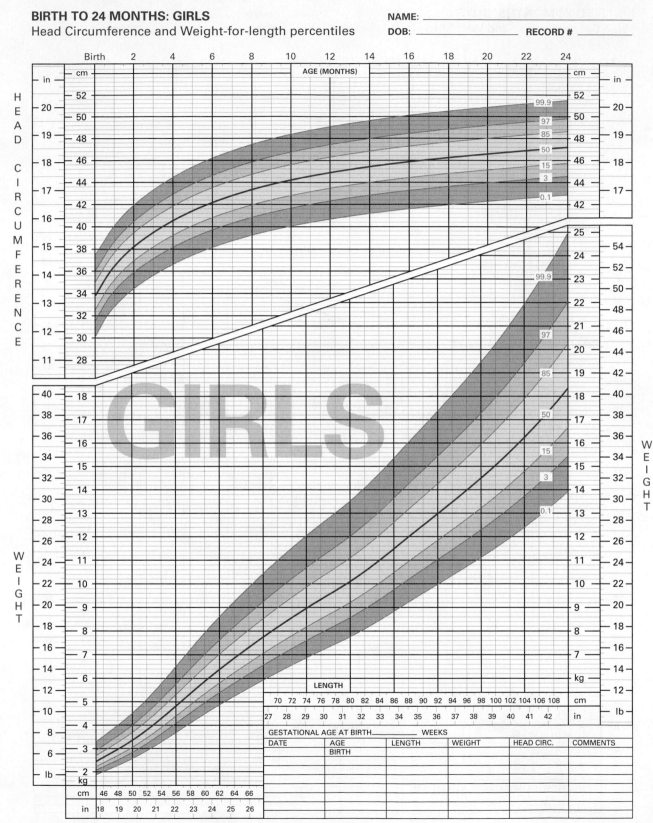

SOURCE: Based on the World Health Organization (WHO) Child Growth Standards (2006) adapted for Canada by Dietitians of Canada, Canadian Paediatric Society, the College of Family Physicians of Canada and Community Health Nurses of Canada.

WHO GROWTH CHARTS FOR CANADA

BOYS

2 TO 19 YEARS: BOYS
Height-for-age and Weight-for-age percentiles

NAME: _____

DOB: _____ RECORD # _____

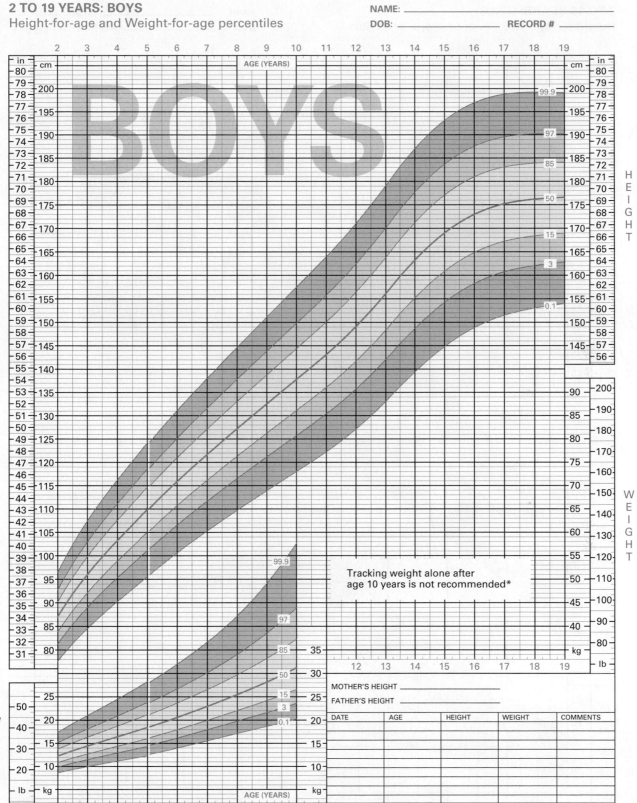

Tracking weight alone after age 10 years is not recommended*

MOTHER'S HEIGHT _____
FATHER'S HEIGHT _____

DATE	AGE	HEIGHT	WEIGHT	COMMENTS

SOURCE: Based on the World Health Organization (WHO) Child Growth Standards (2006) and WHO Reference (2007) adapted for Canada by Dietitians of Canada, Canadian Paediatric Society, the College of Family Physicians of Canada and Community Health Nurses of Canada.

© Dietitians of Canada. 2010. May be reproduced in its entirety (i.e. no changes) for educational purposes only. www.dietitians.ca/growthcharts
*BMI is a better measure due to variable age of puberty.

WHO GROWTH CHARTS FOR CANADA

GIRLS

2 TO 19 YEARS: GIRLS
Height-for-age and Weight-for-age percentiles

NAME: _____

DOB: _____ RECORD # _____

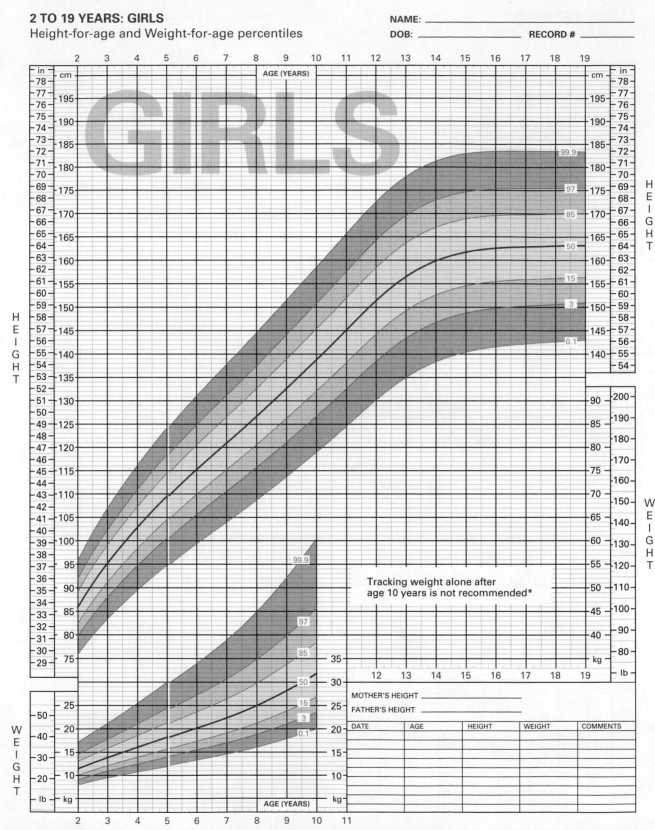

Tracking weight alone after
age 10 years is not recommended*

MOTHER'S HEIGHT _____
FATHER'S HEIGHT _____

DATE	AGE	HEIGHT	WEIGHT	COMMENTS

SOURCE: Based on the World Health Organization (WHO) Child Growth Standards (2006) and WHO Reference (2007) adapted for Canada by Dietitians of Canada, Canadian Paediatric Society, the College of Family Physicians of Canada and Community Health Nurses of Canada.

© Dietitians of Canada. 2010. May be reproduced in its entirety (i.e. no changes) for educational purposes only. **www.dietitians.ca/growthcharts**
*BMI is a better measure due to variable age of puberty.

WHO GROWTH CHARTS FOR CANADA

BOYS

BIRTH TO 24 MONTHS: BOYS
Length-for-age and Weight-for-age percentiles

NAME: _____

DOB: _____ RECORD # _____

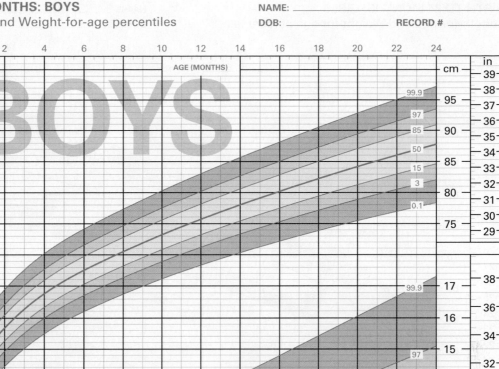

MOTHER'S HEIGHT _____

FATHER'S HEIGHT _____ GESTATIONAL AGE AT BIRTH _____ WEEKS

DATE	AGE	LENGTH	WEIGHT	COMMENTS
	BIRTH			

SOURCE: Based on the World Health Organization (WHO) Child Growth Standards (2006) and adapted for Canada by Dietitians of Canada, Canadian Paediatric Society, the College of Family Physicians of Canada and Community Health Nurses of Canada.

WHO GROWTH CHARTS FOR CANADA

GIRLS

BIRTH TO 24 MONTHS: GIRLS
Length-for-age and Weight-for-age percentiles

NAME: _____

DOB: _____ RECORD # _____

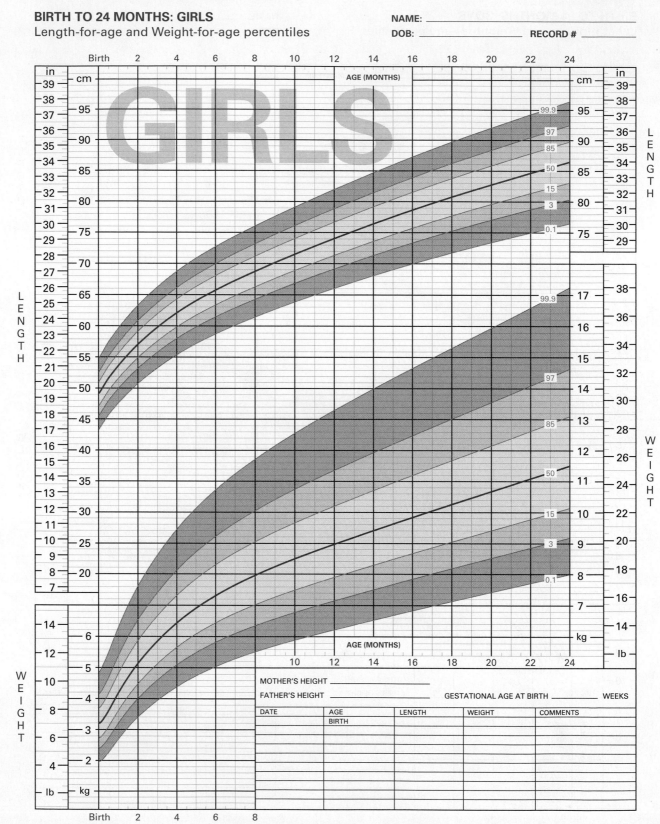

SOURCE: Based on the World Health Organization (WHO) Child Growth Standards (2006) and adapted for Canada by Dietitians of Canada, Canadian Paediatric Society, the College of Family Physicians of Canada and Community Health Nurses of Canada.

© Dietitians of Canada. 2010. May be reproduced in its entirety (i.e. no changes) for educational purposes only.
www.dietitians.ca/growthcharts

Answers to Review Questions

The answers to Review Questions appear here and also on the Companion Website, at www.pearsonhighered.com/thompsonmanore

Chapter 1

1. **d.** micronutrients.
2. **d.** all of the above.
3. **b.** contain 90 kcal of energy.
4. **c.** measurement of height.
5. **c.** "A high-protein diet increases the risk for porous bones" is an example of a valid hypothesis.
6. Organic nutrients contain carbon that is an essential component of all living organisms. Carbohydrates, lipids, proteins, and vitamins are organic. Minerals and water are inorganic because they do not contain carbon.
7. The new dietary standards (DRIs) are harmonized standards—meaning that both Canada and the United States have agreed on the definitions for recommended intake values. The new standards are aimed at preventing and reducing the risk of chronic disease and promoting optimal health.
8. A primary deficiency occurs when a person does not consume enough of a nutrient in the diet. Therefore, a nutrient deficiency occurs as a direct consequence of an inadequate intake. A secondary deficiency occurs when a person cannot absorb enough of a nutrient in his or her body, when too much of a nutrient is excreted from the body, or when a nutrient is not utilized efficiently by the body. Thus, a secondary deficiency is secondary to some other disorder.
9. In a well-designed experiment, a control group allows a researcher to compare between treated and untreated individuals, and therefore to determine whether or not a particular treatment has exerted a significant effect.
10. The Estimated Average Requirement, or EAR, represents the average daily nutrient intake level estimated to meet the requirement of half of the healthy individuals in a particular life stage or gender group. The Recommended Dietary Allowance, or RDA, represents the average daily nutrient intake level that meets the nutrient requirements of 97% to 98% of healthy individuals in a particular life stage or gender group. The EAR is used to estimate the RDA.
11. I would explain to Marilyn that the term "nutritionist" does not guarantee that this particular person who suggested the supplements is qualified to give nutritional guidance. I would recommend that she is be better off talking with a qualified healthcare professional about her fatigue. To find reliable nutrition information, I would suggest she talk with a registered dietitian. She can find registered dietitians in her local area by contacting Dietitians of Canada. She can also access free, reliable information from the websites of organizations such as Health Canada and the Public Health Agency of Canada.
12. The source of funding can be a good indicator of the level of bias in a research study. For instance, if this particular study was funded by chocolate manufacturers and conducted by their own scientists, the results could be potentially biased in that the chocolate manufacturer could make a substantial profit by discovering positive findings related to chocolate. Having an independent research team conduct the study can reduce this type of bias.
13. There are numerous aspects of this study that limit its relevance to your mother. Some of these are:
    a. Limited number of participants. Only 12 women participated in this study. This very small number of participants significantly limits the ability to generalize the results to a larger population.
    b. Age. The women in the study were all older than your mother.
    c. Blood pressure. Your mother has blood pressure at the upper end of the normal range, and all of the participants in this study had high blood pressure.
    d. Activity level. Your mother is physically active. She walks daily and swims once a week. The participants in this study were sedentary or inactive.
    e. Smoking. Your mother is a non-smoker, and only half of the participants in this study were non-smokers, with the other half being relatively heavy smokers.

Chapter 2

1. **d.** The % Daily Values of selected nutrients in a serving of the packaged food.
2. **b.** provides enough of the energy, nutrients, and fibre to maintain a person's health.
3. **a.** at least half your grains as whole grains each day.
4. **b.** Foods with a lot of nutrients per kilocalorie such as fish are more nutritious choices than foods with fewer nutrients per calorie such as candy.
5. **a.** nuts.

6. John's requirement is 8–10 servings/day. He is consuming five servings a day: banana/orange (1); ½ cup apple sauce (1); 2 cups orange juice (2); apple or ½ cup grapes (1). Yes, he should listen to his girlfriend because he isn't eating any vegetables and especially no dark green or orange vegetables.

7. The %DV can be used to compare products, to find whether a product has a little or a lot of a specified nutrient. The %DV does *not* tell you anything about an individual's requirements or about how much additional food an individual needs in a day.

8. As humans, we are all different in terms of body size, physical activity level, religious and ethnic beliefs, and disease risk factors. No single diet can meet the needs of every single human being, as our needs are very different. It is necessary to vary a diet based on individual needs.

9. Answers will vary. Be sure labels contain all four of the primary components of information identified in Figure 2.2.

10. *Eating Well with Canada's Food Guide* suggests a range in the number of daily servings of each food group because energy needs are dependent upon physical activity level and body size, and therefore are different for everyone. The lower end of the range applies to inactive women and small individuals, while the higher end of the range applies to more active people and larger men. In fact, highly active people may need to eat even more servings than those recommended at the higher end of the range. People should not eat fewer than the lowest recommended number of servings as this could lead to nutritional deficiencies.

11. At least 4 grams per serving.

12. It is not accurate. The Mediterranean diet is actually relatively high in fat, not low in fat. However, this diet recommends consuming foods that contain more healthy mono- and polyunsaturated fats. Bread and pasta are a daily part of the Mediterranean diet, but this diet does not recommend unlimited consumption of these foods. If Sylvia eats more energy than she expends, even while consuming the Mediterranean diet, she will not be able to lose weight.

Chapter 3

1. **b.** peristalsis.
2. **d.** emulsifies lipids.
3. **c.** hypothalamus.
4. **a.** gastric acid into the esophagus.
5. **a.** a bean and cheese burrito.
6. Pierre would feel full longer since he has incorporated some protein into his breakfast. Protein is the most satiating macronutrient. Pierre also has some insoluble fibre, which helps a person feel full longer, and some fat in the peanut butter that slows gastric emptying. Katia on the other hand has no protein or fibre source in her breakfast, but she does have fat in the donut that will delay gastric emptying.

7. The surgery will affect both mechanical and chemical digestion. The reduction in the size of the stomach means that only small amounts of food can be eaten at any meal or snack; therefore, the food must be nutrient-dense. The shortening of the intestines will reduce the amount of contact with digestive enzymes and the amount of absorption that can occur, further reducing the nutrients available to meet the individual's needs.

8. Our bodies are composed of cells, which are the smallest unit of matter that exhibits the properties of living things. That is, cells can grow, reproduce themselves, and perform certain basic functions, such as taking in nutrients, transmitting impulses, producing chemicals, and excreting wastes. The human body is composed of billions of cells that are constantly replacing themselves, destroying worn or damaged cells, and manufacturing new ones. To support this constant demand for new cells, we need a ready supply of nutrient molecules, such as simple sugars, amino acids, and fatty acids, to serve as building blocks. These building blocks are the molecules that come from the breakdown of foods. All cells, whether of the skin, bones, or brain, are made of the same basic molecules of amino acids, sugars, and fatty acids that are also the main components of the foods we eat. Thus, we are what we eat in that the building blocks of our cells are composed of the molecules contained in the foods we eat.

9. **No.** The main function of the small intestine is to absorb nutrients and transport them into the bloodstream or the lymph system. To do this effectively, the surface area of the small intestine needs to be as large as possible. The inside of the lining of the small intestine, referred to as the mucosal membrane, is heavily folded. This feature increases the surface area of the small intestine and allows it to absorb more nutrients than if it were smooth. The villi are in constant movement, which helps them to encounter and trap nutrient molecules. Covering the villi are specialized cells covered with hair-like structures called microvilli (also called the brush border). These intricate folds increase the surface area of the small intestine by more than 500 times, which tremendously increases the absorptive capacity of the small intestine.

10. The stomach does not digest itself because it secretes mucus that protects the lining from being digested by the hydrochloric acid it secretes.

11.

Digestive Disorder	Area of Inflammation	Symptoms	Treatment Options
Celiac Disease	Small intestine	• Fatty stools • Diarrhea or constipation • Cramping • Anemia • Pallor • Weight loss • Fatigue • Irritability	• Modified diet that excludes foods that contain gluten or gliadin (for example, wheat, rye, and barley)
Crohn's Disease	Usually ileum of small intestine but can affect any area of gastrointestinal tract	• Diarrhea • Abdominal pain • Rectal bleeding • Weight loss • Fever • Anemia • Delayed physical and mental development in children	• Combination of prescription drugs, nutritional supplements, and surgery
Ulcerative Colitis	Mucosa of large intestine (or colon)	• Diarrhea (which may be bloody) • Abdominal pain • Weight loss • Anemia • Nausea • Fever • Severe urgency to have bowel movement	• Anti-inflammatory medications • Surgery if medications are not effective

12. It is possible that your roommate could be suffering from heartburn or gastroesophageal reflux disease (GERD). Eating food causes the stomach to secrete hydrochloric acid to start the digestive process. In many people, the amount of HCl secreted is occasionally excessive or the gastroesophageal sphincter opens too soon. In either case, the result is that HCl seeps back up into the esophagus. Although the stomach is protected from HCl by a thick coat of mucus, the esophagus does not have this mucous coating. Thus, the HCl burns it. When this happens, a person experiences a painful sensation in the region of his or her chest above the sternum (breastbone). This condition is commonly called heartburn.

If your roommate experiences this painful type of heartburn more than twice per week, he may be suffering from GERD. Similar to heartburn, GERD occurs when HCl flows back into the esophagus. Although people who experience occasional heartburn usually have no structural abnormalities, many people with GERD have an overly relaxed or damaged esophageal sphincter or a damaged esophagus itself. Symptoms of GERD include persistent heartburn and acid regurgitation. Some people have GERD without heartburn and instead experience chest pain, trouble swallowing, burning in the mouth, the feeling that food is stuck in the throat, or hoarseness in the morning.

Chapter 4

1. **b.** the potential of foods to raise blood glucose and insulin levels.
2. **d.** carbon, hydrogen, and oxygen.
3. **d.** sweetened soft drinks.
4. **a.** monosaccharides.
5. **a.** phenylketonuria.
6. Soluble fibres dissolve in water. They are viscous, forming a gel when wet. They are also fermentable, meaning that they are easily digested by bacteria in the colon. Soluble fibres are typically found in citrus fruits, berries, oat products, and beans. Soluble fibre intake is associated with reducing blood cholesterol levels and thus reducing cardiovascular disease risk. It is also thought to help slow down the absorption of glucose and thus improve the body's regulation of insulin production and blood glucose levels.

   Insoluble fibres, on the other hand, do not typically dissolve in water. They are non-viscous and cannot be fermented by bacteria in the colon. They are generally found in whole grains such as wheat, rye, and brown rice and many vegetables. These fibres are known for promoting regular bowel movements, alleviating constipation, and reducing the risk of diverticulosis.

7. The glycemic index refers to the potential of foods to raise blood glucose levels. Foods with a high glycemic index cause a sudden surge in blood glucose, which triggers a large increase in insulin. This may be followed by a dramatic drop in blood glucose.

   Some nutrition experts believe that the glycemic load is more useful than the glycemic index. The glycemic load is the amount of carbohydrate in a food multiplied by the glycemic index of the carbohydrate.

8. Insulin is a hormone secreted by the beta cells of the pancreas in response to increased blood levels of glucose. When we eat a meal, our blood glucose level rises. But glucose in our blood cannot help the nerves, muscles, and other tissues function unless it can cross into them. Glucose molecules are too large to cross the cell membranes of our tissues independently. To get in, glucose needs assistance from insulin. Insulin is transported in the blood to the cells of tissues throughout the body, where it stimulates special molecules located in the cell membrane to transport glucose into the cell. Insulin can be thought of as a key that opens the gates of the cell membrane and carries the glucose into the cell interior, where it can be used for energy. Insulin also stimulates the liver and muscles to take up glucose.

9. **a.** Fibre adds bulk to the stools, which aids in efficient excretion of feces.
   b. Fibre keeps stools moist and soft, helping to prevent hemorrhoids and constipation.

c. Fibre gives the gut muscles something to push on, making it easier to eliminate stools. Diverticulosis can result in part from trying to eliminate small, hard stools.

d. Fibre may bind with cancer-causing agents and speed their elimination from the colon, which could in turn reduce the risk for colon cancer.

10. Grain-based foods contain carbohydrates, and sometimes these foods are processed, meaning that many of the important nutrients we need for health are taken out of them. Fibre-rich carbohydrates contain not only more fibre, which is important for the health of our digestive tract, but they also contain many vitamins and minerals that we need to be healthy. The foods Lilly listed are examples of foods in the "grains" group that are processed. Examples of healthier fibre-rich alternative choices include whole-wheat saltine crackers, whole-wheat or pumpernickel bagels, brown rice, and whole-wheat spaghetti.

11. Kenton explains to his wife that his doctor told him that diabetes more commonly runs in families, but just because no one in the family has diabetes does not mean that someone cannot get it. Being overweight increases a person's risk for this type of diabetes even if no one else in the family has it. Since Kenton is overweight, he is more at risk for type 2 diabetes than he would be if he was not overweight. Overweight and obesity trigger insulin insensitivity, or insulin resistance, which in turn causes the pancreas to produce greater amounts of insulin so that glucose can enter the cells and be used for energy. Eventually, type 2 diabetes develops because either (1) there is an increasing degree of insulin insensitivity; (2) the pancreas can no longer secrete enough insulin; or (3) the pancreas has entirely stopped producing insulin.

12.

Carbohydrate	Molecular Composition	Food Sources
Glucose	Six carbon atoms, twelve hydrogen atoms, six oxygen atoms	Fruits, vegetables, grains, dairy products; does not generally occur alone in foods, but attaches to other sugars to form disaccharides and complex carbohydrates
Fructose	Six carbon atoms, twelve hydrogen atoms, six oxygen atoms	Fruits and some vegetables
Lactose	One glucose molecule and one galactose molecule	Milk and other dairy products
Sucrose	One glucose molecule and one fructose molecule	Honey, maple syrup, fruits, vegetables, table sugar, brown sugar, powdered sugar

Chapter 5

1. d. found in flaxseeds, walnuts, and fish.
2. b. exercise regularly.
3. a. lipoprotein lipase.
4. d. high-density lipoproteins.
5. a. monounsaturated.
6. Fatty acid chain length is important because it determines the method of lipid digestion and absorption and affects how lipids are metabolized and used within the body. For example, short- and medium-chain fatty acids are digested, transported, and metabolized more quickly than long-chain fatty acids.
7. Bile is produced in the liver and stored in the gallbladder. The gallbladder secretes bile, which mixes with dietary lipids to emulsify them. At the same time that bile is mixing with the lipids, lipid-digesting enzymes produced in the pancreas travel through the pancreatic duct into the small intestine. Each lipid product requires a specific digestive enzyme for digestion.
8. The straight, rigid shape of both *trans* and saturated fatty acids appears to raise blood cholesterol levels and to change cell membrane function and the way cholesterol is removed from the blood. For these reasons, many health professionals feel that diets high in *trans* and saturated fatty acids can increase the risk of cardiovascular disease. Because of the concerns related to *trans* fatty acid consumption and heart disease, manufacturers are required to list the amount of *trans* fatty acids per serving on the food label.
9. Dietary fat enables the transport of the fat-soluble vitamins, specifically vitamins D and K. Vitamin D is important for regulating blood calcium and phosphorous concentrations within the normal range, which indirectly helps maintain bone health. If vitamin D is low, blood calcium levels will drop below normal, and the body will draw calcium from the bones to maintain blood levels. Vitamin K is also important for proteins involved in maintaining bone health.
10. This is not particularly good advice for someone doing a 32 km walk-a-thon. Fat is a primary source of energy during rest and during less-intense exercise. In addition, we use predominantly more fat as we perform longer-duration exercise. This is because we use more carbohydrate earlier during the exercise bout, and once our limited carbohydrate sources are depleted during prolonged exercise, we rely more on fat as an energy source. Although carbohydrates are an important source of energy during exercise, loading up on carbohydrates is typically only helpful for individuals who are doing longer-duration exercise at intensities higher than those experienced during walking. As the primary goal of this walk-a-thon is to raise money and not to finish in record time, you can walk at a pace that matches your current fitness level. Thus, it would be prudent to consume

adequate carbohydrate prior to and during the walk-a-thon, but loading up on carbohydrates is not necessary.

11. Caleb's father probably had a blood test to determine his blood lipid levels, including total cholesterol, LDLs, HDLs, and triglycerides. Unfortunately, switching to cottage cheese and margarine will not improve his blood lipid values. Margarines may be high in *trans* fatty acids, and these increase blood lipids and increase our risk for heart disease. In addition, cottage cheese contains saturated fatty acids which also increase blood lipid levels. Both *trans* and saturated fatty acids will increase Caleb's father's risk for heart disease. A non-dietary lifestyle choice that might improve his health is regular physical activity. Regular physical activity can help people maintain a more healthy body weight, can increase HDLs, and can also cause other changes that reduce our risk for heart disease.

12.

Type of Fat	Maximum recommended intake (% of total energy intake)	Maximum recommended calorie intake
Saturated fat	7%	140 calories
Linoleic acid	10%	200 calories
Alpha-linolenic acid	1.2%	24 calories
Trans fatty acids	0%	0 calories
Unsaturated fat	None; amount equal to remainder of total fat calories after you account for intake of saturated fat and linoleic and alpha-linolenic acids	336 calories

Calculations used:
- Total energy needs = 2000 calories per day
- Maximum AMDR for fat = 35% of total energy intake = $0.35 \times 2000 = 700$ calories
- Saturated fat = 7% of total energy intake = $0.07 \times 2000 = 140$ calories
- Linoleic acid = 10% of total energy intake = $0.10 \times 2000 = 200$ calories
- Alpha-linolenic acid = 1.2% of total energy intake = $0.012 \times 2000 = 24$ calories
- *Trans* fatty acids = 0 calories

Chapter 6

1. **d.** mutual supplementation.
2. **a.** rice, pinto beans, acorn squash, soy butter, and almond milk.
3. **c.** protease.
4. **b.** amine group.
5. **c.** carbon, oxygen, hydrogen, and nitrogen.

6. There are several methods of determining protein quality: biological value (BV), protein efficiency ratio (PER), amino acid or chemical score, and the protein digestibility corrected amino acid score (PDCAAS).
   - The BV of a protein refers to the proportion of absorbed protein from foods that are incorporated into body proteins. Egg protein has a BV of 100, which indicates that 100% of the nitrogen absorbed is retained and used by the body.
   - The PER measures the amount of weight gained by a growing animal and compares it to that animal's protein intake. It is expressed as:

     PER = weight gain (g)/protein intake (g)
   - The amino acid or chemical score is a comparison of the amount of the limiting amino acid in a food with the amount of that same amino acid in a reference food (usually egg protein). The amino acid that is found to have the lowest proportion in the test food as compared with the reference food is defined as the limiting amino acid. Thus, the amino acid or chemical score of a protein gives an indication of the lowest amino acid ratio calculated for any amino acid in a particular food.
   - The PDCAAS is the most preferred method and has been adopted by the WHO and the FDA to determine protein quality. This technique measures the quality of a protein based on the amino acid requirements (adjusted for digestibility) of a 2- to 5-year-old child (considered the most nutritionally demanding age group).

7. Unlike carbohydrates and lipids, proteins are made according to instructions provided by our genetic material, or DNA. Proteins also contain a special form of nitrogen that the body can readily use. Carbohydrates and lipids do not provide nitrogen. In addition, two amino acids (the building blocks of protein) contain sulphur.

8. Adequate protein is needed to maintain the proper balance of fluids inside and outside of the cells. When a child suffers from kwashiorkor, the protein content of the blood is inadequate to maintain this balance. Fluid seeps from inside of the cells out to the tissue spaces and causes bloating and swelling of the abdomen.

9. In general, only people who are susceptible to kidney disease or who have kidney disease suffer serious consequences when eating a high-protein diet. Consuming a high-protein diet increases protein metabolism and urea production. Individuals with kidney disease or those who are at risk for kidney disease cannot adequately flush urea and other by-products of protein metabolism from the body through the kidneys. This inability can lead to serious health consequences and even death.

10. There are various classifications of vegetarianism. Many people feel that if a person eats any meat or products from animals (such as dairy or eggs), then they cannot be a vegetarian. People who eat only plant-based foods are classified as vegans. If you believe this, then you would argue that your Dad is not a true vegetarian. However, there are others who believe a vegetarian is someone who can eat dairy foods, eggs, or both in addition to plant-based foods. There are also people who classify themselves as pescovegetarians, meaning they eat fish along with plant-based foods. Semi-vegetarians may eat lean meats such as poultry on occasion in addition to plant-based foods, eggs, and dairy products. If you believe in these broader definitions of vegetarianism, then you would agree with your Dad's opinion that he is now a vegetarian.

11. Use Figure 6.4 as a guide. Amino acids should be joined at the acid group of one amino acid and the amino group of the next amino acid. Multiple amino acids joined in this way make a protein.

Chapter 7

1. **a.** lactic acid.
2. **b.** power plant.
3. **a.** hydrolysis.
4. **d.** None of the above statements is true.
5. **d.** catabolic hormones.
6. Liver glycogen is our primary source of stored carbohydrate. Once liver glycogen has been depleted, the body must make glucose to supply the brain and central nervous system with energy. Glucose via gluconeogenesis can be synthesized from glucogenic amino acids, glycerol from stored triglycerides, and lactic acid that has been produced through muscle glucose metabolism.
7. Acetyl CoA is considered a metabolic crossroads, which means the metabolism of protein, fat, carbohydrate, and alcohol can produce acetyl CoA. Acetyl CoA, in turn, can be used to form triglycerides to be stored in adipose tissue, ketones as an alternative fuel for the brain and central nervous system, and can enter the TCA cycle to produce ATP.
8. The final stage of glucose oxidation is called oxidative phosphorylation and occurs in the electron transport chain of the mitochondria. In this step, a series of enzyme-driven reactions occur in which electrons are passed down a "chain." As the electrons are passed from one carrier to the next, energy is released. In this process, NADH and FADH$_2$ are oxidized and their electrons are donated to O$_2$, which is reduced to H$_2$O (water). The energy released when water is formed generates ATP.
9. Fatty acids released from the adipose tissue or fatty acids that come from the foods we eat are transported on albumin in the blood. They are then transported to the cells that need energy, such as the muscle cells. The fatty acids move across the cell membrane into the cytosol, where they are activated by the addition of CoA and then transported to the mitochondria, where fatty acid oxidation occurs. Once in the mitochondria, the fatty acid is systematically broken down into two-carbon units that lead to the formation of acetyl CoA, which can enter the TCA cycle for energy production.

10. Without insulin, the body cannot utilize the glucose derived from food. Since glucose cannot enter the cells, the body begins the process of breaking down body fats to fatty acids, which can be used to produce ketones and alternative fuel for the brain when glucose is not available. These ketones are acidic and can build up in the blood, leading to ketoacidosis. Under these conditions more ketones are produced than can be utilized or eliminated from the body, so they build up in the blood.

11. When children with PKU go off their diet they increase the levels of the amino acid phenylalanine in the body. They cannot metabolize phenylalanine correctly because of a genetic enzyme disorder that can result in the toxic build up of phenylalanine in the body, which causes organ tissue damage.

12. We can assume that Aunt Winifred has been eating so little food that her need for carbohydrate (to maintain blood glucose) has not been met. Since the brain, red blood cells, and other types of cells, are all dependent on glucose for fuel, her body has no doubt been breaking down muscle protein to use some of the amino acids—known as glucogenic amino acids—to synthesize new glucose (gluconeogenesis). So, not only has Aunt Winifred been losing body fat, she has been also losing muscle mass, our main pool of body protein.

Chapter 8

1. **d.** vitamin A.
2. **b.** hypertension.
3. **a.** biotin.
4. **a.** lutein.
5. **c.** reduce the risk of allergies in infants.
6. The absorption of vitamins and minerals depends on their chemical form, the presence of other components in the same food, and the composition of the meal.
7. Canadian regulations are more restrictive than U.S. regulations; however, this is an advantage for Canadian consumers. The Canadian regulations for natural health products require that all health claims be truthful and not misleading or deceptive. Further, disease risk reduction or therapeutic claims are only allowed once a regulatory amendment specifying the conditions for their use has been completed.
8. Most well-controlled studies in cells, animals, or people typically research only one phytochemical or food. However, we know that phytochemicals can interact

with macronutrients, micronutrients, and one another. Consequently, no RDA or AI for phytochemicals has been established for any life-stage group.

9. Even though we know a lot about the various vitamins and minerals needed for health, there is still much more to discover. Several compounds are being explored as potential required nutrients, for example, boron and nickel. Further, a varied diet contains many phytochemical compounds that may be protective against a wide variety of chronic diseases. A limited diet such as the one Amy has chosen would be missing these components.

10. Probiotics in yogourt promote healthy colonic bacteria. Some research has been published that supports the observation of increased transit time with regular consumption of 125 mL of probiotic yogourt per day. Further research is needed to better understand this effect. Typically, probiotic yogourts are not more costly than regular yogourt, so you may as well eat them.

Chapter 9

1. **d.** thiamine, pantothenic acid, and biotin.
2. **d.** Choline is necessary for the synthesis of phospholipids and other components of cell membranes.
3. **a.** iodine deficiency.
4. **b.** tuna sandwich on whole-wheat bread, green peas, banana, 1 cup of low-fat milk.
5. **d.** It is water soluble.
6. High alcohol intake contributes to thiamine deficiency in three ways: it is generally accompanied by low thiamine intake; at the same time it increases the need for thiamine to metabolize the alcohol; and it reduces thiamine absorption.
7. Biotin deficiency can occur in people who consume a large number of raw egg whites over a long period of time. This is because raw egg whites contain a protein called avidin that binds with biotin and prevents its absorption.
8. People from inland regions are more prone to goiter because they consume fewer seafoods, which are high in iodine.
9. Vitamin B_6 is important in the transamination of essential amino acids to non-essential amino acids.
10. Vitamins and minerals added to foods can help improve our nutritional status for these micronutrients. Not everyone is able to eat enough variety or the quantity of the foods they need to get all the micronutrients they need, for example vitamin D; thus, fortification and enrichment help these individuals maintain their nutritional status.
11. Dialysis can remove water-soluble vitamins from the blood, which need to be replaced with either foods high in these nutrients or supplements.
12. Sally might be suffering from iron-deficiency anemia due to the elimination of all heme iron from her diet. Other micronutrients most likely to be low in Sally's diet

are zinc, calcium, and vitamin B_{12}. These are all micronutrients that are found in animal products such as dairy and meat. Low vitamin B_{12} may also be contributing to Sally's fatigue.

Chapter 10

1. **b.** It can be found in fresh fruits and vegetables.
2. **d.** a healthy infant of average weight.
3. **a.** extracellular fluid.
4. **b.** It is freely permeable only to water.
5. **b.** normalizing body weight.
6. People with kidney disease may have trouble excreting excess potassium and difficulty regulating their blood potassium levels. As a result, hyperkalemia or high blood potassium levels can occur. Because of potassium's role in cardiac muscle contraction, severe hyperkalemia can alter the normal rhythm of the heart, resulting in heart attack and death. Thus, people with kidney disease should monitor their potassium intake very carefully and should avoid consuming salt substitutes, as these products are high in potassium.
7. *Eating Well with Canada's Food Guide* and the DASH diet plan both recommend eating foods low in fat and high in fibre. Both plans recommend eating whole-grain foods and low-fat or non-fat milk and alternatives. The DASH diet also emphasizes foods that are rich in potassium, calcium, and magnesium and recommends 10 servings of vegetables and fruit each day. This is the upper end of the recommended number of servings from *Eating Well with Canada's Food Guide* for an adult male (8 to 10 servings daily) but higher than that recommended for adult females (7 to 8 servings daily). The sodium content of the DASH diet is about 3000 mg. *Eating Well with Canada's Food Guide* does not have a recommended sodium intake. It simply recommends limiting foods and beverages high in salt.
8. Chronic diarrhea in a young child can lead to severe dehydration very quickly because of his or her small body size. Diarrhea causes excessive fluid loss from the intestinal tract and extracellular fluid compartment. This fluid loss causes a rise in extracellular electrolyte concentration, and intracellular fluid leaves the cells in an attempt to balance the extracellular fluid loss. These alterations in fluid and electrolyte balance change the flow of electrical impulses through the heart and can lead to abnormal heart rhythms and eventual death if left untreated.
9. One possible cause of these symptoms is dehydration. You most likely lost a significant amount of fluid during the cross-country relay race. In addition, you consumed a few beers after the race. Beer is a diuretic, which causes you to lose even more fluid. The "pins and needles" feeling in your extremities is consistent with a fluid loss of about 3% to 5% of body weight. To maintain your health

and support optimal performance, it is critical that you make every effort to consume enough fluid (preferably water, a sport beverage, or some other beverage that is not a diuretic) to regain any body water you have lost because of your athletic efforts.

10. Although there are many things to consider when consuming foods prior to exercise, one important factor is consuming an optimal balance of fluid and electrolytes. In this case, lunch (b) would be the better choice. Lunch (a) is very high in sodium. While our bodies need adequate sodium to function properly, lunch (a) is filled with very high-sodium foods, such as chicken soup, ham, and tomato juice. It is likely that consuming lunch (a) will lead to excessive thirst due to a rise in blood sodium levels. This excessive thirst could cause distraction or even lead to consuming so much fluid that you feel nauseated during practice. Lunch (b) has a more desirable balance of sodium and fluid, should not cause excessive thirst, and should provide ample energy for hockey practice.

11. Many over-the-counter weight-loss pills are diuretics, which means that they cause fluid loss from the body. Your cousin should avoid diuretics as she needs to maintain her fluid levels at a higher-than-normal level on account of breastfeeding. If she becomes dehydrated, she cannot produce adequate milk for her infant. In addition, it is possible that the substances in the weight-loss pills could be passed along to her infant in her breast milk, which could cause serious health consequences for the infant.

12. Your grandmother's muscle cramps may be prompted by an electrolyte imbalance brought on by dehydration.

Chapter 11

1. **d.** It is destroyed by exposure to high heat.
2. **b.** an atom loses an electron.
3. **a.** cardiovascular disease.
4. **d.** nitrates.
5. **a.** vitamin A.
6. The UL for vitamin C for a 19–70-year-old woman is 2000 mg (or 2 g) per day. With a 4000 mg dose, Allysa is king twice the UL for this nutrient. Even though vitamin C is water soluble, and therefore not stored in the body in high concentrations, she should be cautious of this practice. High dose supplements of vitamin C for a prolonged period are known to cause nausea, diarrhea, nosebleeds, and abdominal cramps. Vitamin C at this dose can also act as a prooxidant. Further, research does not support a role for vitamin C in preventing the common cold.
7. Beta-carotene is an antioxidant and because of this role is often recommended for its cancer-preventing properties. Numerous research studies have shown a positive correlation between foods containing beta-carotene and a decreased risk of some types of cancer. However, when

beta-carotene supplements are taken their protective properties are not as clear. In the ATBC and CARET studies, beta-carotene was shown to increase the number of deaths in smokers taking the supplement; these studies showed that beta-carotene increased the risk of prostate and stomach cancer.

8. Free radicals steal electrons from the stable lipid molecules in our cell membranes. This stealing can destroy the integrity of the membrane and lead to membrane dysfunction and potential cell death.
9. Cancer development has three primary steps: initiation, promotion, and progression. During the initiation step, the DNA of normal cells is mutated, causing permanent changes in the cell. During the promotion step, the genetically altered cells repeatedly divide, locking the mutated DNA into each new cell's genetic instructions. During the progression step, the cancerous cells grow out of control and invade surrounding tissues. These cells then metastasize, or spread, to other sites of the body.
10. Vitamin E may help reduce our risk for heart disease in a number of ways. Vitamin E protects LDLs from oxidation, thus helping to reduce the buildup of plaque in our blood vessel walls. Vitamin E may also help reduce low-grade inflammation. Vitamin E is known to reduce blood coagulation and the formation of blood clots, which will reduce the risk of a blood clot blocking a blood vessel and causing a stroke or heart attack.
11. Trace minerals such as selenium, copper, iron, zinc, and manganese are part of the antioxidant enzyme systems that convert free radicals to less damaging substances that are excreted by our bodies. Selenium is part of the glutathione peroxidase enzyme system. Copper, zinc, and manganese are part of the superoxide dismutase enzyme complex, and iron is a part of the structure of catalase.
12. Yes, you should be concerned. Vitamin E acts as an anticoagulant, and combined with the prescription anticoagulant Coumadin, the effects are magnified, which could cause uncontrollable bleeding. This could lead to both internal bleeding and prevent the cessation of bleeding caused by a cut or other external injury. In some people, long-term use of standard vitamin E supplements may cause hemorrhaging in the brain, leading to a type of stroke called hemorrhagic stroke. It would be prudent to tell your mother about your concerns, and suggest that she stop taking the supplement until she has discussed with her healthcare provider the potential interactions with her medication and this supplement.

Chapter 12

1. **a.** calcium and phosphorous.
2. **c.** has normal bone density as compared with an average, healthy 30-year-old.

3. **d.** It provides the scaffolding for cortical bone.
4. **d.** structure of bone, nerve transmission, and muscle contraction.
5. Bone remodelling is a two-step process that includes the breakdown of existing bone by osteoclasts and the formation of new bone by osteoblasts. Osteoclasts erode the bone surface by secreting enzymes and acids that dig grooves in the bone matrix. Osteoblasts work to synthesize new bone matrix by laying down the collagen-containing organic component of bone.
6. The bioavailability of calcium depends on a person's age, his or her need for calcium, how much calcium is consumed throughout the day or at any one time, binding factors such as phytates and oxalates, and consuming calcium at the same time as iron, zinc, magnesium, or phosphorous.
7. Active transport of calcium across the cells of the small intestine is dependent on the active form of vitamin D. Thus, consuming too much vitamin D can lead to an excessive amount being absorbed in the small intestine, leading to high blood levels of calcium.
8. Researchers have proposed three theories to explain this: soft drinks may be displacing calcium-rich beverages, such as milk, in the diet; the acidic properties and high phosphorous content of soft drinks may cause an increased loss of calcium because calcium is drawn from bone into the blood to neutralize the excess acid; and the caffeine found in many soft drinks causes increased calcium loss through the urine. A recent study suggests that it is probably the first theory that explains the association between soft drink consumption and poor bone health.
9. Because vitamins D and K are fat-soluble vitamins, they are absorbed with the fat we consume in our diets. If a person has a disease that does not allow for proper absorption of dietary fat, there will also be a malabsorption of the fat-soluble vitamins, which include vitamins D and K.
10. The two processes behind this phenomenon are bone resorption and bone formation. The combination of these processes is referred to as bone remodelling. To preserve bone density, our bodies attempt to achieve a balance between the breakdown of older bone tissue and the formation of new bone tissue.

    One of the primary reasons that bone is broken down is to release calcium into the bloodstream. We also want to break down bone when we fracture a bone and need to repair it. During resorption, osteoclasts erode the bone surface by secreting enzymes and acids that dig grooves into the bone matrix. Their ruffled surface also acts much like a scrubbing brush to assist in the erosion process. Once bone is broken down, the products are transported into the bloodstream and utilized for various body functions.

Osteoblasts work to form new bone. These cells help synthesize new bone matrix by laying down the collagen-containing organic component of bone. Within this substance, the hydroxapatites crystallize and pack together to create new bone where it is needed.

In young healthy adults, the processes of bone resorption and formation are equal so that just as much bone is broken down as is being built. The result is that bone mass is maintained. At around 40 years of age, bone resorption begins to occur more rapidly than bone formation, and this imbalance results in an overall loss in bone density. This loss of bone density affects all bones, including the vertebrae of the spine, and thus results in a loss of height as we age.

11. This meal does not ensure that your calcium needs for the day are met because our bodies can only absorb about 500 mg of calcium at one time. Although this meal contains more than 100% of the DRI for calcium, you cannot absorb all of the calcium present. To meet your daily calcium needs, it is recommended that you eat multiple servings of calcium-rich foods throughout the day and try to consume no more than 500 mg of calcium at one time.
12. The sunlight is not sufficient in Toronto, Ontario, during the winter to provide adequate vitamin D for anyone. Thus, all people living in this climate in winter need to consume vitamin D in foods and/or supplements to meet their needs.

Chapter 13

1. **b.** vitamin K.
2. **b.** Iron is a component of hemoglobin, myoglobin, and certain enzymes.
3. **c.** by-product of incomplete methionine metabolism.
4. **a.** plasma cells.
5. **d.** antibodies.
6. The micronutrients that are particularly important for effective immune function include vitamins A, C, and E, and the trace minerals zinc, copper, iron, and selenium. Obesity has been associated with increased incidence of infection, delayed wound healing, and poor antibody response to vaccination. If Hannah is obese, this may be contributing to her illness. Before she considers taking a supplement, it would be important for Hannah to see a dietitian for a complete nutritional assessment. This would help to identify if, in fact, she has any nutritional deficiencies. Some of the micronutrients (such as vitamin A, zinc, iron, and selenium) can cause toxicity and/or interfere with the absorption of other micronutrients if taken in excess.
7. Iron deficiency anemia cannot be treated by diet alone within a reasonable time period. Iron supplements are needed to treat this disorder. Ferrous iron salts are the

most bioavailable form of iron supplements and therefore would be the type that would most likely be recommended. This means that they are more readily absorbed by the body.

8. Mr. Katz's doctor probably did not give him the vitamin in pill form because Mr. Katz is 80 years of age, and it is more likely that he suffers from low stomach acid secretion. This is a condition known as atrophic gastritis, and it is estimated that about 10% to 30% of adults older than 50 years have this condition. Stomach acid separates food-bound vitamin B_{12} from dietary proteins. If the acid content of the stomach is inadequate, we cannot free up enough vitamin B_{12} from food sources alone. Because atrophic gastritis can affect almost one-third of the older adult population, it is recommended that people older than 50 years of age consume foods fortified with vitamin B_{12}, take a vitamin B_{12}-containing supplement, or have periodic B_{12} injections. Because Mr. Katz's condition was so severe, it was critical to treat him with a form of vitamin B_{12} that would be guaranteed to enter his system as quickly and effectively as possible; thus, his physician opted to use a vitamin B_{12} injection.

9. Jessica is at a higher risk for iron-deficiency anemia because of her menstrual status and the fact that she consumes only plant-based foods. Plant-based foods contain only the non-heme form of iron, which is more difficult to absorb. Consuming vitamin C enhances the absorption of non-heme iron from our foods; thus, it is imperative that Jessica's parents encourage her to eat good plant-based food sources of iron with a vitamin C source to optimize her iron absorption and reduce her risk for iron-deficiency anemia.

10. Based on this diet, Robert does not appear at risk for inadequate micronutrient intake. The foods he consumes contain all of the necessary micronutrients, and as long as he continues to eat a wide variety of foods from these groups, his risk for inadequate intakes of micronutrients is very low.

11. **a.** Janine is of childbearing age. It is recommended that all women of childbearing age consume adequate folate even if they do not plan to become pregnant. This recommendation is made to reduce the risk for neural tube defects in the developing fetus in case a woman does become pregnant.
b. Janine is avoiding foods that are excellent sources of folate, including many vegetables and enriched grain products. Thus, it is likely that her intake of folate is inadequate. If she continues to avoid these folate-rich foods, a folic acid supplement may be warranted.

12. Both underweight and obese people have an increased risk of infection, and if they are infected, an increased risk that the infection will be severe. Undernutrition reduces defence against infection because micronutrient deficiencies impair immune function. In obese individuals, most

studies show a lower ability of B and T cells to multiply in response to infection. Obese individuals also appear to maintain a low-grade inflammatory state currently thought to increase the likelihood that they will develop asthma, type 2 diabetes, and other disorders that would increase the severity of infection.

Chapter 14

1. **d.** body mass index.
2. **a.** basal metabolic rate, thermic effect of food, and effect of physical activity.
3. **b.** take in more energy than they expend.
4. **c.** all people have a genetic set point for their body weight.
5. **b.** ghrelin.
6. 3.3 grams of protein $\times$ 4 kcal/gram = 13.2 kcal
6 grams of fat $\times$ 9 kcal/gram = 54 kcal
33 grams of carbohydrate $\times$ 4 kcal/gram = 132 kcal
Total energy content = 13.2 + 54 + 132 = 199 kcal
7. Bariatric surgery may be recommended for people who are morbidly obese (BMI $\geq$ 40) or for people who have a BMI > 35 who have other life-threatening conditions such as diabetes, hypertension, or elevated cholesterol levels.
8. A weight that is appropriate for your age and physical development; a weight that you can achieve and sustain without restraining your food intake or constantly dieting; a weight that is acceptable to you; a weight that is based upon your genetic background and family history of body shape and weight; a weight that promotes good eating habits and allows you to participate in regular physical activity.
9. *Dietary recommendations for a sound weight-loss program include:*
a. Set reasonable weight-loss goals. Reasonable weight loss is defined as 0.5 to 1 kg per week. To achieve this rate of weight loss, energy intake should be reduced approximately 250 to no more than 1000 kcal/day of present intake. A weight-loss plan should never provide less than a total of 1200 kcal/day.
b. Eat a diet that is relatively low in fat and high in complex carbohydrates. Total fat intake should be 20% to 25% of total energy intake. Saturated fat intake should be 5% to 10% of total energy intake. Monounsaturated fat intake should be 10% to 15% of total energy intake. Polyunsaturated fat intake should be no more than 10% of total energy intake. Carbohydrate intake should be around 55% of total energy intake with less than 10% of energy intake coming from simple sugars, and fibre intake should be 25 to 35 g/day.
Physical activity recommendation: Set a long-term goal for physical activity that is at least 30 minutes of moderate physical activity most, or preferably all, days of the

week. Doing 45 minutes or more of an activity such as walking at least five days per week is ideal.

Behaviour modification recommendations include:

a. Eliminating inappropriate behaviours by shopping when you are not hungry, only eating at set times in one location, refusing to buy problem foods, and avoiding vending machines, convenience stores, and fast food restaurants.

b. Suppressing inappropriate behaviours by taking small food portions, eating foods on smaller serving dishes so they appear larger, and avoiding feelings of deprivation by eating regular meals throughout the day.

c. Strengthening appropriate behaviours by sharing food with others, learning appropriate serving sizes, planning healthy snacks, scheduling walks and other physical activities with friends, and keeping clothes and equipment for physical activity in convenient places.

d. Repeating desired behaviours by slowing down eating, always using utensils, leaving food on your plate, moving more throughout the day, and joining groups who are physically active.

e. Rewarding yourself for positive behaviours with non-food rewards.

f. Using the "buddy" system by exercising with a friend or relative, and/or calling this support person when you need an extra boost to stay motivated.

g. Refusing to punish yourself if you deviate from your plan.

10. You can increase your basal metabolic rate by increasing your lean body mass or by using drugs such as stimulants, caffeine, and tobacco. Stress and certain illnesses can also increase BMR. The healthiest way to increase BMR is to increase your lean body mass by participating in regular strength-training exercises. Attempting to increase your BMR by using drugs or by increasing your stress is not wise and can be dangerous to your health.

11. **a.** Greater access to inexpensive, high-fat, high-calorie foods (for example, fast foods, vending machine foods, and snack/convenience foods)
b. Significant increases in portion sizes of foods
c. Increased reliance on cars instead of bicycles, public transportation, or walking
d. Use of elevators and escalators instead of stairs
e. Increased use of computers, dishwashers, televisions, and other time-saving devices
f. Lack of safe, accessible, and affordable places to exercise

12. One primary question for Misty is: What is her idea of her ideal weight? It sounds as if Misty might have significant body image concerns. If this is the case, it is important that she meet with a healthcare provider or nutrition professional who can assist her with improving her body image perceptions.

Another question is: What weight can she achieve and sustain without trying so hard (in other words, without restricting her food intake or constantly dieting)? The fact that she must try so hard and is still

not losing weight is a good indication that she may already be at the weight that is healthy.

A third question is: How does her current weight and body shape compare to her genetic background and family history? If her body weight and shape are consistent with her genetic makeup and family history, she may have unrealistic expectations of reducing her body weight or significantly altering her shape.

A final question Misty should consider is whether she is able to maintain her current weight by being regularly active and by eating a healthy, balanced diet. If not, then this is another indication that her body weight goals are unrealistic.

Chapter 15

1. **c.** 64% to 90% of your estimated maximal heart rate.
2. **a.** 1 to 3 seconds.
3. **b.** fat.
4. **c.** can increase strength gained in resistance exercise.
5. To increase muscle mass an individual needs to participate in regular resistance exercises and consume an adequate amount of high-quality (complete) protein. The typical Canadian eats protein in excess of the RDA so few Canadians would need to take protein supplements to meet their needs to build muscle. This is also the case for athletes who may have higher protein requirements.
6. This would be a bad decision on Megan's part. To compete at her top performance Megan needs to be well hydrated. Restricting water prior to her event could lead to dehydration, an increased heart rate, fatigue, weakness, and dizziness. All of these outcomes would contribute to poor performance.
7. There are an infinite number of correct answers to this question. The plan outlined here is for a 40-year-old woman who is interested in maintaining a healthy body weight, optimizing her blood lipid profile, reducing her stress, and maintaining aerobic fitness, flexibility, and upper body strength. She works full-time as a research scientist, and most of her occupational activities are sedentary in nature.
   - *Monday and Wednesday:* 60 minutes of fitness walking (including 5-minute warm-up and 5-minute cool-down)
   - *Tuesday and Thursday:* 75 minutes of Power/Ashtanga yoga (including warm-up and cool-down); 45 minutes of morning swimming (substitute with bicycling in the summer months)
   - *Friday:* 60 minutes of fitness walking (including warm-up and cool-down); 30 minutes of gardening
   - *Saturday:* 75 minutes of Hatha yoga (including warm-up and cool-down); 120 minutes of gardening
   - *Sunday:* 30 minutes of Hatha yoga (including warm-up and cool-down); 180 minutes of hiking with a light daypack.

8. To answer this question, you need to know the total energy that is required to maintain body weight and support the previously described activity/exercise routine. This value can be calculated using the EER equation provided in the You Do the Math activity in Chapter 14 (page 497). If the woman described in Question 8 weighs 59.1 kg, is 1.7 m tall, and has a physical activity factor of 1.27 (from Chapter 1), her EER would be:
   $EER = 354 - [6.91 \times 40] + 1.27 \times [9.36 \times 59.1 + 726 \times 1.7] = 2348$ kcal/day

9. The most helpful strategy you might consider is the use of sports drinks. Sports drinks were designed for people who exercise for more than 60 minutes at a time and are specially formulated to replenish the fluid and micronutrients that are lost during intense, long-duration exercise. By consuming sports drinks during training for a marathon, you can ensure that you are maintaining adequate hydration levels and avoid hyponatremia by replenishing sodium.

10. Gustavo is 56 years of age. You would need to know a little bit more about his occupation to determine his level of activity at work. However, Gustavo could most likely benefit from participating in a planned exercise program of low to moderate intensity. This type of program will help keep his blood pressure under control, will reduce his risk for cardiovascular disease, stroke, and type 2 diabetes, will help Gustavo maintain a healthy body weight, and will assist in maintaining bone density. This type of program may also reduce his risk for colon cancer.

   Before Gustavo begins an exercise program, he should get a thorough physical exam by his physician because of his older age and his high-blood-pressure status. His physician can then determine the safest forms of physical activity for Gustavo.

11. Factors that assist Marisa in maintaining a normal, healthy weight include:
    - walking to/from school each day;
    - covering the lunch shift at her university's day care centre, which requires that she be on her feet, walk, and perform light lifting two hours each day; and
    - walking on the weekends

    Factors that contribute to Conrad's weight gain include:
    - driving to school each day;
    - working an office job two hours each day; and
    - going to the movies on the weekends instead of doing some form of physical activity

Chapter 16

1. **b.** neural tube defects.
2. **c.** oxytocin.
3. **c.** iron.
4. **b.** women who begin their pregnancy underweight.

5. **d.** iron-fortified rice cereal.
6. There are numerous correct answers to this question. The key is to always offer breast milk or formula first and then offer solid foods when feeding infants. Below is a typical pattern for an eight-month-old infant.
   Breakfast: Breast milk; 30 mL infant cereal mixed with breast milk or formula; 15 mL mashed banana; 15 mL soft tofu
   Snack: Breast milk
   Lunch: Breast milk; 15 mL infant cereal mixed with breast milk or formula; 15 mL sweet potato; 15 mL minced chicken
   Snack: Breast milk
   Dinner: 15 mL infant cereal mixed with breast milk or formula; 15 mL mashed green beans; 15 mL minced pork; 15 mL unsweetened apple sauce
   Bedtime Snack: Breast milk

7. In 1981, the World Health Organization adopted the *International Code of Marketing of Breast-milk Substitutes.* The purpose of the code was to protect, promote, and support appropriate infant and young child feeding practices. It outlined recommendations that the marketing of infant formula be restricted so that mothers are not discouraged from breastfeeding. Since that time, the code has been implemented in countries around the world (for additional information see www.who.int/nutrition/publications/code_english.pdf).

8. *Advantages:* Optimal nutritional quality; protects infants from infections and allergies; reduced risk of sudden infant death syndrome; quickens the return of the uterus in the mother to prepregnancy size and reduces postpregnancy bleeding; suppresses ovulation, which lengthens the time between pregnancies and gives the mother's body time to recover before conceiving again; provides for mother–infant bonding and attachment; more convenient than bottle-feeding; less expensive than bottle-feeding.
   Disadvantages: Passage of drugs (caffeine, prescription drugs), alcohol, and irritating components of foods such as onion, garlic, etc.; allergic reactions to foods mother eats such as wheat, peanuts, and cow's milk; transmission of HIV from mother to infant in mothers who are HIV-positive; balancing the challenges of regular breastfeeding with job duties; sleep deprivation of mother due to feeding every two to three hours; social concerns such as exposing breasts in public and discomfort of others who may observe breastfeeding in public.

9. After reviewing the girl's typical dietary intake, I would discuss the importance of appropriate prenatal weight gain (not too much, not too little), the importance of taking folic acid, iron, and possibly calcium supplements, and the need to avoid alcohol, street drugs, and (unless prescribed by her healthcare provider) medications.

10. It is possible that your cousin is partly right and partly wrong. If she is very careful and consumes a wide variety of nutrient-dense foods, she is likely consuming adequate amounts of the macronutrients and many of the micronutrients she needs to support her pregnancy. However, there are some nutrients that are extremely difficult to consume in adequate amounts in the diet during pregnancy, as a woman's needs are very high for these nutrients. One of these nutrients is iron.

During pregnancy, the demand for red blood cells increases to accommodate the needs of the growing uterus, placenta, and the fetus itself. Thus, more iron is needed. Fetal demand for iron increases even further during the last trimester, when the fetus stores iron in the liver for use during the first few months of life. This iron storage is protective because breast milk is low in iron.

Because of these risks, the RDA for iron for pregnant women is 27 mg per day, compared with 18 mg per day for non-pregnant women. Even though your cousin feels her eating habits are sufficient, it is highly likely that she had low iron stores prior to pregnancy, as this is a common problem in many women. Women have a difficult time consuming 18 mg of iron per day in their diets; consuming twice this amount is extremely difficult if not impossible for most women. Thus, women of childbearing age typically have poor iron stores, and the demands of pregnancy are likely to produce deficiency. To ensure adequate iron stores during pregnancy, an iron supplement (as part of, or distinct from, a total prenatal supplement) is routinely prescribed during the last two trimesters. In addition, consuming vitamin C will enhance iron absorption, as do dietary sources of heme iron.

11. Based on this description, it is possible that Katie has a condition referred to as colic. Overstimulation of the nervous system, feeding too rapidly, swallowing of air, and intestinal gas pain are considered possible culprits, but the precise cause is unknown. As with allergies, if a colicky infant is breastfed, breastfeeding should be continued, but the parents should try to determine whether eating certain foods seems to prompt crying and, if so, eliminate the offending food(s) from the mother's diet. Formula-fed infants may benefit from a change in type of formula. In the worst cases of colic, a physician may prescribe medication. Fortunately, most cases disappear spontaneously, possibly because of maturity of the gastrointestinal tract, around three months of age. It is important that Katie's parents discuss her condition with her pediatrician before making any decisions about changing her diet.

12. The primary information to share with this woman is that breastfeeding is recommended for all children up to at least two years (or 24 months) of age. Thus, an 11-month-old child is not too old to be breastfed. In addition, it is also possible that this woman is offended by seeing your sister breastfeed in public. If this is the case, it is important to point out that all women have the right to breastfeed in a public place. If this woman is offended, she can leave the area or choose not to observe your sister as she breastfeeds her child.

Chapter 17

1. **d.** greater than that for young children, adults, and pregnant adults.
2. **c.** 45% to 65%.
3. **b.** skipping breakfast.
4. **b.** 30 mL of plain yogourt, 30 mL of applesauce, 30 mL of fortified whole-grain oat cereal, and 125 mL of calcium-fortified orange juice.
5. **a.** Cigarette smoking can interfere with the metabolism of nutrients.
6. Snacks are an important component of the diet for most preschoolers. Preschoolers have small stomachs and consequently are not able to consume all the energy they need in three meals. Instead, they need smaller meals and snacks dispersed throughout the day (every two to three hours). They also need to make every meal and snack count from a nutritional perspective. To meet a preschooler's micronutrient needs, the foods must be nutrient-dense. If the snacks that are provided are of low nutrient-density, then the preschooler will "fill up" on these foods and not be hungry when more nutrient-dense foods are presented to them.
7. Adequate calcium intake is critical to achieve peak bone density. The RDA for calcium for adolescents is 1300 mg/day; you would need to drink over 1 litre of milk daily to obtain this amount of calcium. After peak bone density has been achieved, there is a slow gradual loss of calcium from bone that is not reversible. Consequently, it is important to have maximum bone density prior to the loss of bone density with age. Adolescents who replace milk with soft drinks are not able to meet their calcium needs and are at risk to achieve a lower density of bone at their peak bone density.
8. *Advantages:* Improved access to a wider variety of affordable, fresh, healthy foods from around Canada and the world; improved access to nutrition and health information from a variety of sources, including television and internet sources; improved access to interactive nutrition and healthy lifestyle programs that encourage family participation
Disadvantages: Reduced energy expenditure due to increased television viewing and computer use leading to obesity; lower fitness levels and higher risk for chronic

diseases due to the lack of physical activity; increased exposure to advertisements promoting junk foods rather than healthy foods; failure to acquire important physical skills because not much time is spent engaged in physical activities; inhibition of imagination and creativity in young children because they do not have to develop skills necessary for creative play

9. Toddlers are relatively picky eaters, and they are also small individuals and can only consume small amounts of food at any given time. In consuming a vegan diet, the primary sources of quality proteins are restricted to legumes, meat substitutes, and various combinations of vegetables and whole grains. It is highly likely that a vegan diet will be too low in protein for toddlers, as their protein needs are relatively high. Few toddlers can consume enough legumes and whole grains to provide sufficient protein, and many may not prefer the taste of vegetables and meat substitutes. In addition, certain staples of the vegan diet that are high in protein, such as wheat, soy, and nuts, commonly provoke allergic reactions in children. When this happens, finding a plant-based substitute that contains adequate protein and other nutrients can be challenging.

10. There are numerous correct answers to this question. The key to designing a menu for this age group is to keep in mind that these children need adequate fluid, and they do not eat large amounts of food. The foods should also look fun and attractive to encourage regular snacking and should be easy to eat when the children are active. Here are some foods you may want to offer to these children:
    - Ample water in small, coloured plastic cups
    - Whole-grain crackers that are small and easy to eat
    - Small chunks of different colours and flavours of cheese to eat with the crackers (or you could make peanut butter/whole-grain cracker "sandwiches")
    - Baby carrot sticks
    - Orange slices

11. Here are three of many lunch choices that you could offer to these students:
    - Menu 1: Bean burrito with salsa; rice; low/no-fat milk; fresh fruit
    - Menu 2: Grilled turkey and muenster cheese sandwich on whole-wheat bread; assorted raw vegetables; pineapple/orange yogourt fruit smoothie
    - Menu 3: Chicken and vegetable teriyaki rice bowl; fruit skewers; low/no-fat milk

12. A registered dietitian would be concerned about (1) Lydia's monotonous and unbalanced diet, (2) her lack of physical activity, and (3) Lydia's potential homesickness and isolation. Her poor dietary habits are probably contributing to a lack of protein as well as most vitamins and minerals. Her poor diet and the fact that she lives in a northern region almost certainly mean that she

is vitamin D deficient, and her consumption of soda rather than milk or a calcium-fortified beverage further increases her risk for low bone density. These deficiencies may also account for some of her lethargy and lack of physical activity. By guiding Lydia toward healthier meals and menus, she would feel more energetic and be more likely to ride a bicycle, take an activity class, or join a gym.

A regular routine of physical activity would probably stimulate Lydia's appetite, encouraging her to consume greater amounts of food, hopefully healthy food! Lydia's move from Ottawa to Vancouver could account for her isolation; she may need additional guidance in finding and developing new friendships. If Lydia had always lived at home, where someone else prepared the meals, she would benefit from specific sessions on planning menus, shopping for healthy foods, and preparing daily meals.

Chapter 18

1. **b.** vitamin D.
2. **a.** dysgeusia.
3. **d.** 122 years.
4. **c.** glycosylation.
5. **c.** palliative care.
6. In programmed theories of aging, nutrition has little, if any, potential or practical impact on the progressive deterioration of bodily functions over time. Thus, there is little or no impact on the development of disease, disability, or mortality.
7. There is an increase in body fat and a decrease in muscle mass as we age due to the decreased production of certain hormones, including testosterone and growth hormone. Poor diet and an inactive lifestyle may also contribute to this change in body composition.
8. The RDA for vitamin B_{12} is the same for younger and older adults; however, up to 30% of older adults cannot absorb enough vitamin B_{12} from foods because of atrophic gastritis. Therefore, it is recommended that older adults consume foods fortified with vitamin B_{12} or a B_{12}-containing supplement because the vitamin B_{12} in these products is absorbed more readily.
9. The older population as a whole has a high risk for heart disease, hypertension, type 2 diabetes, and cancer, and these diseases are more prevalent in older adults who are overweight or obese. Obesity also increases the severity and consequences of osteoarthritis, limits the mobility of older adults, and is associated with functional declines in daily activities. Even moderate weight loss can improve functional status. Thus, achieving and maintaining a healthy weight can decrease the risk for the development of chronic disease and improve the quality of life for older adults.

10. Lack of adequate stomach acid can lower the absorption of vitamin B_{12}, calcium, iron, and zinc, increasing the risk for deficiencies of these nutrients.

11. **a.** If not fluent in English, an older immigrant woman may not be confident enough to go out to shop for food on a regular basis, or may not qualify for a driver's licence, which would affect her ability to obtain food. In both cases, she might have to purchase food from the nearest convenience store (not the best source), and/or simply run low on food, leading to possible malnutrition.
    b. If isolated, with no southeast Asian friends or relatives nearby, the woman could easily become depressed, which often results in poor food intake and rapid onset of nutrient deficiencies.

12. Older adults may purposefully limit fluid intake to avoid embarrassing "accidents" due to poor bladder control; they may be taking medications that act as diuretics, increasing urinary output; many older adults fail to perceive thirst and may not drink adequate amounts of fluid during the day; and some older adults may not be able to drink enough fluids because of physical limitations related to a stroke, Parkinson's disease, or other neuromuscular disorders.

13. I would first try to determine why my client eats as he does: is he easily tired, does he have a poor appetite, is he inexperienced in planning and producing healthy meals, or is he on a very limited budget? Depending upon his circumstances, I would develop several simple but nutritious meal suggestions that have more protein, fibre, total energy, and a wider range of vitamins and minerals. Finally, I would discuss ways of improving his sleeping habits while limiting alcohol intake. Gentle physical activity during the day, a warm bath before bedtime, and caffeine avoidance during the evening might help him sleep through the night without the need for beer.

14. The death of a spouse often triggers mental and physical declines in older adults. Loss of appetite, depression, loneliness, and fearfulness may contribute to a drastic reduction in food and fluid intake. Malnutrition and dehydration quickly develop, which then contribute to loss of balance, weakness, and fatigue. These factors may have led to Marta's grandmother's fall and fracture.

Chapter 19

1. **a.** sub-Saharan Africa.
2. **c.** It has dramatically increased worldwide production of rice, corn, and wheat at lower costs.
3. **b.** reduced resistance to infection.
4. **b.** single mothers and their children.
5. **d.** all of the above.

6. There are several reasons why iron deficiency is so common. Contributing factors in developing countries include poor availability of the non-heme iron in staple foods, the high cost of animal products, which are the source of the highly absorbable heme iron, and blood loss from intestinal worms and other parasites. Pregnant women and children are most at risk because of their high needs for iron during growth.

7. Females tend to work in lower paying jobs than males and thus have less income for buying food. Further, women are typically responsible for childcare, which can strain an already tight budget. In households led by couples, there is the potential for two people to have jobs and thus an increased income for purchasing food.

8. This refers to the paradox of being overweight and undernourished. This occurs when people consume foods with low nutrient density. They consume excess calories but are still deficient in nutrients because of the poor quality of the foods chosen. As the prevalence of obesity increases, so too does the prevalence of chronic diseases such as type 2 diabetes and heart disease. This is straining public health resources in developing countries.

9. In developed countries such as Canada, food insecurity is often caused by poverty. Despite the availability of sufficient quantity of safe, nutritious foods, many people cannot afford to buy them. Physical, psychological, and social factors can also contribute to the problem. People with chronic diseases or disabilities may not be able to work or may have to accept lower-wage jobs, which reduces their income potential. Divorce frequently leads to financial stressors, especially for women.

10. Women with access to education are more likely to have increased earning potential, access to information about contraception, and information to use better health practices. These circumstances lead to smaller, healthier, more economically stable families.

11. Breast milk contains antibodies that protect against infections. In addition, there is a danger in developing countries of feeding infants with formula because the use of unsanitary water for mixing batches of formula results in diarrheal diseases. Another problem is that overdilution of formula by families who cannot afford adequate amounts results in inadequate intake for the infant, whereas breast milk is likely to contain adequate amounts of the nutrients needed.

12. When undernutrition is endemic throughout an area, growth stunting becomes the norm. In such a population, a person who is of average height by Canadian standards would be considered unusually tall.

13. The family is dependent on the supplies available at the local food pantry. These supplies may provide for good nutrition, but likely do not provide all nutrients regularly. Therefore Davie's nutrition status is likely to be compromised. Davie is at greatest risk of infection from

drinking water from a nearby pond, particularly if his mother does not boil the water prior to consumption. Because they have limited access to medical care, they are likely to wait out infections, prolonging the time that the infection is resolved. This further exacerbates Davie's nutrition status, makes him more susceptible to another infection, and makes it more likely that he will die from a prolonged fight with infection.

14. Mexico is a country experiencing economic growth and the nutrition transition. Obesity is becoming a serious problem for both adults and children. Because of obesity, type 2 diabetes is being diagnosed at younger and younger ages in the Hispanic population. The best solution to type 2 diabetes is prevention, and a concerned pediatrician is likely to be able to make a tremendous beneficial difference in the lives of the children he sees.

Glossary

A

absorption The physiologic process by which molecules of food are taken from the gastrointestinal tract into circulation.

Acceptable Daily Intake (ADI) An estimate made by Health Canada of the amount of a non-nutritive sweetener that someone can consume each day over a lifetime without adverse effects.

Acceptable Macronutrient Distribution Ranges (AMDR) A range of intakes for a particular energy source that is associated with reduced risk of chronic disease while providing adequate intakes of essential nutrients.

acetyl CoA (or acetyl coenzyme A) Coenzyme A is derived from the B-vitamin pantothenic acid; it readily reacts with two-carbon acetate to form the metabolic intermediate acetyl CoA.

acetylcholine A neurotransmitter that is involved in many functions, including muscle movement and memory storage.

achlorhydria Lack of gastric acid secretion.

acidosis A disorder in which the blood becomes acidic; that is, the level of hydrogen in the blood is excessive. It can be caused by respiratory or metabolic problems.

active transport An absorptive process that requires the use of energy to transport nutrients and other substances in combination with a carrier protein.

added sugars Sugars and syrups that are added to food during processing or preparation.

adenosine diphosphate (ADP) A metabolic intermediate that results from the removal of one phosphate group from ATP.

adenosine monophosphate (AMP) A low-energy compound that results from the removal of two phosphate groups from ATP.

adenosine triphosphate (ATP) A high-energy compound made up of the purine adenine, the simple sugar ribose, and three phosphate units; it is used by cells as a source of metabolic energy. Also, the common currency of energy for virtually all cells of the body.

adequate diet A diet that provides enough energy, nutrients, and fibre to maintain a person's health.

Adequate Intake (AI) A recommended average daily nutrient intake level based on observed or experimentally determined estimates of nutrient intake by a group of healthy people.

albumin A serum protein, made in the liver, that transports free fatty acids from one body tissue to another.

alcohol dehydrogenase (ADH) An enzyme that converts ethanol to acetaldehyde in the first step of alcohol oxidation.

aldehyde dehydrogenase (ALDH) An enzyme that oxidizes acetaldehyde to acetate.

aldosterone A hormone released from the adrenal glands that signals the kidneys to retain sodium and chloride, which in turn results in the retention of water.

alkalosis A disorder in which the blood becomes basic; that is, the level of hydrogen in the blood is deficient. It can be caused by respiratory or metabolic problems.

alpha bond A type of chemical bond that can be digested by enzymes found in the human intestine.

alpha-linolenic acid An essential fatty acid found in leafy green vegetables, flax seed oil, soy oil, fish oil, and fish products; an omega-3 fatty acid.

amenorrhea Lack of menstruation in the absence of pregnancy. Primary amenorrhea is the absence of menstruation by the age of 16 years in a girl who has secondary sex characteristics, whereas secondary amenorrhea is the absence of the menstrual period for three or more months after the onset of menstruation.

amino acids Nitrogen-containing molecules that combine to form proteins.

ammonia A highly toxic compound released during the deamination of amino acids.

amniotic fluid The watery fluid contained within the innermost membrane of the sac containing the fetus. It cushions and protects the growing fetus.

anabolic A substance that builds muscle and increases strength.

anabolism The process of making new molecules from smaller ones.

anencephaly A fatal neural tube defect in which there is partial absence of brain tissue most likely caused by failure of the neural tube to close.

angiotensin II A potent vasoconstrictor that constricts the diameter of blood vessels and increases blood pressure; it also signals the release of the hormone aldosterone from the adrenal glands.

anorexia An absence of appetite.

anorexia nervosa A serious, potentially life-threatening eating disorder that is characterized by self-starvation, which eventually leads to a deficiency in energy and essential nutrients that are required by the body to function normally.

antibodies Defensive proteins of the immune system. Their production is prompted by the presence of bacteria, viruses, toxins, and allergens.

antidiuretic hormone (ADH) A hormone released from the pituitary gland in response to an increase in blood solute concentration. ADH stimulates the kidneys to reabsorb water and to reduce the production of urine.

antigens Parts of a molecule, usually proteins, from bacteria, viruses, worms, or toxins that are recognized by specific receptors on lymphocytes and induce formation of antibodies or killing of an organism displaying the antigen.

antioxidant A compound that has the ability to prevent or repair the damage caused by oxidation.

antiserum A pharmacologic preparation that contains antibodies to specific antigens.

appetite A psychological desire to consume specific foods.

ariboflavinosis A condition caused by riboflavin deficiency.

atrophic gastritis A condition, frequently seen in individuals over the age of 50 years, in which stomach acid secretion is low, resulting in decreased production of mucus, HCl, pepsin, and intrinsic factor.

atrophy A decrease in the size and strength of muscles that occurs when they are not working adequately.

autoimmune A destructive immune response directed toward the individual's own tissues.

B

B cells Lymphocytes that can become either antibody-producing plasma cells or memory cells.

balanced diet A diet that contains the combinations of foods that provide the proper proportions of nutrients.

basal metabolic rate (BMR) The energy the body expends to maintain its fundamental physiologic functions.

beriberi A disease caused by thiamine deficiency.

beta bond A type of chemical bond that cannot be easily digested by enzymes found in the human intestine.

bile Fluid produced by the liver and stored in the gallbladder; it emulsifies lipids in the small intestine.

binge eating Consumption of a large amount of food in a short period of time, usually accompanied by a feeling of loss of self-control.

binge-eating disorder A disorder characterized by binge eating an average of twice a week or more, typically without compensatory purging.

bioavailability The degree to which our bodies can absorb and utilize any given nutrient.

biologic age Physiologic age as determined by health and functional status; often estimated and scored by questionnaires.

bleaching process A reaction in which the rod cells in the retina lose their colour when rhodopsin is split into retinal and opsin.

blood volume The amount of fluid in blood.

β-oxidation (or fatty acid oxidation) A series of metabolic reactions that oxidizes free fatty acids, leading to the end products of water, carbon dioxide, and ATP.

body composition The ratio of a person's body fat to lean body mass. Also, the amount of bone, fat, and muscle tissue in the body.

body fat mass The amount of body fat, or adipose tissue, a person has.

body image A person's perception of his or her body's appearance and functioning.

body mass index (BMI) A measurement representing the ratio of a person's body weight to his or her height.

bolus A mass of food that has been chewed and moistened in the mouth.

bone density The degree of compactness of bone tissue, reflecting the strength of the bones. Peak bone density is the point at which a bone is strongest.

brown adipose tissue A type of adipose tissue that has more mitochondria than white adipose tissue and can increase energy expenditure by uncoupling oxidation from ATP production. It is found in significant amounts in animals and newborn humans.

brush border A term that describes the microvilli of the small intestine's lining. These microvilli tremendously increase the small intestine's absorptive capacity.

buffers Proteins that help maintain proper acid–base balance by attaching to, or releasing, hydrogen ions as conditions change in the body.

bulimia nervosa A serious eating disorder characterized by recurrent episodes of binge eating and recurrent inappropriate compensatory behaviours to prevent weight gain, such as self-induced vomiting, fasting, excessive exercise, or misuse of laxatives, diuretics, enemas, or other medications.

C

calcitonin A hormone secreted by the thyroid gland when blood calcium levels are too high. Calcitonin inhibits the actions of vitamin D, preventing reabsorption of calcium in the kidneys, limiting calcium reabsorption in the intestines, and inhibiting the osteoclasts from breaking down bone.

calcitriol The primary active form of vitamin D in the body.

calcium rigour A failure of muscles to relax, which leads to a hardening or stiffening of the muscles; caused by high levels of blood calcium.

calcium tetany A condition in which muscles experience twitching and spasms due to inadequate blood calcium levels.

calorimeter A special instrument in which food can be burned and the amount of heat that is released measured; this process demonstrates the energy (caloric) content of the food.

Canada's Food Guide A practical pattern of food choices that incorporates variety and flexibility, and is based on current science for nutrient recommendations.

Canadian Food Inspection Agency (CFIA) A government agency that is responsible for the safety of the food supply, protecting the environment, and contributing to the health of Canadians.

Canadian Physical Activity Guidelines Recommendations for the type and amount of activity that should be done weekly to achieve health benefits.

cancer A group of diseases characterized by cells that reproduce spontaneously and independently and may invade other tissues and organs.

carbohydrate One of the three macronutrients, a compound made up of carbon, hydrogen, and oxygen that is derived from plants and provides energy.

carbohydrate loading Also known as *glycogen loading*. A process that involves altering training and carbohydrate intake so that muscle glycogen storage is maximized.

carbohydrates The primary fuel source for the body, particularly for the brain and for physical exercise.

carbon skeleton The unique "side group" that remains after deamination of an amino acid, also referred to as a *keto acid*.

carcinogen Any substance or agent capable of causing the cellular mutations that lead to cancer, such as certain pesticides, industrial chemicals, and pollutants.

cardiorespiratory fitness Fitness of the heart and lungs; achieved through regular participation in aerobic-type activities.

cardiovascular disease A general term that refers to abnormal conditions involving dysfunction of the heart and blood vessels; cardiovascular disease can result in heart attack or stroke.

carnitine A small organic compound that transports free fatty acids from the cytosol into the mitochondria for oxidation.

carotenoids Fat-soluble plant pigments that the body stores in the liver and adipose tissues. The body is able to convert certain carotenoids to vitamin A.

cash crops Crops grown to be sold rather than eaten, such as cotton, tobacco, jute, and sugar cane.

catabolism The breakdown or degradation of larger molecules to smaller molecules.

cataract A damaged portion of the eye's lens, which causes cloudiness that impairs vision.

celiac disease A disorder characterized by an immune reaction that damages the lining of the small intestine when the individual is exposed to a component of protein called gluten.

cell differentiation The process by which immature, undifferentiated stem cells develop into highly specialized functional cells of discrete organs and tissues.

cephalic phase The earliest phase of digestion in which the brain thinks about and prepares the digestive organs for the consumption of food.

ceruloplasmin A copper-containing protein that transports copper in the body. It also plays a role in oxidizing ferric to ferrous iron (Fe^{2+} to Fe^{3+}).

chief cells Cells lining the gastric glands that secrete pepsinogen and gastric lipase.

cholecalciferol Vitamin D_3, a form of vitamin D found in animal foods and the form we synthesize from the sun.

chronic disease A disease characterized by a gradual onset and long duration, with signs and symptoms that are difficult to interpret, and which respond poorly to medical treatment. Often a result of poor dietary and lifestyle choices.

chylomicron A lipoprotein produced in the mucosal cell of the intestine; transports dietary fat out of the intestinal tract.

chyme A semifluid mass consisting of partially digested food, water, and gastric juices.

coenzyme A molecule that combines with an enzyme to activate it and help it do its job; many coenzymes are B-vitamins.

cofactor A small, chemically simple organic or inorganic substance that is required for enzyme activity; trace minerals such as iron, zinc, and copper function as cofactors.

colic Unconsolable infant crying of unknown origin that lasts for hours at a time.

collagen A protein that forms strong fibres in bone and connective tissue.

colostrum The first fluid made and secreted by the breasts from late in pregnancy to about a week after birth. It is rich in immune factors and protein.

complementary proteins Proteins contained in one or more foods that together contain all nine essential amino acids necessary for a complete protein. It is not necessary to eat complementary proteins at the same meal.

complete proteins Foods that contain all nine essential amino acids.

complex carbohydrate A nutrient compound consisting of long chains of glucose molecules, such as starch, glycogen, and fibre.

conception (also called *fertilization*) The uniting of an ovum (egg) and sperm to create a fertilized egg, or zygote.

condensation An anabolic process by which smaller, chemically simple compounds are joined with the removal of water.

conditionally essential amino acids Amino acids that are normally considered non-essential but become essential under certain circumstances when the body's need for them exceeds the ability to produce them.

cone cells Light-sensitive cells found in the retina that contain the pigment iodopsin and react to bright light and interpret colour images.

constipation A condition characterized by the absence of bowel movements for a period of time that is significantly longer than normal for the individual. When a bowel movement does occur, stools are usually small, hard, and difficult to pass.

cool-down Activities done after an exercise session is completed; should be gradual and allow your body to slowly recover from exercise.

cortical bone (compact bone) A dense bone tissue that makes up the outer surface of all bones as well as the entirety of most small bones of the body.

cortisol A hormone produced by the adrenal cortex that increases rates of gluconeogenesis and lipolysis.

covert symptom A symptom that is hidden from a client and requires laboratory tests or other invasive procedures to detect.

creatine phosphate (CP) A high-energy compound that can be broken down for energy and used to regenerate ATP.

cretinism A unique form of mental retardation that occurs in infants when the mother experiences iodine deficiency during pregnancy.

Crohn's disease A bowel disease that causes inflammation in the small intestine leading to diarrhea, abdominal pain, rectal bleeding, weight loss, and fever.

crop rotation The practice of alternating crops in a particular field to prevent nutrient depletion and erosion of the soil and to help with control of crop-specific pests.

cystic fibrosis A genetic disorder that causes an alteration in chloride transport, leading to the production of thick, sticky mucus that causes life-threatening respiratory and digestive problems.

cytotoxic T cells Activated T cells that kill infected body cells.

D

DASH diet Term for Dietary Approaches to Stop Hypertension, this diet plan emphasizes fruits and vegetables, whole grains, low/no-fat milk and dairy, and lean meats.

de novo synthesis The process of synthesizing a compound "from scratch."

deamination The process by which an amine group is removed from an amino acid. The nitrogen is then transported to the kidneys for excretion in the urine, and the carbon and other components are metabolized for energy or used to make other compounds.

dehydration Depletion of body fluid that results when fluid excretion exceeds fluid intake.

denaturation The process by which proteins uncoil and lose their shape and function when they are exposed to heat, acids, bases, heavy metals, alcohol, and other damaging substances.

diabetes A chronic disease in which the body can no longer regulate glucose.

diarrhea Condition characterized by the frequent passage of loose, watery stools.

dietary fibre The non-digestible carbohydrate part of plants that forms the support structures of leaves, stems, and seeds.

Dietary Reference Intakes (DRIs) A set of nutritional reference values for the United States and Canada that apply to healthy people.

digestion The process by which foods are broken down into their component molecules, either mechanically or chemically.

direct calorimetry A method used to determine energy expenditure by measuring the amount of heat released by the body.

disaccharide A carbohydrate compound consisting of two monosaccharide molecules joined together.

diseases of aging Conditions that typically occur later in life as a result of lifelong accumulated risk, such as exposure to high-fat diets, lack of physical activity, and excess sun exposure.

disordered eating A general term used to describe a variety of abnormal or atypical eating behaviours that are not severe enough to make the person seriously ill.

diuretic A substance that increases fluid loss via the urine. Common diuretics include alcohol as well as prescription medications for high blood pressure and other disorders.

docosahexaenoic acid (DHA) A metabolic derivative of alpha-linolenic acid; together with EPA, it appears to reduce the risk of heart disease.

doubly labelled water A form of indirect calorimetry that measures total daily energy expenditure through the rate of carbon dioxide production. It requires consumption of water that is labelled with non-radioactive isotopes of hydrogen (deuterium, or ^{2}H) and oxygen (^{18}O).

dual energy X-ray absorptiometry (DXA or DEXA) Currently the most accurate tool for measuring bone density.

dysgeusia Abnormal taste perception.

dysphagia Abnormal swallowing.

E

eating disorder A psychiatric disorder characterized by severe disturbances in body image and eating behaviours. Anorexia nervosa and bulimia nervosa are two examples of eating disorders for which specific diagnostic criteria must be present for diagnosis.

edema A disorder in which fluids build up in the tissue spaces of the body, causing fluid imbalances and a swollen appearance.

eicosanoids Physiologically active signalling molecules, including prostaglandins, thromboxanes, and leukotrienes, derived from the 20-carbon fatty acids arachidonic acid and eicosapentaenoic acid.

eicosapentaenoic acid (EPA) A metabolic derivative of alpha-linolenic acid. Commonly found in fatty fish and fish oils.

electrolyte A substance that disassociates in solution into positively and negatively charged ions and is thus capable of carrying an electric current.

electron transport chain A series of metabolic reactions that transport electrons from NADH or $FADH_2$ through a series of carriers resulting in ATP production.

elimination The process by which the undigested portions of food and waste products are removed from the body.

embryo Human growth and developmental stage lasting from the third week to the end of the eighth week after fertilization.

endocytosis An absorptive process by which a small amount of the intestinal contents is engulfed by the cell membrane (also called *pinocytosis*).

energy cost of physical activity The energy that is expended on body movement and muscular work above basal levels.

energy expenditure The energy the body expends to maintain its basic functions and to perform all levels of movement and activity.

energy intake The amount of energy a person consumes; in other words, it is the number of kilocalories consumed from food and beverages.

enriched foods Foods in which nutrients that were lost during processing have been added back so the food meets a specified standard.

enteric nervous system The nerves of the GI tract.

enterocytes Specialized absorptive cells in the villi of the small intestine.

enzymes Small chemicals, usually proteins, that act on other chemicals to speed up body processes but are not changed during those processes.

epinephrine A hormone produced mainly by the adrenal medulla that stimulates the release of glucose from liver glycogen and the release of free fatty acids from stored triglycerides.

epiphyseal plates Plates of cartilage located toward the end of long bones that provide for growth in the length of long bones.

ergocalciferol Vitamin D_2, a form of vitamin D found exclusively in plant foods.

ergogenic aids Substances used to improve exercise and athletic performance.

error theories of aging Aging is a cumulative process determined largely by exposure to environmental insults; the fewer the environmental insults, the slower the aging process.

erythrocyte hemolysis The rupturing or breakdown of red blood cells, or erythrocytes.

erythrocytes Red blood cells; they transport oxygen in the blood.

esophagus A muscular tube of the GI tract connecting the back of the mouth to the stomach.

essential amino acids Amino acids not produced by the body or not produced in sufficient amounts so that they must be obtained from food.

essential fatty acids (EFAs) Fatty acids that must be consumed in the diet because they cannot be made by the body. The two essential fatty acids are linoleic acid and alpha-linolenic acid.

Estimated Average Requirements (EAR) The average daily nutrient intake level estimated to meet the requirement of half of the healthy individuals in a particular life stage or gender group.

Estimated Energy Requirement (EER) The average dietary energy intake that is predicted to maintain energy balance in a healthy person.

evaporative cooling Another term for sweating, which is the primary way in which we dissipate heat.

exercise A subcategory of leisure-time physical activity; any activity that is purposeful, planned, and structured.

extracellular fluid The fluid outside of the body's cells, either in the body's tissues (interstitial fluid) or as the liquid portion of the blood or lymph (intravascular fluid).

F

facilitated diffusion The absorptive process that occurs when nutrients are shuttled across the enterocytes with the help of a carrier protein.

FAD (flavin adenine dinucleotide) A coenzyme derived from the B-vitamin riboflavin; FAD readily accepts electrons (hydrogen) from various donors.

failure to thrive (FTT) An unexplained condition where the infant's weight gain and growth are far below usual levels for age and previous pattern of growth.

famines Widespread, acute food shortages that affect a substantial portion of a population, often associated with starvation and death.

fat-soluble vitamins Vitamins that are not soluble in water, but are soluble in fat. These include vitamins A, D, E, and K.

fatty acids Long chains of carbon atoms bound to each other as well as to hydrogen atoms.

female athlete triad Refers to the interrelationship between three conditions seen in female athletes: inadequate energy intake, menstrual dysfunction (for example, amenorrhea), and reduced bone strength (for example, stress fractures, osteopenia, osteoporosis).

fermentation The anaerobic process in which an agent causes an organic substance to break down into simpler substances and results in the production of ATP.

ferritin A storage form of iron found primarily in the intestinal mucosa, spleen, bone marrow, and liver.

ferroportin An iron transporter that helps regulate intestinal iron absorption and the release of iron from the enterocyte into the general circulation.

fetal alcohol effects (FAE) A milder set of alcohol-related birth defects characterized by behavioural problems such as hyperactivity, attention deficit disorder, poor judgment, sleep disorders, and delayed learning.

fetal alcohol spectrum disorder (FASD) A set of serious, irreversible alcohol-related birth defects characterized by certain physical and mental abnormalities.

fetus Human growth and developmental stage lasting from the beginning of the ninth week after conception to birth.

FIT principle The principle used to achieve an appropriate overload for physical training. Stands for frequency, intensity, and time of activity.

flexibility The ability to move a joint through its full range of motion.

fluid A substance composed of molecules that move past one another freely. Fluids are characterized by their ability to conform to the shape of whatever container holds them.

fluorohydroxyapatite A mineral compound in human teeth that contains fluoride, calcium, and phosphorous and is more resistant to destruction by acids and bacteria than hydroxyapatite.

fluorosis A condition marked by staining and pitting of the teeth; caused by an abnormally high intake of fluoride.

folate deficiency anemia (stage IV) The stage of folate deficiency in which the number of red blood cells has declined due to lack of folate, and macrocytic anemia develops.

folate deficiency erythropoiesis (stage III) The third stage of folate depletion in which folate levels are so low that the ability to make new red blood cells is impaired.

folate depletion (stage II) The second stage of folate depletion in which both serum and red blood cell folate are low.

food The plants and animals we consume.

food allergy An allergic reaction to food, caused by a reaction of the immune system.

food insecurity Condition in which the individual is unable to regularly obtain enough food to provide sufficient energy and nutrients to meet physical needs.

food intolerance Gastrointestinal discomfort characterized by certain foods that is not a result of an immune system reaction.

food security Exists when all people, at all times, have a physical and economic access to sufficient, safe, and nutritious food to meet their dietary needs and food preferences for an active and healthy life.

food shortage Condition in which food production and import in an area are not sufficient to meet the needs of the population in that area.

food/population ratio The amount of food available for each individual; also food available per capita.

fortification The addition of nutrients to a food that were either not originally present in that food or were present in insignificant amounts.

fortified foods Foods in which nutrients are added that did not originally exist in the food or existed in insignificant amounts.

free radical A highly unstable atom with an unpaired electron in its outermost shell.

frequency Refers to the number of activity sessions per week you perform.

fructose The sweetest natural sugar; a monosaccharide that occurs in fruits and vegetables. Also called *levulose*, or *fruit sugar*.

functional fibre The non-digestible forms of carbohydrate that are extracted from plants or manufactured in the laboratory and have known health benefits.

functional food A food that provides a health benefit beyond basic nutrition.

G

galactose A monosaccharide that joins with glucose to create lactose, one of the three most common disaccharides.

gallbladder A pear-shaped organ beneath the liver that stores bile and secretes it into the small intestine.

gastric juice Acidic liquid secreted within the stomach; it contains hydrochloric acid, pepsin, and other compounds.

gastroesophageal reflux disease (GERD) A painful type of heartburn that occurs more than twice per week.

gastrointestinal (GI) tract A long, muscular tube consisting of several organs: the mouth, esophagus, stomach, small intestine, and large intestine.

gene expression The process of using a gene to make a protein.

geriatric failure to thrive Inappropriate, unexplained loss of body weight and muscle mass; usually results from a combination of environmental and health factors.

gestation The period of intrauterine development from conception to birth.

gestational diabetes mellitus Insufficient insulin production or insulin resistance that results in consistently high blood glucose levels, specifically during pregnancy; condition typically resolves after birth occurs.

ghrelin A protein synthesized in the stomach that acts as a hormone and plays an important role in appetite regulation by stimulating appetite.

glucagon A hormone secreted by the alpha cells of the pancreas in response to decreased blood levels of glucose; causes breakdown of liver stores of glycogen into glucose.

glucogenic amino acid An amino acid that can be converted to glucose via gluconeogenesis.

glucokinase An enzyme that adds a phosphate group to a molecule of glucose.

gluconeogenesis The synthesis of glucose from noncarbohydrate precursors such as glucogenic amino acids and glycerol. Also, the generation of glucose from the breakdown of proteins into amino acids.

glucose The most abundant sugar molecule, a monosaccharide generally found in combination with other sugars. The preferred source of energy for the brain and an important source of energy for all cells.

glutathione A tripeptide composed of glycine, cysteine, and glutamic acid that assists in regenerating vitamin C into its antioxidant form.

glycemic index Rating of the potential of foods to raise blood glucose and insulin levels.

glycemic load The amount of carbohydrate in a food multiplied by the glycemic index of the carbohydrate.

glycerol An alcohol composed of three carbon atoms; it is the backbone of a triglyceride molecule.

glycogen A polysaccharide stored in animals; the storage form of glucose in animals.

glycolysis A sequence of chemical reactions that converts glucose to pyruvate.

glycosylation Addition of glucose to blood and tissue proteins; typically impairs protein structure and function.

GOBI UNICEF campaign to eliminate common infections of childhood by four inexpensive strategies: growth monitoring, oral rehydration therapy, breastfeeding, and immunization.

goiter Enlargement of the thyroid gland; can be caused by iodine toxicity or deficiency.

grazing Consistently eating small meals throughout the day; done by many athletes to meet their high energy demands.

Green Revolution The tremendous increase in global productivity between 1944 and 2000 due to selective cross-breeding or hybridization to produce high-yield grains and industrial farming techniques.

H

haustration Involuntary, sluggish contraction of the haustra of the proximal colon that moves wastes toward the sigmoid colon.

health A multidimensional, lifelong process that includes physical, emotional, and spiritual health.

Health Canada The federal department responsible for helping Canadians maintain and improve their health.

healthy diet A diet that provides the proper combination of energy and nutrients and is adequate, moderate, balanced, and varied.

heartburn The painful sensation that occurs over the sternum when hydrochloric acid backs up into the lower esophagus.

heat cramps Muscle spasms that occur several hours after strenuous exercise; most often occur when sweat losses and fluid intakes are high, urine volume is low, and sodium intake is inadequate.

heat exhaustion A heat illness that is characterized by excessive sweating, weakness, nausea, dizziness, headache, and difficulty concentrating. Unchecked heat exhaustion can lead to heat stroke.

heat stroke A potentially fatal response to high temperature characterized by failure of the body's heat-regulating mechanisms. Symptoms include rapid pulse, reduced sweating, hot and dry skin, high temperature, headache, weakness, and sudden loss of consciousness. Commonly called sunstroke.

heat syncope Dizziness that occurs when people stand for too long in the heat or when they stop suddenly after a race or stand suddenly from a lying position; results from blood pooling in the lower extremities.

helper T-cells Activated T-cells that secrete chemicals needed to activate other immune cells.

heme The iron-containing molecule found in hemoglobin.

heme iron Iron that is part of hemoglobin and myoglobin; found only in animal-based foods such as meat, fish, and poultry.

hemoglobin The oxygen-carrying protein found in red blood cells; almost two-thirds of all iron in the body is found in hemoglobin.

hemosiderin A storage form of iron found primarily in the intestinal mucosa, spleen, bone marrow, and liver.

hephaestin A copper-containing protein that oxidizes Fe^{2+} to Fe^{3+} once iron is transported across the basolateral membrane by ferroportin.

high-density lipoprotein (HDL) A lipoprotein made in the liver and released into the blood. HDLs function to transport cholesterol from the tissues back to the liver. Often called the "good cholesterol."

high-yield varieties Semi-dwarf varieties of plants that are unlikely to fall over in wind and heavy rains and thus can carry larger amounts of seeds, greatly increasing the yield per acre.

homocysteine An amino acid that requires adequate levels of folate, vitamin B_6 and vitamin B_{12} for its metabolism. High levels of homocysteine in the blood are associated with an increased risk for vascular diseases such as cardiovascular disease.

hormone A chemical messenger that is secreted into the bloodstream by one of the many endocrine glands of the body. Hormones act as a regulator of physiological processes at a site remote from the gland that secreted them.

hormone-sensitive lipase The enzyme that breaks down the triglycerides stored in adipose tissue.

hunger A physiological drive to eat. Chronic hunger results in physical discomfort, weakness, or pain.

hydrogenation The process of adding hydrogen to unsaturated fatty acids, making them more saturated and thereby more solid at room temperature.

hydrolysis A catabolic process by which a large, chemically complex compound is broken apart with the addition of water.

hypercalcemia A condition marked by an abnormally high concentration of calcium in the blood.

hyperglycemia A condition in which blood glucose levels are higher than normal.

hyperkalemia A condition in which blood potassium levels are dangerously high.

hyperkeratosis A condition resulting in the excess accumulation of the protein keratin in the follicles of the skin; this condition can also impair the ability of epithelial tissues to produce mucus.

hypermagnesemia A condition marked by an abnormally high concentration of magnesium in the blood.

hypernatremia A condition in which blood sodium levels are dangerously high.

hypertension A chronic condition characterized by above-average blood pressure readings; specifically, systolic blood pressure over 140 mmHg or diastolic blood pressure over 90 mmHg.

hyperthyroidism A condition characterized by high blood levels of thyroid hormone.

hypertrophy An increase in strength and size that results from repeated work to a specific muscle or muscle group.

hypocalcemia A condition characterized by an abnormally low concentration of calcium in the blood.

hypoglycemia A condition marked by blood glucose levels that are below normal fasting levels.

hypokalemia A condition in which blood potassium levels are dangerously low.

hypomagnesemia A condition characterized by an abnormally low concentration of magnesium in the blood.

hyponatremia A condition in which blood sodium levels are dangerously low.

hypothalamus A region of the forebrain below (*hypo-*) the thalamus and cerebral hemispheres and above the pituitary gland and brain stem where visceral sensations such as hunger and thirst are regulated.

hypothesis An educated guess as to why a phenomenon occurs.

hypothyroidism A condition characterized by low blood levels of thyroid hormone.

I

immunocompetence Adequate ability to produce an effective immune response to an antigen.

impaired glucose tolerance Fasting blood glucose levels that are higher than normal but not high enough to lead to a diagnosis of type 2 diabetes.

incomplete proteins Foods that do not contain all of the essential amino acids in sufficient amounts to support growth and health.

indirect calorimetry A method used to estimate energy expenditure by measuring oxygen consumption and carbon dioxide production.

infant mortality Death of infants between birth and one year.

inorganic A substance or nutrient that does not contain the element carbon.

insensible water loss The loss of water not noticeable by a person, such as through evaporation from the skin and exhalation from the lungs during breathing.

insoluble fibres Fibres that do not dissolve in water.

insulin A hormone secreted by the beta cells of the pancreas in response to increased blood levels of glucose; facilitates uptake of glucose by body cells.

intensity Refers to the amount of effort expended during the activity, or how difficult the activity is to perform.

interstitial fluid The fluid that flows between the cells that make up a particular tissue or organ, such as muscle fibres or the liver.

intracellular fluid The fluid held at any given time within the walls of the body's cells.

intravascular fluid The fluid in the bloodstream and lymph.

intrinsic factor A protein secreted by cells of the stomach that binds to vitamin B_{12} and aids its absorption in the small intestine.

invisible fats Fats that are hidden in foods, such as the fats found in baked goods, regular-fat dairy products, marbling in meat, and fried foods.

iodopsin A colour-sensitive pigment found in the cone cells of the retina.

ion Any electrically charged particle, either positively or negatively charged.

iron depletion (stage I) The first stage of iron deficiency caused by a decrease in stored iron, which results in a decrease in blood ferritin levels.

iron-deficiency anemia (stage III) A form of anemia that results from severe iron deficiency.

iron-deficiency erythropoiesis (stage II) The second stage of iron deficiency, which causes a decrease in the transport of iron and leads to a decline in the ability to produce heme and make new red blood cells.

irritable bowel syndrome (IBS) A bowel disorder that interferes with normal functions of the colon. Symptoms are abdominal cramps, bloating, and constipation or diarrhea.

K

Keshan disease A heart disorder caused by selenium deficiency. It was first identified in children in the Keshan province of China.

keto acid The chemical structure that remains after the deamination of an amino acid.

ketoacidosis A condition in which excessive ketones are present in the blood, causing the blood to become very acidic, which alters basic body functions and damages tissues. Untreated ketoacidosis can be fatal. This condition is found in individuals with untreated diabetes mellitus.

ketogenic amino acid An amino acid that can be converted to acetyl CoA for the synthesis of free fatty acids.

ketone bodies Three- and four-carbon compounds (acetoacetate, acetone, and β- or 3-hydroxybutyrate) derived when acetyl CoA levels become elevated.

ketones Substances produced during the breakdown of fat when carbohydrate intake is insufficient to meet energy needs. Provide an alternative energy source for the brain when glucose levels are low.

ketosis The process by which the breakdown of fat during fasting states results in the production of ketones.

kwashiorkor A form of protein-energy malnutrition that is typically seen in developing countries in infants and toddlers who are weaned early because of the birth of a subsequent child. Denied breast milk, they are fed a cereal diet that provides adequate energy but inadequate protein.

L

lactase A digestive enzyme that breaks lactose into glucose and galactose.

lactate (or lactic acid) A three-carbon compound produced from pyruvate in oxygen-deprived conditions.

lactation The production of breast milk.

lacteal A small lymph vessel located inside of the villi of the small intestine.

lactose Also called *milk sugar*, a disaccharide consisting of one glucose molecule and one galactose molecule. Found in milk, including human breast milk.

lactose intolerance A disorder in which the body does not produce sufficient lactase enzyme and therefore cannot digest foods that contain lactose, such as cow's milk.

large intestine Final organ of the GI tract consisting of cecum, colon, rectum, and anal canal, and in which most water is absorbed and feces are formed.

lean body mass The amount of fat-free tissue, or bone, muscle, and internal organs, a person has.

leisure-time physical activity Any activity not related to a person's occupation; includes competitive sports, recreational activities, and planned exercise training.

leptin A hormone that is produced by body fat that acts to reduce food intake and to decrease body weight and body fat.

leukocytes White blood cells; they protect the body from infection and illness.

life expectancy The expected number of years remaining in one's life; typically stated from the time of birth. Children born in Canada in 2010 could expect to live, on average, 80.7 years.

lifespan The highest age reached by any member of a species; currently the human lifespan is 122 years.

limiting amino acid The essential amino acid that is missing or in the smallest supply in the amino acid pool and is thus responsible for slowing or halting protein synthesis.

linoleic acid An essential fatty acid found in vegetable and nut oils; also known as omega-6 fatty acid.

lipids A diverse group of organic substances that are insoluble in water; lipids include triglycerides, phospholipids, and sterols.

lipogenesis The synthesis of free fatty acids from nonlipid precursors such as ketogenic amino acids or ethanol.

lipolysis The enzyme-driven catabolism of triglycerides into free fatty acids and glycerol.

lipoprotein A spherical compound in which fat clusters in the centre and phospholipids and proteins form the outside of the sphere.

lipoprotein lipase An enzyme that sits on the outside of cells and breaks apart triglycerides so that their fatty acids can be removed and taken up by the cell.

liver The largest auxiliary organ of the GI tract and one of the most important organs of the body. Its functions include production of bile and processing of nutrient-rich blood from the small intestine.

long-chain fatty acids Fatty acids that are 14 or more carbon atoms in length.

low birth weight A weight of less than 2500 g at birth.

low-density lipoprotein (LDL) A lipoprotein formed in the blood from VLDLs that transports cholesterol to the cells of the body. Often called the "bad cholesterol."

low-intensity activities Activities that cause very mild increases in breathing, sweating, and heart rate.

M

macrocytic anemia A form of anemia manifested as the production of larger-than-normal red blood cells containing insufficient hemoglobin, which inhibits adequate transport of oxygen; also called *megaloblastic anemia*. Macrocytic anemia can be caused by severe folate deficiency or by vitamin B_{12} deficiency.

macronutrients Nutrients that the body requires in relatively large amounts to support normal function and health. Carbohydrates, lipids, and proteins are macronutrients.

macular degeneration A vision disorder caused by deterioration of the central portion of the retina and marked by loss or distortion of the central field of vision.

major minerals Minerals we need to consume in amounts of at least 100 mg per day and of which the total amount in our bodies is at least 5 g (or 5000 mg).

malnutrition A nutritional status that is out of balance; an individual is either getting too much or not enough of a particular nutrient or energy over a significant period of time.

maltase A digestive enzyme that breaks maltose into glucose.

maltose A disaccharide consisting of two molecules of glucose; does not generally occur independently in foods but results as a by-product of digestion; also called *malt sugar*.

marasmus A form of protein-energy malnutrition that results from grossly inadequate intakes of protein, energy, and other nutrients.

mass movement Involuntary, sustained, forceful contraction of the colon that occurs two or more times a day to push wastes toward the rectum.

maternal mortality Death rate of women from pregnancy-related causes, including in the immediate post-partum period.

matrix Gla protein A vitamin K–dependent protein that is located in the protein matrix of bone and also found in cartilage, blood vessel walls, and other soft tissues.

maximal heart rate The rate at which your heart beats during maximal-intensity exercise.

meat factor A special factor found in meat, fish, and poultry that enhances the absorption of non-heme iron.

medium-chain fatty acids Fatty acids that are six to twelve carbon atoms in length.

megadosing Taking a dose of a nutrient that is 10 or more times greater than the recommended amount.

memory cells Lymphocytes that differentiate from B cells and T cells, recognize a particular antigen for an infectious disease, and remain in the body after the disease is resolved to be ready to respond if the disease is encountered again later. The purpose of vaccination is to create memory lymphocytes.

menaquinone The form of vitamin K produced by bacteria in the large intestine.

menarche The beginning of menstruation, or the menstrual period.

metabolic syndrome A clustering of risk factors that increase one's risk for heart disease, type 2 diabetes, and stroke, including abdominal obesity, higher-than-normal HDL cholesterol levels, higher-than-normal blood pressure (greater than or equal to 130/85 mm Hg), and elevated fasting blood glucose levels.

metabolic water The water formed as a by-product of the body's metabolic reactions.

metabolism The sum of all the chemical and physical changes that occur in body tissues when food is converted from large molecules to small molecules.

metabolites The form that nutrients take when they have been used by the body. For example, lactate is a metabolite of carbohydrate that is produced when we use carbohydrate for energy.

metallothionein A zinc-containing protein within the enterocyte; it assists in the regulation of zinc homeostasis.

micelle A spherical compound made up of bile salts and biliary phospholipids that transports lipid digestion products to the intestinal mucosal cell.

microcytic anemia A form of anemia manifested as the production of smaller-than-normal red blood cells containing insufficient hemoglobin, which reduces the ability of the red blood cells to transport oxygen; it can result from iron deficiency or vitamin B_6 deficiency.

micronutrients Nutrients needed in relatively small amounts to support normal health and body functions. Vitamins and minerals are micronutrients.

microsomal ethanol oxidizing system (MEOS) A liver enzyme system that oxidizes ethanol to acetaldehyde; its activity predominates at higher levels of alcohol intake.

minerals Inorganic substances that are not broken down during digestion and absorption and are not destroyed by heat or light.

Minerals assist in the regulation of many body processes and are classified as major minerals or trace minerals.

moderate-intensity activities Activities that cause moderate increases in breathing, sweating, and heart rate.

moderation Eating the right amounts of foods to maintain a healthy weight and to optimize the body's metabolic processes.

monosaccharide The simplest of carbohydrates. Consists of one sugar molecule, the most common form of which is glucose.

monosaturated fatty acids (MUFAs) Fatty acids that have two carbons in the chain bound to each other with one double bond; these types of fatty acids are generally liquid at room temperature.

morbid obesity A condition in which a person's body weight exceeds 100% of normal, putting him or her at very high risk for serious health consequences.

morning sickness Varying degrees of nausea and vomiting associated with pregnancy, most commonly in the first trimester.

multifactorial disease Any disease that may be attributable to one or more of a variety of causes.

muscle cramps Involuntary, spasmodic, and painful muscle contractions that last for many seconds or even minutes; electrolyte imbalances are often the cause of muscle cramps.

musculoskeletal fitness Fitness of the muscles and bones.

mutual supplementation The process of combining two or more incomplete protein sources to make a complete protein.

myoglobin An iron-containing protein similar to hemoglobin except that it is found in muscle cells.

N

NAD (nicotinamide adenine dinucleotide) A coenzyme form of the B-vitamin niacin; NAD readily accepts electrons (hydrogen) from various donors.

negative folate balance (stage I) The first stage in folate depletion, in which the body has less folate available to it and serum levels of folate begin to decline.

neonatal Referring to a newborn.

neonatal mortality Death rate of newborns between birth and 28 days.

neural tube Embryonic tissue that forms a tube, which eventually becomes the brain and spinal cord.

neural tube defects The most common malformations of the central nervous system that occur during fetal development. A folate deficiency can cause neural tube defects.

night blindness A vitamin A–deficiency disorder that results in the loss of the ability to see in dim light.

night-eating syndrome Disorder characterized by intake of the majority of the day's energy between 8:00 p.m. and 6:00 a.m. Individuals with this disorder also experience mood and sleep disorders.

non-essential amino acids Amino acids that can be manufactured by the body in sufficient quantities and therefore do not need to be consumed regularly in our diet.

non-heme iron The form of iron that is not part of hemoglobin or myoglobin; found in animal-based and plant-based foods.

non-nutritive sweeteners Also called *alternative sweeteners*; manufactured sweeteners that provide little or no energy.

non-specific immune function Generalized body defence mechanisms that protect against the entry of foreign agents such as microorganisms and allergens; also called *innate immunity*.

nucleotide A molecule composed of a phosphate group, a pentose sugar called deoxyribose, and one of four nitrogenous bases: adenine (A), guanine (G), cytosine (C), or thymine (T).

nutrient-dense foods Foods that give the highest amount of nutrients for the least amount of energy (or calories).

nutrients Chemicals found in foods that are critical to human growth and function.

nutrition The scientific study of food and how it nourishes the body and influences health.

Nutrition Facts table The label on a food package that contains the nutrition information required by Health Canada.

nutrition paradox Coexistence of undernutrition and overnutrition in the same region or in the same family.

nutritive sweeteners Sweeteners such as sucrose, fructose, honey, and brown sugar that contribute calories (or energy).

O

obesity Having an excess amount of body fat that adversely affects health, resulting in a person having a weight that is substantially greater than some accepted standard for a given height.

oligosaccharide Complex carbohydrates that contain 3 to 10 monosaccharides.

opsin A protein that combines with retinal in the retina to form rhodopsin.

organic A substance or nutrient that contains the element carbon.

osmosis The movement of water (or any solvent) through a semi-permeable membrane from an area where solutes are less concentrated to areas where they are highly concentrated.

osmotic pressure The pressure that is needed to keep the particles in a solution from drawing liquid toward them across a semi-permeable membrane.

osteoblasts Cells that prompt the formation of new bone matrix by laying down the collagen-containing component of bone that is then mineralized.

osteocalcin A vitamin K–dependent protein that is secreted by osteoblasts and is associated with bone turnover.

osteoclasts Cells that erode the surface of bones by secreting enzymes and acids that dig grooves into the bone matrix.

osteomalacia Vitamin D–deficiency disease in adults, in which bones become weak and prone to fractures.

osteoporosis A disease characterized by low bone mass and deterioration of bone tissue, leading to increased bone fragility and fracture risk.

overhydration Dilution of body fluid. It results when water intake or retention is excessive.

overload principle Placing an extra physical demand on your body to improve your fitness level.

overnutrition A situation in which too much energy or too much of a given nutrient is consumed over time, causing conditions such as obesity, heart disease, or nutrient toxicity.

overpopulated Characteristic used to describe a region that has insufficient resources to support the number of people living there.

overt symptom A symptom that is obvious to a client, such as pain, fatigue, or a bruise.

overweight Having a moderate amount of excess body fat, resulting in a person having a weight that is greater than some accepted standard for a given height but is not considered obese.

oxidation A chemical reaction in which molecules of a substance are broken down into their component atoms. During oxidation, the atoms involved lose electrons.

oxidation–reduction reactions Reactions in which electrons are lost by one compound (it is oxidized) and simultaneously gained by another compound (it is reduced).

oxytocin A homone responsible for the "let down" of milk.

P

palliative care Reducing an individual's pain and discomfort without any attempts at a treatment or cure.

pancreas A gland located behind the stomach that secretes digestive enzymes.

pancreatic amylase An enzyme secreted by the pancreas into the small intestine that digests any remaining starch into maltose.

parathyroid hormone (PTH) A hormone secreted by the parathyroid gland when blood calcium levels fall. It is also known as parathormone, and it increases blood calcium levels by stimulating the activation of vitamin D, increasing reabsorption of calcium from the kidneys, and stimulating osteoclasts to break down bone, which releases more calcium into the bloodstream.

parietal cells Cells lining the gastric glands that secrete hydrochloric acid and intrinsic factor.

passive diffusion The simple absorptive process in which nutrients pass through the enterocytes and into the bloodstream without the use of a carrier protein or the requirement of energy.

pellagra A disease that results from severe niacin deficiency.

pepsin An enzyme in the stomach that begins the breakdown of proteins into shorter polypeptide chains and single amino acids.

peptic ulcer An area of the GI tract that has been eroded away by the acidic gastric juice of the stomach. The two main causes of peptic ulcers are *Helicobacter pylori* infection or use of nonsteroidal anti-inflammatory drugs.

peptide bonds Unique types of chemical bonds in which the amine group of one amino acid binds to the acid group of another to manufacture dipeptides and all larger peptide molecules.

peptide YY (PYY) A protein produced in the gastrointestinal tract that is released after a meal in amounts proportional to the energy content of the meal; it decreases appetite and inhibits food intake.

percent daily values (%DVs) Information on a Nutrition Facts table that is a benchmark to evaluate the nutrient content of a food, and is based on a set of standards for a 2000-kcal healthy diet.

peristalsis Waves of squeezing and pushing contractions that move food, chyme, and feces in one direction through the length of the GI tract.

pernicious anemia A special form of anemia that is the primary cause of a vitamin B_{12} deficiency; occurs at the end stage of an autoimmune disorder that causes the loss of various cells in the stomach.

peroxidation The oxidative deterioration of an organic compound, such as a lipid, resulting in the formation of a peroxide.

pH Stands for percentage of hydrogen. It is a measure of the acidity—or level of hydrogen—of any solution, including human blood.

phospholipids A type of lipid in which a fatty acid is combined with another compound that contains phosphate; unlike other lipids, phospholipids are soluble in water.

phosphorylation The addition of one or more phosphate groups to a chemical compound.

photosynthesis A process by which plants use sunlight to fuel a chemical reaction that combines carbon and water into glucose, which is then stored in their cells.

phylloquinone The form of vitamin K found in plants.

physical activity Any movement produced by muscles that increases energy expenditure; includes occupational, household, leisure-time, and transportation activities.

physical fitness The ability to carry out daily tasks with vigour and alertness, without undue fatigue, and with ample energy to enjoy leisure-time pursuits and meet unforeseen emergencies.

phytic acid The form of phosphorous stored in plants.

phytochemicals Chemicals found in plants (*phyto-* is from the Greek word for plant), such as pigments and other substances, that may reduce our risk for diseases such as cancer and heart disease.

pica An abnormal craving to eat something not fit for food, such as clay, paint, etc.

placenta A pregnancy-specific organ formed from both maternal and embryonic tissues. It is responsible for oxygen, nutrient, and waste exchange between the mother and fetus.

plasma The fluid portion of the blood; it is needed to maintain adequate blood volume so that the blood can flow easily throughout the body.

plasma cells Lymphocytes that have differentiated from activated B cells and produce millions of antibodies to an antigen during an infection.

platelets Cell fragments that assist in the formation of blood clots and help stop bleeding.

polypharmacy Concurrent use of five or more medications.

polysaccharide A complex carbohydrate consisting of long chains of glucose.

polyunsaturated fatty acids (PUFAs) Fatty acids that have more than one double bond in the chain; these types of fatty acids are generally liquid at room temperature.

portal vein A vessel that carries blood and various products of digestion from the digestive organs and spleen to the liver.

prebiotics Fibres that are preferentially fermented by the beneficial lactobacilli and bifidobacteria in gut flora and thus encourage their growth.

pre-eclampsia High blood pressure that is pregnancy-specific and accompanied by protein in the urine, edema, and unexpected weight gain.

preterm Birth of a baby prior to 38 weeks of gestation.

primary deficiency A deficiency that occurs when not enough of a nutrient is consumed in the diet.

probiotics Live beneficial microorganisms in foods that can colonize the intestine and optimize the intestinal bacterial environment. There is promising research suggesting various health benefits from consuming probiotics.

programmed theories of aging Aging is biologically determined, following a predictable pattern of physiologic changes, although the timing may vary from one person to another.

prolactin A hormone responsible for milk synthesis.

prooxidant A nutrient that promotes oxidation and oxidative cell and tissue damage.

proteases Enzymes that continue the breakdown of polypeptides in the small intestine.

protein digestibility corrected amino acid score (PDCAAS) A measurement of protein quality that considers the balance of amino acids as well as the digestibility of the protein in the food.

protein-energy malnutrition A disorder caused by inadequate consumption of protein. It is characterized by severe wasting.

proteins Large, complex molecules made up of amino acids and found as essential components of all living cells.

proteolysis The breakdown of dietary proteins into single amino acids or small peptides that are absorbed by the body.

provitamin An inactive form of a vitamin that the body can convert to an active form. An example is beta-carotene.

puberty The period in life in which secondary sexual characteristics develop and people are biologically capable of reproducing.

Public Health Agency of Canada (PHAC) A government agency that is responsible for health promotion in Canada. Its mandate is to prevent and control chronic and infectious diseases and injuries and to prepare and respond to public health emergencies.

purging An attempt to rid the body of unwanted food by vomiting or other compensatory means, such as excessive exercise, fasting, or laxative abuse.

R

raffinose An oligosaccharide composed of galactose, glucose, and fructose. Also called *melitose,* it is found in beans, cabbage, broccoli, and other vegetables.

reactive oxygen species (ROS) A specific term used to describe an oxygen molecule that has become a free radical.

Recommended Dietary Allowance (RDA) The average daily nutrient intake level that meets the nutrient requirements of 97% to 98% of healthy individuals in a particular life stage and gender group.

registered dietitian (RD) A professional designation that requires a minimum of a bachelor's degree in nutrition, completion of supervised internship experience, a passing grade on a national examination, and maintenance of registration with a provincial regulatory body. RDs are qualified to work in a variety of settings.

remodelling The two-step process by which bone tissue is recycled; includes the breakdown of existing bone and the formation of new bone.

renin An enzyme secreted by the kidneys in response to a decrease in blood pressure. Renin converts the blood protein angiotensinogen to angiotensin I, which eventually results in an increase in sodium reabsorption.

resistance training Exercises in which our muscles work against resistance.

resorption The process by which the surface of bone is broken down by cells called osteoclasts.

resveratrol A potent phenolic antioxidant found in red wines as well as grapes and nuts.

retina The delicate light-sensitive membrane lining the inner eyeball and connected to the optic nerve. It contains retinal.

retinal An active, aldehyde form of vitamin A that plays an important role in healthy vision and immune function.

retinoic acid An active, acid form of vitamin A that plays an important role in cell growth and immune function.

retinol An active, alcohol form of vitamin A that plays an important role in healthy vision and immune function.

rhodopsin A light-sensitive pigment found in the rod cells that is formed by retinal and opsin.

ribose A five-carbon monosaccharide that is located in the genetic material of cells.

rickets Vitamin D–deficiency disease in children. Symptoms include deformities of the skeleton such as bowed legs and knocked knees.

rod cells Light-sensitive cells found in the retina that contain rhodopsin and react to dim light and interpret black-and-white images.

S

saliva A mixture of water, mucus, enzymes, and other chemicals that moistens the mouth and food, binds food particles together, and begins the digestion of carbohydrates.

salivary amylase An enzyme in saliva that breaks starch into smaller particles and eventually into the disaccharide maltose.

salivary glands A group of glands found under and behind the tongue and beneath the jaw that releases saliva continually as well as in response to the thought, sight, smell, or presence of food.

salt resistance A condition in which certain people do not experience changes in blood pressure with changes in salt intake.

salt sensitivity A condition in which certain people respond to a high salt intake by experiencing an increase in blood pressure; these people also experience a decrease in blood pressure when salt intake is low.

sarcopenia Age-related progressive loss of muscle mass, muscle strength, and muscle function.

sarcopenic obesity A condition in which increased body weight and body fat mass coexist with inappropriately low muscle mass and strength.

saturated fatty acids (SFAs) Fatty acids that have no carbons joined together with a double bond; these types of fatty acids are generally solid at room temperature.

secondary deficiency A deficiency that occurs when a person cannot absorb enough of a nutrient, excretes too much of a nutrient from the body, or cannot utilize a nutrient efficiently.

segmentation Rhythmic contraction of the circular muscles of the intestines that squeezes chyme, mixes it, and enhances digestion and absorption of nutrients from the chyme.

seizures Uncontrollable muscle spasms caused by increased nervous system excitability that can result from electrolyte imbalances or a chronic disease such as epilepsy.

selenocysteine An amino acid derivative that is the active form of selenium in the body.

selenomethionine An amino acid derivative that is the storage form for selenium in the body.

senescence The progressive deterioration of bodily functions over time, resulting in increased risk of disability, disease, and death.

sensible water loss Water loss that is noticed by a person, such as urine output and sweating.

set-point theory A theory that suggests that the body raises or lowers energy expenditure in response to increased and decreased food intake and physical activity. This action serves to maintain an individual's body weight within a narrow range.

severe acute malnutrition A state of extreme energy deficit defined as a weight for height more than three standard deviations below the mean or the presence of nutrition-related edema, and associated with a risk of death five to twenty times higher than that of well-nourished individuals.

short-chain fatty acids Fatty acids fewer than six carbon atoms in length.

sickle cell anemia A genetic disorder that causes red blood cells to be shaped like a sickle or crescent. These cells cannot travel smoothly through the blood vessels, causing cell breakage and anemia.

simple carbohydrate Commonly called *sugar*; a monosaccharide or disaccharide such as glucose.

small for gestational age (SGA) Infants whose birth weight for gestational age falls below the 10th percentile.

small intestine The longest portion of the GI tract where most digestion and absorption take place.

soluble fibres Fibres that dissolve in water.

solvent A substance that is capable of mixing with and breaking apart a variety of compounds. Water is an excellent solvent.

specific immune function The strongest defence against pathogens. Requires adaptation of lymphocytes that recognize antigens and that multiply to protect against the pathogens carrying those antigens, also called *adaptive immunity* or *acquired immunity*.

sphincter A tight ring of muscle separating some of the organs of the GI tract and opening in response to nerve signals indicating that food is ready to pass into the next section.

spina bifida Embryonic neural tube defect that occurs when the spinal vertebrae fail to completely enclose the spinal cord, allowing it to protrude.

spontaneous abortion (also called *miscarriage*) Natural termination of a pregnancy and expulsion of pregnancy tissues because of a genetic, developmental, or physiologic abnormality that is so severe that the pregnancy cannot be maintained.

stachyose An oligosaccharide composed of two galactose molecules, a glucose molecule, and a fructose molecule. Found in the Chinese artichoke and various beans and legumes.

starch A polysaccharide stored in plants; the storage form of glucose in plants.

sterols A type of lipid found in foods and the body that has a ring structure; cholesterol is the most common sterol that occurs in our diets.

stomach A J-shaped organ where food is partially digested, churned, and stored until release into the small intestine.

stunted growth A condition of shorter stature than expected for chronological age.

subclinical deficiency A deficiency in its early stages, when few or no symptoms are observed.

subsistence crops Crops grown to be eaten by a family or community, such as rice, millet, and garden vegetables. Surpluses may be sold locally.

sucrase A digestive enzyme that breaks sucrose into glucose and fructose.

sucrose A disaccharide composed of one glucose molecule and one fructose molecule; sweeter than lactose or maltose.

sudden infant death syndrome (SIDS) The sudden death of a previously healthy infant; the most common cause of death in infants more than one month of age.

sustainable agriculture Term referring to techniques of food production that preserve the environment indefinitely.

T

T cells Lymphocytes that mature in the thymus gland and are of several varieties, including helper T cells.

TCA cycle The tricarboxylic acid (TCA) cycle is a repetitive series of eight metabolic reactions, located in cell mitochondria, that metabolizes acetyl CoA for the production of carbon dioxide, high-energy GTP, and reduced coenzymes NADH and $FADH_2$.

teratogen Any substance that can cause a birth defect.

theory A scientific consensus, based on data drawn from repeated experiments, as to why a phenomenon occurs.

thermic effect of food (TEF) The energy expended as a result of processing food consumed.

thirst mechanism A cluster of nerve cells in the hypothalamus that stimulates our conscious desire to drink fluids in response to an increase in the concentration of salt in our blood or a decrease in blood pressure and blood volume.

thrifty gene theory A theory that suggests that some people possess a gene (or genes) that causes them to be energetically thrifty, resulting in them expending less energy at rest and during physical activity.

time of activity How long each exercise session lasts.

tocopherol The family of vitamin E that is the active form in our bodies.

tocotrienol A second family of vitamin E that does not play an important biological role in our bodies.

Tolerable Upper Intake Level (UL) The highest average daily nutrient intake level likely to pose no risk of adverse health effects to almost all individuals in a particular life stage and gender group.

total fibre The sum of dietary fibre and functional fibre.

trabecular bone (spongy bone) A porous bone tissue that makes up only 20% of the skeleton and is found within the ends of the long bones, inside the spinal vertebrae, inside the flat bones (breastbone, ribs, and most bones of the skull), and inside the bones of the pelvis.

trace minerals Minerals we need to consume in amounts less than 100 mg per day and of which the total amount in our bodies is less than 5 g (or 5000 mg).

transamination The process of transferring the amine group from one amino acid to another to manufacture a new amino acid.

transcription The process through which messenger RNA copies genetic information from DNA in the nucleus.

transferrin The transport protein for iron.

transgenic crops Plant varieties that have had one or more genes altered by the use of genetic technologies; also called *genetically modified organisms,* or *GMOs.*

translation The process that occurs when the genetic information carried by messenger RNA is translated into a chain of amino acids at the ribosome.

transport proteins Protein molecules that help to transport substances throughout the body and across cell membranes.

triglyceride A molecule consisting of three fatty acids attached to a three-carbon glycerol backbone.

trimester Any one of three stages of pregnancy, each lasting 13 to 14 weeks.

T-score A comparison of an individual's bone density to the average peak bone density of a 30-year-old healthy adult.

tumour Any newly formed mass of undifferentiated cells.

type 1 diabetes A disorder in which the body cannot produce enough insulin.

type 2 diabetes A progressive disorder in which body cells become less responsive to insulin.

U

ulcerative colitis A chronic disease of the large intestine, or colon, indicated by inflammation and ulceration of the mucosa, or innermost lining of the colon.

umbilical cord The cord containing arteries and veins that connect the baby (from the navel) to the mother via the placenta.

undernutrition A situation in which very little energy or too few nutrients are consumed over time, causing significant weight loss or a nutrient-deficiency disease.

underweight Having too little body fat to maintain health, causing a person to have a weight that is below an acceptably defined standard for a given height.

urinary tract infection A bacterial infection of the urethra, the tube leading from the bladder to the body exterior.

V

vaccination Administering a small amount of antigen to elicit an immune response for the purpose of developing memory cells that will protect against the disease at a later time.

variety Eating many different foods from the different food groups on a regular basis.

vegetarian A person who does not eat meat, poultry, or fish or products containing these foods.

very-low-density lipoprotein (VLDL) A lipoprotein made in the liver and intestine that functions to transport endogenous lipids, especially triglycerides, to the tissues of the body.

vigorous-intensity activities Activities that produce significant increases in breathing, sweating, and heart rate; talking is difficult when exercising at a vigorous intensity.

viscous Term referring to a gel-like consistency; viscous fibres form a gel when dissolved in water.

visible fats Fat we can see in our foods or see added to foods, such as butter, margarine, cream, shortening, salad dressings, chicken skin, and untrimmed fat on meat.

vitamins Micronutrients that contain carbon and assist us in regulating our bodies' processes. They are classified as water soluble or fat soluble.

W

warm-up Also called preliminary exercise; includes activities that prepare you for an exercise bout, including stretching, calisthenics, and movements specific to the exercise bout.

wasting A condition of very low body-weight-for-height or extreme thinness.

water-soluble vitamins Vitamins that are soluble in water. These include vitamin C and the B-vitamins.

X

xerophthalmia An irreversible blindness due to hardening of the cornea and drying of the mucous membranes of the eye.

xerostomia Dry mouth due to decreased saliva production.

Z

zygote A fertilized egg (ovum) consisting of a single cell.

Index

Note: Page numbers followed by "f" indicate figures. Page numbers followed by "t" indicate tables.

Credits

Photo Credits

Chapter 1

Chapter Opener: © Elenathewise/Fotolia; **p.3:** Fotocrisis/Shutterstock; **p. 4:** © Andrey Kiselev/Fotolia; **p. 5:** Lester V. Bergman/Corbis; **Fig. 1.1:** © Kurhan/Fotolia; **p. 11:** © twixx/Fotolia; **p. 12:** © Yuri Arcurs/Fotolia; **p. 14:** © luca fabbian/Fotolia; **p. 15:** © tan4ikk/Fotolia; **p. 16:** © Maridav/Fotolia; **p. 18:** © AVAVA/Fotolia; **p. 22:** Michelle Del Guercio/Photo Researchers, Inc; **p. 23:** © Jacob Berthelsen/Fotolia; **p. 28:** © Monkey Business/Fotolia; **p. 29:** © Yuri Arcurs/Fotolia; **p. 32 top:** © Odua/Fotolia; **bottom:** © Kzenon/Fotolia; **p. 39:** Randy Jirtle, Laboratory of Epigenetics and Genomic Imprinting, Duke University; **p. 40:** © BlueOrange Studio/Fotolia.

Chapter 2

Chapter Opener: © cindymmcintyre/Fotolia; **p. 43:** © Mist/Fotolia; **p. 44:** © Monkey Business/Fotolia; **p. 45 top:** Photosani/Shutterstock; **bottom:** forest badger/Shutterstock; **Fig. 2.1:** Creative Digital Visions/Pearson Science; **p. 47 top:** © Konstantin Kulikov/Fotolia; **bottom:** © Monkey Business/Fotolia; **Fig. 2.2:** Courtesy of PepsiCo Foods Canada; **p. 48:** © Nitr/Fotolia; **p. 52 top:** © iofoto/Fotolia; **bottom:** © Maridav/Fotolia; **p. 54:** © al62/Fotolia; **p. 55:** © evgenia sh/Fotolia; **p. 56:** © Okea/Fotolia; **Fig. 2.11aa:** Image Source Pink/Alamy. **Fig. 2.11ab:** © Chris Brignell/Fotolia. **Fig. 2.11ba:** © alexfiodorov/Fotolia. **Fig. 2.11bb:** © Ruslan Olinchuk/Fotolia; **p. 63:** Kzenon/Shutterstock; **p. 68 top:** © Dmytro Sukharevskyy/Fotolia; **bottom:** © Dmytro Konstantynov/Fotolia; **p. 69:** Sigrid Estrada/Getty Images; **p. 74:** © Marco Mayer/Fotolia.

Chapter 3

Chapter Opener: © Tomo Jesenicnik/Fotolia; **p. 77:** © allyb208/Fotolia; **p. 78 top:** © Suprijono Suharjoto/Fotolia; **bottom:** © Lasse Kristensen/Fotlia; **Fig. 3.2:** © Deklofenak/Fotolia; **p. 81:** © Ramon Grosso/Fotolia; **p. 84:** © Image Source IS2/Fotolia; **p. 91:** SPL/Photo Researchers; **Fig. 3.13a:** Steve Gschmeissner/SPL/Photo Researchers. **Fig. 3.13b:** Dr. David M. Phillips/Getty Images; **p. 97:** Shippee/Shutterstock; **p. 101:** © Roman Sigaev/Fotolia; **Fig. 3.19:** BIOPHOTO ASSOCIATES/Photo Researchers/Getty Images; **p. 102:** © Maridav/Fotolia; **p. 103:** Ben Fink/Dorling Kindersley; **p. 104:** © Elenathewise/Fotolia; **p. 106:** © Marco Mayer/Fotolia; **p. 107:** Alex Robinson/Dorling Kindersley; **p. 114:** © pressmaster/Fotolia; **p. 115:** Glutenpro Inc.

Chapter 4

Chapter Opener: © Viktor/Fotolia; **p. 117:** Anatoliy Samara/Shutterstock; **p. 119:** Brocreativ/Shutterstock; **p. 121 left:** © volff/Fotolia; **right:** © Paul Fleet/Fotolia; **p. 123:** Monkey Business Images/Shutterstock; **p. 124:** © rafer76/Fotolia; **p. 129 left:** © volff/Fotolia; **right:** © Elenathewise/Fotolia; **p. 130 top:** © Maridav/Fotolia; **bottom:** © auremar/Fotolia; **p. 131:** Peter Weber/Shutterstock; **p. 132:** © Dorling Kindersley; **p. 134 top:** Justin Sullivan/Getty Images; **bottom:** © gemphotography/Fotolia; **p. 137:** © Elenathewise/Fotolia; **Fig. 4.15a:** Ildi Papp/Shutterstock. **Fig. 4.15b:** © motorlka/Fotolia. **Fig. 4.15c:** Subbotina Anna/Fotolia. **Fig. 4.15d:** © dusk/Fotolia; **p. 140:** Courtesy of Snowcrest Foods; **Fig. 4.16:** Creative Digital Visions,Pearson Science. **Fig. 4.17a:** © kostrez/Fotolia. **Fig. 4.17b:** © Giuseppe_R/Fotolia; **p. 143:** Kristin Piljay/Pearson Education; **Fig. 4.19:** Courtesy of Roche Diagnostics; **p. 147:** Courtesy of Animas Corporation; **p. 148:** Tim Mosenfelder/Getty Images; **p. 150:** © Christian Jung/Fotolia; **p. 157:** Brian Buckley/Alamy Images; **p. 158:** © Rtimages/Fotolia; **p. 159:** © Islemount Images/Alamy.

Chapter 5

Chapter Opener: © Barbara Dudzinska/Fotolia; **p. 161:** Martin Garnham/Shutterstock; **p. 162 top:** © Ocean/Corbis; **bottom:** Clive Streeter/Dorling Kindersley; **p. 165 top:** © 1999istek/Fotolia; **bottom:** © dinostock/Fotolia; **p. 166:** © Stephen VanHorn/Fotolia; **p. 168:** © Igor Kolos/Fotolia; **p. 170:** Dorling Kindersley; **p. 171:** © Elena Schweitzer/Fotolia; **p. 173:** Quest/Photo Researchers Inc.; **p. 175 top:** © Maridav/Fotolia; **bottom:** © Jörg Engel/Fotolia; **p. 177 top:** © Alison Bowden/Fotolia; **bottom:** Danny E. Hooks/Shutterstock; **p. 179:** © Maridav/Fotolia; **p. 180:** Wilmy van Ulft/Shutterstock; **p. 184:** © 14ktgold/Fotolia; **Fig. 5.14:** © Louella Folsom/Fotolia; **p. 186:** © renamarie/Fotolia; **Fig. 5.17a:** Science Photo Library/Photo Researchers. **Fig. 5.17b:** Wikipedia; **p. 190 top:** © Jeffrey Banke/Fotolia; **bottom:** altafulla/Shutterstock; **p. 198 top:** David McNew/Getty Images; **bottom:** © Monkey Business/Fotolia; **p. 199:** Dorling Kindersley.

Chapter 6

Chapter Opener: Dorling Kindersley; **p. 201:** © Elenathewise/Fotolia; **p. 202:** Andresr/Shutterstock; **p. 203:** © Maridav/Fotolia; **Fig. 6.7b:** Andrew Syed/Photo Researchers; **p. 208:** © robynmac/Fotolia; **p. 209 top:** © Mark Stout/Fotolia; **bottom:** © Maridav/Fotolia; **Fig. 6.8a–d:** Creative Digital Visions/Pearson Science; **Fig. 6.11a:** © Nobilior/Fotolia. **Fig. 6.11b:** Medical-on-line/Alamy; **Fig. 6.13a:** © bonniemarie/Fotolia. **Fig. 6.13b:** Andrew Holdbrooke/Corbis. **Fig. 6.13c:** © Maridav/Fotolia; **p. 222 top:** Ranald MacKechnie/Dorling Kindersley; **bottom:** Pearson Education; **p. 224:** BananaStock/Alamy Images; **p. 225:** Ekaterina Nikitina/Shutterstock; **p. 226:** © Lilyana Vynogradova/Fotolia; **p. 227:** Andy Crawford/Dorling Kindersley; **Fig. 6.15a:** Paul Almasy/Corbis. **Fig. 6.15b:** © Stephen Morrison/epa/Corbis; **Fig. 6.16:** Dr. Stanley Flegler/Visuals Unlimited/Getty Images; **p. 234 top left:** © erwinova/Fotolia; **top right:** © Rohit Seth/Fotolia; **bottom left:** © steverts/Fotolia; **bottom right:** © michelstock/Fotolia.

Chapter 7

Chapter Opener: colorvsbw/Shutterstock; **p. 237:** © Picture Partners/Fotolia; **p. 238:** © Vibe Images/Fotolia; **p. 244:** © Inga Nielsen/Fotolia; **p. 249:** © Joshua Resnick/Fotolia; **p.252:** © Gary Scott/Fotolia; **p.254:** © Nitr/Fotolia; **p.257:** © Rob Stark/Fotolia; **p.258 top:** © Maridav/Fotolia; **bottom:** © Valua Vitaly/Fotolia; **p.260:** © Nitr/Fotolia.

Chapter 8

Chapter Opener: © auremar/Fotolia; **p. 273:** Alexandr Makarov/Shutterstock; **p. 276 top:** © fredredhat/Fotolia; **bottom:** Paul Prescott/Shutterstock; **p. 278:** © Laurent Renault/Fotolia; **p. 280 top:** Perry Correll/shutterstock; **bottom:** © fotogal/Fotolia; **p. 281:** © Shariff Che'Lah/Fotolia; **p. 282:** © Julián Rovagnati/Fotolia; **p. 283:** © Chariclo/Fotolia; **p. 284:** © Anna Kucherova/Fotolia; **Fig. 8.1a:** Southern Illinois University/Photo Researchers. **Fig. 8.1b:** © www.doglikehorse.com/Fotolia. **Fig. 8.1c:** © phiseksit/Fotolia. **Fig. 8.1d:** © Igor Dutina/Fotolia. **Fig. 8.1e:** Joy Brown/Shutterstock; **p. 286:** © Serghei Velusceac/Fotolia; **p. 287:** © stockstudios/

Chapter 15

Chapter Opener: Racheal Grazias/Shutterstock; **p. 535:** © Paul Maguire/Fotolia; **p. 536:** © Magalice/Fotolia; **p. 538:** © micromonkey/Fotolia; **p. 539:** © erwinova/Fotolia; **Fig. 15.3a:** © mr.markin/Fotolia. **Fig. 15.3b:** © Vibe Images/Fotolia. **Fig. 15.3c:** © laurent hamels/Fotolia; **p. 546 top:** © Monkey Business/Fotolia; **bottom:** © Brocreative/Fotolia; **p. 548:** © Maridav/Fotolia; **p. 551:** © Moreno Novello/Fotolia; **p. 554:** Sian Irvine/Dorling Kindersley; **Fig. 15.10a–f:** Laura Murray/Pearson Education; **p. 555:** © Serhan Sidan/Fotolia; **p. 557:** © Vladimir Voronin/Fotolia; **p. 558:** © soupstock/Fotolia; **p. 559:** © Dzmitry Fedarovich/Fotolia; **p. 560:** © violetkaipa/Fotolia; **Fig. 15.12:** © Gudellaphoto/Fotolia; **p. 561:** © auremar/Fotolia; **p. 564:** AP Photo/Kansas City Star, Kelley Chin; **p. 565:** © huaxiadragon/Fotolia; **p. 566 top:** © Pumba/Fotolia; **bottom:** © alexandru verinciuc/Fotolia; **p. 568:** Matthew Ward © Dorling Kindersley; **p. 575 top:** © Vyacheslav Baranov/Fotolia; **bottom:** © Africa Studio/Fotolia; **p. 576 top:** © Monkey Business/Fotolia; **bottom:** © Nomad_Soul/Fotolia.

Chapter 16

Chapter Opener: © sonya etchison/Fotolia; **p. 579:** Douglas Freer/Shutterstock; **p. 580:** David Phillips/The Population Council/Photo Researchers; **Fig. 16.4a:** Dr G. Moscoso/Photo Researchers. **Fig. 16.4b:** Petit Format/Photo Researchers, Inc. **Fig. 16.4c:** Neil Bromhall/Photo Researchers, Inc. **Fig. 16.4d:** © Marcin Sadlowski/Fotolia; **Fig. 16.5:** Ron Sutherland/Photo Researchers; **Fig. 16.6:** ingret/Shutterstock; **p. 586:** Ian O'Leary/Getty; **p. 587:** © Barbara Dudzinska/Fotolia; **Fig. 16.7:** Biophoto Associates/Science Source/Photo Researchers; **p. 589:** © Dani Vincek/Fotolia; **p. 592:** © Monkey Business/Fotolia; **p. 593 top:** © Graça Victoria/Fotolia; **bottom:** © Dmitry Rukhlenko/Fotolia; **p. 594:** © nyul/Fotolia; **p. 595:** © dalaprod/Fotolia; **p. 596:** George Steinmetz Photography; **p. 597:** © Andrey Bandurenko/Fotolia; **Fig. 16.9:** © Jeanne Hatch/Fotolia; **p. 601:** © Oleg Kozlov/Fotolia; **p. 603:** Darama/Corbis; **p. 605:** © dalaprod/Fotolia; **p. 606:** © Jkeen/Fotolia; **p. 610:** © Monkey Business/Fotolia; **p. 611:** © Melastmohican/Fotolia; **p. 613:** © Tom Grill/Corbis; **p. 615 left:** © Maridav/Fotolia; **right:** Hospital Archives, The Hospital for Sick Children, Toronto; **p. 616:** © Vivid Pixels/Fotolia; **p. 617:** © criminalatt/Fotolia; **Fig. 16.13:** Dr. Pamela R. Erickson/Pearson Education; **p. 624:** © Monkey Business/Fotolia; **p. 625:** © Dimitrios Rizopoulos/Fotolia.

Chapter 17

Chapter Opener: © sdenness/Fotolia; **p. 627:** © Vojtech Vlk/Fotolia; **p. 628 top:** Garry Wade/Taxi/Getty Images; **bottom:** © rouakcz/Fotolia; **Fig. 17.2:** © zest_marina/Fotolia; **p. 633:** © Stephanie Frey/Fotolia; **p. 634 top:** © 1999istek/Fotolia; **bottom:** © volff/Fotolia; **p. 635:** Courtesy of Vitasoy USA, Inc.; **p. 636:** debr22pics/Shutterstock; **p. 637:** © michaeljung/Fotolia; **p. 638 top:** © Donald Swartz/Fotolia; **bottom:** © Anatoliy Samara/Fotolia; **p. 640:** Zurijeta/Shutterstock; **Fig. 174a:** © Ivonne Wierink/Fotolia. **Fig. 17.4b:** © Fotoksa/Fotolia. **Fig. 17.4c:** © Monart Design/Fotolia; **p. 641:** © Maridav/Fotolia; **Fig. 17.5:** www.sghi.org; **p. 643:** © Amy Myers/Fotolia;

p. 644: © klikk/Fotolia; **Fig. 17.7:** Data from: Dairy Farmers of Ontario. www.milk.org.; **p. 646 top:** Laura Murray/Pearson Education/Pearson Science; **middle:** Karl Prouse/Catwalking/Getty Images; **bottom:** © micromonkey/Fotolia; **p. 647:** © Peter Kim/Fotolia; **p. 648:** © fuzzbones/Fotolia; **p. 649:** © Monkey Business/Fotolia; **p. 651:** © sonya etchison/Fotolia; **p. 661:** © gzorgz/Fotolia.

Chapter 18

Chapter Opener: © auremar/Fotolia; **p. 663:** © Yuri Arcurs/Fotolia; **p. 664 top:** © diego cervo/Fotolia; **bottom:** Richard Koek/Stone/Getty Images; **p. 665:** Claro Cortes IV/Reuters/Corbis; **p. 667:** © michaeljung/Fotolia; **p. 668:** Raymond Gehman/Corbis; **p. 670 left:** © Yuri Arcurs/Fotolia; **right:** © nyul/Fotolia; **p. 671:** © Frantab/Fotolia; **p. 673:** © Lisa F. Young/Fotolia; **p. 674:** © goodluz/Fotolia; **p. 675:** © Maridav/Fotolia; **p. 676:** Jed Share/Getty Images; **p. 678:** © Fenton/Fotolia; **p. 679:** © Anna Kucherova/Fotolia; **p. 680:** © Marty Haas/Fotolia; **p. 682:** © Monkey Business/Fotolia; **p. 684:** Karen Preuss/The Image Works; **p. 685:** © James Steidl/Fotolia; **p. 690:** © Mihai Simonia/Fotolia; **p.691 left:** © PHB.cz/Fotolia; **right:** © Monkey Business/Fotolia.

Chapter 19

Chapter Opener: © erikdegraaf/Fotolia; **p. 693:** © Elwynn/Fotolia; **p. 694:** Peter Turnley/Corbis; **Fig. 19.3:** AP Photo/Brennan Linsley; **p. 697:** © Borderlands/Alamy; **p. 698 top:** © Kevin R. Morris/Bohemian Nomad Picturemakers/CORBIS; **bottom:** Neil Cooper/Alamy Images; **p. 699:** Reuters/Corbis; **p.700:** Oli Scarff/Getty Images News/Getty Images; **p. 701 top:** Nik Wheeler/Corbis; **bottom:** © Ruud Morijn/Fotolia; **p. 703:** David Turnley/Corbis; **p. 704:** © JanMika/Fotolia; **p. 707:** © Maridav/Fotolia; **Fig. 19.5:** © TravelPhotography/Fotolia; **p. 709:** © .shock/Fotolia; **p. 710:** © rebecca abell/Fotolia; **p. 717:** © Monkey Business/Fotolia; **p. 718:** © Monkey Business/Fotolia.

Figure and Text Credits

Fig. 11.11 From Marieb, E. Human Anatomy and Physiology, 5/e, Fig. 16.7, Copyright © 2003 Benjamin Cummings. Used by permission of Pearson Education, Inc. **Fig. 14.13** Pearson Science. **Fig. 15.2a–e** Canadian Physical Activity Guidelines, © 2011. Used with permission from the Canadian Society for Exercise Physiology, www.csep.ca/guidelines. **Chapter 15 Highlight** Coaching Association of Canada/www.coach.ca **Chapter 15 See for Yourself** Centers for Disease Control and Prevention. 2005. Physical activity for everyone: Making physical activity part of your life: Tips for being more active. Available at www.cdc.gov/nccdphp/dnpa/physical/life/tips.htm. United States Department of Health and Human Services. 2005. Get active: Goals. Available at www.smallstep.gov/step_3/step_3_goals.html. **Fig. A.3** TimVickers **Fig. A.11** Pearson Science.

Tolerable Upper Intake Levels(UL[a])

Vitamins

Life-Stage Group	Vitamin A (µg/d)[b]	Vitamin C (mg/d)	Vitamin D (µg/d)	Vitamin E (mg/d)[c,d]	Niacin (mg/d)[d]	Vitamin B$_6$ (mg/d)[d]	Folate (µg/d)[d]	Choline (g/d)
Infants								
0–6 mo	600	ND[e]	25	ND	ND	ND	ND	ND
7–12 mo	600	ND	38	ND	ND	ND	ND	ND
Children								
1–3 y	600	400	63	200	10	30	300	1.0
4–8 y	900	650	75	300	15	40	400	1.0
Males, Females								
9–13 y	1,700	1,200	100	600	20	60	600	2.0
14–18 y	2,800	1,800	100	800	30	80	800	3.0
19–70 y	3,000	2,000	100	1,000	35	100	1,000	3.5
>70 y	3,000	2,000	100	1,000	35	100	1,000	3.5
Pregnancy								
≤18 y	2,800	1,800	100	800	30	80	800	3.0
19–50 y	3,000	2,000	100	1,000	35	100	1,000	3.5
Lactation								
≤18 y	2,800	1,800	100	800	30	80	800	3.0
19–50 y	3,000	2,000	100	1,000	35	100	1,000	3.5

Elements

Life-Stage Group	Boron (mg/d)	Calcium (g/d)	Copper (µg/d)	Fluoride (mg/d)	Iodine (µg/d)	Iron (mg/d)	Magnesium (mg/d)[f]	Manganese (mg/d)	Molybdenum (µg/d)	Nickel (mg/d)	Phosphorus (g/d)	Selenium (µg/d)	Vanadium (mg/d)[g]	Zinc (mg/d)
Infants														
0–6 mo	ND	1	ND	0.7	ND	40	ND	ND	ND	ND	ND	45	ND	4
7–12 mo	ND	1.5	ND	0.9	ND	40	ND	ND	ND	ND	ND	60	ND	5
Children														
1–3 y	3	5	1,000	1.3	200	40	65	2	300	0.2	3	90	ND	7
4–8 y	6	5	3,000	2.2	300	40	110	3	600	0.3	3	150	ND	12
Males, Females														
9–13 y	11	3.0	5,000	10	600	40	350	6	1,100	0.6	4	280	ND	23
14–18 y	17	3.0	8,000	10	900	45	350	9	1,700	1.0	4	400	ND	34
19–50 y	20	2.5	10,000	10	1,100	45	350	11	2,000	1.0	4	400	1.8	40
51–70 y	20	2.0	10,000	10	1,100	45	350	11	2,000	1.0	4	400	1.8	40
>70 y	20	2.0	10,000	10	1,100	45	350	11	2,000	1.0	3	400	1.8	40
Pregnancy														
≤18 y	17	3.0	8,000	10	900	45	350	9	1,700	1.0	3.5	400	ND	34
19–50 y	20	2.5	10,000	10	1,100	45	350	11	2,000	1.0	3.5	400	ND	40
Lactation														
≤18 y	17	3.0	8,000	10	900	45	350	9	1,700	1.0	4	400	ND	34
19–50 y	20	2.5	10,000	10	1,100	45	350	11	2,000	1.0	4	400	ND	40

Data from: Adapted from the Dietary Reference Intakes series, National Academies Press. Copyright 1997, 1998, 2000, 2001, 2011 by the National Academy of Sciences. These reports may be accessed via www.nap.edu. Courtesy of the National Academies Press, Washington, D.C.

[a] UL = The maximum level of daily nutrient intake that is likely to pose no risk of adverse effects. Unless otherwise specified, the UL represents total intake from food, water, and supplements. Due to lack of suitable data, ULs could not be established for vitamin K, thiamin, riboflavin, vitamin B$_{12}$, pantothenic acid biotin, or carotenoids. In the absence of ULs, extra caution may be warranted in consuming levels above recommended intakes.

[b] As preformed vitamin A only.

[c] As α-tocopherol; applies to any form of supplemental α-tocopherol.

[d] The ULs for vitamin E, niacin, and folate apply to synthetic forms obtained from supplements, fortified foods, or a combination of the two.

[e] ND = Not determinable due to lack of data of adverse effects in this age group and concern with regard to lack of ability to handle excess amounts. Source of intake should be from food only to prevent high levels of intake.

[f] The ULs for magnesium represent intake from a pharmacological agent only and do not include intake from food and water.

[g] Although vanadium in food has not been shown to cause adverse effects in humans, there is no justification for adding vanadium to food, and vanadium supplements should be used with caution. The UL is based on adverse effects in laboratory animals, and this data could be used to set a UL for adults but not children and adolescents.

Dietary Reference Intakes: EAR

Life-Stage Group	Vitamins										
	Vitamin A (µg/d)[a]	Vitamin C (mg/d)	Vitamin D (µg/d)	Vitamin E (mg/d)[b]	Thiamin (mg/d)	Riboflavin (mg/d)	Niacin (mg/d)[c]	Vitamin B$_6$ (mg/d)	Folate (µg/d)[d]	Vitamin B$_{12}$ (µg/d)
Infants										
0–6 mo										
7–12 mo										
Children										
1–3 y	210	13	10	5	0.4	0.4	5	0.4	120	0.7
4–8 y	275	22	10	6	0.5	0.5	6	0.5	160	1.0
Males										
9–13 y	445	39	10	9	0.7	0.8	9	0.8	250	1.5
14–18 y	630	63	10	12	1.0	1.1	12	1.1	330	2.0
19–30 y	625	75	10	12	1.0	1.1	12	1.1	320	2.0
31–50 y	625	75	10	12	1.0	1.1	12	1.1	320	2.0
51–70 y	625	75	10	12	1.0	1.1	12	1.4	320	2.0
>70 y	625	75	10	12	1.0	1.1	12	1.4	320	2.0
Females										
9–13 y	420	39	10	9	0.7	0.8	9	0.8	250	1.5
14–18 y	485	56	10	12	0.9	0.9	11	1.0	330	2.0
19–30 y	500	60	10	12	0.9	0.9	11	1.1	320	2.0
31–50 y	500	60	10	12	0.9	0.9	11	1.1	320	2.0
51–70 y	500	60	10	12	0.9	0.9	11	1.3	320	2.0
>70 y	500	60	10	12	0.9	0.9	11	1.3	320	2.0
Pregnancy										
≤18 y	530	66	10	12	1.2	1.2	14	1.6	520	2.2
19–30 y	550	70	10	12	1.2	1.2	14	1.6	520	2.2
31–50 y	550	70	10	12	1.2	1.2	14	1.6	520	2.2
Lactation										
≤18 y	885	96	10	16	1.2	1.3	13	1.7	450	2.4
19–30 y	900	100	10	16	1.2	1.3	13	1.7	450	2.4
31–50 y	900	100	10	16	1.2	1.3	13	1.7	450	2.4

Data from: Reprinted with permission from the Dietary Reference Intakes series, National Academies Press. Copyright 1997, 1998, 2000, 2001, 2011 by the National Academy of Sciences. These reports may be accessed via www.nap.edu. Courtesy of the National Academies Press, Washington, DC.

Note: This table is adapted from the DRI reports; see www.nap.edu. An Estimated Average Requirement (EAR) is the average daily nutrient intake level estimated to meet the requirements of half of the healthy individuals in a group.

[a] Given as retinal activity equivalents (RAE).
[b] Also known as calciferol. The DRI values are based on the absence of adequate exposure to sunlight.
[c] Also known as α-tocopherol.
[d] Given as niacin equivalents (NE), except for infants 0–6 months, which are expressed as preformed niacin.
[e] Given as dietary folate equivalents (DFE).